LUNAR PROSPECTOR

Against all Odds

Alan B. Binder

Ken Press

Tucson

Publisher's Cataloging-in-Publication

Binder, Alan B.

    Lunar Prospector : against all odds / Alan B. Binder. — 1st ed. — Tucson, AZ : Ken Press, 2005.

      p. ; cm.
      ISBN: 1928771319

      1. Lunar Prospector (U.S.) 2. Space flight to the moon. 3. Moon—Exploration. 4. Aeronautics—United States—Government policy. 5. Space flight—Government policy. 6. United States. National Aeronautics and Space Administration. 7. Truthfulness and falsehood—United States. I. Title.

TL799.M6 B56 2005   2004115171
629.43/53/0973—dc22   0503

Published by Ken Press, Tucson, Arizona USA
(520) 743-3200 or office@kenpress.com

Printed in Canada

This book and the
Lunar Prospector Mission
are dedicated to . . .

Preston and Gregg,
who were there in the beginning.

Bill, posthumously,
whose early interest as a NASA/JSC manager was critical.

The Lunar Exploration Inc. volunteers for all their efforts.

The OMNI Systems Inc. engineers,
who did the original design of the spacecraft.

Tom, my Deputy and best friend,
who helped me build and test the spacecraft.

All the engineers who helped me design,
build, test, and launch the spacecraft.

The Mission Operations Team members,
who helped me fly the spacecraft and,

The American public,
who paid for the mission and
who deserve a much better
national space program than
NASA has provided.

CONTENTS

PREFACE

Purpose

This book was written for several reasons. The first and foremost is to show the American taxpayer just how badly the national space program and the large aerospace companies, at least Lockheed, are run. While NASA and the aerospace industry use a carefully managed PR front to cover up their poor management, incompetence, and lack of direction, many cracks have appeared in that façade over the past decades, cracks that have given the public a glimpse into the bungling NASA and aerospace bureaucracies. The most notable examples of this bungling include the International Space Station, that was to have cost $8 billion of taxpayers' money and was to have been finished years ago. It is a poorly managed program that has already cost approximately $40 billion and will cost up to $80 billion by the time the "Core Space Station" (the Core is not the entire station, but just enough to make it look finished) is finished in a few years; the January 1986 loss of Challenger and its crew, because NASA managers and Morton Thiokol upper management would not listen to the Morton Thiokol engineers who said that it was far too cold to launch the Shuttle; the incorrectly made mirror in the Hubble Telescope; the loss of the Mars Observer (1993), the Mars Climate Observer (1999), and the Mars Polar Lander (1999). All three Mars failures were due to poor engineering and poor management. As if those failures were not sufficient, the crowning failure was the February 2003 loss of Columbia and its crew, because NASA managers ignored the concerns of NASA engineers regarding the magnitude of the damage done to Columbia's left wing when it was hit by foam insulation debris during launch.

The Lunar Prospector Mission was conceived as a private mission to demonstrate to NASA, Congress, and the American taxpayer how missions could be done inexpensively, efficiently, and reliably, or as NASA puts it, "Faster, Better, Cheaper." This book gives the story of how the $65 million Lunar Prospector Mission was conceived by a small group of people outside of NASA and eventually brought to a successful conclusion eleven years later. It is meant to give the reader a detailed picture of just how the mission was accomplished, despite the bungling and mismanagement on the parts of NASA and Lockheed managers.

In addition, the book is meant to give the reader a firsthand account of the personal side of the struggle that brought the mission from it fledgling start in late 1988, as a private mission, to its triumphal conclusion at 2:52:00.8 AM PDT on July 31, 1999.

Finally, this book is meant to show the reader the technical side of the Lunar Prospector Mission — the technical challenges of designing, building, testing, launching, and commanding the spacecraft on its way to the Moon and as it orbited the Moon 384,000 km from Earth — and how the technical decisions were made.

Viewpoint

As the reader will quickly find out, this book is the highly personal tale of my role in the mission. The way I frequently and critically characterize some of the people, events, NASA, and Lockheed throughout the book reflect my own personal views of the individuals, events, and institutions and may or may not be correct and may or may not be fair — but they are my views and, as such, are subject to my personal biases and expectations. While I judge several people, NASA, and Lockheed very harshly most of the time, I guarantee that if any of a number of managers in the NASA or the Lockheed bureaucracies had written this book instead of me, I would be the one characterized in a very harsh way. I leave it up to the reader to decide if I am the villain or not, and if my critical judgments of the people, events, and institutions involved are valid or not.

Historical Accuracy

I have tried to make this history of the Lunar Prospector Program as accurate as possible. While I have an excellent memory for events, I am terrible at remembering dates. Thus, while the events are accurately described, there is some question about exactly when some of the events occurred. All stated dates are accurate, but there are a few periods of time when I could not determine the specific date on which an event occurred, but even in those cases, I have been able to place the event within a specific week or a specific month. Nevertheless, as detailed in the following, the availability of information giving the exact dates and the exact details of the various events depicted in this book is as follows:

Prolog — Most of the pre-Apollo and Apollo events described in the Prolog are derived from the open literature and are accurately dated. The accounts of the pre-Lunar Prospector activities at the Space Studies Institute and in the National Space Society were given to me by Gregg Maryniak and Peter Kokh, respectively, and are assumed to be accurate. The account of my pre-Lunar Prospector activities was derived from my memory and various documents.

Part One — The dating of the events during the "Early Years" of the project is checkered. The dating of events from late November 1988 through March 1989 is poor, since only a few of the events were recorded in documents. Once our Lunar Prospector Team started getting organized in March 1989, there are more dated records of events from then on through August 1989. Between October 1989 and November 1990, our Lunar Prospector newsletter and my monthly progress reports to Lockheed (which provided support for my work on Lunar Prospector during that period) provided accurate dates and information for essentially all events described. Unfortunately, from December 1990 through February 1995, when events in the development of the mission were few and far between, there are only occasional dated records, except for a few short periods when Lockheed gave me support to work on the mission, periods of time that the reader will easily recognize.

Parts Two, Three, and Four — Right after I was informed in February 1995 that Lunar Prospector had been selected for flight, my new wife, Rebecca, insisted that I start recording the day's events on tape, so I would have accurate information for this book. From March 1995 to just after the end of the mission in July 1999, I recorded the day's events almost every night after work. In all, there are 44 tapes that my sweet wife laboriously transcribed and they served as the very accurate basis for dating and describing all the events in the bulk of the book. In addition, there are numerous documents, letters, reports, videos, newspaper articles, TV interviews, etc. from those periods of time that add to the accuracy of the events described in Parts 2, 3, and 4.

Epilog — The Epilog was written more or less as the events happened, thus the dating of the events in the Epilog is also very accurate.

Quotes — In an effort to keep the book lively, I have taken artistic license and written the essence of numerous conversations that occurred during the eleven years of the project as dialogue within quotation marks. However, with the exception of a few cases where the quotes are verbatim, taken from videotapes of press conferences, the dialogues in the quotes are close approximations to the real conversations and, since I did record the day's events almost every night, the quoted dialogues are quite accurate, but, of course, not verbatim.

Terminology

One of my pet peeves is the use of the terms geology, geophysics, geochemistry, etc. by planetary scientists to describe the study of other solar system bodies besides the Earth. As everyone knows who has taken a geology course, geology is derived from Greek, in which *geo* means the Earth and *logy* means science or study. When *geo* is combined with other suffixes, we get geography, geophysics, geochemistry, geodesy, geocentric, etc.; in some cases, geo is a suffix, as in perigee and apogee (the nearest and farthest points of an orbit around the Earth).

Since the earliest beginnings of the study of the planets, astronomers have used the same linguistic logic to name the study of each planet, i.e., selenology is the study of the Moon, where *Selene* is Greek for the Moon, areology is the study of Mars — *Ares*, hermeology is the study of Mercury — *Hermes*, zenology is the study of Jupiter — *Zen*, etc. and, e.g., selenography, selenophysics, etc. follow the same linguistic logic used in the geosciences for the naming of these branches of the study of the Moon. Thus, there is a rich literature in which astronomers have used the proper terminology in discussing the various planets (and the Sun, e.g., helioseismology, perihelion, aphelion, etc.) for over four centuries.

Unfortunately, when geologists, geophysicists, etc., became involved with the study of the Moon, mainly during the Apollo era, and later with the rest of the planets, they were either ignorant of the correct terminology and/or they took the lazy way out and just called everything geology. Hence, today we see in the literature and hear in scientific talks the incorrect phraseology of *the geology of the Moon*, *the geology of Mars*, etc. — though no one ever talks about the *geology of the Earth*, because — gee — that would be redundant!

I not only object to the use of the term geology to describe the study of the Moon and the other planets from the linguistic and historical standpoints, but also from the scientific standpoint. When we look at the terrestrial bodies in the solar system, i.e., the Earth, the Moon, Mars, Venus, and Mercury, and the rocky and/or metallic asteroids, we find that the Earth is *very atypical* among the terrestrial bodies — the Earth has abundant water, very active erosion, plate tectonics, few impact craters, a highly evolved atmosphere containing abundant oxygen, and abundant life, to mention just a few things. In contrast, the other terrestrial bodies have little or no water, very low erosion rates, no plate tectonics, un-evolved atmospheres of carbon dioxide (if they are big enough to hold an atmosphere), no life (unless Mars proves to have some primitive life forms), and impact craters are a major or the dominant land form.

Thus, the Earth is the worst possible body to serve as a reference point for the study of the other planets (the general term for which is planetology) and I have heard more than one "planetary geologist" objecting to some conclusion regarding one of the properties or characteristics of one of the terrestrial bodies, e.g., the Moon, by saying, "But that's not the way it is — or works — on Earth."

To which I say, "So what, it's not the Earth, it's the Moon." Thus, the geocentric thinking of many "planetary geologists" has, at times, led them down the path to incorrect conclusions that might have been avoided if they would accept the fact that they are studying selenology, areology, etc., instead of the geology of the Moon, Mars, etc.

Thus in keeping with my philosophy and the fact that Lunar Prospector was sent to the Moon to study it and not the Earth, the reader will see the correct prefix or suffix "seleno" when I refer to the Moon and "geo" when I refer to the Earth.

Metric System

The USA should have adopted the metric system and gotten rid of the antiquated English system of weights and measures years ago. I will not go through the arguments and counter argument regarding that topic, but it suffices to point out that NASA lost the $125 million Mars Climate Observer in 1999 because Lockheed Martin engineers in Denver were using the English system when they were supposed to have been using the metric system!

The first thing I did, when I got to Lockheed in Sunnyvale, CA, to start the final design, construction, and testing of Lunar Prospector, was to tell the engineers, "We will use the metric system and only the metric system on this project," and we did, with one exception. The propulsion engineers argued strongly that, since all the test data on the all important engines and fuel tanks, when referring to the pressure, were in pounds/square inch (psi), we should use psi in our testing and mission operations to insure that there were no mistakes. Though that is the same argument engineers always use to keep from being forced to switch over to the metric system, in part to keep things simple and in part to keep peace in the family, I reluctantly agreed to use psi instead of kilopascals as our measure of pressure. With that exception and with the exception of quoted dialogue in which my discussion partner used pounds, miles or inches on his side of the conversations, I use the metric system throughout the book.

Appendices and Photographs

In order to keep the purchase price of this book as low as possible, the photographs have been printed in black and white. However, a collection of 84 color photographs, including all of the black and white pictures found in this book, is given on the Lunar Research Institute's website, www.lunar-research-institute.org.

Similarly, all the appendices referred to in the text of this book are also found on the Lunar Research Institute's website.

Have Fun

Finally, as I told my Lockheed engineers at the beginning of the work on the final design, construction and testing of Lunar Prospector, "Lunar Prospector is supposed to be an interesting and fun program to work on. If you are not having fun, then go find another program to work on that is fun," and they did have fun, as did I. In the same sense, this book is meant to let the reader share in the fun of the Lunar Prospector Mission. As the reader will see throughout the book, unlike NASA, I firmly believe that Lunar Prospector (and all space missions) belongs to the American taxpayer who paid for it and thus you, the reader, the taxpayer, has the right to share in the fun of the mission. Thus, I wrote this book, in part, to give you that opportunity and to be able to say thank you for giving me the opportunity to do Lunar Prospector.

Alan B. Binder, Ph.D.
Lunar Prospector
Principal Investigator
Lunar Research Institute
Tucson, Arizona
August 2003

PROLOG

Lunar Prospector's Prehistory

1865 through
late November 1988

1865 to December 1968: Pre-Apollo

Like most historical events, there is no clear-cut beginning to the Lunar Prospector Mission; it was the result of the evolution of the exploration of the Moon. However, from my perspective, the historical beginning of Lunar Prospector goes back to July 1971 when, for the first time, lunar orbit mapping experiments were carried in the SIM (Science Instrument Module) Bay of the Apollo 15 Service Module and on the sub-satellite released into lunar orbit during that mission. Nevertheless, it might be argued that Lunar Prospector's roots go back to the pre-Apollo era, or to the pre-Sputnik era or even to an earlier time since the concept of examining the Moon from orbit dates back decades in the scientific literature and nearly a century and a half in the science fiction literature.

The most notable early science fiction account of a lunar orbital mission is Jules Verne's 1865 Novel, *From the Earth to the Moon,* and its 1870 sequel, *A Trip Around It,* in which Verne describes a circumnavigational trip to the Moon by three intrepid adventures. That story, like many of Verne's novels, has many interesting parallels in the real world — in that case, Apollo 8, the first manned lunar orbital mission. Some of the parallels are: Verne's space capsule had roughly the same shape, size and mass as the Apollo capsule (the Verne capsule's diameter, height and mass were 2.74 m, 4.57 m and 8732 kg, respectively, while those of the Apollo Command Module were 3.91 m, 3.66 and 5545 kg), the crews of both consisted of three men, both missions were carried out by Americans (the Baltimore Gun Club in Verne's version and NASA in the real world), both missions started in Florida (from a fictitious "Stone Mountain" near "Tampa Town" on Florida's west coast in Verne's story, just 225 km SW of the Apollo 8 launch pad at the Cape on Florida's east coast), the Verne mission orbited the Moon for about two days, while Apollo 8 orbited the Moon for 20 hours (10 orbits), both crews made scientific observations of the Moon from orbit, and both missions ended with a water splash down in the Pacific!

Fast-forwarding nearly a century to the pre-Sputnik 1950s — in the March 22, 1952 issue of *Collier's* Magazine, Werner Von Braun and several other prominent scientists and engineers published the description of a manned circumnavigational flight to the Moon as part of their historical, pre-space age series of articles on the exploration of space. While the *Collier's* articles served to educate the pre-Sputnik public on the possibilities of space flight, led to several books, spacecraft model kits, Disney TV films, and Disney comic books, and fueled the imaginations of numerous future space scientists (me for one) and aerospace engineers, the Von Braun/*Collier's* lunar orbital mission had no direct bearing on the course of the unmanned orbital exploration of the Moon. But it did foretell the first manned orbital mission to the Moon — Apollo 8.

Similarly, several 50s books on the exploration of space by authors such as Willy Ley, Arthur C. Clark, Harold Goodwin, and Martin Caidin all foretold the use of orbiting manned and unmanned spacecraft for mapping the Moon. The visions of those authors were correct, but their vague discussions of lunar orbiting missions served only to show the way to the future exploration of the Moon, not how to do it.

Once the space age began with the launch of Sputnik 1 on October 4, 1957, lunar orbital exploration became feasible. The first attempts to reach and orbit the Moon were made in later 1958, when the US Air Force made three unsuccessful attempts to launch Pioneer spacecraft using their newly developed Thor-Able rocket. Each of those simple, small, spin-stabilized, battery powered spacecrafts carried a primitive TV camera to photograph the then unknown lunar far-side, a micrometeoroid detector, a magnetometer and a cosmic-ray detector — but none of the Pioneers even reached the Moon, let alone went into orbit around it!

After those three USA failures and two successful Soviet lunar missions (the first lunar flyby by Luna 1 in January 1959, and the first lunar impact by Luna 2 in September 1959), the Soviets made the first successful circumnavigational lunar mission, Luna 3, in October 1959, which resulted in the first photographs of the lunar far-side.

Those three Soviet successes were followed in late 1959 and late 1960 by three more unsuccessful attempts to orbit the Moon by the US Air Force using its more powerful Atlas-Able rocket and a more sophisticated, larger, spin-stabilized, solar cell powered Pioneer spacecraft. Thus ended the USA's first two series of unsuccessful lunar orbital missions, leaving the lunar science community with none of the coveted data on the Moon it had so long wanted.

After a long string of failed landing attempts and two months after their Luna 9 made the first semi-soft landing on the Moon in February 1966, the Soviets succeeded in putting Luna 10, the first successful lunar orbiting mission, into a low lunar orbit in April 1966. Unfortunately, propaganda drove that mission since, after demonstrating Soviet technological prowess by orbiting the Moon, Luna 10 played back the *Soviet International* from lunar orbit, and that was about the extent of its mission. All in all, between April 1966 and June 1974, the Soviets put five spacecraft into lunar orbit for the purpose of mapping the Moon, but none of them produced any significant scientific data. Thus, while the early Soviet orbital missions proved their technical feasibility, except for their Luna 3 circumnavigational mission, none provided any real science data.

The first scientifically significant lunar orbiting missions were the five Lunar Orbiters that NASA successfully launched on three-month intervals between August 1966 and August 1967. Those orbiters were designed to obtain high-resolution photographs of potential Apollo landing sites and hence were meant to achieve technical, not scientific goals. However, unexpectedly, all five missions were successful and thus the Apollo support objectives were accomplished on the first three missions. That allowed NASA and the lunar science community to use Lunar Orbiters IV and V to photograph the entire Moon with unprecedented resolutions, providing scientists with a rich harvest of data that are still being evaluated nearly forty years later.

As a totally unexpected bonus, P. Muller and Bill Sjogren, using the extremely precise Doppler tracking data of the Lunar Orbiters, detected gravity variations over the lunar surface and showed that the major circular maria (Imbrium, Serenitatis, Nectaris, Crisium and Humorum) all have positive gravity anomalies of up to a few 100 mgal, (1 mgal is a gravitational acceleration of 0.001 cm/sec^2; for comparison, the lunar surface gravity is 162 cm/sec^2 and the Earth gravity is 980 cm/sec^2). Muller and Sjogren called the positive gravity anomalies Mascons (short for Mass Concentrations) and their work opened a new field of orbital investigation — Doppler Gravity Mapping.

That first truly successful series of lunar orbital missions was led by Boeing Project Manager Jim Martin, whose role in both my career and in the Lunar Prospector Mission more than 30 years later is chronicled in Part Two of this book. Despite the technical and scientific successes of the five Lunar Orbiters, those missions were of limited scope and hence, in my mind, they are not true precursors to Lunar Prospector. However, Jim told me during the first review he conducted during Lunar Prospector's construction that, at the end of the five planned missions, he suggested to NASA that they put one of the gamma-ray spectrometers built for the Ranger Program (all the Ranger lunar impact missions that carried a gamma-ray spectrometer failed) on the spare, sixth orbiter and map the composition of the Moon. The mission would have cost just $11 million, but, unfortunately, NASA said, "No, it's too expensive," so a great opportunity was lost and we had to wait over 30 years for Lunar Prospector to do the job!

There was one more successful USA unmanned lunar orbiting spacecraft that preceded the Apollo Program — Explorer 35. That "Particle and Fields" satellite was one of many Explorer missions launched to study the Earth's magnetic field, the Van Allen Belts, and the interactions between them and the Solar Wind. Explorer 35 was put into a relatively high altitude, elliptical orbit around the Moon where it was "anchored by the Moon's gravity" and would therefore pass through the geomagnetic tail once per month — it was not sent there to study the Moon. Nevertheless, Explorer 35 did define the interaction between the Moon and the Solar Wind and confirmed earlier results that showed the Moon probably did not have any significant dipole magnetic field (the field strength at the lunar surface was found by Explorer 35 to be less than 1 nT; 1 nT = 10^{-5} Gauss; for comparison the Earth's field strength at the surface is some 35,000 nT) — though some unexplained, small, lunar magnetic signatures were observed by Explorer 35.

December 1968 through December 1972: Apollo

Once the Apollo Program started its manned lunar mission phase in December of 1968 with the Apollo 8 lunar orbit mission, lunar Doppler gravity data were obtained via the S-band tracking transponders on the Command and Service Modules and LM's (Lunar Excursion Modules — except for Apollo 8) of the first five missions. Also the astronauts made visual observations and took hand-held camera photographs of the Moon from lunar orbit. However, true lunar orbital science really began with the more advanced missions — Apollo 15, 16 and 17. The first two of those missions are, in my opinion, the real forefathers of Lunar Prospector.

Because of their increased payload capabilities, the last three Apollo Missions not only provided for longer stay times on the surface (3 days vs. a maximum of 1½ days) and in lunar orbit (6 days vs. a maximum of 3 days) than the first three missions, but also allowed orbital mapping instruments and a sub-satellite (on Apollo 15 and 16 only) to be carried in the SIM Bays of the Service Modules. The sub-satellites were deployed in lunar orbit just prior to the departure of the Command and Service Modules (plus, of course, the three astronauts and the lunar samples) from lunar orbit. The Apollo 15 and 16 SIM Bay instruments were i) a gamma-ray spectrometer — *the direct forefather of the Lunar Prospector Gamma-Ray Spectrometer (GRS)*, ii) an alpha particle spectrometer — *the direct forefather of the Lunar Prospector Alpha Particle Spectrometer (APS)*, iii) an X-ray spectrometer, iv) a mass spectrometer, v) a laser-altimeter, vi) a 1-m resolution panoramic film camera and vii) a metric mapping film camera. Doppler gravity data were provided as usual by the S-band transponders on board the Command and Service Modules and the LMs. The Apollo 15 and 16 sub-satellites carried i) a magnetometer — *the direct forefather of the Lunar Prospector Magnetometer (MAG)*, ii) an energetic-particle telescope, iii) an electrostatic analyzer — *the direct forefather of the Lunar Prospector Electron Reflectometer (ER)*, and iv) an S-band transponder — *the direct forefather to the Lunar Prospector Doppler Gravity Experiment (DGE)*. Finally, *the simple, little, spin-stabilized Apollo 15 and 16 sub-satellites themselves are the forefathers of the Lunar Prospector Spacecraft*.

The Apollo 15 and 16 orbital mapping, together with that done on Apollo 17 (with the exception of the two cameras, the Apollo 17 payload was completely different from those carried by Apollo 15 and 16 and had no direct bearing on the Lunar Prospector payload), provided the lunar science community with extremely high value data sets that allowed the samples collected by — and the observations and measurements made by — the astronauts on the lunar surface to be put in the proper context on the local, regional and even global scales. However, because the Apollo landing sites were all near the equator, the orbital mapping was limited to the near equatorial regions of the Moon and covered only 10 to 20% of the Moon. Thus, as the Apollo Program came to its premature end (21 Apollo Missions had been originally planned; that was cut to 18 and then to 17 — the three remaining Saturn V launch vehicles are lawn ornaments at the Johnson Space Center [JSC], the Kennedy Space Center [KSC] and the Marshall Space Flight Center [MSFC]) the lunar science community was extremely keen on getting the entire surface mapped from orbit. That led to the suggestion that, instead of landing on the Moon, the last Apollo should be sent into a polar orbit with a crew of just two and with the LM (which would carry no fuel since it was not going to land and hence could carry a lot of supplies) serving as a warehouse for the extra food, oxygen, water, film, etc. that would be needed to support a 1-month, manned orbital mapping mission using all — or most — of the SIM Bay and sub-satellite instruments carried on the Apollo 15, 16, and 17 Missions. Unfortunately, NASA promptly turned down that exquisite idea, so another unique opportunity in the exploration of the Moon was lost (better to have the launch vehicles rust away than to do something useful with them — despite their having already been bought and paid for). Nevertheless, *because of the Apollo 15, 16, and 17 Missions, the concept of mapping the Moon from a low polar orbit using multiple mapping techniques had become a permanent fixture in the world of lunar science and the basis of the Lunar Prospector Mission over a quarter of a century later.*

1973 to 1985: Lunar Polar Orbiter Missions — DOA

With no chance of having the last Apollo do the global mapping of the Moon, lunar scientists turned to JPL (the Jet Propulsion Laboratory in Pasadena, CA) to do an unmanned polar orbiting mission with the Apollo SIM Bay and sub-satellite instruments. Thus was born the unmanned Lunar Polar Orbiter (LPO) Mission concept that is also a forefather of Lunar Prospector. However, the LPO concept was born under an evil star. The Apollo Program had provided the lunar science community with a wealth of samples and data on the Moon, information that would take decades to analyze and digest, so the space science community at large turned its sights on the rest of the solar system. Also, NASA had the "been there, done that" attitude and turned its attention to the Shuttle and later to the infamous International Space Station. Thus, there was little support for LPO in NASA. Nevertheless, NASA slyly put LPO into its yearly budget requests to Congress for a number of years — but NASA always gave LPO a low priority compared to the other proposed solar system exploration missions, so LPO was used for years as a sacrificial lamb that NASA would "reluctantly give up" in order to get its higher priority missions funded.

A trick lunar scientists, JPL, and NASA used to keep the LPO concept alive (probably because NASA did not want to lose their sacrificial lamb) was to periodically change its name, e.g., to Lunar Geochemical Mapper and Lunar Geosciences Observer. The reason that was done (and is done on other proposed programs) is because, after seeing the same proposed mission for a few years in a row, NASA Headquarters and Congress say, "That old thing again, don't you have something new?" Well, because the science goals really don't change, the only thing to do is to change the spacecraft a little, change the payload a little and then change the name and — *voila*, you have "something new"! But despite that trick, as the seventies slipped into the eighties, and as the eighties began to tick by, LPO and its various derivatives remained on the DOA list of NASA missions with the final blow coming in 1985 when NASA canceled any plans to use the backup to the Mars Observer spacecraft to do a Lunar Observer Mission (again — a new name).

In part, because of NASA's lack of support of a LPO mission, the small European lunar and planetary science community (of which I was a member from June 1973 to June 1983 when I taught and did lunar research in Germany) tried to get the European Space Agency (ESA) to support a mission that we named Polar Orbiting Lunar Observatory or POLO. Though we had some initial success in getting a Phase A Study of the proposed mission done, we were unable to get through the considerable political barriers that existed in ESA and the effort eventually failed. Nevertheless, the work I did on POLO laid the groundwork for my later thoughts about a simple orbital mapping mission that eventually led to Lunar Prospector.

Finally, each and every time that NASA or ESA began to make what sounded like serious noise about a LPO mission, the Soviets would respond with, "Yes, we are also planning such a mission," and that was all we ever heard about a Soviet LPO.

Thus, by 1985, it was clear that neither NASA, nor ESA, nor the Soviets were ever going to do a LPO mission, so discussions about trying to do a simple LPO began to occur outside of those governmental agencies.

1985 to November 1988: The SSI Effort

The Space Studies Institute (SSI) in Princeton, NJ, a private institute devoted to the exploration and utilization of the resources of the Moon and planets, had started trying to push NASA into doing small lunar mapping missions in lieu of the full $1 billion LPO missions that JPL had unsuccessfully promoted. That effort got started in early 1985 when SSI's founder, Dr. Gerard O'Neill, was appointed by President Reagan to the President's National Commission on Space. O'Neill was a leading proponent of the use of lunar resources for constructing solar power satellites and space colonies. He and Gregg Maryniak, the Institute's Executive Vice-President, were intrigued by the possibility that permanently shadowed regions near the Moon's poles could hold water ice and other trapped volatiles as had been suggested by Jim Arnold and others. As such, O'Neill asked Maryniak to brief the President's Commission on a series of alternative approaches to space development and those included considering whether a very small spacecraft in a polar orbit around the moon could effectively map its chemical resources.

In July 1985, SSI contracted with Jim French, a well-known and well-respected JPL engineer who was given permission by his management to "moonlight" on a small contract, to consider just how small such a "Lunar Polar Probe" could be. Jim's final report was submitted to SSI on December 1, 1985, in which Jim indicated that a small probe carrying a gamma-ray spectrometer could map the Moon for about $50 million. Maryniak presented those results to the National Commission on Space on December 16, 1985, and explained to the commission the impact the discovery of lunar volatiles would have on the exploration of the Moon and planets. That SSI effort to put lunar mapping on the front burner bore some fruit in that the Commission's report, *Pioneering the Space Frontier,* published in early 1986 said, "It is a first priority to search the permanently shadowed craters near the lunar poles, where ices containing carbon, nitrogen, and hydrogen may be found. We, therefore, recommend: A robotic lunar polar prospector to examine the entire surface of the Moon from low orbit."

By early 1987, O'Neill published an article, *Forward to the moon,* in which he urged NASA to launch a small lunar polar probe by the mid-1990s. However, the notion of such a small spacecraft was not popular within the NASA of the 1980s. As SSI pro-

moted the idea, Maryniak learned that several small spacecraft concepts had been proposed by the JPL staff. One idea was to use a tiny, ion-engine propelled spacecraft that
was small enough to fit into the Getaway Special containers flown on many Space Shuttle missions. Another concept proposed using one of several surplus Atlas E launchers,
then available, for a program called Lunar Quicksat.

Armed with that information, O'Neill and Maryniak twice briefed NASA Administrator James Fletcher, who had returned to the helm of the Space Agency after the Challenger accident at the request of the President. Fletcher (a former member of SSI's
Board of Directors) was sufficiently interested in the small lunar satellite concepts that,
during a subsequent visit to JPL, he requested a meeting with Kerry Nock, one of the
originators of the Lunar Getaway Special concept.

Despite the apparent interest generated by those SSI activities, NASA and JPL
could not be moved to go back to the Moon. One suspects that JPL had little motivation
to follow SSI's push towards small, inexpensive missions ($50 to $100 million) when it
had its eye on doing a $1 billion LPO mission and NASA simply did not have any inter-
est in going back to the Moon — period. Thus by 1987 SSI decided to try to do a Lunar
Polar Probe on its own. SSI knew that financing such a private mission would be a
greater challenge then the technical issues of building the spacecraft. SSI wrote a letter
to Peter Ueberroth, whose work on the Los Angeles Olympics was well known. The letter discussed the enormous impact that lunar water would have on space development
and suggested that a $50 million mission could find those resources should they exist.
Ueberroth's office was friendly, but gave what was to become a familiar response, "If this
is so important why doesn't NASA do it?" — the famous "Catch 22" of all private lunar
exploration efforts.

The SSI "go-it-alone-to-the-Moon" effort got into high gear in early 1988 when SSI
asked NASA to provide the Institute with the Apollo Gamma-Ray Spectrometer that had
been bumped from the Apollo 17 SIM Bay payload and was still sitting in Al Metzger's
office at JPL (Al had been the Principal Investigator on the Apollo Gamma-Ray Spectrometer Experiment). At first the Institute's efforts appeared to fall on deaf ears, but
with the help of Jim Muncy and Rick Tumlinson, Tim Kyger, the legislative assistant to
Congressman Dana Rohrabacher, was advised of the Lunar Prospector Program and
Maryniak requested that Rohrabacher ask NASA to give SSI the use of the Apollo
Gamma-Ray Spectrometer, which he later did.

Finally, Dr. Gay Canough, a high-energy physicist from Notre Dame who had
worked at Fermilab, and who had been "turned on to the mission" by Peter Kokh of the
National Space Society (see below), was providing SSI with information on the capabilities of gamma-ray and other spectrometers that could be used for orbital lunar mapping. In an effort to recruit support for a private SSI mission, Maryniak contracted with
Canough in 1988 to canvas the lunar science community. A sense of the "shoestring"
nature of the budget for that effort comes from a clause in Canough's contract that
required that she travel in the "lowest cost seats in the pressurized portion of the aircraft." Gay agreed and, on her own time and, in part, on her own money ($25,000 to
be exact), began to try to find support for the SSI Lunar Polar Mission as time rolled on
towards November of 1988.

1985 to November 1988: The NSS Efforts

Prior to 1985, members of the National Space Institute and the L5 Society, which
merged in 1986 to form the National Space Society (NSS), had discussed how to initiate

a lunar mission since they had become convinced that NASA was not going back to the Moon. Those "hallway" conversations became more intense in 1985 when, as a result of NASA's canceling the Lunar Observer Mission, JPL's Jim French, Boeing's Gordon Woodcock, and science fiction author, Greg Bear, began pushing the NSS/L5 membership to get behind a private LPO mission. Those efforts picked up in May 1987 during the 6th International Space Development Conference in Pittsburgh. SSI's Rick Tumlinson started an effort from the floor to raise money for the mission. That resulted in some $2000 being pledged, of which about $700 was actually received by Lori Graver at the NSS.

At the 1988 NSS Conference in Denver, Peter Kokh and Mark Kaehny of the Milwaukee Chapter (called the Lunar Reclamation Society) of the NSS became very active in promoting a NSS lunar polar mission and "fired-up" Gay Canough at the Conference when they convinced her that the mission was possible. Also, Peter Kokh and Morris Hornick suggested that the NSS approach institutions like *National Geographic* for financial support for the mission. Finally, Peter started the discussion about the name of the mission and Prospector 1 was selected from about five suggestions that had been floated around the Conference; the Lunar in Lunar Prospector was added a little later.

Within two weeks after the 1988 NSS Conference, Gay approached SSI's Gregg Maryniak about her working on the SSI mission as discussed above, and Jim Davidson of the Houston Chapter of the NSS began actively working with his chapter members on their version of the mission. Unfortunately, there was little cooperation or trust between those various groups, as demonstrated in part by the fact that Rick Tumlinson and his followers split off from the NSS at the end of the 1988 Conference (and later from SSI) to form the Space Frontier Foundation and to pursue their own lunar mission, and the fact that Houston Chapter also "went-at-it-alone." Nevertheless, Jim Davidson and his Houston colleagues started a serious effort to make the mission a reality and began to recruit people from the Johnson Space Center (JSC) area to work on the mission as late November 1988 approached.

Fall of 1982 to November 1988: My Road to Lunar Prospector

My road to Lunar Prospector started in 1982 when I was teaching and doing lunar research at the Universität Kiel in Germany and how and why I got there is as follows: I had been invited to go to Germany in 1973 by Dr. Hugo Fechtig at the Max Planck Institut für Kernphysik (Nuclear Physics) in Heidelberg because he was interested in introducing into Germany the type of planetary science I do. He had applied for and received a one year Senior Scientist Stipend for me (from June 1973 to June 1974) from the Alexander von Humboldt Stiftung. Fechtig's interest in planetary science had grown from his participation in the analysis of the Apollo samples and data. While at Heidelberg, I met Professor Dr. Meißner, Director of the Institut für Geophysik at the Universität Kiel. Meißner had been a guest investigator on the Apollo Seismometer Team and was keen on having me come to his Institute to teach and do lunar research when I was finished at Heidelberg and before I had to return to the USA to participate in the 1976 landings of the Viking Mars Landers (I was a Principal Investigator on the 1976 Viking Mars Lander Camera Team). While in Kiel, Meißner and I discussed the possibility of my returning permanently to Kiel after the Viking Missions were over. Meißner said he would try to get me research funding and eventually a University staff position if I wanted to return to Germany and I agreed.

While I was at JPL in Pasadena, CA (from February 1976 to March 1977), to carry out my role as the leader of the uplink half of our Viking Lander Camera Team, the German scientific community and the Deutsche Forschungs Gemeindschaft (DFG, equivalent to the National Science Foundation in the USA) wrote a White Paper on the need to teach and promote planetary science in the German research and university communities. They recommended a good level of funding for the program and that some university should offer a Lehrstuhl (Chair) in Planetary Science. Meißner wanted the Lehrstugh at his Institut and wanted me in it. As Viking came to its active operational end, I returned to Germany.

I knew that if Germany was to have an active program of teaching and doing planetary science, it also had to have a series of exploration missions, otherwise there would be no jobs for students when they were finished with their studies and there would be no reason for them to study planetary science in the first place. Since my interests are focused on surface activities (e.g., studying the petrological, compositional, age, etc. data obtained from the Apollo samples, and the seismic, heatflow, magnetic, etc. data obtained via the four ALSEP stations [Apollo Lunar Surface Experiments Package]), I decided to define an unmanned lunar surface exploration program that I called Selene (Greek for the Moon) that would serve as a focal point of the budding German planetary science effort and get the international lunar science community back into the business of actively exploring the Moon.

The Apollo Program had, among numerous other things, showed us two things in terms of what I had in mind: First, we needed a global selenophysical network of seismometers, heatflow probes, magnetometers, etc. to get an accurate picture of the interior of the Moon. I found that the minimum number of stations needed to get a global view of the Moon selenophysically was 16. Second, we needed samples from the numerous petrological units over the entire Moon. Since the walnut sized (1 to 3 cm in diameter) rocks collected by the astronauts using a rake proved to be the most useful of all the samples for characterizing the petrology, composition, age, etc. of the landing sites, I proposed that we collect 1 kg (about 100 individual walnut sized rocks) of rake samples from a number of different lunar sites and bring them to Earth for analysis. Given that we needed 16 Selenophysical Stations and the very large number of interesting selenological sites over the Moon, I decided that we would have 18 sample return missions for a total of 34 Selene Lander Missions in the entire program (I also hoped that, once started, Selene would continue well past the original 34 missions). The idea was to develop a simple lander that would deliver either a) a Sample Return Vehicle or b) a Selenophysical Station to the Moon. By building the same systems over and over on an assembly line (the way cars are made), the cost of each mission, and hence the cost of the entire program would be low and that would make it feasible. Since Germany did not have a launch vehicle capability, I proposed that the program be done jointly with the USA — Germany would build the lunar spacecraft and NASA would launch the missions using the at-that-time-thought-to-be-inexpensive Shuttle (the Shuttle was not only supposed to have been cheap, but also it was also supposed to fly every 2 weeks like a commercial airplane). I got Mike Duke, then the Chief of the Solar System Exploration Division at JSC, interested and he became my American partner in that venture.

I proposed and got funding to do a full Phase A study of the Selene Project from the DFG and proceeded to fully define and justify the science goals of the program with the aid of several of my German colleagues who were heavily involved with Apollo sample analysis work. When it was finished, I sent copies of the study to three or four German aerospace companies and one of them, ARNO in Bremen, liked the idea and decided to do a preliminary design study of the spacecraft on their own nickel! The ARNO study (which was completed in August 1982) showed two basic things, a) the concept was both engineering-wise and financially feasible and b) the Selenophyscial Station

Mission payload was considerably lighter than the Sample Return Mission payload (no surprise there). The standard mission profile I wanted to use for all the missions was to put the landers and their payloads into a 100-km altitude, parking, polar orbit for up to two weeks, i.e., until the spacecrafts were over their respective landing sites. Thus I decided that the extra payload capability on the 16 Selenophysical Station Missions would be used to carry 16 small, simple, spin-stabilized sub-satellites — like the Apollo 15 and 16 sub-satellites — into polar orbit. If each of the sub-satellites carried one or two instruments, we could do all the LPO global mapping as a cheap add-on to the Selene Lander Missions and thus the germ of the Lunar Prospector Mission idea began to infect my thoughts as early as 1982.

By early 1983, any hope of my getting a Lehrstuhl and of doing Selene in Germany had faded, so I returned to the USA in June 1983, specifically to JSC where I had received a two-year Senior Scientist Fellowship from the National Science Foundation. While at JSC, Mike Duke and I were able to get NASA support for small, student summer studies of Selene, but nothing ever came of those efforts.

However, a year or so later, in 1986, I got involved with Mitch Mitchell, a Houston area developer, who had the bright idea that he could build a commercial lunar base and was trying to get public help, support and financing for the base that he called "Lady Base One," the lady being Mother Earth and the base being the first one that Mother Earth would build on another celestial body! Since NASA was doing nothing to support lunar exploration, since I had begun to think about commercial space exploration as the way to get around NASA's lack of doing-anything-real-about-the-Moon, and since I had nothing better to do (by that time I was a Lockheed employee working for the New Initiatives Office at JSC on defining manned lunar and Mars missions and bases, but that effort was going nowhere), I joined Mitch's volunteer group to see if we really might be able to build a commercial lunar base. My first act as Mitch's Program Scientist was to suggest that we do a lunar polar orbit mapping mission using a simple, inexpensive spin-stabilized spacecraft carrying a gamma-ray/neutron spectrometer, an alpha particle spectrometer, a magnetometer, and an electron reflectometer and do gravity mapping using the Doppler transponder. I explained to Mitch that, in my opinion, if we did that mission it would give his idea and the team credibility, it would also result in a lot of good PR and public exposure, and all that would help to get investors. Mitch liked the idea and agreed, but Mitch's efforts to start Lady Base One quickly collapsed. Nevertheless, I had unknowingly fully defined what two years later — in late November 1988 — would became Lunar Prospector.

November 1988

Thus, by November of 1988, serious consideration had been given to doing a small polar orbiting mission outside of NASA by the Houston Chapter of the NSS, by SSI, and by me. Though the chances that a small, private effort would succeed in doing a lunar orbiting mission were vanishingly small, those three entities were about to converge — in late November — and their efforts would eventually result in my successfully doing Lunar Prospector over a decade later — AGAINST ALL ODDS.

PART ONE

The
Early Years

Late November 1988
through February 23, 1995

Chapter 1-1
The Beginning

Late November 1988: Phase A

As far as I am concerned, Lunar Prospector really began just before Thanksgiving in November 1988. Early one morning, Larry Friesen, a co-worker of mine at Lockheed Engineering and Science Company (LESC) in Houston, TX, told me that the Houston Chapter of the National Space Society (NSS) wanted to do a lunar orbit mapping mission to search for the proposed water ice deposits near the lunar poles. Larry, who was a member of the chapter, wanted to know if I would be interested in helping. Given that NASA was doing nothing about the Moon and that I had long believed that if anything was to be done, it had to be done outside of NASA, I said, "Yes." I added I would only be interested if the mission were driven by science goals, if I would be the Project Scientist, and if I would have full authority over the scientific goals and science payload of the mission. I asked Larry to find out if those conditions were acceptable to the other members of the Houston Space Society (HSS), and he said he would.

I had three reactions to the HSS's interest in doing a lunar orbital mission. First of all, I knew that the HSS members had no idea of what they were getting into. While all of the nation-wide NSS members are enthusiastic supporters of the space program, many are dedicated fans of Star Trek and/or of Gerard O'Neill's concept of a space city at the 5th Lagrangian Point (L-5) in the Moon's orbit. Only a fraction of them have any experience in aerospace engineering and/or space science of any kind. As such, only a small number of the NSS members have any real concept of how lunar spacecraft and lunar missions are done.

Second, getting back to the HSS specifically, having given a talk or two at the Houston Chapter's meetings, I knew that most of the HSS members were, at best, on the very fringes of the space program. Two, who were inseparable and because of their physical appearances and mannerisms I always thought of as Tweedledee and Tweedledum, were perpetual students at the University of Houston and were always responsible for the audio-visual equipment used at the meetings. A few, like Howard Stringer and Jim Davidson, had jobs in space-related fields and the others were just space and science fiction buffs. As such, the HSS had even less of the technical capability needed to pull off a lunar exploration mission than the NSS in general.

Third, on the other hand, despite their lack of having any real understanding of the technical issues, those people were willing to work hard to try to do something positive. They belonged to a national organization that could potentially draw enough attention and possibly money to such a mission to make it happen. Since I knew NASA was doing nothing — and would do nothing — about the Moon, I thought maybe those enthusiastic amateurs could help get us back into the lunar exploration business, if I could get the necessary science and technical team behind the idea. I was willing to help them if I had control over the science and technical issues.

A few days later, Larry informed me that the other members of the chapter agreed that I would be the Project Scientist under the conditions I had set, so I got started working with the HSS team at the end of November 1988.

The team, which was led by Howard Stringer — a quiet, soft-spoken person, held weekly meetings, mainly at a pizza parlor about one block from my apartment in Clear Lake, TX. Larry had told me earlier that the plan was to ask NASA for the Gamma-Ray Spectrometer (GRS) that had been bumped from the Apollo 17 payload by another instrument, have it modified so it could detect water ice, build a spacecraft, and fly it to the Moon — so simple!

As I carefully explained to the team at the first pizza parlor meeting I attended, a mission with just one objective — searching for water ice — was a bad idea. If there were no water ice, the public and the space science community would consider the mission a failure, no matter how well we conducted it. A small, multi-instrument payload, the same one I had suggested for the "Lady Base One" mission, would produce valuable lunar science data, and, even if there were no water ice in the lunar Polar Regions, the mission would be a success in the eyes of the world.

I then explained the Lunar Exploration Science Working Group (LExSWG, a NASA science advisory committee) objectives for lunar orbiter missions and our need to have a payload that would fulfill as many of the LExSWG goals as possible, especially some of the higher-level goals. However, to be doable with our expected meager resources, the payload had to consist of instruments with low masses, low power requirements, low data rates, few command requirements, and no pointing requirements so it could be flown on a simple, spin-stabilized spacecraft with minimum launch and ground support requirements. I ended by telling them that such a payload — the payload I wanted to fly — consisted of a Gamma-Ray/Neutron Spectrometer (GRS/NS) to do global compositional mapping and to look for the proposed polar ice deposits (LExSWG first level goals), a Magnetometer/Electron Reflectometer (MAG/ER) to map the lunar magnetic fields and help determine the size of the suspected lunar core (LExSWG third level goals), and an Alpha Particle Spectrometer (APS) to look for gas release events (LExSWG sixth level goal). In addition, we would use the Doppler tracking data to map the lunar gravity field and to gain additional information on the size of the suspected lunar core (LExSWG second level goals; I called that experiment the Doppler Gravity Experiment or DGE).

I also explained that we had to produce complete, high quality data sets. If not, we would just muddy the water and hurt lunar science in the long run. The reason is that neither NASA nor Congress care about detailed science. If we got some of the data, e.g., found some evidence for water ice and got partial or low quality gravity, magnetic, and compositional data, it would be next to impossible for the lunar science community to get the money for follow-on missions to finish or upgrade the botched mapping we began. As far as I was concerned, either we did it right, or we did nothing at all. Everyone accepted my payload and rationale, with one exception.

Everyone wanted a camera on Lunar Prospector to take pictures of the Moon. I told them that we had plenty of low and medium resolution imagery from the Lunar Orbiter Missions and that the only scientifically useful imagery programs, i.e., the global metric mapping and very high resolution imagery started during the Apollo 15, 16, and 17 Missions, as well as the multi-spectral imagery the lunar science community needed, were all well beyond the capabilities of our small mission. Nevertheless, they argued that we at least needed a few simple pictures for the newspapers, for TV, and as mementos for the supporters of the mission. I explained that there was no such thing as a simple picture from a spacecraft. Adding a camera would raise the cost and complexity of the mission well beyond what we could handle.

I said, "It's not like throwing your little Kodak camera in the car when you are going on vacation and just taking a snapshot every now and then. It's a major undertaking."

After some more discussion, everyone finally, but reluctantly, agreed and with that, I considered that both the payload and mission were defined. In terms of the NASA mission development sequence, we had just finished Phase A — the Definition of the Mission Objectives and Payload.

December 1988:
Enter Lunar Prospector, SSI, Brad Roscoe, and Gay Canough

The next few meetings were dedicated to getting organized and developing a plan. Aside from that, two important events marked that early period.

First was the naming of the spacecraft. I had been told earlier that most people wanted to call the spacecraft "Lunar Prospector" and they already had an idea for the logo — a 49'er type Lunar Prospector with his mule, both in tinny looking spacesuits, ambling across the lunar surface. I did not like either the name (an error on my part) or the logo. I said that our first job, if we were to have any chance of getting the financial and institutional support we needed, was to gain total credibility and not to appear like a bunch of amateurs or worse.

I said, "We need a more conventional name like Lunar Explorer, Lunar Polar Orbiter or the like."

No one agreed with me, so we said that we would all think about it and resolve the issue at the next pizza meeting. We did and I lost. Everyone wanted the mission to be called Lunar Prospector, so I agreed (the name turned out to be very useful in the publicity arena much later).

Second, as we discussed organizational issues at the second or third meeting, Howard told me that the Space Studies Institute (SSI) at Princeton, NJ, was proposing the same mission and there had been some talk about merging both efforts. Like everyone I knew in the NASA, aerospace, and space sciences communities, my view of SSI was that it was a group of L-5 and Star Trek devotees all gathered around their L-5 guru, SSI's founder and President, Gerard O'Neill. While I had doubts about trying to do the mission with the HSS and the NSS in general, I was even less happy about hitching up with SSI. Nevertheless, I knew that SSI did raise small amounts of money and distributed it to scientists for space research. Given the inevitable (the NSS and SSI were related because most, if not all, SSI members and supporters were also members of the NSS — lots of inbreeding there), and because SSI had at least raised some money for space research and did have a functioning organization, I asked, "OK, but who is in charge of Lunar Prospector, You guys or SSI?"

Howard's answer was, "We don't know."

I said, "Well, you had better sort that out ASAP, before we waste any more time."

It was reported at the very next pizza meeting, that SSI was in charge and that the HSS would play a supporting role with Jim Davidson leading the politicking, fundraising, and publicity efforts. SSI had accepted me as the Project Scientist and the payload I had chosen. I was also told that a young woman, Gay Canough, was the SSI Project Manager and that she would come to see me sometime before Christmas.

By that time, I had started to think about whom I could ask to be on the Science Team, though I was not ready to ask my colleagues to get involved until we were further along in the development of the project. Since we wanted to fly the old Apollo 17 GRS, modified to search for water ice, Al Metzger at JPL (Jet Propulsion Laboratory, in Pasadena, CA), who had been the Principal Investigator (PI) of the Apollo Gamma-Ray Spectrometer Team, was the logical choice to lead the GRS/NS experiment. Bill Sjogren, also at JPL, had led essentially every lunar and planetary mission gravity experiment since P. Muller and his discovery of the lunar Mascons using the Lunar Orbiter Doppler data. I really wanted Bill to lead the DGE. Lon Hood (at the Lunar and Planetary Laboratory, U of Arizona, Tucson) had done a large part of the analysis and interpretation of the Apollo Magnetometer data. Lon is the foremost expert in lunar magnetism and hence was my choice for the leader of the MAG part of the MAG/ER effort. Kinsey Anderson (UC Berkeley, Berkeley, CA) is the father of Electron Reflectometry, so he was my choice for the ER part of the MAG/ER experiment. I knew of no one I could ask to lead the APS part of the effort and would have to ask around about someone who might take on that responsibility. I had no idea how those colleagues would react when I asked them, at the appropriate time, to be part of a non-NASA lunar mission, but I was optimistic they would join us.

The most memorable meeting we had in December had been set up towards Christmas by Tweedledee and Tweedledum. In an apparent attempt to add some class to our meetings, they obtained a meeting room at the Johnson Space Center (JSC) cafeteria one quiet Saturday afternoon. Though most of us had arrived on time for the meeting, Tweedledee and Tweedledum came, uncharacteristically, quite late. The problem was that the JSC security guards would not let those suspicious looking characters on base. Only after several calls to the rather deserted administration was it verified, "Yes, there was a Lunar Prospector meeting at the cafeteria and yes, those two had set it up." The guards finally let them pass and they came, quite annoyed, to the meeting. Most of us had a good laugh as they explained their plight.

Once the meeting got started, one of the HSS members who had not been at any of the earlier meetings, objected to my payload on two grounds. First, he argued since Lunar Prospector was supposed to be a polar ice mapping mission, why was I trying to have it do global mapping of the Moon and why did I not have the all-important camera onboard Lunar Prospector?

While attempting to answer his first concern, it quickly became apparent that he thought that a polar orbiting spacecraft somehow (magically?) sat or orbited above one pole or the other to get the polar ice data and hence it would never see the rest of the Moon! To say the least, I was stunned that he had no understanding of the fundamental fact that an orbiting satellite goes around the body it is orbiting and that the name, polar orbiting spacecraft, referred to the fact that the spacecraft's orbit has an inclination of 90°, i.e., it passes over the north and south poles once per orbit. As a result the spacecraft passes over the entire body, yielding complete global coverage of the body — in the lunar case, once every two weeks. I explained all that, but it was clear that he did not really trust what I said. (Disheartening as that guy's ignorance was, I recalled a story about a former NASA Administrator who had once asked, "Why don't the aurora physicists put up a geostationary satellite over the pole to watch the aurora instead of going around the Earth all the time?" — but then, I never have expected too much from NASA bureaucrats).

After the first gross misconception was more or less cleared up, I tried to explain why I did not include a camera on Lunar Prospector. Though he reluctantly accepted that Lunar Prospector might not be able to do the type of imaging required by lunar science, he still wanted a camera for PR purposes — no matter what.

In order to justify a camera for "scientific purposes," he said, "We've got to get pictures of the ice deposits in the permanently shadowed regions."

I was astounded by that comment and replied, somewhat annoyed, "The reason the ice could be there in the first place and the reason we call them permanently shadowed regions is that the Sun never shines in them — they are always dark, so there is no light there to take pictures."

Not to be stopped by such a trivial breach of the laws of physics he retorted, "Well, then we'll just have to fly a CCD camera and take long exposures using the light from cosmic-ray flashes."

That did it; the guy was an idiot. He knew absolutely nothing about anything he was jabbering about.

I was really annoyed and said, "That's absurd. You don't know what you're talking about and you're wasting our time. Shut up."

At that, the rest of the team told him, "Yeah, shut up or get out!"

He kept quiet for the rest of the meeting and was never again involved with Lunar Prospector.

On the very positive side, Brad Roscoe came to the meeting. I did not know Brad before that day, but I was very happy to have met him. Brad is a physicist at Schlumberger, the worldwide and world famous oil and mineral resource company, and builds gamma-ray spectrometers and other such equipment for Schlumberger's resource exploration branch. He had heard about Lunar Prospector and wanted to build the GRS for the mission. I explained that we were hoping to get the Apollo 17 GRS and hence would not need a new GRS. I explained further that we would modify the Apollo GRS by putting a boron shield around its detector, so it could be used to search for the proposed water ice deposits. Brad was disappointed that we would not need a new GRS and was concerned that the boron shield would mess up the gamma-ray spectra and we would get poor information on the elemental composition of the rest of the Moon. He suggested that we consider flying a separate Neutron Spectrometer (NS) to search for the water ice and leave the GRS alone, so it would produce the best compositional data possible. Given our limited (then nonexistent) resources, I said I did not believe we could afford a separate NS and we would probably have to stick to the shielded GRS to do both jobs.

Not wanting to have Brad lose interest, and because I knew of no one I could ask to do the APS, I ask if he would be interested in building the APS and flying it. He said he would, but that I should keep in mind his comments about the problems with a shielded GRS and his willingness to build both a new GRS and a separate NS if that became an option. Of course, I agreed.

I was extremely glad to have Brad onboard. He was an experienced instrumentalist who would help to bring credibility to the program. Things were looking more and more interesting.

Gay Canough flew into Houston one Saturday morning to meet with me. As I understood her involvement, Gay was associated with SSI and had grown tired of SSI and NSS members always talking about doing a polar ice mapping mission and told SSI's Executive Vice-President, Gregg Maryniak (who I did not know at that time), that they ought to do something instead of just talk. Gregg had given Gay a small amount of money (Gay also spent a lot of her own money) to travel around the country trying to get something going. Since the original SSI mission was just a polar ice mapper and SSI had, already in 1988, asked Congress to authorize NASA to give SSI the Apollo 17 GRS, she had already visited Al Metzger to discuss his involvement with their mission.

Gay arrived just before lunch, so we started our discussions over Mexican food. Gay and I had a good meeting and agreed on all issues. We agreed the first thing we had to achieve was credibility within the science and aerospace communities; without that we were dead as a doornail.

I said, "To me, the first step in achieving credibility is having a solid science mission, a solid science team, and a solid mission plan. I believe we have a solid science mission with the payload I defined and I am fairly certain that, along with Al Metzger, I can put together a solid science team. My basic mission plan is in place and I will firm it up when we have a good spacecraft design, but my concept of having a simple spinner is the first step in the right direction." Gay agreed with all that and we turned to schedules and organization.

We both had essentially the same concepts of a realistic schedule and we agreed the final schedule had to be rigorously maintained. We could not, as was endemic in NASA missions, have slip after slip in the schedule — no one would have any faith in us if we could not keep on track. Also, since a major part of our effort had to be based on volunteer support, we knew one couldn't keep unpaid volunteers working on an ill defined or eternally slipping schedule.

Finally we discussed the organization. Gay expected to be the Project Manager, supported by SSI and, of course, I was already the Project Scientist — so we had a start.

I said, "I know several, young, excellent engineers in the JSC area who could be the Project Engineer," and Gay agreed that I should explore that avenue.

With that, there was little more we could do at our first meeting, which had gone extremely well. Gay got ready to leave and we both felt that we had made important progress.

I then called Al Metzger at JPL to verify that he wanted to be on the Science Team and to get him to fill out the science instrument data forms I needed for the GRS/NS. As I already knew, Al wanted to fly the Apollo 17 GRS on Lunar Prospector, so we got down to business. I asked Al about how the GRS would work in the NS mode, e.g., would we have to switch the spectrometer from one mode to the other each time we passed over one of the poles and he said, "You will like my answer," and went on to explain, "No switching is necessary because the GRS is the detector for both the gamma-rays and the neutrons. When neutrons hit the boron shield around the sodium-iodide (NaI) gamma-ray detector, they cause nuclear reactions that yield gamma rays of specific energies. Thus we measure gamma rays all the time, obtaining elemental compositional data on the crust and simultaneously searching for water ice deposits." Al was correct; his explanation did make me happy. Like the other instruments I wanted to fly, we would just turn the GRS/NS on and let it go about its business of collecting data without our having to command it from one mode to the other.

As 1988 ended, we seemed to have the beginnings of an organization that might just work. Nevertheless, I had no illusions about how very low the probability was that we would ever succeed. First, NASA does hundreds of Phase A Mission Definition Studies for all kinds of missions, most of which never get to Phase B (Engineering Study), and only a small fraction of those that get to Phase B get funded for Phase C/D (Construction, Integration, and Test) and even some of those are canceled before flight — so thinking up a mission is easy, getting it to fly is nearly impossible, even for NASA. Second, NASA had killed each and every one of the few attempts that had been made outside of NASA (excluding, of course, foreign powers) to do a space mission. Third, it would be nearly impossible for us to raise the kind of money needed and to get the big aerospace companies to donate hardware, let alone get a launch. While I thought we had a somewhat better chance than "a snowball in hell," I would not have bet the farm on Lunar Prospector.

January and February 1989

Work on the organization proceeded during January and February, but the main effort of our HSS team was to organize a Lunar Prospector Workshop, to be held the weekend before the 20th Lunar and Planetary Science Conference (LPSC) at JSC. The idea was to bring everyone from the NSS and SSI membership and all other interested parties, as well as anyone else we could get involved, to meet for a couple of days, discuss all the many open issues (launch, finance, organization, etc.), and develop our final plans. I would present my payload and mission plan, and, hopefully, we would gather momentum and move rapidly forward in the development of the mission.

I also felt it was time to tell Lockheed, my employer, what I was up to, since it would not help our cause if Lockheed was against my being involved with something like that. I told Mick Culp, my supervisor, what was going on.

I also said, "I feel that it's premature to discuss Lunar Prospector with (Lockheed) upper management until after the March workshop. If the workshop is a bust, we can just forget about it. But if the workshop produces positive results, I think we need to discuss Lunar Prospector with Max (Max Parks, Mick's boss) and let him decide what the next step should be." Mick was very positive about the whole idea and agreed with my plan. The stage had been set for the next step in the development of the project.

Chapter 1-2
The Spring 1989 Workshops

Saturday, March 11, and Sunday, March 12, 1989: The HSS Workshop

I was more than pleasantly surprised when I got to the meeting to find that over 50 people were attending. One of the attendees, Jason O'Neil, was a representative of Defense Systems, Inc. (DSI), a small aerospace company in McLean, VA (in the Washington DC area), that was very interested in building the spacecraft. The HSS had really done a very good job of setting up and advertising the workshop, which was held at the Hilton across from JSC.

I presented the payload, its rationale, and the basic mission plan early Saturday morning, and, of course, everyone wanted to know why I had not included a camera in the payload — they wanted pictures. I went through the arguments as to why Lunar Prospector could not and would not carry a camera (an exercise I would have to repeat many, many more times over the next ten years). Despite my explanations, the grumping continued until I stated very clearly, that as Project Scientist, it was my responsibility, and mine alone, to define the science payload and that was it, period. That formally ended the debate, though I had no doubts it continued behind my back.

The second bone of payload contention was the GRS. Brad Roscoe discussed the relative merits and issues of the different GRS detectors and the question was raised as to why I was flying the old, low-resolution Apollo 17 NaI GRS instead of a newer, high-resolution Germanium (Ge) GRS. The first part of the answer was, of course, that we hoped to get the Apollo 17 GRS free! The second part was that a Ge GRS is very expensive (the one that was being prepared for the Mars Observer Mission cost about $20 million — $10 million for the Ge GRS and $10 million for its cryogenic cooler) and it has to be cooled to cryogenic temperatures to work — a requirement that cannot be satisfied on a spinning spacecraft. The reason is that the cryogenic cooler's radiator has to point to deep space, which is at 3° Kelvin at all times, if cryogenic temperatures are to be achieved, and that can only be done on an expensive three-axis stabilized spacecraft. On an inexpensive spinning spacecraft that is in a polar orbit, the radiator will always point to the Moon during part of each spin period during part of each orbit. Since the Moon is essentially never colder than about 100° Kelvin and reaches 400° Kelvin at noon at the equator, the radiator never gets cold enough to cool the system down to cryogenic temperatures. It would be impossible for Lunar Prospector to carry a Ge GRS, even if we could afford the spectrometer, unless we could also afford to build a three-axis stabilized spacecraft — both of which were out of the financial question.

I was very impressed with some of the other contributions, especially that of one young lady, Dee Ann Davis. She had considerable experience in fund-raising and explained in convincing detail that the cost of raising money is 10 to 20% of the amount you needed! Since we would need roughly $5 million in cash (as well as a lot of donated hardware and a donated launch at a minimum), we had to have $500,000 to $1 million to even get started raising the money needed! That was very sobering.

Also, a young space engineer named Dennis Wingo from Huntsville, AL, had a number of innovative suggestions. Though I felt that Dennis's ideas were too unproven to be useful for Lunar Prospector, he clearly had his head on right.

However, the most critical thing for me was when the SSI representative, Rick Tumlinson, said that SSI had $75,000 for a Phase B Engineering Design Study. That was to me the single most important statement during the whole workshop and during the entire program up to that point; it made the mission a real possibility in my mind. If we not only had a good science payload, a good science team, and a good mission design, but also a well engineered spacecraft design to put in our "showcase window" and a realistic cost estimate based on all that, then we would have the credibility we needed to have a chance of getting the financial support we needed for Lunar Prospector. After Rick had finished his short talk, I spoke with him (that was the first time we had met) to make sure that I had not misunderstood what he had said about the $75,000. Rick assured me that SSI would put up the money for the Phase B Design Study.

I said to him, "Rick, that drastically increases our chances of success."

It was at that point I decided I would tell Mick Culp — and then we would tell Max Parks — I thought Lunar Prospector could succeed. Then I would talk to Lon Hood, Kinsey Anderson, and Bill Sjogren about being on the Science Team, and I would ask some of my young engineering friends about being the Project Engineer. Lunar Prospector had become a lot more real and I was excited about the possibility of a successful mission.

Monday, March 13, through Saturday, May 6, 1989: Building the Team

The workshop ended late Sunday afternoon and, of course, the 20th LPSC began about the same time. For me, the conference was an opportunity talk to Lon Hood about leading the MAG effort. Lon, who is scientifically and politically very cautious, was interested, but said that he wanted to ask the opinion of the other members of LExSWG (Lon was a member of LExSWG) if being part of a non-NASA mission was a good idea or not before saying yes or no. He promised to get back to me in a few weeks. When he did, he said LExSWG thought both the idea of the mission and his being involved were OK, so the answer was a cautious, "Yes."

Also Brad, Gay, Al Metzger, and I used the opportunity to get together at the LPSC to discuss the GRS, so the development of the Science Team was coming along just fine.

After the LPSC ended, I called Bill Sjogren at JPL to ask him to do the DGE. Bill answered with a resounding, "Yes." We discussed the DGE and the issue of a sub-satellite. Classically, the only way one obtains highly sensitive gravity data is to obtain line-of-sight Doppler Residual data. This is accomplished by getting a good, low harmonic gravity model of the body, using the model to predict the Doppler shifts of the satellite expected for each orbit, and then to subtract the observed Doppler shifts from the predicted shifts. The differences between the observed and predicted Doppler shifts, the so-called Doppler Residuals, give one the desired data on the gravity anomalies, i.e., the higher harmonic features. The catch is that this can only be done when line-of-sight Doppler data are obtained and hence, only when the satellite is visible from Earth if there is only one satellite in orbit. Thus, this method only works for the lunar near-side, as was done during the Lunar Orbiter and Apollo Mission days.

There are two solutions to this dilemma. First, one can fly a communications sub-satellite to act as a relay between the Earth and the main-satellite when the latter is behind the Moon, i.e., provide a line-of-sight link between the Earth and the relay-satellite and simultaneously between the relay-satellite and the main-satellite. Second, one can fly a repeater sub-satellite behind or ahead of the main-satellite that has a second transmitter/receiver. The main-satellite sends a signal to the repeater-satellite that is immediately bounced back to the main-satellite, allowing Doppler Residual data to be obtained between the co-orbiting lunar satellites. The data from the lunar far-side is stored in the main-satellite and is played back to Earth when the main-satellite comes back in view from the Earth.

Bill wanted to get the Doppler data from the far-side using either of those two techniques, but I said I doubted we would have the resources to do either of those things, but I would keep the issue open as long as possible.

When I called Kinsey Anderson at UC Berkeley to ask if he would lead the ER effort, I got another, "Yes." At that point, I had PIs for each experiment ready to go and, at my request, they were preparing the instrument data sheets (giving the mass, power, data rate, dimensions, etc. for each instrument) I needed to start defining the Spacecraft and Mission Requirements.

My next task was to get a Project Engineer. There were several friends and co-workers of mine at Lockheed and NASA who I thought I would ask — David Weaver, Bret Drake, Ron Humble, and Preston Carter. All of these guys are bright, young engineers who I trust and who I felt could do the job. Because David, Bret, and Ron all worked in the same big room as I did, I talked to them first.

David had worked in the same Lockheed group that I worked in, supporting NASA's advance mission planning, but had just become a NASA employee (or as we NASA contractors said — a NASA wienie, in contrast to NASA considering us — contractor scum). David is always full of ideas, but had no experience with real missions — just NASA paper studies. When asked, David liked the idea, but was concerned about conflicts of interest that could arise and decided he had to say no (David later became a lawyer [!] and reappears in that capacity in the Epilog of this book).

Bret, who also worked in the same Lockheed group as me (but later became a NASA wienie and, as it turned out, worked on Lunar Prospector from the NASA side years later) is very conservative and was concerned about working on a private program outside of both NASA and Lockheed and said, "No."

Dr. Ron Humble (one of the few engineers to have a PhD in engineering), also a Lockheed co-worker of mine and, like me, a non-establishment, politically incorrect, *persona non grata* at NASA (i.e., a competent, capable person who is tired of NASA's incompetence and who is not quiet about it) liked the idea, but thought he had too little experience to take on the responsibilities of the Project Engineer, but wanted to be involved.

Preston was a Lockheed employee, but worked in a different group and on a different program than me. In addition to being a "take charge kind of guy," Preston is of the same ilk as Ron Humble and me (that is the reason we three got along so well), and he was Ron's close friend and mentor. Preston and I had supported each other's ideas in the past, so when I found him and asked him if he wanted to be the Project Engineer, his answer was a resounding, "Yes." Preston had no doubts he could do the job of the Project Engineer and that, together, we would get the job done.

With that, I had the leaders of the Science and Engineering Teams put together and I informed the HSS and the SSI of my choices. The HSS accepted my choices; SSI liked the Science Team and tentatively accepted Preston as Project Engineer, but wanted to get acquainted with him, since they didn't know him from Adam (with or without the fig leaf).

The next thing I did was to tell Mick Culp the workshop had gone well, I had the Science Team, Preston was most probably going to be the Project Engineer, and I thought that Lunar Prospector had a chance of succeeding. I also said I wanted to ask Lockheed to support Preston's and my involvement with Lunar Prospector as a donation to the project. I told Mick that as Project Engineer and Project Scientist, Preston and

I would, in effect, control the entire program and if Lockheed supported us, Lockheed would get most of the credit for Lunar Prospector.

Mick said, "Great, let's go see Max."

We did and as a result of our discussion, Mick and Max told me to write a formal memo to Max, describing the Program and asking for LESC's financial support. I wrote a four page memo to Max dated March 23, 1989, in which I described all the details of the project, the benefits to Lockheed, and asked for $360,000 of support for Preston and me.

Once Max had the memo in hand and at Max's suggestion, Max, Mick, and I went to have a meeting with Moe Miller to get LESC's OK for what I was doing with Lunar Prospector. Moe, a very large man with enormous ears, was a high-up Lockheed mucky-muck and one of the dumbest people I had ever met (a characteristic I feel is an essential prerequisite for one to become a Lockheed upper manager and one that, along with his appearance, always made me think of him as being Moe in the famous trio, Curley, Joe, and Moe). In addition to that, and to put it mildly, Moe had a drinking problem, so when one talked to Moe, he was always half asleep or in a daze. Despite that handicap, I successfully explained to Moe what we were doing with Lunar Prospector and what kind of financial support I was seeking. That was all OK by Moe (assuming that he really understood what I had told him) and then, as expected, Moe added that Preston and I could work on Lunar Prospector as long as we did it on our own time and as long as it was clear to everyone involved that Lockheed was not formally involved with the project (i.e., Lockheed was not to blame for the mess we were making), unless or until Lockheed decided to give the project some formal support. Like a good little Lockheed employee, I said I understood; and with that, LESC's upper management was formally informed about Lunar Prospector and I had high hopes it would respond positively to my request for support.

Also during that period, SSI finished setting up a second workshop to be held at Princeton, NJ, on May 8 and 9, 1989. The workshop was being held to discuss all the technical and science issues, but also for SSI to get acquainted with Preston and me, face-to-face.

In preparation for the workshop, Preston and I got busy with the task of defining the mission requirements so we would know in some detail what had to be discussed at the meeting. I had already pulled together all the data about the science instruments and had a firm definition of the payload requirements — the starting point for defining the spacecraft. Preston had also started to recruit engineers like Mike Matthews and Gregg Grant from Lockheed to help us with the tasks ahead. Thus, by April 28, Mike and Gregg had produced our first, albeit very incomplete, version of the Mission Requirements Document (MRD). Things were moving right along.

Sunday, May 7, through Tuesday, May 9, 1989: The SSI Workshop

Preston and I flew (on our own nickels) from Houston to Princeton on May 7 and arrived at our hotel for a late supper. Gregg Maryniak and Gay Canough met us to get acquainted and to break bread together. After we sat down and got to know each other, Gregg said he was happy with Preston being the Project Engineer and then we discussed programmatics. Other than that, there were three memorable events at the workshop, one of which was quite personal.

Jim Burke from JPL was there, a fact that made me very happy. I had known and respected Jim since the sixties when I was a graduate student at the Lunar and Planetary Laboratory at the University of Arizona. At that time, my mentor, Dr. Gerard P. Kuiper, was the Principal Investigator (PI) on the Ranger Program that was run by JPL, and Jim Burke was the Project Manager. Jim, who is unquestionably one of the best space-engineers around, was held responsible when the first five rangers failed and his career as a JPL manager came to an end. Jim still continued to work at JPL, doing many good things, but that was that. While I fully agree that people have to be held accountable for their work and suffer the consequences of failure, I, like everyone else I know, still think Jim is one of the best in the business. I respect and like him very much. As such, I was taken aback when Jim ran into Preston and me, as we were taking a walk around the grounds the second evening of the workshop, and Jim said, "I am glad you're on board, Alan. If anyone can make this happen, it's you."

I was flattered, but literally speechless at Jim's statement. After a few seconds I managed to say, "Thanks, I'm glad you think that."

After we finished chatting and went our separate ways, Preston said, "That was quite a compliment."

I replied, "Yeah, but I have no idea why he said that!"

The meeting was well attended — there were more than 20 people there. However, the meeting itself was a fiasco. As the Project Manager, Gay was supposed to run the meeting, but it very quickly became very clear that she could not handle either job. While a Project Manager and Meeting Chair are supposed to give direction, keep order, and make decisions, Gay could do none of these things, so the meeting was chaotic.

After I had presented the mission objectives, payload, and mission plan, Andy Cutler, a bright young PhD, who seemed to have no practical sense at all, argued vehemently against our flying the low resolution NaI GRS instead of a high resolution Ge GRS, and against not having a camera onboard Lunar Prospector.

When I tried to explain the cost and complexity rationales for not having a Ge GRS and camera in the payload, Andy interrupted and said, with regard to not being able to cool a Ge GRS to cryogenic temperature on a spinning spacecraft, "All we have to do is freeze the GRS in a big block of frozen methane, wrap it in a garbage bag and that will keep it cold for a long time."

I thought, *what crap. Doesn't he have any idea about the engineering of a spacecraft, especially a spinning spacecraft that has to be kept spin balanced throughout the mission?* With the help of others, mainly Al Metzger (one of the worlds leading GRS experts, as well as our expert), we got that issue, and Andy, quieted down.

Gay said, "Well, clearly we have to look at the GRS issue in more detail," and the whole mess erupted again. That time it took even longer to quiet everyone down since there was a contingent, led by Andy, who objected to the Project Scientist — me — dictating to the group what the science payload was to be. At that point I explained, backed by Jim Burke, that space missions are not democracies. They are dictatorships, or they failed.

Defeated on those points, Andy then turned to the absent camera and said, "All we have to do is put a pin hole in one side of the spacecraft and a photodiode on the inside of the opposite side and the whole thing becomes a simple spin camera."

Once again I thought, *crap, that's fine for a grade school demonstration, but it's not worth a damn on a spacecraft*.

Before I could say anything, Jim Burke stood up and said in his loudest and most authoritative voice, "Lunar Prospector was never meant to be a photographic mission and Alan's payload is what we are flying, end of discussion." That ended the argument, but not the chaos.

Gay could not control the meeting and a little while later, when things were again out of control, John Lewis, one of the leading space resource scientists in the business, looked straight at me and said, "Will someone please take control of this meeting?"

I replied, "It's not my meeting." I had no intention of trying to take control of an SSI meeting at which I was an invitee, regardless of what my position was on Lunar Prospector. At that point it was clear that Gay could not handle her responsibilities and the meeting chugged chaotically along until we broke up into working groups. In the end, my payload and mission plan were accepted by those of us who were in charge and Andy and his backers left, not wanting anything more to do with Lunar Prospector.

The final, memorable event of the meeting was on the last night when Jim, Gregg, Gay, Preston, and I had an executive meeting. At the very beginning of our meeting, Jim Burke made a moving and prophetic statement. He said, like all space missions, "As Lunar Prospector proceeds, some of us will change our areas of responsibility, some of us will leave altogether, and newcomers will take our places."

Having been a PI on Viking, I certainly agreed; but unlike Viking, where I was just a PI, I was playing a major role in defining and managing Lunar Prospector. Jim's words hit home and I looked around, wondering who would be doing what in the future, already knowing that Gay had to go (I suspected that Jim had that issue in mind when he made his little speech). However, as the years passed and, one by one, the original Lunar Prospector Team leaders and members dropped away, I often thought back on Jim's statement, which I can still hear in my head as if he just said it.

After Jim's moving words, we got down to business. We agreed that Preston and I would be responsible for all the science and engineering (spacecraft, launch, tracking, etc.) aspects of the mission and that SSI would be responsible for the overall management, fundraising, and politicking. Gregg reaffirmed that SSI had $75,000 for a Phase B Design Study, so Preston and I said we would write an RFP (Request For Proposals) for the Phase B Study and have it ready for release in just one month. We all agreed that it was absolutely necessary to keep on schedule; if not, we all felt we would lose credibility. Our schedule for the Phase B Design Study activities was: Release of the RFP — June 12, 1989; Proposal Due Date — August 11, 1989; Contractor Selection — September 15, 1989; Contract Start — October 15, 1989; Contract Completion — March 31, 1990. We also agreed that our ultimate goal was to launch Lunar Prospector in late 1991 or early 1992.

From my standpoint, although we had been working on Lunar Prospector for less than six months, we had already made tremendous progress and were moving forward at an excellent pace. I really thought we had a good chance of flying Lunar Prospector to the Moon in two and a half to three years.

Chapter 1-3
The RFP, LEI, and the Proposals

Wednesday, May 10, through Tuesday, June 13, 1989:
Getting the RFP Out

Preston and I discussed the mission, the meeting, SSI, and the RFP on the flight home. We agreed that Gay had to go ASAP and that Jim Burke should be the Project Manager. Our opinion of SSI had not changed; if anything, it was even lower than before. As far as we were concerned, SSI was the weak link in our very short chain. However, if Jim Burke took charge for SSI, we figured we would be OK.

As soon as we were back in Houston, I went to see Mick to tell him that things looked really good for Lunar Prospector. By that time, our group had been moved from Max Parks's section and to Bill Beatty's section. Bill is an interesting character, who seems to be enthusiastic about everything, and had already begun to fall in love with Lunar Prospector. Anytime I needed to do anything for Lunar Prospector or needed to see anyone in LESC's upper management, Mick and I would go to Bill and he would say, "Sure, go ahead and do it," or, "Yeah, I'll call his secretary and see if we can see him right now."

My favorite response of Bill's was the one he used when I needed a couple of days to take a trip for the Lunar Prospector or the like. Bill would say, "Don't you have the lunar flu? You should be home in bed," so with Bill's unofficial sanction, I took sick leave to work on Lunar Prospector. When Mick and I told Bill how the Princeton meeting had gone, Bill was 100% behind our efforts.

After talking with Mick and Bill, Preston and I started to write the RFP. Preston, who has a great talent for organizing people and things, laid out a great RFP format and we got very busy working on the text, tables, and figures. I had received the Science Instrument Data Forms from Lon, Kinsey, Al, Bill, and Brad in April, so I already knew the payload parameters, which, of course, drove the design of our spacecraft. I quickly went ahead and made the ΔV (change in velocity capability a spacecraft has to have to accomplish its mission) calculations and determined the rest of the capabilities the spacecraft had to have to support the science payload and the mission. Unlike all NASA missions I knew about, the Lunar Prospector Science Objectives drove the spacecraft requirements and our developing RFP clearly reflected that.

In the midst of our RFP work (May 31), I got a fax from Gay, who was busy organizing her end of things. The good news was that SSI had had positive discussions with Congressman Torricelli (NJ) and Senator Gorton (WA) about their asking NASA to donate the Apollo 17 GRS to the project and letting us use NASA test, launch, and tracking facilities. The other news was that Gay and Gregg were going to be at the International Space University (ISU) in France from July 14 through August 31. Preston and I were astounded and angry. Here we were putting out an RFP in a few weeks, asking for responses by mid-August, and two of the principals were about to vanish for most of the summer! That was total nonsense and confirmed to us that we were dealing with rank amateurs, or worse.

We called Gregg and voiced our concerns to no avail. Gregg's attitude was that we could communicate via telephone when necessary and he would be back in the states once during the summer, so we could get together if we needed to. He and Gay were going to France! Preston and I were disgusted and concerned, knowing that their absence during that critical period was bound to cause trouble, but we pressed on with the RFP.

As we did, Jim Davidson and the other HSS guys started raising small amounts of money, as we assumed SSI was also doing, so we had a little money to work with.

Since Brad Roscoe had asked me if we could get him a surface barrier silicon detector (the type he needed for the APS) so he could make some tests before designing the APS, Jim Davidson took some of the money the HSS had raised and bought the detector. The HSS than held a press conference in mid-June, with coverage from two of the local radio stations and the Houston Chronicle, announcing the purchase of the first piece of Lunar Prospector hardware. That ticked Gregg off and he sent an angry letter to Jim, indicating that all money collected was to be sent to SSI for disbursement and no press events were to be done without SSI's involvement.

Preston and I finished the RFP on schedule and sent it off to Gregg early in June. The final product, which hit the streets just one day late on June 13, 1989, was a 46-page document that, when SSI put it together with a nice cover, a cover letter, and section dividers, was up to anyone's professional standards. Preston and I were very pleased with the RFP's professional appearance, since our main concern was always getting and maintaining credibility.

We had announced on the cover that "Proposals were due on August 15, 1989" (in just two months), that "Replies (our selection) would be on September 15, 1989," and that "Work would Commence on October 1, 1989" and, inside, we stated that the spacecraft had to be ready to launch by the fall of 1991, essentially what we had agreed to at the SSI meeting. We had reached another important milestone in the Program, a milestone that told the world that Lunar Prospector was real and that we meant business.

The only fly in the RFP ointment was when Preston and I sent the RFP to Gregg, we had put on the cover sheet that Preston and I were its authors, as well as the Project Engineer and Project Scientist, respectively, and that Gay was the Project Manager (which she still was). But, when the RFP came out, all three of us were missing from the document (except at the very end in a list of workshop participants) and the cover showed that the RFP came from SSI! That did not please Preston and me. Clearly, SSI was trying to make the world think that Lunar Prospector was their project, and theirs alone.

We were concerned for two reasons, the personal one, of course, and more importantly because of the credibility issue. We knew what the professional space community thought of SSI, and if the community thought the RFP and the mission were just SSI ventures, the community would laugh the whole thing off.

SSI's lame and transparent excuse for taking Preston's, Gay's, and my names off the RFP was that SSI wanted to save us from getting phone calls and having to answer questions! Since the only point of contact on the RFP was SSI's main secretary, Bettie Greber, that excuse was a joke. But it was too late to do anything about it, so Preston and I kissed the whole thing off and hoped for the best. However, we took the incident as a second warning that we could not trust SSI and had to watch our backs.

The Rest of June through Wednesday, July 19, 1989: Getting Moving

I got a memo dated June 15 from a Mr. G.E. Swiggett stating that LESC could not support my request for funding for Preston and me and suggesting that I submit the request to Anthony (Gus) Guastaferro at Lockheed Missiles and Space Company (LMSC) in Sunnyvale, CA. Mr. Swiggett had spoken with Gus and he was willing to consider the request. I showed Mick the memo and we decided that we would take it to Bill Beatty before acting on Swiggett's suggestion. Bill said we should discuss it with Moe Miller and then set up a meeting for the three of us with him. Moe agreed that LMSC was the right place to seek support and that I should go ahead and send my request to Guastaferro. I took my March 23 memo to Max Parks, updated it and the budget (I asked for $481,000 for wages and travel) and sent it to Guastaferro, hoping I would get a positive response.

With the RFP out of our hair, Preston and I started getting ready for the work ahead and continued to worry about SSI. But as July came and Gregg, Gay, and Jim Burke headed off to France, everything seemed to be going smoothly, and someone called Preston and told him the RFP had demonstrated to the aerospace community that we knew what we were doing and that Lunar Prospector was to be taken seriously. Thus, we had begun to achieve the credibility we would dearly need if Lunar Prospector were ever to reach to Moon.

As the summer proceeded, Preston and I were very busy with Lunar Prospector and things were getting exciting. We frequently exchanged faxes with Gregg and Gay, so our communications between Houston and France were working well to Preston's and my relief. We were also getting more engineers from the JSC area to help work on all the technical details of the mission. In order to recruit even more people, we wrote a short article on Lunar Prospector and our need for volunteers and sent it to the NASA/JSC *Space News Roundup* in early July.

July 20, 1989: The Apollo 11 Anniversary and the SEI

On the 20th Anniversary of the July 20, 1969, Apollo 11 landing on the Moon, President Bush announced the Space Exploration Initiative (SEI) from the steps of the Smithsonian Air and Space Museum in Washington, DC. The main objectives of Bush's SEI was, "to return man to the Moon permanently and go on to Mars." That sounded very good, but what it meant for Lunar Prospector was unknown.

Thursday, July 27, through Tuesday, August 8, 1989

On July 27, Preston responded to a request for clarification of two points in our RFP from Wayne Stevens, the President of OMNI Systems Inc., a small, new aerospace company in El Segundo, CA (in the LA area), that was responding to our RFP; it was comforting to know that someone beside DSI (the small aerospace company that had attended the NSS Workshop) was responding!

Also, by the end of July, Preston had re-initiated contact with John Champa, President of AMSAT (the Ham-Radio Operators' organization that had put up some 30 ham communication satellites), seeking their help in setting up a tracking network for Lunar Prospector. John had been at the NSS March Workshop and, at that time, felt the mission was not possible. He had since changed his mind and was greatly interested in having AMSAT become part of the Lunar Prospector Team, so much so that AMSAT had joined up with Dennis Wingo from Huntsville, to write a proposal for the Spacecraft Design Study.

Preston and I were also busy getting science and engineering budgets together so Gregg and Jim would know how much money the project would need. I had also written a letter to Gregg on August 2 stating it appeared unlikely that Lockheed would give us the money we had requested so Preston and I could work on Lunar Prospector, and reminded Gregg that we could not do our Lunar Prospector work in the evenings and on the weekends. Two days later, we found out that Lockheed might pay half of our costs if SSI paid the other half, and Preston informed Gregg of that development via fax. Gregg replied immediately with some other news and the statement, "raising an extra 100 K in a relatively few months does not appear to be viable." SSI was already failing to do its part of the project — the fundraising.

Finally, after some delays, our article about Lunar Prospector appeared in the August 4, 1989 issue of the NASA/JSC *Space News Roundup* (Appendix 1-1, also see www.lunar-research-institute.org) and in a few days we had some 30 volunteers who wanted to work on Lunar Prospector, and that number was growing.

Wednesday, August 9, through Thursday, August 24, 1989: Trouble with SSI — the First Delay

Everything was going along nicely until Wednesday, August 9, when, just before the proposals were due, we received a major setback from SSI. Preston got a maddening fax from Gregg and Gay stating that, because some aerospace companies had asked for more time, Gregg had — with just six days to go — extended the due date of the proposals to October 15 — by two full months! Gregg also stated that part of the delay was caused by a cash flow problem, but tried to assure us, "the money (the $75,000) is around, but cannot be accessed at the moment." As far as we were concerned, all that was BS. We had originally allocated two months for the companies to respond to our RFP and that had just been extended to four months! Preston's and my first reaction was that we simply did not believe that any competent company would need twice the time we had allocated to respond to the RFP, and we did not believe that Gregg had the $75,000. We smelled a rat and we believed the rat was SSI.

Our second reaction was that, besides there being no $75,000, the delay was due to Gregg and Gay being in France instead of at home tending to Lunar Prospector business.

Our third reaction was — LAWSUIT. We were fully aware that, by changing due dates at essentially the end of the response period, those companies that were bidding and that had finished on time could sue for unfair practices. Not surprisingly, Gregg got a letter from Wayne Stevens of OMNI. OMNI was about to submit its proposal for an on-time delivery on the August 15 due date and were "concerned" that other companies would have an advantage over them by having an extra two months to improve their proposals. SSI and Gregg had opened a can of potential legal worms, had caused the project to slip two months in violation of our agreed upon ground rule that no schedule slips would be tolerated, and had started to destroy the credibility Preston and I had been working so hard to develop.

Our fourth reaction was that, if SSI put out an RFP with no money to back it, SSI was asking for lawsuits and that would totally destroy the project's fledgling credibility.

All of a sudden, Preston and I were glad our names were not on the RFP. If someone sued, they would sue SSI and we would be in the clear! For the first time, we were happy with SSI's self-serving ways. Nevertheless, Preston and I were ticked off and very concerned, so I composed a letter for us to send to O'Neill. In the letter, dated August 15, we made our concerns unquestionably clear about the poor way Gregg and Gay were doing things and asked that O'Neill replace both of them before they wrecked the program and/or got SSI, and perhaps us, into legal hot water (Appendix 1-2, also see www.lunar-research-institute.org).

Since we received no response from O'Neill, we began to believe that Bettie Greber and Gregg had intercepted the letter. We did however receive a message from Bettie indicating that Gregg would soon be back at SSI for a short break from the ISU and that he, Preston, and I were to have a conference call.

When we had the conference call, Preston and I played "good cop — bad cop," a game Preston loved to play (he liked the bad cop role), but one I always thought was dumb. Regardless of our *modus operandi*, we told Gregg what we thought of the way he and SSI were doing their part of the job, about the potential damage that could be caused by the delay, and that Gay had to go. We also said we believed the delay was due to SSI's not having the $75,000 and demanded to know if SSI had the money or not.

Gregg, being a lawyer (or just being Gregg — we didn't know him well enough then to know which), held his ground, but he did admit in a "Clintonian" way that he and Bettie had intercepted our letter to O'Neill (a federal crime, though Gregg did not openly admit it) and that some of our concerns were legitimate.

Gregg agreed with us about Gay and said that SSI was looking for an experienced Project Manager and that Gay would be his or her understudy to learn how to become a Project Manager. That issue was being solved to our satisfaction.

We had a frank discussion about all the rest of our points of concern, but, as I said, Gregg held his ground. When we pressed the point about the $75,000, Gregg assured us that SSI had the money, but Preston and I remained unconvinced.

The conference call lasted close to an hour. As it ended, Gregg said he was pleased that we had aired all our concerns and that was a good sign we could work together and get Lunar Prospector done successfully. Preston and I were not so sure. The fact that they had intercepted our letter had, once again, indicated to us that SSI could not be trusted and we still had big doubts about the reality of the $75,000 for the Spacecraft Design Study.

Friday, August 25, through Sunday, September 24, 1989: The Beginnings of Lunar Exploration Inc.

As a result of our August 4 article, the number of volunteers for our Lunar Prospector Engineering Team had grown to over 40, so Preston and I held our First Engineering Team Meeting on Friday evening, August 25, in room 23M at the Lockheed Plaza 2 building (the meeting announcement had gone out on August 10). The first order of business was to order several pizzas (the meeting occurred immediately after work, so food was on everyone's mind) and then we got down to organizing the team. Preston and I went over all aspects of the project's structure and participating organizations, the mission, the schedule, and the RFP, and we showed the volunteers the management hierarchy we were using for the project and outlined the tasks ahead of us.

At that point the PROJECT was led by Gregg Maryniak (SSI) with SSI providing the PROJECT MANAGER (Gay Canough — still on paper, but soon to be changed). Preston was the PROJECT ENGINEER and was responsible at the next level for the GROUND SEGMENT, SPACECRAFT, LAUNCH, COST, and DOCUMENTATION — the lead engineers for each of these divisions were yet to be found. I, of course, was the PROJECT SCIENTIST and under me was the Science Team, with GRS/NS PI — Dr. Al Metzger (JPL) and TBD Co-Investigators (Co-Is), MAG PI — Dr. Lon Hood (U of Arizona) and Co-Is Dr.

Chris Russell (UCLA) and Dr. Bob Snare (UCLA, the MAG Engineer), ER PI Dr. Kinsey Anderson (UC Berkeley) and Co-I Dr. Robert (Bob) Lin (UC Berkeley), me as the APS PI with Dr. Brad Roscoe (Schlumberger, the APS Engineer), and DGE PI Dr. William (Bill) Sjogren (JPL) with TBD Co-Is.

What we needed to do was to fill out the rest of the engineering management matrix under Preston. We asked the volunteers to decide what areas or mission segments they each had the most experience in and therefore would best serve the mission in. They should then get together to form the various Mission Segment Teams, start having their own Mission Segment Team Meetings and address the issues we had outlined during the meeting. We began to call the latter the "Big Meeting" to distinguish the "all hands" meetings we had just started from the much smaller and more frequent, Mission Segment Meetings.

In addition to the engineers, there was a secretary (Diana Pavlow), a lawyer (Angela Davis), and other support personnel among the volunteers, people we would dearly need to help do all the work ahead of us. Preston and I also encouraged the team members to get their spouses and families actively involved, so they could not only help us in the support areas, but also share in the great experience we believed the mission would give us all. Lunar Prospector was a grassroots effort and needed to continue to be so if it was going to be successful.

Finally, the schedule Preston and I showed had us launching in just over two years, in December of 1991 — so we had a lot of work to do.

One of the volunteers, Larry Spratlin, worked for Control Data, a company that built and sold space computers. Control Data was interested in helping us put together our Command and Control Center as a way of getting good PR for their products. Also Tim Russell, Larry's boss at Data Control, put us in touch with John Reed who ran the Applied Technology Center (ATC) on the other side of Clear Lake from JSC.

ATC was a small service company that provided the usage of high-powered computers to small companies that could not afford the computers themselves and who only needed to use the computers on a part time bases. When we met with John, he offered us the possibility of the free use of his facilities for our meetings and his computers for our work.

On Thursday, August 31, Preston sent a memo to our Team stating that our second Big Meeting was set for Thursday, September 7, at the JSC Gilruth Center and giving the agenda. We also informed our members (who by then had reached more than 50 in number) that, in addition to our Houston team, a small group of interested engineers in California had contacted us and wanted to know what they could do for Lunar Prospector. We were really moving full speed ahead.

Preston and I wrote a memo on Tuesday, September 5, to SSI reporting those activities and the potentially donated support, and laid out eight requirements that we felt should be in the contract between us (Preston, our volunteers, and me) and SSI in order to get the job done (in terms of compensation, legal protection, levels of responsibility, etc.), and suggested three different ways of legally setting up the project for everyone's benefit and protection.

Our second Big Meeting, held on Thursday, September 7, was as productive as the first and, as was the case at our first meeting, pizza played a critical role in the event. However, besides eating pizza at the meeting, Preston and I verified that the work defining the requirements for the different segments was well under way and we began to see who were the natural leaders for the different segments of the project.

One such person, Paul Bailey, took the dozen or so members of the Command and Control (C&C) Team off to one corner, saying he was going to conduct a "Paper

SIM." Since C&C is one of my main mission interests, I went over to see what Paul was up to. As everyone knows, the most effective training tool for C&C personnel is the computer simulation or "SIM" of a spacecraft's activities and of possible failure modes. SIMs are practiced over and over before, and even during, the flight phase of a mission. Since we had neither computers, nor a spacecraft design, nor a spacecraft simulation program at that time, Paul took the bull by the horns and wrote down various data on small pieces of paper and gave several of them to each of his controllers. He then said that a fictitious spacecraft had just been launched and that they should look at the first of their scraps of paper, each of which represented a computer screen in a real mission. Paul then asked if the spacecraft was OK or if there were any anomalies indicated on their "screens." Everyone had blank looks on their faces and only after another prompt by Paul did they reluctantly start to say, in turn, that everything was OK. Perplexed, Paul then asked one controller in particular what his screen showed and he read what was written on the piece of paper with a puzzled look on his face.

Paul then said, "Doesn't that mean your subsystem is failing?"

The poor guy said, "I guess so."

To which Paul asked, "Why didn't you say so immediately when I polled you instead of saying everything was OK?"

Clearly, the controller had no answer. Paul then said every controller had to respond quickly and correctly and said, "Lets try again."

I was delighted and impressed with what Paul had done using the most primitive means and I was sure that Paper SIMs would be a very useful tool in training our C&C people until we had a real computer simulation capability. I was also certain we had a lot of the right people to get the tough job ahead of us done.

On the other side of the coin, because of our suspicions about the reality of the $75,000 and because of Gregg and SSI's other questionable activities during the previous months, Preston and I decided we had to protect both our growing team of volunteers, our interests, and ourselves against SSI. Since SSI was a non-profit, tax-exempt corporation, we decided we had to fight fire with fire by forming our own non-profit, tax-exempt corporation and thus, Lunar Exploration Inc. (LEI) was born.

Since Lunar Prospector was a labor of love for us, LEI was to be a volunteer based corporation whose charter was to provide the scientific, technical, and aerospace engineering support needed to build, test, and fly the spacecraft — and that was all.

Having no idea about how to set up such an organization, we first sought legal advice on Tuesday, September 12 from Art Dula, a well-known Houston "space lawyer" (who had a somewhat shady side — we found out later he had been disbarred from doing patent law because he had changed the dates on some patent applications). Art told us we needed to get incorporated, that being incorporated would protect all the involved individuals (especially the LEI officials — us) from legal action, and what we had to do to get incorporated.

Art also told us something we thought was irrelevant at the time; he said when we got done with Lunar Prospector we should legally disband LEI. He explained that if we wanted to do any follow-on missions for profit and kept LEI as the responsible corporation by changing it into a for-profit entity, every one of our ex-volunteers would expect a job and/or part of the profits from any follow-on ventures. If they did not get what they wanted, Art said they would sue us for everything the company had. Since we had no idea of doing anything beyond building and flying Lunar Prospector, we took little note of that sage advice.

Shortly after that meeting, I began getting the information and forms to start the process of incorporating LEI as a non-profit, tax-exempt Texas corporation.

A few days later, we received a letter dated September 15, 1989, from Gregg and a package of the proposals from OMNI and DSI. The letter stated, "Proposals for the Lunar Prospector have arrived from two of the spacecraft manufacturers. The deadline from the proposals has been shifted by two months. Therefore the companies that worked hard to meet the deadline would like to get a chance to answer our questions about their proposals before the new deadline (October 15)." Gregg asked that we evaluate those proposals and send our questions to SSI by September 29 in order to give those two companies a fair shake, given the postponement of the deadline (as it turned out, the only other proposal we received was a totally inadequate one from American Microsat Inc. in Sunnyvale, CA, sent on October 10 — close to the extended deadline, but that proposal was so inconsequential it could not have taken nearly four months to write. Also, to our disappointment, Dennis Wingo and AMSAT did not submit a proposal as they said they would).

Having received those two proposals by the original deadline, Preston's and my suspicion was heightened that the two-month delay in the program was not caused by companies asking for more time to prepare their proposals, rather that Gregg had delayed everything because he did not have the $75,000 for the study.

On Tuesday, September 19, Preston and I sent out the announcement for the Third Big Meeting, to be held on Thursday, September 28 at Lockheed Plaza 2. The announcement also contained the management matrix we had begun to fill out in some detail.

Brian Cox, a young and enthusiastic Lockheed software engineer, was selected to be Preston's assistant; John Gruener, a young Lockheed aerospace engineer and close friend of mine, had become my assistant, and we selected Larry Spratlin from Control Data to be the GROUND SEGMENT ENGINEER. Under Larry was COMMAND AND CONTROL, led by Paul Bailey with a ten member team, COMMUNICATIONS AND TRACKING, led by Bob Noteboom with a five member team, COMPUTER HARDWARE AND SOFTWARE, led by Steve Koontz with a three member team, and TRAINING AND VERIFICATION, led by Bill Conroy with a five member team.

We had dropped the COST and DOCUMENTATION SEGMENTS from our structure and added HOUSTON (SUPPORT) STAFF that was staffed by Richard (Rick) and Diana Pavlow and Fred Becker. Rick was "between jobs" and he thought Lunar Prospector might be a new start for him and Diana, his wife, who was a secretary at Data Control where Larry Spratlin worked.

Thus, except for the TBD SPACECRAFT and LAUNCH SEGMENT engineers, we had a well-developed Engineering Team staff. Our membership (excluding the eight Science Team members) was over fifty, of which some 70% was actively working on the project.

Though SSI was primarily responsible for raising the money for the project, I made my first attempt to get money beyond the support I was requesting from Lockheed for Preston's and my time and travel. I had written the Hobby Foundation, a local Houston philanthropic organization, requesting financial support for Lunar Prospector. The Foundation replied in a letter dated September 10, 1989; not unexpectedly, the answer to my request was a polite "No."

By Sunday, September 24, Preston and I had finished reviewing the DSI and OMNI proposals and had sent our questions about each proposal to Gregg so he could forward them to OMNI and DSI. However, it was already clear to us that OMNI had by far the best proposal and that they clearly knew what they were doing. In fact, the bulk of the OMNI proposal was a first cut at a complete Lunar Prospector spacecraft design! If OMNI were selected to do the Design Study, their job would be mainly to refine the basic design they had in their proposal — we were impressed. In contrast, the DSI proposal had several holes in it and worse, they were asking for a 10% fee on our volunteer based, non-profit effort — and I wanted to know why.

Monday, September 25, through Wednesday, October 11, 1989: The Apollo 17 GRS, Gus, and Jim French

On Wednesday, September 27, we received a fax from SSI of a letter to SSI from NASA's Lynn Heninger to Congressman Rohrabacher stating that, in response to his letter of August 8,1989; NASA was considering donating the Apollo 17 Gamma-Ray Spectrometer to SSI for use on the Lunar Prospector Mission! We might get the GRS, but more importantly, Lunar Prospector had been legitimized by Congress's support, so we thought that NASA would (however reluctantly) donate the GRS to us.

We got a call from Gregg who told us SSI had hired Jim French to be the new Project Manager. Jim, who I did not know at that time, is an outstanding spacecraft engineer who had started his career at JPL. Like many really good people, Jim could not stand the JPL/NASA bureaucracy and soon left to become a freelance agent doing contract engineering. Preston knew of Jim and his reputation and was pleased that Gregg had hired him to be the Project Manager.

We told the Team at the fourth Big Meeting on Thursday, the 28th, that Jim French was the new Project Manager and that he and Gregg would be visiting us during our next team meeting in October. Also, we added a MISSION PLANNING SEGMENT (trajectory and navigation) to our management matrix with Preston's and my good friend, Ron Humble, as its lead engineer.

Finally, the month of October began on a financial note. To both my great delight and surprise, I received a copy of an internal LESC memo dated October 6 indicating that LMSC had asked LESC for time and cost estimates for my requested support for Lunar Prospector. That was a very positive sign.

However, in order to seal the deal for the money Preston and I had requested, I flew to Sunnyvale, CA, to have a meeting with Gus at LMSC. When I went into Gus's office, he immediately asked me, "Weren't you a PI on Viking?"

I answered, "Yes, I was a PI on the Lander Camera Team."

Gus then turned around and got a book about the Viking Mars Lander Program off his shelf, thumbed through it until he found the page he was looking for and said, "Yeah, here you are (referring to a list of Viking PIs), I thought I remembered you. I was a NASA manager on Viking, so you worked for me before," and with that, the deal for my support was essentially sealed! Nevertheless, I told Gus all about Lunar Prospector, about NASA's probably donating the Apollo GRS to us and about all the progress we had made. In the end, Gus said that he would probably support our funding request, his assistant, Carol Lane, would be my contact, and he had arranged for me to give a talk on Lunar Prospector to his top management and engineering staff.

After leaving Gus's office, I went to the meeting room he had reserved for my talk and met the members of his staff. I gave them my spiel and then asked them two questions. First, I wanted to know if they thought our design, construction, test, and flight readiness schedule of two years was realistic, and second, if they thought we could do Lunar Prospector for the small amount of money (real dollars and dollar equivalents in donated hardware and personnel time) we were estimating. They answered, "Yes," to both questions and clarified that LMSC did spacecraft on that kind of schedule and for those kinds of dollars all the time for the military (but not for NASA) and that there was enough surplus hardware around LMSC to build a small spacecraft like Lunar Prospector without any trouble! I was pleased and relieved by both answers, since that meant Preston and I did know what we were doing and we were credible in LMSC's eyes.

I left Sunnyvale and headed home to Houston with the first external financial support for Lunar Prospector nearly in my pocket and with increased credibility for the program.

With that positive news, plus the fact that NASA was considering giving us the Apollo 17 GRS and that Jim French was the new Project Manager, things were looking very good indeed.

Thursday, October 12, through Thursday, October 26, 1989: Everything is Falling into Place

Having received the word that Jim French was on board, Preston wrote Jim a long memo on October 12, introducing us (he enclosed our resumes), the mission goals (he enclosed my discussion of the mission and the science goals), explained where we were in terms of our efforts at LEI, and expressed our concerns about how badly SSI had managed the project to date. Both Preston and I were encouraged that someone of Jim's stature and experience was becoming the Project Manager, but we were still very concerned about SSI's amateurish management methods and hoped very much that Jim would take our concerns to heart and finally get SSI moving in the right direction.

October 15, the deadline for the receipt of the proposals for the Spacecraft Design Study, came and went without any new proposal arriving. Thus, the three proposals we had received were the extent of the responses to our RFP, so Gregg, Jim, Preston, and I began to prepare for the selection of the winning proposal.

Since a large part of our effort was keeping the flow of information moving to our Houston staff, SSI, and the growing number of additional groups supporting the effort, Brian Cox and Mike Mathews took on the responsibility of writing a newsletter called *Lunar Prospector News*. Volume 1, Number 1 of *Lunar Prospector News* came out on October 16, 1989. The first issue told our team that ATC had agreed to donate permanent meeting space to LEI, that Gregg and the new Project Manager, Jim French, would attend our next general meeting on Friday, October 27, that NASA Administrator Truly was supportive of Lunar Prospector and hence that we might get the Apollo 17 GRS, and it contained a number of other work and organizational issues. Brian and Mike had done a great job of putting out a professional looking newsletter that was of considerable help to our cause.

I had taken a two-week vacation (starting on Monday, October 9, my birthday) and drove to New Mexico, the Grand Canyon, and Tucson to do a lot of hiking and camping. While in Tucson, I held a Science Team Meeting at the University of Arizona where Lon Hood worked. That was a good opportunity and a good location for the meeting since most of my Team was from Arizona and neighboring California.

When I returned to work after my vacation on Monday, October 23, I was greeted by the news that on October 16, NASA Administrator Truly had written Congressman Dana Rohrabacher stating that NASA would provide SSI with the Apollo 17 Gamma-Ray Spectrometer in return for SSI making the data available to the scientific community. Truly also warned that the GRS refurbishment costs might run into several million dollars. Also, Truly indicated he had designated Joseph Alexander as the contact between NASA, Congressman Rohrabacher, and SSI. That was great news since, in addition to our getting our first science instrument, it meant that Lunar Prospector was recognized as a legitimate and credible program by NASA and, of course, several members of Congress.

Also, when I got back, I received a copy of a full-blown LESC cost proposal dated October 18, and sent on October 23, to LMSC for the $489,999 for Preston and me. That was a very encouraging sign that the money would come, especially when the period of performance on the form was from November 1989 through December 1992. If that got approved (and it looked like it would), Preston and I would have money in just a week — hot diggidy dog!

Just after finding out about the cost proposal, Preston dropped a small bomb on me — he was leaving Lockheed and, as of Oct. 30, starting to work for Space Industries, a small Houston aerospace company headed by the famous designer of the Mercury, Gemini, and Apollo capsules, Max Faget and ex-astronaut, Joe Allen! That changed nothing in terms of Preston's participation in Lunar Prospector, and it came as a very big surprise.

On Monday, October 23, Preston sent Gregg a schedule of the meetings for the two days (Friday and Saturday, October 27 and 28) that Gregg and Jim would be visiting us in Houston. The list of meetings for Friday was an encapsulation of all the work LEI staff members had done in getting support from the extensive aerospace community surrounding the Johnson Space Center and was as follows:

8:00 AM (Friday) — Meeting with Control Data;

9:00 AM — Meeting with Ford Aerospace about their outfitting the Mission Control Center;

10:30 AM — Meeting with John Reed about ATC's support, its providing free office space, and a $5,000 membership for use of ATC's computers;

12:45 PM — Meeting with Disney and the JSC Visitor Center management about putting our Mission Control in their new Visitor Center as an added attraction;

2:00 PM — Meeting with Glenn Lunney of Rockwell International about Rockwell support;

3:30 PM — Meeting with McDonnell Douglas about its support for Lunar Prospector

After dinner, we would all meet at 7:00 PM for our Fourth LEI Engineering Team Meeting. Clearly, anyone seeing that list of meetings would understand just how far LEI had brought Lunar Prospector in the six months since the SSI Meeting in May.

Saturday, the 28th, was reserved for a meeting between Gregg, Jim, Preston, and me to discuss the three proposals we had received and to decide which company we were going to select to do the design study.

Friday, October 27, 1989: The SSI Visit

Gregg and Jim French spent all day Friday visiting the various companies that were interested in supporting our efforts and that evening they met our volunteers at our Team Meeting in the McDonnell Douglas Tower. Jim and Gregg were impressed with what Preston, our Engineering Team, and I had accomplished and with the prospects of support we had found among the various companies in the JSC area. In turn, Preston and I were impressed with Jim and very happy to have someone of his experience and qualifications leading the effort and, hopefully, getting SSI finally on the right track. All in all, the day's events, especially the joint meeting with our full Engineering Team in the evening, had created a lot of good will on both sides of the Program.

Saturday, October 28, 1989: OMNI's Selection

Saturday morning Gregg, Jim, Preston, and I met in a room at Gregg and Jim's hotel to go over the three proposals. Jim started the discussion with a bang when he said that the Feds had raided DSI the day before because of alleged illegal activities. DSI had been shut down and a couple of satellites that were under construction had been confiscated! Jim added, partly tongue-in cheek and partly seriously, that the raid should not influence our decision about possibly selecting DSI for the design study (after all, they had not been proven guilty). After that sobering revelation, we got started with our review.

Given what Jim had just told us about DSI and given the fact that we had all exchanged our views on the proposals over the previous few weeks, we took an immediate straw poll to see where we all stood. We all agreed hands down that the OMNI proposal was by far the best, that the DSI proposal was adequate, and that the proposal from American Microsat Inc. was a joke and was not worth spending any time on.

We got down to the details of both the OMNI and DSI proposals, discussing the pros and cons of each and the companies themselves. Though the OMNI proposal was the superior of the two, OMNI was completely unknown, while DSI had a reasonable track record. In the end, though, we all felt the OMNI proposal was technically very convincing and that fact outweighed OMNI's being new and untried (though we knew that all of the OMNI staff were Hughes Aircraft Company employees who were moonlighting to start their own little aerospace company — so all the staff had experience even if OMNI, as a company, did not). We decided to go with OMNI with the proviso that Jim (who lived in the LA area) would visit OMNI to get a face-to-face impression of their capabilities. If Jim turned up anything he did not like, we would then reconsider DSI. Barring a bad report from Jim, it looked like we had a winner. Preston and I expected we would make the final decision about OMNI very soon and they would be able to get started on the Design Study no later than the 1st of December, two months later than we had agreed upon when the RFP had been released — but that was not too bad.

By the time Gregg and Jim left Houston Saturday evening, everything seemed to going very well for Lunar Prospector.

Sunday, October 29, through Saturday, November 11, 1989: Finalizing OMNI's Selection, Support from LMSC and Others

A couple of days after our meetings, SSI's Bettie Greber sent Preston and me a copy of the letter from OMNI's Wayne Stevens dated October 26 with their replies to our questions. The replies were excellent and strengthened our opinion that OMNI was the correct choice for the Phase B Design Study.

On Thursday, November 2, I received formal word from Gus Guastaferro that he had agreed to fund Preston's and my Lunar Prospector activities. However, since Preston had left LESC, LESC had to prepare a new budget with my effort increased from halftime to two-thirds time and with an increase in my travel budget of 50%. The new budget was sent to LMSC on the 14th, but that wouldn't stop me from starting my work on Lunar Prospector using the original contract with the original budget as soon as the paperwork came through from LMSC.

As we had discussed during our proposal evaluation meeting, Jim went to visit OMNI at their home base immediately upon returning to LA. OMNI was located in a large, nearly empty building they had rented on the assumption they would fill it up with equipment and staff if they were not only selected to do the design study but were also selected to build Lunar Prospector. As Jim reported to us, he was satisfied that OMNI could both design and build our spacecraft. Clearly, as a startup company, they had no equipment or test facilities, but Jim said they convinced him they had access to facilities where they could rent services, e.g., thermal-vacuum and acoustic test facilities, and there were enough engineering and technical talent in the LA area so they could staff up as needed. OMNI's main assets were the talented young engineers that had formed the small company.

As a result of Jim's visit and questions, Wayne Stevens wrote Jim a letter dated November 6 with the formal answers to Jim's questions. After Jim's report and after receiving Wayne's letter, we all agreed that OMNI was it and that Gregg should inform Wayne that OMNI had been selected to do the Phase B Study and get the contract negotiated ASAP so we could start on the Design Study in early December.

On November 9, while Wayne's wife, Peggy, was in labor with their second child, Michael, Wayne called me from the hospital to see if there was any news about the selection (Gregg had not yet informed Wayne, who was getting increasingly worried about the selection). I told Wayne we had decided to go with OMNI and Gregg would soon officially notify him of our decision. I said further we hoped to have the contract done very soon so we could get started with the Design Study in early December. I must add here, years later Peggy told me, much to her consternation, that instead of Wayne comforting her during her labor, he was out in the hallway on a pay phone talking about Lunar Prospector with me!

Preston was also underway for Lunar Prospector. He attended an AMSAT Conference in Des Moines, IA, on November 4 and 5, where he gave a talk on the project and suggested several ways AMSAT could support the mission. One way that interested me was for AMSAT to build a small, sub-satellite that would be launched with Lunar Prospector and put into a high lunar orbit. That small satellite would carry a magnetometer that would monitor the background solar wind magnetic field, a data set that would enhance the magnetic measurements of the lunar magnetic fields made by Lunar Prospector in its low altitude orbit. It might also provide a communication link so we could get the line-of-sight Doppler residual measurements from the lunar far-side as Bill Sjogren hoped.

In support of AMSAT's interest in the mission, Dennis Wingo and John Champa of AMSAT submitted an article on Lunar Prospector that was published in the November issue of the AMSAT Journal.

We got the news from Sharon Lackey that the Center for Corporate Innovation was considering giving LEI free office space in the South Shore Harbor Office Building where ATC was located.

Finally, we found we needed more legal assistance in setting LEI up, so Rick Pavlow took it upon himself to contact Vinson & Elkins (V&E), a major, Houston based, international law firm of great reputation and asked if they would help us *pro bono*. They said they would, so Rick set up a meeting between V&E's James (Jay) L. Cuclis, Preston, Rick, and me. The three of us drove to downtown Houston and had an excellent meeting with Jay. He told us he would get LEI incorporated in Texas and then get our tax-exempt status and, in addition to his *pro bono* work for LEI, V&E also would pay the various fees associated with the applications! We were floored at how prepared V&E was to give us free help and were grateful to get it. That meeting with V&E was to bear fruit not only for LEI's immediate needs, but also those well into the unforeseen future.

Monday, November 13, 1989: A Very Good Day

LESC received the LMSC paperwork for my support, so I was able to start working on the mission two-thirds time and I had travel money. The revised contract, based on the new budget LESC was about to send LMSC (sent on the 14th), would follow, but that had no impact on my getting started right then.

Preston, Fred Becker, and I released Version 1.0 of the Mission Requirements Document (MRD) to the Team. The MRD was, of course, based on the requirements Preston and I had spelled out in the RFP and represented a revision and refinement thereof. It was — as expected — the first of many versions. The MRD was the standard reference for the Spacecraft Design Study and we sent OMNI a copy immediately.

Besides that, I was putting the final touches on our first "Big Paper SIM" to be held next evening during the Command and Control (C&C) Team meeting. Because I had been so impressed with Paul Bailey's Paper SIM two months earlier, I set up a much more sophisticated SIM based on the spacecraft design OMNI had in its proposal. The SIM covered the first hour or so after launch, starting just after the spacecraft had been turned on. I had typed lines of engineering data (voltages, currents, temperatures, tank pressures, engine temperatures, etc.) for every minute after turn-on for each subsystem on sheets of paper and taped a paper frame (representing the frame of a computer screen) on each of the engineering data sheets with just enough space between the frame and the data sheets so a slightly smaller piece of paper could slide between them, thereby covering up the lines of data. The idea was that someone would call out the time in minutes after spacecraft turn-on and each controller would slide the obscuring sheet of paper down one line, revealing the engineering data for that minute. That way we could step through the engineering data in a real-time Sim. I had set up the SIM on the assumption that we had had an under-burn of the third stage during launch, so it was necessary to have an immediate corrective burn, using Lunar Prospector's engines, to save the mission.

In addition to preparing the Sim, I had begun to write what later became the Mission Operations Document (MOD). The purpose of that document was to instruct the controllers on how to run the spacecraft and what to do in case something failed or it was not working properly. At that point in the training, the parts I wrote were related only to the emergency procedures so we could get through the Paper Sims. However, I began to find that preparing Sims and writing both the MRD and the MOD are the best possible ways of understanding the spacecraft and of determining ways to improve its design and the mission's design.

I had spent a lot of time preparing the SIM and the emergency procedures, so I was looking forward to seeing how well it all would work and how well the C&C guys would do.

Tuesday, November 14, 1989: The First Big Paper Sim

The SIM was a blast. Mick Culp read off the times and I was the Mission Director. Though he did not know it, Ron Humble, who was both the Mission Planning Team Leader and the Controller for the Propulsion Subsystem, was in the hot seat.

Mick counted down to spacecraft turn-on and at T=0 the guys pulled down the obscuration sheets one line and saw their first lines of data. Interestingly, they were all rather tense; in fact, Ron said afterwards he was really nervous and it felt like the real thing — despite the simplicity of the paper computer screens. Ron immediately noted that the spacecraft's velocity was too low and that they had to do an emergency engine burn to get the spacecraft back on track. He went through the emergency procedures I had written up and found out what to do, but he took too long to do so and thus missed the first window for the burn. At that point, I had to stop the SIM because the engineering data sheets I had typed up assumed that the corrective burn had gotten off on time. Since it had not, the rest of the pre-prepared engineering data were, of course, incorrect. That was the weakness of the Paper SIM — it was not interactive. If the controllers did not get it right, there was nothing to do but stop.

After I stopped the Sim, I asked the controllers what they thought of it and they had a number of good suggestions on to how to improve it. Most importantly, they wanted all the out-of-spec data highlighted in red (as is the case on the real computer screens during computer Sims and during a real mission, the color codes for which are as follows: Green — the data are within spec; yellow — the data are OK, but close to the limits; and red — the data are out of spec) so they could easily tell if something was wrong. There were a few other good suggestions, but it was clear to me that the main problem was that none of them had any idea of what the spacecraft was really supposed to do. That was mainly because they had not yet seen the Preliminary Design and would not be able to do so until the contract between OMNI and SSI was signed. Despite that failing, we had learned a lot about how to proceed with training and everyone had enjoyed their first attempt to fly the mission — even if it did make them nervous.

Wednesday, November 22, 1989: The GRS Meeting With NASA

Gregg and I had received word from Joe Alexander at NASA that we were to have a meeting at Headquarters to discuss the transfer of the GRS to SSI, the transfer of Lunar Prospector's data to NASA, and other issues. We set up the meeting for November 22. I flew to Washington the night before and met Gregg at the Air and Space Museum on the morning of the 22nd, well before our meeting with Joe, so we could discuss the pending issues between ourselves before going to NASA. Gregg diplomatically let me know he was concerned because, as a scientist, I was not used to dealing with NASA upper management, whereas he thought he was — so he wanted to do most of the talking. I silently laughed at his assumptions, but said nothing to the contrary. Then we went to the meeting.

In addition to Joe, who was then the Assistant Associate Administrator and the official NASA Liaison to the Lunar Prospector Project, NASA's Project Scientist for Advanced Studies, Bevan French, and NASA's Congressional Liaison, Mary Kerwin, were also present at the meeting. The meeting started out cordially, but cool as Joe immediately made it very clear that we were getting the GRS only because members of Congress had asked (more like told) them to give it to us and then Joe and Bevan asked about the details of the science, the spacecraft, and the mission. Despite Gregg's previous assumption about our relative levels of experience dealing with NASA, Gregg could not tell Joe and Bevan what they wanted to hear, whereas I could and did.

Despite their typical NASA — not invented here, so we don't care what you are doing — attitudes, Joe and Bevan were clearly surprised (I would like to have been able to write impressed, but surprised was more like it) at what I told them. We discussed the transfer of all of the Lunar Prospector data — not just the GRS data — to NASA at the end of the mission, the allocation of NASA employees' time to the project (paid for by the project) for those NASA scientists who were Science Team Members, and permission for other NASA employees to do volunteer work on the project. Since all of those issues were concerned with LEI Team Members or LEI activities, I did essentially all the negotiating, contrary to what Gregg had expected. In the end, the final tenor of the meeting was very positive with Joe, Bevan, and Mary expressing considerable interest in Lunar Prospector and its positive impact on the NASA Lunar Exploration Program. Joe finished by telling Gregg and me that the agreements would be formalized by written contract between NASA and SSI in the immediate future.

As Gregg and I left the NASA building, Gregg said to me, "Boy, you did a really great job in there."

I replied, "Thanks," but I laughed to myself at Gregg's naiveté.

Monday, November 27, 1989:
Agreement Between OMNI and SSI and the Money Issue

A few days after Gregg's and my successful meeting with Joe Alexander, Wayne wrote a letter to Gregg, dated November 27, indicating that he believed, "Omni Systems' position on these topics (discussed during a November 20 telephone call) are (sic) now fully compatible with that of Space Studies Institute." At the end of the letter, Wayne stated, "I believe you and I can work out to our mutual satisfaction any remaining contractual aspects of the design of the Lunar Prospector Spacecraft." OMNI and SSI were finalizing the contract, but it was still not done and our hoped-for start in early December looked like it would slip again.

Seeing no real reason for slipping the start of the study, Preston and I were again worried that Gregg was stalling because, as we still believed, SSI did not really have the $75,000. In reality, as we learned later, SSI did have at least some of the money, but even at that late date Gregg *did not have permission* from the SSI Board of Directors to use SSI money for the Phase B Study! Also, we learned very shortly, SSI only *intended to underwrite the $75,000* for the Design Study, not actually to pay for it! SSI expected the project to pay back the $75,000 as soon as it began to get donations, or better yet, that SSI would never have to pay OMNI, since SSI hoped that the project would get donations before OMNI was to be paid! In short, SSI never intended to support the project financially.

Tuesday, November 28, 1989: LEI Becomes Incorporated

We got the word that our application for LEI's incorporation in Texas was accepted on the 28th — though the Certificate of Incorporation was not signed by the Secretary of State until December 5, 1989, and we still had to get our tax-exempt status from the IRS. Nevertheless, LEI was soon going to be a legal entity, and with that important step nearly behind us, I began working on a Consortium Agreement that would legally define the roles of LEI, SSI, and any other organization that might join the Consortium in the future, e.g., AMSAT.

From Preston's and my standpoint, since we did not trust SSI or believe that it could really manage the project, we wanted equal voting rights for SSI and LEI, so SSI could not stop us from doing what we needed to do to bring the mission to a successful conclusion (actually, we wanted LEI to have the majority voting rights so we would not even have to compromise with SSI, but we knew that SSI would not allow that). SSI was intent on keeping the majority voting rights since it wanted to keep control of the mission for its own purposes. Unfortunately, from LEI's standpoint, SSI was providing the $75,000 (we hoped) for the Phase B Study and was responsible for the fundraising activities. Since the "Golden Rule," i.e., "He who has the gold — rules," always applies, SSI had the leverage in the battle between LEI and SSI concerning the Consortium Agreement terms that had just begun and would continue well into the future.

Also on the evening of the 28th, we had our second Paper SIM that was as much fun as the first one.

The End of November 1989: One Year and Counting

As November 1989 drew to a close, the Lunar Prospector Project had been underway for one year and we had made tremendous progress in that year. First, LEI had been officially founded as a Texas corporation and had a well-structured group of some 50 experienced JSC area engineers and support personnel, most of whom were working very hard on the project; second, I had defined an excellent payload and built a Science Team of excellent and experienced scientists and instrument engineers; third, LMSC had donated two-thirds of my time and all my travel to the project; fourth, OMNI had been selected to do the Phase B Spacecraft Design Study and had already presented the project with a very good preliminary spacecraft design in its proposal; fifth, SSI had obtained support from several members of Congress and had hired Jim French as the Project Manager; sixth, in large part thanks to SSI, NASA had donated the Apollo 17 GRS to the project; seventh, NASA was (even if reluctantly) cooperating with us; and eighth, we had achieved a high level of credibility within the space science and aerospace communities. Lunar Prospector was clearly off to a good start and we had every reason to believe that we had more than a good chance of launching the mission in two years. All of that was more than remarkable when one considered how few financial resources we had. Lunar Prospector's future looked bright indeed after only one year's effort.

Sunday, December 3, through Wednesday December 6, 1989

In response to a request by Jim and Gregg for Preston and me to write down how we wanted the Design Study with OMNI to be managed, Preston and I wrote a letter dated December 3, in which the five main points were as follows: First, the Consortium (that we were trying to hammer out) must control the project; second, the Design Study Contract must be between the Consortium (not SSI) and OMNI with SSI underwriting the contract; third, Jim French should be the Director of the Lunar Prospector Consortium; fourth Jim French should also be the Spacecraft Segment Engineer under the Project Engineer — Preston; and fifth, Jim should "be completely responsible for the technical and administrative monitoring of the design study contract," as well as should "be the primary contact person for the design study contract."

That letter to Jim and Gregg was followed the next day by a fax of the first draft of the Consortium Agreement I had written and that Jay Cuclis of V&E had proofed. In that draft, SSI and LEI had equal voting rights, LEI was responsible for all scientific, engineering, and technical aspects of the project, and SSI was responsible for the main funding, political, and publicity activities of the project. Further, Gregg had no real title, but was responsible for the funding activities, Jim was the Spacecraft Engineer and Project Manager, Preston was the Project Engineer, and I was the Project Scientist and Mission Director.

Also on Monday, December 4, the 4th issue of *Lunar Prospector News* appeared, in which the next Big Meeting was announced. It was to be held on Wednesday, December 6 and the Board of Directors was to be elected at that meeting. Also, the next Paper SIM was announced via the amusing statement, "Another of Alan Binder's famous mind-bending simulations, guaranteed to leave you with nightmares about failed thrusters and sub-nominal TLI burns. . ."; the date of which was to be Tuesday, December 12.

Jim, Gregg, Preston, and I had a telecon during which we discussed both the letter Preston and I had sent them on the 3rd and the Consortium Agreement draft. To say the least, it was not a good telecon — Gregg rejected essentially everything Preston and I had sent to them. Gregg was bent on keeping absolute control of the project in SSI's hands and would not consider anything else. He insisted that the Design Study Contract had to be between SSI and OMNI and that Jim, an SSI employee, must be in full control of the study and future work, i.e., be a classical NASA type Project Manager. Gregg argued that it was SSI's $75,000 that was being spent on the Design Study (not true, we already knew that SSI was just underwriting the study — not paying for it), and hence that SSI personnel be responsible for the money and how it was spent.

That was all BS. It was clear that Gregg and SSI's sole interest was having Lunar Prospector be an SSI venture and SSI's alone, shutting out LEI, regardless of what it cost (and Preston and I believed that the cost would be mission success). In contrast, Preston's and my sole interest was having a successful mission, regardless of all other issues. Thus, SSI and LEI were working at cross purposes and SSI's "dog in the manger" attitude put LEI at a negotiating disadvantage — we were not willing to damage the project for our own benefit, while SSI was — and that ticked off Preston and me. The telecon got heated and was going nowhere. Interestingly, Jim was very quiet during all of that and we found that strange for a Project Manager.

Given SSI's stance, I said that I was no longer willing to have Jim be the point man for the Design Study; rather that Preston must have that responsibility. I said, "Since LEI is providing all the science, engineering, and mission requirements, it makes no sense for LEI to discuss the requirement with Jim in LA, who then relays them to OMNI. Doing so will only insure that there are numerous misunderstandings and will lead to inefficiencies. If Preston is the point man, then the information will be transmitted directly from LEI to OMNI. As long as LEI is doing all the technical work, there is just no way Jim can be a real Project Manager and the contract point man unless he lives in Houston and works directly with us at LEI, and that is a fact whether you (Gregg) like it or not." I then reminded Gregg that his-way was the same as NASA's-way and that we were trying to demonstrate that there was a better-way of doing missions, i.e., the LEI/Preston/Alan and even Jim-way. I had several other points and in the end Gregg said that I should write down my points and send them to him — an exercise in futility as far as I was concerned.

Finally, the useless telecon ended with Preston and I knowing for sure that SSI was going to cause nothing but trouble and that SSI was going to try to keep itself in the spotlight at LEI's expense — just as it had been doing during the previous several months. Two comments I wrote at the bottom of my prepared notes (Appendix 1-3, also see www.lunar-research-institute.org) during the telecon underscored that conclusion. They are: "(1) We (Preston and I) are letting Gregg get his way. (He) Cuts off discussion when (it) goes against him and postpones it as (a) delay tactic. (Gregg) Did not discuss point man with Jim or us — just do it his way. (2) Writing arguments is delay tactic."

Despite my knowing that it was a useless exercise, I sent Gregg my 2½ pages of notes as a memo the next day (December 5), giving my four points about why Preston should be the point man (Appendix 1-3, see also www.lunar-research-institute.org). That memo is a clear statement of how I believe missions must be done, what is wrong with NASA's way of doing anything, and the fact that Jim (despite his capabilities and experience) had only a cosmetic role as Mission Manager in Lunar Prospector. I also pointed out, that despite Gregg's insistence that SSI have control of the project because it was SSI's $75,000 that was being spent, SSI was only underwriting the $75,000, while I would be spending $65,000 of real Lockheed money, and hence, I had more responsibility to Lockheed to see that its money was correctly spent than Gregg did to SSI (Given the importance of that memo in setting the tone of Lunar Prospector for years to come and my future commercial lunar exploration activities, I encourage the reader to read it since it remains a clear statement of the managerial and programmatic issues that have always faced NASA, their solutions [in my view], and the real purpose of the Lunar Prospector as a demonstration of those solutions. That memo also contains the prophetic statement, ". . . *one of the major goals of the Lunar Prospector Project is to demonstrate a quicker, less costly and better way of doing . . . missions,*" in which the phrase "*quicker, less costly and better*" predates by several years the "*Faster, Better, Cheaper*" mantra NASA used for its new way of doing business in the late nineties.).

On the brighter side, as a result of *Perestroika* and *Glasnost*, a Russian delegation, led by Cosmonaut Alexander Laveikin, visited the USA and specifically the Clear Lake Area Economic Development Foundation to look for launch vehicle and other space related business for the Soviet Union. LEI's Denis Dillman presented the Lunar Prospector Project to the delegation and Alexander Martinov, Director of the Plenipotentiary of Glavkosmos, expressed great interest in the project and requested more information, which Preston began to provide essentially immediately via a fax on December 6 and letters on December 11 and 22 with the requested information.

On Wednesday evening, December 6, 1989, LEI had its fourth Big Meeting, during which Preston and I were elected as Co-chairmen, Larry Spratlin was elected as the Secretary, and Richard (Rick) Pavlow was elected as the Treasurer. LEI was officially under full steam as we moved into the Spacecraft Design Study.

Chapter 1-4
The Spacecraft Design Study

Thursday, December 7, and Friday, December 8, 1989: The Kick-Off Meeting

Although OMNI had not yet signed the contract with SSI, we all wanted to get started with the Design Study ASAP since Gregg's delays had already cost us over two months of time. In addition, there were contractual questions about the schedule and deliverables that needed to be answered before the contract could be finalized. Jim and I met with OMNI in LA on December 8 and in effect, though not contractually, that was the Design Study Kick-Off Meeting.

I flew to LA on the afternoon of the 7th. Wayne Stevens had booked a room for me with an adjacent meeting room at the Embassy Suites Hotel just south of LAX. I had never been to an Embassy Suites Hotel before and I liked it very much. Like all Embassy Suite Hotels, the rooms are built around — and look into — a beautiful, interior atrium. The only drawback was that it was expensive and since Wayne had me down to pay for both my room and the meeting room, the cost of the rooms was well above what Lockheed allowed. OMNI was going to have to pick up some of the hotel bill.

Given Gregg's intransigent and counterproductive attitude about SSI's dominating the project — in part via Jim French — Preston and I had decided that I would take over the meeting and would assume the role of the Project Manager. Our decision was in no way directed against Jim personally, for whom we had the highest regard, rather we decided that we had to do so because there was no way that Jim could be an effective Project Manager while living in LA, remotely working for SSI in Princeton, and being remotely responsible for all the technical work that we were doing at LEI in Houston. To have Jim do so, as Gregg insisted, was just asking for a NASA-type mission mess and mission failure. Uncharacteristically, Preston wanted me to subtly take over the Project Manager role as the meeting progressed, but I had decided otherwise.

Early Friday morning, I met Jim, Wayne, and the other members of the OMNI staff for breakfast down in the hotel atrium. I told Wayne I could not pay for both of the rooms and he said OMNI would pay for the meeting room, a solution that worked.

While Wayne and the others got their things together, I went up to the meeting room and deliberately sat down at the head of the table where the Project Manager would normally sit. As everyone else came into the room and before they could even sit down I said, "OK, let's get this meeting started," thereby taking control of the meeting at its onset and I never let go of that control for even a second after that. Jim never blinked an eye, but sat rather quietly during most of the meeting, in part, because Jim is a quiet person, but mainly because he had essentially no knowledge of what we had been doing at LEI regarding the spacecraft design and the Mission Requirements — just the problem we knew would exist if Jim were to remain the Project Manager and the point man.

We discussed the MRD that I delivered to OMNI, the contract schedule, and the contract deliverables as planned, but the main issues I brought up were the changes we wanted to be made to the preliminary design of the spacecraft that OMNI had in their proposal.

First, we wanted the axial thruster, that would be used for the big Lunar Orbit Insertion (LOI) burn, to have 4 or 5 times the thrust that OMNI proposed. That change would cut the burn time from as much as 90 minutes to less than 20 minutes, thereby greatly reducing the inefficiencies of the burn due to gravity and thrust vector mis-alignment losses.

Second, we wanted a single solid motor for the Trans-Lunar Injection (TLI) maneuver rather than the two-motor configuration that OMNI had proposed.

Third, we needed the science instrument boom configuration changed to reflect new science requirements that eliminated the need for a multi-step boom deployment to get science instrument calibration data at different distances from the spacecraft bus and a new GRS requirement regarding its orientation on the boom.

Part of the reason for the changes in the boom configuration was that, when I had first asked the MAG/ER Teams to give me the specifications for their hardware, they had given me those for the Mars Observer package that had a common electronic package, the ER and two magnetometers (MAGs) — an inboard and an outboard MAG. That was what Preston and I had assumed when we wrote the RFP, and what OMNI used in their proposal design. In the meantime, I had found out the reason for the inboard MAG and had dropped it from the package.

The reason for two MAGs in the MAG/ER package is that, while the outboard MAG is used to measure the magnetic fields of a planet or satellite, the inboard MAG data is needed to correct the outboard MAG measurements for the magnetic fields created by the spacecraft itself. This is necessary because few NASA spacecraft are magnetically clean, so an inboard MAG is necessary to make sense of the data.

However, because of our limited resources, I told the MAG Team that they could have only one MAG — the outboard MAG, and I would see to it that the spacecraft was magnetically clean. Based on their bad experiences with MAG experiments on NASA spacecraft that were promised to be magnetically clean, but in the end were not, the Team protested, but I said that they could have only one MAG, period.

OMNI said they would take care of those changes, so we had agreement on all the issues.

The Kick-Off Meeting resulted in a great start for the Design Study. We had all got-ten acquainted and it was clear we could easily work together, and, most importantly, I had set the precedent that LEI and I were in charge and not SSI and Jim.

When the meeting broke up, Jim offered to drive me to LAX for my flight back to Houston. I accepted, in part, because I wanted to talk to Jim about the problems Pre-ston and I saw between LEI and SSI, and because I wanted to be sure Jim understood both why I had taken over his role as Project Manager and my doing so was not meant to show any disrespect to him. As we drove to LAX, I did both.

Jim said he understood LEI's viewpoints and did not disagree with Preston and me, but added he also saw the situation from SSI's standpoint and that Gregg was not altogether wrong either. What Preston and I did not know at that time — but Jim did — was that Gregg and SSI had invested a fair amount of time and money in the idea of a small, lunar polar orbiter before we all had gotten together and had already spent a year's effort on the idea (see the Prolog). Because of that prehistory, Gregg and SSI felt Lunar Prospector was their baby. Nevertheless, Preston and I knew SSI hadn't a clue as to how to do the mission, so there was no baby without LEI, regardless of how pater-nal Gregg and SSI felt.

Then Jim dropped a real zinger. He said, regarding his role vs. mine in the project, "Well, since SSI has no money to pay me, there's not much that I can do any-way."

Now that put the frosting on the cake! SSI could not afford to pay Jim (a fact that made me worry even more about SSI possibly not having the $75,000 for the OMNI contract)! Thus, SSI's "hiring" Jim as the Project Manager and Gregg's arguing that SSI and Jim had to run the project was just a façade (however, I did not believe that Gregg was trying to trick us, rather I believed that SSI had hired Jim with the best of intentions, but just did not have the money to pay him). No matter what, that new fact, added to all the other concerns, showed conclusively that Jim could not be an effective Project Manager, so either Preston or I would have to take over the job if Lunar Prospector was going to be successful. Armed with that information and a very successful Kick-Off Meeting, I flew home to Houston thinking things were working out quite well for Lunar Prospector and LEI.

The Second Half of December 1989

After the Kick-Off Meeting, SSI and LEI were busy finalizing a number of administrative issues and receiving calls and letters from additional groups who were interested in becoming involved with Lunar Prospector.

Dr. Nebil Misconi of the Florida Institute of Technology (FIT) in Melbourne, FL, had contacted Gregg about becoming a major player in the project. Preston and I followed up that initial contact and exchanged information about Lunar Prospector and FIT with Misconi.

Most importantly, Gregg and Wayne finally signed the Spacecraft Design Study Contract between OMNI and SSI on December 26, 1989 (actually, we at LEI thought it was signed, but the contract was only initialed by Wayne and Gregg so OMNI could officially get started to work — Gregg dragged out the negotiations for more than another month before the contract was actually signed). Thus, (or so we thought) that major step was finally behind the project and we could finally move forward rapidly with the already "kicked-off" Design Study. Hooray!

Also on the 26th, the agreement for LEI to become a member of ATC was finalized. Thus we had a permanent place for our meetings, we could use the ATC computer facilities, and Preston and I had a place to work until we received our free office space, just down the hall from ATC, from the Center for Corporate Innovation.

The decade of the eighties ended well for Lunar Prospector — our major contracts were in place, the Design Study had started and we were all looking forward to a launch in late 1991 or early 1992.

First Half of January 1990

Our Mission Segment Teams, as well as Preston and I, continued to work diligently defining the Consortium Agreement, the budgets and requirements for the various segments of the mission (i.e., tracking and communications, mission control, and launch), and, of course, the spacecraft itself. Along these lines, Brian Cox had investigated the launch options for Lunar Prospector and had provided the project with a list of 20 possible launch vehicles, both domestic and foreign, along with their technical data. Preston had put together — and sent off to Gregg — a very detailed project budget with a total mission cost of $14.7 million (assuming very large amounts of donated time, hardware and services), a pittance in terms of a NASA Project, but still a lot of money for us to find, and I sent a second version of the Consortium Agreement to Gregg. The major changes in that draft were that SSI had three votes to LEI's two, Gregg had a title — Project Finance Officer — and I was also the Deputy Project Manager (a change that Gregg had already agreed with) with, of course Jim still officially being the Project Manager — but in Preston's and my opinion, in name only.

I was also busy getting ready for our First Monthly Design Study Meeting on January 19 at OMNI's headquarters in El Segundo, CA.

Finally, Preston had been contacted by the Aerospace Department at his alma mater, University of Texas at Austin, whose staff was interested in joining Lunar Prospector and they had invited Preston to give a talk on Lunar Prospector at UT, which he did on February 22. We just kept getting letters and calls from various organizations that wanted to be part of the project.

Friday, January 19, 1990:
The First Monthly Spacecraft Design Meeting

I had flown to LAX during the afternoon of the previous day, gotten my rental car, and driven the couple of miles to the Hacienda Motel that is just to the south of LAX and just north of where OMNI had its headquarters in El Segundo. Since I had explained to Wayne at our Kick-Off Meeting a month earlier that I could not stay in expensive hotels, Wayne suggested I try the Hacienda, where a lot of Hughes visitors stayed. As one might guess from the name, it was a Spanish style motel and I liked it a lot.

Friday morning I drove the couple of miles to OMNI and as I did, I decided it was not worth the expense of renting a car for the few miles between LAX, the Hacienda, and OMNI and hence, that in the future, I would take the Hacienda van from LAX to the motel, have Wayne take me between OMNI and the hotel for our meetings, and have him take me to LAX after the meetings were over — a much cheaper scheme that worked very well during the remainder of the Design Study.

Jim and I were the only project personnel at the meeting, during which we reviewed the progress OMNI had made. I gave OMNI a computer disk copy of the MRD they had requested, and we discussed three propulsion issues, two from LEI's side and one from OMNI's side.

First, as I had brought up during the Kick-Off Meeting, LEI was still concerned that OMNI's initial propulsion design, which had two axial engines with a combined thrust of only 44 Newtons, would result in a spacecraft acceleration of only 0.2 m/sec^2, so the LOI burn would be some 65 minutes long. Such a long burn would have large gravity and thrust vector misalignment losses and we did not like that. We wanted engines with 4 or 5 times the thrust and OMNI was considering the alternatives.

Second, because Preston and I wanted the simplicity and reliability of a monopropellant, hydrazine propulsion system and were prepared to accept its relatively low Isp (a measure of the fuel's efficiency), we had called for that propulsion system in the RFP. Though OMNI had, as required in the RFP, used the monoprop system in their initial design, they felt the complications of a bipropellant system were more than offset by its higher Isp and hence lower fuel mass, considering the large ΔV requirements of the mission. OMNI wanted us to let them consider using a bipropellant system in their design and we said that they could.

Third, though OMNI had planned to use two 22 Newton engines for the main, axial engines, they planned to use much smaller, 4.4 Newton engines for the two radial engines that were primarily there to control the spin rate of the spacecraft, one engine for spin-up and one for spin-down. However, OMNI had pointed out that the radial engines, that fired nearly perpendicular (they had a cant angle of just 12°) to the spacecraft's spin axis, could act as backups for the main axial engines. The idea being that, if the main engines failed, we would rotate the spacecraft 90° and alternately fire the two radial engines a large number of times in a pulse mode, i.e., alternately fire each engine many times for a very short period of time once every half revolution of the spacecraft, when each engine was pointing in the correct direction. Thus, we could very slowly do burns equivalent to those of the main engines.

However, since each pulse burn has to be short, about one-sixth of a spin period, a pulse burn maneuver would take six times longer than a normal, continuous burn on the axial engines — if the radial and the axial engines had the same thrust levels. Since OMNI planned to have the radial engines only one fifth as powerful as the axial engines, an equivalent pulse burn on the 4.4 Newton radial engines would take 30 times as long as an axial burn. Since, for example, our LOI burn would take over an hour with the two 22 Newton axial engines OMNI had planned on using, the equivalent pulse burn on the radial engines would last some 30 hours and that would just not work. I asked OMNI to change the axial engines from 4.4 Newton engines to 22 Newton engines and they agreed.

By the time the meeting was over, Jim and I were satisfied OMNI was doing a very good job, so we left for our respective homes feeling quite good about everything.

While Jim and I were attending the Design Study Meeting, Gregg was busy with a series of letters and faxed copies thereof on a number of issues. First, having received a fax of a letter dated January 18 from Drs. Misconi and Kaplan of FIT, Dr. Weinberg of the Institute for Space Science and Technology at the University of Florida, and Dr. Webb of the University of Central Florida with the specifics of their proposal to join the Lunar Prospector Project, Gregg wrote a reply to Misconi on the 19th. FIT was offering their services in seeking a subsidized launch, the project's use of their staff and facilities, a potential investment of up to $1 million, and a number of other good things — all subject to negotiation. All that sounded pretty good and all they wanted in return was *to take over the project and to have SSI and LEI work for them — a major point that Preston and I, and apparently Jim and Gregg, too, had overlooked due to our hectic levels of activity*. Except for their last point, their offer was certainly worth pursuing, so Gregg and Misconi began setting up a meeting at FIT to discuss the issues.

Good news, Gregg received a letter dated the 19th from NASA's Bevan French with a copy of the draft for the agreement giving the GRS to SSI for his approval. As NASA had promised us at our November 22 meeting, they were moving ahead as rapidly as they could with the transfer of the GRS to the project.

Also on the 19th, Gregg and Wayne signed an agreement that would allow OMNI to proceed with the Design Study until the contract was to be ready for final signature on or before February 7. Unfortunately, it appeared to Preston and me that Gregg was dragging out the contract negotiations so long that there was a real chance the Study would be done before the contract was signed!

Monday, January 22, 1990

Sharon Lackey and I signed the lease for the donated office space for LEI on the 22nd and I would to be able to move in on February 1. Diana Pavlow, LEI's secretary, began looking for office furniture. I also asked Jim Davidson if the Houston Space Society could try to find some furniture for our new office and Jim said, "Yes" (Jim did so in early April, when the HSS coughed up $500 for the furniture after both Diana and Jim had been unsuccessful in finding any donated furniture).

I also informed Gregg about the office and asked if SSI, which was responsible for all things financial, would get telephone service set up and Gregg answered, "Yes, SSI will underwrite LEI's telephone service until the project could take over the account and pay SSI back."

Gregg then added that SSI had received a donation of ten voicemail accounts from a company called "VoiceMail," so each of the principals of Lunar Prospector would have an account, which would greatly increase our ability to efficiently communicate with one another.

Tuesday, January 23, 1990

Though SSI had the main responsibility for raising funds (a task that we assumed SSI was very busy at, since we expected to start building Lunar Prospector by August 1, a month after the Design Study was finished), LEI had the responsibility of seeking money from the aerospace community. In order to get started on that activity, we had an LEI Board Meeting to determine how LEI was going to begin its fund-raising. We decided on three initial courses of action: First, we would make a Lunar Prospector Brochure to be used as a fund-raising tool; second, I would have a meeting with Gerry Griffin of the Houston Chamber of Commerce to solicit the Chamber's support for our fundraising activities; and third, we would contact the local news media to start getting the public informed about our activities.

Wednesday, January 24, 1990: The Japanese Reach for the Moon

Japan's Institute of Space and Astronautical Science launched an engineering research satellite called Muses-A. Muses-A was put into a highly elliptical orbit around the Earth and was to make multiple flybys of the Moon in order to obtain the engineering and technical experience Japan needed for its future lunar exploration missions. The 193 kg Muses-A Spacecraft carried an 11 kg lunar orbiter (again, an engineering spacecraft) called Hagoromo that was to be injected into a very high, 10,000-km altitude lunar orbit as Muses-A flew by the Moon at a distance of 9000 km on March 20 (an orbital attempt that could not be confirmed when Hagoromo's transmitter failed early in the mission, though the ignition of Hagoromo's orbital-kick-motor was confirmed). Though the Muses-A mission was purely an engineering effort, it was the first lunar mission of any kind in 14 years!

Upon hearing about Muses-A, Preston and I requested — and had — a meeting with Yukio Haruyama, the Houston liaison officer to NASA for Japan's National Space Development Agency (NASDA), the office of which was on the first floor of the Nova Building in which I worked! We discussed the possibility of NASDA joining the Lunar Prospector Project, providing a launch, and tracking and building the sub-satellite we were considering. We gave Mr. Haruyama all our Lunar Prospector information and documents and never heard another word from either Mr. Haruyama or NASDA again!

Amidst the excitement caused by Muses-A, Gregg was busy writing a letter to the editor of the *Final Frontier* in response to an attack on the Lunar Prospector Project made by Louis Friedman of the Planetary Society in letter he wrote to the *Final Frontier* on October 24, 1989. Louis, who is typical of the Planetary Society leadership that is all for Mars and hates the Moon, complained that an inexpensive, private lunar mission, "may well be impractical,. . .the scientific value of anything that could be done cheaply was insignificant," that nevertheless, "I (Louis) hope that some creative ideas can be found in order to make the Lunar Prospector idea useful. We searched and found none," and so on. Gregg countered Louis's sour grapes letter, but over the following years Louis continued to attack Lunar Prospector.

Monday, January 29, 1990: The FIT Fiasco

For reasons that I have forgotten, I took a very late flight from Houston to Orlando, FL, Sunday evening. After getting my rental car, I still had more than a two hour drive between Orlando and Melbourne where FIT is located. It was late and I was very tired, but fortunately the night was quite cool, so I drove with the windows wide open so I would not fall asleep. I arrived at my motel in Melbourne well after 1:00 AM, checked in, and plopped into bed for a few short hours of sleep.

Monday morning I drove to FIT and met Gregg, Jim, Misconi, and the rest of the leading members of the Florida group. FIT had laid out what to us — given SSI's and LEI's meager resources — was an impressive spread of donuts, breakfast pastries, fruit, coffee, and juice, from which it was clear that they were really serious about impressing us with their resources and their interest in Lunar Prospector. After some food and chitchat, we went to a large meeting room where we got down to business. The agenda was simply that SSI and LEI would lay out the mission and our organizational structure in the morning, and FIT would tell us what they had to offer in the afternoon.

Gregg started off our pitch and then I spent most of the rest of the morning with the details of the mission philosophy, the science objectives, the science payload, the Mission Profile, and the spacecraft design, while Jim was characteristically quiet.

Towards the end of my presentation, Misconi said that FIT wanted to add a few instruments of their own to the payload, none of which had anything to do with the Moon, rather they were all directed toward space and solar physics. As such, there was no reason in the world for them to be on a lunar orbiting spacecraft. Thus it was clear that FIT had no interest in the Moon, they just wanted a spacecraft on which to hang their instruments. I said the Lunar Prospector Payload had been set in concrete and was not going to be changed, the spacecraft was being designed to support only that payload, and I saw no reason for their instruments to be on a lunar spacecraft when all they really needed was to be in a high Earth orbit. Both Jim and Gregg strongly backed me up.

Not willing to lose so quickly, Misconi argued they needed to be in lunar orbit so one of their instruments could study the sun's outer-corona during the twice-yearly lunar eclipses (which, from the Moon's viewpoint, are solar eclipses). That was also a load of hogwash, since if that instrument was on a spacecraft in a high Earth orbit with an occulting disk, it could observe the outer corona all the time, not just twice a year.

Misconi gave up on the idea that FIT would put its non-lunar instruments on Lunar Prospector, but then suggested we build two spacecraft, one for them and one for us. That suggestion went over as poorly as his first since Gregg, Jim, and I knew that it was going to be hard enough for us to get the resources for one spacecraft, let alone two. Nevertheless we agreed that a two spacecraft program was worth considering — in part, because the idea would at least keep our discussions alive. However, as we broke for an (to our minds) extravagant, catered lunch, Gregg, Jim, and I all had the feeling that we had fallen into a snake pit.

After lunch, we reassembled and FIT presented its story. Misconi reiterated all that FIT was offering to the project, but we noted that essentially everything he promised was hypothetical; he really had nothing but promises. Then he presented their idea of the organization. His chart showed that, except for the oversight Consortium consisting of "Binder, Carter, French, Kaplan, Maryniak, Misconi, Webb, (and) Weinberg," Misconi was taking over the project with Kaplan, Weinberg, Webb, and other Florida personnel having all the primary areas of responsibility, and French, Preston, the other LEI members, and me all working for the Florida managers, with Gregg pushed off to the side doing fundraising, marketing, and politics!

Jim, Gregg, and I were struck speechless at their audacity (as I indicated earlier, Misconi had sent us that chart in his letter of January 19, but somehow we had not taken note of it). Jim was the first to recover and said, uncharacteristically, "If I were Alan and Preston, I would be mad as hell at what you just proposed, given all the work they have put into the project!"

Jim's statement broke the ice and I regained my wits and added my two cents worth by stating something to the effect that Preston and I would not submit to such an arrangement. Gregg added, in his lawyer-like way, that he saw problems with such a structure and suggested they consider something else. Though the discussion dribbled on politely for a few minutes, we already knew the meeting was over and FIT was out of the picture. Nevertheless, as we prematurely parted, Gregg and Misconi agreed to keep the dialogue between our organizations going, and then we left as fast as we could.

As Gregg, Jim, and I walked to our cars, Gregg assured us that he would stonewall Misconi and added he was shocked at what they had proposed. I was glad to hear Gregg say that, but I also thought, *gee, Gregg, how does it feel to have some group that has little or nothing to offer want to kick you downstairs, run the show, and get all the credit for what you are doing?* But I left it unsaid in the vague hope that Gregg might get the picture himself. Nevertheless, the FIT fiasco had brought Gregg, Jim, and me closer together as a team since, for the first time, we had acted together against a common foe instead of arguing amongst ourselves — and that was a good feeling.

Thus ended the first hectic month of the nineties. Despite the FIT fiasco, the project was in fine shape and we were all looking forward to finishing the Design Study in the next few months and to proceeding with our other activities.

First Half of February 1990

After the hectic level of activity during January, the first half of February was relatively calm. We were busy reviewing the Mission Requirements developed by the various Mission Segment Groups, prior to the requirements being integrated into the next version of the MRD. We expected to release the next version by the end of the first week in March. Also, Preston and I were preparing for the "all hands" Preliminary Design Review (PDR) that was going to be held at OMNI on February 16 and 17.

Wayne and Gregg had finally finished a draft copy of the final Design Study Contract on the 6th, just in time for the February 7 deadline they had set in their January 19 agreement, but the contract was still not signed as of the 7th!

Given that the Spacecraft Design Study was almost half over, I got busy and wrote version 1.0 of the Mission Profile that would eventually give the exact sequence of events and commands that would be required to get the spacecraft from its launch through the end of the mission. I wanted to start getting comments on the Mission Profile from the LEI and OMNI staffs, since the spacecraft's capabilities and the Mission Profile had to be iterated until they matched — a never ending process that would last to the end of the real mission. The development of an evolving Mission Profile is, along with the writing of the MRD and the MOD, the best way to understand a spacecraft and what it has to be able to do in order to support a successful mission.

Version 1.0 of the Mission Profile was, of course, very sketchy since I still had few details of the workings of the spacecraft, even though OMNI was diligently refining the Preliminary Design they had given us as the main part of their proposal. Nevertheless, starting the development of the Mission Profile, primitive as it was, started the iterative process of merging the developing spacecraft's capabilities with the evolving mission.

Version 1.0 of the Mission Profile was written assuming a transit time to the Moon of 100 hours, approximately that for the type of minimum energy trajectory we were going to use, and a three burn Lunar Orbit Insertion (LOI) sequence. The latter already differed from the Mission Profile that Preston and I had in the RFP, in which there was a single, long LOI burn to put the spacecraft into a slightly elliptical orbit with its periselene at 100 km, followed two days later by a short, circularization burn. The reason for the three burn LOI sequence was that OMNI still had the two 22 Newton engines in their baseline design. The Mission Profile ran from spacecraft turn-on at its separation from the Trans-Lunar Injection Stage through the final LOI circularization burn that would put Lunar Prospector into its 100 km altitude, 118-minute, polar mapping orbit. I had also written the Mission Profile for a typical lunar Orbit Maintenance Maneuver (OMM) that we would have to do periodically to keep Lunar Prospector in its correct lunar mapping orbit.

Also, when writing the Mission Profile, I thought it would be a very good idea to have a fail-safe LOI burn sequence programmed into the spacecraft before launch, just in case there was a communications failure and we were initially unable to command the spacecraft. By having such a fail-safe LOI burn sequence, I hoped that, in case of such a command failure, there would be a reasonable chance Lunar Prospector might achieve some kind of lunar orbit on its own and then, if and when we regained command capability, we could save the mission. My idea was that after launch and each time we got a better navigation solution for the transfer orbit and/or corrected it with a mid-course burn, we would up-date the fail-safe LOI burn sequence. Thus, Lunar Prospector would have an ever-increasing chance of putting itself into some kind of lunar orbit in case we temporarily lost command capability before we had been able to put Lunar Prospector into the desired lunar orbit ourselves.

While I thought the fail-safe LOI sequence was a great idea, Wayne and the OMNI engineers thought I was nuts. Wayne forcefully convinced me that the complexity and cost of having a fail-safe capability built into the spacecraft far outweighed the very low probability of being able to save the mission if there were a communications failure, which was also of very low probability. Despite OMNI having rejected my brilliant idea, Version 1.0 of the Mission Profile had served its purpose by starting the iterative process of matching the spacecraft's capabilities and the mission requirements.

Thursday, February 15, 1990: The Presentation to LMSC

I made a detour to LMSC in Sunnyvale on my way to LA for the PDR, so I could give Gus and his staff a status report on Lunar Prospector. In addition to Gus, Jack Houle (Gus's Exploration Programs Manager), Lee Lunsford, Eric Laursen, Carol Lane, and several others attended the presentation. I reviewed all the progress we had made and discussed our fundraising activities, our requests for donated hardware, and the donated use of test facilities from the aerospace companies — with a special emphasis on getting those kinds of support from Lockheed — and our test and verification schedule. Except for Jack Houle, the LMSC staffers were both impressed and surprised at the progress we had made and were supportive of our efforts. When I left LMSC to fly down to LA, I was satisfied that Lockheed was still behind the project, even if they had not yet committed to giving us the really high level of support that we would soon need.

Friday, February 16, 1990: Preliminary Design Review

We had a really good turnout of project personnel for the "all hands" PDR. Gregg was there from SSI (but, unfortunately, Jim French was not), Preston and I represented LEI, and Al Metzger, Bill Sjogren, Lon Hood, and Bob Snare were there from the Science Team.

We carefully reviewed all the science interface action items that had arisen during the Design Study with the Science Team guys. The main science questions discussed were as follows: What were the requirements for the mechanical attachment points between the instruments and the spacecraft that were needed to secure the instruments during launch; what were the requirements for the mechanical interfaces between the booms and the instruments; how would static charge buildup between the booms and the instruments be prevented; what were the formats for command uplink and science downlink; and what were the instrument heater power requirements during the night-time parts of the orbits and during lunar eclipses?

We reviewed the results of the trade studies that OMNI had done on the space-craft and accepted the following suggested changes to the baseline design: Use of a bipropellant propulsion system instead a monopropellant system; use of a 440 Newton biprop, onboard engine for the Trans-Lunar Injection burn instead of a solid fuel motor in case Lunar Prospector was launched into a geostationary transfer orbit as a piggyback payload on a geostationary satellite launch; use of the 440 Newton biprop engine for the LOI burn instead of the two 22 Newton engines; and the use of the omni antenna (on top of the spacecraft) for uplinking commands with a backup, uplink omni antenna on the bottom of the spacecraft rather than using the medium gain antenna as the backup command antenna.

As the PDR ended, all of us, OMNI, Gregg, Preston, the Science Team members, and I felt that we had made great strides towards our goal, and the science guys, being used to NASA meetings, were pleasantly surprised at how well the PDR had gone and how readily and non-bureaucratically we were making progress and were solving engineering issues.

Thursday, February 22, 1990

I was the guest speaker at the Annual Dinner of the Houston Chapter of the American Institute of Aeronautics and Astronautics (AIAA). In addition to telling the AIAA members all about the science and the mission and the spacecraft, I asked them to support our efforts by joining LEI and finding donated spacecraft and ground support hardware for us. In addition to having a nice free dinner, I was successful in getting several new volunteers for LEI, including the twin brothers, Andy and Andre Sylvester! Andy and Andre are bright young engineers from Preston's alma mater — the University of Texas — who were NASA employees.

Early March 1990

Gregg had more or less accepted the second version of the Consortium Agreement I had sent him in early January. He had made a few minor changes, but he had accepted all the main points that, unfortunately from our standpoint, left SSI in charge. Nevertheless, I was officially the Deputy Project Manager, though in practice I was the Project Manager. I sent the final version to Gregg and Jay Cuclis at Vinson & Elkins for preparation for signature on the 3rd, and we hoped that we would soon have a legal working agreement between LEI and SSI.

As had been expected and verified at the PDR in February, the power requirements during the twice-yearly lunar eclipses (as seen from the Moon and a lunar orbiting spacecraft, a lunar eclipse is really a solar eclipse) were drivers for the spacecraft design, so I had been working on the eclipse power budget. I had modeled the power required by the spacecraft during the roughly three-hour eclipses under different orbital conditions and found there were significant differences depending on when we launched.

If we launched at a time when the spacecraft would initially be in one of its twice-yearly periods of maximum nighttime pass (47 minutes), or at $\beta=0°$ (β is the angle between the plane of the orbit as seen from the Sun and the vector between the Sun and Moon), the spacecraft would remain in total darkness for 168 minutes and in partial darkness for another 110 minutes during a lunar eclipse. If we launched when the spacecraft would initially be in one of its twice-yearly periods with no nighttime passes, or at $\beta=90°$, the spacecraft would remain in total darkness for only 128 minutes and in partial darkness for another 200 minutes during a lunar eclipses. Even though, at $\beta=90°$ the total duration of the eclipse as seen from the spacecraft is 5½ hours vs. a little over 4½ hours at $\beta=0°$, the spacecraft is in total darkness for 40 minutes longer during the latter than during the former. Further, though the spacecraft spends nearly an hour longer in the partial phases of the eclipses at $\beta=90°$ than at $\beta=0°$, the spacecraft does get some solar power and solar heat when it is in partial sunlight. The accumulated effects on the power requirements for all phases are less severe for a $\beta=90°$ eclipse than for a $\beta=0°$ eclipse. Thus, I concluded that if we had the choice, we should launch during the twice-yearly periods when we could get the spacecraft into an orbit that would result in the eclipses occurring when the spacecraft's orbital β angle was at, or close to 0°. That also meant that our first two launch windows were November of 1991 and May of 1992. However, since it was unlikely we would have a choice of launch dates, we would have to plan for the worst case. Regardless, I had the power budget information OMNI needed to design the power subsystem of the spacecraft and I passed that critical information on to OMNI and SSI.

Tuesday, March 6, 1990: Another Paper Sim

As they say, "Practice makes perfect." The March 6 "Paper SIM" consisted of a typical orbit maintenance burn and involved putting all the science instruments into standby mode, uplinking the attitude and burn parameters, verifying the configuration, performing the burn, verifying the post-burn attitude, and reconfiguring the spacecraft for normal operations. The burn went well in the SIM, but there was a problem during the reconfiguration sequence when the Electron Reflectometer (ER) was switched from standby to the data collection mode — a power spike was detected in the power subsystem. The Command and Control Team responded immediately and correctly by shutting down the ER to prevent possible damage to it or the spacecraft. I was extremely pleased, the entire SIM had gone well and the C&C Team had performed flawlessly.

The maturing of our Ground Support Segments was becoming apparent, not only by the successful SIMs we were conducting, but also by the fact that we started getting ready to turn over the SIMs to the Training and Verification Team. The T&V team was ultimately responsible for training the C&C Team, as well as training all of the other ground support teams, and for verifying their readiness to support the mission. LEI was making great strides in preparing for the mission.

Friday, March 23, through Sunday, March 25, 1990: Ron's Reference Trajectory, LMSC, and the OMNI Monthly Review Meeting

As the leader and sole member of the Mission Planning Team, Ron Humble had been very busy calculating a Preliminary Trans-Lunar Reference Trajectory. He finished that important task and turned in his report to Preston on the 23rd. Thus we began to have the details we needed about how Lunar Prospector was going to get to the Moon.

As I usually did when I went to California for the monthly review meeting at OMNI, I stopped off at Sunnyvale to give Gus and his staff an update on our progress, and on that side trip, I kicked off LEI's efforts to get major support from LMSC and all the aerospace companies. I had sent Gus a memo on March 6 asking for further support for the mission beyond what LMSC was already giving me and I used that trip to make the same pitch — but in person — for the $1 million in cash plus the donated hardware, the donated personnel time and charges, and the donated use of test facilities we were seeking from LMSC.

I emphasized to Gus that I was then not only the Project Scientist, but also the Mission Director, officially the Deputy Project Manager, and in reality, the Project Manager. As such, Lunar Prospector was mainly under my control, and since I was a Lockheed employee, Lockheed was going to get most of the credit for the mission. Gus certainly appreciated that fact, but was concerned that SSI was still keeping official control of the project. Since he (and Lockheed in general) thought as little of SSI as Preston and I did, Gus emphatically stated, "If Lockheed is going to give you the kind of support you're requesting, it will do so only if you are in total control of the project and not SSI," a sentiment that I heartily agreed with.

Gus then suggested, in addition to my presenting my request to LMSC, I should present it to the Managers at Lockheed Corporate Headquarters in Calabasas, CA (just north of LA). Gus specifically said I should contact Brenda Forman at Calabasas who would most probably want to help push my agenda forward.

Though Gus hadn't said yes to my request, he hadn't said no, either. That, plus the fact that he wanted me in control of the mission and that he wanted me to go to Lockheed Headquarters to ask for support, made me feel very hopeful about our getting Lockheed to support Lunar Prospector as I left Sunnyvale to wing my way to LA.

Jim and I attended the review meeting at OMNI. OMNI had come up with a weight saving idea that they were quite proud of — they wanted to design the spacecraft so it could be launched in the inverted position! That would allow the bipropellant tanks to be mounted directly on the separation ring, thereby reducing the need for 4 to 5 kg of tank support structure. However, there were three problems with that configuration. First, as OMNI pointed out itself, the fuel lines from the tanks to engines would be filled with blow-down gas rather than oxidizer and fuel until each engine was fired. During the first burn of each engine, gas bubbles would interrupt the burn and the resultant irregular flow could cause a catastrophic engine failure! OMNI was in the process of getting the data on the tolerances of the engines to gas ingestion.

I did not like the idea because, if we had a bad launch, the chances were high we would have an under-burn rather than an over-burn. In such a case, when time was of the essence, we would have to flip the spacecraft 180° before we could make a corrective maneuver, an operational complication I did not like.

Further, if we launched an inverted spacecraft, the antennas could no longer be permanently mounted on top of the spacecraft; rather they would have to be deployable. Jim, Preston, and I were dead set against having any more deployables than absolutely necessary — it was bad enough that we had to deploy the science instrument booms, but there was no way around that.

As a result, Jim and I were not too excited about flying an inverted spacecraft just to save 4 to 5 kg, and, after giving OMNI a few days to get the data on the gas ingestion question, we rejected OMNI's idea of inverting the spacecraft.

We then discussed the results of the eclipse power budget data I had sent to OMNI. Earlier, OMNI had made worst-case calculations indicating that the drain on the battery used in the Proposal Design of the spacecraft would be 150% during the eclipses, i.e., the spacecraft would die! However, based on the real eclipse data I had sent OMNI, the drain on the proposed battery would be 75% to 90%, values that were still too high for safety. A somewhat bigger battery would be required, but not as bad as OMNI had feared.

OMNI was also concerned that the cost of a two-way Doppler system with a stability of 5 parts in 10^{12}, as required for the gravity measurements, would be $2 million. OMNI wanted to have Bill Sjogren determine if he could do the gravity mapping using a one-way Doppler system that cost only $200,000. I said I would find out from Bill what the answer was (it was no).

Also, OMNI gave us the details of the new Command and Control (C&C) system, which meant that I could improve the Mission Profile (write Version 1.1) by using real C&C command information — a task I started as soon as I was back in Houston.

After the meeting was over, I drove down to Disneyland where I spent Saturday evening and most of Sunday enjoying myself until I left for Houston Sunday night.

Monday, March 26, 1990: The Russian Proton Launch Offer

The March 26 issue of *Space News* reported that the Soviet Union had offered to sell SSI a Proton rocket for Lunar Prospector's launch (a nice way for LEI to find out what its Consortium partner was up to). OMNI had been in the loop with the Proton discussions, but LEI wasn't — just another indicator that SSI considered LEI not its partner, but its employee. Vjacheslav Filin, Deputy Chief Designer of the Energiya Enterprise Design Bureau and leader of a Soviet delegation that was touring the USA and that had visited SSI, was quoted as saying, "The first step is to search the technical possibilities, . . . then we can talk about business." Filin was quoted further as saying, "The moon is very important to us and very little research on it is being done. We are very eager to work (with the U.S.) on lunar programs because it is very expensive."

Chris Faranetta, who was Gregg's Special Assistant, told *Space News*, "We're just in the discussion stage." We had a possibility of having Lunar Prospector launched as a secondary payload on a Proton. That was very exciting, but we were disturbed about the way SSI kept LEI out of the loop.

Thursday, March 29, 1990

As promised, Gregg had been stonewalling Misconi and his Florida cohorts. Kaplan had sent Gregg a letter dated March 19 with a revised version of FIT's proposed role in Lunar Prospector. It was clear from the letter that the FIT crowd had not caught on to the fact that we were not interested in their taking over the project or even having them involved. Gregg had ignored both the letter and a call from Misconi, who then faxed Gregg a letter, whose somewhat pleading tenor suggested Misconi was finally catching on to the fact that we were not interested in FIT.

In response to the fax, Gregg asked Preston and me to write out the conditions under which FIT could join the project, conditions we knew would be unacceptable to FIT. We replied two days later and indicated 1) there would be no second Lunar Prospector Spacecraft, 2) all the science on Lunar Prospector and any sub-satellite that we might fly would be directed towards lunar science and nothing else, and 3) if FIT joined the Consortium, it would have to accept the existing administrative structure and it would be a non-voting member of the Consortium. Then we outlined what FIT could do, i.e., seek money and a launch, build a tracking station in Florida, and join the existing Science Team. I assumed Gregg sent our conditions to Misconi since we never heard from him or FIT again (though Weinberg was not as easy to get rid of)!

Early April 1990

The April issue of *Astronomy* had a short article about Lunar Prospector based on an interview with Gregg. As was always the case, Lunar Prospector was described as an SSI mission with absolutely no mention of LEI. Preston and I were again annoyed, so I wrote a short letter to the editor of *Astronomy* that appeared in the July, 1990 issue, explaining the partnership between SSI and LEI, correcting a number of technical errors in the article, and sent a copy to Gregg. SSI's continual misrepresentation of the real situation and pretending that LEI did not exist was getting very old, and it was going to have serious consequences for the project in the very near future.

Gregg received a letter from Jerry Weinberg dated April 3. Having realized much quicker than Misconi and the FIT bunch that they had blown it in January, Jerry had called us earlier to let us know that he had — to his supposed horror — recognized at the meeting that FIT had completely overstepped their bounds by proposing they take over Lunar Prospector. As such he was approaching us independent of FIT. However, we were not impressed with Jerry any more than we were with FIT. Our impression of him was that he was arrogant and self-serving, so Gregg stonewalled him, too.

Finally, as Gus suggested, I called Brenda Forman, who was more than enthusiastic about Lunar Prospector and more than willing to champion my efforts to get the Lockheed Corporation to give us the support we needed. She asked that I send her a memo with the details of my request and then she would arrange a meeting for her and me with the appropriate corporate staffers ASAP.

Tuesday, April 10, 1990: Enter Congressman Mike Andrews

As part of my continuing efforts to gain support for Lunar Prospector, I had called the Houston office of Congressman Mike Andrews, the Democratic Representative from the JSC area of Houston, to ask for a meeting and got one for the 10th. We had a good meeting; I told him what Lunar Prospector was all about and what its status was and I asked him to join the other Congressmen who were supporting the project. Mike was greatly interested and committed himself to helping us and assigned one of his Houston staffers to be the contact between his office and LEI.

Monday, April 16, and Tuesday, April 17, 1990: Exchange with Brenda

As I had promised Brenda Forman, I faxed her a memo on the 16th that included descriptions of the current status of Lunar Prospector and the support we had from NASA and the various Congressmen, as well as the requests I was making for financial, personnel, and material support from Lockheed, my requests for the use of the Lockheed test facility and test personnel, and backup letters, reports, etc. The next day, Brenda faxed me a memo she had written to Chris Caren informing him I would be coming to Calabasas on April 30 to brief him on the project. She also gave him the materials I had sent her so Chris would have some idea about what I would be telling him and requesting of him. I was impressed — Brenda did not let grass grow under her feet, and I felt one step closer to getting major Lockheed support.

Early Friday, April 20, 1990: Telecon with McDonnell Douglas

David Strack, one of LEI's leading young members and a McDonnell Douglas (or, as everyone called it, MacDac) employee, had prepared the way for him and me to discuss our standard mission support request ($1 million plus personnel, hardware, and facility support) with his management. David had wanted to be in on the meeting, which was logical since he was a MacDac employee, because he wanted to learn how to solicit support from the major companies. Since one of Preston's and my goals for the project was to give bright, young engineers experience in doing major projects, I was happy to have David participate in the meeting and to come along when I visited other aerospace companies in the JSC area to ask for support.

Our effort to get MacDac support started with a telecon to McDonnell Douglas Corporate Headquarters in California on the 20th. The telecon went well and ended with MacDac Headquarters telling the Houston office personnel that they should handle our request. They, in turn, told David to set up a meeting in a couple of weeks between them and us in order to go over the details of our request. I left and David got busy setting up the meeting that was eventually scheduled for May 9.

Friday Afternoon, April 27, through Monday, April 30, 1990: The Monthly OMNI Meeting and Calabasas

As usual, Jim and I represented SSI and LEI, respectively, at the monthly review meeting, during which we finalized the following subsystem issues.

The original requirements I had given OMNI in the RFP were that the three science booms were of different lengths (from 1 to 6 m). However, OMNI found that such a configuration caused spacecraft stability problems that would be alleviated, or at least minimized, if the booms were all of equal length, so their resonance frequencies were similar. That solution was scientifically acceptable, so I set the boom lengths at 3.5 m.

A second issue with the booms was, because the GRS is far heavier than either the APS or the MAG/ER, the mass of the APS had to be increased (by adding ballast) from 4 to 7 kg. Also the angles between the GRS boom and the APS and MAG/ER booms were set at 135° and the angle between the APS and MAG/ER booms was set at 90° in order to balance the spacecraft.

The final boom issue concerned the MAG/ER science package, which consisted of the MAG, the ER, and their common electronics unit, and the requirement that the MAG had to be mounted at least 1 m from the other two components. The solution was to mount the electronics at the end of the MAG/ER's main boom and have a 1 m long mini-boom for the MAG mounted on top of the electronics unit. That mini-boom would be mounted perpendicular to the main boom and parallel to the spin axis of the spacecraft. The ER would be similarly mounted on the bottom of the electronics unit at the end of a very short (0.2 m) mini-boom. That configuration would satisfy all the science requirements and keep the MAG/ER package balanced with respect to its boom.

There were two changes we made to the spacecraft itself. First we changed the cant angle of the two radial engines from 12° to 90° to facilitate the spacecraft spin up and spin down maneuvers, thereby changing them from radial to tangential engines, but their functions (spin up, spin down, and pulse burns) remained the same. Second, we increased the height of the spacecraft from 91 cm to 120 cm so we could increase the number of solar cells and get 202 w of power instead of just the 175 w the original design gave. By doing so, we minimized the effects of power loss due to the shading of the solar array by the science instruments.

All in all, the meeting was very successful and the design of the spacecraft was maturing very nicely. Jim and I left the meeting feeling very satisfied and I was looking forward to both a weekend of sightseeing (the Queen Mary and other local LA attractions) and my meeting at Lockheed Headquarters in Calabasas the following Monday.

When Monday morning arrived, I drove up to Calabasas, which took a lot longer than I had thought, and met Brenda. Though we had talked on the phone, we had never met face to face. I was impressed with her interest, her willingness to support our efforts, and her "let's get going" attitude. After getting to know each other a little, we discussed the upcoming meeting and then proceeded to Chris Caren's office.

The meeting with Chris went very well. He was impressed with what we had already done with the project and with the support we had from the various members of Congress and NASA. He suggested that the logical place we might get the $1 million we were requesting was from the Lockheed Public Relations Department, since Lunar Prospector would result in a lot of good PR for Lockheed. That was the case since as Project Scientist, Mission Director, and, in reality, the Project Manager, I was the major player in the program, and, of course, a Lockheed employee. Like Gus, Chris appreciated the importance of those facts.

We also discussed our requests for the use of Lockheed test facilities and test personnel, Lockheed's continued support of my time (I was asking for fulltime support) and travel, and all the rest of the things we needed. Chris was very positive in his response to our presentation and requests and said he would take them up with the rest of the Lockheed Corporate Management.

When Brenda and I left Chris's office, we both felt we had done a good job and I was ready to fly back to Houston with two successful meetings behind me.

Friday, May 4, 1990: Back to NASA Headquarters

Joe Alexander had asked Gregg and me to come to Headquarters on May 4 to finalize the agreement between NASA and SSI for the transfer of the Apollo 17 GRS. The meeting was successful, though uneventful. More importantly, Gregg and I spent quite a bit of time together talking about the mission and the issues separating LEI and SSI, as well as doing some sightseeing.

Gregg knew Washington much better than I did, so he showed me around a little bit — I was especially impressed with the Union Train Station that had been turned into a very attractive, but still functional, tourist attraction with many stores and restaurants. As a result, Gregg and I began to understand and respect each other's viewpoints more and more, though we still disagreed on many issues, and Gregg finally understood Preston's and my views on the thorny issue of the Project Manager. Gregg then conceded that I was, in reality, the Project Manager, though we did not formally make the change until early June.

That meeting of the minds, like the FIT fiasco, helped draw Gregg and me somewhat closer together as partners in our endeavor, a necessity if we were to be successful in trying to do the impossible. However, it did not draw us close enough to remove the main problem of SSI's continually trying to keep up the façade to the outside world that Lunar Prospector was solely an SSI project.

Monday, May 7, through Friday, May 11, 1990

May had started off with a bang with Gregg's and my trip to see Joe Alexander at NASA Headquarters. Then it just kept going at a fast and more promising pace as OMNI neared the June 16 end of the Phase B Design study and LEI began planning for the start of the construction of the spacecraft in early August with November 1991 still our target launch date.

Our LEI team was maturing nicely as our members began to learn to take on more and more responsibilities, such as Brian Cox setting up and supervising the next SIM between the C&C and T&V teams, and as new members joined us. Regarding the latter, we were getting several new volunteers per week due to luncheon talks that Preston and I had been giving and due to articles that Marianna Dyson, our LEI publicist, had been writing. Needless to say, we also lost volunteers — as is always the case in volunteer efforts — but our gains were more than our losses. As expected, the really dedicated and good people were staying with us, while the less useful and less interested ones dropped out quickly.

SSI sent us a full list of the Congressmen and National Space Council members who were supporting the project; most of them were with us because of Gregg and SSI's efforts, but we had also done our part. The Congressional supporters were Robert Torricelli (D-NJ), Thomas McMillen (D-MD), Tom Campbell (R-CA), Dana Rohrabacher (R-CA), George Brown (D-CA), and Mike Andrews (D-TX). The National Space Council members were Courtney Stadd and Pete Worden (Mike Andrews and Courtney Stadd were destined to appear later in this story — in the Epilog, and Pete Worden will be back in Part Three of this book).

On Wednesday the 9th, David Strack and I had our first meeting with Bob Thompson, a local McDonnell Douglas official. During the meeting we made our standard request for $1 million, contributed hardware, etc. Bob had two responses to our pitch.

First, he asked why should they (MacDac specifically and the aerospace companies in general) help us demonstrate that lunar and planetary missions could be done for the equivalent of several tens of millions of dollars when the aerospace companies were getting NASA to pay 10 times that much for such missions. My answer was simple; "Because NASA won't have the money for expensive missions much longer. If you don't learn how to do inexpensive missions, you won't be doing anything." Despite my being correct, that explanation fell on deaf ears.

Second, despite his first question, Bob's position regarding our request for support was, "If Lockheed kicks in a million and gives you the other support you need, we will probably do the same." Our success with MacDac hinged on Lockheed starting the ball rolling (a clear indication MacDac considered that Lockheed was primarily responsible for the project since I was a Lockheed employee). That was not exactly the response we had hoped for, but Bob also said he would look into what MacDac had in the way of hardware and facilities they might be able to donate to us. Then he asked David and me to come back to discuss what he had found the following week. That was encouraging.

Monday, May 14, through Friday, May 18, 1990

On Monday the 14th, Dave and I met for a second time with Bob Thompson of MacDac, a meeting that was to lead to a third meeting in late June.

Joe Alexander requested information he needed to set up the negotiations between NASA and LEI, so we could get official permission for those of our volunteers who were NASA employees at JSC and for those Science Team members who were employees at JPL (Bill Sjogren and Al Metzger, plus any support people they would need) to work on the project. Joe also needed information to set up our usage of the JPL facilities Al Metzger would need to get the GRS ready for flight. NASA was really getting behind Lunar Prospector and making everything official, a very encouraging situation. I very quickly got the information together and faxed it to Joe in an effort to keep the ball rolling as fast as possible.

I also got a call from Paul Hoversteen of *USA Today* who was doing a story on Lunar Prospector for *Discover* magazine that would appear in about three months — so Lunar Prospector was beginning to get press on its own — a very good sign.

The week ended when Dave Strack and I met with Glynn Lunney of Rockwell on the 18th to ask for Rockwell's support. Glynn is a retired NASA manager of great accomplishment and experience who had taken a post-Apollo job at Rockwell. Glynn's fame was that he was one of the Mercury, Gemini, and Apollo Mission Directors and thus had greatly contributed to NASA's successfully getting man on the Moon. Because of his intimate involvement with the earlier NASA manned programs and because he knew NASA well, Glynn was unhappy with the bureaucratic mess NASA had become and the fact that the USA and NASA together had thrown away their manned and unmanned lunar exploration capabilities. In contrast, and because of that, Glynn was very enthusiastic about our efforts to do the Lunar Prospector Mission and promised to get all the help he could from Rockwell.

Thus, a week full of promise ended on a very high note.

Monday, May 21, through Friday, May 25, 1990

In preparation for my hitting up Martin Marietta in Denver, CO, for a possible Titan 2 piggyback launch for Lunar Prospector and a $1 million contribution, I called

Carolyn Cooley, a Martin Marietta colleague from the good-old Viking days. It was nice to talk with one of the old Viking gang again and it was especially nice when she told me that she worked for Al Schallenmuller and with Terry Gamber. Al had been one of the Martin Marietta Viking managers for whom I have an enormous amount of respect and Terry was one of the Martin Marietta engineers on our Lander Camera Team and he had worked for me on the "Uplink" half of our Team I led. As such, Al, Terry, Carolyn and I had spent untold hours working together in various ways and were old friends. I was pleased at the prospect of getting back involved with them in any capacity, especially on Lunar Prospector.

As it turned out Carolyn was going to be in Houston on the 24th, so we could, and did, have an initial meeting on the topic of Martin Marietta supporting Lunar Prospector. Our Houston meeting went very well and Carolyn said she would set up a meeting in Denver ASAP. I was ready to go to Denver with high hopes of getting a Titan 2 launch, some cash, and seeing many of my old Viking friends.

In addition to my efforts to find aerospace community support for Lunar Prospector, Preston had started looking for money — via unnamed contacts he had gotten at Space Industries — from non-aerospace companies and he said that we might get money to the tune of $3 million within the next three months!

Gregg too had been very busy on the project and had had a second round of talks with the Soviets about a Proton launch. We were attacking the launch issue from at least a couple of promising angles.

Tuesday, May 29, 1990: The Pictures and Martin Marietta

During the previous week, we had arranged for a professional photographer, Gary Fox, (the husband of one of our volunteers, Marcha Fox) to take documentary pictures of the entire LEI volunteer staff as a group and of each of the individual Mission Segment Teams. Everyone was there for the pictures, except me — I was in Denver and not feeling very well.

Immediately after our initial meeting in Houston on the 24th, Carolyn had set up the Denver meeting for the 29th and it was not possible for us to arrange for Gary Fox to come on a different date on such short notice. Clearly the Denver meeting took precedence, but I regretted missing the picture taking session.

Unfortunately, I was not feeling well the day I left Houston for Denver and as the airplane got close to Denver, the ride got very bumpy. The result was that I got very airsick. By the time we landed, I had a splitting headache and was nearly throwing up — a hell of a way to go to a meeting to ask for a piggyback Titan 2 launch and a million dollars. Somehow I avoided tossing my cookies in the airplane — and in the Stapleton Airport — and at the Hertz counter. I also managed to leave Stapleton and start driving to Martin Marietta on the far southwest side of Denver, but decided I had no choice but to stop and rest in the vague hope that the headache and nausea would pass and I would not vomit. Luckily, it was quite cool in Denver and as I lay back in the car with the windows wide open along the side of the road, I slowly began to feel better. After about a half an hour, I felt good enough to continue driving and by the time I was at Martin Marietta, I was feeling well enough to get through the presentation and the meeting.

When I arrived, Al, who was the Vice President for the Space Exploration Initiative at Martin Marietta, met me and we went to a fairly big presentation hall where Terry, Carolyn, and a number of other old friends and some new faces were waiting. Al introduced me and then I went through my viewgraph presentation and told them I wanted a million dollars, a Titan rocket, and anything else they did not have nailed down.

Al and the rest of them were very impressed with what we had accomplished and thought our chances of succeeding were quite good. Al also joked that he wished we had been the secondary-payload on their last Titan 2 launch. As he explained, the last launch had been of a single spacecraft with no secondary- or piggy-back-payload and because someone had forgotten that fact, he or she had not reprogrammed the payload/upper stage separation sequence that normally was set for a two spacecraft deployment. As a costly result, nothing happened when separation was to have occurred, so the spacecraft was lost. I said to Al, "Well, we'll let you pay us to launch us as insurance against that type of failure," but somehow that suggestion did not work.

On the serious side, Al said that, unfortunately, they did not have any commercial launches going during the timeframe that would help us and suggested we ask the Department of Defense to provide us a launch on a refurbished military Titan 2 and said further that Congressman Martin Packard (D-CA) might be able to help us get such a launch. Finally, Al said Martin Marietta was interested in supporting Lunar Prospector, but any major cash contribution or other support would be contingent on the project receiving similar support from the other aerospace companies, especially, of course, Lockheed. Again, it all boiled down to my getting Lockheed to cough up major support and then we would probably be in very good shape.

I left Martin Marietta feeling good about the prospects of their supporting Lunar Prospector and feeling a lot better in terms of my airsickness. Happily, my return flight was uneventful regarding my physical state — a fact that I was more than pleased about.

Saturday, June 2, 1990: The Big Picnic

Since Preston and I were always trying to have LEI be just one big happy family, we had asked Diana Pavlow and some of our other volunteers and their wives to set up a "company picnic" on Saturday, June 2, at the Challenger Memorial Park near JSC. Like all such picnics, everyone brought most of their own food and some dish for the common good. I brought one of my telescopes so our staff and their wives and kids could look at the Moon, the target of our efforts, and I was very surprised to find out that most of them had never looked at the Moon through a telescope! All in all, everyone had a very good time at what we expected was the first of several "Annual LEI Picnics."

Monday, June 4, 1990: First Meeting with Bill Huffstetler

Using the information that I had faxed to him on May 14, Joe Alexander had immediately (the same day) written Aaron Cohen, the Director of JSC, asking Aaron to start negotiations between JSC and LEI so the JSC volunteers in LEI could get official recognition of their work on Lunar Prospector. Aaron had in turn asked William Huffstetler, Jr., Manager of the New Initiatives Office (NIO) at JSC, to conduct the negotiations with me. I was pleased about that because Bill's office had the contract with Lockheed that I worked on, so I actually worked for Bill in an administrative sense. More importantly for Lunar Prospector, Aaron's assigning Bill the task of negotiating with me resulted in the development of an important professional friendship between Bill and me.

Our meeting was set up for June 4 and I went to Bill's office that was just a few doors from mine and I explained the project to Bill. Bill immediately became a very enthusiastic supporter of the project, because of its private enterprise nature, its timely impact on president Bush's Lunar/Mars Program, and the way we had organized it and were conducting it. Bill said that he would arrange a meeting with Aaron Cohen and me to garner further JSC support for Lunar Prospector and that he would call Gus at LMSC to discuss Lockheed's interest and support of the mission (and thereby showing Gus that JSC was behind us too). Boy-o-boy, that was just the support I thought would tip Gus and Lockheed's hand, so they would finally give us the $1 million and the other support I had been requesting and it was great having someone in NASA like Bill who was enthusiastic about the mission.

Wednesday, June 6, 1990:
Bendix's Turn and the Consortium Agreement

Dave Strack and I met with Don Smith of Bendix to make our standard request for support. Bendix was already helping us by letting two of its employees work on Lunar Prospector on company time! Thus, Don was quite positive about Bendix giving us major support and said further that the Bendix group supporting the NASA/Goddard Space Flight Center (GSFC) might be able to supply us with a lot of surplus communication, tracking, and C&C hardware, and he would see what else Bendix might be able to supply. He also said he would relay all our requests to Bendix Corporate Management for further consideration.

Finally, after another revision, the long awaited and long suffering Consortium Agreement between SSI and LEI was signed on the 6th. I was finally and officially the Project Manager, as well as Project Scientist and Mission Director, Gregg was the Project Director, Preston was the Project Engineer, and Jim was the Deputy Project Manager and Spacecraft Engineer. Though SSI still had the majority voting rights, LEI had all the key positions, as was always the case in practice and as should have been acknowledged by SSI in the very beginning.

Thursday, June 7, 1990: Hernandez Engineering

David and I met with Hernandez President, Mike Hernandez, to request possible support from his small, minority owned, aerospace, engineering company. Until then, I had been hitting up the major aerospace companies for the standard $1 million contribution plus the use of facilities and donated hardware, etc. However, while small JSC area companies like Hernandez could not afford to give the project that kind of support, they could still play an important role in helping us. Given Hernandez's areas of expertise and experience, we asked Mike if they could help us set up the C&C Center, help train the C&C Teams, and help us with spacecraft and launch safety issues. Like all the other companies we had talked to, Mike said he was potentially interested and would get with his staff to see what they could do for us.

Tuesday, June 12, through Wednesday, June 20, 1990:
The Big Trip — The CDR and Lots More

The middle part of June was chock-full of major and minor activities. The OMNI Spacecraft Design Study was starting to wind down and the Critical Design review

(CDR) was scheduled for June 16. As he had done with JSC, Joe Alexander had also written Lew Allen, JPL's Director, on May 14 to initiate the negotiations between JPL and LEI for the Science Team members' time and for the project's use of JPL laboratories to prepare the GRS for flight; so I was to meet with JPL managers on June 15. Since I would be at JPL, I was also planning to meet with my JPL Science Team guys, Bill Sjogren and Al Metzger. Also, since I would be on the west coast, I was, as always, planning to see Gus at LMSC on the 13th, and while I was in the Bay Area, I would also visit Bob Lin and Kinsey Anderson at UC Berkeley. Then I would go to Tucson to meet with Lon Hood and to meet with my good old friend, Don Davis at the Planetary Science Institute (PSI) to see if he and PSI wanted to help with the Lunar Prospector Trajectory work. Don had helped develop the programs for — and then calculate — the Apollo trajectories to the Moon and I have great faith in his abilities. I was going to make one long — and I believed fruitful — trip of it.

After flying to the Bay Area the day before, I met with Gus during Wednesday morning, the 13th. When I went into his office, I knew instantly that something was very wrong. Gus angrily handed me a copy of an aerospace magazine in which there was a full-page ad from SSI asking for donations for "SSI's Lunar Prospector Mission." There was no mention of LEI, the Consortium, or Lockheed — just SSI. Given that Lockheed had already donated some $65,000 for my wages and travel, Gus was furious that Lockheed was not mentioned as the major aerospace partner or contributor, and that Lunar Prospector was represented as solely a SSI program. Gus chewed me out for being associated with such an underhanded bunch and said again, even more forcefully than in March, if Lockheed were to contribute anything beyond what it had already committed to, LEI — not SSI — would have to have full control and full responsibility for the project. Since I could not have agreed more with Gus on that point, I said that I would take that message to Gregg and SSI and get the issue resolved once and for all. Gus added, "You had better."

With that, Gus had calmed down enough so I could tell him about the excellent progress we had made and then, though still annoyed about SSI, Gus agreed that he would pay for me to go to full time on the project and that he would support my efforts to get Lockheed Corporate to donate the $1 million to us — *if, and only if, LEI was in total charge of the project.*

Though still concerned that SSI's greed had soured my chance of getting the support of Lockheed that we needed so badly, I left Gus and Sunnyvale to drive to Berkeley to meet with Bob and Kinsey (Kinsey had retired somewhat earlier and Bob had become the ER Team Leader by the time of that meeting). I brought them up to date on the current status of the project. We then reviewed their instrument development schedule and budget and the proposed ER Team contract with LEI.

After the meeting, I left Berkeley to fly down to LA for my JPL meetings on the 14th and 15th. The meetings on the 14th were with Bill, the DGE Team Leader, and Al, the GRS Team Leader. The purpose of those science meetings was basically the same as that in Berkeley, except the DGE required no instrument, and the GRS was to be provided by NASA. Thus, the topics of those two meetings were mainly the state of the project and their schedules and budgets. However, Bill mentioned that JPL might have a spare S-Band transponder (worth about $1 million) and suggested I ask JPL to donate it to the project — a good suggestion.

The next day, Friday, June 15, was very important. In addition to the discussions about the contracts between JPL and LEI for Bill's, Al's, and their staff's time and their use of the JPL facilities for Lunar Prospector, I was asked by Pete Lyman, JPL's Deputy Director, and Walt Downhouser to give a talk on the project to the JPL Section Managers. Pete and Walt explained that JPL was very interested in Lunar Prospector and had already initiated several internal tasks to see how JPL could support the mission! I then told them what Bill Sjogren had said about a spare S-band transponder. Pete said he would look into it (in a letter dated June 29, Pete confirmed that a test transponder did exist, but that its current configuration, status, and pedigree needed to be clarified).

I really enjoyed giving the JPL top brass a rundown on Lunar Prospector. As Pete, Walt, and I entered the conference room, it was full of the Section Heads and Pete introduced me and explained why I was there. He then added, "I don't want you to start telling Alan how to do the mission (a bad habit that JPL has), listen to what he says and to what they have accomplished with essentially no money and maybe we can learn a thing or two." Everyone laughed (because they all knew they would normally do the former and not the latter) and agreed they would shut up and just listen and that was what made it so much fun for me.

It is an understatement to say that the JPL managers were very surprised at how well we had the mission and the spacecraft in hand, but that will do. Rather than trying to tell me how we should really be doing Lunar Prospector, the managers found themselves complimenting me on just how well we had defined the mission, the spacecraft, mission operations, and our organization. Not only was it fun to get that kind of response from the people who had built and flown almost every USA lunar and planetary mission conducted up to that time, but it was also an important validation of the entire project. Clearly, I was a very happy camper when I left JPL to drive down to El Segundo and the Hacienda.

Finally, it was Saturday, June 16, the big day — the CDR day. Gregg, Jim French, Jim Burke, and I were there from the project and, of course, the OMNI staff was present in full force — all eight or nine of them! The only major player who was missing was Preston, the Project Engineer, the second most important man in the project, and I was annoyed. Preston, who is a bulldog, absolutely dominant, my-way-or-the-highway, master-of-all-at-work, is an absolute pansy when it comes to Nancy, his loving wife. When Nancy says jump, Preston just asks, "How high?"

Unfortunately, Preston had been on a lot of travel for Space Industries just prior to our CDR, and despite its criticality to the entire project (the "C" in CDR stands for Critical for a reason) and when Preston told Nancy that he needed to go to the CDR, she said, "NO!" No matter how much he begged and pleaded, the answer remained, "NO!"

When Preston told me he could not go to the CDR, I said, "Are you nuts? You can't miss the CDR, that's crazy!" but he could and he did and I was ticked. The Project Engineer could not come to the Spacecraft CDR, because his wife would not let him, bah-hum-bug and much worse.

Despite Preston's prominent absence, the CDR went extremely well (after all, Jim French and I had been to a review meeting every month since the start of the study to make sure that every thing was OK — but it was the CDR, and that was the time to find anything we might have overlooked), and we found no major problems with the spacecraft design. Each of the OMNI subsystem engineers went through the details of his or her subsystem and we grilled them on the details.

I was very glad that Jim Burke was there; he asked innumerable, probing questions (as is his nature), while Jim French was characteristically quiet, only interjecting a few comments into the discussions. Since I am a scientist and was not then a practicing engineer (I am now), I was relying on both of the Jims to catch anything that we had missed, so I was a little disappointed at French's quiet performance and relieved at Burke's very active participation. When the CDR ended, I felt we, as a group, had done a good job of probing for any weaknesses in the OMNI spacecraft design and hence, we had a spacecraft that could do the job we wanted done.

We, the project personnel, then told OMNI that we would review the CDR documentation in detail and send our final comments back to them by July 17 in preparation for the start of construction a few weeks later.

When the CDR was formally over, we started the two fun parts of the meeting. One of the OMNI contract deliverables was a full-scale engineering model of the spacecraft. We had, of course, seen it briefly before the CDR started and during our lunch break, but it was after the CDR was finished that we got to play with the model and started taking pictures of it and of various combinations of the OMNI and project staff members standing beside it like proud parents. The thing was kind-of tinny, but it was real. Lunar Prospector was no longer just a paper design, it stood before us as metal and plastic, not the real spacecraft, of course, but a full scale engineering model and that made the spacecraft seem real and the Moon seem a lot closer than it had just a few hours earlier.

After we stopped playing with our new toy, OMNI's entire upper management (Wayne, Mike Chobotov, and Asif Ansari) took Gregg, Jim, Jim, and me out to a nice dinner (at OMNI's expense) to celebrate our successful CDR.

The next morning I flew to Tucson and spent the rest of the day, Sunday, hiking in my beloved desert and mountains around my equally beloved Tucson.

Monday morning, June 18, I met with Lon Hood, Leader of the MAG Team, and went through the same issues that I had gone through with my Berkeley and JPL Science Teammates.

Finally, I met with Don Davis at PSI on Monday afternoon and on the morning of June 19 to discuss PSI's working on the Lunar Prospector Trajectory task. Don thought PSI could spend several man months of effort per year on the project, a task he would enjoy given his Apollo trajectory experience over two decades earlier.

After finishing my meeting with Don, I reluctantly left Tucson to fly back to Houston, thus ending a very successful trip. We had a good spacecraft design. We had what appeared to be viable promises of money and support from the aerospace community. We had an excellent start on the mission operations side of the project at LEI. We had NASA Headquarters' (somewhat reluctant) support, JPL's apparently sincere support and JSC/Bill Huffstetler's enthusiastic support and the possibility of a Soviet launch. We expected to start building Lunar Prospector sometime in August and we expected to make our launch date in late 1991. Thus, it really looked like we were going to pull off the miracle and successfully conduct the very first private exploration mission to the Moon within the next couple of years.

Chapter 1-5
Where's The Money?

The Last Ten Days of June 1990

When I returned from my trip, everyone at LEI was keen on getting started with spacecraft construction and the development of our C&C Center in August, but first we needed a few million dollars. The possibility of us soon getting major financial support and donated hardware and services from the aerospace community as a result of LEI's efforts looked very good, and we assumed that SSI was doing even better since fundraising was essentially its only job in the Consortium, though Preston and I had been far too busy to even ask Gregg about SSI's success in that all important arena.

In order to get all of the LEI volunteers ready to review the OMNI CDR Documentation and to prepare for the beginning of construction, we held an "All Hands" meeting on Friday the 22nd. During the meeting I reported the results of the CDR and Preston and I adjusted the LEI organization to reflect the change over from the planning phase (Phase B) to the implement phase (Phase C/D).

Also, on the 22nd, David Strack and I met with MacDac's Tom Parkinson to further discuss MacDac's support of the project. That was our third meeting without concrete results and when we were finished, we scheduled a fourth meeting!

Finally, and most encouraging, our discussions with the Soviets for a Proton launch had reached the point where Chris Faranetta, representing SSI, and LMSC's Eric Laursen, representing LEI, flew to Moscow to initiate formal negotiations. We were all hoping that we would soon have a Proton launch!

July 1990

In anticipation of the coming storm of activity that would break over LEI once we got started with construction in August, I decided I would take a long needed vacation. I spent three weeks during July in Germany, spending most of my time on my cousin's farm near Ansbach in northern Bavaria (or Mittelfranken to be exact) and seeing the sights in the nearby vicinity.

However, in my absence, things just kept plowing ahead. First, the agreement between NASA and SSI for the transfer of the GRS to the Consortium was formally signed. Second, as a result of Eric's and Chris's trip to Moscow, NPO Energia sent the Lunar Prospector Consortium a "Letter of Intent" in which they expressed their willingness to launch Lunar Prospector, either on a direct insertion trajectory or to a geostationary transfer orbit, for a nominal fee that we understood would probably be around $1 million. LEI began to send the technical data on Lunar Prospector to NPO Energia they needed to determine how best they might launch it.

After I returned from Germany, Larry Spratlin, Diana Pavlow, and I met with Panda Production, a TV and film Production Company that was building a facility in Nassau Bay, close to JSC. Panda was considering doing a TV series called "Mission Control" about the lives, loves, trials, and tribulations of fictitious mission controllers at JSC. They were considering giving us space in their new building for our Lunar Prospector

Mission Control that they could then use as one of their TV/film sets! We also promised them we would provide technical advice for their series. Larry then took on the responsibility of getting Panda all the technical data (power, space, etc. requirements) needed for them to evaluate if they could accommodate us.

Meanwhile, our LEI engineers were busy reviewing the CDR Documents. Specifically, John Muratore, a leading JSC engineer, had taken the lead on reviewing the Command and Data Handling Unit; Bob Noteboom was the lead reviewer for the Telemetry Encoding Subsystem; Mike Matthews was the Attitude Control Subsystem lead; David Strack was responsible for the Communication Subsystem; Brian Cox was the Power Subsystem lead; the Propulsion Subsystem leader was Paul Bailey; while Preston, Larry Spratlin, and I reviewed everything. The comments and questions we derived were transmitted to OMNI on July 31.

OMNI sent us a 35-page draft of a *Fixed Price Contract Between TBD and OMNI Systems Incorporated for (the) Lunar Prospector Satellite and Services* on July 31 for our information and comments.

Finally, also on the 31st, Preston and I met with Chairwoman, Ms. Robinson, of Barrios Technology, another small minority (in this case, a woman) owned technical company in the JSC area, to ask for Barrios's support and for support from the Texas Space Commission that was chaired by Ms. Robinson. Ms. Robinson asked that we come back the following week to give a formal presentation to the entire Barrios' management as the next step in obtaining Barrios's support.

Early August 1990

Since it was by then August, the month we had planned to start construction, we began to ask SSI, "Where's the money?" and, of course, we continued our own efforts to get financial and other support from the aerospace community.

As part of that effort, Preston, who worked for Max Faget at Space Industries, set up a meeting between Max and me for Friday the 3rd. I asked Preston why he didn't meet with Max himself since he worked there. Preston said he felt that, since I was the "elder statesman," Max would be more inclined to listen to me than to him, and I gave a better pitch than he did. Preston added he would be there anyway, but planned to keep his mouth shut.

The meeting with Max went well. The most interesting point was when we asked him if our approach to building Lunar Prospector using commercial, not space-rated hardware was sound. Max answered, "Yes," and added that even Radio Shack electronic components were of such high quality that one could use them in a spacecraft. Beyond the engineering advice, Max said Space Industries would help by letting us use their facilities, etc., but because it was so small, Space Industries could not donate money to the project. We were not surprised about the latter, so were happy with what Max offered.

On Tuesday, August 7, of the following week, I gave a formal presentation to Barrio's staff, as earlier requested by Ms. Robinson. She then asked me to give a presentation to the Texas Space Commission as a way of possibly getting the State of Texas to support Lunar Prospector and, of course, I said I would be very happy to do so (but that never happened).

Also, during the first half of August, the remaining contracts between LEI and the Science Teams were signed and came trickling in. Thus, we had all of the formalities between LEI and the scientists behind us.

Monday, August 13, through Wednesday, August 15, 1990:
A Trip to Toronto

As usual, Gregg and Jim Burke were at the International Space University (ISU) during the latter part of the summer. That year the ISU was held in Toronto, Canada, and Gregg had asked me to give a talk on Lunar Prospector to the students. The trip would also give me the opportunity to talk with Gregg about A) SSI's ticking off Gus and Lockheed with its "SSI/Lunar Prospector ad," B) the resulting requirement that LEI be fully responsible for the project if Lockheed were to continue supporting it, C) how much money SSI had raised, and D), since it was already the middle of August and we had not yet started construction as planned, our setting September for the start of spacecraft construction.

I flew to Toronto on Monday the 13th. When I got to the ISU, I found Gregg who told me that Scott Mandry of Rutgers University wanted to meet with me the next day to discuss Rutgers's participation in Lunar Prospector. Rutgers wanted to provide the project with computer hardware and software support in the area of science data synthesis, databasing, and graphics. As expected, Gregg also said that Jim Burke, he, and I would also meet to discuss the project's status and a September construction start date. I then told Gregg that he and I needed to talk about a couple of things independent of Jim. The next day's activities were set up and I went to my room to get some sleep.

After I gave my talk to the students and met with Scott on the morning of the 14th, I cornered Gregg. I told him about Gus's angry reaction to the SSI add and said that SSI's continued efforts to portray Lunar Prospector as solely a SSI program might well have killed any chance of my getting $1 million and other donated support from Lockheed, and hence any similar support from the other aerospace companies, since all the other companies had tied their promise of financial, hardware, and service support to Lockheed's "leading the way."

Gregg was clearly taken aback and embarrassed by what I had just said, since he could not look me in the eye as our discussion continued. To avoid looking at me, Gregg turned slightly to his left to stare past me, so I stepped to my right to again gain eye contact. Gregg then turned a little further to his right and I again kept pace as we talked. That little dance continued until we had made nearly a full circle by the end of the conversation!

As we were doing our little dance, Gregg said SSI had ordered the offending ad several months earlier before our Consortium relationship had been legally defined and before Lockheed's support had been granted. I was not buying that excuse and replied, even if that were the case, SSI had plenty of time to change the ad to reflect the true situation before it appeared. Then I dropped the second bomb and told him that unless LEI and I were in full charge of the project, Gus would not give us any further support — period. Thus, we had to change the Consortium agreement to reflect Gus's demand or else. Gregg reluctantly agreed to do so, but did nothing about it.

That settled, I then asked Gregg about their fundraising activities and how much money was available to get started with construction. I was absolutely shocked by Gregg's answer. He said SSI had not yet started to raise any money, it was just getting ready to hire a fundraising company to seek the money and the now infamous ad was SSI's first attempt to get money!

I could not believe my ears. While Preston and I had been busting our butts doing all the technical and organizational tasks to get ready for an August construction start date, as well as looking for financial and other support from the aerospace community, Gregg and SSI had done nothing — absolutely nothing — to get the money needed to start construction and keep the project on track. To say the least, I was not happy. SSI had totally failed to uphold its side of the Consortium Agreement, while at the same time it kept trying to keep the world believing that Lunar Prospector was SSI's project, and its alone! SSI was far worse than I had ever imagined, and it was crystal clear to me that Lunar Prospector could succeed only if LEI not only did all the technical tasks as planned, but also raised all the money.

With that knowledge, the meeting between Jim, Gregg, and me concerning the status of the project and our construction schedule had no meaning for me, but Jim, who was apparently unaware of SSI's failure to do its part of the project, asked me over to his apartment for a glass of wine to celebrate Lunar Prospector's great progress. Despite Gregg's maddening revelations and my not drinking alcohol in any form unless I can't get out of it, I accepted Jim's sincere invitation and guzzled a glass of wine, toasting Lunar Prospector's success to date.

The next day I flew back to Houston to tell Preston and the rest of our staff of SSI's failure, and therefore, that it was necessary for us to find all the money. In short, I reported to them we finally had the answer to the question we had been asking SSI for sometime, i.e., "Where's the money?" The answer was a frustrating and aggravating, "Nowhere!"

Chapter 1-6
To the Moon Using Pepsi and Pizza for Fuel?

Friday, August 17, 1990:
A Shift of Emphasis and Two Important Meetings

Having returned from the Toronto trip with the knowledge that SSI had raised no money and hence that we could not start construction until LEI found the necessary funding, we shifted LEI's efforts from the science and engineering aspects of the project, all of which were in excellent shape, to raising money — and raising it fast. That led to the rather quick disintegration of LEI's volunteer engineering staff since, having finished essentially all the documentation and preparation for the construction phase of the project, there was little for most of the engineers to do until we had the money to start construction. We assumed that when we got the money, most of our volunteers, plus many new ones, would quickly return to LEI to continue with the work they had started. However, in the meantime, LEI's staff was reduced to a core of several stalwarts — mainly Rick Corbell, Brian Cox, Mike Matthews, Diana Pavlow, David Strack, Jana Rebmann, Larry Spratlin, Andy and Andre Sylvester, and, of course, Preston, and me — who kept LEI alive and sought the needed money.

As had been arranged by Bill Huffstetler, Bill and I met with Aaron Cohen and Dan Remington of the JSC Legal Department and others from JSC's upper management to discuss the legality of JSC personnel working on Lunar Prospector and the status of the project. Cohen and the legal staff agreed that JSC volunteers could work on Lunar Prospector, but that their doing so would have to be approved on an individual basis to avoid any "conflicts of interest." By allowing JSC engineers to work on Lunar Prospector, JSC was officially blessing the project — another very important step in increasing our credibility, thanks in large part to Bill.

As cryptically mentioned by Preston towards the end of May, there was a possibility of us getting a few million dollars from non-aerospace companies. That possibility was via a Mr. Mike Lawson who had an advertising company, Space Marketing Concepts of Atlanta, in Atlanta, GA, that specialized in space ads. Mike had worked with Space Industries' Joe Allen when he was an astronaut flying in the Shuttle. One of the minor problems encountered by the astronauts (and cosmonauts) during space flights was that everything tasted flat and their drinks gave them gas. In addition to NASA having spiced up the food for the astronauts, Mike had arranged a "Coke-Pepsi Drink Off" on one of Joe's shuttle flights that, of course, gave those two companies a lot of good press and advertising. As a result, Mike had continued to work with Joe after he had retired from NASA and started Space Industries with Max Faget. As a further result, Preston and Mike had become acquainted and Preston had, to put it mildly, excited Mike about the space advertising possibilities that Lunar Prospector offered as a private mission. Mike had set out since May to try to get Coke, Pepsi, and Pizza Hut (Pepsi owns Pizza Hut), and other big companies to support Lunar Prospector for the advertising rights. Mike had made considerable progress in that arena, enough so Mike's company and we (the Consortium) had signed a "Representation Agreement" on August 9. Then Mike and Preston had set up a meeting with me to discuss the issues on the 17th.

Mike indicated at the meeting that he had had some initial talks with Pepsi and Pizza Hut, whom he then represented, and suggested that we could get $2.4 to $5 million from them in a few months — an interesting possibility. In our minds, if we got that kind of money from Pepsi and Pizza Hut for advertising, then the odds were very good that Lockheed and the other aerospace companies would follow suit and make good on their promises of support. If so, then we would be on our way to the Moon.

Important as the possibility was that we could get a few million dollars from Pepsi and Pizza Hut, I felt quite uncomfortable with Mike's advertising style of addressing the issues. To put it simply, Mike's ideas did not seem to be constrained by the physical, engineering, and scientific requirements of a space mission, and, worse, Preston did not seem to care or to try to straighten Mike out on those important issues. It was as if Mike believed the real world ran like an advertising cartoon rather than being forced to follow the laws of nature.

Some of his suggestions were, of course, very good, like having Pepsi and Pizza Hut advertisements on the side of the Proton launch vehicle, having Lunar Prospector models sold or given away at Pizza Huts, and the like.

Though perhaps acceptable, I was bothered by Mike's grand idea of having contests for kids in the USA and in the Soviet Union, the winners of which — a USA boy or girl and a Soviet boy or girl — would get to simultaneously punch the "Launch Buttons" in our Lunar Prospector Control Center and in the Soviet Launch Center. While Preston did tell Mike that such buttons could not be connected to anything and hence would not launch the Proton rocket and Lunar Prospector to the Moon, I was bothered by the thought of our having fake launch buttons to deceive the poor kids, by having the kids possibly punching the buttons when nothing was going to happen if we had a last second launch hold and having kids — or anyone — in the Mission Control Centers at such a critical time.

Worse, and totally unacceptable from engineering standpoints, was the idea of making Lunar Prospector in the shape of — and painted like a Pepsi can. First, because of moment of inertia constraints, spinning spacecraft need to be as short and squat as possible and hence not tall and skinny like a Pepsi can and second, the outside of the spacecraft would be covered with blue solar cells, not with paint. That and similar non-realistic and unconstrained, but enthusiastically presented ideas, made me worry we were entering a never-never land of advertising that could do more harm than good.

After our meeting I told Preston that I was very concerned about Mike's lack of reality. Preston countered with the arguments A) that Mike made lots of money and hence knew his trade, while we had no idea about advertising issues, B) in order for us to get the much needed money, we might (or would) have to compromise some of our principles and let the sponsors dictate some of the terms, and C) since he (Preston) had fully supported my efforts to get money from Lockheed and the aerospace community (efforts that had not yielded the level of support we needed to continue with Lunar Prospector), I should fully support his efforts and work with Mike to get the few million dollars. Though I still felt very uneasy, I reluctantly said I would support Preston and Mike.

Shortly after our meeting, Gregg and Mike met to discuss the same issues Mike, Preston, and I had discussed. Interestingly, Gregg came away from his meeting with Mike with the same uneasy feelings I had after my meeting with Preston and him. Thus, like the abortive meeting with the Florida gang the previous January, Gregg and I again found ourselves on the same side of an issue. Nevertheless, we were preparing to move ahead with Mike Lawson, whose first major move was to have us (LEI) hold our first press conference in order to get the nationwide press we would need to convince the commercial world we were for real and hence to support us. In exchange, some commercial company would use Lunar Prospector as a major ad theme during the 1992 International Space Year — since, with any financial luck, we still hoped to be able to launch by the beginning of 1992.

The Last Two Weeks of August 1990

Since we were following Mike Lawson's lead, we started thinking about making a PR video and getting together the press conference. Andy Sylvester had started dating a talented young lady named Sherri Koepnick who had done PR work for a Houston physician — the star of local TV and radio "Ask the Doctor" type of program. As such, Sherri was well versed in the arts of PR videos and press conferences and had become highly motivated to help with Lunar Prospector after Andy had explained to her our efforts and goals. Also, given her and Andy's relationship, she, Andy, and his twin brother, Andre, took the lead in developing the video and had an excellent product in a few weeks. Their efforts were supported by Mike Truly (the son of NASA Administrator and ex-astronaut, Admiral Richard Truly), whose beautiful computer animations of the Lunar Prospector Spacecraft on its way to the Moon and in lunar orbit helped make the video a first rate PR instrument. Also, when the video was finished, Judy Humble, Ron Humble's wife, who speaks Russian, translated the videotext and did a voice-over in Russian so we could send the Soviets the video to help seal the Proton launch deal.

Sherri, who had become LEI's Publicity Director, began to put out press releases, the first of which went into the August 24 issue of JSC's *Space News Roundup*. The article reviewed the progress we had made since we had asked for volunteers to help with the mission in our first *Space News Roundup* article that had appeared one year earlier. Sherri's article had a picture of the spacecraft model and quoted Bill Huffstetler as saying, "Their objectives are excellent and collection of data is something we need. The premise of the project is very good."

During that period, in fact during the previous few weeks and the following few weeks, LEI and SSI had a flurry of correspondence with the Russians regarding the launch, with Panda Productions regarding their helping to set up the Command and Control Center in their studio, and with all the other sources of potential support in an effort to finalize the promises those organizations made regarding our much needed support.

Though we were spending most of our time at LEI dealing with the PR and money aspects of the project, we still had technical issues to resolve. Specifically, the OMNI spacecraft design had a 4 watt radio frequency (wrf) output transmitter that required 31 watts of input power to transmit at the 9600 bit/sec (bps) data rate we required. That system required 20 m diameter receiving antennas and there were few such antenna available to us. Since there are a great number of 5 to 10 m dishes around the world, we needed to find a way of using those smaller receiving antennas. There were two approaches we were looking at — or a combination of both.

First, I found out we could "data compress" the data from the GRS to reduce its data rate from 3000 bps to just 750 bps, thereby reducing the entire spacecraft's downlink data rate from 9.6 kbps to 4.8 kbps and allowing us to use 10 m dishes.

Second, we could upgrade the transmitter to have a 6 or 8 wrf output, with a corresponding increase in the input power of 15 to 30 watts. That would require us to give up the 29 watt margin in the design of the solar array (a bad thing to do), and/or increase the solar array output by using expensive gallium arsenide solar cells instead of the standard, cheaper silicon cells.

In the end, we opted for cutting the data rate to solve the problem, rather than adding to the expense of the mission that was already strapped for money.

Finally, though we did not know it at the time, the last issue of *Lunar Prospector News* — Volume 1, Number 10 — was issued on August 28, 1990.

September 1990

September opened on two sour notes. The first was the September issue of *Discover* came out with a nice article about Lunar Prospector, but SSI had been up to its old tricks of pretending that Lunar Prospector was solely an SSI project in crass violation of the Consortium Agreement signed in June. That, and similar problems of SSI failing to follow the Consortium Agreement to the detriment of both the project and LEI, led us to consider legally nullifying the Consortium Agreement and going our own way, unless the Agreement were changed to give LEI full authority over the project as Gus had demanded back in June, and as I had told Gregg was required two weeks earlier in Toronto. I wrote a draft letter and sent it to Jay Cuclis at Vinson & Elkins so he could prepare it as a legal document and send it to SSI (Appendix 1-4, also see www.lunar-research-institute.org). We stated in the letter that SSI had to respond by September 12, giving LEI total control of the project in a new agreement, or else.

Just a couple of days later, and adding more insult to injury, we got a copy of a "Dear Friends" letter SSI had put in the September issue of *Frontier* magazine soliciting funds for SSI's Lunar Prospector Project (Appendix 1-5, also see www.lunar-research-institute.org). Jay sent our letter to SSI and we waited for their response.

On Friday the 7th, Brad Roscoe and I got together to discuss the design of the APS. As it was originally designed, it had eleven detectors, one on eleven of the twelve faces of a pentagonal-dodecahedron (the twelfth face was to be used to attach the APS to its boom), with a total collecting area of 33 cm^2. Brad felt that we should increase the sensitivity of the APS by putting two detectors on each of the eleven faces, thereby doubling the collecting area and the sensitivity. In order to keep the resulting increase in the APS's mass and power consumption to a minimum, Brad proposed we retain the original design of having just one pre-amp and amplifier per face. That arrangement would slightly increase the noise in the system, but that slight increase would be acceptable. Brad's suggestion represented a great improvement in the APS's performance at an absolute minimum of cost in terms of dollars, mass, and power, so I agreed wholeheartedly.

On Monday, the 10th, Preston, Sherri, Mike Lawson (who by then was also representing Amway in our discussions), and I met to discuss the potential of our getting $3 million from one of the non-aerospace companies and to outline the Press Conference we were targeting for October 4, the 33rd anniversary of the beginning of the Space Age by the launch of Sputnik 1.

In response both to Gus's insistence that, if Lockheed were to continue supporting Lunar Prospector, LEI had to have total responsibility for the project, and to Jay Cuclis's letter, Gregg and I signed a Memorandum of Understanding giving LEI total control of the project on the 13th.

However, one of the stipulations was that SSI would be repaid for all its expenses, including the $75,000 it had spent on the Spacecraft Design Study and LEI's use of the Apollo GRS NASA had donated to SSI for the project! Eric Laursen, who was my liaison with Gus, fired back a memo stating that repayment of SSI's past funding and future efforts would be unacceptable to Lockheed and would torpedo any efforts to get funding from any other sources, since "Nobody wants to invest in or contribute to ventures which require significant portions of new funds to go to debt service or payoffs to past investors; this is a basic rule of investment . . . not just a Lockheed concern." Eric stated further, as I had in the past, "There is the broader issue of whether SSI can really claim to be 'supporting' Lunar Prospector in any meaningful way if their costs are completely reimbursed."

In addition to the above comments, Eric addressed the issue of who should be the Project Manager and who should be in charge of the project as follows: "Binder should be the Project Manager. He has done the vast majority of the work pulling this project together, and it is his drive that is moving the project forward. I thought about our discussion regarding Jim French (for whom I have the greatest respect), but finally decided that Alan's drive and initiative make him the best choice for the job. Lockheed has made its investment to-date in Alan, even more so than in the project itself." With that memo Eric and Lockheed finally put a lid on the LEI-SSI pot that had been boiling over about those issues for months.

As a result of Eric's memo, a new Memorandum of Understanding, with the offending stipulation removed, was signed and it went into effect on the 19th. Finally, LEI and I had full control of Lunar Prospector.

With that important piece of organizational structure finally behind us, we continued working on the Press Conference, which had in the meantime slipped to October 9 — my 50th birthday! We were making arrangements for Apollo astronaut, Gene Cernan, the Commander of the Apollo 17 Mission and the last man to stand on the Moon, and astronaut Joe Allen to initiate the Press Conference, for a Soviet representative to indicate their intentions to launch Lunar Prospector, and for representatives of those companies that were supporting the project to be at the Press Conference. Also, we would show the PR video and the spacecraft model publicly for the first time.

By that time it was beginning to look like the refurbishment costs of the Apollo GRS would be prohibitive, so Al Metzger, Brad Roscoe, and I began developing a backup plan. We started to look into the development costs and issues of building a new GRS that would have a BGO (barium germinate oxide) detector instead of a NaI (sodium iodide, like the Apollo GRS had) detector and having an independent ^{3}He Neutron Spectrometer (NS) for mapping the suspected polar water ice deposits. It wasn't too long before we opted for the much cheaper BGO GRS and ^{3}He NS systems.

Finally, I flew to Sunnyvale for a meeting on the 24th with Gus and Eric to discuss Lockheed's future support for the project. Gus said he would pursue the topic with LMSC President McMahon the following week.

Thus, as September came to an end, our hopes were high that the new Consortium Arrangement with LEI and me in total charge of the project and the upcoming Press Conference would break the money logjam, and that we would then be back on track with spacecraft construction starting in a couple of months and a late 1992 launch to the Moon.

The First Two Weeks of October 1990:
Preparing for the Press Conference

During the two weeks prior to the Press Conference (which by then had slipped to the 17th), LEI's small, but dedicated, residual staff spent late nights (after our day jobs) getting the press package together, making viewgraphs for Preston's and my pre-

sentations and writing invitations to the print media, television networks, and radio stations. To ensure that we had a good showing of media representatives, Sherri and I
called each of the local radio and TV stations and newspapers and then we went to each
of them to hand deliver their invitation.

The dubious highlight of that period of hectic activity occurred when we were trying to get OMNI to send us the Lunar Prospector Model on time for the Press Conference. OMNI had taken the model to Japan as part of their display at an aerospace expo-
sition and had not gotten it back from Japan until it was too late to ship it to us via an
inexpensive surface carrier. Thus, it had to be shipped via a very expensive air carrier
and OMNI was shy by $1000 to cover the air shipping costs.

Preston announced that little fact when we were all putting the final touches on
the Press Conference. As every one in our little group knew, I was the oldest and hence
the best paid member of our group, I was single and had no debts and I had a reasonable amount of savings; while the rest of our members were young engineers, some married and with children, they had lower paying jobs, debts, and little or no savings. When
Preston announced that someone had to cough up $1000 for the cause, everyone turned
and looked at me. Then everyone laughed and Preston explained why. "You should see
the look on your face. You look just like a fish that has just been hooked and can't find
a way out of your predicament," and that was exactly how I felt. Needless to say, I paid
the $1000 to get the model shipped to us for the all-important Press Conference.

In addition to springing the $1000 surprise on me, Preston had hidden another
little item from me that he knew I would really object to. In order to satisfy the PR
desires of Pepsi, Coke, etc., Mike and Preston had promised them Lunar Prospector
would add a slow scan camera to the payload to document the receding Earth and the
approaching Moon as we headed to the latter and to periodically take pictures of selected lunar areas during the orbital mapping phase of the mission. Needless to say, I was
not happy when I found that out. I had fought having a costly and scientifically useless
PR camera onboard Lunar Prospector from its inception, and, thanks to Mike's ignorance and Preston's "do anything and promise anything attitude," they had snuck a useless camera on board behind my back. When I raised hell with Preston, he argued we
had to have the camera to get advertising money and I said, "If we get the advertising
money, I will make sure that whoever gave us the money will understand the camera is
a costly burden to the mission and I will get rid of it as I have done in the past."

Preston retorted, "Who cares after we get the money!"

Tuesday, October 16, through Thursday, October 18, 1990:
A Pepsi Meeting, the Press Conference, and Bad News

Preston, Mike Lawson, and astronaut Gene Cernan had flown to New York for a
formal meeting at Pepsi Corporation on the 16th to present our case for their supporting Lunar Prospector to the tune of $3 million for the advertising rights. Pepsi promised
they would make their decision in two weeks (Amway was also considering the same
deal for about the same amount of money). Preston and Mike flew on the red-eye from
New York to Houston to get back on the 17th, just in time for our 10:00 AM Press Conference (Gene Cernan did not come with them since neither he, nor Joe Allen, nor the
Russians were going to participate in our Press Conference, much to our disappointment). When Preston and Mike arrived — directly from the airport — at the Holiday Inn
Crown Plaza in Houston where we were holding the Press Conference, they were very
tired and looked like hell after sleeping poorly in the airplane.

Just after they arrived and just before the press conference started, Preston told me about their meeting, the $3 million, and the time-scale of the Pepsi decision. That was good news, but then Preston said he and Mike had decided, in order to make the necessary impact, they were going to say the Russians were going to launch Lunar Prospector and the Pepsi deal was solid and hence the $3 million was "in the bag." I strongly objected, saying if the Russians and Pepsi said, "No," we would kill our credibility with the press. But Preston was adamant, replying that Mike knew advertising and the press, that everything would be OK and that to do less, i.e., to admit that we had no money, would undermine our efforts to get good press and would kill our chances of getting any commercial support. I strongly did not agree, but it was too late to do anything more since it was 10:00 and Sherri had already started introducing Preston, Mike, and me.

I presented first. I gave the background of the mission, our overall programmatic philosophy and goals, our science objectives, and the Mission Profile, all of which seemed to have been well received by the press.

Preston discussed the spacecraft, the Russian launch, and the other engineering aspects of the mission and all that went over quite well.

Finally, Preston and Mike talked about the funding aspects of our efforts and about how Pepsi was paying $3 million for the advertising rights to the mission, and the Pepsi money represented an excellent start on our getting the full $11.7 million we needed for the mission — but, as I feared, the press smelled a rat.

One of the TV reporters stood up and asked skeptically, "Do you really have the $3 million, or is that just a promise; and if it is just a promise, how much money do you really have?"

Preston, looking like a deer caught in a car's headlights, sputtered and tried, in a Clintonian way, to say we had the money without really saying we had the money and looked for help from Mike, who was figuratively, if not literally, "heading for the hills."

Again, the reporter wasn't buying it and asked, "Well, you really don't have any money do you? You're just standing there with your hat in your hand asking for money, isn't that true?"

With that, Preston, looking very tired and very sheepish, had to admit the reporter was correct — and with that admission, the press conference ended on a very bad note.

Needless to say, after the press left, I let Preston and Mike know how I felt about their performances. Nevertheless, though some damage had been done, the overall assessment of the Press Conference by our staff and the press was quite positive. We left Houston to drive back down to Clear Lake to get ready for the evening's Press Reception we were holding at 6:00 PM at the Clear Lake Golf Course Clubhouse.

The Press Reception was a lot of fun. We had some donated food and drink and a lot of people showed up besides our LEI staff and the press. There were several JSC people there, including Bill Huffstetler and other local, non-aerospace people. One of the latter was a local contracts lawyer, David Juist. David introduced himself to me and said he thought what we were doing was very exciting and he offered his services, *pro bono*, to the cause. David's services were welcome and were very useful over the next few years.

Since we had had to take the booms and antenna off the model to transport it from the Holiday Inn in Houston to Clear Lake for the Reception, we had to reassemble the model just as the Reception was getting started. For some reason, the *Houston Post* press photographer was fascinated by those activities and kept taking pictures as we reassembled the model. The next morning's issue of the *Houston Post* (Thursday, Oct. 18, 1990, Appendix 1-6, also see www.lunar-research-institute.org) had a great article about the mission and a picture of the spacecraft model with me working on one of the booms. I was assembling the boom and, since my hands were full of the boom and its guy-wire, I was holding a bolt between my lips; but in the picture the bolt looked like a cigarette. Since I don't (never did and never will) smoke and think smoking is a filthy, stinking habit, I was not happy with the impression the photo delivered. Nevertheless, the article was very good, and, despite the pseudo-cigarette, the picture was impressive.

Though the newspaper article had started the day out well, I got word from Sunnyvale that the meeting between Gus and McMahon had been postponed. Worse, when I called Joe Kerwin and Frank Martin at LMSC to see what was going on, they indicated that Lockheed might not be in a position to make further contributions to Lunar Prospector. If so, our hopes for support from the rest of the aerospace community would be dashed. Just as our prospects for support from the conventional commercial sector were growing, Lockheed was apparently getting ready to pull the rug from under us!

Friday, October 19, through Monday, October 29, 1990

Despite the possible lack of support from Lockheed and hence, from the rest of the aerospace community, we pressed ahead, hoping our success on other fronts would persuade Lockheed and the rest of the aerospace community to support us after all.

We received a lot of good national and international press and many offers of support as a result of the Press Conference. For example, reporters for *Scientific American, Aviation Week, Runways,* and *Breakthrough* were preparing articles about Lunar Prospector for their respective journals. The Press Conference had paid off well.

On Tuesday the 23rd, Gregg sent us an angry letter via fax (Appendix 1-7, also see www.lunar-research-institute.org). Justifiably, he was angry about Preston's having said at the Press Conference that the Soviets were going to launch Lunar Prospector, even though the deal had not been finalized, and was very concerned Preston's statement might tick off the Russians and wreck SSI's negotiations with them. Further, Gregg was very, very concerned because he had received an urgent call from the U.S. Department of Commerce regarding our supposed use of a "non-Western Block launch" without getting their appropriate approval.

While I agreed fully with Gregg's first concerns about the launch misstatements and though I agreed with a second set of complaints about our not having kept SSI completely in the loop and our apparently not having mentioned SSI's role in Lunar Prospector (SSI role was discussed at the Press Conference and in the Press Kit, though admittedly, not very prominently and hence SSI was ignored by the press), I had to laugh about the latter set of gripes — clearly SSI did not like it when the shoe was on the other foot.

Tuesday, October 30, through Friday, November 2, 1990: The Space Exploration 90 Conference and the Russian Launch

The Johnson Space Center Alumni Association held a "Space Exploration 90 Conference" from October 30 through November 1, and donated free display space in their exhibition hall to LEI. Our display consisted of the spacecraft model and a TV that continually showed our PR video plus written materials. Sherri and I "manned" the booth most of the time, but others from our small staff took their turns, too.

During one of my turns, Yuri Semyenov, the General Designer of NPO Energia, and Boris Artemov, also of NPO Energia, came over to our booth to see the model and to talk with me. Yuri said NPO Energia wanted to commit to the launch of Lunar

Prospector and wanted to invite us to go to Moscow in December to finalize the deal! He added he was sending us a letter to that effect. The letter was written on November 1 and delivered the very next day (see Appendix 1-8, also see www.lunar-research-institute.org). We had a promise of a launch, and boy, were we happy.

Shortly after I received that good news from Yuri, Bill Huffstetler came by and I told him the good news. Bill congratulated me and said that was really great news.

The very next day, Friday, November 2, we faxed Eric and Frank Martin a copy of Yuri's letter, telling them to give it to Gus so he could add it to his pitch to McMahon. We hoped and expected the Russian promise of a free or very inexpensive (a token $1 million at a maximum) launch would convince McMahon to give us the $1 million and the other support we were requesting from Lockheed.

We learned from Mike that one of the potential commercial sponsors had committed to a $3 million contract that was being prepared for signature by the sponsor and Mike's company. The money would follow in 30 days and Mike was working on additional commercial sponsors. It really looked like the money problem was being solved in a big way and that we would soon be building Lunar Prospector in preparation for a late 1992 launch on a Soviet rocket.

Monday, November 5, through Friday, November 16, 1990

Dave Strack, who had been elevated to be my deputy, i.e., the Deputy Project Manager, and I had yet another meeting with Tom Parkinson of McDonnell Douglas and his staff. Given the progress we had made in getting the Russian launch and the commercial backing, McDonnell Douglas was preparing a request to corporate management asking that it donate cash, our use of their construction and test facilities, and support for McDonnell Douglas employees to work on Lunar Prospector. Further, Tom was preparing a meeting between LEI and McDonnell Douglas upper management. It appeared that MacDac was getting much more positive about its support of the project than Lockheed was. Thus, the thought crossed my mind that if Lockheed did not want to give us the support we needed, even though I, a Lockheed employee, was in full charge of the project, then maybe I should quit Lockheed and become a McDonnell Douglas employee and do the mission under their banner. I did not act on that idea, but in retrospect, maybe I should have.

David and I then met again with Glynn Lunney of Rockwell, and like Tom Parkinson, Lunney was willing to ask his corporate management for the same types of support McDonnell Douglas was being asked to give Lunar Prospector. Again, I felt Rockwell was being more supportive than Lockheed.

On the 14th, we got a letter from astronaut Tom Stafford, Chairman of the Synthesis Committee (a committee Congress had set up to find out what to do about NASA's decaying situation), inviting us to present Lunar Prospector to his committee on Monday, November 19! That was just great. Presenting Lunar Prospector to the Synthesis Committee would dramatically increase our credibility. Though our credibility within the aerospace and space sciences communities was already very high, it never hurt to be even more credible.

We all got busy, that is, Gregg and Chris Faranetta of SSI, Mike Lawson and John Reed of Space Marketing Concepts of Atlanta, and Preston and I from LEI, preparing for a trip to Washington DC a few days hence to present to the Stafford Committee and then to go to Moscow (in the dead of winter — burrrrr) to finalize our launch deal with NPO Energia. Boy, were we on a roll again.

Though the project was on a roll, SSI was not. Someone sent us a copy of a confidential letter Gregg had sent to the Directors and Governing Members of SSI on November 8 regarding SSI's financial situation, which was not good to say the least. According to the letter, SSI was facing a cash flow deficit of $50,000 during November and December, mainly because the cash-cow stock SSI had in a communication satellite company called Geostar had tanked.

That bit of information seemed to explain some of the difficulties we had had and were still having with SSI. First there had been the concerns Preston and I had had about SSI not really having had the $75,000 for the Spacecraft Design Study (by then we had also learned from OMNI that SSI still owed them $10,000 for the study, a bill that was never ever paid). Though SSI probably had had the $75,000 two years earlier when they pledged it, they had lost some of it by the time we had started the Design Study. Second, apparently SSI had failed to get money for the project because they had no money for themselves, let alone for hiring a company to seek funding. Third, SSI's continual attempts to tell the world that Lunar Prospector was solely an SSI project was apparently their attempt to impress old, and potential new, SSI donors to give SSI money to survive on (though the larger part, in my mind, was simply SSI's greed in not wanting to share the credit for the project).

Though our finally knowing about SSI's poor financial situation helped to clarify some of the difficulties we had been having with them, the project had suffered because SSI had not been straight with us about their situation. Had Preston and I known about SSI's financial problems, we might have reacted differently to all the uncertainty and delays SSI had caused. Nevertheless, there was no excuse in our minds for SSI having hidden important information from its Consortium Partner under any circumstances, and certainly not when we were trying to do something as difficult as a private lunar exploration mission.

However, in retrospect, I have to give Gregg a lot of credit for sticking his neck way out the way he did to try to keep Lunar Prospector financially afloat while he was on a sinking SSI ship. Years later, after Lunar Prospector was in orbit, Gregg told me that, even after SSI had let three of its seven member staff go in order to pay OMNI as much of the $75,000 as possible, the remaining four staffers went without pay for extended periods of time in order to send OMNI its money! Because he had pushed the mission very hard at SSI and at a financial loss, Gregg was eventually removed from his position as the Executive Vice-President and he left SSI. As it turned out, Gregg was not the first to sacrifice himself on the Lunar Prospector altar, but while at SSI, he did as much as he could for the project, even though Preston and I did not see it that way at the time.

Monday, November 19, 1990: The Synthesis Committee Presentation

I gave the formal presentation to the Stafford Committee. The Committee showed a very high level of interest in the project and the impact it would have on the future development of the national space effort. One of the Committee leaders said Lunar Prospector was one of the most interesting projects they had heard about since they began their work. Stafford and the other Committee members said they were particularly interested in our having obtained non-aerospace commercial support and the Soviet launch. They were also impressed with the positive impact that our low cost mission and data would have on the Space Exploration Initiative. Stafford said that he would write a letter (which he did on November 28, see Appendix 1-9, also see www.lunar-research-institute.org) indicating the Committee's interest in Lunar Prospector, a letter we could use in our promotional material as we continued seeking financial and other support for the mission. We returned home the next day, feeling as though we had made another good step forward.

The Remainder of November 1990:
Lockheed Pulls the Rug and the Plug

Shortly after we returned from our successful meeting with the Synthesis Committee, I got the news that Lockheed Corporate was not going to grant our request for support. Gus called and said that he had left the decision to Jack Houle, Gus's Exploration Programs Manager, as to whether his office would continue supporting my work on Lunar Prospector. Every time I had seen Jack, he was negative about Lunar Prospector, so I knew what Jack's decision was going to be, as did Gus. Thus, I found Gus's not telling me directly that he was cutting off my support, rather, letting his subordinate make the decision and tell me, a little gutless. Just when we apparently had a donated Soviet launch and the possibility of non-aerospace support to the tune of $3 million, Gus and Lockheed pulled the rug out from under Lunar Prospector and pulled the plug on my support!

With Lockheed pulling out, our hopes of getting the other aerospace companies to support us went down the drain, though both McDonnell Douglas and Rockwell remained friendly to the cause. Unless we found support via Mike Lawson and found it fast, Lunar Prospector was in deep trouble. Happily, Mike was diligently working with Amway, Coke, Pepsi, and Pizza Hut to that end, but the promised fast decision on a deal kept slipping.

At the same time, SSI's Chris Faranetta had laid out the schedule for our December trip to Moscow where we would finalize the deal for the Soviet launch. Chris was to leave for Moscow on December 12. John Reed of Space Marketing Concepts and I would follow on December 18, to be picked up by Chris at the Moscow Airport on the 19th. We would then go to our hotel for a short rest and then meet informally with Vjacheslav Filin of NPOE. The next day we would start our formal meetings and visit Red Square and Lenin's Tomb (which I was willing to endure for Lunar Prospector) and then spend the next two days discussing technical issues. I was also to meet with Professor Vjacheslav Balebanov of the Space Research Institute to discuss the science objectives of the mission. Finally, we were to return to New York on the 23rd.

As Chris was getting the schedule set up, we were busy getting visas and making preparations for the trip. However, since Gus was cutting off my support at the end of November, I had no money for the trip, and, as we knew from the pirated SSI letter, SSI did not have money either. There was a big question mark as to how we were going to pay for the trip.

Thus, by the end of November, and hence by the end of our second year of effort, we had made tremendous technical and organizational progress on our journey towards a successful Lunar Prospector Mission. We had experienced science and engineering teams, an excellent payload, a completed spacecraft design, and a promise of a donated, inexpensive launch. We had a promise of money from the non-aerospace world, but we still did not have the few million dollars we desperately needed to move forward. Though we did not know it at the time, we had passed the zenith of our success in doing Lunar Prospector as a private effort. What lay ahead was a several yearlong struggle to keep the mission alive — until a way was found to do it.

December 1990

Because of our financial set backs, things slowed down, but did not stop. First, we pushed ahead with AMSAT and finished a Memorandum of Understanding, dated December 7, regarding their providing a tracking network for Lunar Prospector. Second, our trip to Moscow slipped until January and Gregg sent all of us a memo on the 14th regarding visas and the new trip schedule. On December 20, Pizza Hut wrote Mike Lawson about a business deal that might end up with $4 million for Lunar Prospector — keeping our hopes for support alive.

Also by that time, Brad Roscoe and I had decided it would be more cost effective and better scientifically to forgo using the donated Apollo GRS and build a new BGO GRS and a separate NS as Brad, Al Metzger, and I had begun to discuss in September. When Brad and I reached that decision, I called Al and he concurred, but added, since we were not going to use the Apollo GRS (that was still stored in his office), he no longer wanted to be on the team. I said I understood and thanked him for all his interest and help.

Al's quitting opened the door for Brad to be the GRS Team Leader and to build the Lunar Prospector GRS, as he had always wanted to do. When I called Brad, he was very happy with the news and accepted the position as the GRS Team Leader. That left me with the problem of finding someone to take over the new position of the NS Team Leader and to build the NS. Brad also said, since his GRS experience was in oil and terrestrial resource exploration, he would need some team members who had experience doing space GRS experiments. I immediately got busy on both issues.

Though I found Jerry Weinberg, who was part of the Florida fiasco back in January, to be arrogant and objectionable at a minimum, I decided to call him to see if he was interested in being involved with the GRS mapping. When I called Jerry, he astounded me by aggressively saying, "You owe me an explanation as to why I have not been involved in the mission." Since I did not owe him anything (except maybe a kick in the butt), I ignored his arrogance and explained that we had decided to build a BGO GRS and asked him if he was interested in being part of the GRS Team. His attitude was if he was not in charge of the GRS, he was not interested (OK, Jerry, then go to hell).

I then asked him if he would recommend anyone else and he said, "Yes, Penny Haskins," who worked in his research group.

I called Penny, who was absolutely delightful to talk with (and later to work with), explained the situation, and asked if she would like to help with the BGO GRS. She said, "Yes," and explained that she and her instrument engineer, Jack Kisson, were flying BGO GRSs on the Space Shuttle to determine the radiation hazard. I asked her how much Jerry would be involved, since she was in his research group. Without my having said anything negative about Jerry, Penny knew exactly why I had asked and said, "Yes, Jerry is a pain and impossible to work with, but you don't have to worry about that. Jack and I have our own little company outside of the University and we can work with you through that company." I was relieved that I would not have to put up with Jerry and said that would be great. I then asked her if she knew anyone who could do the NS. She said, "Yes, Bill Feldman at Los Alamos," and she gave me Bill's number. I thanked Penny and that ended our first interaction.

I called Bill Feldman and asked if would want to lead the NS Team and build the spectrometer and Bill said, "Yes," with great enthusiasm. That telephone conversation started a personal and collegial friendship that would play a very important role in the Lunar Prospector Mission.

On the personal side, since I no longer had support from Gus to work on Lunar Prospector, I had to return to working on the Space Exploration Initiative (SEI) activities and I broke my wrist just before Christmas — ouch. Regarding the former, in part because I had been away working on Lunar Prospector, but mainly because the NASA managers, Ed Lineberry and Barney Roberts, for whom I worked directly (though Bill Huffstetler ran the New Initiatives Office, the day to day work was led by lower level managers), did not like the way I did things, I had been ostracized from the Lunar/Mars Mission planning activities of the SEI.

The reason for my situation was simple. Both Ed and Barney were engineers who knew absolutely nothing about the Moon and Mars, and not a whole lot about engineering (a fact witnessed by Barney's later being fired from NASA because of his incompetence [and perhaps because of his well known extracurricular activities with attractive female contractor personnel] — a nearly impossible feat given that, like all NASA employees, Barney was a civil servant of the Federal Government. Ed Lineberry died a little later). Like most NASA managers, Barney and Ed could and would only make decisions by committee and only after numerous and senseless trade studies. That way, no one, especially the manager(s), can be blamed for failures; but nothing ever really gets decided or finished — one is in a perpetual cycle of trade studies. I don't work that way (as witnessed by Lunar Prospector's success) and that became quickly clear to Ed and Barney. When our work on defining a SEI Lunar Base began, I suggested, since NASA had done extensive work on that subject at the end of the Apollo Program, we should just dust off those studies and go from there — a suggestion that was briskly rejected. After all, if we did not start from scratch, how could Ed and Barney justify their jobs and the money for their programs (the reader should also return to the discussion in the Prolog about the evolution of the NASA Lunar Polar Orbiter Program, where every few years, in order to look like something new, the mission was changed a bit and was renamed — that is just part of the same misguided philosophy of NASA management). Instead of building on what had already been done, we had to start all over again. My objecting to the way we were wasting time and effort (and hence taxpayers' money), plus the fact that incompetent managers do not trust anyone who actually knows something about the subject and has some experience (after all, if an exalted manager does not know something, how can a mere underling, worse a contractor, know anything at all), rather quickly led to my being eased out of the SEI planning activities.

Luckily, Bill Huffstetler was not a typical NASA manager and believed that what I was doing with Lunar Prospector was of great importance for JSC, NASA, and the national space program. Bill told Mick, my Lockheed supervisor, not to worry about my having nothing to do on the SEI contract, he wanted me to keep working on Lunar Prospector — but, of course, under the table. Without anyone except Bill, Mick, and me knowing it, NASA was supporting my efforts to find a way of getting Lunar Prospector done. For that, and much, much more, I owed Bill a great debt of gratitude and I was very happy that he lived to see Lunar Prospector become a complete success, before his untimely death at the beginning of June 1999.

As a result of Bill's support, I was able to spend considerable time over the next few years improving the OMNI spacecraft design, writing and revising Mission Profile 1.1, the Mission Requirements Document, the Mission Operations Document, and the Controllers Training Manual. As a result, when Lunar Prospector's time finally came, it was at a very high state of development and ready to go.

January 1991 to the Spring of 1991

The New Year started with the publication of a very nice article in the January issue of *Scientific American* (p. 116) called *Another small step?* In addition to the one page article, they had a picture of the spacecraft model with me standing in front of it. It was a good piece of PR material that we used extensively in our funding efforts.

Given that money — or better, the lack thereof — was our main problem, we had pinned our hopes on getting the $4 million Mike was trying to get from Pepsi and Pizza Hut. The main company, Pepsi, seemed serious, but since we had not received the major financial support we had requested from Lockheed and the other aerospace companies, Pepsi was dragging its feet. However, Preston was convinced Pepsi would buy in if we could convince them we could fly Lunar Prospector for the $4 million, Pepsi was willing to pay for the advertising rights to the mission. Preston had easily convinced Mike we could do it for $4 million, so Mike was off telling Pepsi everything was OK. However, when Preston told me we had to slash the Lunar Prospector budget from $11.6 million to $4 million, I thought he was nuts, as did the rest of our LEI staff and Gregg. Nevertheless, Preston insisted we could do the mission for $4 million and argued we had no other choice but to try and, if Pepsi did gave us the $4 million, we stood a good chance that some of the aerospace companies would kick in a few million, even if Lockheed wouldn't. Though Preston had a point, Gregg and I were still very skeptical and very concerned, because, if we received no money beyond the $4 million from Pepsi, we were fairly certain we could not do the mission and then Pepsi would kill us for breach of contract.

Despite our grave reservations, and at Preston's insistence, the LEI staff went through the (self-deceptive) task of shoving a size 11.6 million foot into a size 4 million shoe. As far as I was concerned, the numbers we came up with were pure fiction, but we did come up with a budget that to the untrained eyes of Mike and Pepsi looked realistic on paper.

Pepsi, certainly supported by Mike's unbridled (and unconstrained by reality) enthusiasm, bought the idea we could do Lunar Prospector for $4 million, plus, of course, a free Soviet launch (the deal which had yet to be finalized, since our trip to Moscow was on permanent hold until we got some money). By the time spring rolled around, Pepsi was in basic agreement with us and had turned the decision regarding the $4 million deal over to its advertising agency. Pepsi had told the agency to meet with us, to listen to our pitch and to see if they thought they could build a successful advertising campaign for Pepsi and Pizza Hut on the basis of the Lunar Prospector Mission.

April 1991: The Pepsi Advertising Pitch

The meeting, of which Preston had told me very little, was held in the Space Industries' conference room. Those present were Mike Lawson, two representatives from the advertising company, Ed White, Jr. (the son of Apollo astronaut, Ed White, who was killed in the Apollo 1 fire along with Gus Grissom and Roger Chaffee), who had a space paraphernalia business, Preston, and me. Not knowing exactly what was going on, I asked Preston what Ed White, Jr. was doing at the meeting. Preston replied Pepsi was considering a deal that might include another company Ed was representing. That seemed strange to me, but what did I know? Then Mike asked me a very strange question about how angles could be so accurately related to π. Not really understanding the reason of his strange question, I answered that, since there were 2π radians in a circle of 360°, all angles could be, and often were, represented as a function of π. Mike looked even more puzzled about my answer than I was about his question.

Finally the meeting got started and I gave my presentation (Preston had declined to present anything on his usual grounds that I did a better job — being the elder statesman and all).

White got up and started talking about the infamous "Face on Mars," of which he had a video made by the nut cases (whom he was representing) who believe the natural feature was carved by intelligent beings and it is surrounded by a city of pyramidal shaped buildings (mainly apartment buildings), all of which are aligned with respect to the face at very specific angles that are exact fractions of π, i.e., like π/2, π/3, π/6, etc. White's pitch was to sell that nonsensical video as part of an advertising package along with Lunar Prospector!

When White started his presentation, I was stunned. Then I realized I had been had by Preston. Preston knew I would never, never in a million years, have been part of that meeting had I known what kind of wacko, pseudo-scientific crap was going to be presented along with Lunar Prospector. I was about to say something when Preston turned to me, put his forefinger to his lips to make the "shhh" motion and mouthed silently, "Don't say anything." I realized I was trapped and then I realized why Mike had asked about the "magical" relationship between π and angles before the meeting had started; he actually believed the pseudo-numerological nonsense I was having to sit through. I was really trapped and had no choice but to sit there fuming, unless I wanted to create a scene by strangling Preston on the spot (a difficult task at best, since Preston is much younger, much bigger, and much taller than I am).

Finally, the very painful meeting was over and the advertising agency representatives said they would give us their decision in a week or two. I dreaded the possibility the agency would buy both the "Face on Mars" crap and Lunar Prospector. I had been worried enough about the possibility of our having to try to do Lunar Prospector for just $4 million, and that worry was compounded by the "Face on Mars" nonsense! When Preston and I were alone, he said — before I could say anything, "I knew you would have a fit if you knew what was going on, so I didn't tell you. If we get the money, we can deal with the Mars face stuff later." Since the dirty deed had been done, there was nothing I could say to change it, so I shut up and left.

Mercifully, we were informed a couple of weeks later by Pepsi that the advertising agency had decided against using Lunar Prospector for an advertising theme. The reason we were given was that advertising dogma states in good times one uses avant-garde advertising themes and in bad times, conservative themes. The USA was in a recession at that time, so Lunar Prospector, which was about as avant-garde a theme as was possible, was out. Though we badly needed money for Lunar Prospector, I was relieved that Pepsi had bowed out since I did not believe we could do Lunar Prospector for $4 million and I was sick to death of Mike Lawson's wacky advertising schemes.

Though Preston still held out hope Mike would somehow find us money, he had to admit that the Pepsi deal had fizzled (pardon the pun) and therefore there was little or no hope for any non-aerospace funding for some time to come. After SSI had failed to get money and was in no position to get money for the project or even for itself, after I had failed to get aerospace support, and after Preston's attempt to get advertising money failed, I started to try, once again, to find financial support for Lunar Prospector.

Chapter 1-7
The Political Approach

May through Early September 1991

After the Pepsi fiasco, the only approach left to solving our money problem I could think of was to try to get Congress to support our efforts. Since NASA was a mess and Congress knew it (Congress had set up the Stafford and the Augustine Committees to find out how to correct the mess), and since one of the purposes of Lunar Prospector was to demonstrate how to do missions better and cheaper than NASA could, I naively thought Congress might be talked into funding Lunar Prospector directly. After all, SSI had gotten Congressmen Torricelli, McMillen, Campbell, Rohrabacher, and Brown to write to NASA requesting that it give the Apollo GRS to the project and I had gotten Texas Congressman Andrews to actively support us. Thus I hoped there was a chance of getting even more Congressional backing, given the enormous progress we had made and given we could show there was a better way of exploring the Moon and planets than the NASA way.

However, since I was in Texas, I did not have access to the Congressmen that SSI had originally gotten to support Lunar Prospector, but I thought I should have access to Texas politicians besides Congressman Andrews. I started writing letters to Governor Ann Richards, Senators Lloyd Bentsen and Phil Gramm, Congressman Jack Brooks (from the Beaumont/JSC area district), and Henry Cisneros, the former Mayor of San Antonio, to ask for meetings and their support.

Except in the cases of the Governor and Henry Cisneros (who would not be concerned with the inadequacies of a federal agency like NASA), I explained in my letters that one of the reasons we were doing Lunar Prospector was because NASA was screwing up (I was more polite in my letters), and we wanted to demonstrate how to do space exploration right. I got some interesting replies.

Ann Richard's response began with, "Thank you for your letter concerning problems at the Texas Department of Criminal Justice." Getting a form letter is bad enough, but it should at least be the correct form letter — so much for the Governor.

Senators Bentsen and Gramm wrote back that they had forwarded my letters to NASA. Since I had clearly stated NASA was the problem and I was seeking their support to solve the problem, sending my letters to the "enemy" ensured the answer was, "What problem? There is no problem." So much for the Senators!

Cisneros was willing to see me and a meeting was set up, but when I went to San Antonio, Cisneros had another commitment, so I just talked with his aide and that, of course, led to nothing.

Happily, there was Jack Brooks. Jack, if I remember correctly, was then the second ranking member of the House of Representatives — an elder statesman — and a real old-time Texas politician. Like Mike Andrews, Jack was a believer in JSC and the space program, but Jack, being a very senior Congressman at that time, had a lot more clout than Mike did and could therefore more readily help us. Jack was also a believer in his hometown of Beaumont, TX, and anything he could do to help those three things — NASA, JSC, and Beaumont — he tried to do. Happily, Jack's Beaumont office said they would set up a meeting for me as soon as possible.

Not wanting NASA to think that I was going behind its back, I also wrote NASA Administrator, Admiral Truly on June 17. I reviewed the Lunar Prospector Mission and the progress we had made and told Truly, because we had been unable to raise the $11.6 million we needed to do the mission, I was asking various Senators and Congressmen for direct Congressional funding of the project. I further wrote that I assumed that the Senators and Congressmen would ask him about the mission and when they did, "I hope that you will find that our effort to help the national space program is worthy of such support."

I was very careful not to even hint in the letter that I wanted NASA support for the mission, rather direct Congressional support. Nevertheless, I got a reply dated June 25 (Appendix 1-10, also see www.lunar-research-institute.org) and written by Wes Huntress, then the Director of the Solar System Exploration Division or Code S, showing that NASA had ignored what I had written and assumed I wanted NASA support for the mission. Wes's answer was the classic NASA refrain that had kept lunar science missions from happening for over two decades — the mission must pass the peer review process and it must be part of the "Strategic Plan." Even though I had not asked for NASA help, Code S was trying to drive the nails in Lunar Prospector coffin. Wes's letter was an embodiment of the reasons why we were trying to do Lunar Prospector completely outside of NASA.

As I was busy with those efforts, Preston dropped a bombshell — he was leaving Space Industries and going to Lawrence Livermore Labs in California in August! Preston is a brilliant engineer and I have the greatest respect for him; I like him and I like working with him very much. However, like many exceptional people, Preston is outspoken, brisk, and does not even know the word "tact" (at least I know the word and can even spell it). Thus Preston does not hesitate to tell his bosses (who are usually nowhere near as competent as Preston) what he thinks of them and their instructions. That endearing trait, plus the fact that Preston had spent considerable time working on Lunar Prospector instead of doing what he was supposed to be doing, led his Space Industries superiors to take Preston off all the engineering projects he was heading and to sidetrack him into being a liaison person for existing contracts and for seeking new business. Since Preston is no idiot, he saw the handwriting on the wall, so, on one of his first liaison trips, he sought and got an offer from Lawrence Livermore Labs. Thus Preston would be leaving Houston in August.

Given that Preston was leaving, given that I had started to get meetings (at least one) set up with Texas politicians, given that I did not want Mike Lawson involved with Lunar Prospector anymore, and given that I was going to remove the offensive slow scan camera from the payload, I wanted to get the computer disk on which we had all our Lunar Prospector viewgraphs so I could remove all references to Mike's company and the camera in order to prepare a modified pitch for the politicians.

Preston had come to my house so we could discuss the impact on Lunar Prospector of his move to California. When I asked Preston to give me the computer disk so I could change the viewgraphs, Preston surprisingly said he would not give it to me because he did not want Mike Lawson written out of our efforts. I said that was crazy and I again asked him to give me the disk. Preston again said no and explained that he had other deals going on with Mike and he did not want me spoiling them if Mike got mad because I removed him from the project. With that, our conversation quickly devolved into a shouting match (one of only two times I lost my temper during the entire ten and a half years it took to do Lunar Prospector), and Preston left. I did not get the disk, so I had to "cut and paste" the existing viewgraphs to make the new ones rather than have nice, clean, presentable ones. Though I was annoyed, our little war did not affect our friendship, and in August Preston left Houston and Lunar Prospector for good.

However, with Preston on his way out of both Houston and Lunar Prospector, and because of several events that had transpired during the project, I decided two related things had to be done regarding the LEI/Lunar Prospector Organization. The reasons for my decision were first, it had been a mistake for Preston and me to have shared the responsibility of running LEI as Co-Chairmen — to be successful, there can be only one person in charge — a dictatorship is the best form of corporate government. Second, it was clear Preston had other agendas that were beginning to interfere with what needed to be done to keep Lunar Prospector alive, and third, when Preston went to California, he could no longer effectively interface with us in Houston. Thus, I decided it was necessary to remove Preston from all responsibility in LEI and from LEI itself.

I called together the remnants of LEI for an organizational meeting, explained the situation and asked that we do four things — which we did. We removed Preston from his position as Co-Chairman. We changed the bylaws so LEI had a President with a Vice-President rather than two Co-Chairmen. We then voted me in as the President, and, with much twisting of David Strack's arm, David as Vice-President. Finally, we removed Preston LEI's membership. Those things done, we were ready to face a very uncertain future for Lunar Prospector.

Immediately after our LEI reorganization meeting, I called Gregg, who was then my only partner in running the Lunar Prospector Consortium. First, I wanted to bring him up to date about Preston and Jack Brooks. Second, since he had written the contract between the Consortium and Mike Lawson's company, I asked him to write Mike a contract termination letter — a request Gregg was more than willing to fulfill, thus ending Mike's role in Lunar Prospector.

At that point, Gregg and I were the only ones still left out of the original leaders of Lunar Prospector, after some two and a half years of activity (I thought back on Jim Burke's prophetic words at the Lunar Prospector Workshop back in May 1989, "As Lunar Prospector proceeds, some of us will change our areas of responsibility, some of us will leave altogether and newcomers will take our places").

In the meantime, Jack Brooks's office had set up a meeting for me while Jack was attending some other meeting at the South Shore Harbor Hotel across Clear Lake from JSC and just across the street from the LEI office. I went to the hotel at the appointed time and met Jack in the lobby. Jack said to come on up to his room where we could talk and he could relax a bit. When we got there, Jack got a drink, lit a cigar, took off his shoes, sat down, and asked me to sit down and tell him what I wanted. I did, and when I was finished, Jack summed up his reaction with the offhanded, but sincere compliment, "I think you're crazy, but I like you and what you're trying to do and I will try to help you all I can," and he did.

Jack's first approach was to go to JSC to talk with Aaron Cohen, who, of course, was already trying to help Lunar Prospector at Bill Huffstetler's urging. Thus, while my political efforts were achieving some initial resonance, other events overtook Jack's efforts. However, Jack remained a useful ally and continued to play a role in the development of Lunar Prospector.

Chapter 1-8
Lunar Prospector —
The First SEI Mission

Most of September and November 1991: Enter Mike Griffin

As the fall of 1991 approached, over two years after President Bush had announced the Space Exploration Initiative (SEI), NASA was finally gearing up to seriously start looking into how to build a Lunar Base and put man on Mars. It did so by creating a new Associate Administrator (AA) post — the AA for Exploration. Rumors had started to circulate that Mike Griffin, a hotshot engineer who had been heavily involved with President Reagan's Star Wars Initiative and who had multiple degrees in engineering and management was to be the new AA.

When it got to the point where it was certain Mike was going to be the AA, I called him to see if I could interest him in flying Lunar Prospector as part of the SEI. When I reached Mike, I introduced myself and before I could say anymore, Mike cut me off. He said, "Yeah, I know all about Lunar Prospector and I want to fly it as the first mission in the SEI." I about fell over — just like that, Lunar Prospector was not only going to fly, but to fly as the first step in putting man back on the Moon! Then Mike said he was up to his ears trying to leave his current position and getting ready to join NASA, but once "the dust had settled" and he had the time, we would talk about how to proceed and then our short, but surprisingly gratifying conversation was over!

I immediately called the LEI staff to tell them the good news and to ask Brian Cox to set up a LEI meeting as soon as possible. After several months of minimal activity on the technical side, our first task was to get LEI running at full speed again, to get all our volunteers back and to get many new ones.

I called Gregg to tell him the good news and asked him to again get working on the Russian launch deal that had, of course, languished during the previous several months. Gregg said he would and then informed me the reason Mike "knew all about Lunar Prospector," was that he and Jim French were the best of friends, they had collaborated on a book or two on spacecraft engineering, and Jim had kept Mike informed about Lunar Prospector from the beginning of the project — well, it is a small world after all.

I called Wayne Stevens at OMNI and told him the good news and asked him if OMNI could set up shop in the JSC area so we could have the spacecraft built where LEI was and Wayne said, "Yes."

Finally, I went to see Bill Huffstetler to tell him the good news and Bill was really pleased.

Mike became the AA for Exploration during the last week of September and the October 14–20, 1991 issue of *Space News* carried an interview with the new AA in which Mike said many questions about the Moon, "can be answered with some fairly simple, straightforward, unmanned, precursor missions . . . in a few years . . . ," and "Many concepts exist for such a mission, from a simple Lunar Prospector satellite . . . ." There it was, in print. Mike was apparently serious about Lunar Prospector.

It took a couple of months for "the dust to settle" and for Mike to get around to dealing with Lunar Prospector. In the meantime, an article appeared in the November 1991 issue of *Spaceflight* (vol. 33, p. 370), entitled *Return to the Moon?*, lamenting the uncertain state of lunar missions, including Lunar Prospector, all of which were reviewed in detail in the article.

Finally, during the last week of November, Mike was ready to discuss Lunar Prospector. Mike had decided to fly four lunar missions — three Orbiters and one Lander — to get the SEI underway. The first was to be Lunar Prospector, followed by three NASA missions: A Lunar Resource Mapper, a Lunar Geodetic Mapper, and a lander mission using the Common Lunar Lander. The Common Lunar Lander was derived from the Selene Program I had developed while I was in Germany, and which Mike Duke and I had kept alive when I came to JSC in 1984, and which we were finally developing at JSC.

It was time to get Lunar Prospector underway and Mike asked me to give him and his staff a formal briefing, which I did. I described the Consortium, LEI's organization, the science goals and instruments, my Science Team, the spacecraft design, OMNI, the Mission Profile, the promise of AMSAT tracking, the promise of a Russian launch, the schedule, and, of course, the $11.6 million price tag. When my presentation ended, Mike and his staff were full of praise for what we had done and extolled the virtues of our having international cooperation via the Russians and everything else about the project. It was as if we could do no wrong.

Mike asked me to put together a short, unsolicited proposal and told Hum Mandell, who was the Manager of the Program Development and Control Office in JSC's Lunar/Mars Exploration Program Office, to take care of the details, since the contract was to be run through JSC, not Headquarters. Mike then told me our budget was too tight, that he did not want us coming back asking for more money once we got started, so he wanted me to increase the budget by a third to be on the safe side. That was fine by me and I left the meeting feeling great.

I immediately called another LEI meeting and we got started writing the proposal and began to prepare to build and fly Lunar Prospector. I also again called Wayne and Gregg to get the ball rolling on their fronts.

Shortly thereafter, Jay Green, Mike's Deputy, asked me for LEI incorporation papers and the IRS documentation regarding LEI's non-profit, tax-exempt status, all of which I delivered, posthaste, to Hum Mandell as requested. A few days later, Hum said our documentation was all in order and they hoped to get us a contract by Christmas so we could get started right after the New Year! After all our efforts, Lunar Prospector was finally on track again — a year later than we had planned, but we were on our way to the Moon.

Tuesday, December 10, 1991: The SEI Proposal

We finished the proposal and I delivered it to Hum on December 10. As requested, and as was necessitated by our limited resources, the proposal was short and sweet — just 28 pages, including the cover. We had increased the budget to a grand total of $16,171,000, of which $9.7 million was for OMNI to build the spacecraft, $1.8 million for the science instruments, $1.5 million for operations, $1.5 million for the launch and $1.7 million for administration. Those numbers compared favorably with the actual costs of the spacecraft as built by Lockheed — $20 million, the science instruments — $3.5 million, and operations — $3 million. The reader should remember that a lot of our efforts were going to be done by volunteers and that Lockheed has a very high overhead. Our calculated costs, about 50% of those of the final mission cost, were very realistic, assuming, of course, the Soviets really would have given us a launch for $1 million or less. Hum accepted the proposal with a great deal of enthusiasm and reassured me we would be ready to start after New Year's.

Friday, December 13, 1991: Ready To Go

After having looked at our proposal for a couple of days, Hum and several other JSC personnel had nothing but praise for every aspect of Lunar Prospector, from our science and simple spacecraft to our Soviet launch. All that was music to my ears, but to be on the safe side, I suggested we have a short meeting to air out any questions that might have come up when they read the proposal and before JSC started writing the contract. Hum set up a meeting for the following Monday and all the LEI personnel, the OMNI personnel, Gregg, and I started the weekend full of confidence that in a couple of weeks we would have the money for Lunar Prospector.

Monday, December 16, 1991: The Monday Massacre

Full of great expectations, I walked in to the meeting room where Jay Green, Hum, and, if I remember correctly, Doug Cook (a JSC Lunar/Mars Exploration Program Office engineer and manager) were sitting. I left about thirty minutes later feeling as if Jay had stuck a double barrel shotgun in my mouth and pulled both triggers!

After I came in, Jay asked, "Well, it's your nickel, what do you want to talk about?"

I answered that I wanted to address any questions that may have arisen after they had read the proposal. As Hum and Doug sat quietly — never saying a word, Jay said there were a whole host of problems and they were rejecting the proposal! To say the least, I was stunned. Jay began, in rapid succession, to list all the project's many deficiencies: It was not acceptable that we were using a Soviet launch; the AMSAT tracking network did not yet exist; we were using JSC volunteers and that resulted in conflicts of interests, and on and on and on. I tried to counter Jay's onslaught by saying, "You were all for the Soviet launch just last Friday," and, "Of course the AMSAT tracking network does not yet exist, because we first have to have the money to pay AMSAT to set it up," and, "We met with Aaron Cohen and the legal staff of JSC and cleared the JSC volunteers," and so on.

Jay just brushed all my arguments aside and admitted that it was a "Catch 22" situation — no matter what I said, he would just say, "No."

Finally, Jay used what he considered to be his final argument, "Besides, if you get killed in a freeway accident, Lunar Prospector is over." Of all the negative things Jay had said in the previous twenty or so minutes — that one nearly made me speechless.

I sputtered, "That's just not true. If I get killed, someone else would carry on — someone always does."

Jay said, "No, without you, there is no Lunar Prospector, period, end of debate."

That was it; just like that, everything that was positive about Lunar Prospector on Friday had turned into a negative over the weekend! Just as quickly as the Griffin/SEI support for Lunar Prospector had begun, it had ended in what I immediately called the "Monday Massacre."

As I left the meeting, I thought about Jay's statement regarding my getting killed in a freeway accident, and decided in jest that, *when I'm on the freeway, I'm going to watch out for NASA vans and keep out of their way!*

Still stunned, I went to tell Bill Huffstetler what had happened. Like me, Bill was floored, but immediately said, "This stinks to high heaven. I smell a rat. Don't worry, I'll find out what is going on." We talked a little more about what could be behind the sudden reversal and Bill was certain it had to be political. Shortly thereafter, I left Bill's office, really feeling as though Jay had stuck a double barrel shotgun in my mouth, pulled the trigger and blown my head off.

Chapter 1-9
JSC to the Rescue, Again, and Again

Wednesday, December 18, and Thursday, December 19, 1991: Another Chance

The gloom and doom caused by the Monday Massacre were still settling over the project when, on Wednesday, I got an amazing call from Doug Cook. Doug said Aaron Cohen wanted to find a way for JSC to fund Lunar Prospector and I was supposed to meet with him and Henry Flagg, Jr., the head of JSC's Legal Department and JSC's Chief Counsel, the next day! I was both stunned and elated. Just a couple of days after the Monday Massacre, Lunar Prospector, like the fabled Phoenix, was again rising from its ashes (depending on how you wanted to count, for the fourth time during the previous 18 months).

The next day I met with Henry and Doug in Henry's office in Building 1 (the JSC Administrative Building). Henry verified that Aaron wanted Lunar Prospector to fly and asked me to fill him in on the details of the project. I explained everything about the mission, the science, the spacecraft, the Consortium, our political support, the Russian launch, etc., as well as the various ups and downs we had endured during the previous three years. When I was finished, Henry expressed his amazement at — and admiration for — what we had accomplished with so few resources and said he understood why Aaron wanted to find a way to support the mission. He said further, because Christmas and the New Year were upon us, nothing would happen until early January when I was to meet with Aaron and others in the upper level of JSC management to lay out a plan. Once again, it looked like a way would be found for Lunar Prospector to get the USA back in the Moon business. Also, though Aaron had instructed Henry and Doug to spearhead a new Lunar Prospector plan, I knew full well Bill Huffstetler had once again urged Aaron to do so and I was grateful for Bill's undying support.

January 1992: The Second Monday Massacre

The meeting Henry had set up occurred on either the first or second Monday in January and was in the big meeting room in Building 1. The meeting room has two entrances in the rear, one on the left and one on the right. Bill and I went in the right door and found Aaron, Henry, Doug, and a host of Directors of the various engineering and bureaucratic divisions in JCS sitting on the right side of the large U-shaped table — it was an impressive group of JSC officials. Bill and I sat down next to Aaron, who was sitting at the back end of the table near the door and Henry was just off to Bill's right. The meeting was about to begin when suddenly, Mike Griffin and Jay Green walked in the door on the left and took seats on the left side of the large table — opposite to the main JSC contingency. Surprised, and with a foreboding feeling in the pit of my stomach, I turned to Bill and asked him what Mike and Jay were doing there. Bill did not know, and he was also concerned.

I do not remember the details of that devastating meeting, but somehow Mike and Jay had become aware of what Aaron and JSC were up to and came to put a stop to it. Though the odds (in terms of the number of people on both sides of the ensuing, short little war) were more than ten to one, Mike and Jay simply said JSC was not going to support Lunar Prospector and that was that. Though Aaron and others tried to argue against Mike and Jay's position, their arguments were as fruitless as those I had tried to make during the first Monday Massacre. Such was the power of an Associate Administrator and his hatchet man when pitted against a Center Director and his entire upper management staff. As suddenly as the meeting had begun, when Mike and Jay walked in, it was over.

Mike and Jay exited using the door on the left to avoid any contact with the JSC personnel and me and we exited the door on right for the same reason. Everyone on our side was dejected. When Bill and I got in the elevator with several of the JSC managers, they all said I had gotten a rotten deal and they all encouraged me to keep trying, since they all thought Lunar Prospector was an important program. Nice as those words were and as much as I wanted to have Lunar Prospector fly, I surely did not see any light at the end of the tunnel at that depressing moment. However, life — and Lunar Prospector — did go on.

The Remainder of January 1992:
Discovery and JSC to the Rescue — Again

Later in January, Wes Huntress, in Code S at NASA Headquarters, announced the creation of the Discovery Program. Discovery was set up to enable lunar and planetary scientists to propose, and if selected, to conduct their own small, simple, low cost missions that were supposed to be "Faster, Better, Cheaper" than previous NASA missions. Though the Discovery Program was to become the final solution to Lunar Prospector's dilemma, I was completely unaware of the Discovery Program. That was a somewhat surprising situation, since Headquarters was fully aware of the "small, simple, low cost mission" called Lunar Prospector and yet made no attempt to notify me of the up and coming opportunity — a portent of things to come. Thus, Wes's announcement provided no ray of hope for Lunar Prospector at that point.

However, a ray of hope did come several days after the Second Monday Massacre, once again in the familiar form of Bill Huffstetler. Bill called me to his office and told me, even though Griffin had stopped Aaron from fully funding Lunar Prospector, Aaron wanted to keep the mission alive until a way was found to fully fund it. He was going to give me $100,000 of study money to keep it going. Once again, I knew I had Bill to thank, and I did, and I took off to get the LEI troops ready to get active once again.

Since one of Jay Green's arguments against Lunar Prospector during the first Monday Massacre was that some of the LEI volunteers were JSC employees, I decided I had better get clarification from Henry Flagg as to the true status of the JSC volunteers. I called Henry's office and asked for a short meeting to clarify the situation.

I met with Henry a day or two later and explained that Aaron was going to get me $100,000 of study money, and, given Jay's comments, I needed clarification about the status of the JSC volunteers. I said we had addressed the issue with Dan Remington from the Legal Department in August 1990 and it was determined that everything was OK, though each case had to be decided on an individual basis. Henry said he would look into it.

A day later I got a call from an angry Bill Huffstetler asking me to come to his office immediately. I did and when I arrived, Bill was visibly mad and immediately said, "You blew it!"

I had no idea what he was talking about and then Bill said, "After talking to you, Henry told Griffin about the $100,000 and Griffin put a stop to it." I felt like crap; here Bill and Aaron had once again gone out on a limb for me and I had blown it and made them look bad. Feeling very low, I explained to Bill why I had talked to Henry and, though Bill was still annoyed — but more with the situation than with me — he saw I was just trying to do the correct thing and it had backfired. We both asked ourselves why Henry told Griffin when Henry was clearly on our side. We suspected, just like me opening that "can of worms" by wanting to "go by the book," the lawyer in Henry required that he inform Griffin. Regardless of the reason, the damage was done. Clearly, even if I had gotten the money, Griffin would have eventually caught wind of that fact and would have raised hell. However, Bill and Aaron's attitude was if I already had the money, what could Griffin do; but knowing how he operated, I suspected Mike would have done plenty. Nevertheless, that was a good lesson about the old saying, "It's better to ask for forgiveness, than for permission," a lesson I would not soon forget.

Even though Bill was no longer mad at me, I still felt very bad about having let Bill down, even though my intentions were honorable. When I went to tell Mick Culp about the latest defeat for Lunar Prospector, I asked Mick if he would join me for dinner. Though Mick clearly had something else to do, he saw that, for the first time, I was really dejected and said, "Sure, let's go have a nice dinner and forget all that crap." I really appreciated Mick's company and, to a lesser extent, the food; but I really did not "forget all that crap."

Sunday, February 8, 1992

Frank Bass of the *Houston Post* had interviewed Bill and me in early February and the ensuing article appeared on Saturday, February 8. It was a good article with the emphasis on our lack of money and though it did not do Lunar Prospector any good at the time, it helped keep Lunar Prospector alive and good publicity is always desirable.

Wednesday, February 12, through Wednesday, February 19, 1992

I read in the February 12 issue of the *Post* that Admiral Truly had been forced to resign by President Bush and then, on February 19, that Aaron Cohen was to become the Acting Administrator starting March 1. After reading that, I went to see Bill who immediately said, "With Aaron going to Headquarters, Lunar Prospector will get done."

Just like that, the relative power positions of Mike Griffin and Aaron Cohen had been reversed; Aaron would soon be Mike's boss and would not have to put up with Mike's negative attitude towards Lunar Prospector. Even though Aaron was only the Acting Administrator, Bill said he would be in a position to influence the new Administrator when he was appointed, so things again looked good for Lunar Prospector.

March 1992: Enter Dan Goldin

It was announced that Dan Goldin was the nominee for the new NASA Administrator in early March, and his appointment was confirmed shortly after the Congressional Confirmation Hearings that occurred on March 28. Further, Aaron was to remain at Headquarters as Goldin's Deputy during the transition period. Thus, as Bill had predicted, Aaron was in the right spot to get Lunar Prospector back on track and he started trying to do so very quickly — but before Aaron got going, I got sidetracked to Sunnyvale on a related matter that turned out to be of great importance to Lunar Prospector.

Thursday, April 9, through Early May 1992: The Lunar Resource Mapper Proposal

Though Mike had brutally torpedoed Lunar Prospector, he was pushing ahead with the Lunar Resource Mapper, the Lunar Geodetic Mapper and the Common Lunar Lander Missions. He had put out a "Request for Proposals" (RFP) for the development of the Lunar Resource Mapper with the idea that the spacecraft bus designed for that mission would also be used for the Geodetic Mapper. LMSC, and hence Gus's division, was going to bid on the project and LMSC needed help in preparing their proposal in the areas of science, communications, and structures. Domenick Tenerelli, who was the lead engineer and manager of the proposal effort, called LESC on April 9 asking for help. LESC told Warren Holdenbach (a communications expert), and me from our group, and George Singer (a structural engineer and quality control engineer) from another group to go to Sunnyvale for three weeks to work on the LMSC proposal. The three of us were in Sunnyvale by Sunday evening.

Warren had spent a lot of time in Sunnyvale working on other LMSC proposals and knew the best motels and best eating spots, so we ended up at the Maple Tree Inn, a motel I would spend a lot of time in over the following eight years. Early Monday morning, we went to Lockheed and were met by Frank Martin and Dr. Domenick (Dom) Tenerelli (Dom is one of the few engineers to have a PhD and he got it at Stanford). Dom, a New Yorker of slight build and clearly of Italian heritage, was full of energy and the "can do" attitude I like so much. I immediately thought, *now this is the kind of manager and engineer I can work with,* and was very much looking forward to the next three weeks of intense effort that always characterize the preparation of a proposal.

We then met with the rest of the LMSC proposal team that Dom had put together. Dom introduced Warren, George, and me to the group, and they brought us up to speed. Dom and his engineers had gotten started a few days earlier and were still trying to sort out what NASA wanted in the proposal (NASA RFPs are seldom well written and it is usually hard to figure out exactly what NASA expects). The only fly-in-the-ointment was that NASA wanted a flight-proven spacecraft for the mission and LMSC did not have one. The best it had was the F-Sat that was under development as a standard, medium sized spacecraft bus for Earth orbiting missions. Our job was to try to put together a proposal based on the F-Sat that would satisfy the requirements of a lunar orbiter and circumvent the NASA requirement for a flight proven spacecraft.

During the following three weeks and under Dom's driving leadership, we succeeded in putting together a fully credible proposal based on F-Sat, and, as was critically important for the future development of Lunar Prospector, Dom and I forged a collegial friendship based on mutual respect. I liked Dom's no-holds-barred management style, his disdain for Lockheed upper management (which I share), his willingness to do anything and everything to get the job done (twisting arms, cajoling, bribing — "I'll give you a case of beer if you get that done on time," and, when necessary, berating). Dom quickly found out, as I told him about Lunar Prospector, that I not only knew lunar and planetary science, but that I also knew spacecraft engineering (unheard of at Lockheed for a scientist), mission planning, and mission operations. The latter two skills, plus the science, of course, were completely lacking at LMSC.

Surprise, surprise, Dom gave me the responsibility for the science, mission planning, and mission operations parts of the proposal. The Geochemical Mapper was a classic Lunar Orbiter Mission, just like Lunar Prospector. I simply took the Lunar Prospector Mission Profile and Mission Operations information, modified them to account for the differences between the Lunar Prospector payload and spacecraft and those of the F-Sat Lunar Geochemical Mapper, and wrote my sections of the proposal.

Like all proposal efforts, that one came down to the wire. At the very end, Dom worked with — cajoled, bribed, and twisted the arms of — the reproduction people, until early morning of the due day, to get the proposal reproduced in time for it to be sent to Houston, so it would arrive there before the 5:00 PM deadline.

Thinking that my work was done, I had gone to bed early to finally get some rest before Warren, George, and I had to catch our early flight back to Houston. However, Dom, who was nervously checking all the details of the proposal even at that (too) late date, called me three times that night to get me to come to LMSC to help him check things. I went in to LMSC in response to the first two calls, but balked at the third. The next day, Warren, George, the proposal, and I winged our way to Houston.

As it turned out, despite our Herculean effort, the LMSC proposal was rejected and Boeing won the contract. The reason we lost was simple — the F-Sat was not a flight-proven spacecraft as required by the RFP. However, when Dom and I attended the post-selection review of our proposal at JSC in June, we were informed that, except for the fact that we did not have a flight-proven spacecraft, our proposal was rated as the best proposal! Also, to Dom's and my gratification, the sections I wrote had all received very high marks. When we heard the scores, Dom said to me, "Jeez, Alan, Lockheed has never gotten such high scores on science, mission planning, and mission operation. You did a really great job." Though our proposal had lost, we showed NASA that LMSC had the talent to do lunar and planetary missions, even though they had never done any in the past. Thus, we had opened a new area of business for LMSC — and unknowingly, began to lay the groundwork for the ultimate success of Lunar Prospector.

The final footnote to that episode is that though Boeing won the contract, the Lunar Resource Mapper Program was canceled before they even got started, thus ending the start of the SEI, but not the SEI itself — it took a little longer for the SEI to die.

The rest of May 1992: A Strange Meeting with Griffin and the Second Attempt at the JSC $100,000

Towards the end of the Lunar Resource Mapper Proposal effort I received a call from Mike Griffin's secretary who told me that Mike wanted to set up a meeting between him, Jay Green, Hum Mandell, and me as soon as I got back to Houston. I told her when I would be back and we set up a meeting date. However, Mike's request for a meeting left me wondering what on Earth he wanted after already stabbing Lunar Prospector and me in the back several times.

When I arrived at Mike's office for the meeting, I was very surprised that neither Jay nor Hum was there, just Mike, and that made me very suspicious (no witnesses to the perfect crime?) and I expected the worst, but I was wrong. What followed was one of the most bizarre conversations I had ever had in my life, especially when one remembers that Mike was the Associate Administrator for Exploration, the head of the entire SEI, and I was just a lowly scientist and Lockheed employee.

Mike immediately went into a tirade, demanding I stop trying to do Lunar Prospector, saying I was embarrassing him and NASA with that nonsense and if I didn't stop, he would tell all the aerospace companies they were to forbid their employees from doing volunteer work on the project. I replied that Lunar Prospector was a private effort and as such, neither he nor NASA had any right to tell me I couldn't pursue trying to find support for the mission and it was illegal for him to try to blackmail the aerospace companies into stopping their employees from working on the project.

Mike then repeated his demands and threats, but with less force and with a hint of pleading in his voice and I repeated my reply. Then we went around again, with more pleading and less force from Mike — and again.

Finally I had had enough and said, "Mike, we're just going around and around in circles and getting nowhere. You have no legal right to do what you are saying and I will not stop working on Lunar Prospector, so let's stop this nonsense."

With that, Mike, looking as dejected as a wet poodle, said, "OK, but I'll have to talk with the my (NASA) lawyers to see if it's all right."

I thought, *what crap, you have to ask your lawyers if it's OK for you to stop harassing my LEI coworkers and me — you must be nuts!*

Thus ended Mike's pathetic attempt to bully me into killing Lunar Prospector and I left his office thinking how pathetic he and others like him at NASA were for him to have tried such a rotten trick.

On the rational side, with Aaron Cohen as Goldin's Deputy, Mike could no longer interfere with Bill Huffstetler's and Aaron's efforts to help Lunar Prospector (maybe that was what had set Mike off to make such a fool of himself?). Bill made a second attempt to get me $100,000 to keep Lunar Prospector alive. That time the money was to be laundered through Lamar University in Beaumont, TX. The reason for that was simple. When I had talked with Congressman Jack Brooks a year earlier, Jack had asked me to get Lamar University involved in Lunar Prospector, since Jack wanted his hometown university to benefit as he tried to help get Lunar Prospector funded. I had made contact with Jim Jorden, a Beaumont hometown boy who had made good and who taught and did lunar research at Lamar. Jim had worked on lunar science problems in the same group as I had at the Max Planck Institut für Kernphysik in Heidelberg, but several years after I was there, so we had a lot in common. Also, Jim was understandably enthusiastic about having Lamar involved with Lunar Prospector. Jim arranged for me to meet with the Lamar University President who was also very much in favor of Lamar being involved with the mission. Thus, as Lunar Prospector's fortunes had evolved and devolved during the previous year, I had kept Lamar as part of the ever-changing picture as I had promised Jack Brooks I would do.

Thus, when, with Goldin, Aaron, and Jack's support, Bill again wanted to get me $100,000 of study money through JSC, Jack asked that the money be funneled through Lamar University and that was OK by me. I liked Beaumont and Lamar and thought it would be great to have a small University involved where I could perhaps become a faculty member when Lunar Prospector was over. However, the President with whom I had talked a year earlier and who was all for having Lamar involved had been removed because he was far too progressive for the conservative Lamar administration. Also, when Bill started the discussions with the Lamar administration about running the $100,000 contract through the University, they told Bill they wanted $10,000 off the top for the University! That was highway robbery and it annoyed both Bill and me; but to keep Jack happy, we would have to let Lamar take its blood money.

When I went to Lamar to discuss how the University would actually be involved, I made it clear that the mission would have to be run out of the JSC area, perhaps via an off campus facility, since all my volunteer engineers and staff were there. Beaumont was just too far from the JSC area (140 km) to do otherwise. That was OK by the administration, so it appeared that, except for the $10,000 swindle, everything was going to work out.

My next step was to give a seminar about the mission to the interested students and faculty. I started my talk by telling them that Beaumont was already on the map, i.e., the lunar map. Then I showed them a slide of Mare Nectaris, on whose SW edge, between the large, prominent craters Fracastorius and Theophilus is the 52 km diameter crater named Beaumont. The audience loved that and the rest of my talk was greeted with great enthusiasm. When I was finished, many of the students asked how they could participate in the mission. Mission accomplished.

While my negotiations with Lamar were going on, Code S sent out a "Dear Colleague Letter," describing some of the details and opportunities of the Discovery Program to everyone in the lunar and planetary science community — except me. Thus, as was the case in January when Wes Huntress announced the Discovery Program, Code S was ignoring Lunar Prospector.

However, events that were about to transpire at Lockheed Corporate Headquarters in Calabasas, CA, would put the efforts with Lamar onto the backburner.

Chapter 1-10
Goldin Asks Lockheed to Do Lunar Prospector

Early June 1992: Support from Parten and LECS

As June started, I learned from Bill Huffstetler that Goldin and Aaron went on a "get acquainted trip" to visit all the major aerospace company CEOs. When they visited Lockheed, Goldin, at Aaron's urging, asked Lockheed CEO Dan Tellep to finally get behind Lunar Prospector and get it done, a request I did not hear about from either Lockheed Corporate Headquarters or LMSC! I decided to see if LESC would stand by me after the new NASA Administrator had asked the Lockheed CEO to get behind Lunar Prospector.

I told Mick Culp the news and said I wanted to see if the new LESC President, Dick Parten, would help put pressure on Tellep and LMSC to finally give me the support I needed for the mission. Mick replied, "Lets go see Beatty." We did and, true to form, Bill called Parten's secretary and set up a meeting for us.

We met with Parten a short time later. Before I got started, Dick said Jay Green had been to see him somewhat earlier and had told him essentially the same things Mike Griffin had said to me in our meeting a few weeks earlier. Jay had vilified me, as well as Lunar Prospector, and had threatened Lockheed with repercussions if Dick didn't stop me from pursuing Lunar Prospector. Apparently, Dick told Jay where he could go, because, when I asked Dick how he had responded (fearing the worst), Dick said, "I'm not worried about the likes of Jay Green."

Very relieved (but amazed at the ends to which Mike and Jay were willing to go to kill Lunar Prospector — what were they so afraid of?), I told Parten a quick version of the Lunar Prospector story and that Goldin had asked Tellep to get behind the mission. Parten was impressed and said he would support my efforts and would set up a meeting with Tellep for him and me! He also said, in his opinion, Lockheed Corporate could and should pay for Lunar Prospector out of its very large PR budget because, Lunar Prospector would give Lockheed a great deal of excellent PR. Parten said he would give me five weeks of "time and charges" to get things going again and then we would see what would happen after that. That was all very good news; Lunar Prospector was starting to roll again.

I called Gus and Dom to let them know what I had accomplished with Parten and to find out what, if anything, was happening at LMSC as a result of Goldin's request to Tellep. Gus said Aaron Cohen had called him to ask that he get behind Goldin's request. Gus said his first reaction was to take the F-Sat Lunar Resource Mapper Design we had worked so hard on for the proposal and change it into Lunar Prospector. I was very happy to hear that Aaron had called Gus personally, but I was dead set against using F-Sat for the mission.

First, F-Sat did not exist. Second, F-Sat was going to be a very complicated spacecraft if it was ever developed (it never was) and certainly very complicated in comparison to the simple spinner I wanted to build. If Lockheed were to have used the F-Sat for the Lunar Prospector Mission, it would negate all the programmatic engineering goals set for the spacecraft and its operations. Third, it was clear if Lockheed went the F-Sat route, Lunar Prospector would be managed, built, and flown by LMSC, not by LEI and OMNI, and that would negate all the programmatic management and organizational goals set for the Program.

Happily, I was able to convince Gus that NASA wanted our version of Lunar Prospector and not an F-Sat/Lockheed version. That done, we got down to the business of deciding how to proceed and, once again, it appeared that Gus, along with Frank Martin and, certainly, Dom, were all behind my efforts and LMSC was considering building the spacecraft. After that discussion with Gus, I once again called the faithful LEI troops and told them we needed to get going again.

By that time, a Lockheed co-worker of mine, Tom Polette, and I had become close friends and I had asked him to become part of the LEI/Lunar Prospector Team. Tom, a space architect, had joined our mission planning group at Lockheed a year or so earlier to help design the lunar bases we were studying. As was found out during the Sky Lab Program (NASA's first space station that was launched on May 14, 1973), living and work facilities designed by engineers are not very livable. NASA and the aerospace contractors supporting a lunar base and Mars manned mission studies began to bring in architects to help do the job correctly. Tom has a Masters Degree in Space Architecture from the University of Houston's Sasakawa International Institute for Space Architecture, and therefore, is well suited for the task of designing space habitats. However, Tom's capabilities go far beyond architecture; he is great at attending to details and getting the job done, no matter what is asked of him — characteristics that I admire very much and need in a co-worker that I can totally depend on. As our friendship grew, Tom became loyal both to me personally and to my goal of getting Lunar Prospector done. Thus, Tom had become the trusted co-worker I needed and whom I could totally depend on to help me get Lunar Prospector done. When Parten gave me some support and the hope that we might get full support from Lockheed Corporate Headquarters, I asked Tom to take a more active role in the mission and Tom agreed. That was the beginning of Tom's becoming a major player in Lunar Prospector.

Thursday, June 11, through Thursday, June 18, 1992: Getting Underway — Again

All of a sudden, after many months of relative inactivity on the engineering and science sides of the project, the pace really picked up. The first thing my core group at LEI did was to start reassembling our volunteers and getting new ones.

After that, I quickly put the final touches of Version 1.2 of the Mission Profile and issued it to the team on the 16th so they could start getting back-in-the-saddle and I finalized Version 2.3 of the MRD in preparation for its distribution on the 30th. I sent copies of the Mission Profile, the MRD, the MOD, the budget, the spacecraft construction schedule, and everything else that was of use to Dom, Frank, and Gus so they could set up a construction plan for the spacecraft.

I then went to see Joe Allen at Space Industries to discuss the possibility of them building the GRS, NS, and APS under a contract that would include a significant amount of donated time on their part. Joe and I reached a verbal agreement and the actual contract negotiations were to follow within a few weeks.

I contacted Wayne Stevens regarding LEI's purchase of a license to use OMNI's Lunar Prospector spacecraft design and to see if LEI could contract OMNI for Mike

Chobotov and Asif Ansari to be the project's Spacecraft Engineer and the Launch Engineer, respectively. We easily reached verbal agreement on all points and the contract negotiations were to begin on Friday, June 20.

I set up a meeting with Don Smith for the 26th to see if Bendix was still willing to donate personnel and equipment to set up our world wide tracking network as it was when we discussed the same issues one year earlier. Similarly, I set up a meeting with Daryl Curry to discuss donated space for the LEI offices and the Mission Control Center.

Lastly, I called Chris Faranetta to get him started, once again, on preparing for contract negotiations with the Russians for the launch of Lunar Prospector.

It had been a very busy week, but it really felt good to be back in business and working hard on the mission after so many months of hopes and disappointments, and it was good to see LEI getting built up again to do the mission.

Friday, June 19, through Thursday, June 25, 1992

Because many of our volunteers were new and because most of the older ones had had little time to get to know the OMNI spacecraft Design before everything had slowed down towards the end of 1990, I started a series of tutorials on the spacecraft and started writing a *Lunar Prospector Controller Training Manual*, so the Controllers would know how to fly the spacecraft.

Dom came to Houston for the Lunar Resource Mapper Proposal debriefing, so we met, after the debriefing, to discuss the presentation we were preparing for Gus. Gus was once again going to try to get McMahon to support Lunar Prospector in view of Goldin's request to Tellep.

Bill Huffstetler called to tell me Aaron Cohen had again called Gus about Lunar Prospector and asked me to come over to his office so I could give him a status report on how Lockheed was responding to Goldin and Cohen's requests — which I immediately did.

Since Gus, Dom, and LMSC needed to know exactly what they were to build if they decided to build Lunar Prospector, I called Wayne and asked him for permission to send the Critical Design Review Documents to Gus. Wayne agreed and then I talked to Gus about setting up a Spacecraft Design Review so OMNI, LMSC, and LEI could go over the design together.

I called John Hamrick of Loral and set up a meeting for the 29th to discuss the possibility of Loral donating a million dollars and a Command and Control center to the project.

Finally, Brad Roscoe and I finalized the design of the GRS, NS, and APS and sent the designs to Pete Williams and Joel Sills, two young engineers I had worked with on the Lunar Resource Mapper Proposal, and who had volunteered to analyze the instruments' structural and thermal performances.

Friday, June 26, through Thursday, July 2, 1992

I had my meeting at Bendix/Allied Signal (they had just merged) with Vice-President Ed Briggs on Friday, the 26th. Ed said that the new CEO of Allied Signal, Larry Bossidy, was interested in supporting us by setting up the tracking network and perhaps even become the major sponsor of the mission. Bossidy wanted to have some major, showcase project for the new corporation and that might be Lunar Prospector!

After our meeting, Ed Briggs sent the Lunar Prospector information materials throughout Allied Signal. As a result, Mike Stoop in Allied Signal's facilities in Huntsville, AL, called to discuss our communication subsystem and tracking needs, and he informed me that other Allied Signal personnel would be calling for information about the other subsystems!

I got a similar response from John Hamrick of Loral. Loral was interested in providing, or, at least, helping to set up the Command and Control Center, and, like Allied Signal, perhaps even becoming the major sponsor. John said he would set up a meeting for me with the local President of Loral, Clinton Denny. After which, John expected I would be able to see Loral's CEO, B. Schwartz, who much earlier had expressed considerable interest in Lunar Prospector and had sent out instructions throughout Loral asking how it might best support the mission.

The Allied Signal and Loral meetings seemed to be pointing to real support that would take the pressure off us if Lockheed decided again that it was not going to support the mission, despite Goldin and Cohen's repeated requests.

Regarding the Lockheed support, it was time for me to approach Lockheed CEO Tellep and LMSC president, McMahon, so I requested a meeting with them by July 15.

Still seeking money from additional sources, I wrote Ross Perot a letter on the 29th asking for his financial support.

Friday, July 3, through Thursday, July 9, 1992:
McMahon Does It Again

McMahon's response to my request to see Tellep and him was swift and deadly — he wrote, "we do not find it within Lockheed's plans to participate at this time," (see Appendix 1-11, also see www.lunar-research-institute.org) and that was that — what a slap in the face for Goldin and Cohen and how stupid of Lockheed upper management. That answer strengthened my exceptionally low opinion of Lockheed and its corporate managers.

Given Lockheed's latest stab in the back, I got very busy on all other fronts (while I still had a couple of weeks support from Dick Parten, support that was sure to dry up given Tellep and McMahon's rejection of our request for support).

First, I got back to getting the $100,000 Bill wanted to funnel through Lamar University. Bill needed a short proposal from Lamar and LEI, so I took the proposal we had written for Mike Griffin and changed it into a $100,000 Pre-Phase C Activity Proposal and made an appointment to see a Lamar administrator for his signature. Bill wanted the proposal by the 17th.

Second, I phoned Allied Signal's Mike Stroop (Huntsville, AL) and Peter Dachel (Columbia, MD) in order to pursue setting up a meeting with Allied Signal's CEO, Larry Bossidy. Mike and Peter indicated that Bossidy would probably give Lunar Prospector major support if Goldin and Cohen expressed their interest to him in the project as they had done with Tellep and Guastaferro, because Allied Signal was actively seeking a way of supporting Goldin and the SEI — that sounded good to me.

Third, not wanting to wait for a response to my letter of the 29th to Ross Perot, I contacted Perot's private secretary to ask for a meeting with Perot and she said the answer was forthcoming — when it came, it was, "No."

Fourth, I called my friend Al Schallenmuller at Martin Marietta in Denver to see if there was any chance that Martin Marietta might support us as I had requested some two years earlier. Unfortunately, Al's answer was, "Unlikely."

Fifth, I called Loral's John Hamrick to push for the promised meetings with President Denny and CEO Schwartz.

Friday, July 10, through Friday, July 17, 1992:
The Storm of Activity Ends

Like a sudden summer storm in the Arizona desert, the storm of feverish activity and great expectations that had so suddenly started just a few weeks earlier, ended just as suddenly. McMahon's negative response had taken the wind out of the sails of the Lunar Prospector ship and the project began, like so many times during the previous two years, to flounder.

As the handwriting on the wall was again being reluctantly read by Tom, the rest of LEI, and me, I met with Bill Huffstetler to discuss with him "What next?" and that was, of course, getting LEI the $100,000 through Lamar University and seeking the major support from Loral and Allied Signal. Regarding the latter efforts, I wrote letters to the respective CEO's of Loral and Allied Signal asking for meetings with them. However, with Lockheed again out of the picture, the promise of major support from Loral, Allied Signal, and everyone else quickly faded and those meetings never took place. Somehow, Lockheed was the key to getting Lunar Prospector done, whether I liked it or not.

My support from Dick Parten ended on Friday, July 17, so I wrote my final Weekly Report to him and thanked him for his efforts and with that, another major attempt to get Lunar Prospector fully underway came to an abrupt stop.

Chapter 1-11
Keeping Lunar Prospector Alive and Keeping Gainfully Employed

The Rest of July to November 1992

With the latest unsuccessful effort behind us, I was off to Lamar with a draft of the $100,000 proposal in my hand and some hope in my heart. I drove the 140 km to Beaumont to see the Lamar bureaucrat, who I needed to have sign for the University, to get his comments on the draft proposal. When I got there, to my great surprise and annoyance, he gave me the runaround. Very quickly I understood the very conservative Lamar administration wanted nothing to do with something as progressive as a lunar mission. They liked their little, backwater University just as it was and had absolutely no interest in bringing it into the twentieth century.

When I got back to Houston, I informed Bill that the Lamar administration wanted nothing to do with the mission; he could hardly believe it and just shook his head.

A little later, I again asked to see Jack Brooks to see if he could exert some pressure on Lamar. When I saw Jack at his Beaumont office and told him what had happened, he was disgusted with the idiots that ran Lamar, but admitted there was no way he could force them to accept the contract. Thus ended another attempt to get Lunar Prospector some funding and I was getting weary of being continually jerked around, but I still believed Lunar Prospector was going to fly — someday, somehow.

After the hectic few weeks in June and July ended with both Lockheed and Lamar bailing on Lunar Prospector, all our activities slowed nearly to a halt as the few faithful LEI troops, Bill Huffstetler, and I tried to regroup and tried to find some shimmer of light at the end of what had become a very long and very dark tunnel.

I continued refining the Lunar Prospector Mission Documents and spacecraft design and tried to get Tom Polette to spend time learning about the mission and the spacecraft, since by that time, he had become my second in command. However, given our lack of progress, I was finding it hard to motivate Tom — or anyone else.

Regarding the spacecraft design, I found the propulsion sub-system OMNI had designed had a big flaw, and after calling Wayne Stevens to discuss it, I corrected it. The problem was, as ex-Hughes employees, the OMNI engineers were used to designing spin-stabilized communications spacecraft that operated in Geosynchronous Orbit, some 36,000 km above the Earth's surface, where there was plenty of time and space to maneuver. Lunar Prospector was going to operate in low lunar orbit, just 100 km above the Moon and would whip around the Moon in 118 minutes. We knew we would have to do periodic Orbital Maintenance Burns (OMBs) to keep the spacecraft in the correct mapping orbit, and that was the source of the problem.

The final OMNI design had two 22 Newton engines firing out the bottom of the spacecraft for all major maneuvers and two 22 Newton engines firing tangentially to the spacecraft's sides for spin control and as backups for the main engines as discussed in Chapter 1-4. OMNI assumed, when we needed to do an OMB, we would reorient the spacecraft so the axial engines would fire in the right direction, do the burn, and then reorient the spacecraft back to its mapping attitude. However, the reorientation maneuvers associated with an OMB would use, on average, almost as much fuel as the OMB itself, and the reorientation maneuvers would last up to an hour. That was OK for a Geosynchronous orbiting spacecraft that does such maneuvers very infrequently and had plenty of time and space in which to do the maneuvers, but not for a lunar orbiting spacecraft: First, because of the waste of precious fuel; second, because of the fact that every time one fires an engine, something can go wrong, so one does as few burns as possible; and third, because of the long duration of the maneuvers.

Given those issues, I decided the best way to do the OMBs was to leave the spacecraft in its nominal attitude and do, what I called a "Vector Burn." Such a burn would consist of a continuous burn on the axial engines and a pulse burn sequence on the tangential engines, so the resulting velocity vector was the one needed for the OMB. There were two issues to be addressed with the Vector Burn concept.

First, because of the fact that the individual engine pairs are not generally firing in the direction of desired velocity vector, there are large thrust vector alignment losses that add up to some 30% on average. However, 30% is small compared to the nearly 100% losses that would occur if the spacecraft were reoriented twice during an average OMB sequence as originally planned. Thus the Vector Burn sequence won hands down on that issue.

Second, since OMNI planned to have axial engines only on the bottom of the spacecraft (–Z direction in the spacecraft's coordinate system), a Vector Burn would work only when the desired velocity vector was pointed somewhere in the lower hemisphere (–Z hemisphere) of the spacecraft. When the OMB velocity vector was in the upper hemisphere (+Z hemisphere, as it would be statistically half of the time), we would have to flip the spacecraft 180° to do that OMB and that would cost a lot of fuel. The obvious solution was to add two axial engines at the top to the spacecraft. By doing so, we could conduct a Vector Burn in the +Z hemisphere by using the upper axial engines plus the tangential engines in exactly the same way we would do a Vector Burn in the –Z hemisphere using the bottom axial engines plus the tangential engines; and that is what I did.

The addition of the two upper axial engines would also have a further benefit. As a consequence of the final OMNI design, reorientation maneuvers would be done using just the lower axial engines, so there would be no opposing thrust in the +Z direction of the spacecraft during the reorientation burns. Thus, there would be a significant change (Δ) in the spacecraft's velocity (V) during each reorientation maneuver — a ΔV that would adversely affect the spacecraft's orbit unless canceled out by yet another burn. By adding a pair of upper engines, the reorientation maneuvers could be carried out using paired upper and lower engines, thereby eliminating the unwanted ΔV during the reorientation maneuvers. I killed two birds with one stone.

Having made the decision to add two axial engines to the top of the spacecraft, I finalized the spacecraft's engine configuration and I adopted the following terminology. The axial (A) engines on the bottom of the spacecraft were named A1 and A2, while those on the top were named A3 and A4. The tangential (T) engines were named T1 and T2, with T1 being the spin-down engine and T2 being the spin-up engine.

Having made that change to the Spacecraft's Propulsion Subsystem, I then proceeded to change the Mission Profile, the MRD, the MOD, and the Training Manual, since the new engine configuration made a big difference in how we would build and fly the spacecraft and what the backup possibilities and emergency procedures were.

I also made some changes to the way we were going to do the science. First, after talking with Bob Lin, the leader of the MAG/ER Team on the Mars Observer that had been successfully launched on September 25, we decided we would ask NASA for the backup MAG/ER hardware for use on Lunar Prospector. If NASA agreed, that would save us a lot of money. The only differences between the Mars Observer package and the Lunar Prospector package were that we were going to fly just one magnetometer instead of two and the software of the electronics had to be reprogrammed to account for the fact that Lunar Prospector was to be a spin-stabilized spacecraft, while Mars Observers was a three-axis stabilized spacecraft.

A consequence of our having decided to ask NASA for the backup Mars Observer MAG/ER package was a change in the MAG and ER Teams. Lon Hood was originally the MAG Team PI and he and his UCLA colleagues and Co-Is, Chris Russell and Bob Snare, were going to build the MAG and integrate it into the ER package that Bob Lin and his Berkeley colleagues were going to build. However, our decision to try to get the Mars Observer backup MAG/ER meant we would have nothing to build and there was no need for Russell and Snare to be involved, so I had dropped them from the team. Since all of the Mars Observer MAG/ER hardware had been built under Bob's leadership, I made Bob the PI of the combined MAG/ER Team, whose sole Co-I was then Lon Hood.

Second, Brad Roscoe had moved from Houston to Ridgefield, CT, where he still worked for Schlumberger, but at a different facility. Because Brad is such a great guy and great instrument builder, I hoped I could keep him involved in the mission, but that proved difficult. I asked Bill Feldman if he could build all three spectrometers and he said he could. I combined the GRS, NS, and APS Teams into one Spectrometer Team and made Bill its Leader.

Finally, still trying to gather political support for Lunar Prospector, and because the 1992 Presidential Campaign was well under way, I had written to Presidential Nominee Bill Clinton, telling him about Lunar Prospector and asking for his support if he became President. I received a reply from George Stephanopoulos dated October 24, indicating that he had, "shared them (the material I had sent with the letter) with our advisors who handle space issues," and never heard from them again.

November 1992: San Juan Capistrano and Discovery

NASA held its first Discovery Meeting in San Juan Capistrano, CA, in November. The purpose of the meeting was to have scientists present their ideas for Discovery Missions. Based on those presentations and accompanying proposals, NASA intended to select about a dozen of the most promising ideas and give those teams some seed money to help them prepare for the proposal efforts that would occur after the Discovery Announcement of Opportunity (AO) came out in the spring of 1994.

I found out about both Discovery and the San Juan Meeting after the fact and was really annoyed that NASA had not even given me a chance to present Lunar Prospector at the meeting. I called Pat Dasch, a friend of mine and the wife of a very good friend of mine, Julius Dasch (both of whom will appear many times throughout the rest of this book). Julius and Pat lived and worked in Washington, DC; Julius worked at NASA and Pat at SAIC, a contractor that supported NASA. Pat worked for Code S and hence, the people running the Discovery Program. I assumed Pat would know what had gone on.

When I called, Pat said that she had been surprised that I was not there. Because of that, she looked through the invitee list (SAIC personnel had sent out the invitations) and found I was not on it! She was astounded, but thought that it was an oversight. I replied I did not believe that, since Code S had previously made it clear to me it did not want Lunar Prospector and the San Juan Meeting slight proved to me beyond a shadow of a doubt that Code S wanted nothing to do with Lunar Prospector.

The reader might want to pause here and reflect on the mentality of the NASA managers who were doing everything to stop Lunar Prospector, while the NASA Administrator, Dan Goldin, had tried to get Lockheed to do the mission just a few months earlier. Further, one has to reflect on the fact that just a little over two years later, Lunar Prospector was selected by an almost completely non-NASA Review Committee to be the first peer reviewed and competitively selected Discovery Mission. Finally one has to reflect on the fact, that less than eight years later, we had completed the most cost effective and one of the most scientifically and programmatically successful lunar missions ever flown. When one does reflect on all that, it is rather clear that NASA is very badly managed.

February 1993

As a result of my work on the Lunar Resource Mapper Proposal, Dom had asked me to work halftime on the science instrument part of a very big proposal LMSC was preparing for NASA's EOS Program (Earth Observation Satellites — a long series of very expensive and therefore very lucrative weather and climate satellites). Dom's offer was welcome, since there was little for me to do back at LESC and I enjoyed working with Dom on my frequent trips to Sunnyvale.

Goddard Space Flight Center (GSFC) in Greenbelt, MD, just north of DC, was responsible for the EOS Program and Dom asked me to go to GSFC for a week or so to dig out as much information as possible about the science instruments that EOS was to carry. While at GSFC, I took the opportunity to drive down to NASA Headquarters to talk to Carl Pilcher, who was the Chief of the Advanced Studies Branch of Code S. Since Carl was, before joining NASA, a scientist and hence one of the more knowledgeable people in Code S regarding the Moon and planets, I hoped that Carl might be sympathetic to the Lunar Prospector cause, but I was wrong. Carl's closing statement summed up his attitude towards Lunar Prospector nicely, "Nobody is interested in Lunar Prospector. It is never going to fly; so why don't you quit wasting your time and go do something useful?" (Again, the reader might want to pause here and reflect on the mentality of NASA managers, in this case, Carl Pilcher, given that two years later, Lunar Prospector was selected by an almost completely non-NASA Review Committee for flight.) Once again, I left NASA Headquarters with little hope in my heart for Lunar Prospector.

Given the negative attitudes of Code S to Lunar Prospector, I decided once again to write Ross Perot to ask for his support of the mission. Like the first time I tried to interest Perot in helping with the project back in June 1992, I got the same negative response the second time.

April 1993

I was out in Sunnyvale for a few weeks in April to work on a proposal with Dom for the MESUR/Network — a series of simple Mars Landers that would be used to set up a global seismic and meteorological network. A few days into that effort, Dom came to me and handed me a short RFP from the University of Michigan for a mission called MAUDEE (an aeronomy satellite to study the upper atmosphere of Mars) it was going to propose for the Discovery Program. The MAUDEE Team, led by Dr. Tim Killeen, had received some study money after the San Juan Capistrano Meeting and was looking for an Industry Partner, hence the RFP. Dom asked me to look it over and to tell him if I thought we should propose.

The basic MAUDEE Mission was patterned after the highly successful Pioneer Venus Orbiter that, among other things, produced a large amount of information about the Venus upper atmosphere. Like all the Pioneer Spacecraft, Pioneer Venus was a simple, spin-stabilized spacecraft, not unlike Lunar Prospector, and carried a simple set of aeronomy instruments as part of its payload. The MAUDEE Team, many whom were on the Pioneer Venus Aeronomy Team, saw Discovery as an opportunity to do for Mars what Pioneer Venus did for Venus, so they took the basic Pioneer Venus concept and turned it into MAUDEE.

I liked the simple spacecraft and the simple mission profile. Upon arriving at Mars, MAUDEE was going to go into a highly elliptical, polar orbit and then slowly, via aerobraking, change the elliptical orbit into a circular orbit. While doing that, it would continuously gather data on the Martian upper atmosphere and its interaction with the solar wind. So far so good. However, there were three flies in the MAUDEE ointment. Included in the RFP was the letter from NASA with the comments of the Review Team that had reviewed all the mission proposals presented at the San Juan Meeting. Though the MAUDEE proposal had received high marks, the Review Team had three major concerns.

First, though the basic MAUDEE Proposal was based on a simple-spinner mission like Pioneer Venus, Option A, the MAUDEE Team had an Option B that was based on a three-axis stabilized spacecraft. Option B could do a lot more science than A, but the B spacecraft and mission were much more expensive and more complicated than those for A. The Review Team gave MAUDEE the study money based on Option A, but was "very concerned that the MAUDEE Team would not be able to resist the temptation to go to Option B."

Second, the Review Team stated that MAUDEE had too many instruments and the Team needed to reduce the payload to be consistent with Discovery guidelines and budget.

Third, the Review Team stated that the MAUDEE Science Team itself had far too many Co-Investigators (Co-Is) and their number needed to be reduced.

Despite those three concerns, the science, the simple spacecraft, and the simple mission all looked very good to me, so I told Dom that I thought we should propose. He thought so too, so we went to Frank and Gus with our recommendations and they also agreed. Dom and I got very busy since the proposal was due in just a few days.

As usual, I took over the science, mission profile, and mission operations parts of the proposal. Everything we did was based on Option A, which was the only real option when one considered the Review Team's comments. We knocked out the short proposal on time and sent it to Michigan.

June 1993

I got a call in Houston from Dom in June; Dom told me that MAUDEE had selected us for its Industry Partner and that we had a Kick-Off Meeting at the university in a few days. Hence I needed to get out to Sunnyvale ASAP so we could prepare for the Kick-Off Meeting. That was great. Even if Lunar Prospector was experiencing hard times, maybe I would be part of another Mars Mission — I liked that idea.

I flew to California and we got our viewgraph presentations together. Then we flew to Detroit and drove to Ann Arbor where the University of Michigan is located. The

Kick-Off Meeting went well — to a point. After the usual introductions, PI Tim Killeen started off by welcoming us to the MAUDEE Team and indicated we had been selected because our proposal was the best, by far, they had received. They were impressed that a top engineer/manager, Dom, and experienced lunar and planetary scientists, who knew Mars as well as mission planning and the like, were leading the LMSC Team. Then, Tim went over the MAUDEE Mission, and, of course, Options A and B. After that, Dom and I did our parts and the Kick-Off Meeting followed the usual pattern.

Later, towards the end of the meeting, Tim got up to summarize what we had accomplished, where we were going and then took a left turn when he should have gone straight. Tim, who I believed had made up his mind months earlier, said it was clear from our discussions (which we, LMSC, had limited to Option A) that we could and should do Option B and waste no more time on Option A! Frank, who was sitting way up in the back of the classroom, reacted immediately and warned, "This is a Volkswagen mission, not a Cadillac."

I said, "Tim, you guys are waving a red flag in front of a bull. The Review Committee clearly warned you guys about not resisting going to a three-axis stabilized spacecraft, about having too many instruments, and about having too large a Science Team. If you dump Option A and go to B, you'll turn NASA off and that will be the end of MAUDEE."

Regardless of what Frank, Dom, and I said, Tim and the MAUDEE Science Team were going to have their three-axis stabilized spacecraft, all their science instruments, and their big Science Team — come hell or high water. However, taking our sincere criticisms to heart, they decided to keep MAUDEE a spinner in form (Option A), but with a "one revolution per orbit" spin rate (right back to Option B) — a subterfuge that was as transparent as glass. Further, they decided to reduce the number of instruments by combining two or three related instruments into "Instrument Packages," thereby, on paper, having fewer instruments — again a subterfuge that was as transparent as glass. Similarly, the number of Science Team Co-Is was reduced by having one Co-I per Instrument Package. However, each Co-I had a Science Team of his own! In fact, since, as an astronomer and Viking Lander Camera PI, I knew the surface of Mars and they didn't, they even put me on the Scanning Imager Instrument Package Team, thereby making the real Science Team even bigger than before!

When that exercise in self-deception was over, Tim and the original MAUDEE Team congratulated themselves on having responded in a positive manner to all three of the Review Teams concerns! However, though MAUDEE rolled on for the next year and a third, Tim and his team had insured, right then and there, that MAUDEE would not do well in the Discovery evaluation process (MAUDEE came in 14th out of the 28 proposals that were submitted to the Program 16 months later).

Nevertheless, MAUDEE continued to play a role in the development of Lunar Prospector in a couple of ways, one positive and the other negative. The positive side was that working on MAUDEE helped keep me gainfully employed at LESC via support from LMSC and kept Gus and Frank impressed with my capabilities in lunar and planetary mission development.

The negative aspect of MAUDEE on Lunar Prospector came about slowly and did not manifest itself until the fall of 1994 when the Discovery proposals were being written. The problem began when Dom was taken off the MAUDEE pre-proposal effort to again work fulltime on the big EOS proposal. Gus put Pete Williams in charge of the MAUDEE effort, and Pete was too young and too inexperienced for the job. Over the next several months, in a vain attempt to keep the customer happy at any cost, Pete responded to every request that Killeen made with, "Yes, we can do that," — regardless of whether it was possible engineering-wise or budget-wise (I don't think Pete was try-ing to be deceptive, he was just too inexperienced to know what was possible and what was not, and he didn't want to blow his big chance at being a Project Manager).

Every time Pete promised Killeen something, I would check it out against the mis-sion profile I was developing and usually it wouldn't work, i.e., there was not enough power to support it or not enough downlink capacity to get the data transmitted to Earth and the like. Pete just ignored what I said; after all, I was just a hired gun from another Lockheed company and worse, a scientist — not an engineer.

Similarly, Pete consistently underestimated the costs. Killeen wanted the Phase C/D costs kept around $100 million so MAUDEE would be well below the Discovery Phase C/D cap of $150 million and would therefore be very competitive cost-wise. No matter what or how much Killeen added, the cost never got more than $105 million according to Pete. Though I had little experience in detailed costing, it was clear to me that Pete's budget was full of very big holes.

Finally, in the late winter of 1994, Pete was removed from managing MAUDEE and Dom was put back in charge. I found that out when I got out of my rent-a-car at the hotel where we were all staying the night before a MAUDEE meeting in Michigan, and Dom was also getting out of his car. I said, "Dom, you're back! Great! This thing is screwed up so bad that it isn't funny." It didn't take Dom very long to find out just how right I was.

When Dom began to try to correct the mess Pete had made and figure out a real-istic budget, Killeen and Len Fisk (a former Associate Administrator of Space Science [Code S] who had retired from NASA and became a member of the University of Michi-gan's Administration) were not pleased. Their position was, "Lockheed (Pete) promised us a $105 million mission and Lockheed is going to deliver a $105 million mission, period, end of discussion." Thus when we were writing the MAUDEE and Lunar Prospector proposals a half a year later, Dom, and what little staff was available to help, had to put all their time and effort into trying to save MAUDEE at Lunar Prospector's and my expense, as later described in Chapter 1-15.

Friday, July 16, 1993: The Unsolicited Proposal

Though I was enjoying working on MAUDEE, despite my concerns that Tim Killeen and his Team had already blown their chances of being selected, and despite Pete's mismanaging the Lockheed's part of the pre-proposal efforts, I had not stopped trying to find support for Lunar Prospector. Thus, notwithstanding Carl Pilcher's rejec-tion of the mission a few months earlier, I decided to try the direct approach. I submit-ted an Unsolicited Proposal for Lunar Prospector to Code S on July 16, 1993. The pro-posal was based on our original SEI proposal to Mike Griffin.

Part of my motivation for submitting the Unsolicited Proposal was that, during the past year, things had changed for the worse at LESC and my co-workers and I were look-ing for a little security. The Lockheed/JSC Support Contract that our Mission Planning Group (Mick Culp — our supervisor, Tom Polette, John Gruener, Warren Holdenbach, and a few others) worked on, as well as a large fraction of all of the LESC groups, had come to its end. JSC had put out the usual RFP to all the aerospace companies for the new contract. Money was very tight at NASA and every effort had to be made to keep the proposed budget as low as possible. In his infinite wisdom (helped out undoubt-edly by large amounts of alcohol), Moe Miller had decided that the LESC proposal would be based on young, inexpensive new hires (direct from the universities — who were also *inexperienced*) rather than us older, more expensive employees (who were very *experienced*, but could be fired). However, even NASA could figure out that inexperienced, young kids could not deliver the quality work we had done on the old contract, and, of course, LESC lost the contract — McDonnell Douglas won it.

As a result of Moe's outstanding leadership, things were getting pretty tight at LESC. It didn't really affect me, because I had not been working on the JSC contract to any extent for some time, and many other LESC employees were picked up on subcontracts by McDonnell Douglas. However, it was clear that Mick was in jeopardy (he was soon let go, and later got a job at JSC). As a supervisor, he cost a lot and since our group was falling apart due to the loss of the contract, there was little for him to supervise. As a result, like me, he began to spend a lot of time working on Lunar Prospector, in the hopes that we would somehow get it funded and he could work for me on the mission. Thus, Mick, Tom, and I spent time working out the new budget and upgraded LEI organization for the Proposal, and Mick, as well as Tom, became more involved with my efforts to keep Lunar Prospector going.

Because so much time had passed since we had done the original SEI proposal, I could no longer assume we could get a free, or low cost, launch from the Russians. Part of the original motivation for the Soviets to launch Lunar Prospector was to demonstrate the Proton's commercial launch potential. Since then, they had started selling Proton launches to the West, so they no longer needed Lunar Prospector as a PR tool. Thus, I had begun to look around for an inexpensive launch vehicle that could do the job.

Lockheed in Sunnyvale was developing its LLV (Lockheed Launch Vehicle) series of inexpensive rockets, so I got a bid for a LLV2 launch to Trans-Lunar Injection that came to $22.5 million. Similarly, I got a $20 million bid for a Russian Proton launch from a new American company, International Space Enterprises. Also, the spacecraft and mission costs had crept up to $19.5 million; so the total budget was just over $40 million — still a bargain by a factor of five to ten over NASA mission costs.

I tried to convince Code S that Lunar Prospector would make the ideal initial mission for the Discovery Program in the cover letter for the Proposal (Appendix 1-12, also see www.lunar-research-institute.org).

Wednesday, August 18, 1993:
A Visit with Mary Kicza Regarding the Proposal

In order to plead the case for Lunar Prospector being the first Discovery Mission in person, I went to DC to see Mary Kicza, the Acting Program Manager of the Discovery Program, at Headquarters. I told her that Lunar Prospector was the ideal mission to start Discovery because it was simple, it had good science, it was inexpensive, and it was ready to go (and history proved me right). Mary quasi-rejected my arguments by saying, "The problem with Lunar Prospector is that it is embarrassingly inexpensive."

I was astounded — NASA didn't want *really* inexpensive missions, it just wanted *less* expensive missions. If the missions were too cheap, then NASA would not get as much money from Congress to spend, NASA would not need as many bureaucrats, and the big, fat aerospace companies would not make as much money as they did. The philosophy was, "Lets just keep everybody fat and happy, but just a little less fat and just a little less happy." Nevertheless, Mary reminded me about the spring release of the Discovery AO and said I should re-submit my proposal in response to the AO.

Saturday, August 21, 1993:
The One Billion-Dollar Mars Observer Disappears

On Saturday, August 21, NASA suffered a major setback — it lost the $1 billion Mars Observer (MO) just three days before it was to insert itself into Mars orbit! The loss was just one more example of the consequences of the bad management and bad engineering I felt plagued NASA and had earlier led to the loss of the Challenger and its crew of seven, the flawed Hubble Telescope mirror, and other embarrassing and costly failures.

The cause of the loss of MO will never really be known, because the transmitter was off when the failure occurred, but the NASA Failure Review Board had at the top of its list of probable failure modes leaky propellant valves, and the story goes like this. MO's Mars Orbit Insertion Propulsion Subsystem was a standard biprop system using hypergolic monometyl hydrazine and nitrogen tetroxide (they ignite on contact) and the MO transponder was the type that utilizes a traveling wave-guide amplifier that is susceptible to shock. The original plan was to pressurize the propellant tanks five days after launch by explosively opening the pyro-valves to the helium pressurant tank. Because of the transponder's susceptibility to shock, it was to be shut off for the 10-minute pressurization/pyro-event. However, to be on the safe side and to protect the propellant tanks from being under high pressure for a long time (for which they are designed), the engineers decided to change the mission profile and pressurize the propellant tanks just before MO reached Mars — 11 months after launch. However, the valves were not designed to withstand prolonged exposure to the space environment (hence the original plan to pressurize the tanks a few days after launch). Despite that fact, the valves were not replaced by ones that were designed for long exposure to the space environment! It was concluded that during the 11 months between launch and the pressurization event, the valves leaked, allowing small amounts of hydrazine and nitrogen tetroxide to get into the propellant lines. When the valves were finally opened — after the transponder was turned off, so no data was obtained during the event — the hypergolic propellants in the lines mixed and instantly ignited, destroying the propellant lines, the propulsion subsystem, and the spacecraft.

For me, and many, many others, the loss of the MO was just one more example of how incompetent NASA had become. The failure also underscored the importance of our somehow getting Lunar Prospector done so we could show NASA, Congress, and the American taxpayer there was a better way of doing space exploration than the incompetent NASA way.

Also, I immediately changed Lunar Prospector's bipropellant propulsion subsystem OMNI had talked us into early in the Spacecraft Design Study back to the simple and reliable monopropellant, hydrazine subsystem Preston and I had requested in our RFP for the Spacecraft Design Study.

Further, the loss of the Mars Observer meant, if NASA flew a back up mission (which they did — Mars Global Surveyor), they might (and did) use the backup MAG/ER package we had hoped to get for Lunar Prospector. If so, then we would have to build our own MAG/ER package. But we would just have to duplicate the MO MAG/ER package, minus one MAG and with different software. That would not be too costly or difficult to do because all the plans were available and there would be no costly development work to be done. Though Bob and his Berkeley coworkers had built the ER and done the integration, Mario Acuña from GSFC had built the MO MAG and was responsible for the common electronics, but Bob was sure Mario would do the same for Lunar Prospector, so we were most probably OK there.

Thursday, August 26, 1993: Letter To Goldin

As a result of the MO failure, I felt even more strongly than ever about the importance of using Lunar Prospector to demonstrate that small, simple, inexpensive, reliable missions should be flown instead of big, complicated, very costly, put-all-your-eggs-in-one-basket missions. I wrote Dan Goldin in hopes that, since he had told Tellep and Lockheed to get behind me and do Lunar Prospector over a year earlier, he would tell Wes and the rest of Code S to fund the unsolicited proposal I had submitted on July 16.

September 1993: Mary's Letter and Wes's Answer to My Goldin Letter

I received a letter from Mary dated September 3, in which she reiterated her suggestion that I re-submit the proposal in response to the AO. She also wrote, "Your name has been added to the Discovery mailing list." At last, Code S was willing to officially acknowledge that Lunar Prospector and I existed and that was, at least, a start.

Later in the month, I received a letter from Wes Huntress, the Associate Administrator for Space Science, dated September 14, in response to my August 26 letter to Goldin. Like Mary, Wes referred to the up and coming Discovery AO (by then it had slipped from spring to mid-1994) and wrote he was looking "forward to reviewing your proposal in response to the forthcoming solicitation."

Like it or not, if I wanted NASA to fund Lunar Prospector, I would have to submit it as a Discovery Proposal and I didn't see any hope in that.

First, Code S had made it clear they were not interested in Lunar Prospector. Though Wes and Mary had invited me to submit a proposal to Discovery when the AO came out in the summer of 1994, they were just following procedures as far as I was concerned, and being polite.

Second, because Code S had no interest in Lunar Prospector, or the Moon, and clearly resented the fact that we had done everything outside of NASA, there was no way in hell that Code S would select Lunar Prospector as a Discovery Mission. Their good-old-boy peer review system would see to that. I was certain any proposal we submitted would end up in the wastepaper basket — unless NASA had a truly independent review committee with none of NASA's biases and hidden agendas. But I saw no way NASA would not keep tight control over the Discovery review process and would therefore reject a Lunar Prospector Proposal.

Third, none of us, LEI, OMNI, or SSI, had any money and it would cost $100,000 to a million dollars to produce a credible proposal that could compete with those from Lockheed, Boeing, McDonnell Douglas, Bell, and the other aerospace companies that would certainly be the Industry Partners of the other teams.

Fourth, the only way we could compete would be to ask LMSC to be our Industry Partner. If we did, I was fairly certain LMSC and Gus would completely take the project over and Gus would use the Lunar Resource Mapper/F-Sat Proposal as the basis of the Discovery Proposal. If that happened, then I had the same programmatic concerns I had had when Goldin had asked Tellep and Gus to get behind Lunar Prospector back in June of 1992.

Since I did not see any hope for Lunar Prospector if my only choice was to propose to the Discovery Program, I kept trying to find a way around the Code S bureaucracy, and a new opportunity had already begun.

Chapter 1-12
Galvan, ISE, and Goldin

September To Late November 1993: Larry Bell, Mike Simon, and ISE

Larry Bell, the Director of the Sasakawa International Institute for Space Architecture (SIISA) at the University of Houston, called and wanted to talk to me about Lunar Prospector and a new company he was involved with. The San Diego, CA, based company, International Space Enterprises (ISE), was the brainchild of its President, Mike Simon, an ex-employee of General Dynamics, and Larry Bell was one of its several Vice-Presidents.

ISE had been set up to exploit the chaotic and decaying economic situation in Russia after the fall of the Soviet Union. The idea was to utilize very inexpensive Russian lunar landers to put commercial payloads on the Moon, thereby keeping Russian rocket scientists gainfully employed by the West, rather than their making mischief with third world bad guys, and making lots of money for the US participants. ISE was a union of two companies, the new American one and a much older Russian one, Lavochkin Association of Moscow that had built the Soviet Lunakhod rovers. By having Lavochkin as a corporate partner, SEI could not only utilize the Russians to build inexpensive lunar landers, but, being a Russian company, Lavochkin could buy Proton launch vehicles directly and very cheaply from its Russian vendor, thereby eliminating the need for ISE to go through the expensive red tape of the USA bureaucracy — an ideal situation!

Mike, Larry and the other founders of SEI were looking for a way to get the whole thing off the ground and to get some good publicity. Since I had taught a class for three semesters at SIISA about the Moon to the students who wanted to design lunar bases and lunar structures, I had interfaced with Larry Bell quite a bit. Thus, Larry knew all about Lunar Prospector and thought it was a great idea. He also knew Lunar Prospector already had a lot of notoriety, and was accepted by the space science and aerospace communities as being something that would be very worthwhile. Larry also believed if ISE launched Lunar Prospector, all its good attributes would automatically be transferred to ISE and that would instantly jump start their company.

That belief was strengthened when Larry talked to Bill Huffstetler about ISE to see how NASA would react to their forming the company and to see if there was anything Bill could suggest that could help get ISE going. Bill, of course, also immediately suggested ISE launch Lunar Prospector as their first mission, thereby helping lunar science and establishing their company via a mission many people wanted to see go to the Moon.

Larry told me part of that on the telephone and asked me to come up to SIISA to discuss the details, which I, of course, did. Since Tom Polette had become my deputy and, as a former SIISA student, knew Larry far better than I did, I asked Tom to come along. The reason for my doing so was twofold. First, as my deputy, I wanted Tom to be involved with everything that was going on and for Larry to understand Tom's involvement. Second, Larry is a notorious wheeler-and-dealer and I didn't trust Larry as far as I could throw him. Since Tom knew Larry very well and also did not trust him, I figured Tom could help me watch out for Larry.

With our concern about Larry in the not too far back parts of our minds, Tom and I met with him at SIISA and discussed Lunar Prospector in detail, as well as the aspects of ISE's possible involvement with it. As it turned out, Larry was actually interested in my becoming part of ISE since I knew payloads and understood the Moon and the ISE guys knew nothing about either of those very important issues. That was a strange situation considering they had just formed a company to launch commercial lander missions to the Moon!

Larry asked me what missions I thought ISE could do (again, a strange question from someone who had just helped set up a commercial lunar exploration company). I told him about the missions I had in my Selene Lunar Lander Program, i.e., sample return missions, setting up the Selenophysical Array, landing rovers, setting up telescopes, and all the other things that the lunar and space science communities had suggested. I explained further that over 70 such missions had been described in various NASA position papers. I also said I championed what they were trying to do and, if they gave Lunar Prospector a free launch to Kick-Off their company, it would certainly help us as well as help ISE get on the map.

After a couple of similar meetings, Larry told the rest of the ISE group how useful and important I could be to ISE and suggested I lead a Houston office to promote ISE activities and to do payload definition and mission planning. Then Larry, Mike Simon, and I had a few telephone conversations about all those issues. Mike, of course, knew of Lunar Prospector and was quite interested in Larry's various ideas and the impact they would have in getting money from potential investors.

In our telephone conversations, Larry brought up the possibility and utility of getting a meeting set up with a certain Israel Galvan.

Israel is a very active and very interesting person who is very well connected in the Democratic Party and in the political arena in general. However, though he really prefers Democrats, Israel will support anyone who is pro-space in either party. All the Texas politicians I either had contact with, or had written to (Mike Andrews and Jack Brooks) were people that Israel had ready access to. Israel is also a friend of Goldin's and had easy access to him, which was why we wanted him involved with ISE and Lunar Prospector. We first wanted to meet with Israel and then have him set up a meeting for us with Goldin to try to get him to again support Lunar Prospector as a NASA science mission and whatever he could do for ISE.

Larry called me up in late October and said we had a meeting with Israel at his office that was not very far from JSC. Larry, Tom, and I went there and discussed Lunar Prospector and ISE with Israel. There had been some earlier contact between Larry and Israel about ISE, so ISE's activities were not totally foreign to him, but Israel knew nothing about Lunar Prospector. I told him the history of Lunar Prospector and what we wanted to do with it. When I was done, Israel saw the value of Lunar Prospector, both in helping the Space Program and in helping ISE get off the ground. As a result, Israel fell in love with Lunar Prospector and was ready to do whatever he could to see that Lunar Prospector got funded.

Israel had two approaches to getting that funding; the first was to go to Goldin directly as we wanted to do and the second was via George Abby. Abby, a close friend of Israel's (it seems like everyone in power in NASA and in the Government is a friend of Israel's) was head of the Astronaut Office back in the Apollo days and was *the member* of the Stafford Committee who had set up our meeting with the Committee. After Goldin had become the NASA Administrator, Aaron Cohen had been relieved of his duties as the Director of JSC. Israel was lobbying Goldin to appoint Abby as the new Director of JSC. If that didn't work, Israel wanted Abby to become a personal advisor to Goldin or be appointed to some other high position at Headquarters. Israel believed if Abby were in any of those three positions, he would make sure that Lunar Prospector got done.

However, Abby's possible appointment to any of those positions was yet to occur, so Israel immediately started with Dan Goldin. I was amazed at the access Israel had to Goldin (and various Congressmen and Senators too); Israel just swiveled his chair around, picked up his telephone, and said, "Well, I'll just call up Dan and see when we can set up this meeting."

When Israel got Goldin on the phone and said he wanted to set up a meeting and why, Goldin said, "Just pick a date and time and come on out." Larry and I assumed we were going to get to see Goldin right away and get our shows on the road, but it didn't happen that way — it was January 27 before we actually got to meet with Goldin, but Israel had certainly set the stage. As Larry, Tom, and I went away from that first meeting with Israel, we felt that we would soon be able to present our cases to Goldin and maybe get the support we needed to do Lunar Prospector and to get ISE rolling.

ISE's basic concept was to sell NASA two Proton missions for about $100 million (an absolute bargain) to get their business started. Remember that a Proton could launch several tons to the Moon, so Lunar Prospector's 299 kg was just so much ballast, as the Russians liked to tell us. The first Proton was going to place Lunar Prospector and a "commercial" payload in lunar orbit — not just on trans-lunar trajectories. The commercial satellite was going to take movie pictures of the Moon that could be used in commercial films or the like. That first launch was also going to place a lunar communications satellite in a halo orbit at the L-2 point. The second Proton was going to launch a lunar lander with whatever payload NASA wanted and a NASA orbiter of their choice.

In addition to the hoped-for NASA support, ISE was also looking for commercial support and investors. ISE was not trying to get NASA to pay the full $100 million, but as they found out, when you go out to the commercial world to try to get people involved, they always say, "Well, if this is so good, why isn't NASA involved?" — the old Catch 22. Without NASA, you can't get the investors and without investors, NASA won't do anything — NASA is not in the business of setting up private enterprises.

After we had had our initial meeting with Israel and as we were waiting for a firm date for the meeting with Goldin, Mike Simon and I began to work on our common technical issues. But as 1993 slipped away with no date set for the meeting — there was always some delay because of Goldin's full schedule — we were getting very anxious. The ISE staff kept busy working on its presentation for Goldin. As they did, they got the bright idea that ISE would do Lunar Prospector, i.e., Lunar Prospector would become part of ISE's program and they would build it and fly it. When I heard about that (shades of the Florida gang?), I called Mike and said, "NO WAY."

Also during October, there were two good articles about Lunar Prospector. On October 4 there was an extensive article about the mission and the possible cooperation between LEI and SEI to get it done as a commercial venture in the *Houston Business Journal*. The business world was beginning to understand what we were trying to do with Lunar Prospector in terms of commercial space exploration. The second article, also quite extensive, but oriented towards the technical aspects of the Spacecraft, appeared in the October issue of *The ISSO Newsletter (International Small Satellite Organization)*.

There was an interesting consequence of the *Houston Business Journal* article. A few days after the article appeared, a young Houston businessman called and wanted to meet me for lunch to find out more about Lunar Prospector. That sounded very interesting, so I said, "Yes." A couple of days later, he, Mick Culp, and I met for lunch and he said, even though we had no money to do Lunar Prospector, we had considerable assets that businessmen would pay a lot of money for. I was puzzled and said, "We don't have any assets."

He countered with, "Yes, you do. You have all kinds of political contacts and contacts within the aerospace community that are very valuable assets for any business." Since I knew nothing about the business world, that was news to me, but after he told us that, it made sense. Second, he warned us if Lunar Prospector were successful, we had to dissolve LEI and start a new company if we wanted to do any follow-on commercial missions. If we didn't, everyone who had worked with us, or as he said, "anyone who had even walked by our door," would want in on the profits and if they didn't get what they wanted, they would sue us. His words were both an echo and a reinforcement of those of Art Dula back in September of 1989 when we were just getting started setting LEI up. The guy then told us why he was giving us that advice. When he started his business (the equivalent of Teleflora, but using computer email instead of telephones) he wasn't doing well and several of the investors backed out. A little later, his business began to payoff and all the ex-investors sued him for their money! Enough said. Though we still had no plans to do anything beyond Lunar Prospector, I kept that sage advice in mind — just in case.

While waiting and preparing for the Goldin meeting was going on, there was an abrupt change in my solitary personal life.

November 1993: Enter Rebecca

Nearly a year earlier, after being alone for a decade — and finally tired of it, I decided I was in dire need of feminine companionship. Since I am not Mr. Social Butterfly and don't go to bars or clubs and since the engineering world I worked in at Lockheed is not known for its attractive women, I had joined Great Expectations, a video dating service, to look for Ms. Right. I had spent the intervening year meeting and going to lunch or dinner with a number of attractive, interesting, and usually intelligent ladies, none of whom was the Right One. I found that dating, or trying to, at 53 is a lot harder than at 18 and after a year I had begun to wonder if it was worth the $1700 I had paid for my one-year membership. I had decided when my membership was over — it was over.

Sometime during the first or second week of November, while thumbing through the books containing the biographies and pictures of the Great Expectations Ladies, I ran across a cute little newcomer named Rebecca (no last names, just first names and membership numbers). Like me, she is from farm country (Rebecca — a farm near Wetmore, KS, with 300 inhabitants; me — a farm village, Chemung, IL, with 300 inhabitants), likes reading, movies, and being alone. All that was interesting enough for me to go to all the trouble to look at her video. She still looked cute and sweet in the video (can't really trust the pictures in the books) and sounded OK, too. But, since I had been down that road many times during the previous year, I had few expectations when I decided to inform Rebecca, via the standard Great Expectations postcard with my name (just Alan — no last name) and membership number (so she could check out my biography, picture, and video before committing a grievous error), that I would like to meet her.

As it turned out, Rebecca's daughter was having her first child and Rebecca was in St Louis, MO, to participate in the event. I did not get an answer, yeah or nay, for over two weeks — long enough for me to have figured that her answer was probably nay.

Thursday, December 2, 1993: The Telephone Calls

Nevertheless, when, on December 2, I arrived at Great Expectations for another attempt to find Ms. Right, I was told that Rebecca wanted to meet me and I received her work and home phone numbers. It was nearly 5:30 PM, so I first tried to reach her at work (she was the Legal Secretary for the Vice-President of Legal Affairs at the Baylor College of Medicine in downtown Houston) and she was there, but about to leave for home. She said she would be home in about an hour and to call her then. As she drove home, I drove from Great Expectations (also in downtown Houston) back down to my home in Santa Fe, TX, several kilometers south of JSC.

When I got home, I called Rebecca and we began to get acquainted. The more we talked, the more we found we had a lot in common (besides being farm/small town hicks). I loved Arizona and wanted to get back there; she liked Tucson and had a niece there and a sister in Phoenix. She liked to read self-help books and I had read *Men Are From Mars And Women Are From Venus* (she thought that meant I was sensitive and caring — I just thought the book was interesting and right on the money). After more than an hour, I asked her if she wanted to meet for dinner Saturday evening (I didn't want to give her more than a couple of days to think about it, otherwise she might back out) and she said, "Yes." I then asked her where she would like to go to dinner (we lived more than an hour away from each other and I assumed she would like to go somewhere near where she lived) and she suggested a Steak and Ale restaurant that was about in the middle of the city, though much closer to her far-west-side home than my far-south-side home.

Saturday, December 4, 1993: The First Date

Since it was a long drive from Santa Fe to the restaurant, and since I hate being late for anything, especially a first date, I left home with plenty of time and, as usual, arrived about a half an hour early for our 6:00 o'clock dinner date. I drove around a while and then parked and sat in the car for a while. At about 10 till 6 and still somewhat early, I went into the restaurant — where Rebecca was waiting! She too had been early (another thing we have in common), had driven around a while and then went into the restaurant to wait for me. We had a glass of wine while we waited for our table (I don't drink, but when I started at Great Expectations, my young engineer friends at NASA and Lockheed told me I had to drink wine, or the ladies would think I was out of it). I guzzled down the evil tasting stuff for the sake of romance — but I did have a coke with my prime rib, no sense in getting too far out of character.

Our table was soon ready, so we started our dinner and continued the conversation we had started over the wine. We had a great time talking and getting acquainted, so good in fact that the restaurant was closing before we decided we had better call it an evening.

During that several hour conversation, I told her about Lunar Prospector (certainly, in much more detail than she was interested in) and, as she told me much, much later, she figured Lunar Prospector was just one more masculine pipe dream of the type she had heard many times before. At least the previous pipe dreams were about getting rich, not going to the Moon. Despite that, we had a great time and clearly wanted to see each other again.

Saturday, December 11, 1993: The Second Date

A week later we had our second date — we were originally just going on a picnic at Brazos Bend State Park to the SW of Houston, but the date lasted all afternoon and well into the night, but first things first. I was sufficiently confident that Israel would get Goldin to help ISE and support Lunar Prospector that I had begun to build a full scale model of the spacecraft (the one OMNI had built had been destroyed because OMNI, which was operationally defunct by that time, did not have the money to keep it in storage). I had started with the science instruments and their booms and needed more electrical wire to finish modeling the long instrument cables. On the way to Rebecca's I had stopped at a Radio Shack, but they did not have enough wire to fulfill my needs. After I picked her up (I did not want to be late), I asked her if it would be OK if I stopped at another Radio Shack to buy more wire and she said, "Sure." She would soon learn that Lunar Prospector, like any child, was always going to be tagging along with us — one way or another.

After picking up my all-important wire, we drove to the park and had a nice picnic and a long walk along the river where we watched the alligators that abound there. By the time we left the park, it was late enough for dinner and since there was a nice Mexican restaurant very close to where Rebecca lived (Mexican food — another thing we have in common), we had dinner there. Not wanting the date to end, we decided to go to a movie at a close-by theater and saw the film *Geronimo*. Then we went to her house and watched a film from her video collection and finally, thirteen hours after I had picked her up, at 1:00 AM, I left to drive back home, thinking I had possibly found Ms. Right.

The Rest Of December 1993

The following weekend we drove to San Antonio, one of her and my favorite places, and enjoyed the River Walk and each other. By the end of that weekend, it was clear we were going to be spending a lot of time together, perhaps the rest of our lives — though our relationship had not yet advanced that far. However, we did decide we would go inactive at Great Expectations, i.e., be removed from the books since we were going to date each other exclusively. The irony of that was, I had spent $1700 and a year of dating various ladies, which was more work than pleasure (everyone I met there said the same thing, "It's hard work trying to find the right person at our age."), while Rebecca had spent $1700 for a three year contract (sex discrimination — my $1700 covered just a year) and had met just one guy on her first date!

We spent Christmas together with her daughter, son-in-law, and grandson, and New Year's Eve, growing closer all the time. When 1993 ended, I had a very happy personal life with Rebecca and high hopes that Goldin and Israel would finally get Lunar Prospector off the ground — to which it seemed to be chained.

January 1994: Getting Prepared for the Goldin Meeting

By the time January 1994 rolled around and during January, Israel and I had had several meetings. Israel was really gung-ho about Lunar Prospector and wanted to make sure no one screwed it up. When Israel called and said he had received the ISE viewgraph package for the Goldin meeting for our review, we intended to make sure all the i's were dotted and the t's were crossed. After getting the call, Mick Culp and I went to Israel's office to look at the viewgraphs and when we did, we were ticked off. Despite my telling Mike in the fall that ISE was not going to be responsible for Lunar Prospector, his last viewgraph showed that ISE was going to do the mission and LEI was going to play a support role as part of ISE! When I saw that, I said, "Hell no, that is not the way it is. Lunar Prospector is totally independent of ISE and has nothing to do with it, except for the launch."

Though we had talked about the possibility of LEI and ISE doing a joint venture, where LEI would build the instruments (and maybe even the spacecraft), rather than having the Russians do so, since everyone knew that the Russians instruments were crap, I intended to keep LEI as a separate entity that would only work with ISE, not for it. I didn't want Lunar Prospector and LEI to be dragged down with ISE if it failed, and I intended to keep LEI independent of ISE. Israel felt the same way.

Israel immediately called Mike Simon and we said, "The last viewgraph is not acceptable, neither Lunar Prospector nor LEI are parts of ISE. What you can show is that ISE is offering us a free ride as a demonstration of your capabilities and our cooperative effort, but in no way are you going to tell Goldin you are going to build Lunar Prospector or fly it or anything else."

Mike apologized and said that was not what he meant, but he had gotten it all screwed up on the viewgraph — that was a lame bunch of BS. I didn't really think Mike was trying to screw us, but he was certainly trying to maximize the advantage for ISE and to exploit LEI's capabilities and publicity successes. Whatever the case, we were ready for the Goldin meeting that had finally been set for January 27, 1994.

Wednesday, January 26, 1994: A Winter Trip

Since I had to pay for my own transportation and everything else, I had called Pat and Julius Dasch to ask if, as I usually did when I went to DC, I could stay with them and the answer was, as always, "Yes." I flew off to DC on Thursday in high hopes that we would be successful.

As it turned out, the winter of 93/94 was one damned cold winter in DC. DC had had some killer snowstorms and people had been sent home from work because there were power and heating outages. Coming from warm Houston, I had, of course, forgotten to bring a heavy coat, gloves, and a hat; I just had on my suit coat. Also, I had all the Lunar Prospector documentation with me — the MRD, the MOD, the Mission Operations Manual, plus my viewgraphs, and my little bag. As such, I had an arm-full, so I couldn't even put my hands in my pockets to keep them from freezing.

In the past, Julius had always picked me up at the National Airport, but since he really didn't like to do that, I said I would take the Metro to the station that is several blocks from their apartment and walk the rest of the way.

When I got out of the airplane, I didn't know where the damned Airport Metro Station was and it was cold as hell, icy and snowing — really very unpleasant. I asked for direction to the station and was told that it was a few blocks away. I froze my tail off walking there. I got my ticket and then had to stand on the platform in the icy cold, winter weather waiting for the train in the early evening, winter darkness. The train finally came and, after switching trains once, I arrived, somewhat warmed up, at the station near Julius and Pat's apartment. Then I had to walk the five or six blocks to their apartment complex and it was again just as cold as hell (for those readers who have never read Dante's *The Inferno*, Satan is frozen in eternal ice in the ninth circle of Hell)!

When I got there, Julius had his famous meatloaf dinner waiting for me. After dinner we brought each other up to date on everything that was going on, and then I went to bed in their guest room.

Thursday, January 27, 1994: The Meeting with Goldin

I walked to NASA with Julius in the morning, and since our meeting was not until 10:30 AM, we went to Julius's office to talk a little while I waited. While there, I talked Julius into giving me one of the magnetite crystal complexes he had from an iron lava flow and then we decided to have a midmorning snack. We went down to the little deli in the NASA building and, as we were snacking, Frank Martin waltzed in!

Frank, more than a little surprised to see me there, asked, "What are you doing here?"

I answered, "I have a meeting with Goldin about Lunar Prospector."

We chatted a little bit and then, as he left, he said, "Well, good luck."

By then, it was nearly time for the meeting. As I was about to go up to Goldin's office, I saw Mike and he was not alone. That concerned me. We had all agreed that only Mike, Israel, and I were going to meet with Goldin — and no one else. Despite our agreement, Mike had brought a representative from Rockwell International, the aerospace company that was supporting ISE, and Valery Aksamentov, the ISE Vice President from the Russian part of their company. Clearly, Mike was trying to bring all his big guns to sell their program, and I was annoyed about that for two reasons. First, Mike had again pulled a fast one in violation of our agreement, and second, the fewer people that are at a meeting like ours, the fewer distractions there are and the more you can get done. It was too late to do anything about Mike's little trick, so we introduced ourselves to each other and then we went up to the top floor of the building to Goldin's office.

The Administrator's office (and several others) is behind the "Golden Doors." According to Pat and Julius, NASA is really run from behind those Golden Doors. If you are behind the Golden Doors, things got done and you are running programs and deciding what to do. If you are outside the Golden Doors, where 99% of NASA is, you have nothing to say. Getting into the inner sanctum is a big deal. As I was soon to find out, none of that is really true.

After passing through the Golden Doors, we were invited to sit in very comfortable chairs and wait until Goldin was ready for us. Unfortunately, Israel wasn't around and we were getting a little concerned because he had set up the meeting and he was the key for everything we wanted. As we waited, we talked among ourselves and the engineer from Rockwell International tried to grill me about Lunar Prospector. He didn't know much about the mission, but when I got done, I had made it very clear to him what Lunar Prospector was, who in the hell was in charge of it, who knew what the hell they were doing and how to do it — and it wasn't ISE as he had hinted at. Finally, to our collective relief, Israel got there just minutes before the meeting.

Almost simultaneously with Israel's arrival, some high-up lackey came in, introduced himself as Goldin's assistant and said he would take us to Mr. Goldin. Along with him was a guy whose face was very familiar. He introduced himself as Al Diaz, but the name didn't ring a bell, and, as usual, I couldn't place him. Al then said, "Yeah, it's been a long time since Viking," and that rang the bell. It was Al Diaz from Viking. Al had been on the Mass Spectrometer Team and we had known each other well then and interfaced with each other quite a bit during the Viking Missions. Al was the Deputy Associate Administrator of Code S, i.e., Wes Huntress's Deputy. Al seemed to be very positive about everything we were trying to do with Lunar Prospector, so I thought, *well, this is pretty good*. Then we walked into Goldin's office and introduced ourselves to him.

The meeting got started with Mike explaining what ISE was all about and the fact that they wanted NASA to buy into two Proton launches. That immediately set Goldin off. Somewhat angrily, he said, "All you commercial guys do is come in here and want me to pay you to get your company started. As a Federal Agency, NASA is not in the business of setting up commercial companies and subsidizing you so you can make a profit. When you have your own investors and can produce a product that NASA is interested in, then come and we will talk. NASA is not an investment company."

Mike held his ground and replied that it was impossible to get investors unless NASA was involved with the mission (the old Catch-22; "If this is so good, why isn't NASA involved?"). Mike also used the analogy about building the railroads in the early west. Because America needed the railroads to develop the west, the Government heavily subsidized the railroad companies. Goldin wasn't buying it and he and Mike argued back and forth for about forty minutes and I was beginning to wonder if I was going to get a chance to say peep about Lunar Prospector before our one-hour meeting was over.

Israel was wondering the same thing and finally broke into the argument saying we had a second topic to discuss — Lunar Prospector. That stopped Goldin and he turned to me and Al Diaz, who, in a rather "kiss-ass" way, said, "Yes, we (Code S) know all about Lunar Prospector and the progress Alan has made."

I started to tell Goldin about our science goals and the mission. I had just said a few words when I mentioned we would produce the first complete lunar gravity map. Goldin sat up and said, "You're going to get a gravity map?"

I answered, "Yes."

Goldin said, "Good, that's what we want, let's do it." He then immediately turned back to Mike and began haranguing him about his wanting NASA to subsidize ISE. Just like that, after only a couple of minutes and a few sentences on my part, Goldin had said, "Let's do it."

However, the joy was very short-lived. After a few more minutes of arguing with Mike, Goldin stood up and began to walk us to his door. He put his arm around Mike's shoulders and said, what Mike was trying to do was really good and he hoped Mike would succeed, but NASA just couldn't subsidize their operation. As that was going on, I turned to Al and attempted to give him the Lunar Prospector Mission Documents I had carried around and asked, "What is the next step?"

Al answered, "There is no next step. Nothing is going to happen with Lunar Prospector."

I was floored. Just minutes earlier Goldin had said, "Let's do it," and Al rejected what his boss had said without batting an eye. The trip and meeting had been a colossal waste of my time and money and Al Diaz's ass kissing was just a show for Goldin — a way to keep Goldin from knowing what Code S's true attitude towards Lunar Prospector was.

Only years later did I come to completely understand what had happened. I was told by someone who had asked Goldin how he ran NASA and he replied, "I tell my staff what I want done and they go off and do what they want to." Well, I had just seen a perfect example of that and it confirmed what I already knew from talking with Joe Alexander, Carl Pilcher, and Mary Kicza, and from the letters I had gotten from Wes Huntress — Code S wanted nothing to do with Lunar Prospector, or the Moon, and that was that. Goldin or no Goldin, Code S was not going to fund the mission, no matter how good or how inexpensive it was, period.

Later, perhaps after he realized that Code S was not going to do anything about Lunar Prospector, Goldin called Israel and told him to have me put in a Discovery Proposal for Lunar Prospector when the AO came out in the spring (sage advice given Code S's attitude towards Lunar Prospector). Goldin also said I should go see Sam Venneri, the Director of the Spacecraft and Remote Sensing Division in Code C (Advanced Concepts and Technology) about Code C possibly doing Lunar Prospector.

Chapter 1-13
Rebecca, Sam Venneri, and Code C

Wednesday, February 23, 1994: Meeting Sam Venneri

Given Goldin's suggestion and Israel's insistence that Goldin really wanted to find a way to fund Lunar Prospector, I had a brief meeting with Sam Venneri at Headquarters on February 23. Sam was willing to talk with me and thought Code C might be able to fund the mission, but was not overly enthusiastic about the whole thing. Sam wanted more details and I promised I would get him the information ASAP.

Monday, February 28, through Saturday, March 12, 1994: MAUDEE

Almost as soon as I got back from Washington DC, I flew out to Sunnyvale to work on MAUDEE for two weeks — as I had been doing regularly since June of 93. Though I was sure MAUDEE was nearly a lost cause, there was still hope for it and I was doing everything I could to help make it a success. If it were selected as a Discovery Mission and if Lunar Prospector kept on being rejected, I would have a job on MAUDEE for several years and that was a good incentive to work hard on it.

Tuesday, March 15, 1994: Rebecca and I Get Engaged

The personal highlight during that period was on Tuesday, March 15, the day Rebecca and I got engaged. The previous couple of months had proven to both of us that we were going to be together for the rest of our lives and that it was only a matter of time before we became engaged. I had already asked her to marry me, but — being gun-shy from her past experiences with marriage — she answered she would think about it and would say yes when she felt comfortable with the idea of being married again. On the evening of the 15th, Rebecca cautiously said to me, "Maybe it's time for us to get engaged."

Never one to let an opportunity go by, I said, "Great, let's go get the ring right now."

She had not expected such a quick reaction, but said, haltingly, "Well, OK." We got in my car and drove the few blocks to a nearby Mall, went to a Helzberg Jewelry Store, and picked out and bought her engagement and wedding rings. When we got to her house, to make it official, I again asked her to marry me and she said, "Yes," but added, "The next time I agree to something, I'll know you not joking around about it."

Wednesday, March 16, 1994: Sam Venneri

Since Sam was dragging his feet, I wrote him a letter on the 16th to try to light a fire under him. A month later, I got a letter dated April 18, 1994 from Gregory Reck of Code C that, while not eliminating the possibility of Code C support for Lunar Prospector, poured cold water on the idea.

Tuesday, March 22, 1994: Letter to Goldin

However, well before I got the reply from Code C, and hoping to put some pressure on Sam to respond positively, I wrote Goldin a letter on March 22. I first thanked him for giving us the opportunity to meet with him in January and then asked him very politely to get Sam and Code C to fund Lunar Prospector. However, the April 18 reply from Reck ended that hope.

Spring 1994: Congressman Tom Delay

Since my efforts with Code C had gone nowhere, despite Goldin's seemingly wanting the mission to fly, I decided to again try to get some political pressure applied to NASA on behalf of Lunar Prospector. Israel suggested I approach the powerful Texas Congressman, Tom Delay. I called his Houston office and easily got an appointment set up.

The day of the meeting, Mick Culp and I took off to drive to Delay's office, but I had gotten the directions all screwed up and ended up driving all over the place before finally landing in the right spot. As a result, we were nearly half an hour late and when we went into his waiting room, a couple of other people were there waiting to see Tom. They seemed quite annoyed when Mick and I were ushered into Tom's office ahead of them. I apologized to Tom for being late and then, talking as fast as I could to make up for our tardiness, I explained to Tom all about Lunar Prospector and my desperate need for his political help. Tom seemed genuinely impressed with what we were trying to do and promised to do what he could to help, but whatever he did, it made no difference as far as I could tell.

June and Most of July 1994

After trying unsuccessfully to get Code C and Tom Delay to do something about Lunar Prospector, I was beginning to think that Lunar Prospector had about reached the end of its rope. There just didn't seem to be any way to get the mission funded — except via a Discovery Proposal and I had no hope at all that would yield the desired result, given Code S's hostility towards the mission. As the summer of 1994 marched on, I was busy helping MAUDEE get ready for its Discovery Proposal effort and looking for a miracle.

During the summer, John and Barbara Gruener and their kids had gone to Green Bay, WI, to visit Barb's relatives. While there, John met George French who owns an advertising agency where Barb's brother worked. That meeting occurred because George is a space enthusiast, and since John works in the space program, John's brother-in-law thought George would like to meet John. During their conversations, John told George about Lunar Prospector and me and said we (George and I) should get acquainted. When John got back to Houston from their vacation and told me about George, I gave him a call.

We had a nice conversation and George told me about his work with the lunar resource utilization group at the University of Wisconsin at Madison and the fact that they were going to put in a Discovery proposal for a lunar rover that would do lunar resource utilization experimentation. He also told me about the educational program he was developing as part of the proposal. I also learned that George was well connected in the Republican Party, had access to Congressman Sensenbrenner who was on the House Space Science Committee, was a founder and official of the Aerospace States Association and had many other important contacts in the space business. Clearly, George was a good guy to know. I told him more about Lunar Prospector and George was very interested in what I was doing and wanted to help in any way he could. By the time we finished talking, we had begun a personal friendship that would soon prove to be mutually beneficial.

Chapter 1-14
"What have you got to lose?"

The Last Thursday or Friday of July 1994:
Bret Drake's Critical Question

Since I did not have a lot to do at LESC, I went over to the Lunar/Mars Exploration Office at JSC about once a week to see what my old co-workers were up to. Bret Drake, who had worked in our group at Lockheed, had become a NASA employee sometime earlier and was a member of the University of Arizona/JSC Team that was going to propose a full up Lunar Polar Orbiter with Boeing as their Industry Partner. That Team, led by Bill Boynton of the University of Arizona, was proposing the same orbiter Boeing had proposed for the Lunar Resource Mapper in the spring of 1992, before the program and the SEI were canceled. Since Boeing had already won once with that orbiter, they figured they had an excellent chance to win again.

Bret brought me up to date on their efforts and he asked me if I was going to submit a Lunar Prospector Proposal and I said, "No, what's the use? Code S would never in a million years select Lunar Prospector." I reminded Bret of all the rejections I had already had from Code S. Then I said, as I had said so many times during the previous year, "If I put in a proposal, Code S would not even look at it before they throw it in the wastepaper basket. If they didn't and if the proposals were evaluated outside of NASA and not by their good-old-boy review teams, Lunar Prospector would win hands down, but that will never happen. Besides, LEI doesn't have the resources to write a competitive proposal and I don't trust LMSC to do Lunar Prospector the way it needs to be done if I did ask them to be my Industry Partner."

Then Bret asked the critical question, "*Well, you've tried everything else, what have you got to lose?*"

I will be forever grateful to Bret for that simple question, for which I really didn't have an answer, so I said, "Well, maybe you're right, I'll think about it," and I did.

As I drove back to Lockheed, I turned Bret's question over and over in my mind and decided in the few minutes it took to get to Lockheed that I didn't have anything to lose, except maybe, just maybe, a chance to get Lunar Prospector to the Moon. Also, since Gus and LMSC had previously agreed to do Lunar Prospector my-way and not their-way, back when Goldin had asked Tellep and LMSC to do Lunar Prospector, I decided LMSC would probably let me do it my-way in the Discovery Program and not interfere (too much) with my plans.

As soon as I got back to Lockheed, I called Dom and told him what I was thinking, and Dom agreed wholeheartedly and with great enthusiasm. He said he would go see Gus and Frank right away and call me right back with their reaction to Lockheed becoming my Industry Partner in a Discovery Proposal.

Dom called back about a half an hour later and said Gus was supportive of the idea, but we would have to agree on the details and then present our case to the LMSC New Business Council at their next meeting that was on August 22. Further, Dom said I should hop on the next plane and get my tail out to Sunnyvale to discuss the details with Gus and Frank and to prepare for the new Business Council Meeting. I immediately started setting up my travel plans to fly to California on Sunday, July 31.

I then found Tom Polette and told him what I was up to and asked him if he wanted to be my Deputy in the proposal and go to Sunnyvale for the three or four years that the project would take if we somehow won. Tom said, "Yes, I would."

After that, I called Wayne Stevens to tell him about my plans to propose Lunar Prospector to Discovery and to discuss LEI's purchasing the OMNI Spacecraft Design. Though I had asked him about getting a license to use the design back in June of 1992, I decided it would be simplest if LEI owned the design when I was trying to deal with LMSC and NASA/Discovery. I also wanted OMNI to get a reasonable amount of money for their design work (the $65,000 that SSI had paid OMNI was way below the value of the design). Thus I suggested LEI (meaning me) would pay $1 for the design for use in the proposal and if we won, then OMNI would get another $99,999. That way, they would get a grand total of $165,000 for their work, still a lot less than such a design is worth, but a lot better than a poke in the eye with a sharp stick. Wayne was most agreeable with that idea, but wanted to add if the proposal lost, the ownership of the design would revert back to OMNI and that was fine with me.

I also wanted to know if Mike Chobotov, Asif, or he (Wayne) could or would want to work on the project if we were selected. That would mean they would have to work for LMSC, but, like me, that would be the price they would have to pay to see their work come to fruition. Since Mike was in Santa Rosa, CA (just north of San Francisco), starting up his own little engineering company, Wayne thought he might just want to be a consultant. Since Wayne was in Boston, the best he could do was to be a consultant, but it was possible that Asif would want to work on Lunar Prospector at LMSC and Wayne said he would talk to him about that.

Then I called Gregg. Though SSI was out of the picture and had been since the Mike Griffin/SEI fiasco, I knew that without Gregg (as much as he annoyed Preston and me at times) there would be no Lunar Prospector and hence no proposal. Out of respect and gratitude for all he had given the project (e.g., his job at SSI), I wanted Gregg to know I was making one last gigantic effort to make all of our efforts finally pay off.

Then I called a meeting of the remaining few faithful of LEI. I told them what was up and asked if they had any objections. After all, if I did propose with Lockheed, none of them, except Tom, would be part of the mission if we won. As I expected, that was fine with them. Certainly they all wanted to continue working on the mission, but if the only chance for success was my going with LMSC and leaving them behind, so be it. If Lunar Prospector were successful, then all their work would not have been in vain. With that, we had our last group LEI meeting, closing a chapter that had lasted five years, during which we had accomplished a great deal and during which they had all stuck by me through all the numerous ups and downs the project had endured.

Finally, I called all my Science Team guys to let them know I was going to propose to Discovery and to make sure that they were willing to be part of the proposal.

When I called Bob Lin, he certainly wanted to be in on the proposal and we talked about Mario Acuña and some French colleagues. While Mario had been willing to build the MAG and common electronics without being on the Science Team when we were doing Lunar Prospector as a private venture, Bob thought Mario would want to be a Co-I in the proposal. I asked Bob to see what Mario wanted to do and if he wanted to be a Co-I, that was OK by me. Then Bob pointed out that some French teammates had actually built some of the electronic boards that were in the Mars Observer MAG/ER electronics, and asked if I was willing to add them to the MAG/ER Team — a possibility according to the Discovery rules. However, I wanted to keep the Lunar Prospector Science Team as small as possible and I didn't like the complication of having international team members — it was bad enough dealing with one national agency, let alone two,

so I said, "No, unless there is no way we can build the electronics without the French."
Bob assured me Mario could do the whole package without the French, so that was that.

I called Bill Sjogren to see if he wanted to be in the proposal. Bill exclaimed, "Oh
no, I just signed an agreement with Bill Boynton to be on his Lunar Orbiter Team (the
same one that Bret Drake was on) and according to the agreement I can't be on any
other proposal."

I was disappointed and very surprised that Boynton would require such a thing.
There were going to be numerous proposals submitted to Discovery and since there
are not a large number of lunar and planetary scientists in the USA, or in the world,
most scientists were going to be asked to be on several proposals, otherwise there just
wouldn't be enough scientists to go around. That also meant most scientists had a fair
chance of being on the winning proposal(s) — just like buying more than one lottery
ticket. The fact that Boynton had made his Co-Is sign an exclusive contract was really
dirty pool and hurt the scientists involved, but, of course, increased Boynton's chances
of winning by eliminating some possible proposals or forcing other PIs to have less
qualified Co-Is. Bill said he would check with the JPL lawyers to see if he could be on
my team, too, but if not, Bill suggested that his protégé, Alex Konopliv, could do the
DGE for me. Bill said he would get back to me on both issues. When he did, he said
the lawyers said he was screwed and Alex was willing to be on my team.

Having learned from Bill Sjogren about Boynton's dirty trick, I called Bill Feldman
immediately to see if Boynton had snatched him too. When I asked Bill, he said, "Yes,
Bill (Boynton) asked me to be on his team and I said I would, but when he said I had
to sign the exclusive agreement I said no. I told him that I didn't know if you were going
to propose or not, but if you did, I would be on your team since we had worked together so long on Lunar Prospector."

Boy, was I relieved, for without Bill, I had no mission. Then Bill added, "When I told
Bill (Boynton) that, he said he still wanted me on his team, but I didn't have to sign the
agreement, and I said OK." Boynton was playing both ends against the middle — if he got
to someone he needed as a Co-I first, he or she had to sign the exclusive agreement; but
if some other PI got to that Co-I first, then he or she didn't have to sign the exclusive agreement to be on Bill's team. My opinion of Bill Boynton sunk considerably at that point.

With that done, I had my Science Team Co-Is; Bob Lin, Lon Hood, and Mario
Acuña for the MAG/ER, Bill Feldman (and me) for the GRS, NS, and APS, and Alex Kono-
pliv for the DGE. Now all I needed was for Gus and LMSC to agree to be my Industry
Partner.

Sunday, July 31, through Thursday, August 4, 1994: Agreement with Gus

I flew to California on Sunday afternoon the 31st and checked into the good old
Maple Tree Inn (by that time I was practically a resident there).

Monday morning I went to Lockheed and met with Gus, Frank, and Dom. Gus
was quite interested in the idea of our proposing, though Frank came across as having
reservations about it or even being opposed to it, but he never came right out and said
so. Gus had several issues he wanted to get agreement on, as did I, before we would
proceed. Those issues were mostly related to the rules about how Discovery Missions
were to be set up and those rules were as follows:

First, the management of the project was the sole responsibility of the PI and the
PI could be from a university, a private institute, or an aerospace company.

Second, the PI's Mission Team consisted of his Science Team, an Industry Partner that would build the hardware, and, if the PI wanted one, a NASA Center Partner, but the latter was not mandatory

Third, the PI's home institution would have the main contract with NASA, the PI would run the project from his home institution, and the Science Team members, the Industry Partner and, if he had one, the NASA Center Partner would work on the project as sub-contractors.

The related issues Gus wanted to resolve were as follows:

First, Gus insisted I lead the effort as a Lockheed employee, i.e., as an Industry PI, and not as a LEI Institute PI. As an Industry PI, Lockheed would be my home institute and would have the main contract (in effect, I would be working for the company I had hired to build my spacecraft under my direction). I had expected that and saw no way around it, since LEI had neither the staff nor the means to run such an effort, and I said, "Sure."

Second, I was to kill LEI (Gus wanted no trace of the past — Lunar Prospector was to be an all Lockheed show and Lockheed was to get all the credit). I again agreed (but I did not intend to carry through with that, since I did not trust Gus or Lockheed and I needed LEI as a backup).

Third, Gus insisted I choose the NASA/Ames Research Center as my NASA Center Partner. Ames is just across the street from LMSC and LMSC wanted to get brownie points with NASA/Ames to keep in their good graces — and hence those of NASA Headquarters. I had a lot of heartburn about that. I had had no intention of having a NASA Center Partner. As far as I was concerned, I wanted as little involvement with NASA, in any form, as possible, since I firmly believed NASA would only screw up the mission. I aired my concerns and Gus said, "Take Ames or forget the proposal." There was to be no discussion on that point, so I reluctantly agreed.

Fourth, I could do my job, as either an LESC or an LMSC employee, whichever way would work best. A point that I would have to discuss with LESC when I got back there.

We got to my issues, which were:

First, we would use the OMNI design and do the project the way I had planned it; that was fine with Gus.

Second, we would pay OMNI the $99,999 so I (LEI) would own the Spacecraft Design and then I would donate the Design to Lockheed as my part of the deal. Gus agreed about the $99,999 and was very happy about my giving the Design to Lockheed.

Third, Tom would be my Deputy and be written into the proposal. That was fine with Gus; he didn't care who I brought with me, just as long as it was only one or two people.

Fourth, we would bring on some of the OMNI engineers as consultants or as employees since they designed the spacecraft. Gus agreed, but was not too happy with that idea.

We had ironed out how we were going to proceed and then Gus, Frank, Dom, and I spent the next two days deciding how to structure our presentation to the New Business Meeting. As expected, Gus would introduce the idea and me. Then I would discuss the science, the mission, and the spacecraft, and Dom would discuss our budget, organization, and schedule.

Regarding Ames's participation as my NASA Center Partner, Gus had already talked to his good friend and ex-protégé, Jeff Briggs, who had been exiled from Headquarters to Ames. Jeff is a very competent lunar and planetary scientist and generally nice guy, and we had known each other for years and were both PIs on Viking; Jeff was a PI on the Orbiter Camera Team. As a Viking Scientist, Jeff had become acquainted with Gus and when Viking was over, Gus asked Jeff to join his staff at Headquarters as his protégé, and Jeff did and did a very competent job there. Later, after Gus had retired from NASA and took a managerial role at LMSC, Jeff fell into disfavor at Headquarters (probably because he is competent) and was, literally, exiled to Ames where he had a very small office in a back hallway and was given unimportant jobs to do. When Gus was considering whether to support my Discovery Proposal effort, he went to see Jeff to determine if Ames would want to be part of the team, and Jeff said it probably would.

After our discussions were over and Gus and I were in agreement, we went over to see Jeff. While Jeff was supportive of Lunar Prospector and me, he was all too aware of his lowly status at Ames and said we would have to talk to someone else and suggested a certain Mr. Scott Hubbard, who was the Acting Chief of the Space Projects Division. We went to meet and talk with Scott.

I explained the science and engineering goals of Lunar Prospector to Scott and gave him copies of some of my documents. We also discussed Lunar Prospector's programmatic goals and those of the Discovery Program and Scott and I seemed to be on the same wavelength on all of the programmatic issues. In the end, Scott was impressed with Lunar Prospector and felt Ames should and would become my NASA Center Partner.

As it turned out, the Discovery AO was released (several months late) while I was at LMSC. The official release date was Thursday, August 4, but it was sent out with a cover letter on July 28. Thus, we got our copies and began to try to understand it — always a difficult task, trying to figure out what NASA wants from a poorly written and often contradictory AO.

Several things were clear; First, a Notice of Intent (to propose) was due at NASA on September 2, 1994; second, a Pre-proposal Conference was being held in late August at the Crystal Gateway Marriott in Arlington, VA; third, the proposals were due in Houston at the Lunar and Planetary Institute on Friday, October 21, 1994 at 4:30 PM; and fourth, NASA's target for announcing their selection was January 1995. However, it was the fifth thing that was most encouraging and that was *the purpose of the AO* — stated as follows: "This announcement solicits proposals for the third, and possibly fourth, Discovery Missions. These proposals must be for complete missions from project initiation (either Phase A, Phase B, or Phase C/D) through operations (Phase E) … NASA will select several proposals which will be subject to competitive down selection at the end of each phase." So far so good, but the last sentence in that paragraph was just what I was looking for — and it read, *"In addition, NASA may select a small mission (one with total mission costs less than $150 million) to proceed directly to launch (down selection is waived), if such a mission is proposed which is sufficiently well defined to allow a launch near the end of 1998"* (the italics are mine). At that point, we believed Lunar Prospector would cost under $50 million and would be ready for launch by June of 1997. The door was open for us to be selected directly for launch and we were going to go for the gold!

Just as important to me was the definition of the PI's responsibility and it was, *"The PI is expected to be the central figure in each Discovery mission, with full responsibility for all aspects of the mission* (the italics are mine)." All of a sudden, things were getting exciting and I began to see a very bright light at the end of the tunnel.

In addition to the above information, the AO clearly defined the programmatic goals of the program, three of which were essentially identical to those we had had for Lunar Prospector from its inception. Those common goals were: Perform high quality science, pursue innovative ways of managing and doing missions, and enhance public awareness and education. The only programmatic goal that Discovery had that we didn't have was to encourage the use and transfer of new technology — the technological philosophy behind Lunar Prospector was to use inexpensive, flight proven, reliable hardware. We would have to add some new technology hardware to the spacecraft to qualify for the Discovery Program, a requirement that made no sense if mission were to be "Faster, Better, Cheaper," as the mantra for Discovery required.

One thing that puzzled me was Gus and Frank kept trying to steer me away from having Dom be my Project Manager, and they kept trying to get me to accept someone else who I hardly knew, but thought was a dunce. Since I knew, respected, and trusted Dom, and since he was anti-establishment (would fight the system and would do everything that was necessary to get the job done right), I fully intended to have Dom be my Project Manager, and kept countering Gus and Frank's suggestions that I do otherwise. In the end, Dom was my Project Manager.

Having finished what I could do on that trip, I flew home on Thursday, August 4, feeling very good about everything and not even worrying about how NASA would treat our Lunar Prospector proposal. Somehow, I thought everything was finally going to work out OK and I wouldn't get the rug pulled out from under me for the nth time.

Friday, August 5, through Saturday, August 20, 1994:
Prepared for the New Business Council Meeting

Once back in Houston, I had two things to do. First, I set up a meeting with LESC President Dick Parten to see if he wanted me to stay an LESC employee or just become a LMSC employee. If I stayed at LESC, LESC would have the main contract and LMSC would be a subcontractor to LESC and me. That would have great advantages for both LESC and me. Thus, I was greatly surprised when Parten showed no interest in my running Lunar Prospector form LESC and told me to join the LMSC staff. In fact, Dick seemed hostile to my doing Lunar Prospector and that was even more surprising since he had so enthusiastically supported me and the project back in the summer of 1992. I had no idea why he had changed his mind so dramatically, but he did — and that was too bad.

Second, I began to prepare my presentation for the New Business Council Meeting. Dom and I discussed our presentations via phone and faxed the viewgraphs back and forth until we (Gus, Frank, Dom, and I) all thought we had the right pitch to get the New Business Council to OK our doing the proposal.

Sunday, August 21, through Friday, August 26, 1994:
The Decision to Propose

I flew to California on Sunday, August 21 to give the pitch to the New Business Council Monday morning, the 22nd. Gus, Frank, Dom, and I went to the meeting room where ten to twelve top LMSC managers were waiting. The Council was led by LMSC President Sam Araki, who was about to retire and frankly didn't seem to give a damn about what was going on. The only people I knew on the Council were Executive Vice-President Mel Brashears and Vice-President Arnie Aldrich, the rest were complete strangers.

As planned, Gus introduced Lunar Prospector, and discussed the fact that he had given me support over the years and explained how much I had done with the project. Then he gave me the floor. In addition to giving my standard pitch about the history, science, spacecraft, and Mission Profile, I pointed out, if LMSC supported my effort, I would be turning over the Spacecraft Design to the company and I would be using a LLV2 launch to get Lunar Prospector to the Moon. Further, I was asking LMSC to set up the Lunar Prospector Command and Control Center at LMSC in Sunnyvale and to set up the world-wide Lunar Prospector Tracking Network of at least three 6 m antennas. I said, "If you did all that, then LMSC would have a complete turnkey, totally in-house capability to do follow-on lunar missions and simple orbital missions for the Earth, Mars, Venus, and Near-Earth asteroids." The prospect of follow-on business was attractive to all of them. Then Dom went through the budget (estimated at $50 million), the schedule (22 month C/D), and the organization we needed to do the job.

When we were done, Mel Brashears was enthusiastically behind us, Arnie was supportive and made the comment, "For you guys to succeed on such a short schedule and for so little money, Lockheed is going to have to give you all the support you need and the best engineers we have," and everyone else agreed. Nevertheless, Sam Araki still didn't give a damn either way and the rest of them seemed neutral as to whether LMSC should support my effort and become my Industry Partner. As such, it was Mel who saved the day by saying Lunar Prospector was a great mission and should result in a lot of good PR and follow-on business for Lockheed. He said further that I was the type of forward thinking person LMSC needed in the new era of smaller, cheaper missions that were the future of the space business. With that, everyone more or less agreed that Lockheed would support my proposal effort.

Sam asked Gus if he had any money left in his budget for such an effort and Gus replied that he still had $100,000. I was taken aback — a full proposal effort would cost upwards of $1 million. To be sure, I already had the OMNI Spacecraft Design, the Mission Profile, the MRD, MOD, and a lot of other stuff ready to go, but I still expected the effort would cost at least $300,000. Sam said, "That's fine, that will do." So much for the idea, "Lockheed is going to have to give you all the support you need," and we hadn't even gotten out of the room yet! Disappointed as I was about the relatively small amount of money I was going to get to do the proposal, Lockheed had at least bought into the idea (thanks largely to Mel) and I was one step closer to my goal of getting Lunar Prospector to the Moon — I hoped.

After the New Business meeting was over, Dom and I spent the rest of the day and the next one preparing for the proposal effort. We also went over to see Scott to tell him Lockheed was going to support the proposal and to find out if Ames was going to join us. The answer about Ames's participation was, "Yes."

Then there was the question about who I wanted to lead the Ames's part of the effort. Scott said that there were several people who could do the job, but since I knew no one at Ames except Jeff, who was out of the picture, and since Scott and I seemed to agree on everything, I asked him if he wanted the job and he answered, "Yes, if that's what you want?"

I answered, "Sure, why waste time looking for someone else? If you want to do it, that's fine with me."

I had a second question for Scott. Since Mario had joined the MAG/ER part of the Science Team, there were more MAG/ER guys (three) than Spectrometer guys (two) and since the GRS and NS were the top priority instruments, adding Scott to the Spectrometer Group would balance the Science Team. Since Scott had a BS in physics and had had some experience with gamma-ray spectrometers, I had thought about asking him to be on the Spectrometer part of the team, both to balance the Team and for NASA political reasons. When I asked Scott if he also wanted to be on the Science Team, he said, "Yes."

Finally, we discussed other ways Ames and Ames personnel could support the project, e.g., using Ames's Pioneer Mission Control Center as the Lunar Prospector Mission Control Center, and having some of the Ames technical personnel support the mission. Scott and I ended up with a list of such possibilities that would become part of the proposal. With that, the Ames part of the deal was sealed.

On Wednesday the 24th, Frank, Dom, and I flew to Michigan for a MAUDEE meeting and then we expected to fly on to DC for the Pre-proposal Conference across the river in Arlington. However, we still had one more hurdle to get over before we could proceed with the proposal. Because the MAUDEE Team had made such a stink about Dom's realistic revisions of both the MAUDEE budget and engineering that Pete Williams had so badly messed up, Lockheed was very sensitive about doing anything that might further upset Michigan, especially putting in a competitive proposal that might easily win over MAUDEE. Gus insisted I had to get Tim Killeen's OK before I could propose.

As soon as we arrived, Dom, Frank, and I sat down with Tim and I explained that I had asked Lockheed to support my doing a Lunar Prospector Proposal, but that we would only proceed with the effort if he had no objections. Clearly, I put Tim between a rock and a hard place. If he said yes, Tim knew more than enough about Lunar Prospector and me to know I had an excellent chance of winning, possibly at MAUDEE's expense. If he said no, then he would be violating the unofficial code between scientists that is supposed to stop us from stabbing each other in the back (but which often does not succeed in doing so — remember Bill Boynton's exclusivity agreements?). As I expected, Tim did the correct and gentlemanly thing and said he had no objection to my putting in a proposal. He added, "If MAUDEE doesn't win the first slot, there is no one I would rather see win it than you, Alan." His gracious statement touched me.

We went to the MAUDEE meeting, but before we did Dom and I decided not to go on to the Pre-proposal Conference. Rather, we would finish up the MAUDEE meeting and then head straight home. Frank was going to the Conference anyway and therefore he could fill us in on what went on there. Also, since Dom and I knew exactly what we had to do, we felt the Conference would only be a waste of precious time, given we had just over eight weeks to do the Proposal. We finished up the MAUDEE meeting on the 25th and I flew back to Houston on Friday, August 26 and prepared to fly right back to California on Sunday to start work on the proposal.

Chapter 1-15
The Proposal

Sunday, August 28, through Wednesday, September 14, 1994: Getting Started

I flew out to California on Sunday, August 28, and checked into the Maple Tree Inn for an extended period of nearly eight weeks — a period that was filled with intense activity and that was the single most satisfying period of my entire life, in terms of what I accomplished and the extremely high levels of both mental and physical stamina that were required to accomplish it. Once I got started on the proposal, I lived on very little sleep, high levels of adrenaline my body generates when I am pushing myself to my limits, and sheer willpower. The willpower was generated by my strong desire to finally get Lunar Prospector to the Moon. Because of the long work days and short sleep periods, most of the eight weeks is a mish-mash of memories, with a few events that stand out in my mind.

I was approaching the ripe old age of 56 when I started the proposal (and I was 56 when it was finished), and, like many older people, I wake up very early, usually by 4:00 AM. That gave me the advantage of getting to work three or four hours before most of the other Lockheed employees, so I had time to get some serious work done before all the interruptions of a normal workday began. Monday morning, I was up and ready to go to Lockheed by about 4:30. During my previous stays at the Maple Tree Inn, I had found a local donut shop where I could get a donut or sweet roll and a coke (the real breakfast of champions) on the way to LMSC, so I stopped there and fortified myself for the day ahead.

Since I had already been assigned a cubicle in Building 107 and someone had set up a Mac PC there, I was ready to roll when I entered the nearly empty building (only the cleaning crew was there). I stashed the Lunar Prospector Documents and the OMNI Spacecraft Design Study Documents I had brought along in a bookshelf. Then got started on the tasks of carefully reading the AO to figure out exactly what was supposed to be in the Proposal and laying out its basic structure, tasks that took a couple of days.

The Proposal was to be done in three volumes. Volume I, the "Executive Summary," was limited to five pages, and was to have a "Fact Sheet" about the mission. Volume I was to be attached to the front of both Volumes II and III. Volume II was to give the "Science and Technical Approach" and was limited to 75 pages, including no more than five foldout pages, and was to have all the signature pages. Volume III was to be the "Cost and Management Plan" and was also limited to 75 pages. One could have as many appendices as one wanted, but the reviewers were under no obligation to read or consider them in their evaluation of the proposal. There were numerous other instructions regarding page size, font type and size, etc., all of which had to be religiously followed or your proposal could be rejected out of hand.

Volume I and the Fact Sheet couldn't be done until Volumes II and III were finished, and Volume III, the Cost and Management Sections, was Dom's domain. My job was to do Volume II and by mid-week, I started that major task using all the Lunar Prospector materials we had developed during the previous six years.

The first major section of Volume II was the *Science Section* and was to have four main parts, *Science Goals and Objectives, Measurement Objectives and Anticipated*

Data, Instruments, and the *Science Team.* I called my Co-Is and asked them to write up and send me their biographies, the technical descriptions of their instruments, and their data handling procedures. Then I got busy writing the sections on the *Science Goals* and the *Measurements and Data.* I had what I thought were good first drafts of those sections in a couple of days and sent them off to my Co-Is for their comments.

Lon Hood called me a day or so later and suggested he rewrite the *Science Goals* part since, having served on the LExSWG and other NASA science advisory boards, he was well acquainted with the way NASA expects to have science goals described. That was just fine with me. Lon is a much better writer than I am, and, as an accepted member of the NASA science establishment, he is more in tune with the NASA mass psyche than I am. He could clearly do a much better job on *Science Goals* than I could. Also, Lon's writing the *Science Goals* would save me a lot of time and work, which was very good, since I had little of the former and a lot of the latter.

I also got started on the appendices since I had the MOD, MRD, Mission Profile, Controller's Training Manual, the OMNI Design Study, newspaper clippings, letters of support, and the like, all of which were important to show the maturity of the project. All in all, we ended up with nine appendices to Volume II. However, though Dom had been ecstatic about the quality and quantity of the backup material I had, he said the MRD and MOD needed to be broken up into different documents that corresponded more closely to how NASA did its documents. I didn't see the sense in that; Dom originally had nothing but praise for the MRD and MOD the way they were, so why take the time to change them around? I had seen that behavior in Dom when I had worked with him on other proposals and on MAUDEE, and I could never figure out why he would so often reverse himself for no apparent reason. But, since Dom had much more experience in spacecraft proposal writing than I did, since I wanted to win, and since Dom's changes wouldn't take too much time, I went ahead and put the various parts of the MOD and MRD in the appendices the way he wanted.

During the first couple of weeks of the proposal effort, my daily routine started with my getting to work between 4:00 and 5:00 AM. During the early morning quiet period, I wrote on the proposal until other employees arrived and I could ask them questions, call my Co-Is, or go over to Ames to talk with Scott about administrative issues or about Ames mission support and personnel issues and the like. Once that started, I got little writing done until evening when Lockheed had again cleared out. Then I would again work undisturbed until 9:00 or 10:00, after which I went back to the Maple Tree Inn for five or six hours of sleep. Breakfast was always a donut or the like and a coke purchased on the way to Lockheed and eaten at my desk. Lunch was either a quick bite in the little cafeteria in building 107 or Francisco Andolz, Richard Lynch, and I would go to a nearby McDonald's, Taco Bell, or Pizza Hut. Dinner was sometimes McDonald's, but usually I went to Marie Callenders Restaurant or the Black Angus Restaurant that are both within a half a block of the Maple Tree Inn, or to the Hofbrau Haus that is a couple of miles away from the Maple Tree Inn.

Except for the few hours of sleep, lunch and dinner were the only times I got to relax a bit during the normal work week, though, as time went on, food became more fuel than something to enjoy. I also worked on the weekends, though on either Saturday or Sunday morning I usually took a walk at a local mall, or, if work permitted, I drove up to a beautiful walkway along the Lower Crystal Spring Reservoir about 30 kilometers to the NW of Sunnyvale. The narrow, five-kilometer long lower reservoir and the 3 kilometer long upper reservoir fill a valley that was carved out by erosion along the San Andreas Fault Line. The walking/skating/biking path is on the American Plate and the Pacific Plate is on the west side of the middle of the reservoir. It was neat to walk along the boundary of those two major geological units that are slowly grinding past each other and periodically giving rise to the famous or infamous California earthquakes.

Francisco Andolz and Richard Lynch, my lunch companions and co-workers are two young engineers from Purdue who worked for Dom. Francisco is from Puerto Rico, quite bright, well schooled, has a laid back Latin temperament, and his background is in launch vehicles and spacecraft propulsion systems. Richard Lynch is a couple of years older than Francisco, less bright and less well schooled, but is more aggressive and more driven than Francisco. Richard's background is launch vehicles, celestial mechanics, and navigation. I had worked with both of them on earlier proposals and we were good friends, despite my being old enough to be their father. They were supposed to work with me about halftime, but they were off helping Dom try to save the MAUDEE proposal most of the time.

Because of the enormous pressure the University of Michigan was putting on LMSC to deliver what Pete Williams had erroneously promised at too low a cost, Lockheed was putting more resources, both personnel and dollars, on the MAUDEE proposal than I was given. Thus, Dom spent essentially all his time on the MAUDEE proposal, Francisco and Richard were spending at least three-quarters of their time on it, and I had what was left over. That was not critical during the first couple of weeks of work because they couldn't help with the science sections anyway, and I really only needed Richard to help me with two issues. First, I needed him to keep the dilapidated Mac PC running I was given to work on. Second, since he had already worked with the Lockheed Launch Vehicle crew that was developing the LLV series of launch vehicles, I wanted him to be my interface with them. Though I had the $22.5 million bid for a LLV2 launch from them back in August 1993 for the Unsolicited Proposal, that bid was for LEI, not LMSC, so I would have to get a new bid for the Proposal and I wanted Richard to help with that. Other than that, not having Richard and Francisco helping me halftime was not critical then; but later, when I was working on the engineering parts of the proposal, the lack of their being able to spend more time with me put me in a real bind.

Even during the first week or two, I was feeling the pressure of trying to do a full proposal nearly by myself, and because of the long work hours and lack of sleep, I was already tired and frequently frustrated. One source of the frustration was the piece-of-junk Mac I had. It had the habit of locking up or just doing what it wanted to do right in the middle of what I was writing. Since I habitually did not save the document I was working on as frequently as was prudent, I tended to lose a portion of what I had been typing every time the Mac decided to do its own thing. Then I would go and find Richard and he would get the Mac working again, leaving me with an uneasy feeling about how soon that snake would bite me again.

The worst example of a Mac snakebite occurred towards the end of the second week. My Co-Is had sent me their final corrections for all four parts of the *Science Section*. I had come in bright and early (well before 4:00) to put the finishing touches on that section in order to get it out of my hair until the final editing. It was close to 7:00 AM and I was almost done when the Mac crashed, taking with it what I thought was most of the previous three hours of work — since I was so tired, I couldn't remember if or when I had saved the document. It was too early for Richard to be in and I felt defeated and helpless — *how was I going to finish the Proposal in just six more weeks with no help and a piece of junk to work with?* If I were the type, I think I would have cried out of frustration and fatigue at that point; instead, I just got angry. *Had the Business Council not said just a few weeks earlier I would need the best that Lockheed had to offer if Lunar Prospector was to succeed? Had not everyone said Lunar Prospector was a winner? If so, then why in hell was I sitting there at seven in the morning with three hours of work down the drain?* Since there was nothing to do but to wait for Richard, I took a walk round Lockheed to relieve some of the frustration. As it turned out, after Richard got the Mac working again, I had saved the majority of the corrections and had to repeat only about an hour's worth of work, which was bad enough.

Another frustrating and time wasting event occurred during the second week of the effort. Soon after I had gotten started writing, I realized that I sorely needed some of my computer disks from Houston. I called Tom Polette and asked that he immediately Fed-Ex the needed disks to me, which Tom did with his usual efficiency. Nevertheless, the next day passed without the Fed-Ex package arriving. I called Tom to make sure he had gotten the package off on time for the next day's delivery and he said he had done it himself to make sure it had gotten on its way that day. He then gave me the tracking number and I called Fed-Ex to see where the package was, only to find out that it had been delivered to LMSC shipping rather than to me in Building 107, as was requested. I called shipping and they said they had never seen the package, but promised to look around since Fed-Ex insisted someone in shipping had signed for the package, but, of course, that someone was not there when I called. Well, time was a wasting and I was getting annoyed. Another day went by and still no package. Then I told Dom about the screw up and he got on the phone with shipping and raised holy hell as only Dom can do. Finally, after three or four days and after I had already spent the time necessary to recreate what I had on the disks, shipping found the missing package in another building! Why in hell it was not even delivered to the correct building was more than I could fathom. I was ticked-off, frustrated, tired, and even more convinced that Lockheed was full of idiots.

Having more or less finished the *Science Section* by the end of the second week, I got seriously started on the *Technical Approach Section*. That section was to consist of eight parts: *Mission Design* (launch, trajectory, ΔV budget, mission profile, etc.); *Flight System* (the spacecraft); *Payload Integration*; *Manufacturing, Integration, and Test*; *Ground* (tracking, communications and mission control center) *and Data*; *Mission Operations*; *Product Assurance and Safety*; and *Phase A/B Preliminary Analysis and Definition Study Plans*. I had gone over the *Technical Approach* Section requirements with a fine-toothed comb during the first couple of days of the effort and knew I would need help in a few of those areas.

First and foremost, I needed help doing the *Ground* segment. Early on, I told Dom I needed someone with a lot of experience in that area and Dom suggested that we get Tim Bridges. Tim had just retired from Lockheed and was willing to do part time work on various projects. He had a lot of the needed experience and had been involved with the ground segment of some of the Pioneer Missions that were run by Ames. I had worked with Tim during my previous stints at LMSC and liked him a lot, so I was pleased with Dom's suggestion. Also, as a retiree, Tim wouldn't cost a lot of money, so his working with me would not seriously impact my small budget. Dom and I asked Gus if we could bring Tim on part-time and Gus agreed and started the necessary paperwork. Dom called Tim and Tim said he would like to work on the proposal and was ready to start right then — and he did. As I was doing the *Science Section*, Tim was busy finding and costing a tracking system for us. Within a few days he found a company that built turnkey tracking stations with 6 m dishes that could serve our tracking needs and each cost about $1 million. Tim was off to the races on the tracking system and then got stopped dead in his tracks.

Gus found out that Tim was already working with us even though the paperwork had not yet gotten through the system and that ticked Gus off. Typically (as was absolutely necessary, given our time limitations), Dom had ignored standard procedures (one reason I liked Dom) and that always irked Lockheed and Gus (hence, one of the many reasons why Dom is not popular at LMSC). Gus said, "If you guys can't follow procedures, I'm not going to hire Tim." I was astounded that Gus would cut the support I desperately needed and jeopardize the Proposal effort just because he got mad at Dom and me — but he did. That left me frustrated and again wondering how in hell I was going to get the Proposal done. Such nonsense only added to my sense of urgency and my state of fatigue (about a wasted week later, Gus reversed his dumb decision and hired Tim).

In addition to needing Tim's help on the *Ground* segment, I needed major support in the part on *Manufacturing, Integration and Test*, as well as the part on *Product Assurance and Safety*. Also, since we had to use some new technology in the spacecraft to be in compliance with the proposal requirements, we had to modify the OMNI design. Dom had suggested that we use graphite epoxy, a new technology that was being pioneered by LMSC, to build the spacecraft's structure instead of aluminum as OMNI had planned. That meant redesigning the basic load bearing structure of the spacecraft, so I would need help there. Dom also suggested we use the new nickel-hydrogen battery utilized by the Clementine Mission, rather than a standard, flight proven nickel-cadmium battery. In addition to the new technology changes to the OMNI design, neither Dom nor I (nor anyone else except OMNI) liked the OMNI science boom design, so we began to explore what Lockheed had to offer in that area. Finally, I needed a complete check of the thermal properties of the spacecraft, given the number of changes we had to make to the OMNI design. As I got seriously started on the Technical Approach Section of the Proposal, I relied on Dom to find bits and pieces of support in several key engineering areas, a task that Dom is excellent at.

Also, Dom thought it would be a good idea to introduce the *Technical Approach* section with a short blurb about where we were in the development of Lunar Prospector and how Lockheed was going to carry out the rest of the project. Given that I had no idea of how LMSC actually worked and since what was needed was NASA/Lockheed bureaucratic gobbledygook, Dom asked Bob Goldin to write it. Bob, another working Lockheed retiree, a great guy, and a great engineer with extensive experience, was Dom's closest associate. Like Tim Bridges, I knew Bob from my earlier work in Sunnyvale and had a great deal of respect for him. As Bob was writing the introduction, I got started on the serious stuff.

The first part — the *Mission Design* — was straightforward and had been defined in great detail for years, so it didn't take long to finish. Among other things, that part was to contain a short description of the Mission Profile. I, of course, had a completely defined, mature Mission Profile. I described its major phases in the text and added the entire Mission Profile as an appendix, since I wanted to demonstrate fully how mature the entire Lunar Prospector Mission was.

By that time, nearly two and a half weeks had gone by and as preplanned, Rebecca was getting ready to wing her way from Texas to California for a little R&R and some preliminary house hunting — just in case we won.

Thursday, September 15, to Monday, September 19, 1994: Rebecca's Visit

Rebecca arrived at the San Francisco Airport at mid-day on Thursday and I drove up there to get her. Tired as I was, seeing her and being with her after two and a half weeks did a lot to boost my state of being. We drove down to Sunnyvale, put her luggage in the Maple Tree Inn, had a late lunch and then drove to Lockheed where I continued working that afternoon. Because I had so little help working on the proposal, I didn't have any time to do anything with her Friday, so Rebecca stayed at the Maple Tree to read and relax, her two favorite pastimes.

However, I took Saturday and Sunday off, first to look around the area to find a place where we might want to live and second so we could have some fun together. Long before Rebecca came, I had asked Dom where we might look for a place to live. As country bumpkins, neither Rebecca nor I wanted to live in the metropolitan area. I asked Dom if there was some place not too far away that was small-town or rural and he suggested Morgan Hill, a small community about 50 kilometers south of Sunnyvale, that was fast becoming a bedroom community for the San Jose and Sunnyvale area. Not too bright and early Saturday morning, Rebecca and I drove down Highway 101 to look around Morgan Hill.

We found a real estate lady at Coldwell Banker and asked some questions about buying a house. She said she could show us some properties after lunch in order to give us an idea about the costs and what was available, so we arranged to meet after lunch.

Rebecca and I then drove around a little to get a feel for the town and stopped for lunch. When we were finished and ready to go, we found that the car had broken down! I called Hertz and asked for a replacement and they said it would take about an hour. I called the real estate lady and told her about our predicament and we reset our meeting time.

When we finally got together, she showed us a few homes that cost $300,000 or more, homes that in Houston would cost $100,000, and those homes were even on the low side of the market! She suggested, if we wanted something less expensive, we should take a look at Gilroy, a farming community about 15 kilometers to the south on 101. Though I was not too excited about the prospect of having a 65 kilometer commute, we drove down to Gilroy to look around and decided we liked Morgan Hill better. Also, having found out how expensive houses were and knowing, even if we won, the project could be canceled at any time or the launch could fail, we decided we would just rent and wait to see what happened.

Having accomplished our Saturday objectives, we had fun on Sunday. We went for a walk at the Lower Crystal Spring Reservoir in the morning and then drove over the mountains to Half Moon Bay on the Pacific where we had lunch. During the afternoon, we drove south along Coastal Highway 1 to see the coastal scenery and finally drove back to Sunnyvale.

Our short weekend was coming to an all too quick end and I already knew I wouldn't have time to fly to Houston for the weekend of September 23 through 25, as I had planned, nor worse, for my birthday on October 9. Rebecca had bought tickets for a Sousa March Music Concert in Galveston for my birthday, since I played the drums in the high school band (and had considered becoming a concert percussionist for a while — until astronomy won out) and I love march music. Alas, science won (again) and I knew I would have to forgo the concert (Rebecca took her friend, Edwina Morris, instead of me). When I took her to the airport early Monday morning, we knew it would be six weeks before we would see each other again.

Monday, September 19, through Tuesday, October 18, 1994: Just Five Short Weeks Left

Despite having taken Rebecca to the San Francisco Airport in the early morning, I got to Lockheed about the same time as everyone else did. I picked up where I had left off the previous Friday and started working on the second part of the *Technical Approach* Section — the *Flight System* (spacecraft) — and that was the part of the whole proposal I most enjoyed working on.

Over the years, Dom had developed a great format for describing a spacecraft and its subsystems. In that format, each subsystem section begins with a one or two sentence statement of its "Relevance" to the spacecraft. That is followed by all the "Requirements" the subsystem has to fulfill. Then the "Background/Approach" of the subsystem follows, in which a full description of the subsystem, its components and their functions are given. Since I already had a full list of spacecraft commands (there were only 59 spacecraft commands — that is how simple the OMNI Design of Lunar Prospector was), I enhanced Dom's format by adding the command list for each subsystem and what each command did. Also, since I had descriptions of the emergency procedures for each subsystem in the MOD I had written and refined over the years, I added all the emergency procedures for each subsystem to its section. Finally, in Dom's format, each subsystem section ends with a full page of schematics, diagrams, and charts of the subsystem and its components — a page that rounds-out the section in a very convincing manner. Again, since the spacecraft design was so well advanced, I even had tables of subsystem's parts and their vendors on that final page, thus fully demonstrating how mature the spacecraft design was. Tim and the other engineers had helped put together the parts and vendor data, and, in the process, we also had the cost information for the spacecraft hardware, information that was vital for the budget people when we got to that point.

The first spacecraft subsystem in Dom's format is *Structures and Mechanism*. Since we had decided to use graphite epoxy structures and we wanted to find a boom design Lockheed might have that fit our needs, I could not use much of the information from the original OMNI design, so I needed support from LMSC engineers. Thus, that section took a while to develop.

The process of finding a new boom design had already begun via some discussion we had had with the boom engineers in another part of LMSC. They soon provided me with data, pictures, and information about the boom design we chose, so that part of the redesign was done fairly quickly.

Dom then introduced me to Tom Chinn, Lockheed's leading expert on graphite epoxy structures. Tom is quiet, very good at what he does, a really nice guy, and eager to help. Tom was fast approaching retirement, but said he would gladly work on the project after retirement as a part-time employee. Tom got started immediately and quickly sketched out a new load-bearing structure based on graphite epoxy technology. He replaced the OMNI aluminum truss structure that held the fuel tanks with an inverted cone sitting on the OMNI designed equipment shelf (that could also be made of honeycomb graphite epoxy instead of honeycomb aluminum) and sent it over to some stress engineers for analysis. When the stress engineers came back with their analysis, they said that if we flipped the cone over, the entire load-bearing structure would be much stronger, so Tom made the adjustments to his design and I had a redesigned spacecraft structure, and that section was finished.

As Tom was explaining to me how graphite epoxy parts were manufactured, from the main structural pieces down to the smallest bracket, it occurred to me we might be able to make the GRS casing and thermal shield out of graphite epoxy rather than aluminum and stainless steel, as was usually done. If we could, there would be two advantages in doing so. First, a graphite casing and thermal shield would have significantly less mass than those made of aluminum and steel. Second, since we would be mapping the distributions of iron and aluminum (and several other elements) over the lunar surface with the GRS and since any iron and aluminum in the casing and shield would make it more difficult to measure their lunar abundances, having a graphite epoxy casing and shield would increase the accuracy of the data. I asked Tom if he could do that and he answered, "Yes."

I called Bill Feldman and asked him if he thought it was a good idea to make the GRS casing and thermal shield out of graphite epoxy, and Bill answered a resounding, "Yes, that's a great idea!" Just like that, we made a significant improvement to the design and function of the GRS, thanks to Tom Chinn's graphite epoxy.

The next section is *Thermal Control* Subsystem and that could not be finished until most of the other subsystems were fully defined, so it took a while to do. In the meantime, Dom had found some excellent thermal engineers who could spare some time to run the needed thermal models of the spacecraft and redesign the thermal system, which they did when we provided them with the necessary spacecraft redesign information.

The third subsystem is *Power* and was something I could sink my teeth into. The Mission Profile drives the power requirements in large part and I had a mature Mission Profile at hand. Also, the real driver of the Power Subsystem is the demand on the system, especially on the battery, during the twice-yearly lunar eclipses, and I had worked all that out in March of 1990 during the OMNI Phase B Design Study. I figured that part of the power discussion would be a very strong point in our Proposal since none of the scientists I knew who were going to submit Discovery Proposals for lunar missions had an astronomical background, and I did. Thus, I strongly suspected they would not know and/or pay much attention to the demands a lunar eclipse puts on the *Power* Subsystem and, more importantly, how to minimize those demands. Similarly, I figured that most spacecraft engineers would know even less about lunar eclipses than did the typical lunar and planetary scientist — in part because no NASA spacecraft had been sent to the Moon in nearly twenty-five years. Since not accounting for lunar eclipses in the power budget calculation (and thermal calculations) would result in a dead spacecraft orbiting the Moon after an eclipse, I really thought an in depth discussion of the issue would show we knew what we were doing. I made sure that part of the *Power* Subsystem discussion was very well done. Since there were no changes in the subsystem from the way OMNI had designed it, except for the use of the nickel-hydrogen battery instead of a nickel-cadmium battery, that section required little additional work.

However, in addition to my own engineering work on the power issues, I looked up Woody Woodcock, a physicist/power engineer, with whom I had worked on early proposals. Like me, Woody had spent several years working in Germany and he spoke fluent German, so we had always had fun babbling at each other in German when we discussed some power issue. Woody was working on the very big and very expensive EOS proposal when I found him. When I asked him if he wanted to work on the Lunar Prospector Proposal and, if we won, on the project, Woody said he couldn't, but said that he would answer any questions that I might have while writing my proposal. With a little bit of help from Woody, I finished the *Power* Subsystem, feeling it was in great shape and a strong point in the proposal.

Next came the *Communications* Subsystem. We used the OMNI Design unchanged and since Tim Bridges was again working with me, Tim helped me whip the *Communications* section into good shape.

The following Subsystem — *Propulsion* — is again something I knew a lot about and I made sure that key section was well done. I had, over the years, redesigned the OMNI Propulsion Subsystem. First I had added a pair of upper engines to the spacecraft and then, after the Mars Observer failure in August of 1993, I had gone back to the simple monopropellant, hydrazine propulsion subsystem Preston and I had originally requested in the RFP. Despite those changes, the subsystem was still largely the same as that designed by OMNI, so that subsection was finished fairly quickly.

However, when I had gone looking for Woody, I also found Ron King, who was also working on the EOS proposal, sitting in the next cubicle. Ron is a propulsion engineer with whom I had worked earlier and respected. When I asked Woody if he wanted to work on Lunar Prospector, I asked Ron the same question and got the same answer. In addition to saying he was busy with EOS, Ron said I had already completely designed the *Propulsion* Subsystem, so there was nothing left to do, except build it. Nevertheless, I asked Ron to give the section the once-over just to make sure I had made no mistakes, and he did so.

Next came the *Attitude* Subsystem. For a simple spinner like Lunar Prospector that uses its Propulsion Subsystem to control the spacecraft's attitude and spin rate, the Attitude Subsystem consists of a Sun sensor and an infrared Earth/Moon limb-crossing sensor, and that's it. Thus that part was quickly finished using the OMNI information.

The penultimate subsystem was the *Command and Data Handling* Unit and I also used the OMNI design for that. Thus that subsection was quickly dispatched.

Finally, the last subsystem, *Flight and Ground Software*, was next. Since Lunar Prospector would not have an onboard computer — a unique feature of the spacecraft; it would also have no flight software — so that part was simple. All the software would be in the Command and Control Center, and Tim Bridges knew a lot more about that than I did. Tim helped me finish that subsection and with that, the Spacecraft Engineering section was finished — for the time being.

While I was working hard on the spacecraft sections, Richard had started our talks with the LLV crew that was led by Don Damon. Richard and I met with them a couple of times to discuss the details of the launch and its price. I had hoped, if we could keep Lunar Prospector's mass down, it could be launched by the smaller and less expensive LLV1, rather than the bigger and more costly LLV2. However, Richard and I soon found out our using a LLV1 was out of the question. First, based on the LLV1 and LLV2 performance data I had back in 1993, I knew the LLV1's performance was marginal to launch Lunar Prospector and its Trans-Lunar Injection (TLI) Stage into low Earth orbit. Second, when we started our discussions with the LLV engineers, we immediately found out the performance numbers had dropped. I asked why and the reason given was the vendor of the light weight engine bells for solid fuel, Castor 120 rocket stages they had planned to use went out of business and the only other engine bells available were considerably heavier than the original ones. Thus I was stuck using the bigger and more costly LLV2, as originally planned.

As our discussions with the LLV crew proceeded, I reminded them I wanted a launch through TLI, not just to low Earth orbit (LEO). We would have enough to do getting the Lunar Prospector Spacecraft designed, built, tested, and readied for launch without having to concern ourselves with the TLI Stage. From my standpoint, the launch vehicle and the launch itself were issues for the launch service vendor, not for us, so, by a launch, I meant a launch to TLI. However, the LLV crew wanted their responsibility to end at LEO. They wanted the TLI Stage to be our problem, but I said, "No. I want a launch through TLI, not to LEO." The LLV crew kept trying to bring up the TLI issue, but both Richard and I made it very clear that we both expected the bid to be based on a launch to TLI.

Finally Damon and his crew agreed and sent me a letter dated October 10, but which was unsigned — a point that I did not take notice of in my haste and high state of fatigue. The bid for a LLV2 launch to TLI was $25 million, higher than the 1993 bid by $2.5 million and thus higher than I had expected.

Before leaving the *Spacecraft Design* section, there is one important point about the OMNI/Discovery Proposal Design that needs to be mentioned — all the electronic units had a primary and a backup unit, so the spacecraft had redundancy everywhere possible — the common practice for all NASA and commercial spacecraft.

By that time in the proposal effort, I was really fatigued and feeling the pressure. I was sleeping only three to four hours a night, but because of the adrenaline pumping through my body, I was never sleepy. When I went to bed, even though my mind was still going a mile-a-minute, I fell quickly into a deep sleep and woke up just three or four hours later — immediately wide awake and ready to go. I would jump out of bed, quickly shower, and drive to Lockheed where I would have to call a security guard to let me in Building 107. Since it was too early for even the donut shop to be open, I would get a sweet roll and a coke when the Building 107 cafeteria finally opened for breakfast.

As is the practice at LMSC, as a proposal is being developed, the various section authors tape their pages of text, figures, etc. on a long, blank wall. As a result, everyone working on the proposal can walk along the wall and see what is finished and can easily refer to and review the various sections. That practice provides a very efficient way for one to work his or her way through the proposal and get to the desired parts of it without having to sift through a stack of papers on one's desk.

Since I was effectively the only one working on my Proposal, I had started putting up the pages on the walls of my cubicle. Dom came to take a look every so often and was pleased with my progress. One day, I met Frank coming out of Building 107 as I was going in and Frank asked me how things were going. I said, "Fine. You should stop by my cubicle and take a look at the proposal."

Instead of saying he would, Frank just said, "You've got a winner there," and continued out the door. I was a little perplexed since he seemed totally indifferent to the proposal effort, even though he claimed that Lunar Prospector was "a winner."

Nevertheless Frank did show up at my cubicle a little while later, but took only a cursory look at the numerous pages on my wall and said, without reading a single word, "It looks great." Either Frank didn't give a damn or he had supreme confidence in Lunar Prospector and me, but I doubted the latter. On the other hand, Frank at least came by — I can't remember if Gus ever came by to look at the proposal. If he did, his visit left no mark on my tired brain.

After finishing the first draft of the *Flight System*, I started on the remaining six parts of the *Technical Approach* Section, of which I could write only three — *Payload Integration, Mission Operations,* and *Phase A/B Preliminary Analysis and Definition Study Plans* — without substantial engineering support. Dom asked Kim Foster to write the part on *Manufacturing, Integration, and Test* and Bob Goldin to write the part on *Product Assurance and Safety.* Then I asked Tim Bridges to do the ground part of *Ground and Data,* while I did the data part.

By that time, Dom had gotten the technical parts of the MAUDEE under quasi-control, so both Francisco and Richard were able to spend more time helping me, in large part by making the illustrations, tables, and diagrams that I needed. Nevertheless, with only three weeks to go, it was clear that I could not finish on time without some more dedicated help. I told Dom that I needed Tom Polette to come out and help me finish Volume II. Though we were certainly going to go over the $100,000 budget Gus had given us if Tom came out, that didn't bother Dom in the slightest (by the time the accountants noticed that we had a cost overrun, the proposal would be done). I then called Tom and asked him if he could come out and help me finish the proposal. He said that he could come out for a long week, fly out the next Saturday and fly back to Houston the Sunday of the following week, but no longer. I said that would help a lot and gave him my LMSC contract number so he could get airline tickets, pay for a Maple Tree Inn room, and get paid.

Tom flew in the next Saturday. I picked him up and we immediately went to work. Characteristically, Tom saw what I needed done and did it. He took over managing the work Francisco and Richard were doing for me, got busy finishing up all the appendices and began to pull together the Table of Contents — all things that needed to be done, but that I never got to because I was too busy doing the body of the proposal. Without Tom's help, even though he was there only a long week, I would not have gotten the Proposal done on time.

It was also nice having my good friend Tom around, someone that I trusted implicitly and whose loyalty to Lunar Prospector and me was unquestionable. Knowing that I had someone to help me who I could totally rely on took some of the pressure off me and reduced my level of frustration considerably. Also, having Tom to talk to and joke around with when we were eating dinner or driving to and from Lockheed helped me relax a little bit. Nevertheless, the clock was ticking and the time remaining was getting shorter and shorter. Tom had had to adapt to my three to four-hour sleep, twenty-hour workday, seven-day week work schedule and that was hard on Tom, despite his being some fifteen years younger than I am. The main reason is that Tom had polio when he was young and was suffering from post-polio problems and some other health issues. The secondary reason was that, though Tom was loyal to me and totally supportive of my goal of getting Lunar Prospector done, Lunar Prospector was my baby and I was the one that was fiercely driven to get it to the Moon. I was the one living on adrenaline, not Tom.

My daily routine changed only in that when I popped awake at 3:00 AM, I called Tom's room to wake him up and then got ready to go to Lockheed. Tom, needing more sleep than I could allow, took a good half an hour to wake up and get ready, so we arrived at Lockheed a little later than I usually did. Then Tom would frequently take a half hour or hour nap on the floor of my cubicle as I worked on the Mac, trying to be as quiet as possible. Despite being exhausted from the lack of sleep and the heavy work schedule, Tom was always in great spirits, gave his all to the effort, and did a great job of helping me get the proposal done.

As the week Tom was there was coming to an end, I asked if he could stay longer and he said that he just couldn't; he was a supervisor and just couldn't stay away from his work any longer. I understood and reluctantly agreed he could not jeopardize his job back at LESC, since there was no guarantee Lunar Prospector would win.

The Saturday morning before Tom left, he and I celebrated his coming out and doing such a great job by taking my favorite walk along the Lower Crystal Spring Reservoir, and then it was back to work. The next day I took Tom to the airport and returned to my regular work-sleep routine, with one exception: my sleep time dropped to two hours per night as I pushed even harder to get the Proposal done.

By the time Tom left, the *Technical Approach* section of Volume II was in good shape, thanks to Bob, Kim, and Tim doing the parts I needed them to do, and I was beginning to see the light at the end of the tunnel. All that was left to do on Volume II was the third major Section — *Opportunity*, the final editing, and getting the page count down to 75, the latter is always a major undertaking. I had been very careful to keep the page count as low as possible in the *Science* and *Technical Approach* Sections I had been working on, so I wouldn't be too far off when the final cutting down to size began. Part of that effort was to carefully cut sentences so that I wouldn't waste a whole line with just one or two words in it at the end of a paragraph. Similarly, I had made sure tables and figures were sized and placed in the text so they took as little space as possible.

One day Richard and Dom came to look at the proposal pages on my wall. Dom didn't like the fact I had chosen the single column rather than the double column style for the text (both were allowed according to the AO). I had chosen the single column style since I am used to writing science papers that way and since it saves a small amount of space. Dom said his experience was that proposal reviewers liked the double column style because it was easier to read than the single column, so using it would give us a slight psychological advantage (everything counts — even if just a little bit). I wasn't convinced it made a hill of beans difference, but Dom was well experienced in writing big aerospace proposals, while I had only written small science proposals, so I said, "OK."

Dom asked Richard if it would be difficult to change from single to double columns, given all the work that was done, and Richard said, "No, I just have to change one command," so he did. In a few seconds the entire text (except for the section on the Spacecraft Design that was to stay in the single column format) was transformed into double columns. Satisfied, Dom and Richard walked away and I started to take a look at the newly formatted text in detail, only to find that the change had increased the page count by a few pages! There were numerous dangling words at the ends of paragraphs that required an extra line for just one or two words and the placement of the figures, diagrams, and tables was totally messed up. Richard's simple change had undone all the careful editing I had done throughout the past weeks!

I called Dom and Richard back and showed them what had happened and said we should go back to the single column format, but Dom insisted it was much better to leave it as it was, even though I would have to straighten out the mess the change had caused, a task Richard said shouldn't take me too long. I was not convinced, since I had to do the work and time was getting very short, but Dom insisted, and, since he had more experience than I did, I again said, "OK." However, I thought, *whose proposal is this anyway and who is the PI, you (Dom) or me?* But I let it go while still feeling that Dom had overstepped his bounds.

I got busy carefully straightening out the formatting mess and re-editing, a task that took the good part of two days! I was annoyed at Dom, but more so at Richard for having cost me so much time. Had Richard known what he was talking about, i.e., had not told Dom it was just a simple command change and my reformatting wouldn't take long, I figured Dom would have left it as it was. I went to Richard and told him what his misinformation had cost me in time and effort and told him not to make the same mistake again. Unfortunately, Richard has a bad habit of "leaping before he looks," as I would find out over the course of the next couple of years.

At about that time Dom, who was always thinking of ways to strengthen the Proposal, suggested we add some of the faculty of San Jose State University, with whom Dom had some loose ties, to our Team. I said, "No," it was bad enough to have had to add Ames, but I saw no advantage in adding San Jose State. Doing so would have just added another partner to the Team for namesake only, a partner that had nothing to offer, either scientifically or engineering-wise. Also, that would have just added one more inefficient (university) bureaucracy to the mix, when I already had to deal with the Lockheed and Ames bureaucracies and they were bad enough. I was already spending too much time keeping Scott informed about our progress and dealing with Ames in general. I did not want to have to spend hours informing San Jose about Lunar Prospector and trying to make up a story about how they would be useful to the project, especially when I was fast running out of time.

Dom was not pleased with my answer and rationale and said rather arrogantly, "You can lead a horse to water, but you can't make him drink." I was becoming aware that even though Lunar Prospector was my Program and Dom worked for me, Dom expected me to follow his directions, not the other way around. At that point, I didn't care; all I wanted to do was prepare a winning proposal. I would figure out how to deal with Dom's apparent need to be in total control later — if we won.

By that time we had just over a week to go. Though I was physically fatigued, I was never sleepy and always woke up wide-awake and ready to go, despite my sleeping only two hours per night. I had started the final section of Volume II — *Opportunity* — that was to deal with *Technology Transfer*, *Educational Program Activities*, *Socio-Economic Benefits*, and *Public Awareness*. Since we had little technology to transfer, that was simple to treat. The educational and PR parts were largely based on what LEI had long planned for Lunar Prospector and were done quickly. The social/economic aspects were dealt with largely by demonstration we had the minimum required number of small businesses and minority owned small businesses involved as subcontractors. Finally, I had a complete draft of Volume II and the appendices. The next several days were spent, in part, combing through the entire Volume, cutting it down to the 75 pages and making sure everything required was in it.

Also during the last couple of weeks, Dom had begun putting together the Budget for Volume III. He was still involved trying to get the MAUDEE budget down, but began to spend more time on the Lunar Prospector Budget — he had to, or we would not get done in time. The Budget was being put together mainly by Dom, Fred DeFrank (a contracts person in Gus's group who had a long working relationship with Dom), and Peggy McDougall, a LMSC Financial Operations Controller. Peggy had been working with Dom and Fred for weeks trying to save the MAUDEE budget and fighting with Dom all the time.

The problems, for both MAUDEE and Lunar Prospector, were that Peggy insisted on doing the budgets the LMSC standard way — regardless of what the AO required and that Dom expected Peggy (and everyone else) to do things his way and was very vocal about that. The end result was that Peggy and Dom could not — and would not — communicate with each other. To those personal conflicts was added the fact that she and Dom had spent all their time trying to save the MAUDEE proposal, so they had left Lunar Prospector's budget to the very end, when there was neither the time nor the resources left to do even a reasonable job on it. All that was compounded by the fact that Peggy came down with the flu when she was trying to do Lunar Prospector's budget!

I was busy trying to get volume II done and spent little time with the budget issue, except for two areas. First, since Tim, the other engineers, and I had gotten together the lists of parts, vendors, and costs for the spacecraft hardware given in the spacecraft subsystem sections, Peggy asked Tim and me to fill out the Program Hardware Software List (PHSF) forms in as much detail as possible. Tim and I did the PHSFs. Then she needed the information for the labor for each phase and each task of the entire project, so we filled out those forms. Those forms, plus the science budgets I had previously gotten from each of my Co-Is, provided her with a large fraction of the data she needed to do the budget.

Second, though I had little time to spend on the budget discussions, I did keep track of what was going on and I had two concerns. The cost I had used for Lunar Prospector during my attempts in 1993 and early 1994 to get NASA to support the Mission was $40 million. I knew it would cost more to do Lunar Prospector with LMSC than with OMNI and a lot of volunteer help, but I had hoped that we could still come in under $50 million. However, as the total cost started to come in, it crept up over $50 million and just kept going. I was concerned because one of Lunar Prospector's strengths was its very low cost. Since Goldin had wanted missions that were one third to one half the cap of $250 million, or just $80 to $120 million, and since I assumed the other PIs would try to keep their mission costs in that range, I was afraid we would price ourselves out of a win. Dom was just as sensitive about that issue as I was, but I still kept an eye on the budget goings on. Also, when I looked at the budget, I could not find where the Lockheed fee of $4 million was mentioned, but I was told it was in there and not to worry about it. In the end, the cost of Lunar Prospector was $59 million (we had at least kept it under $60 million, but just barely) and the price (cost plus fee) was $63 million.

As the tussle between Dom and Peggy about the Budget finally reached its crescendo during the last week of the effort, I finished Volume II. That left the *Executive Summary* — Volume I, the Fact Sheet, and Volume III to be done, with Peggy working hard to get the first half of Volume III finished. In order to get the Fact Sheet done, Dom had asked Gerry Grismore, an engineer I didn't know at that time, to go through Volume II and what existed of Volume III and start the Fact Sheet, while I worked on Volume I. Gerry did a really good job and had a first cut of the Fact Sheet for me in just a day. I went through it, corrected it and after a couple more revisions, the Fact Sheet was done thanks to Gerry and it only took me a couple of days to do Volume I. Then, with only about four days to go, and as Volumes I and II were almost ready to go to Scott for his approval and then to the printer, LMSC upper management dropped a small bomb on me.

Since Volumes I and II, the appendices, and the Fact Sheet were ready to go, all I had to worry about was Volume III — until I was told that *Lockheed was no longer willing to set up the tracking network!* I couldn't believe it. The bastards had agreed to set up the tracking using the turnkey stations Tim had found and for which we had money in the budget, and then, when it was essentially too late to respond, Lockheed decided it would not be responsible for the tracking network! I was dumbfounded and at a loss as to what to do. The 6 meter dish tracking stations were a mainstay of the Proposal since, by design and because it would not have a computer on board, Lunar Prospector had to be tracked 24 hours per day. If it wasn't, we could not get the data back and we could not save the spacecraft if something went wrong. There was no question in my mind that we could not get 24 hour tracking using the very expensive (about $1 million per month) and very over loaded NASA Deep Space Tracking Network with its very large antennas. Without a dedicated, Lunar Prospector Tracking Network, I had no Proposal.

As I sat at my desk trying to absorb what had just happened to Lunar Prospector and me, the thought occurred to me that maybe, just maybe, if I called Ed Briggs at Allied Signal and explained the situation, Allied Signal might come to my rescue, since they had been so positive about providing the tracking network in the past. However, I was quite embarrassed to have to call Ed, first, because I had gone off to Lockheed to do the proposal without asking them if they wanted to participate, and second, because I worked for — and had chosen — such a back stabbing company.

Despite my embarrassment, I called Ed and explained the situation. He did not seem surprised at Lockheed's behavior and said, "Sure, we'll help you out. We'll set up some of our small mobile stations at the DSN stations, since we have the contract to run them anyway."

I thanked Ed profusely and asked if he could fax me a letter to that effect ASAP, since there was no time to get a letter via the mail and Ed said he would. Despite Lockheed's leaving me in the lurch at the last minute, I had a tracking network. I told Dom, and he was as relieved as I was.

I quickly made the minor changes to Volume II regarding who was going to set up the tracking network and took everything, Volumes I and II, the Fact Sheet, and the appendices, to Scott for his signature and then to the printer with three days to spare.

The only thing left was the *Management Section* of Volume III, since Peggy had also delivered her *Budget Section* with a couple of days to spare, and we had just two days to do it.

Wednesday, October 19, through Friday, October 21, 1994: A 27-Hour Day and then "The End"

Dom had finished Lockheed's part of MAUDEE and sent it off to Michigan by late Tuesday and so, Dom, Francisco, Richard, and I were ready to start the last major section of the Proposal — the *Management Section* of Volume III — starting Wednesday morning. Though it may seem to the reader like a hopeless task to try to do a major section, some 35 to 40 pages, of a proposal in 48 hours, the situation was not as bad as it might seem. First, though the Lunar Prospector Management scheme was very simple and streamlined — Dom and I would be the only managers — there was a lot of commonality between the MAUDEE management scheme and that of Lunar Prospector. The plan was to modify the existing MAUDEE management section to make it satisfy our needs. Second, Dom had told Richard a couple of days earlier to take the MAUDEE plan and cannibalize it, so we would have something to start working with on Wednesday morning.

When Dom came to work at about 9:00 AM Wednesday, we got started. The only problems, besides the short time available to do the job, were the fact that Dom, Richard, Francisco, and I were exhausted (so exhausted in fact that Francisco was nearly zombiefied when we started and was completely zombiefied within 24 hours) and Dom was very, very sick. He had come down with the flu or a very bad cold that he probably got from Peggy. I am sure that if that were the case, Peggy would have been very happy considering all the abuse Dom had heaped on her during the previous few weeks. Whatever the cause, Dom was very sick and had gone to his doctor to get some strong medication so he could get through the last 48 hours.

Despite those handicaps, we got started reviewing the rough draft Richard had prepared. Richard had assembled the parts of the MAUDEE management section and had had the Mac change all references from MAUDEE to Lunar Prospector, those to the PI from Tim Killeen to me, and the like. However, when we went through the draft, it was a mess and it quickly became apparent that the job ahead of us was a lot bigger than Dom had anticipated. We got started on the next draft.

Since I knew very little about the details of management, there was little I could do except help proofread the text (a task that I am terrible at) and Francisco was so out of it that he mainly stood there looking half dead. The majority of the work fell on Dom and Richard's shoulders. Dom paced back and forth, dictating the changes he wanted and Richard typed them into the Mac. As time went on, Richard's fingers got so stiff and tired he had to periodically stop Dom and just let his fingers rest for a few minutes.

As Wednesday drew to a close, we had what we thought was a good first draft and we thought we would be finished with the Management Section by early Thursday. If so, then we could then get it over to Scott for his approval and then get it copied by late Thursday afternoon. That would give me plenty of time for a decent night's sleep and for me to catch my 6:00 AM flight to Houston — *a flight the Proposal and I had to be on if I was going to get the Proposal to the Lunar and Planetary Institute by the 4:30 PM deadline*. Dom went home for some much-needed rest and the rest of us worked on the proofing and the figures and tables. I left for the Maple Tree Inn for my two hours of sleep (for the last time, though I did not know that at that time) and was back to Lockheed by 3:00 AM.

Dom, Richard, and Francisco came in by 7:00 AM and we went at it. However, the work went a lot slower than we had hoped, partly because we were all very, very tired and Dom was very, very sick, and partly because Dom kept making changes to the text, changes I thought made little difference, especially if it ended up that we didn't get finished in time to make the deadline. By early afternoon it was apparent we still had a lot of work to do and Scott was getting very anxious about his not having enough time to read the *Management Section* and properly approving it. Also, the printers had expected to be done with our job by their normal quitting time. I took care of Scott by taking him the latest, but not the final version of the *Management Section*, late Thursday afternoon. Scott was not at all happy with that, but he realized that unless he approved what I gave him, we would not get done on time. He reluctantly signed off on Volume III. Dom took care of the printers by pleading with them to stay and telling them he would buy them a case of beer or anything else they wanted if they would only stay until we were through — and they did.

At about 5:00 PM, Dom said he was going home for an hour or two to rest, have dinner, and take a shower and his medicine so he would feel well enough to finish the job. He left and Richard, Francisco, and I decided to go to the Cattleman's Restaurant near Building 107 for a well-deserved steak dinner. We drove the few blocks to the restaurant, went in, got seated, and were waiting for the waiter when we all simultaneously realized a steak dinner was just going to take too long. We got up, walked out, drove the extra few blocks to McDonald's and bought hamburgers, fries, and cokes. We then drove back to Lockheed and ate our gourmet dinners.

Dom was back by 7:00, so we began the last editing, which lasted until after midnight. Dom had called the print shop a couple of more time as it got later and later and the printers said they would stay, but as we drove up, the place was dark as could be. Our hearts sank, since it appeared the printers were gone, but Richard ran around the building and found there were lights on in the back and an unlocked door. We rushed in and there the printers were, still waiting for us as promised.

We gave them the original copy of Volume III and they began to run off the 24 copies we needed. As they started that, Richard, Francisco, and I stuck the copy number (2 through 25) on each of the 24 copies of Volume II (plus Volume I) and all the appendices, and put them in three boxes. I was going to carry the originals with me, just in case the airline lost the boxes. The printers soon had the 24 copies of Volume III done, but Dom had also put a few foldouts in that volume, foldouts that had to be specially printed and then hand inserted in the text before the copies could be bound and that was taking forever. By then it was about 4:00 AM (I had been up for 25 hours and was dead tired) and I knew we were not going to make it if I waited for the copies of Volume III to be finished.

I said to Dom, "If I don't go now, I will miss my plane."

Dom replied, "It's only a few minutes to the San Jose Airport, so you still have an hour."

I was astonished and said, "I'm booked out of San Francisco, not San Jose!" (LESC's travel agency apparently didn't know, nor did I till that moment, there were direct flights between San Jose and Houston).

Equally astonished, Dom said, "Then, you've got to go now."

I replied, "Yes, I'll take the originals and the three boxes of Volumes I and II and the appendices with me now. Send the copies of Volume III on the next plane. I'll call you when I get to Houston to get the flight number from you. Goodbye."

I said to Richard, "I'll never make it if I have to return my car. Can you drive me to the airport?"

Richard said, "Yes."

Richard, Francisco, and I grabbed the originals and the three boxes and dumped the boxes in Richard's car. I threw my car keys to Francisco and told him to turn my car into Hertz the next day, and then Richard and I drove off in a cloud of dust.

We still had to go to the Maple Tree Inn to get my suitcase and check out and then we headed up 101 going well in excess of the speed limit. It was a major miracle we didn't get stopped or killed or both, but we didn't. Richard pulled up to the curbside check-in and we jumped out and I tried to check-in, only to find out I could not check-in until I had changed my ticket (I was ticketed to go home the weekend of September 23 — remember). Though I had changed the reservations earlier, I still had to change the ticket! I ran into the airport, only to find a very long line at the ticket counter — at 4:30 in the morning, were those people nuts! I could see, in my mind's eye, my plane pulling away from the gate without me as I waited for an eternity in that damned line.

While I was in the line, Richard parked his car and came back to watch over our precious cargo. Finally it was my turn and I got the damned ticket changed and ran out to show the curbside attendant my ticket. We literally threw the three boxes and my suitcase on the conveyor belt and I started to run for the gate with just a few minutes to spare. Richard said, "I'm going with you; I'm afraid you'll fall asleep on the way to the gate." We both ran as fast as we could and reached the gate just as they were preparing to shut the door. I ran to the door, showed my ticket to the attendant, waved to Richard, and walked to the plane as the door closed behind me.

I found my seat; it was a window seat on the right side near the front, squeezed over the first two passengers and plopped into my seat. I buckled up and immediately fell fast asleep — even before the airplane had pulled away from the gate. I had made it, but barely!

I slept solidly for nearly the entire flight, stirring slightly only a couple of times trying to get comfortable. The next thing I was really aware of was the sound of the captain's voice saying we had begun our descent into the Houston International Airport. I had slept longer than I had in weeks, but I was still dead tired.

When we landed, as prearranged, Tom was there to meet me. With his usual efficiency, he had gotten a Lockheed van. We went down to the baggage area and waited for the three boxes — I didn't care about my luggage — just those boxes. Finally, my suitcase came on the conveyor and then one, two, and three boxes. Man was I relieved. We loaded up the van and Tom drove like hell (but not as fast as Richard had done just a few short hours earlier) and we got to the Lunar and Planetary Institute next to JSC by 2:00 PM. We carried the boxes in and found the young lady who was checking in the proposals and gave her the originals of all three volumes and the appendices and the three boxes containing 24 copies of Volumes I and II and the appendices. I told her the box with the 24 copies of Volume III had been mistakenly put on a plane going to Hobby Airport by the airlines (I wasn't going to tell her that we were guilty of that) and would be at Hobby at about 3:00 PM (Francisco had called Tom with the flight information while I was asleep in my airplane). She said she could not check in my proposal until all the copies were there. I was worried, but I said we would have the last box there no later than 4:00 PM, still ahead of the deadline.

Tom and I took off for the Hobby Airport that is only about a half an hour from the Institute. When we got there, we found out to our horror that the plane was delayed in Dallas and would be over an hour late — too late for us! I immediately called the check-in-lady and told her the bad news. To my relief, she said she would go ahead and check us in, but added we had better get the fourth box there as soon as possible.

Tom and I killed time until the airplane finally arrived at nearly 4:30! Miraculously, our box was the first to come out on the conveyor and it was beat all to hell. One side was split open and the copies were falling out onto the conveyor. We grabbed the box and counted the copies — all 24 were there! I looked at Tom and said, "Given the box's condition, the check-in girl will surely believe our story that the airline sent the box on the wrong airplane." We took off as fast as we could for the Lunar and Planetary Institute.

When we arrived at the Institute, it was night. The Institute was dark and locked up (had that not just happened to me at the LMSC printers only a few hours earlier?). We were just about to bang on the door when John Connolly, a NASA friend of ours with whom we worked in the advanced planning group, and a friend of his came out the door. John laughed and asked innocently, "Do you guys want in?"

We answered, "YES." We walked down the dark hall towards the bright office where the check-in-lady was still fast at work. We gave her the last box and I thanked her for checking us in and grumped about the airline causing so much trouble for her and us. I than asked her how many proposals had come in and she answered, "Twenty-eight." Then Tom and I left.

Somehow I had made it; the Proposal was officially checked-in on time (thanks to that young lady and a small white lie). I had done everything possible during the past several years to find a way to do Lunar Prospector, and the Proposal was my last conceivable chance for success. Now it was up to the reviewers and NASA and I would know in a couple of months whether Lunar Prospector was going to the Moon and if my career was over or not. All I could do was wait for the news from NASA.

Chapter 1-16
The Wait

Friday Evening October 21, through Saturday November 11, 1994:
Home at Last

After Tom and I left the Lunar and Planetary Institute, we dumped the van off at LESC and then he drove me up to the Baylor College of Medicine where Rebecca was waiting for me and working late; then he went home himself. It was great to see Rebecca again and despite my being tired, we enjoyed what was left of the evening and then I crashed. As the weekend progressed, I slowly got rested up and was feeling nearly normal by the time the workweek started.

I really had nothing to do at LESC and was looking for something to do to keep me busy. Then I remembered Dom had said, concerning the MAUDEE Team's assumption that MAUDEE was ready for construction, "If they were really ready for construction, they would have an assembly scheme already laid out." With that in mind and since Lunar Prospector was essentially ready for construction, I began to think through and generate computer diagrams of the assembly sequence, the wiring, the propulsion plumbing, and anything else I could think of that would be useful and would keep me busy.

Besides trying to keep myself busy at work while waiting for NASA's decision in January, Rebecca and I planned to get married and to take a couple of vacations. Several months earlier we had received one of those promotional offers in the mail for a "free cruise to the Bahamas." Since neither of us had been on a cruise and we had talked about doing so, we decided to accept the offer, knowing it would not be "free" and probably not very good. However, part of the package was a three days stay at Disney World that we knew we would enjoy, so even if the Bahamas were a bust, we would have some fun.

Saturday, November 12, through Monday, November 21, 1994:
The Trip to Hell

Our great adventure stated with our flight from Houston to Fort Lauderdale on Saturday and then we drove up to Orlando to go to Disney World. However, we were greeted by Hurricane Gordon, which came out of the Gulf, wandered back and forth across lower Florida and then went out into the Atlantic by way of the Bahamas. Basically, Gordon chased us during the whole trip.

Because the hurricane was far to the south when we got to Disney World, we had nice weather for the first two days and we had a great time. By the third day, the weather had turned bad and we started to drive to Fort Lauderdale to start the cruise on the following day, November 16 — Rebecca's birthday. The drive was something out of a disaster movie; there were high winds, driving rain, flooding and very few cars on the turnpike. Rebecca was scared to death, but we made it to the hotel in Fort Lauderdale, where we were to spend the night before boarding the cruise ship the next morning. The hotel was full of people — one of the two cruise ships had canceled its trip the day before, because of high seas, so those passengers were going to Grand Bahama Island on our ship. The other ship went, but we were told that the passengers were tied to the seats!

The morning of the 16th, we got ready to board and the stewards handed out Dramamine pills (I had already taken two and took the additional two to be on the safe side, since I am prone to motion sickness) and told us we were to travel at our own risk, before we were allowed to board. Then we left the dock and the crossing began in very high seas. Shortly thereafter, people were throwing up all over the place. With four Dramamines in me, I just fell asleep while Rebecca sipped Jack Daniels and watched a movie about vampires starring Tom Cruise. Finally, the several hour transit cruise was over and we reached Freeport. We were driven to our dilapidated hotel in a driving rain in a taxi that was filled to the top with luggage and tourists.

Once we got settled in our "luxury" hotel, we wanted to have a nice dinner to celebrate Rebecca's birthday, so we wandered out into the rain. There were no good restaurants within blocks (maybe even farther, we couldn't tell in the rain), so we ended up at the only choice — a Burger King. Needless to say, Rebecca was not impressed (nor was I). After we ate, we trudged back to the hotel, soaking wet and I, still heavily under the influence of four Dramamines, flopped on the bed and went fast asleep, while Rebecca tried to watch TV — and that was the highlight of our stay in Freeport.

As we gratefully left the Bahamas a few days later, the weather had improved, so the voyage back was actually pleasant, but as we headed home on the 21st, we labeled that part of our vacation "The Trip to Hell" and swore never to go to the Bahamas again — it's no place to go if, like us, you don't like to gamble, swim, play golf, and play tennis, and it's too flat and ugly to enjoy a good hike.

Sunday, December 4, 1994: Getting Married

When I proposed to Rebecca and she finally accepted on March 15, we said we would wait a year after we met to get married. Since I (like most men) can never remember birthdays and anniversaries, I said, "Let's get married exactly one year after our first date — on December 4 (1994)," and hoped she would think I was being romantic instead of just wanting to have only one date to remember instead of two, for two of our anniversaries.

Rebecca said, "OK."

Sunday, December 4, 1994, we went to the Clear Lake City Hall and had a small civil ceremony. Rebecca wore a dark green velvet, cocktail length dress, black satin high heels, and sheer dark green nylons; she was, as always, beautiful — a beautiful bride. Lisa Major, a young friend of Rebecca's, was her Maid-of-Honor and Tom was my Best Man. Besides the Justice of the Peace and the four of us, Lisa's mother — Gayle, Tom's wife — Pauline, my good friend John Gruener and his wife — Barbara, and Rebecca's close friend — Patt Denson were there. After the ceremony, we went to a fancy Mexican Restaurant in Kemah for a lunch and then Rebecca and I drove down to Galveston for our wedding night.

Christmas and New Year's Eve, 1994

The holidays closed out the year 1994 with no fanfare. I had worked on Lunar Prospector for just over five years and would presumably know in a few weeks if all the effort was going to pay off or not. I fervently hoped we would be celebrating Lunar Prospector during the next Christmas and New Year's.

January 1995: Moving and Waiting

Regardless of what happened with Lunar Prospector, I was going to sell my house in Dickinson, TX, and my ultra-light airplane. If we won, Rebecca and I would be moving to California and I would not have time to fly (besides, it's too windy in the area where we hoped to live to fly an ultra-light airplane). If we lost, I would soon be let go from LESC, Rebecca and I would buy the house she was renting, and I would not be able to afford to keep my ultra-light airplane. Starting the weekend of January 8, I began to pack up my things and take them to Rebecca's house where we stored them in the garage. They would stay packed until we either moved to California or knew we were going to stay in Texas. The packing and moving process lasted exactly one month.

January slowly passed by and there was no word from NASA about the selection that was supposed to have been announced during January. As a result, as January slowly came to an end, all 28 PIs and our numerous teammates began to get very anxious and very annoyed. NASA expects us to meet all their deadlines and if we don't, our work is rejected, but NASA does what it wants and when it wants — regardless of its own deadlines.

Early February 1995

January turned into February and the days slowly rolled by with no word from NASA. The tension in the lunar and planetary community increased rapidly with each passing day. We were all like a bunch of "Cats On A Hot Tin Roof," each of us wanting to be the last cat on the roof after the others had jumped off, but NASA just left us up there, hopping around as our paws burned — hoping to be the winner.

In frustration and concern, I called Dom and asked if we should get Gus and Frank to put some pressure on NASA to choose Lunar Prospector and get it over with. Dom called back a little while later and told me both Gus and Frank (both ex-NASA managers) said it would only annoy NASA and would reduce our chances of winning.

Tim Killeen went a step further and *demanded* that Lockheed CEO Dan Tellep write NASA, telling them MAUDEE was vital to the nation's Mars exploration effort and demanding that NASA select MAUDEE — Lockheed declined to do so.

I am sure almost all, if not all, of the other teams also tried or wanted to try to influence NASA's decision in their favor, but NASA was uncharacteristically quiet about the selection process and the selection itself.

Though NASA was quiet as the weeks went by, the rumor mill kept churning out all possible combinations of winners. Bill Feldman had called. He had been at JPL and saw a list on which there were six missions, none of which was Lunar Prospector. The University of Arizona/JSC full up lunar mapping mission was on the list. Bill added gloomily, "If that list is true, then, of course, we have lost. However, I heard of another list on which we are the winner," and added, "I hope that's the case."

I had heard Bruce Murray's supposedly low cost lunar ice Mapper had won, and, of course, the MAUDEE crew knew for certain they had won — and on and on went the rumor mill. Frustrating as the rumors were, their diversity suggested no one really knew what was going on and those who thought they did were just trying to impress the rest of us with their supposed insider knowledge.

Then there was the ever present, pleasant situation at LESC — more and more of the over fifty crowd were getting axed. Tom kept fighting what I knew would soon be a lost battle to keep me off the "to be axed" list. I figured I would be a member of that elite group the next go-around — and then what? There were no known jobs for an over fifty planetary scientist, certainly not with the American space program in an apparent state of fatal decline. I guessed I would soon be flipping hamburgers at McDonald's.

Friday, February 17, through Monday, February 20, 1995: A Trip to Louisiana

During the midst of the waiting in February, Rebecca and I decided to take a break and drive over to New Orleans for a long weekend vacation. When we got to the Texas/Louisiana border, we stopped at an information center and picked up some literature, because we wanted to see some of the old plantation mansions. As we looked through the materials, we found a couple of plantations where one could actually stay overnight. That sounded like fun, so Rebecca called one and arranged for us to rent one of the small houses that were part of the slave quarters for the night. We enjoyed seeing several of the mansions along the Mississippi River and staying in the slave quarters. The next day we drove to New Orleans and spent the day and the next sightseeing. Then we drove back to Houston to continue our vigil.

Tuesday, February 21, through Thursday, February 23, 1995: More Waiting

I had the vague hope there would be some news — good or bad — waiting for me when we got back from Louisiana, but that was not the case when I went to work Tuesday morning. Thus, I went back to my time-killing routine of working on Lunar Prospector construction issues and engineering diagrams, but the time went agonizingly slowly as Tuesday turned into Wednesday and then Wednesday turned into Thursday, all without hearing one peep from NASA — just more rumors.

As Thursday, February 23, finally came to an end, I went to bed wondering what the next day would bring and hoping we would finally hear who had been selected and hoping it was Lunar Prospector.

PART TWO

Success at Last

February 24, 1995
through September 7, 1995

Chapter 2-1
The Call

Friday, February 24, 1995: The Call

Friday, February 24 began just like every workday during the previous several weeks and ran the same course, as had all the long days of all those long weeks. I worked on Lunar Prospector wiring diagrams to kill the time as I waited and hoped to hear what mission(s) NASA had selected for Discovery. The selection announcement was already five or six weeks overdue, and I, like all the other PIs and Co-Is, kept wondering what in hell was taking NASA so long. Having heard nothing from anyone about the selection during the morning and early afternoon, and since I was bored and frustrated at work, while at the same time, I was looking forward to a pleasant weekend with Rebecca, I left work early — about 3:30 — to fight the Friday rush hour traffic to drive home.

I had been home just a little while and was sitting in the living room reading, when, at about 5:00, I got a frantic call from Arthurine (Frank Martin's secretary) who said NASA was trying in vain to call me. NASA could not reach me because, of course, according to the proposal I was supposed to be at LMSC! Since LMSC did not want to hire me unless Lunar Prospector won (and I suspected not even then, as was shortly confirmed), I was not at LMSC, rather still in Houston working for LESC. Earlier in the day, when NASA had asked where I could be reached, Arthurine or some other secretary would not tell them — why, I did not know! Finally, after more calls, NASA indicated it was imperative that they get in touch with me because they had some very urgent questions about Lunar Prospector. At that point, someone gave NASA my old home number in Dickinson, but not my LESC number! Naturally when they called Dickinson, that telephone was disconnected since my house was up for sale and Rebecca and I were living at her house. After that, NASA was finally able to get my LESC number from LMSC, but by that time I had left work, so they left a message on my answering machine and then tried Arthurine again. At last she responded by calling me at Rebecca's home with the above tale of incompetence and gave me a NASA Headquarters number to call immediately.

Despite the not-so-fun game of telephone tag, I finally knew NASA was after me. I was fairly certain it was far too late in the game for NASA to have any technical or budgetary questions about the proposal. I was pretty sure that the call meant I had finally succeeded and Lunar Prospector had been selected as the next Discovery Mission — if I was right, Lunar Prospector was finally on its way to the Moon.

I immediately called Headquarters and got what turned out to be Mark Saunders's secretary. She said they had been trying to reach me all day and there were some questions they had and I had to get in touch with Wes Huntress and Mark Saunders right away. She said Mark had just left the building and she would run downstairs and try to catch him. She left the phone and came back a few minutes later, completely out of breath. She said she had just caught Mark and he would be there in a minute. I knew damn well they didn't have any questions about the proposal; they were trying to reach me to tell me I had won — that was the only logical conclusion.

Mark came on the phone a few minutes later and I apologized for being difficult to reach. I explained I was in the process of moving from Houston to Sunnyvale and that was why my house phone in Dickinson was disconnected. Mark said I had to get in touch with Huntress immediately. Huntress was on his way home, so Mark gave me Wes's home phone number, as well as his NASA number and said I had to reach Wes before the weekend was over. It was very important I reach Wes, so I should call him as soon as I possibly could.

I immediately called Wes's home and his teenage son answered and said his father was not yet home. Then, from the background, his mother said to get my number. He did so and then his mom told him to repeat it back to me. He did and I said, "OK, thank you very much."

Rebecca was still not home, but I knew for sure I had won. Wes Huntress was not trying to get me under those circumstances to tell me he needed a new price on Lunar Prospector or some silly thing like that. I was elated and excited. I tried to read and instead listened to Wagner's enthralling music to pass the time until Wes called.

Around 6:00 Rebecca came home — a little bit earlier than usual. As she drove up, I ran out and yelled, "Honey, I got Lunar Prospector," and, of course, she kind of looked at me with an expression that said, "Oh yeah, I've heard that before." She was not about to get excited and believe that stuff. We went into the house, sat, talked a little bit, and started to have dinner in the kitchen. As we were eating, the call came. I got up and grabbed the phone and it was Wes.

We exchanged pleasantries and I said I was sorry I was so difficult to reach. I explained that Rebecca and I had just gotten married and I was making a double move from Dickinson to Rebecca's house to Sunnyvale. Then Wes congratulated me and said, "Lunar Prospector has been selected for flight." He was very complimentary and said the mission was so good it was an easy task to pick Lunar Prospector, it was just the best by far.

I said, "Thank you, I am very pleased."

I wanted to make sure I had gotten the straight-through slot and he answered my query with, "Yes."

But I still wanted to be absolutely certain and I asked, "Does that mean I don't have to go through down-selection?"

He answered, "That's right, you're going straight through, your mission has been accepted for flight." That was everything I had worked for all those years — I was very, very elated and very, very relieved!

At that point Wes said, "I have two requests for you. First of all, can you come to Headquarters for the news conference set for next Tuesday, February 28?"

I said, "Of course, I'll be there, no problem."

"The second thing I have to ask you will be very, very hard." Wes then said, "You can't tell anyone about this until the news conference, not a soul."

I said, "I can do that," but then I asked, "When can I tell Lockheed?" thinking, *if I go and have a news conference without Gus and Frank knowing it, they will have hemorrhages*.

Wes replied, "You can call them and your co-investigators just before the news conference. You should meet me in my office at 10:00, Tuesday morning. We will discuss how the news conference will be run and then we will go to the news conference which is set for 11:00 AM."

I said, "That's great. I'll keep quiet."

Rebecca finally believed me — SUCCESS AT LAST!

Saturday, February 25, 1995

Since there was no way to get travel orders through Lockheed by Monday, I called and got my airline tickets on my own credit card early Saturday — assuming Lockheed would make the travel orders after the fact given the circumstances (which it did).

I decided to let Tom know since he would know what was up anyway when I told him Monday I had to go to Headquarters, and I knew he would keep quiet. Further, his future was also dependent on Lunar Prospector. I called him at mid-morning and lied. I said Rebecca and I were taking a drive to downtown Houston and we wanted to stop by to say "Hi." He swallowed it hook, line, and sinker. Rebecca and I decided she would sidetrack Pauline and I would tell Tom I wanted to see his stupid birds and turtles so I could get him alone to tell him.

We left right away and drove the few kilometers to the Polette's. Our ploys worked and Tom and I went into his zoo room. I said, "Tom, you have to keep your mouth shut, absolutely shut. You can't tell Pauline or anyone what I am about to tell you. Do you understand?"

He said, "Yes," and then I made him promise on pain of death or worse. He said, "OK, OK. What's going on?"

I then told him of Wes's call and the news conference. Tom, too, was very, very elated and very, very relieved.

When Rebecca and I returned home, I was still concerned about Frank and Gus's reactions if they simply saw me on the news conference or found out about it and hadn't been told. Also I wanted Dom to be able to see the news conference. I called Dom at his home in Sunnyvale. I did not tell him I had won, rather just that Wes had called, I was flying to Headquarters for a news conference and he could draw his own conclusions. I told him the news conference was going to be at 11:00 AM Eastern Time (8:00 AM Pacific Time) — somewhat earlier than Dom's usual arrival time at work, so I wasn't sure he would see it. At first he said, "Well, I can see it at home because I have NASA Select." Then he said, "No, I'll go in early." Dom was also very, very elated.

I then called Pat and Julius to tell them I had to visit Headquarters, that I would be flying in Monday evening and asked if my usual hotel accommodations would be available. Without my saying a word, Pat knew why I was coming. In her position as editor of *Ad Astra* at the National Space Society, she had been invited to the news conference and put two and two together without saying anything directly to Julius. I knew she knew and Julius was still in the dark.

Monday, February 27, 1995

Monday was a busy and exciting day. I talked to Charles Ward in the morning about the legalities of closing down LEI. I picked-up my airline tickets and started doing the innumerable things that needed to be done so I could get out to Sunnyvale, go to the upcoming Lunar and Planetary Science Conference to give a talk on Lunar Prospector at Wes's request, and prepare for the news conference.

I wanted to see Rebecca and have lunch with her on my way to the airport, but time ran out. Tom and I had lunch, after which I drove off to the Houston Intercontinental Airport, where, because of an unexpected frequent flyer upgrade and consistent with my mood, I flew first class to Washington, D.C.

After taking the Metro to the stop nearest Pat and Julius's apartment, I arrived to find that no one was home. When the security guard called to let Julius know I was there, she told me she would let me in. I went into the building, got in the elevator and went up to the 7th floor. In the meantime, Julius had decided to come down and meet me, so he was coming down as I was going up. I walked to the apartment and banged on the door, which was open. I walked in and said, "Where is everybody?" to which there was no reply. I turned around and there was Julius just about to enter the apartment.

His first words were, "Well, what's going on?"

I explained to Julius I had won Lunar Prospector. Julius was ecstatic, just like a little kid; only Julius could act like that. We talked a little while and then Pat came from work. I started retelling the story and she said she had figured it out. She had the memo about the news conference. According to the memo, three missions were selected for further study and one had been selected to go directly to launch, and, of course, she knew it was Lunar Prospector without having to be told.

We discussed things more and I told them the details of what was going on as Julius finished preparing his usual delicious meatloaf dinner that I love so much. We ate dinner and just had a good time talking; both of them were just as excited and happy as I was. It was a dream come true for every one of my friends who wanted and helped it happen.

Julius brought up the possibility of Space Grant supporting some of the Educational and Outreach Programs, and I said, "Of course, I would love for you to do that because I hadn't spent much time thinking about how to get my Educational and Outreach Programs funded. That would be great."

That would also help Julius who was very worried about his job; all the cutbacks were beginning to get to the point where his job was in jeopardy. Julius was trying to find a way to keep himself going and he asked me if there was any way I could mention that Space Grant was going to support the educational program of Lunar Prospector during the news conference. I said I would if I possibly could.

I then called Rebecca to say "Good night," and we all talked to her. Of course Rebecca asked Pat if she would make sure that my tie was straight, that I looked decent and that my hair was combed — all the things that Rebecca just loves to do, but could not do under the circumstances. After that, we finally went to bed and I had a good night's sleep.

Chapter 2-2
The News Conference

Tuesday, February 28, 1995: The News Conference

After breakfast, Julius and I went to his office at NASA Headquarters and Pat went to her office at the National Space Society. Later she would come to NASA for the news conference. Since Julius had to go to Greenbelt, MD, for an all day meeting, he couldn't attend the news conference. I went down to the NASA library and looked through some journals just to pass the time and then went back to Julius's office.

It was now close enough to the time of the news conference that I decided to call Bill Feldman. Through the years, Bill's enthusiasm and support for Lunar Prospector had made him my favorite guy in the whole business, so I wanted to give him a heads-up on what was about to transpire.

When I reached him I said, just to keep up the suspense a little, "Bill, I can't tell you what's happening, but I will tell you I am here at Headquarters for a news conference about the Discovery announcement and you can guess whatever you want to." Of course Bill knew instantly we had won and he went off like a Roman candle. I told him I would talk to him after the news conference and fill in all the details.

Shortly after I talked to Bill, I walked up to Wes's floor and wandered around a little bit since it was still a little early. Finally, I went in Wes's office and sitting there were Richard Goody of Harvard University, and Don Bernett of Cal Tech. I asked, "Are you guys here for Discovery?"

They answered, "Yes," and added, "Are you the one who won the straight through slot?"

I answered, "Yes, I am." We congratulated each other and sat there chatting until Wes came out and invited us into his office. Wes began to wax eloquent about Lunar Prospector, and then Don Brownlee of the University of Washington walked in.

Wes told us we had to wait for a representative of Congressman Brown of California (one of the Congressmen who had signed the original Truly letter to get NASA to give Lunar Prospector the Apollo 17 Gamma Ray Spectrometer), who wanted to talk to us. Wes congratulated all four of us and explained that politically things were very critical. Figuratively speaking, the thing he wanted us to do the minute the conference was over was to get up to the Hill and help get congressional support for Discovery. It was now up to us, the PIs for the three study missions and Lunar Prospector, to help sell the program.

Wes didn't have to tell me that, but I was glad to have that directive from him because it would certainly ease things (so I thought) in the future when I was dealing with Lockheed management.

Wes told us a little about the news conference, it was already scripted, we did not need any of our own materials since PR had selected illustrations from our proposals, we were supposed to sell the Discovery Program, and talk about our science missions.

While we waited for Brown's representative to arrive, Wes told me about a conversation he just had with Congressman Brown, whose district includes McDonnell Douglas in the Los Angeles area. McDonnell Douglas was the real force behind Jeff Taylor's lunar rover mission proposal, "Pele." Brown had called Wes to ask if Pele had been selected and Wes said, "No, it wasn't."

Brown was not happy with that answer and had asked, "Well, who has been selected for the straight-through slot?"

Wes had answered, "Lunar Prospector."

Brown had said, "Oh, well that's great!" so everyone liked Lunar Prospector and that was good politically.

Brown's representative still was not there (he never did show up), so we finished our discussions and trooped down to the room where the Press Conference was going to be held. We were shown the illustrations Public Relations had prepared for each of us. Mine was the artwork of the spacecraft that was on the cover of the Proposal and the photo of the OMNI mock-up of the spacecraft with Mike Chobotov kneeling next to it.

After that we were given more instructions as to what to do and how they wanted us seated. Wes was going to be on the left and I would be next to him, and then came Brownlee, Bernett, and Goody on the right as seen from the audience. Wes told us the coming sequence of events — he would give an introductory discussion of the Discovery Program and how the proposals were reviewed, then he would introduce us and our missions, starting with the programs chosen for further study and ending with Lunar Prospector and me. I would then discuss Lunar Prospector. Brownlee would be next, followed by Bernett, and finally Goody. After we had discussed our missions, the reporters would then ask us questions. The whole thing was to last about an hour.

By that time, it was getting near time for the news conference to begin, so we went up on stage and took our assigned seats. The lights were extremely bright, and all of us squinted, except Wes, who, I guessed, was used to being in the spotlight.

Then the reporters started coming in. Pat came in with one of her colleagues from the National Space Society.

Some 2300 kilometers to the southwest in Houston, Rebecca, Tom, and John Gruener were seated in front of John's TV (John had NASA Select at home) with a tape ready to record. Rebecca had summarily told Sam, her boss at Baylor College of Medicine, I had won Lunar Prospector, I was going to be in a news conference, and she was not coming to work so she could see the news conference, period. Both Tom and John were just going to be a little late for work.

Another 3100 kilometers further west in Sunnyvale, Dom, Frank, Gus, Richard, Francisco, and others had gathered in Frank's conference room in Building 107 to see the event. The stage was set.

Finally, everything was ready and it was 11:00 AM. Doug Isbell introduced Wes and the "Discovery Mission Selection News Conference."

Wes's introduction of Discovery and the evaluation process was brilliant. He started by saying; "Today we are going to announce selections for the third and fourth missions in the Discovery series of low cost planetary missions." He explained further, "The first of the Discovery missions, the Near Earth Asteroid Rendezvous mission, will be launched less than a year from now and will cost less than one-third of the most expensive planetary missions in the history of planetary exploration. The Mars Pathfinder Mission is second in the Discovery series. It will be launched in December, 1996, to place a lander on the surface of Mars for less than ten percent of the cost of the last time we did that back in 1976." He added emphatically, "These are remarkable achievements in cost reduction." He continued, "In addition to being cheaper, the Discovery Missions are also faster and take far less time to develop than had become the practice in planetary exploration — less than three years from the start of development to launch — and it is our intent to launch a Discovery Mission on average about once every eighteen months or so, a far higher flight rate than we have ever had before." NASA was attempting to achieve these goals "by soliciting mission proposals from the general science and aerospace community rather than defining the mission here. These are not NASA defined and executed missions, but these are community defined and executed missions. We more or less turned the old way of doing business upside down. The old way was community support of NASA missions. The new way is NASA support of community missions. The old way was community participation in NASA missions. The new way is NASA participation in community missions and only as an option."

Wes clarified what I consider to be the two most important points for the resurrection and future development of the national space program: "In the Discovery Program the federal government is in essence essentially purchasing missions from the university and aerospace community. Discovery Missions are to be managed by a single Principal Investigator aligned with universities, industry, a federal center, . . . and that PI is solely responsible for the mission." That is, get the space program on a truly commercial basis and let the people who know how to do the job efficiently do it, rather than the government. Wes explained further, in order to get the best science for the least dollars, the scientists had to participate in an open competition. To win, "you have to earn it in the old fashioned American way, face to face competition, a shoot-out at OK Corral. And that's what we had here. That way the space science enterprise and the American people are assured of the best. I am here to tell you that today, that is just what we got."

Wes then came to the point that had concerned me most as I tried to decide if it was worth the effort to put in a proposal since I believed I would win if it were an open and fair competition, but I did not stand a chance if the "good old boy" system prevailed. Wes stated, "Related to competition is a fair and equitable evaluation. In the Discovery competition we just completed, we did some things we have never done before in order to ensure that that was the case. We used an almost wholly external proposal evaluation team from outside the agency, and included experts from a very broad cross-section of the community, including military aerospace."

At that point I looked over at Wes's notes on the evaluation team and process and thought, *how could anyone have gotten through that evaluation?* Then I listened, somewhat in awe to think that I had gotten through that process, as Wes continued, "We had a technical evaluation team of 72 scientists and engineers of which only 8 were from the agency. We had 12 from universities, 2 from the Smithsonian, 4 from non-profit science institutes, 15 from industry, 10 distinguished retired scientists and engineers from government and industry, 13 from the Air Force, 1 from the Navy, 6 from foreign science and engineering institutions, and even one OSTP. I should think that's a very broad team indeed. We had a team of 31 scientists who evaluated the science for each of these proposals, and we had 3 separate independent teams of engineers and experts evaluate the cost, technical feasibility, and the management approach for each of these proposals. One of these teams was an all Air Force team that included former staff from the Strategic Defense Initiative Office. Every proposal was reviewed by each team. In the end all of these teams met together to establish a consensus evaluation score for all of the proposals. We even had an evaluation process here at the agency to evaluate the evaluation process to ensure a thorough, complete, and fair evaluation. That process scored all the proposals, first on cost, second on science, then management, finally technical approach, and in that order of importance. We also rated the proposals on tech transfer, education, public awareness plans, small and disadvantaged business participation. That latter category counted for about 8½% in the score and was done by NASA expert staff. I would like you to note that the cost and science were both most important and almost equally rated. The goal was to get the best science per unit cost.

You could get an A in science, but if your cost was too high, you could get beat out by a B science proposal that cost less."

As was stated in the Announcement of Opportunity, NASA's intent was to select several missions for nine-month definition studies, and then down select to no more than two missions for development and flight. Wes added, "we threw the door open for mission proposals that could prove that they were ready to fly almost immediately. If we found among the proposals a mission that was inexpensive and could be certified ready for immediate flight development by the evaluation team, we would exercise that option for the first of the two flight missions." I was filled with pride as Wes then stated emphatically, "In fact we did find such a mission, so today we are selecting a very low cost mission for flight development." That was the high point of the news conference for me. Wes had yet to mention Lunar Prospector, but that did not matter. NASA had finally recognized the validity of the simple concepts behind Lunar Prospector, and the years of work all the LEI guys and I had put in had finally paid the ultimate dividend.

Wes explained further, in addition to selecting a mission for flight development, NASA had selected three other missions for definition phase and subsequent down selection to one.

Then Wes discussed the proposals. "I have to tell you we got some really dynamite proposals in that program. We got 28 of them. The proposals we received involved 36 universities across the country, 37 aerospace companies, small businesses, 12 national laboratories and FFRDCs, 12 foreign institutions, and 10 non-profit science institutions and observatories. We had proposals in just about every category in Discovery. We had ten mission proposals for comets and asteroids, four fly-bys, one penetrator, two orbiters, and three sample missions. We had two Mercury missions proposed, an orbiter and a fly-by. We had three Venus missions proposed, an orbiter and two probe missions. We had three Mars missions proposed, one polar lander, one orbiter, and one atmospheric balloon. We had six lunar missions proposed, four orbiters, one went to a comet afterwards, and two rovers. We had two Earth orbiters to look out at Jupiter's Io torus. We had one solar wind sample return and we had one mission proposed to search for planets around other stars. As a NASA selection official, I had both a hard and an easy job here. The hard job was to select so few; these were terrific proposals and I wish I could have chosen a dozen of them. The easy job was the selection itself. I just simply picked the highest ranked proposals, not a high ranked one for the Moon and a high ranked from Mercury and the like, I simply just skimmed the cream right off the top."

At that point I thought, *could this get any better?* I thought not, but it did.

Wes then introduced the four missions and four PIs, starting with the three missions selected for definition study. He began, "the first of these . . . is a mission to Venus entitled the Venus Multiprobe Mission. The . . . principal investigator is Professor M. Richard Goody of Harvard University . . . . The aerospace contractor is Hughes Communication and Space Company of El Segundo, California, the launch vehicle is a Delta to launch in June 1999, and the total mission cost proposed is $202 million . . . .

"The second . . . is for a solar matter sample return entitled Suess-Urey . . . . The PI is Professor Don Burnett of the California Institute of Technology . . . . The aerospace contractor is Martin Marietta Astronautics of Denver. The launch vehicle is a MedLite to launch in August 1999, and the total proposed mission cost is $214 million . . .

"The third . . . is for a comet matter sample return mission entitled Stardust . . . . The principal investigator is Professor Don Brownlee of the University of Washington in Seattle. The aerospace contractor is Martin Marietta and the launch vehicle is a MedLite for launch in February 1999, and the total proposed mission cost is $208 million . . . ."

Wes continued, "Finally, the mission selected for immediate flight development is a lunar orbiter mission entitled Lunar Prospector. That mission orbits the Moon to map its surface composition, its magnetic field, its gravity field, and gas release events in order to improve the understanding of the origin and the evolution, current state, and resources of the Moon. It will conduct a search for ice in the permanently shadowed regions of the Moon's South Pole. That was the highest rated of the all the proposals. The evaluation team felt that of all the proposals, that one was the best and most ready to proceed immediately to flight. It was also the least expensive of all the proposals, total mission cost proposed including the LLV launch vehicle was only $59 million and that's for a planetary mission, folks. That's just fantastic! The scheduled launch date is June 1997 and that's just a little more than two years from now. The Principal Investigator is Dr. Alan Binder of Lockheed, Sunnyvale sitting to my left. The aerospace contractor, of course, is Lockheed Missiles and Space Company . . . ." There it was, now the whole world knew Lunar Prospector was on its way to the Moon. I was very, very pleased and very, very proud.

Wes then gave me the floor and I discussed the history of the mission and our objectives. I explained we had started Lunar Prospector as a private effort over seven years earlier. Because we had little or no money to begin with, I had defined a simple, low cost mission with a high science value — just what the Discovery Program wanted seven years later. I went through the early efforts to get aerospace and commercial funding, how Lunar Prospector had been chosen once before by Mike Griffin to start the Space Exploration Initiative, and after all these efforts had failed, along came Discovery. I then discussed the science objectives and mission and then turned the floor over to Brownlee.

In turn, Brownlee, Bernett, and Goody discussed their missions. As they talked, I decided that Stardust was the most exciting of the three and I hoped that it would be selected as number four (which it was the following December).

While Bernett was talking about Suess-Urey, something caught my eye. I looked over and to my surprise there was Mike Griffin! He waved at me and gave me a "thumbs up." I thought, *what in hell is the matter with him?* Obviously Mike liked getting credit for having picked Lunar Prospector earlier to lead off the SEI. I was floored and annoyed that after having stabbed me in the back and vilified me in the way he did in order to try to kill and bury Lunar Prospector, he would now be so happy and give me a "thumbs up."

Wes, too, saw that and asked, "Did you see Griffin?"

I answered, "Yes, kind of unbelievable, huh?" Griffin floored both of us.

Finally, Goody wrapped up his discussion of his Venus Multiprobe Mission and turned the floor back to Doug Isbell who opened the floor to questions from the reporters. As he did, Wes got my attention by pointing to a list of the LExSWG lunar mapping objectives vs. the Clementine achievements and those of Lunar Prospector and the other five proposed lunar Discovery Missions. The list showed Lunar Prospector was doing all the rest of the mapping objectives not done by Clementine. Then he said, not speaking very softly and pointing to the other five missions, "These guys lost," meaning they lost because Lunar Prospector and Clementine nicely complimented each other and completed all the lunar mapping objectives at very low cost while the other missions in part duplicated Clementine and finished the lunar mapping at higher cost.

To which I replied, "Too much, huh?" meaning the other missions tried to do too much and had run up the cost to the point where they were not competitive with inexpensive Lunar Prospector, which had more limited goals.

That was nice. I was happy NASA thought so highly of Lunar Prospector, but I was disturbed they did not seem to understand that Lunar Prospector was only a step in completing the total global mapping and that we still had a lot to do. But right then, it was good enough. The main thing was the program was getting started and if it made NASA happy and got me the money I needed, that was fine with me.

During the question and answer period, the reporters asked a number of questions about our science missions, if we were all going to be launched from the Cape, if the other 24 proposed missions would have chances in the future and could the Discovery concept of having a long series of inexpensive mission succeed when all other NASA attempts to have consistent flight programs based on common hardware had failed. Wes answered several of the programmatic questions and was also asked why NASA wanted more lunar data since we had Apollo. Wes explained the importance of the Moon in planetary science and its unique role as being part of the Earth-Moon system and then asked me to add my comments. I explained how Lunar Prospector was building on the legacy of Apollo, the fact that the Moon was a window into the earliest stage of planetary development and that Lunar Prospector was doing only a part of the required mapping of the Moon — that there was still much more to be done.

Finally the news conference was over and we all left the stage. I was then cornered by a couple of reporters, one was a good-looking blonde and the other was Ralph Vartabedian from the LA *Times*. They asked me a number of questions about Lunar Prospector and then the thing started winding down. Finally after a couple more people came and talked to me, it was over and time for lunch.

As usual, I was hungry, so Pat and I went to lunch. Mark Hopkins wanted to go with us so we could talk about the political backing of Lunar Prospector. Mark was a member of the political arm of the National Space Society, and, as Pat told me later, sort of a loose cannon who you had to watch. We went to the restaurant in the NASA building, had hamburgers, and talked about the politics and the need to get to the Hill. Mark, of course, wanted to help do that. Also Mark and Pat told me there was a National Space Society sponsored meeting that Friday (March 3) which would bring together NASA officials, members of Congress, and supporters of the space program to discuss future programs, and suggested I come and present Lunar Prospector. That would have been an ideal forum, but my main concern was getting to Sunnyvale and getting Lunar Prospector started. If I stayed for the meeting, I would lose the rest of the week and not get to Sunnyvale until the following Monday, so I reluctantly declined.

After lunch, Pat and I went to Julius's office because I needed to make some calls. I checked to see if I could get an earlier flight and then I called Bill Feldman and told him all the good news. I tried to reach some of my other co-investigators without success and finally it was time for me to go.

I walked down to E'Lafont Plaza and got the Metro to the airport. While waiting for my flight, I succeeded in reaching Lon Hood and Alex Konpoliv with the good news, but could not reach Bob Lin and Mario Acuña. I called Tom Polette, and, of course, Rebecca, who by that time was getting much more used to the idea that I had actually done it and that we would be moving to California. I was elated, but tired and ready to go home. Finally my flight was ready and I was soon in the air on my way back to Houston.

Chapter 2-3
On to Sunnyvale

Thursday, March 2, 1995

Because NASA had delayed making its decisions as to who had won, the time available for me to get Phase B done had dwindled from nine to less than seven months. I needed to get out to Sunnyvale fast to start getting things organized and to discuss the details of my transferring to LMSC with Frank and Gus. I had made my travel plans Wednesday to fly to Sunnyvale on Thursday afternoon. Before I left Houston, I had some urgent personal business to attend to.

Bill Beatty had seen an article in a little Lockheed managerial newspaper saying that Lunar Prospector had won and had left a message congratulating me. I called Bill back and said I wanted to come over and see him and Bill Huffstetler (who had retired from NASA and was working for Lockheed) to thank them for all their support.

When I got to the top floor of Building 4, I asked the receptionist to call Bill Beatty and he came upstairs and got me. As we went down one floor, Bill congratulated me again and I thanked him for all the support he had given me during the last seven years. He was very happy and we talked about Lunar Prospector. Then we walked down the hall to find Bill Huffstetler, who had been so instrumental in keeping Lunar Prospector alive. We looked all over for Bill, but couldn't find him and then I saw him down the hall. I pointed at him and said, "Hey, I wanted to talk to you."

Bill came over. He was just ecstatic, and, completely out of character, gave me a big bear hug. I said, "Both of you guys did so much to help it happen."

And they, of course, said, "Oh no, we did nothing, you did it all." But the truth is that without Bill Huffstetler's support — letting me work on Lunar Prospector, getting Aaron Cohen behind me, and everything else he did to keep Lunar Prospector alive and to gain stature at NASA Headquarters — it would have been very difficult, if not impossible to achieve success.

I made sure they both understood how I felt and that I really appreciated their support through all the years. I said I would like to see Parten to thank him. Beatty said, "Let's go on up."

Unfortunately, as we started up to Parten's office, we banged into Moe Miller who was still there even though he was retired. As usual, Moe was in a fog and did not recognize me. He said, "Hi, my name is Moe Miller," like we had never met before! Bill Beatty tried to explain to him what was going on, but you could tell old Moe was in a stupor. We chatted a little, but he still hadn't the foggiest idea of who I was, what Lunar Prospector was or what was going on. I thought to myself in disgust, *how can Lockheed waste money paying that retired SOB, who screwed up at least two contracts and helped run the company into the ground, to sit around there as a consultant with a Golden Parachute?*

I managed to cut that inane conversation short and we continued on our way to see Parten. His secretary said he was busy preparing viewgraphs for a presentation, but I said I just needed a minute to thank him for his support. His secretary let Bill and me in to see him. He was happy too, but surprised because he had forgotten about my proposal effort! We chatted a little bit and then he started lecturing me on how to make sure that LMSC didn't take over Lunar Prospector and wreck it. Even though I had the same concerns about LMSC, I really didn't appreciate him telling me what to do, especially since he had dumped Lunar Prospector and me when I had asked for his support in dealing with LMSC when I started to approach LMSC about doing the proposal as my industry partner.

All in all, I was glad and very happy to have seen Bill Beatty and Bill Huffstetler, since those were the two guys I really wanted to thank. It was good to have talked to Parten since he was useful and supportive in the beginning, but I sure didn't appreciate seeing Moe Miller.

I called Gregg Maryniak, who I had tried to reach earlier, but he was on a trip. In the meantime he had left a message as to where I could reach him. Gregg was very pleased I had called him. He had wanted to call earlier and congratulate me, but he said he didn't want to sound like a boot-licker. He was extremely pleased I had called him. I said I was sorry that it wasn't happening the way we had all wanted, but it was better to do it that way than not at all. Of course, Gregg agreed. We talked about the early days and I said I was writing a book on Lunar Prospector and I wanted information from him about the early years and that made him even happier. Gregg and I had a really cordial and good conversation and I was pleased because I didn't want him to be left out of the success. He had done, risked, and lost a lot for the mission, and like Bill Beatty and Bill Huffstetler, deserved my heartfelt acknowledgment. Making that call and seeing Beatty and Huffstetler during the last hours before I left for Sunnyvale were very important to me.

I also got a call from George French. George had seen the NASA news conference and knew I had won and the lunar rover proposal he was part of had lost. George was extremely happy for me and congratulated me on the big win. Then he said, "As you know, I have this great educational program that was based on our lunar rover and now that we lost, I have no mission to tie it to. Would you be interested in my using Lunar Prospector as the focal point of that program?"

I answered, "In principle, yes, but I have no money in my budget to support any educational programs, not even the small ones I have in my proposal."

George said, "That's OK, I've got the money, I just need a mission to build the program around."

I replied, "In that case, hell yes, I'd be glad to have you be part of Lunar Prospector. Your education program would be a great enhancement of what I already have; so yes, that would be great." With that George and I became partners.

Friday, March 3, 1995 and the Weekend

Despite my having arrived at the good old Maple Tree Inn rather late Thursday night, I was up and into work at about 5:00 the next morning. My main concern, given that only seven months remained for us to finish the Phase B effort in order to be ready to start Phase C/D on Oct. 1, was to get started fast and waste no more time. Clearly some of the problems were my personal need to get hired by LMSC, to get Rebecca and our household things moved out to California, and to get settled so I could concentrate on my work.

I had tried to get Gus and Frank to hire me in January, so our move from Houston to California and getting settled would be behind me when and if I won, but they would have none of that. At exactly the time when I should have been concentrating on starting Lunar Prospector moving forwards, I would have to negotiate with Lockheed about my job and our move, look for a house, get moved, etc. Lockheed was not going to make it easy, and they didn't.

When Dom arrived for work, he was ecstatic. He, Gus, and most of the staff had seen the news conference and everybody was kind of in a tizzy. However, to my complete surprise, Dom complained bitterly to me that I had mentioned Mike Griffin during the news conference, but did not say a word about him. I tried to explain that NASA had told us to discuss the missions and sciences, that I did not intentionally slight him or Lockheed and that I mentioned Griffin only because he was part of the early history of Lunar Prospector. That did not satisfy Dom who continued to grump about it some more and finally let it go (for the time being).

Dom and I spent a good part of the rest of the morning strategizing about how we would have to work the Lockheed system to get Lunar Prospector done and how I could get a decent wage from Lockheed. Dom felt I should get at least $110,000 (we had put my wages as $120,000 in the proposal to cover all bets). Dom pointed out I should get a "win" bonus, Lockheed should buy my house, and make my transition as easy as possible, if they wanted to do things right, which, it turned out, they were not really interested in doing and certainly did not do.

As the day went on, I kept getting messages of congratulations from friends and colleagues in the USA and even from Europe. However, nice as that was, there were also calls from a few people who were going to do me the favor of letting me put them and their experiments on Lunar Prospector!

Gerhard Neukum had called from Germany; actually his call was waiting for me when I got to Sunnyvale. Gerhard blatantly said, "I want to be on the mission." Knowing Gerhard as I do, I would have been surprised if he had not demanded to be on Lunar Prospector and I knew he expected me to fly the camera he had developed. I did not bother to return Gerhard's call.

Alan Stern, who is one of the most self-serving, arrogant, and overbearing people I have ever known (he makes Gerhard look good) also left a message stating he wanted to talk to me right away because he had some very interesting propositions for me. By which I knew he meant, "I know everything better than you, so I will take over your program and then you can get out of my way." Needless to say, I did not return his call.

I had a similar call from Jim Arnold who also asked to be on my team. Jim wanted to help finish the mapping he had helped start during the Apollo Missions. In Jim's case, out of respect, I patiently explained that because of my limited budget I could not expand my team beyond that which was absolutely necessary to develop the instruments and fly the mission. Further, since many people had called and wanted to be on Lunar Prospector, I could not open Pandora's box by inviting him onto my team, despite his qualifications. Jim accepted that and offered any help he could give. I then indicated I would be happy to have him onboard when we got a data reduction contract and then Jim was satisfied.

Then there was still the pressing issue of my new position. The apparent lack of enthusiasm on the parts of Frank and Gus for hiring me was confirmed when Richard Lynch told me, as they all watched the news conference announcing I had won, Frank turned to Gus (or the other way around) and said "Well, I suppose we will have to hire him now."

With that in mind, I finally cornered Frank late Friday afternoon to discuss my contract. Frank gave me the same old Lockheed BS about not being able to get me much of a raise from my rather low $66,000 LMSC salary, despite Dom and I having put an appropriate $120,000 in the proposal, i.e., the money was there, but LMSC was not willing to pay me what I should expect to get as a PI who just brought in a much coveted new contract. He said, "We'll try to get it up, but it's not going to be anywhere near what you expect." Knowing well that Lockheed could pay me a decent wage if they wanted to, I reminded him that not only was I bringing a new program to LMSC, but they were also getting free (the Lunar Prospector contract, not Lockheed, was to pay OMNI systems the $100,000 for the right to use their design) a small, inexpensive spinner spacecraft design. If Lockheed started from scratch, the design would have cost them at least $1 million. To which Frank's attitude was, "So what!" With that annoying lack of support, I then reminded him we had to move rapidly to get Phase B started and done and I needed to get my job, our move, etc. out of the way so I could concentrate on Lunar Prospector. Frank said he was supposed to be gone the following week, but he would stay Monday and Tuesday to get the ball rolling on my position. He then suggested I talk with Rich Vondrak up at Palo Alto. Since Palo Alto was a science rather than an engineering based Lockheed organization, Rich might be able to get me a better wage. I called Rich and made an appointment with him for the next week. Rich liked the idea that I join his group, so I thought I saw a ray of hope LMSC would not screw me as badly as they wanted.

All in all, Friday was shot. Between all the calls, emails, and faxes, and because Dom was more interested in discussing Lockheed politics than getting down to business, I didn't get anything done. In fact, I was only in my office three times for a few minutes all day Friday. I worked all day Saturday and most of Sunday, even though I had wanted to drive down to Morgan Hill to look around for a house. But there was just too much to do, so I didn't get anything personal done.

Since my arrival at Sunnyvale, everything was exciting and hectic, but all the time Dom and I were blithely enjoying Lunar Prospector's success, trouble was brewing, both locally and some 4500 kilometers to the east in Washington.

Chapter 2-4
Trouble in Sun City

Monday, March 6, through Thursday, March 9, 1995

The trouble in Washington had started at the National Space Society's meeting (Friday, March 3) that Pat Dasch had wanted me to address. There were a number of Congressmen there, including Wisconsin Senator Sensenbrenner, who was a member of the Walker Committee and an enthusiastic supporter of the space program in general and the Discovery program in particular. Sensenbrenner was also highly incensed that Goldin had not gotten the Committee the five-year budget NASA was told to present to Congress, rather than the usual one-year budget.

As Pat told me in a call on Monday, she, Mark Hopkins, and some others had lunch with Sensenbrenner, during which he said there would be no new starts in the next fiscal year (October 1, 1996). Immediately Mark stuck his foot in it by asking, "What about Lunar Prospector, you're not going to stop Lunar Prospector are you?" To which Sensenbrenner replied there would be no new starts, including Lunar Prospector!

Of course, if I did not get the money required to start Phase C/D in October, Lunar Prospector would be dead.

Well that caused an earthquake in the community. Everyone was incensed. It appeared, even before the ink was dry on the Discovery Program Selection press release, NASA's attempt to find a "Faster, Better, Cheaper" way of doing business was being killed just three days after the news conference.

My first thought was to get my political activities going to fight that. I immediately tried to call George French, who, as it turned out, was in Washington. After a couple of days of playing a frustrating game of phone tag with George, we finally connected. George (as well as Pat and others I discussed the issue with) felt Sensenbrenner was posturing to put pressure on NASA, but George said he would contact Sensenbrenner about Lunar Prospector.

George immediately got to Sensenbrenner, who was already getting calls, letters, and faxes in support of Lunar Prospector from the space advocacy community, but Sensenbrenner held firm. Needless to say, I was deeply concerned.

The trouble on our side of the continent was that LMSC was just waking up to the fact that it had just won a highly visible (most LMSC missions are secret military missions), very fast, and very, very low cost mission — and upper management was not too happy about it.

That was becoming obvious, in part, because not one person from LMSC upper management, or anyone from LMSC, called to congratulate Domenick on our win. I was not surprised I did not get a call since nobody knew me at LMSC, but everyone knew Dom. It was a big win. Certainly in the past, a $59 million contract would have been of no consequence to Lockheed, but given the current state of affairs — the drastic downsizing due to the loss of military contracts — it was the only thing going.

We had won hands down in competition with 27 other excellent proposals and LMSC did not care. We had won a program with potentially a tremendous impact on how things were going to be done in NASA and Lockheed in the future (though Lockheed did not believe or understand it at that time). As the first peer reviewed and competitively selected Discovery Mission, Lunar Prospector was critical to the success of Discovery and Discovery was critical to NASA in its attempt to prove to Congress and the President it was reforming itself and learning to do things " Faster, Better, Cheaper." But Lockheed was just sitting and saying, "Oh, we're not excited or even interested in it."

Lockheed's indifference to Lunar Prospector was hammered home as we began to hear from a number of people inside and outside Lockheed that NASA Administrator, Dan Goldin, had called Lockheed CEO, Dan Tellep to congratulate him and Lockheed on winning Lunar Prospector and Tellep did not even know what Lunar Prospector was! No one in LMSC congratulated Dom and that hurt Dom's feelings a lot.

Dom and I became quite concerned as we began to find, not only was Lockheed not interested in Lunar Prospector, Lockheed management didn't even want the contract. They were scared of Lunar Prospector because it was highly visible — you can't hide your mistakes on a mission to the Moon like you can in a secret military mission — because it was very low cost, and because it had to be done in two years.

That was typified by the reaction of the vice-president who had signed the certified $1.7 million Phase B budget for the proposal and had just glanced over the $57 million Phase C/D and E budget estimates knowing they were not certified. His reaction to our win was, "What in the hell, I don't understand this. We proposed Phase B and end up getting Phases C/D and E, I never authorized any of this stuff."

We began to get the message that Lockheed might turn the contract right back to NASA and say, "Thanks, but no thanks." Dom and I found ourselves in a hostile environment rather than being congratulated on our success.

Then we began to hear that Lockheed wanted a technical review of Lunar Prospector before we even got started and before Lockheed would accept the contract. Dom and Gus agreed Lockheed would use such a review to kill Lunar Prospector. Dom, who was very skilled at that type of thing, quickly and successfully maneuvered us out of danger. Simply put, Dom flatly said, "There will be no technical reviews until we are ready," and he did a great job of stonewalling upper management.

Lockheed's hostile attitude towards Lunar Prospector's being chosen for flight contrasted dramatically to Martin Marietta's (which had just merged with Lockheed to form Lockheed Martin — from that point in time on, I worked for Lockheed Martin, but for simplicity, I will refer to the new company just as Lockheed in the remainder of the book) reaction to having won two of the three phase B studies (Stardust and Suess-Urey). Martin threw a big party for everyone involved! And even Frank was invited! What irony, Frank was going to Denver to a big party to celebration Martin's win of two lousy little Phase B studies while we had won the whole thing and Lockheed was totally ignoring us. That made Dom even more hurt and angry. Martin Marietta was treating its people with respect and appreciation while we were being treated like lepers. Every other aerospace company and the 27 other proposers were envious of us, they would have killed to be in our position — and Lockheed's reaction was "We don't want this." Needless to say, my opinion of Lockheed sank to even lower depths than I could have ever imagined.

Early in the week, Frank and I met at Ames with Scott and two or three Ames contracts people in order to start the process of getting the Phase B contract. I was told it generally took 30–90 days to get a contract ready for signature. I said, "Look, we have to get started, we have already lost two months because the winner was supposed to have been announced on the 15th of January. According to the schedule in our proposal, we expected the *Authority to Proceed* on the 1st of February and that clearly did not happen. Discovery was supposed to be Faster, Better, Cheaper, we did our part, we got the proposal done on time, NASA did not allow us any delay. I want the contract in less than 30 days. You guys say 30–90 days, I say it's going to be done in less than 30 days." I then set the signing date for the 30th of March and Ames agreed to it. They almost made it.

Scott was at Headquarters on Wednesday and he called Dom and me. Scott was with Mark Saunders and they said there were three problems.

First, Headquarters didn't like Scott having the project office at Ames. They wanted it back at Headquarters, so they were fussing about that and the title of Scott's position. Headquarters was not really going to release control of the project to our Ames-Lockheed team as we had in our proposal and as they had accepted. That problem plagued us for the next several months. So much for doing things a new and better way!

Second, Al Diaz, bless his black heart, didn't want Scott running the program for NASA and also being a member of the science team. It was either — or. If Scott wanted to be on the science team, he could not be the Ames Project Manager for Lunar Prospector.

We resolved that world shaking problem by having Bob McMurray of Ames be acting Co-I, that is, Scott's stand-in until the bureaucratic phase of the mission was over at launch, when Scott would regain his scientific role as one of my Co-Is.

The worst problem was Mark did not want to give us the budgeted $1.7 million for Phase B. Mark was trying to give us just a million dollars and he asked, "What's the impact?"

We answered, "The impact is that we can't do the work."

Mark said, "Well, we'll give you more money at the first of the year," that is, three months after Phase B was to be completed!

Dom said, "No, if you don't give us the full 1.7 million for this phase, then we are going to have a major slip. If you give us a million dollars, the slip is six months in the launch date. If you want us to keep the launch date, you give us all the money."

Mark asked, "What if we gave you 1.5 million?"

We answered, "That would cause a three month slip."

That was the same old trick NASA has always tried for the last 35 years, "We won't give you all the money, but you can make it up later," and it always resulted in major slips and major overruns. NASA never learns, even after they realized they had to do things "Faster, Better, Cheaper" or fail as an agency, they still reverted back to the "old way" even before we got started. But Dom and I held firm and ended up winning. If we had not, Lunar Prospector would have been in serious schedule and cost trouble before we even had the Phase B contract signed!

I went to see Gus in order to thank him for his help and his backing over the past seven years and especially for his helping me get Lockheed management to support my proposal effort. I also wanted to start the discussions of my joining the LMSC staff — I was still annoyed I hadn't been hired in January. Now I had won and there were a million things to do for Lunar Prospector. Simultaneously, I had to get Rebecca and our household goods moved out to California and I didn't even have a contract with LMSC!

When I got to see Gus he was extremely gracious in his congratulations to me on winning Lunar Prospector and praised my persevering in the face of all the obstacles placed in my way over the previous seven years. To my great surprise, Gus then apologized to me for never having been 100% behind Lunar Prospector (a fact which had been obvious to me for a long, long time; nevertheless, I was very grateful for the limited, but critical, support he had given me), but he assured me he was certainly 100% behind it then. However, when I brought up the issue of my contract, he said curtly I would have to talk with Frank about that — so much for his 100% support!

Right after I left Gus's office, I went to the display room because San Jose's TV Channel 4 (or 11) wanted to interview Dom and me for the evening news. The interview was fun; we talked about the science and technological impact of Lunar Prospector's simple and inexpensive mission. Dom was hyper as usual, never finishing a sentence before starting the next and butting in when I was trying to answer the questions asked of me. Nevertheless, the reporter was pleased with her interview and also excited about Lunar Prospector.

Aviation Week also had a major article on Lunar Prospector by James Astor. It was a very good article except it had some mistakes in it, the worst of which was that Lunar Prospector cost $73 million instead of $59 million. Nevertheless, I was pleased about the article.

Frank was at LMSC until Wednesday, and before he left to fly to Denver for the Martin Marietta celebration party, we sat down to discuss my new position at LMSC. Like Gus earlier, Frank assured me he really liked and believed in Lunar Prospector, but unlike Gus, Frank did not mention his earlier lack of support for — and even opposition to — Lunar Prospector. He stated Lunar Prospector was helping to fulfill his dreams; he had wanted to be part of the Hubble Telescope and was, and he also wanted to be part of a lunar orbiter and now that was going to be the case thanks to me. He said when he was at NASA he always tried to get a Lunar Polar Orbiter into the program one way or another and was annoyed because there was never the support needed for it. Maybe so, but I had not noticed any support from him when I tried to get Gus and Lockheed to help fund Lunar Prospector earlier. Also I could not help thinking how easy it is to jump on the bandwagon when someone else has done all the work.

Finally, Frank cut the BS and got down to the business of insuring me I probably wasn't going to get anywhere close to $100,000 or a sign-on bonus or even a win bonus. In short, I was getting *screwed*. Their excuse was, because LESC had low wages, they could not (translation: did not have to) give me the wages I deserved. Lockheed policy prohibits one Lockheed Company from hiring away good employees from another Lockheed Company by offering them much higher wages. If I were not a Lockheed employee at LESC, but came from some other low paying company or university, they could up my wages to whatever level they wanted to. Nice excuse, but I did not buy it. That was followed by the sage advice that if I did not like the wages they would eventually offer me, I did not have to take the job. In essence, I could just walk away from Lunar Prospector or get screwed — it was my choice.

In addition to wanting to be on my team, Jim Arnold and his people at UC San Diego wanted even more of Lunar Prospector. The Discovery selection of Lunar Prospector made for a politically very charged situation — many of the losers were mad at having lost or were trying to exploit my successes and somehow get involved with Lunar Prospector. It turned out Jim had a "great deal for us," which started with the basic premise that "even though we lost and you won, we will tell you how to do your job." Jim, Mick Wischerchen, and another UC San Diego person came to LMSC Thursday morning to see Gus, but not me. However, Gus told me of their call and invited me to "crash" their meeting. They were trying to sell Lockheed on using their students to help build Lunar Prospector! They have a big network of students to do student programs. It was totally idiotic to suggest to Lockheed that students build parts of Lunar Prospector and Gus fended them off. I let Gus do his job, since Jim was trying to get around me by going directly to LMSC management.

As the whirlwind week of March 3 to 9 came towards its end, I was trying to decide when I could get back to Houston. I had planned to stay in Sunnyvale until Friday the 10th because Dom needed a vacation and was going to go to Hawaii. He and his wife were going to leave Wednesday night and come back Sunday. Since there was so much intrigue going on about Lunar Prospector, Dom was worried and felt it was important for one of us to be at LMSC at all times to keep us and Lunar Prospector from being stabbed in the back. I had to be back in Houston by the next Monday to give a talk on Lunar Prospector at the Lunar Planetary Science Conference. Dom said, "Well fine, you are going to be here through Friday and I'll be back Monday. Not too much should be able to happen over a weekend since these guys don't work over the weekend anyway."

Chapter 2-5
Back to Houston

Late Thursday, March 9, 1995

Ever since we knew I had won, Rebecca had great trepidations about her boss's reaction to her terminating her job. She had given Sam her two weeks notice the Wednesday after the news conference and reminded him she had warned him much earlier I might win Lunar Prospector and we would then go to California. Even when I stopped to say goodbye to Rebecca at her office on my way to the airport the previous Thursday and discussed my winning Lunar Prospector with Sam, he still didn't catch on that Rebecca would really be leaving soon — for good.

During the week, as I slaved away twelve hours a day on Lunar Prospector in Sunnyvale, all of Rebecca's friends were very happy for her. They gave her all kinds of parties and gifts and took her out to dinner and lunch and drinks. She loved all that and I was very happy for her — it was great.

Even Sam finally caught on that week that she would soon be gone, so he wanted to take us out to dinner on Friday night to celebrate her six years of loyal, excellent work and my winning Lunar Prospector. He, his wife, and daughter were going to go to Big Bend Park in West Texas that weekend, so the dinner had to be Friday night.

I decided I wanted to get out of Sunnyvale and back to Houston late Thursday. Rebecca and I had all kinds of things to do to get ready for our move and our imminent drive out to California to look for a house. I decided I wouldn't say anything to Dom because he would just get nervous if he knew I was going to fly out late Thursday. I figured the world couldn't fall apart totally if he and I weren't at LMSC one whole day. I changed my flight plans to fly home late Thursday.

I was at Ames shortly before my flight back to Houston and it was raining like crazy. It was a hard rainy season and there was flooding all over California. As I prepared to leave Ames, the water in the parking lot was up to the hubcaps of the cars. I thought, *damn, it's a good thing I am getting the hell out of here today. I hope I make it.*

I drove up to the San Francisco International Airport and dumped the car at Hertz and it was still raining hard. I walked in and there was not a single person in line at Continental. As I walked up to the counter, the man who was doing the ticketing asked, "Are you going to Houston?"

I answered, "Yes I am." I started to explain I had changed my tickets.

He said, "Don't worry about it. The flight you are on is delayed a couple of hours, but don't worry, the earlier flight was also delayed a couple of hours and is about to leave. If you run you can catch it."

I took off running down to the gate. Sure enough, the airplane was still there and I told the person at the gate, "My plane reservations had been changed from tomorrow to today and the guy at the desk told me to run down and get on this one." I walked right in the airplane and it took off. That resulted in my getting home a little after midnight, a whole hour earlier than I would have, so the rain actually helped me. It was great to see my sweetheart again.

Friday, March 10, 1995: Sam's Dinner

After dropping Rebecca off at her office near downtown Houston, I drove down to Clear Lake to LESC to clean out my desk and get everything ready to leave. People were still calling me up to congratulate me. I got a call from Mick Culp and he came to the Lunar and Planetary Science Conference the following week to say Hello.

Tom and I had lunch together and then late in the afternoon I left work, drove up to pick up Rebecca, we went home, got dressed, and then drove to an Italian Restaurant near downtown Houston to meet Sam and his wife. We had an absolutely wonderful evening with them. We had a very expensive meal, but as Rebecca said, Sam would probably just put it on his University charge account. It was kind of disgusting that he might not pay for it himself since that was her going away dinner after six years of working for him and my congratulatory dinner. Even though he was rich, he was too cheap to pay for dinner!

Saturday, March 11, and Sunday, March 12, 1995

Rebecca and I spent most of the weekend getting ready for our drive to California that would begin immediately after my talk on Lunar Prospector at the Lunar and Planetary Science Conference early Wednesday afternoon. Our plan was we would drive to California and look for a house. Then Rebecca would fly back to Houston and come to California as soon as I had my new position and LMSC had arranged to move our household goods.

My good old friend, Chuck Wood, came into town Saturday night for the Conference and to see us. He had called me much earlier and was very happy I had won Lunar Prospector. In light of the fact that neither he nor I are well-liked by many in the lunar and planetary science community (we didn't fit into the various cliques, we didn't jump on the bandwagons, and we didn't kiss the appropriate butts, so a number of our mutual detractors, especially a number of the Building 31 crowd at JSC, were very annoyed I had won Lunar Prospector, especially since their proposals had lost big time), I said to him as we talked on the phone, "Lunar Prospector is the revenge of the Nerds," and we had a good laugh.

Chuck arrived at our house in far west Houston late Saturday afternoon. We chatted for a while and then went for a very nice dinner at a nearby Mexican restaurant. It was really good seeing Chuck. He has been a good true friend since our graduate school days at U of Arizona in the 60s. I was very pleased to be able to share the joy of Lunar Prospector with Chuck.

My other good old friend, Don Davis, had arrived from good old Tucson on Saturday. He called us Sunday afternoon to see if we wanted to go to dinner with him — of course we did! Rebecca and I drove down to Clear Lake where Don was staying. That was the first time Don had met Rebecca, so we talked about us, as well as Lunar Prospector. Of course, Don was his usual self, playing the devil's advocate about Lunar Prospector and the future of space exploration, which Rebecca, who was not used to Don, didn't appreciate very much.

We had a good chat and then decided to go out to dinner — Don wanted barbecue. He wanted to go to a real Texas barbecue place, so we tried to find one, but couldn't. We ended up going to Luther's Barbecue. Rebecca wasn't too happy about that, but it was OK. We got our meal and were talking and having a good time when, all of the sudden, there was a clank on the window next to Rebecca. She looked out and said, "Oh, there's Julius and Pat." Julius loves Luther's and they always go to Luther's whenever they are in Houston. We invited them to come in and join us. That was really nice because we were trying to figure out a time when we could to get together with Pat and Julius. We all had a nice long chat, and finally the evening was over, and we all went home.

Monday, March 13, through Wednesday Afternoon, March 15, 1995: The Lunar and Planetary Science Conference

Rebecca still had two days left to work so I went to the Conference alone Monday and Tuesday.

I drove down to Clear Lake to check into the Conference at JSC early on Monday morning. I was very surprised — I thought I would have to register and pay the conference fees, but now that I was a "big-shot," NASA had already taken care of everything! I just walked in and got my Conference abstracts, schedule, so forth. When I arrived, most people I knew congratulated me, except of course, the Building 31 crowd, most of who would not even say hello. Graham Ryder did manage to say, "Congratulations," — then added, "You Bastard, you!" and Paul Spudis simply walked by me in the hall without even taking note of my disgusting presence. All these events gave me a great deal of satisfaction — there is no revenge like success!

Gerhard Neukum spied me and came right over. Since Gerhard had called from Germany and said he wanted to be on the mission, I was trying to figure out how to politely handle him. That annoyed me, but as Gerhard sat down, he said he had found out more about Lunar Prospector and realized there was no way his (or any other) camera could be flown on it. In response to his rhetorical question about the downlink rate, I answered, "Yes we only have a 3.6 kilobit downlink, Gerhard." That defused that issue. I was pleased since I regard Gerhard as my friend — he is the only German colleague with whom I use familiar rather than formal German when we talk.

Then Bill Feldman came in. It was the first time I had seen him since we had won. He was happy and excited, but concerned. Bill started to tell me, after trying unsuccessfully to get me to let him on our team, Jim Arnold had called him trying to get on my team. Bill replied, "This is Alan's mission, he's the PI. Only he can make any changes like that. I can't make that decision, only Alan can do it."

Bill was also very concerned and insulted that Jim and the rest of the gamma-ray spectroscopy community were very critical of our gamma-ray experiment. At that point, we saw Jim walking towards us.

Given Jim's phone calls and his visit to LMSC, Bill and I knew what was coming. Bill and I knew how politically charged the situation was. Most of our community incorrectly believed NASA picked Lunar Prospector simply because it was inexpensive, and hence, Lunar Prospector must have little science value. They all felt their much more expensive and, in their minds, much better missions got passed over unfairly. None of the other scientists had believed NASA's clear directive that it was after missions costing less than one half of the cap (less than $100 million) and would select the missions based on the science value per dollar — not the most science. Now, because they had not followed NASA's directive and I had, they were all ticked off at Lunar Prospector and me.

The dumbest part of that was, if the lunar science community did not stop complaining about Lunar Prospector, Congress might just cancel the entire Discovery Program. Thus Bill and I were in a delicate position, we had to defuse the considerable antagonism against us without insulting our colleagues or letting them run all over us.

The situation was doubly annoying to me. First, while our detractors were complaining bitterly about our flying a low resolution, but very low cost BGO Gamma-Ray Spectrometer rather than a high resolution, but very expensive Germanium Gamma-Ray Spectrometer, they completely ignored the high science value of our first class Neutron Spectrometer, Alpha-Particle Spectrometer, Magnetometer, Electron Reflectometer, and Doppler Gravity Experiment.

Second, they all ignored the fact that none of the other five lunar proposals had come even close to winning. None of them were among the three missions picked for Phase B study. In fact, none of the other lunar proposals were even among the top seven or eight proposals and the Wisconsin Lunar Rover proposal, headed by Apollo 17 Astronaut Harrison Schmidt, the founding father of Astrogeology, Gene Shoemaker, and my old enemy Mike Griffin, came in last in the evaluation of the 28 proposals. Thus, if Lunar Prospector had not won, we would not have had any lunar mission, period! Why keep stabbing us in the back?

Upon reaching us, Jim said he wanted to talk to us. I said, "Well, why don't we go find a place we can talk quietly." We went to the pressroom which was empty and sat down. Jim congratulated us, then started right into a tirade about how the mission (meaning the gamma-ray spectrometer experiment) had to be done right.

Jim said, "You guys have to fly a sodium iodide or a germanium detector," and so on. He complained, "The mission has to be done right, because we are not going to get another chance," meaning, of course, we did not know how to do it right, but he did (funny, an independent review committee of about 100 scientists, engineers, budgetary personnel, and managers thought we did know how to do our mission, but I guess they were wrong).

I said to Jim, "You have to realize we proposed a very specific mission. It is a very inexpensive mission and we are just a few months from C/D. We do not have the time and money to redefine the mission." Jim appreciated that, or at least he had to acknowledge it. I added, "We appreciate any advice, we are not disregarding anyone's counsel, but basically we are not in a position to change anything. We have very little money and are doing the simplest and least expensive mission we can. That is what NASA wanted and we are going to deliver what we said we would." Jim then assured us he did not want to act the role of a spoiler. He did not want to say anything against the mission because he realized it would be politically devastating if the community destroyed Lunar Prospector out of jealously and stupidity. The community would be destroying not only Lunar Prospector, but also Discovery and then there would be nothing. Though Jim was sensitive to that, he was still putting us in a very difficult position — and though he may not have realized it, he was also putting himself in a very difficult position.

Nevertheless, Jim continued rattling on about how the experiment had to be done — definitely not the way we were doing it. Somewhat annoyed, Bill interrupted and explained how we were doing it. The really sad and annoying part was that Jim didn't have any idea of what we were really doing — he just wanted us to do it his way!

Bill described the BGO detector, its resolution and sensitivity, and that began to mollify Jim. We discussed other aspects of the experiment — the structure of the spectrometer itself, how it was oriented and how we were going to collect the data. As Jim began to understand what we were actually doing, he became more and more relaxed about it — we were obviously undermining all his arguments. Finally he said incorrectly, "Well, you know, the experiment is sitting on the spacecraft."

I immediately retorted, "No it's not, it's on a 3½ meter boom," so the last of his uninformed arguments exploded in his face! Basically I ended the conversation by saying, politely of course, "Yes, we are interested in your comments, but get the hell out of our way and leave us alone. You are not going to run that experiment, we are."

Though our conversation with Jim pretty much defused that situation, there were a lot of negative undercurrents at the Conference. Most people congratulated us, but some turned right around and stabbed us in the back.

Despite these incidences, there were a lot of positives at the Conference. The people who like me and have some respect for me were all very nice. I had hoped to hear Jeff Taylor's talk, but I didn't because of our discussion with Jim. Julius told me later that Jeff, whom I have always liked and respected, pointed out that Lunar Prospector was going to provide a lot of new data from a number of different experiments.

Mike Drake ended his Lunar Science overview talk by discussing Lunar Prospector; he even had a slide of our data sheet showing the instrumentation. Mike said Lunar Prospector was going to fly very soon and it wasn't doing everything perfectly since we were not flying the Germanium Gamma-Ray Spectrometer, but "look at all the good science." He urged everybody to be happy that Lunar Prospector was flying.

I was happy about Mike's comments. Right after his talk, Mike and I met in the hall. He said, "I haven't had a chance to congratulate you." Mike was very complimentary saying, "You understood what was needed and what NASA wanted — you found a niche and did the job right." Mike was a member of Bill Boynton's Lunar Orbiter team and said, of course, "While I am disappointed we lost, you did a marvelous job and I support you all the way."

Mike said Bill Boynton was going to talk to the Walker Committee in a couple of days. Given all the negative comments about Lunar Prospector by the losers, Bill was going to defend Lunar Prospector and the Discovery Program to the Committee. Bill was in the best position to champion Lunar Prospector since he was the PI of one of the losing lunar teams. Needless to say, I was very pleased with Mike's comments.

The next major event at the Conference was the Discovery talks on Wednesday afternoon. Rebecca and I got up that morning and got dressed. I had to put a hated suit and tie on for my talk; I conceded that as a Discovery Program PI, I could not give my talk looking like a slob. Rebecca got all dolled up and looked just absolutely gorgeous. She wore her purple suit and purple high heels — beautiful.

We drove down to Clear Lake in her car, since my car was packed full — ready for our late afternoon departure to California. We arrived at LMSC rather late, picked up Tom, found Julius and Pat over at the Conference, and all went to the "Soup and Salad" and had a light lunch. We came back and got ready for the Special Session on the Discovery Missions.

Mark Saunders was the moderator and he introduced Wes Huntress. Wes talked about Discovery for about 15 minutes, basically it was a short version of what he had so brilliantly said at the news conference just 17 days earlier. How time flies when you are having fun.

The first speaker, from APL, discussed the first Discovery mission, NEAR, which was to be launched in just a little less than one year to the Near Earth Asteroid, Eros. He stressed how inexpensive NEAR was, but I thought, *yeah, but it still cost four times what Lunar Prospector costs.*

Then Matt Golombek, the Project Scientist on Mars Pathfinder from JPL, discussed the second Discovery Mission. Matt was very confident and did a good job; I always liked him. He pointed out that Pathfinder was going to land on July 4, 1997. I thought, *that's a month after we get into lunar orbit, we will beat them if we stay on our schedule!*

Mark then introduced Lunar Prospector and I got up, gave my talk and went through my viewgraphs. My viewgraphs were not fancy like Matt's and APL's, since I had few resources for Lunar Prospector compared to those of JPL and APL. And that reminded me of a funny thing my good friend John Gruener did to aggravate some of the Building 31 guys. John knows my feelings about many of those guys and their feelings about me — and John agrees with me.

John had taken my simple computer drawings of Lunar Prospector from the article that was in *Aviation Week* over to the guys who were part of Boynton's losing team. They had Pat Rawlings, the famous Houston space artist, paint a beautiful and expensive piece of artwork of their lunar orbiter. John said, "Gee, look at that really primitive artwork on that one mission and this really beautiful expensive artwork on the other. No money spent on artwork on the first one and a lot of money spent on the second one, gee I wonder which mission won!" Of course, the guys didn't appreciate that very much, and John then added, "Gee, maybe you should have spent your money on your spacecraft rather than on your artwork."

I answered a few questions at the end of my talk. The ones I didn't like were those from a guy, who was obviously from Clementine. He snottily said, "Your launch vehicle is LLV2, has it ever flown?"

I answered, "No it has not, it's under development."

He asked, "Has LLV1 ever flown?"

I answered, "No, it's on the pad."

He said, "Well, it's not a very reliable rocket, is it?" He was trying to get his digs in, he was doing that to each of us. Every question he asked during each of our question periods was designed to put the Discovery Missions down and make Clementine look better than it was. That was very annoying since the Clementine crew had lied about their costs — they were around $200 million, not $50 million as they reported, and over played their results.

Finally, after my talk, Wendell Mendell said he just heard that the Japanese government called up the Japanese lunar scientists and demanded, "The Americans are flying that very inexpensive lunar mission, why are your costs so high? You are spending too much money!" Wendell and I had a good chuckle about that.

Shortly after that, Rebecca and I were getting ready to leave the Conference and start our drive to California.

Chapter 2-6
Off to California (via Arizona)

Four PM, Wednesday, March 15, through Monday, March 20, 1995:
The Trip West

The Chinese Proverb says, "Each journey begins with one step," so, as Rebecca and I turned and started to leave the conference hall, we began our journey to California and a new and exciting chapter in our lives.

We walked to her car and got in it. Rather than immediately taking off my hated tie, as I usually would, I left it on. Today was not only the beginning of our new life; it was also the one-year anniversary of our getting engaged. I wanted to do something special and surprise her.

It was about 4:00 PM and I was, as usual, starting to get hungry. It would be after 5:00 before we got to her house and changed clothes for our trip, so it would be time to eat before we actually got on the road. As we were driving home and getting near Highway 59, I said, "Honey, aren't we somewhere near the Steak & Ale where we had our first date?"

She answered, "Yes, it's not too far from here."

I said, "Let's go and have supper to celebrate the first year anniversary of our engagement at the place where we met and had our first date."

She responded, "Yes, that's a great idea."

We had a nice meal and then drove home, getting there a little before 6:00 PM. We changed clothes and were soon ready to leave, and my little blue Ford Festiva was fully packed and ready to go — much to her consternation.

Saturday and Sunday I had piled up all the stuff I wanted to take with me; my wooden telescope, the suitcases, pillows, and three boxes of office stuff. Rebecca kept saying, "You're never going to get all that in your car. You're never going to get it in your little tin wagon," insulting my nice little blue car. I had loaded the car the night before. I got everything in very neatly with plenty of room to spare. I made her eat crow every opportunity I had. She had to call my car (which she hated) a "Nice little Cadillac" all the way to California. We got in the car and rolled out of her driveway at 6:20 PM.

We took off and within a few minutes were on my beloved I-10, heading west. It was cloudy and raining off and on. We hoped we could make San Antonio, nearly 300 kilometers and 3 hours to the west, before I was too tired to drive any farther. We also thought about staying in Seguin, about 50 kilometers east of San Antonio, where we had stayed on our first trip to San Antonio when we were falling in love. However, since I was driving like a bat-out-of-hell, as I usually did, we passed Seguin and San Antonio and reached Boerne (some 40 kilometers west of San Antonio) somewhat after 9:00 PM. I had been driving about three hours and had covered almost exactly 320 kilometers and I had to gas up. As we were driving out of the gas station in Boerne, we saw a motel across the street, so I asked, "Why don't we stop here and get some sleep?" We did. We got a room and bedded down at about 10:00 PM. I woke up at 3:30 AM and immediately woke Rebecca up. We stopped at the same place where we had gotten gas the night before so I could get a coke and she could get some coffee. We were on I-10 again at exactly 4:01 AM.

We had planned to stop and see Mark, Rebecca's nephew, in El Paso. The last time I had driven through west Texas — when the US still had the 90 kph speed limit — I had driven from Dickinson starting at 5:00 AM and had reached Van Horn at 10:00 or 11:00 PM, when I stopped and turned in. I thought we might get to El Paso in the evening or possibly in the late afternoon, stay there that night, and see Mark. I just barreled along the flat, straight stretches of I-10 in west Texas at my typical speed of 130 to 140 kph. Rebecca read and we talked and listened to music and had a great time and I just drove and drove towards the west, towards the future, and towards Lunar Prospector.

We called Mark later that morning to arrange to meet him, but it turned out he had to go to Albuquerque for an interview, so we would miss him. We said OK and decided to just keep going.

We were in Van Horn, TX, by 11:00 AM and had a not-so-good Mexican lunch. At 12:30 PM, we passed through El Paso. At the rate we were going, it was clear we would make Tucson that evening! We tried and failed to call Debbie, Rebecca's niece in Tucson, and let her know we were actually going to get to Tucson that evening and not the next day as we had told her before. We called Shirley, Rebecca's sister, and let her know our revised schedule.

I was tooling along at about 120 kph through Las Cruces in a 90-kph-speed zone and got a speeding ticket for $38.00 (the first of the two I expected on that trip — and I was right). Rebecca was a little miffed, but I explained to her that all I was doing was paying my fee so I could drive fast. She seemed to accept my logical explanation. We took off and I behaved myself for a little while, and then, of course, I got going faster.

We went through Deming, NM and then crossed the border to my beloved Arizona. As I drove, I explained the geology to Rebecca and then I saw some brilliant orange-yellow color on the mountains. I said, "Look at the flowers." Rebecca wouldn't believe me. She said it had to be dirt, it could not be flowers, but it was — the Arizona wildflowers were blooming. It was just beautiful.

We drove on and got to Texas Canyon (just east of Willcox, AZ) where I had told her about the beautiful orthoclase crystals in the granite porphyry there. I asked, "Would you like to stop and see them?" and she did. We stopped and stretched and used the bathrooms and I showed her the crystals, some of which I have in my mineral collection. Also, a few kilometers later, I showed her the hills near Willcox where I collected fossil echinoid spines during my graduate student days. I was enjoying seeing my old haunts and teaching her some geology. We were having a great trip. It was wonderful being with her and sharing all of it with her.

Sure enough, we rolled into Tucson just after 6:00 PM; accounting for the hour time difference, it had been just 25 hours since we left Houston. We drove off I-10 at Houghton Road on the east side of Tucson and found Debbie's house without any trouble, but nobody was there (actually, Doug, Debbie's husband, was in the back and didn't hear us at the door). We decided to go to a public phone and call our hotel to see if we could get our room a night early and found out that Debbie had already taken care of it. As we were driving away to go to the hotel, the car right behind us kept honking at us. At the next stop sign, we looked behind us at the pesky driver and found that it was Debbie! As she had passed us going in the opposite direction, she saw the Texas license plates and then recognized my car and me from photographs (she had never met me before). She did a quick U-turn and caught us. We went to Debbie's, sat out on her patio and talked and ended up ordering pizza. Later we went to our hotel, ending the first full day on our trip to Sunnyvale.

The next day (Friday, March 17), Rebecca and I had a great hike in Sabino Canyon. The hike lasted until about 2:00 PM, so we gave up our plan to go to the Desert Museum.

Doug, Debbie, Rebecca, and I then had a nice Mexican dinner, after which we went back to their house and waited for Shirley to arrive from Scottsdale.

After Shirley arrived, she, Rebecca, and Debbie started a marathon gabfest during which I fell asleep on the couch. I woke up an hour later and they were still at it so I said I was going to the hotel. They said they would bring her to the hotel later — which never happened. They talked until 2:00 AM. As a result, Rebecca got very little sleep.

On Saturday, the 18th, Rebecca and I went to the Desert Museum which was just great as always, though it was the first time Rebecca had seen it. Afterwards, we went back to Debbie's for her son's (Luke's) 3rd birthday.

Sunday morning we just relaxed with Rebecca's relatives and we drove to Scottsdale in the late afternoon. We were going to stay at Shirley's Sunday night in preparation for the last leg of our drive to Sunnyvale Monday. After we arrived, we decided to go out and eat Mexican food. Rebecca and Shirley yakked again until the wee hours of the morning as I slept.

I woke up at about 3:30 AM and got Rebecca up off the couch where she had fallen asleep and we left at about 4:00 AM. We drove uneventfully up to Flagstaff, AZ, turned on Highway 40 and headed for California. I got nailed the second time for speeding near Kingman, just before leaving my beloved Arizona. That ticket cost $95 for going 125 kph in a 105 kph zone. I had my two tickets, as I thought I would.

Soon we passed through the border and later we stopped for lunch in Ludlow, where back in the Viking days, Ray Arvidson, Ed Guinness, and I had stopped and eaten when we were on our trip to the volcanoes there. Ludlow is on a piece of old Route 66, so Rebecca and I rode on that for a few blocks and she took some pictures. We got back on Highway 40 and hightailed it to Barstow, then found our way over the pass down into the central valley and started north on Highway 5. We passed over the bridge that had been on the national news because it had been washed out in the storms a week earlier and we could see a lot of the damage and flooding.

It was getting dark and rainy. We found Highway 152 that goes from Highway 5 over to Gilroy, took it over the mountains, got to Gilroy (where we ended up renting a house a few days later) and then drove up Highway 101 to Sunnyvale. We got to the good old Maple Tree Inn at about 6:00 PM. All in all I drove about 3730 kilometers in about 32 hours and my little car got 16 kilometers to the liter (38 miles to the gallon), fully loaded with all the stuff that we were hauling, plus the two of us, at an average speed of 120 kph. Those 32 hours included gas stops and pit stops, so I was probably averaging at least 130 kph on the road. We had arrived and I was prepared to start work on Lunar Prospector the next day.

Chapter 2-7
Trying to Get Started

Tuesday, March 21, 1995

I went to work very early and was raring to go. Even Dom got in fairly early, but, unfortunately, he was preparing for the Hubble Fifth Anniversary and that was taking a lot of his time, so things were off to a slow start, much to my consternation.

I tried to find out what was happening with my LMSC contract. Rebecca and I needed to get our move behind us so I could concentrate on Lunar Prospector. I went to Gus that morning and asked him what was going on and he said the contract was in the mail (who hasn't heard that one).

I went back to the hotel at about 11:00 AM to get Rebecca for lunch and to start house hunting. We drove down to Morgan Hill, had lunch, and went to the Coldwell Banker Realty agent who had helped me look for a house during the proposal effort. After finding out how expensive houses were, we had decided to rent. Rebecca took the ball and that afternoon she found Prospector Realty which could help us, so the house hunting business began in earnest.

Tom called and said Mike Hammal had raised hell about my leaving LESC, saying that LESC should do something about it and try to keep me working there. I said, "Fine, let's see what happens," since LMSC was clearly dragging its feet on hiring me and was definitely going to screw me on my contract. Tom called Jim Adamson, the guy who replaced Moe Miller, and explained the situation, i.e., that I had sought support from LESC, didn't get any, and was told to go out to LMSC to do Lunar Prospector. Adamson wanted to keep my capabilities at LESC, so they started to talk about keeping me there.

Wednesday, March 22, 1995

It was raining like mad. Rebecca called in the morning and said Prospector Realty had two houses for us to look at. We went down there over lunch in the pouring rain. The rent for the first house, which was up in the mountains, was $1700; it was a beautiful gigantic house, but much more than we needed.

Then we went down to the one in Gilroy. The dirt road to it was terrible, full of holes. It was out in the country and had 2.8 acres for horses, which we didn't care about, but the house was suitable, cost only (!) $1500/month, so we rented it. One thing out of the way, now Rebecca could go back to Houston and get ready for the move.

When I got back to LMSC after finding the house, Gus was sitting in the Atrium in Building 107, and asked how things were going. I told him we had just found a house. He asked, "What is LESC saying these days?"

I answered, "Well, they seem to have woken up to the facts that we won the contract and that I am coming out here."

Gus replied, "Well, don't forget you are in a bargaining position, that is a bargaining chip."

That sounded hopeful. Maybe I could get what I was worth through LESC and use it as leverage for Tom also, leave him as an LESC employee working at LMSC, and therefore get him a decent raise and per diem.

Thursday, March 23, and Friday, March 24, 1995

I called Adamson as soon as I could and explained the situation to him. He didn't want to lose me and, after talking with George Abby and Dan Goldin about LESC's future, Jim was trying to build up areas of new business. He wanted to know what I wanted if I were to remain a LESC employee. I told him what I wanted was what I had been promised, the $110,000 per year, the win bonus, and moving expenses. I told him we didn't have much time because we were getting ready to sign the NASA contract on the 30th, and I was told I had a contract offer coming from LMSC. He asked me to put it in writing and he would see what he could do. I did and I sent him a fax.

Things went on like that all day Thursday and Friday — talking back and forth with LESC and trying to get the thing negotiated. Simultaneously, Dom and I were preparing for a talk to the MOB to explain Lunar Prospector to that august body (to alleviate their fears of our scary little program). Dom and I thought we had 30 minutes. I would talk first about the science and the mission and show excerpts from the NASA news conference — mainly what Wes had said. Dom would talk the second 15 minutes about the way we were setting Lunar Prospector up managerially, financially, and technically. Well, just about quitting time on Friday, we got a call saying we had only 15 minutes total! We had to revise the whole thing, so we would have to come in on Saturday morning to revise our presentation.

Understandably, Rebecca was getting bored because she had everything done she came out to do. We were planning to have the weekend for ourselves, but because of the revised schedule, I had to go in Saturday morning for two or three hours and cut the pitch down to 15 minutes.

Saturday, March 25, 1995

Happily, Dom and I were done by noon, so Rebecca and I had lunch and then drove down to Gilroy to look at the house. I was very tired, as I had been working 12 to 14 hours a day since we got to Sunnyvale. We just went to Morgan Hill and walked around to see what it was all about. We went to a lousy movie called *Bye Bye Love*. By that time I was exhausted, so we drove back to The Maple Tree Inn and slept.

Sunday, March 26, 1995

We drove over to Roaring Camp and had a great time riding the train through the Redwood Forest. Then we drove down Highway 1, had a fabulous day, and then had a pizza.

Monday, March 27, 1995

Rebecca and I got up early and I got her to the airport for her trip back to Houston. I went to work at 8:30 for the MOB meeting. Dom was in and was quite nervous about the whole thing. We got over to the meeting place and the other managers came dragging in, picking up a donut and a cup of coffee.

As we stood there, I said to Dom, "Not one single person is coming over and congratulating us." Remembering that not one of those guys had called Dom or me up to congratulate us, I added, "Dom, do you realize they don't have to make the extreme effort of dialing the telephone to talk to us now, all they have to do is walk across the room with their donuts and coffee in their hands to say, Congratulations, but they won't!"

The coldness towards the program was still there, though Tang said one nice thing. Because he was retiring, Dom had congratulated him on retiring and Tang said, "At least you guys gave me a winner to go out with." But again, where was his support when we needed it?

The meeting finally got started. Gus gave us a very short introduction, but Tang and the rest of them didn't seem interested at all. I thought, *what a bunch of bozos, the meeting is not worth the effort.* Clearly, it was not the big deal we were led to believe. In the revised version, Dom was going first and would give me a nice introduction and he wanted to make sure I said nice things about him — he was always very concerned about the fact that most people in the company don't like him. Anyway, we got started.

Dom gave his three viewgraphs and said a couple nice words about the Discovery Program and me. Then I got up and discussed the science and the mission. At the end of my short presentation, I showed our organization chart and I said Dom was the only guy I could do Lunar Prospector with, which pleased Dom to no end. Then I showed the excerpts from the video, so the whole thing went over very well.

Interestingly, Frank had talked to us before we went in and was very negative. He said, "Don't talk about the commercial aspect, they will chew you up and spit you out." Despite his warning, we did discuss the commercial aspects of Lunar Prospector and that was the only thing the managers were interested in! I talked about possible follow-on missions — four or five lunar orbiters, as well as Mars and Near-Earth Asteroid missions.

One of the managers commented afterwards, "You know we should actually build three or four of these right now. We have a really good thing here."

Arnie Aldridge turned around and said, "You guys really hit a home run." Despite the few positive comments, the MOB meeting was not at all important, except it seemed to mark the end of LMSC's opposition to Lunar Prospector, opposition that had slowly melted away.

After that waste of time, I worked very hard the rest of the day — trying to get the Lunar Prospector model started, trying to get the NASA and my contract started, etc. Much to my consternation, Dom was working mainly on the Hubble reunion.

I got a call from Jim Adamson. He was going to be at Cherry Hill on the 29th through the 31st and he wanted to assure me that everything was going well and that I was going to get everything I wanted. They were working on a letter and they would be finished very shortly and if I was satisfied, it was a done deal. I was happy, Rebecca was happy, and Dom was happy (because that would save us a lot of overhead). It would also allow us to bring Tom to Sunnyvale very soon. My remaining an LESC employee would relieve us of some of the burden of trying to work with Frank and I would be totally independent of LMSC. It would be a perfect deal.

Tuesday, March 28, 1995: A Visit to Berkeley

We had a meeting at Berkeley at 1:30 PM, so Dom and I took off about 12:00 and drove up to Berkeley. We had a great meeting with Bob Lin, Dave Curtis, and some other members of Bob's team about how we (LMSC) were going to interface with them (UC Berkeley), about the spacecraft-magnetometer interfaces and especially about the magnetic cleanliness issues. Regarding the latter, we tried to call Mario Acuña and as usual failed to reach him. All in all, it was a very good meeting and Dom and I got home quite late in the afternoon, about quitting time, satisfied with everything on the MAG/ER front.

However, Bob had told us that they were interested in building the Command and Data Handling unit (C&DH). Clearly they could do it, but Dom and I decided on the way back to LMSC that they shouldn't. First, we wouldn't have much control over them. It was clear they were not used to schedules the way we needed and certainly were not able to give us weekly costing. They got their cost data from the University only once every three months, so there was no way they could track their budget on a weekly or even monthly basis. Second, we felt they would have their hands full just getting the MAG/ER ready on time and at cost. Dom and I decided they should stick to doing the magnetic instruments. We weren't going to give them the C&DH, it was just too important to the success of the entire mission.

Wednesday, March 29, 1995

I got a frantic call around noon from Tom saying I had to call Jim Adamson at Cherry Hill. I reached Jim shortly after lunch. He said, "There is a snag in the deal. Up to just a few minutes ago it was a done deal and was waiting for my signature." I would have gotten my $110,000 and a $20,000 bonus, my house in Santa Fe was to be paid for until it was sold, four weeks vacation, and everything else — but the deal was off! Dick Parten had said no! He had prematurely gotten the letter and had just said no!

That didn't make any sense to me, but I said, "Well, OK."

I told Dom and he was really disappointed. We tried to figure out why. Dom was thinking of all kinds of stuff — that Gus had gotten to them and things like that. I thought it was just Parten going back to his original stance of last fall. We wanted to find out what the hell was going on, since all of the sudden I didn't have the possibility of working the mission through LESC, so I had to keep trying to get LMSC's job offer. There I was, the PI and instigator on the hottest thing going in my profession, the envy of the 27 teams that lost, and the envy of companies like Martin Marietta, Ball, McDonnell Douglas, and two major Lockheed companies did not want me!

To add to an already bad day, Bill Feldman called to tell me Jim Arnold had called again, trying to force his way on the team via Bill. He tried again to tell Bill how to do the GRS and Bill had fended him off and Bill was rightfully annoyed and insulted. I had told Bill earlier if Jim called him, he should tell Jim to talk to me directly about his issues (knowing full well that Jim would not face me). As expected, Jim never called me; he just kept trying to get in through a backdoor. As Bill and I agreed, it was never going to happen.

Chapter 2-8
The Fee Crisis and
the NASA Conflict

Black Thursday, March 30, 1995

The day we expected to sign the NASA contract and officially begin Lunar Prospector had arrived, so I put on my suit and tie because we were going to have pictures taken at the signing. I had told Ames on my first trip out there after the NASA news conference that, if NASA wanted things done "Faster, Better, Cheaper" from our side, then NASA had to also do things "Faster, Better, Cheaper." I wanted the NASA contract for Lunar Prospector ready for signature in 30 days, i.e., on the 30th. Ames almost made it. Actually we did get to start the signing on the 30th. Dom signed it and I initialed it, but the real contract was still working its way through the NASA/Ames system and would not be ready for final signatures until the next day (that was too bad since Dom was going to be on vacation — hence his signing it a day early). However, the day was not as simple as that; it was filled with crisis and hectic activity from start to finish, so back to the morning of March 30.

During the previous four weeks Dom and I had been pushing Fred DeFrank, the LMSC contract negotiator dealing with his counterpart at NASA/Ames, Kathleen Christy, to insure that the NASA contract was in place by March 30. We tried to reach him when we got to work to see if the contract was done, but he was over at Ames. Fred came back to LMSC at about 9:00 AM with a copy with some mark-ups, but basically it was finished, except for one disturbing point — THE FEE!

A little historical background might help here: The fixed fee (i.e., Lockheed's profit) was not in the widely quoted $59 million dollars! LMSC's standpoint was the $59 million was the *cost* of the contract and its *price* (cost plus fee) was $65 million — Lockheed's standard, and, supposedly, well understood way of doing business with the government. I had had concerns about that all along. When we were doing the proposal budget, I kept asking, "Where in hell is the fee?" because I never could find it in the budget. Though it didn't make any sense to me, I was told it was OK (after all, I am just a dumb scientist) and everyone else seemed to be happy. That was the way the proposal budget was written. Now back to the future.

I had been talking with Gerry Grismore about his possible role in Lunar Prospector when Dom came in looking like Crisis City (as he frequently did) and said he had to talk to me immediately. We went into Dom's office and shut the door. Dom was very upset because it turned out the fee was not (correctly) in the proposal! Scott had gone through everything very carefully and the fee simply was not (correctly) in there. In reality, the 15% fee or approximately $6 million was on one chart in our proposal, but not in the summary chart. As a result, NASA/Ames's standpoint was the fee was not there and LMSC was going to have to eat it.

Dom became very agitated and started cursing Peggy McDougall for leaving out the fee and screwing everything up. Truly, she did a bad job (I had been concerned about the budget as she was doing it, but my concerns were pushed aside by both Dom and Peggy). That was the case because A) of her arrogance (budget people have their standard way of doing things, regardless of what the AO required), B) she and Dom would not communicate with each other (or anyone else), C) she and Dom had spent all their time trying to save the MAUDEE proposal (which was doomed from the beginning), so they had left Lunar Prospector's budget to the very end when there was neither the time nor the resources left to do a good — or even a reasonable — job on it, and D) she was sick with the flu when she was trying to do Lunar Prospector's budget.

Dom said, "If we don't get any fee, if we get $59 million and Lockheed doesn't get any fee, I'll get canned. If this is true, I'll be out of here in two days. Even if they don't fire me, I'll lose my pay grade and never get another bonus or any other perks." He was very upset.

I tried to calm him down by saying, "This will probably go away. Also, it was not really clear in the AO instructions how in heck the budget was to be reported." Everyone who proposed had trouble understanding the budget requirements, because the way the AO was written, it was just impossible to understand how NASA wanted the budgeting and the fee reported. I said further, "Dom, we did what we thought best and if it wasn't correct, it was an honest mistake."

That did not help; Dom was still sure he would be fired and lose everything. I continued to try to calm him down for a little bit, but soon decided there was nothing more I could do, so I said, "Let's let it ride and see what happens. I think things will be OK." Dom was still in a tizzy, but decided he wanted some ice cream. We went to the cafeteria, talked, had ice cream, and he calmed down (as much as he ever did).

I got a call from Tom (actually three calls from Tom and two from Rich Lyons) telling me to call Rich Lyons at LESC. Rich was not there when I called back, but I talked to his deputy. Lyons and the rest of the guys back at LESC were really upset that the deal to keep me at LESC had fallen apart and wanted to understand why. They couldn't get to Jim Adamson because he was still in Cherry Hill, so they were after me. I explained what I knew of the situation: I told him basically what I wanted and that Dick Parten had not been interested when I talked to him in the fall. I explained that Parten told me to do Lunar Prospector with LMSC, so I did. Then when Adamson said a week ago that LESC would like to keep Lunar Prospector and me, I said, "OK," and then I had explained to Jim what we were doing, what I wanted, and how the contract was going to be run. Lyons's deputy thought the contract, the whole $59 million, would be run through LESC. I said, "No, that's not the case, the only thing that would be done would be that we (Tom and me) would be working at LMSC as LESC employees. LMSC would certainly not allow the contract to be run through LESC." I told him if LESC was still interested and could reverse Parten's decision, I was still interested.

There were advantages for us to do Lunar Prospector through LESC and I would like to have had that option, but I said, "I just had the rug pulled out from under me and I am not too happy about it. I am floored because LESC is at no risk whatsoever. We already won the thing. All LESC has to do is to give me (and Tom) what I want and sit back and enjoy the success. If you guys are interested in doing something, I want ironclad guarantees. Also, we are signing the contract with NASA today and my offer from LMSC is supposed to be here today or tomorrow, so if you are going to do anything, you are going to have to do it now." He said they would call me Monday (April 3) and do what they could.

Another issue, which kept me busy all day, was trying to find engineering personnel to work on Lunar Prospector. I had talked to Grismore about doing the C&DH earlier in the morning before the fee crisis began. Later I talked to Ron King about the propulsion slot and Woody Woodcock about power — Woody was ambivalent (a major

Woody characteristic as I later came to realize). Dom and I had talked to Mark Smith about helping with the management over the last two days, but he was not interested. I had a number of people with whom I wanted to talk and I was anxious to get personnel lined up, both to get started and because we were going to have our kick-off meeting Thursday and Friday (April 6 and 7) with Mark Saunders.

At the kick-off meeting I intended to explain to the team (whoever they were) and Mark the science, the mission, and the spacecraft that won the competition and on which I had worked for the last six years. Dom had a different opinion as to how to run the kick-off meeting. He wanted the subsystem guys to tell how they were going to build their subsystems! The few guys we had rounded up did not even know what the mission, spacecraft, and subsystems were all about, so how in hell could they tell anyone else what they were going to do? I tried to make Dom understand I had to tell the engineers what the mission and spacecraft were all about before they could explain anything to anyone else, especially Mark Saunders (Dom's approach to the kick-off meeting should have rung warning bells in my head, but it did not — at least not then).

As all that was going on, Dom and I were also preparing a pitch about Lunar Prospector to be given to the President of the NASA & Federal Systems Division of LMSC, Al Smith, on Friday, April 7. That was to be the final chapter in trying to get LMSC behind the mission and trying to stop LMSC's threats about not accepting the contract (which was already in the process of being signed).

As Dom and I continued to work on the kick-off and the Al Smith meetings, Dom told me that Mel Brashears, the only person at LMSC who seemed to think highly of Lunar Prospector and me, had replaced McMahon. I thought, *great, Mel is at the top of the ladder*. I said, "Dom, we should thank him for supporting us."

Dom replied, "You know, that's a great idea." Dom immediately called Brashears's office to set up a meeting with Mel to thank him for his support and to let him know how things were going with Lunar Prospector. Brashears, who was supposedly my big buddy, was now running the whole damned place — that was great.

If we could get through the Al Smith meeting on Friday the 7th, which I was sure we would, and then get Mel behind us, we would be in a great position to pull Lunar Prospector off. On that note, the long workday sort of ended.

After leaving Lockheed, I went to my favorite Mexican Restaurant near the Maple Tree Inn and had chili colorado for supper — I was totally stuffed — a nice finish to infamous Thursday. A lot had happened. We got the signing of the contract started; the fee crisis seemed to have subsided by the end of the day; LESC was again trying to get me a contract, etc. etc. What a day!

Black Friday, March 31, 1995: The Day After Black Thursday

Dom was on his trip and my main task for the day was to try to get people lined up to work on the program, but I went to see Fred DeFrank first. There were still problems with the contract and Fred was getting very skeptical that it was going to get signed. The infamous missing fee was rearing its ugly head again, even though Fred thought they had taken care of it on the previous day. He was waiting for a call from Ames.

The morning passed slowly as I also waited and tried to get personnel for Lunar Prospector. It was getting hard to find people because they were all very busy on other programs, and LMSC had laid so many people off there were too few to do the existing work, let alone start a new program.

In the midst of that, I got a nasty call from Ed Boesiger who arrogantly informed me that he was in charge of putting people to work at various jobs in the areas of mechanisms, structures, and whatever else. Ed complained that Dom ignored the system, went about it his way, and, as usual, was making trouble (exactly why I liked Dom — he got things done [or so I thought]), so I just let him yap. Dom hated Ed's guts and I was beginning to also hate him as I listened to him. According to his majesty King Boesiger, we peons were supposed to tell him our requirements and he would find people to fill the slots.

As Dom and I knew, and as even stated by the New Business Council when they backed the Lunar Prospector proposal effort, the Lockheed bureaucratic way was not going to get Lunar Prospector done in 20 months and for $59 million; we needed to "get the best in the company." What we did not need was a pompous little ass like Boesiger telling us who could work on Lunar Prospector. Clearly, we needed to get Brashears and others behind us and get the right people. If we didn't, Lunar Prospector was going to be in trouble. I worked through the morning on that issue.

After lunch, I went over to Ames for a 1:30 meeting with Dave Lozier and Fred Wirth to discuss trajectory and data archiving issues. They were doing a great job on both.

I went to see Scott and about that time all hell broke loose. The whole thing about the fee blew up. Scott knew there was a discrepancy in the NASA/Ames's arguments, because the fee had been identified in the *price* in Table C-6 on page 24 of Vol. III (*Budget and Management*) of the proposal, even through it was not in the final *cost* summary in Table E-1 on page 31. That was either a mistake on Peggy's part or she left it out because she thought that the fee should not be in the summary cost table since it was negotiable. Whatever the reason, I was certain Lockheed was not trying to hide anything or swindle NASA (at least that time). However, the decades of mistrust between NASA and the big aerospace companies caused by enormous program cost overruns, big schedule slips, and each side trying to screw the other (the very programmatic problems my colleagues and I wanted to demonstrate could be overcome using Lunar Prospector and NASA's "Faster, Better, Cheaper" Discovery Program was trying to correct) was driving the fee issue.

Ames, NASA Headquarters, and their bean counters insisted the proposal budget was $59 million; the contract was going to be for $59 million and that meant there would be no fee — period. Well Lockheed would not accept a contract without having its fee. The argument just went back and forth getting nowhere. Mark Saunders called Scott, as we were discussing the problem in his office, stubbornly insisting that Lockheed was not going to receive a penny more than the $59 million.

None of the participants cared about the facts that the AO budgetary reporting requirements were not clear, and that, in addition to the proposal review committee's review of our (and everyone else's) budget, NASA had two — I repeat — two additional reviews of our budget — one by SAIC and the other by an internal NASA review board — and none of the reviewers caught our supposed fee error, discrepancy, or misunderstanding and asked for clarification, as they should have in such a case. But, of course, since Wes stood up at the February News Conference and announced to the world that Lunar Prospector cost $59 million, it had to be $59 million.

In addition to that unyielding NASA logic, there was also the fact that Lockheed had not certified the Phase C, D & E budgets in the proposal. Only the Phase B part of the budget was certified because the purpose of our Phase B effort was to determine the exact cost of the Lunar Prospector Program! By the AO rules, we were allowed a 15% (but no more) growth in the program costs. As usual, NASA felt free to change the rules of the game as long as it was to their advantage (one of my many reasons for disliking and distrusting NASA).

As the arguments got hotter, it was clear Lockheed might just say, "To hell with it," since they were nervous about doing Lunar Prospector anyway. Headquarters was doing something very stupid (what's new) and Lunar Prospector could come crashing down and destroy the Discovery Program just as it was getting started.

Shortly after Mark Saunders and Scott got off the phone, Frank called Scott. I decided to get the hell out of Ames and go back to Lockheed to see Frank personally (he was the only one of the NASA/Ames and Lockheed upper-managers who was acting rationally at that point). When I got over to Frank's office, Fred DeFrank and another bean counter were there and they were not happy. They were concerned about the serious, bureaucratic predicament my program was in. Fred patted me on the back and said, "Don't worry. It will be OK. We'll fix it somehow."

Frank was really annoyed with the whole bunch. He was still on the phone with Scott and thought the whole mess was totally uncalled for. It was also clear to Frank there was either an honest mistake or the error was insignificant. Frank kept saying, "Look, the fee is shown here in the previous table, it wasn't carried over to the other table because it was not clear that we were supposed to carry it over. All you have to do is to look in there and see that one table shows $59 million without fee and the other table identifies the fee — any idiot could add them together."

Frank thought there was no problem, Lockheed had done nothing wrong, and NASA ought to quit screwing around. His said he was going to call one of his ex-buddy mucky-mucks at Headquarters and tell him to get that damn thing straightened out.

Nevertheless, I felt the whole thing was not going to go away so easily, because we still did not have a signed contract. But I did think it would eventually blow over because Headquarters could not simply pull the plug on Lunar Prospector. If it did, it would have had a great deal of explaining to do to Congress, the media, and the space science community. Of course, Lockheed could still tell NASA to go to hell, so Lunar Prospector was far from being out of the woods. Regardless, I decided not to worry about it; I had too many other things to do.

Frank laughed all that off and said it was stupid and called Gus on the phone. Gus also wasn't very concerned, just taking it as business as usual with NASA (and one wonders why nothing ever gets done right and each side distrusts the other).

After Frank finished talking with Gus, I brought up the fact that I still hadn't received my LMSC contract offer. He replied, "Well they thought it was already to go two or three days ago, but it turned out they had to have another signature because the jump in your salary was so big."

I thought, *well, we'll see*, but I still expected to get screwed.

That was the infamous Friday the 31st of March 1995. The next day was April Fools Day, but I thought that the "fools" had come a day early.

The Weekend, April 1 and 2, 1995

During the quiet of the weekend, I updated the Mission Requirements Document and the Mission Operations Document, revised the Mission Profile and worked on the full-scale model of Lunar Prospector. The weekends were the only times I could actually get any work done!

Monday, April 3, 1995: The Fee Agony Continues

The negotiation saga continued unrelentingly with both sides hardening their positions on the fee and cost sheet differences.

Mark Saunders called, more than once, and questioned whether Lockheed was trying to hide the true cost. Mark charged that maybe the costs were twice as much as we said — now it was getting dirty. The situation got even worse (how is that possible you ask?). A Lockheed bean counter named Dennis Brown, who had gotten very upset by the mess, totally exceeded his authority, called NASA Headquarters and ticked them off. Then, compounding his error, he called up a LMSC Vice President, who, in turn, got everybody at Lockheed ticked off. Thus, instead of the thing calming down as we had thought when I had talked to Frank on Friday, the mess was now at fever pitch.

I was over at Ames talking with Scott about personnel for the navigation and the data archiving work and the budget for those tasks when Mark called. I could tell from Scott's comments that things were not good. Afterwards, Scott said things had reached a real crescendo — there was more talk about canceling Lunar Prospector — things were getting completely out of hand. I seriously doubted Lunar Prospector would be stopped. If NASA did, it would destroy Discovery and I would hold a news conference and expose the whole bunch of idiots.

Nevertheless, my feeling at that point was that unless things totally blew up and Lunar Prospector was canceled before Thursday, we would get it resolved on Thursday when Mark came for the kick-off meeting. At that time, all the principals — that is Scott and Mark from NASA, and Dom, Frank, and I, and maybe Gus, from Lockheed — would be there, and I would get us all into one room and we would resolve the absolutely absurd mess.

I was getting really tired of all the nonsense swirling around Lunar Prospector and me — we could not get the Lunar Prospector contract finished and Lockheed couldn't (wouldn't?) get my personal contract finished. Lockheed was still sitting on my contract, so I didn't know if and what I was going to get paid. Every time I asked about my contract and the moving package (Rebecca was still waiting in Houston), I got the usual runaround. LMSC was clearly holding my contract up so that if the NASA contract did not get signed, they could easily dump me.

I was ticked — and there is nothing like ice cream when you are ticked off. I took Francisco and Richard Lynch to 31 Flavors for ice cream. By 4:00 PM I decided enough was enough, so I left work early (early! — my day started at about 5:00 AM), had a nice steak dinner, bought some books, and turned in early to relax and read.

Nevertheless, it was hard to relax. I was disgusted with NASA. I was disgusted with Lockheed. I was disgusted with the problem of getting the personnel we needed. I was disgusted with stupid Ed Boesiger and all the other LMSC jerks I had to deal with. When you get involved with NASA and when you get involved with big corporations like Lockheed, you are in real trouble. Oh, how I wished we could have done Lunar Prospector the way I wanted it done — with OMNI and LEI.

Also, I was seriously beginning to wonder about Mark Saunders. He seemed to be one of the major players in the hysteria surrounding the fee issue and if that was the case, he didn't belong at the head of the Discovery Program.

Tom was coming out the next night, but had to get right back to Houston because he had to sign time cards. Unfortunately, Tom was not able to really learn or participate in the mission to any significant level and I was starting to get concerned about that. He was, of course, the victim of circumstances just as I was and he needed to protect his butt in Houston. On the other hand, he needed to start spending some real time on Lunar Prospector and learn what was going on.

Speaking of LESC at Houston, despite Rich Lyon's promise, I didn't hear a peep from LESC about an offer to keep Tom and me at LMSC, so as far as I was concerned, that was a dead issue (and I was right).

Thus ended black Monday, which had followed black Friday, which had followed black Thursday.

Tuesday, April 4, 1995

Tuesday was the finale to the fiasco of the contract. Dom was back from his trip. I quickly filled him in on the difficulties of the past several days and then we had a meeting at 7:30 AM with Frank, Ray Edinger, and Fred DeFrank. Dom was angry to the point of being red in the face that things had gotten so screwed up. Dom said if they didn't get that straight, he would quit Lunar Prospector — a threat that was part Dom's hysteria and volatility and part bluff.

We then talked with Scott and found to our relief and joy that the fee issue had been resolved — the mess was over without even a whimper after so much noise! Fred DeFrank went over to Ames to work with Kathleen Christy and it appeared that things were actually finally getting back to where they should have been all along.

After all the yelling, cancellation threats, and nonsense, the contract was finally being written up with Lockheed doing the program for $59 million, an amount never to be exceeded or Lunar Prospector would be canceled (no 15% growth margin), plus a negotiated $4 million fee, for a total price of $63 million. The last week had been "much ado about nothing!" But alas, that was not the end. When Peggy was asked to re-do the infamous charts, she screwed up again. Believe it or not, she left off the fee again! The woman was just totally incompetent.

After the charts were finally done correctly and the day progressed, the news got better and better until at the end of the day, when Fred came back without the contract! It was finalized and ready to go, but Christy had made a mistake in it and had to correct it. But her workday ended at 3:30 PM, so she left promptly at 3:30! Fred was to get the contract for signature the next day, Wednesday, April 5, at 7:30 AM.

Except for the final delays in the contract signing, things began to look good again. We made all the arrangements for the kick-off meeting. I got the "Pick Room" for the meeting. The catered lunches were set up and everything was beginning to roll. It finally felt that the momentum was beginning to build. Dom had even started taking care of the business with the personnel.

I talked to Woody, who initially was not going to be able to work with us because of EOS. When I told him we only needed him half time for the first six months, he said he would to be able to work on Lunar Prospector. Basically everything seemed to be finally rolling along.

Tom flew in from Houston for the kick-off meeting and I picked him up at the airport after work and we had supper. I brought him up to date on the program, and, because of my concerns that he was not learning anything about Lunar Prospector, I told him he needed to stop spending all his energy on his job in Houston and start getting busy on Lunar Prospector. Otherwise he would get so far behind that he would be of little use to the program and me. His future was with Lunar Prospector, not with LESC, and he should not sacrifice that future for a company that had just totally neglected his and my interests.

I was looking forward to the kick-off meeting — then Tom and I were going to enjoy ourselves Saturday, before he flew back.

Wednesday, April 5, 1995: The Contract Finally Gets Signed

We finally got the Lunar Prospector contract signed at Ames at 11:30 AM. Lunar Prospector was finally and at last officially underway!

The rest of the day, with Tom's help, Francisco, Richard, and I got the full-scale model of Lunar Prospector from the model shop and put all the details on it so it would be ready for the kick-off meeting. It looked very nice indeed.

Also, Boesiger was causing trouble by trying to stop three of his guys, whom Dom and I had asked to work on Lunar Prospector, from supporting the kick-off meeting. Dom was in the process of going to Boesiger's boss to stop his nonsense (and of course succeeded).

And, of course, though Lockheed had its contract with NASA, I still had no indication at all as to when I was going to get my contract with LMSC. I talked to Mike Ruggeri in the lunch line — he was very snotty about it and said, "It's still in process," which I knew was a bunch of BS. Lockheed had just been delaying it until the NASA contract was signed (or worse). Rebecca was getting very upset about the continual delays in my contract and Lockheed arranging for our move from Houston — we were just left hanging.

As the day progressed, Tom and I finished my viewgraphs for the kick-off meeting. Some of the guys were prepared for the presentation and some were not. We were somehow getting it all together; it was not going to be as smooth as I would have liked, but it was a beginning.

Dom was beginning to concentrate more and more on Lunar Prospector, though strangely, after the contract signing, there was a certain degree of resignation on his part. Although I was certain that Dom knew what was ahead of us, he seemed to be beginning to wonder about the enormity of the task we were starting.

Chapter 2-9
Getting Started at Last

Thursday, April 6, 1995: Kick-Off Day

The first day of the kick-off meeting couldn't have been better. It was an absolutely perfect day in almost every way.

The first thing in the morning Tom, Dom, and I had our debriefing with Mark Saunders. Obviously, we had the best proposal since we won. However, in addition to all the positives, there were a few negative things and Mark went through all the points — good and bad. First he went through the selection procedure and it was amazingly fair and amazingly good. NASA had to be congratulated on defining a perfect way of doing the selection. The process was turned over to the selection team and Wes Huntress did not want to know anything about how it was going. He did not want any interim reports; he just wanted the final list. When he got it, we were number one and were chosen for flight — it was as straightforward as that. The next three were chosen for further study and that was that. Goldin had nothing to do with the selection, which surprised me. It was absolutely a fair and equitable selection.

The scores were poor, good, very good, and excellent. We received a very good. We received a good on science. I asked Mark how we could have done better and he replied, "The only way you could have done better on science was to have more of it, but that would have raised your cost." We had received an excellent on cost, so to get an excellent on science by doing more of it would have meant that we would have only gotten a good or very good on the cost — so that would have been a wash. We had received a very good in management, which was as good as anybody did.

We had gained points because we weren't going to use the DSN (it is always over booked) and we had lost points because we were going to develop and use our own tracking network! The reason for the apparent contradiction was that we didn't yet have our own tracking network firmed up. There were several other issues like that, where in one sense it was positive and in another it was negative.

We had received a very good in the outreach and educational section, which surprised me considering how little time we spent on it.

We had received an excellent on the spacecraft. They loved its simplicity. They loved that it had no computer. They loved all the things we knew they would love. The one thing we got dinged about was the fact that we had changed some things on the OMNI design. We did so because we had to respond to NASA's new technology requirements. Some of those few things we had changed in order to comply with the Discovery rules were criticized and that struck me as being very funny. But who cared, we had won hands down.

After we were through with the debriefing, people started gathering to start the kick-off meeting and they saw the Lunar Prospector model for the first time — everybody liked it.

Ed Boesiger showed up and you could tell he came in thinking he was going to run the place and show us what to do. Dom had called Boesiger's boss and laid the law down. The guys we needed to support the meeting were there, but Ed still came in as haughty as ever.

The meeting got started with Lockheed's Vice-President Klinger giving his welcoming introduction, which was very, very good and then, surprisingly, he stayed! Instead of the fifteen minutes he said he could stay, he stayed nearly an hour and was very pleased with everything he heard.

I gave my introduction and then Gus came to speak. That surprised me because he had been in France and I did not think he was going to be able to be at the kick-off meeting. Even more to my surprise, Gus gave a really glowing personal tribute to me; about how I had stuck to it over the years and that Lunar Prospector was a perfect example of one following his dream and not letting anything or anyone stop him. It was all very complimentary and completely unexpected from Gus!

Then Mark Smith, Scott, and Dom got up in turn to discuss the program — all in very positive terms.

Finally, all of the BS was finished and we got down to business. I presented the spacecraft and the mission in detail and remarkably, we were three-quarters of an hour ahead of schedule.

Then came the science. Bill Feldman started off with the spectrometers and did an absolutely exquisite job of laying out the experiments, the requirements, and the interfaces. Then David Curtis did an equally excellent job on the MAG/ER package. Alex finished the science experiment discussions with a brief, but very good discussion of the interface requirements for the Doppler Gravity Experiment.

That finished the morning session and we broke for lunch at 12:37 (only seven minutes behind schedule). The reader might wonder why I mention our being ahead or only a few minutes behind schedule — well, it is very simple — almost all NASA meetings are seriously behind schedule by that point in a meeting. Lunch breaks are usually taken late, sometime in the early afternoon, at the point in the schedule where the mid-afternoon coffee break is originally planned! If we were going to do Lunar Prospector in two years, we had to keep to our work schedule and that also meant keeping to our meeting schedules as a demonstration of our ability to manage time properly. We did well and I was happy.

As we broke for lunch, I pointed out it was just 26 lunations to launch and just as we had kept on the meeting schedule, we would keep on our launch schedule. Everyone agreed and everyone was in a very positive mood.

After lunch, Dom started his part of the session and it also went very well. Mark Saunders drew me aside two or three times and said he was really pleased with Dom's comments about getting good schedules and requirements. He said he was getting more and more confident we could do the job and the whole meeting — the spacecraft, the science, and the management — just everything pleased him. Then he got me alone by the model and said Lunar Prospector was really a case of perseverance paying off. Everything was just perfect.

The funny part was Ed Boesiger's reaction to all of that. Despite his arrogant entrance to the meeting and the haughty look he gave me that said, "OK, I'm here and you are in trouble now." I noticed as soon as we started and Klinger and everyone else talked, old Ed couldn't look anyone in the face anymore. He kept looking down and it was very clear he had gotten himself into something he shouldn't have, and he left rather quickly.

However, to my surprise the SOB came back in the afternoon. Tom McCloskey from Boesiger's group was there to talk about the booms and their deployment, but I thought Boesiger might horn in and give McCloskey's talk. Happily, McCloskey got up and started — but then said Ed Boesiger should really give the talk (so I was right). Ed started, at first quite subdued, but then he quickly jumped into a self-serving lecture along the lines of, "I am the big shot boss . . . I go to international meetings. . . I am the Chairman of this and that committee . . . I will get the information on the booms . . . , and blah, blah, blah." Everyone just ignored him.

Mark, Alex, and I discussed off line the possibility of an expanded gravity experiment to get far-side line-of-sight Doppler residual data via cooperation with the Japanese. They expected to put their Planet B Spacecraft (which was supposed to drop three penetrator seismic stations on [actually, into] the lunar surface) into lunar orbit about two months after we were to get into lunar orbit. I told Mark if we could put a stable oscillator and another transmitter on Lunar Prospector, and, using Planet B with similar equipment as a relay or repeater satellite, we could do a joint experiment to completely map the higher order gravity anomalies on the invisible (from the Earth) far-side of the Moon.

We also discussed the nominal 1-year mission and the extended mission options I had in the proposal. The evaluation team, realizing the importance of the potentially two year extended mission option I had proposed, said we really should do a three year nominal mission, period. That was quite flattering since it indicated they really understood what I could accomplish with little Lunar Prospector. However, that would have been a "costly" mistake. If we changed Lunar Prospector to a three year base line mission rather than oneyear, we would have to build the spacecraft with more expensive components and have more fuel on board (the spacecraft would get bigger) to insure it would last three years. That would greatly increase Lunar Prospector's cost, development time, and test program. If we left it as a one-year mission, we knew with high probability we would get the extra two years out of it, but with no cost, schedule, etc. impacts. I was not too excited about the three-year option, but it was still nice to know they really wanted the extended mission that badly.

Except for Boesiger, the day went extremely well; we had an excellent exchange of information. Mark Saunders said he just could not have been more pleased with what he heard and he ended the day totally happy.

After the meeting broke up, we all went for a Lockheed pizza party. Tom said while we were eating, Gus told Dom, "We are going to have to get over to finance and make sure we get Alan some good money." Maybe everything would turn out OK after all.

Friday, April 7, 1995

The kick-off meeting finished up with schedule detail and a lot of good discussions. Everything was extremely well done. I was very pleased and very tired!

Gus took my request to the salary board, but he was not allowed to tell me what they had decided! They have to get the final offer through Human Resources, so I would have to wait until Monday. I was very interested to see whether I was going to get a decent salary.

I got more information about the Japanese lunar mission and I became less confident about the possibility of the dual gravity mapping experiment. Planet B would not be in a highly elliptical orbit, rather a 300 km altitude circular orbit. That meant our two spacecraft would see each other only once in a while and then only for short periods of time. I didn't think the experiment would do too much good, and it was not worth the added complexity and cost to Lunar Prospector. I would have loved to do it, but we had more than enough to do in a short time without adding more for a marginal gain.

Monday, April 10, 1995

I met with Denise Young of Allied Signal and we talked to Mike Jordan, also of Allied Signal, on the phone about the Lunar Prospector tracking network. We decided we needed a Memorandum of Understanding to make sure Allied Signal could do the job for less than $2 million. The tracking network was still an open question in the project and hopefully, nothing would go wrong. If it did, Lunar Prospector would be in serious trouble.

Alex Konopliv obtained information on the Loral transponder used on Clementine and they each cost only $400,000 to $500,000 instead of the $1.2 million we had in the proposal budget. That would save us a million and one-half of the two we needed for Lunar Prospector.

Alex had also pursued the Japanese connection for the gravity experiment, but I was getting more and more disenchanted with that idea. In order to do it, the additional transponder or transmitter would take an extra 32 watts of power, and, of course, cost another $400,000 to $500,000. That was just too large an increase in our power and cost budgets and I just didn't want to do it. Also, it was clear the dual coverage would be poor, so I thought the dual gravity experiment would just screw up the mission. Nevertheless, Dom thought we were going to save 25 to 30 watts based on the new electronics packages, but I didn't want to trade the lower power usage for an extra transponder. Lunar Prospector was just too tight in terms of power, mass, and dollars. I felt that we were jeopardizing the mission for a marginal gain and it was just not worth it.

Similarly, there was still the idea of the 3-year nominal mission option, which I was rapidly deciding to kill. Here we were trying to save money and make sure we could do Lunar Prospector within the budget and on schedule, and each of those additions just increased the costs and would take extra time.

Finally, my contract was supposed to have been finished, and, of course, I didn't receive it. I started bugging Frank about every one-half to three-quarters of an hour, but nothing happened. I still didn't have a contract and that really annoyed me.

By the end of the day, I felt everything was moving forward. Though there was an enormous amount of work to do and we were just getting started, I saw positive trends as to how we could cut power and costs and keep Lunar Prospector under control. If we could just get Allied Signal on board, I thought we would be moving in the right directions on all fronts. My thoughts about the dual gravity experiment and the three-year mission were simple — kill them. Explain to all concerned that those options were inconsistent with my philosophy of Lunar Prospector being very simple and cheap and staying within costs. Those issues were much more important than getting 10% more science at the risk of overrunning our budget and schedule and then being canceled.

Tuesday, April 11, 1995

I had a telecon about the data archiving with Ray Arvidson while I was over at Ames with Larry Lasher, who was responsible to me for the data archiving activities. Ray, whom I knew well since he was part of the Viking Lander Camera Uplink Operations Team I ran in 1976, was responsible for the Lunar Prospector data for the Planetary Data Center where our data would be archived. We began the discussions about what needed to be done to get the data archived — I explained to Ray the details of the mission and the types and forms of data we would be getting. Ray explained that his group at Washington University (St Louis, MO) would be responsible for the spectrometer data and that Steve Joy and Ray Walker from UCLA would be responsible for the magnetic data. We decided that Ray, Ed Guinness (Ray's side-kick, and, like Ray, a friend of mine since the Viking days when Ed also worked on my Uplink Team), and Steve Joy would come out the day before the science and engineering team meeting I was planning for the 11th and 12th of May, so we could get together with my Co-Is to begin to finalize the archiving plan. Ray said Ed would send us a modified version of the Mars Observer Archiving Document to serve as boilerplate for the Lunar Prospector archiving plan. It was an excellent telecon and I was happy to be working with Ray again.

I got back to Lockheed and had a call from Bill Feldman about the spectrometers. We decided to use a cube for the basic structure of the APS with two 3 x 3 cm square detectors on each of five of the sides of the cube (the sixth side would be where the APS attached to the boom). That configuration would minimize the number of wires going down the boom to the APS and still give us background data because there would always be one set of detectors pointed away from the Moon no matter where the spacecraft was in its spin cycle. That was a good design change; the APS would cost less and be a much simpler device to build — a square being a lot easier to build than the pentagonal dodecahedron. Bill and I concluded those discussions and I asked him for the information on the wires and structural design changes.

I was rushing around trying to get done so Dom and I could get to the meeting with Mel Brashears at 3:00 PM. I had asked for the meeting so I could thank Mel for his support in getting Lockheed to back the proposal effort.

I was trying to get the subcontracts to my Co-Is so they could get started. I talked to Steve Lowell, Martha Taylor, and Fred DeFrank and it was clear each of them had a different idea on the subcontracts. It was clear to me we had to get together around 4:00 when Dom and I got back from meeting with Mel and try to clarify the subcontracts and get them done.

At 3:00 PM Dom and I went over to talk to Mel. The conversation went extremely well. We gave him copies of the proposal and the video and he praised Lunar Prospector and me and was very, very positive. He said one of the reasons he liked Lunar Prospector was because he respected and liked me and that Lunar Prospector was well thought out, well prepared, and had no flaws in it as far as he was concerned. He said further Lunar Prospector had tremendous potential because it had those three elements, which he believed were required for success. He added that most proposals Lockheed supported just had two. Then he said that after I had met with him and the New Business Council, he went to Gus and Frank and told them he wanted me to be on staff as of the first of the year, rather than waiting for the contract. Of course, nothing happened. He was peeved about that and then asked about my contract. I told him I still didn't have one. Then he was really annoyed and said he intended to do something about it. I said, "It has been six weeks since we got the announcement and I have been working out here for five weeks without a contract." He immediately picked up the telephone and called Mike Ruggeri and politely raised hell. Then he told me to give him a call tomorrow if I didn't have a contract.

Shortly after that Dom and I left Mel's office and Dom immediately began to bitch. He was very upset I had told Mel about my not having a contract. Dom said I just didn't understand Lockheed. Since Mel just raised hell with Gus's staff about my not having a contract, Gus would be mad at Dom and then Gus would only give him a 5% raise instead of 7%. I had put him in jeopardy and on and on. By that time, I knew Dom's self centered concerns and volatility well enough, so I just let him yap on and on.

The ride from Mel's office to building 107 took five minutes and Dom fumed all five minutes and stopped only when we got back to the office.

Martha, Fred, and Steve were waiting when we arrived and we hammered out the science subcontract issues. Since we needed to keep the budget as tight as possible, I had already ask Lon Hood to accept a $15,000 to $30,000 cut and Alex Konopliv to accept a $10,000 to $20,000 cut during the Phase B activities since their work was mainly developing computer software, which could be done during Phase C/D, since we needed the extra money for hardware development then, not later. Dom also wanted to take money away from Bill because we, Lockheed, would be doing the thermal modeling for the spectrometers as well as the mechanical design and construction of the graphite-epoxy casing for the GRS. Dom was also concerned about the common electronics unit Southwest Research was going to do for Bill. I thought that was incorrect and short sighted on Dom's part and I called Bill, who easily convinced Dom his budget was correct as it was. I then said to Dom we could take the $15,000 I had taken away from Lon and use it for the thermal and GRS structures work to be done at Lockheed and leave Bill's budget intact, and Dom agreed.

When I told Bill of our decision, he was very pleased. While that worked out well, I was concerned because Dom seemed to always go off on a tangent without bothering to understand the issues and the consequence of his conclusions, a bad characteristic which was beginning to bother me.

To my surprise, I got a call from Human Resources — lo and behold, my contract was done! Obviously Mel had called up Human Resources and was on their butts. Then the bad news — the bastards offered me $90,000 or $30,000 less than had been written into the proposal budget and $10,000 less than I would accept! That was an unacceptable outrage. I told Herman it was too low by at least $10,000 and said I would get back to him later.

I decided I would tell Herman if he had any questions about the extra $10,000, just call Mel Brashears and discuss it with him. I didn't know if it would be that simple, but that was going to be my tact. I intended to hold out, assuming Mel's high opinion of Lunar Prospector and me would translate at least to my getting $100,000.

Wednesday, April 12, 1995

To add insult to injury, when Dom got in, he again started raving about our meeting with Mel the day before. He was upset because I didn't give him enough credit and say how great he was when we were talking to Mel Brashears. I spent a good 45 minutes reassuring him. I liked Dom, I thought he was a great guy and a good engineer, but I was becoming certain he was just a big, insecure crybaby.

I talked to Frank about my offer and was told, "Take it or leave it." I would get $90,000 and that was it — or forget Lunar Prospector. The dirty SOBs; I brought them a winning proposal, I gave them the design of a spacecraft that would have cost them at least $1 million if they did it themselves and they were going to pay me only ¾ of what had been written in the proposal — money that Lockheed had been awarded — and if I didn't like it, I could quit! I always had a low opinion of Lockheed and its management, but at that point I had nothing but contempt for the company and the unscrupulous people who ran it.

If I wanted Lunar Prospector, I would have to accept Lockheed's insulting offer. Angry as I was, I knew that at the end of a successful Lunar Prospector Mission, I would then be able to free myself from the Lockheeds and NASAs of the world and do what I wanted. That was it. I wrote the letter of acceptance and that was the end of it. I forgot it and went on to better things.

To make things worse, I was getting concerned about Allied Signal. Mike Jordan had called and said it was not clear that Allied Signal's upper management would agree to setting up the Lunar Prospector tracking network! If not, we might be able to use the LEOT (Low Earth Orbit Tracking) stations or something similar since JPL was trying to get in on the Lunar Prospector act by providing tracking capabilities. I figured one way or another we would get tracking. The question was, how and how much would it cost?

Further concerns of the day were that Headquarters was still talking about the three-year nominal mission option and the Japanese-Lunar Prospector Dual Doppler Gravity Experiment. I was not interested in either of those options. If we were going to be successful, we had to keep Lunar Prospector exactly the way it was proposed — just do the job and get it done.

All in all, it was a very tiring day — mainly because Dom's childish bitching had started to wear me out, even as the day got started. It was becoming very clear that it was going to be a challenge to get through Lunar Prospector with him. Dom was the only one at Lockheed I trusted to do the job with, but the man was becoming impossible to work with.

Thursday, April 13, 1995: A Contract at Last

I signed my contract and took it over about noon so that was underway. I hoped I would get the papers quickly so I could send them to Rebecca to start the move and I would be able to start working officially for LMSC Monday. I didn't know if they would get the paperwork done that quickly, but anyway that was it — $90,000 plus maybe a $10,000 signup bonus!

In the afternoon Dom and I went over to deliver our pitch to Al Smith, the President of SSD (Space Systems Division) and it went very well. He was a very sharp guy and asked all kinds of questions about how we were going to do Lunar Prospector. Dom did an excellent job. Al wanted to see our schedules and we had them — Dom knew Lockheed upper management well and was always well prepared. Then Al asked Dom," Well, how did you do the costing and do you have cost sheets?" Clearly, Al was expecting to see just upper level financial statements.

Dom answered, "Yes, we have the cost sheets," and showed Al our cost sheets that went all the way down to the individual parts of each subsystem — and that really impressed him. Then we discussed the funding and Al started making suggestions on how we could do it, though he was skeptical we could do Lunar Prospector for $59 million. Nevertheless, it looked like he was really jumping on the bandwagon, which was very pleasing. He then wanted to have a breakout of the money as a function of WBS (Work Breakdown Structure) and he gave that task to Martha. Al impressed me; he was the sharpest guy I had met at LMSC. Anyway the meeting went well. The last LMSC management hurdle was behind us; the company was at last fully behind Lunar Prospector — 6 weeks after NASA had announced we had won!

In general, as we worked through our budget and costs, we continued to have problems because Peggy had screwed up the proposal budget — like forgetting things or not adding things in right. However, once in a while the error was on our side! Sylvia Cox, Scott's deputy at Ames, was trying to get a budget together for the extended mission Mark Saunders wanted for planning purposes. I was looking high and low in the proposal to figure out how much we had budgeted for mission operations. Lo and behold, it looked like Peggy had double booked the costs of our Lunar Prospector tracking network and for the Command and Control costs during the mission! If so, she had booked an extra $2.3 million in the budget! For the first time one of her mistakes seemed to be a plus rather than a minus. I immediately went in and told Dom. "Look at this," I said, and then added, "We can check this later," but we both agreed it looked like she had double booked the money and we had an extra $2.3 million more than we thought we did — and that was very, very good.

I had a long talk with Bill Feldman about the state of the instruments; he wanted to build two Gamma-Ray Spectrometers. He asked, "What happens if we break something, what happens if we are at the launch pad and something gets broken?" Bill's solution was to have a backup or at least delay the mission until we could get a backup made in two or three months.

I answered, "No, we don't have that kind of money." Bill was doing a good job, but I was worried about the cost and kept telling him he could not go over the cap. I said further, "If an instrument breaks at launch, we just launch. We just go with a broken instrument." That shocked Bill, but that was what was going to be done, regardless of which instrument broke or was not done on time, period.

The morning went well, but I was tired, so I didn't get a whole lot done constructively.

I was very concerned about the tracking and we needed Tim Bridges, so I talked to Dom and then called Tim Bridges to get him started doing the communications, especially trying to figure out the tracking network. What we were going to try to do was have him be hired by Al Howard at Al's little SDB (Small Disadvantaged Business) and then have Tim come and work for us as a subcontractor.

Dom was quite happy with most everything, and it was a good day for me, too. I was getting very tired. I was wearing out because I had a very hard schedule with very long days, but everything was still moving ahead very nicely.

Friday, April 14, 1995

I had a good night's sleep for the first time in a long time, so I was quite rested when I got to work at the start of an interesting day — interesting even though I did not get my contract papers from LMSC, since Herman was on vacation! The day was filled with a lot of little things that had been sitting on my desk until a big surprise came at about 4:30 in the afternoon. Frank called and asked me to come to his office. Frank and Dom were there and they were talking about the meeting with Al Smith the day before. I asked what was up and they surprised me by saying I had been nominated for Lockheed's NOVA Award (that was the second time, the first time was a couple of years earlier in Houston). The NOVA Award (earlier called the Gross Award) is given to the most technically competent person in the entire Lockheed Corporation and it's a big deal just to be nominated for the award.

Frank and Dom said Gus was sponsoring the nomination, but they thought Al Smith had put him up to it — (nice, but why wouldn't they pay me what I was worth if they thought I was so damned good?). I liked the idea of winning it and they thought I probably would, or at least have a good shot at it. The nomination was of course because of Lunar Prospector. Frank and I talked a little bit about it after Dom left (I assumed he was hurt because he was not nominated, but he didn't say anything) and I said, "I'm surprised this happened so quickly." I told him I had been nominated before and he said, "Well, they (SSD) haven't won anything in a long time, not since I've been working here (4 or 5 years). They haven't won any new contracts in SSD and this is the first one." Lunar Prospector was a bigger deal than I thought. Given all that, I still wondered why they wouldn't give me the wages I deserved.

In addition, Dom and I were being set up as the poster boys, as Frank liked to say, for the new way of doing business — "Faster, Better, Cheaper." I was happy Dom was also getting recognition because of Lunar Prospector. A nice ending to a nice day.

Monday, April 17, 1995

I finally got my paperwork and I would officially be hired at LMSC the next day. Other than that nothing spectacular happened the entire day.

Tuesday, April 18, 1995

I finally joined LMSC. I got all my paperwork and all the paperwork for Rebecca to get our household goods move done. It took all morning and then some — but it was done at last. Beyond that, I got a little work done on the IDDs (Instrument Description Documents) for the instruments, but most of the day was shot with stuff related to my joining LMSC. Another hurdle passes — Rebecca just had to get our stuff moved out to Gilroy and we would be all set.

Chapter 2-10
Grinding through Phase B

Wednesday, April 19, 1995

Preston Carter called and we had a good chat. He asked me to come to Lawrence Livermore to give a talk on Lunar Prospector. I answered, "Yes, that would be fun."

Headquarters was becoming more concerned about the tracking network. It turned out that Allied Signal couldn't legally set up a commercial tracking network on the NASA sites in Australia and Spain. Headquarters was thinking more about setting one up as part of the NASA DSN, and Mark Saunders had some contact from whom we could supposedly get the stations for a half a million dollars each. If that were the case, then our tracking network would be set up and my worries would be over. However, we found out during the proposal effort that commercial stations each cost $2.5 million, so I hoped that Mark was right because we did not have $7.5 million in our budget for tracking stations.

My attitude was, *if you (NASA) say we can't use the Allied Signal tracking network we proposed and you initially accepted, then you can't expect us to pay the extra money (which we didn't have) because you changed the rules. You set up the tracking network and then we'll use it.* I hoped that simple logic would resolve that serious issue, because the tracking network issue was our Achilles heel. We had to get it resolved in our favor or the additional $7.5 million for the tracking network would put us well over budget and would almost certainly get Lunar Prospector canceled.

Tim Bridges was finally going to be able to start working on the tracking and communications network issues as an employee of Al Howard's company. That made me very happy because I had a great deal of confidence that Tim would do the job and we would end up with exactly what we needed.

I talked to Frank about overtime and compensatory time for the staff and he said that SSD simply wouldn't allow it! That meant they expected everybody to work 10–12 hours a day, 60–70 hours a week and never get any compensation for it or even time off. It's degrading and disgusting to have to work in that kind of environment. The worker is just a piece of trash with no rights; he is only supposed to work for the benefit of the company and get no benefits for himself.

LESC was also screwing Tom. When they made him a supervisor, they said they were going to raise his grade from level 7 to 9 to make his record look good — but without giving him a corresponding increase in wages! I was trying to make him understand that the best thing to do was to get out to Sunnyvale so we could get a supplement to his basic wages — what a disgusting company Lockheed is!

Bill Feldman called up to find out why he still didn't have his subcontract — he badly needed to start getting money. Bill also said than Jim Arnold had called and tried to wheedle his way onto the team as a no-cost Co-I. Jim tried to tell Bill it was his (Bill's) decision about who was a member of the Spectrometer Group and Bill told him flat out that it was up to me; I was the PI and only I had the authority to do that.

I called Jim and told him I appreciated his interest, but I couldn't add him to the Science Team — even as a no-cost Co-I. I explained I had had similar calls from a number of people wanting to be on the team — either as a paid Co-I or, as he did, for free, and if I let him do it, then I would have to let everybody do it. It was politically just not possible and he understood or at least accepted that. Then he grumbled that everybody was pestering him (why him and not us, he had nothing to do with our mission) because they (in reality Jim himself) all believe that our GRS was worse than the old Apollo GRS. What a load of crap. I explained to him that: First, we were going to cool the GRS passively to –40° C and get 8% resolution; second, we were going to orient the GRS with its cylindrical axis parallel to the spacecraft spin axis and thus eliminate all rotational phase effects; and third, Bill was going to get the best possible BGO detector. All of those things seemed to satisfy him. However, it was annoying to Bill and me that he kept trying to force himself onto the team. I hoped that was the end of it.

Friday, April 21, 1995

I got a lot of little things done. I started discussing the Data Processing Unit with Gerry Grismore. Then I worked on the IDDs for the instruments. Everything was beginning to move better and better. Nothing spectacular happened, but it was just a good day.

Monday, April 24, 1995

Spectrum Astro from Gilbert, AZ, near Phoenix, visited us and spent about three hours telling us about their capabilities. They seemed pretty good, but Dom and I didn't like the attitudes of a couple of them.

On the personal side, Rebecca had finished arranging for the move and I got her tickets to fly out to California Friday — hooray.

Tuesday, April 25, 1995

I wrote the lead article for the new issue of the *Lunar Prospector News*, which had last been published way back in 1989/90. I wanted to start it up again to let everyone know how things were going with Lunar Prospector. Writing the article was fun; I described what had happened in the years since the publication of the last issue — Volume I, No. 10.

The work on Lunar Prospector was moving along quite well. Dom was getting more and more into it and shedding other responsibilities so he could concentrate on Lunar Prospector.

Mark Saunders called and wanted to know if we could delay paying for the launch vehicle! Scott pointed out we only had two years to do the whole program — so when could we delay it to? NASA never ceases to amaze me!

Wednesday, April 26, 1995

We had our first status review and everything went OK. It was clear to me from the questions the engineers were asking about the various subsystems that they still didn't understand Lunar Prospector and the basic spacecraft design — so I had my work cut out to get them to understand that Lunar Prospector was to be built very differently than they were used to.

Dom had the bright idea, because we were having trouble getting the subcontracts done via Steve Lowell, who was slow as molasses, maybe Tom could do them. I talked to Tom to see if he could do the subcontracts. If so, then we would get him out to Sunnyvale right away at full time to do the contracts as well as the other jobs I had for him.

The organization and manpower issues were beginning to get nicely solidified and everything else was beginning to move forward. However, my biggest concern was making even faster progress on all fronts. Though it does take time to get a project like Lunar Prospector started, we just didn't have the usual amount of time to do so. We had to get our people working very hard, which I thought we were, but I felt I would feel a lot better in a couple of weeks (after May 11), when we had our Internal Requirements Review behind us.

In order to get information for Headquarters, Scott and Sylvia came over and asked me about the extended mission options, specifically the priorities and the relative values of A) a short phase of 10 km altitude mapping from an elliptical orbit, B) a longer phase of 50 km altitude circular orbit mapping and C) a 2-year extended mission in the 100 km altitude circular orbit of the nominal mission. I said the value of 2 years of extended mapping in the nominal orbit was about equal to the nominal mission, the 50 km altitude mapping was worth a factor of 10 and since the 10 km altitude mapping could only be done for a few areas on the Moon, it was probably worth a factor of three.

By the end of the day, I was very tired. For weeks I had woken up very early (3:00 or 4:00 AM or earlier) and gone into work. I was working 12 to 13 hours a day and getting tired out. I thought when Rebecca got there and we were in our home, I would sleep better. I would certainly be a lot happier when Friday came and she arrived. I was really looking forward to our having a nice weekend to enjoy ourselves and then, after our household goods arrived, getting settled in Gilroy in a week or so. How nice that would be.

Thursday, April 27, 1995

I finished the IDDs for the MAG/ER, but Bill still owed me about 10% of the information for the IDDs for the spectrometers.

Pat Dasch emailed me that Senator Sensenbrenner was still adamantly against funding Lunar Prospector in the fall. I decided to go to Washington towards the end of following week to start doing politics to make sure Lunar Prospector got funded in the fall — or stand a chance of losing it!

I had long talks with both Ron King about propulsion and Woody Woodcock about the power subsystem in order to get them to understand Lunar Prospector and how I wanted it done. Those were the two most critical subsystems and I had spent a lot of time during the previous several years refining the OMNI designs, and I needed Ron and Woody to understand those subsystems. Unfortunately, a lot of the comments the various subsystem engineers made in the status meetings were just a waste of time because they just didn't know the subsystems and the requirements. I spent a lot of time educating them about the Lunar Prospector Mission and design philosophy.

I talked to the Ames staff about the tracking issues again and then Bob Jackson set up a meeting with the LEOT team for the following Tuesday so we could begin to understand the LEOT capabilities. I was hopeful that issue was going to get resolved soon.

However, the biggest problem right then was the politics and making sure Lunar Prospector didn't get killed.

All in all, it was a good day, especially since it was the last day I would be without Rebecca.

Friday, April 28, 1995

I found out Frank had finished, weeks earlier, my travel reimbursement paper-work for the period when Rebecca and I drove out to Sunnyvale (early March) and for the other travel I did since then and damned Mike Ruggeri had just sat on it. He decid-ed to give it back to Frank because he thought I should be paid through Houston. Rug-geri was absolutely useless and counterproductive. Then Mike found out Dom and I were talking about bringing Tom out earlier than planned to start doing the contract work and he wrote a memo against it, saying how it would cost more money and the like. He had no idea Tom was coming out in the fall, no matter what. Mike Ruggeri was absolutely negative about everything. It was frustrating as hell to have to deal with a per-son that incompetent, a person who threw up roadblocks everywhere he could, when we needed all the help we could get. Unfortunately, Gus liked to surround himself with incompetent lackeys who did all his dirty work. Anyway, Ruggeri was on my list. Inter-estingly, I accidentally caught him playing computer games, which was absolutely ille-gal in the company. It was all I could do to stop myself from calling up the appropriate Lockheed personnel spy office to anonymously get the SOB fired (as it turned out, his days were justifiably numbered anyway).

I also told Frank about my going to Washington. He realized I had to go, but informed me I had to go through Lockheed, that is, have Lockheed set up the meetings and I would have to have the Lockheed liaison person with me at all times. I could tell Lockheed didn't like my having political contacts in Washington and wanted to keep control of me for their purposes. It was really pathetic that I had to continually wade through all the inept and petty bureaucracy and pettiness that went on all the time in that stinking company.

We had a great session in the afternoon doing videotaping and getting still pic-tures of Lunar Prospector. We were going to get a lot more things started with the Pub-lic Relations staff and on the political scene.

By week's end Lunar Prospector was moving ahead, though my biggest engineer-ing concern was to stop the engineers from trying to reinvent Lunar Prospector in the image of the inefficient Lockheed way of doing spacecraft, and get on with the way I had it designed and planned and the way NASA had accepted it. I decided I would have to have a talk with Dom about that.

Anyway Friday ended on a very happy note when I picked Rebecca up at the air-port — she looked as beautiful as ever.

Monday, May 1, 1995

Rebecca was busy with all kinds of things about our rented house since the fur-niture was to come the next day.

Mario Acuña and Dave Curtis came to Lockheed and we discussed what was nec-essary to make the spacecraft magnetically clean — a very important task I concluded would be very easy to do with Mario's help. He knew exactly what had to be done, i.e., the way the cables and various electronics units had to be laid out, the back wiring of the solar panels, etc. and we could do a great job on all of those things. Mario loved the configuration and simplicity of the spacecraft, both as a spacecraft and from the mag-netic cleanliness side and said, "No problem. They (the engineers) just have to make sure the electronics units are clean and it will be fine." I was very pleased with his ver-dict. I had not allowed Bob, Mario, and Lon to have a second magnetometer, which on other spacecraft was located close to the spacecraft bus in order to monitor the bus generated magnetic fields so the data from the first magnetometer could be corrected for the spacecraft generated fields. Instead, I had promised them I would see to it the spacecraft was magnetically clean so they would not need the second magnetometer.

We were using the same MAG/ER package that flew on the ill-fated Mars Observer and that was getting ready to fly on the replacement mission, Mars Global Surveyor. Because that package had the usual two-magnetometer configuration with two magnetometer electronics packages in the MAG/ER common electronics unit, I raised the question about eliminating the unneeded second magnetometer electronics package for simplicity. Mario and David said the redesign and re-testing of the electronics unit would cost both money and time. It would be faster, easier, and cheaper to leave the MAG/ER electronics unit the way it was and to use the second set of electronics as a backup for the first set. That made sense. It wouldn't cost us anything. It would give us redundancy (even though we all felt it was not needed) and the decrease in the electronic unit's mass caused by deleting the second set of electronics would have to be compensated for by adding more lead ballast to the MAG/ER package to keep it in balance with a much heavier GRS package. Clearly I would rather fly redundant electronics rather than lead weights, so I left the MAG/ER electronics the way they were.

Tuesday, May 2, 1995: Moving Day

Spent the day moving into our new home.

Wednesday, May 3, 1995

Wednesday was a long, hard day. I got up really early because I had spent all day Tuesday getting moved into the house, so I wanted to get to work early.

The day started off well — Lockheed had decided to give me a sign-on-bonus of $10,000 to mollify me about paying me only $90,000/year. However, the $10,000 was minus all the taxes, which were over $4,000. I got about $5,800 out of the $10,000, which, as they say, was better than a poke in the eye with a sharp stick.

The previous day, while I was busy moving in the house in Gilroy, there was a tracking network meeting that went pretty well. The LEOT system, which was really two stations up at Poker Flats in Alaska, could meet Lunar Prospector's global coverage needs by moving one of the two elsewhere and adding a third station. The costs of that solution were not yet clear, but most or all of the cost would have to come out of the $2 million we had in our budget.

JPL was, of course, trying to get us to use DSN, but they wanted us to put a recorder on board and downlink just once a day — which I was not going to do. I was not willing to change the spacecraft's simple design and simple operational philosophy just so JPL could get involved with Lunar Prospector by providing the DSN for tracking. The basic design and operations of Lunar Prospector, as a simple spacecraft with no computer, meant it had to be tracked 24 hours a day in case there were any problems. The Russians had lost many lunar, Mars, and Venus missions because they only communicated with their spacecraft once a day — by the time they became aware of a problem, it was too late to do anything about it. Lunar Prospector was going to be built the way I had planned and that was the end of it as far as I was concerned, and Dom agreed. We decided to push hard on the LEOT option and get it done.

I found out Stu Nozette was running around Congress, complaining about Lunar Prospector and Discovery. He had said before the selection was announced that if his Clementine 2 Mission did not win, he would go to Congress and try to stop the Discovery Program. He was causing all kinds of trouble. Headquarters was concerned, so I had to get to the Hill and do my best.

I had a long talk with Gerry Grismore about the C&DH and how his strategy would work. Gerry is pretty sharp and has very good ideas, but he also has a difficult personality. He wanted to make the C&DH a little more complex than I thought it needed to be. Nevertheless, I trusted his judgment and went along with his suggestions.

As a result of our conversations, I found out Gerry didn't like Dom one bit. Gerry said, "I get very annoyed with Dom, since he will never listen and everything has to be done his way." Gerry said further, "I like being able to talk with you, to be able to explain to you what I think we should do and to have you actually listen to me." — something that never ever happened with Dom.

I had realized that about Dom somewhat earlier and was getting both sick of it and concerned about it. Despite my liking and respecting Dom, I found I got along with the engineers much better than Dom did. Dom is just too offensive and aggressive and doesn't give anyone his or her due. Dom doesn't try to work with them, he insists on dominating them. Interestingly, the name Domenick sounds like the verb to dominate!

I talked to David Curtis; he and Bob Lin were getting concerned that Dom was laying too much paperwork on them since the two of them were doing everything. I had to very carefully play the intermediary. I had to keep Dom and Lockheed happy on one side and keep my Co-Is happy on the other side.

Also, all the Co-Is were concerned because Dom had moved up the due dates for the delivery of hardware to May of 96. I didn't know why in hell he did that. I had to look into that and somehow get Dom to realize if he pushed too hard on the science instrument development, he could destroy the mission. I was really getting tired of that type of stuff.

I still felt Dom was very good, but it was becoming clearer and clearer that he was very difficult to work with. That was exacerbated by the fact that Dom was getting more and more frustrated with Frank, Gus, and Lockheed in general — a condition I certainly understood because they were driving both of us nuts. I was beginning to feel it would be a miracle if we got Lunar Prospector done, if I could manage to keep Dom happy, and if I did not blow up myself. It was going to be a tough three years, not because of the task, but just because of the personalities.

Thursday, May 4, 1995

It was a good day. Dom was happy for a change. We had a good status review in the morning and the engineers were beginning to get nicely into their subsystems. Despite everything we had told them, they were surprised to finally understand why we had to have everything in such a rush. Since deadlines had never been kept before, they really hadn't understood that NASA expected us to have the costing done by July 22, 1995. But they had finally caught on, so it was a good review.

Frank pulled me out of the meeting because Gus was at the liaison office in Washington and on the phone. Gus didn't want me to talk to people on the Hill because Lockheed had bigger fish to fry than Lunar Prospector. Frank pointed out to Gus that if I were a PI at a university rather than at Lockheed, I would be going to Washington without any question. Gus had to realize I had a job to do there just like the other PIs and just because I was at Lockheed didn't mean that I didn't have to do it. Frank also reminded Gus that Lockheed was working for me on Lunar Prospector, not the other way around — it was my program, not Lockheed's. Gus had to agree that was the case and that it was my job to go to the Hill and represent Lunar Prospector and Discovery, and that was tough luck on Lockheed.

I had a nice telephone chat with Gregg Maryniak and to my disbelief, he said he had talked to Gus in Washington and Gus had told him we had paid OMNI for the design. I thought, *oh no, now Gregg is going to want us to pay SSI the money it put into Lunar Prospector.* At first it appeared that was not the case, but a few months later, SSI did try to get into Lockheed's pocket.

The guys from Olin, who manufacture the little 22 Newton rocket engines we wanted to use, came for a meeting. Francisco Andolz, Ron King, Richard Lynch, Tom Chinn, and I had a nice meeting with them. We discussed the engines and the tanks and they made some very good suggestions. One suggestion was that we use a bladder tank; that would alleviate the problem of draining the fuel on the pad if we had to and would also stop sloshing. They also said Lockheed owns the company that makes the Centaur 56 cm diameter tanks. There were plenty of those tanks available. They were exactly what we could use and we could probably swap out the tanks of another program (which might not be in such a hurry for their tanks) for ours and hence get our tanks right off the production line, thus cutting our tank procurement time drastically. They also said they make plenty of the 22 Newton engines, so they would be willing to make a similar swap and get our engines to us on time.

Also, they have engines with straight nozzles in the conventional configuration and another type with the nozzle at 90° to the long axis of the engine. They had models of those two engine types with them. The engines are very teeny; the engine bell is only about 4 or 5 centimeters long at most — I was amazed. The neat thing was that, having both the normal and the 90° engine configurations available, we would have a number of options as to how we could mount the 6 engines on Lunar Prospector.

I also had a good discussion with Tom Chinn and Woody about how we could make the solar array. Tom had assumed we would mount the solar cells right on the spacecraft drum. Woody's position was that we should mount the solar cells on separate panels and mount the panels on the drum. We decided, rather than have a solar drum cast in one piece, we would make it in two to four sections and have the solar cells mounted right on the drum sections. That would save having the extra mass of Woody's panels, which I liked.

The other nice thing about that solution was it alleviated part of the assembly problem. Instead of sliding the solar drum down over the load bearing bus structure, we could just mount the drum sections straight onto the bus structure. If we had to take them off during integration and test, it would be quite easy and safe.

Later, Dom came by with a half eaten ice cream sandwich in his hand. He was in a good mood and we were talking about a couple of other things when David Putnam came by. Dom asked him if he could work on mechanisms for us — he said he already was, though I had never met him before! He then made the suggestion that we use Astromast for our booms — I didn't exactly know what an Astromast was at that point. He said they were lightweight, deployment would be passive, and there was an Astromast in the model room.

We headed to the model room and there was an Astromast, a very big one, about 30 cm in diameter; ours would be maybe 6 or 7 cm in diameter. I thought, *man, that would be perfect.* We discussed how we would mount the instruments on them and how they would deploy. The masts are wound around like a spring or slinky in a canis-

ter and when the canister is opened up, they just spring out and uncoil — they are really neat. A damper could slow the deployment of the booms, so there would not be large
dynamic loads on the instruments. Apparently they would be cheap and very reliable. I
thought that was really great.

By the end of the day Dom and I were both optimistic. The engineers were finally learning more and more about the spacecraft from me and were beginning to understand what the hell I wanted done. I wished, as I had wanted in the beginning, I had sat
down with them and made them understand Lunar Prospector's design and design philosophy. That would have saved a lot of time and energy, but for some reason Dom had
hindered my doing so.

Friday, May 5, 1995:
The Beginning of the Never Ending Launch Vehicle Mess

Early in the morning I went to talk to Dom and he said in a strange, accusing way,
"There's something you haven't told me, isn't there."

I was puzzled and asked, "Well, what?"

He said, "The LLV2 guys told me you knew they weren't going to take care of the
Trans-Lunar Injection (TLI) Stage of the launch vehicle."

I was floored and said, "That is a load of BS." I immediately went to my office
and dug out the letter that clearly stated they were responsible for the kick stage, the
integration, and everything to do with the launch through injection. I had repeatedly
told them I wanted them to be responsible for the entire launch vehicle, the LLV2 as
well as the TLI Stage — I expected a launch through injection, not just to LEO and they
had quoted $25 million in the letter for a launch including the injection stage (Appen-
dix 2-1, also see www.lunar-research-institute.org).

Clearly they were trying to get out of paying for the injection stage. They had
already annoyed us and made us mistrustful by trying to get money out of us to do studies they didn't tell us they needed in the beginning. They were trying to say we were
supposed to take care of the kick stage — that was an incredibly dirty lie, made worse
by their saying I had agreed to their not providing the kick stage. Why would I add several million dollars to the program by agreeing to take care of the kick stage? Why would
I take on the responsibility for part of the launch vehicle when we had more than
enough to do just getting Lunar Prospector, the science instruments, and mission operations ready in 2 years? Those SOBs were clearly totally dishonest. Richard and I had
begun to suspect that when we first interfaced with them during the proposal effort last
fall, and then I knew it.

It really ticked me off they told Dom I had hidden something like that from him
and I was annoyed that Dom had even considered I did. He told me he did not believe
them, but still he asked me in a way that said it was possible.

After leaving Dom's office, I found Richard Lynch and told him what had happened. He also remembered that in all our conversations with the LLV2 guys I had
always discussed a launch through injection — not just a launch to LEO — just as the
letter stated. We did note however, that they had cleverly not signed the letter, dated
Oct. 11, 1994, with the $25 million quote for a lunar injection launch, and which they
sent over during the height of the proposal writing effort.

As that evolved during the day, the LLV2 bastards claimed that, since the letter was
not signed, there was no agreement about the launch. Right then and there I decided
to try to find another launch vehicle since the lying bastards could not be trusted.

Monday, May 8, 1995

I had to go home early to get the smog inspection for my car, and the next day, Tuesday, I had to go home at noon to take my driver's license test! As before, I had to spend time away from work, when time was so critical, to do personal things that could have and should have been done before we got started on Lunar Prospector. Gus should have hired me in January as both Mel Brashears and I wanted. Then my contract, the move, and all the associated things would have been done and I could have concentrated on Lunar Prospector as soon as we knew we had won. Instead of helping to make a very hard job simpler, Gus and Lockheed did everything to make it more difficult — I was disgusted.

The first thing that annoyed me in the morning was when I called Michelle at Washington about my appointments with the Congressmen, she had done nothing! Because Gus had initially told her not to do anything and then had neglected to tell her Frank had convinced him I needed to do the politicking, she had continued to do nothing!

I went to Frank who said Gus would be back the next day and I could see him then. They made everything so hard and caused us to waste so much time on trivial things. Working at Lockheed was frustrating, stupid, and very annoying.

Tom arrived for a week's work and was getting excited about working on Lunar Prospector. He was really enjoying himself and that made me happy. I thought everything was going to go well with Tom.

Dom decided to have Bob Goldin take over worrying about the launch vehicle. Dom was going to try to have the interfacing done within SSD and then we wouldn't have to pay those bastards anything. I was not happy about the launch vehicle situation — I saw problems right then and all the way down a very long road.

The tracking network issue was moving forward. Mark Saunders was setting up a special meeting when I was to be at Headquarters the following week. There was also a JPL meeting to try to figure out future DSN needs. Mark apparently did not want Lunar Prospector to support JPL's ambitions, but I had begun to think that was the way it was going to have to be. I hoped the tracking issue would start getting resolved at those meetings.

Tuesday, May 9, 1995

I had to take time off to get my driver's license and get the cars registered in California, so more wasted time when I should have been at work.

I talked to Gus about going to Washington and Gus said he thought it was a useless effort because he couldn't get to see anybody but aides, so how could I do any better — a valid concern. Gus thought if I went to the Hill, I would just be raising a red flag, but I thought it was more likely Gus just didn't like the idea of me going to Washington, since that was his job. However, he acknowledged since Wes Huntress insisted I do it, I had to do it. Further, he didn't feel I should go thank the Texas delegation for their support (I suspected he thought I would take too much credit away from Lockheed).

Not only did Gus want to keep me on a short leash to protect Lockheed and him from me; Michelle also wanted to run the show to protect her little kingdom. How those Lockheed people disgusted me with their little turf battles and big egos.

I decided to have George French try to let Sensenbrenner know I would be in Washington, so if Sensenbrenner wanted to see me there is nothing Lockheed and Michelle could do about it.

We decided to give Tom the subcontracts task, so, unless LESC gave us trouble, Tom would be at Sunnyvale full time very soon, which pleased me very much.

Wednesday, May 10, 1995

Since Michelle had apparently done nothing, I called George French. George was appalled at how politically naive and stupid the Lockheed people were and said he would go ahead and set up some meetings. He called back a few minutes later and said, "Sensenbrenner's aides expected you today at 11:30!"

I asked, "What the hell is this all about?"

George replied, "Somebody from Lockheed set it up." I immediately called Michelle and said, "I just found out somebody called about a meeting at Sensenbrenner's office for today!"

She said, " I set that up, but it is not today, it is a week from today."

I said, "Well, I have news for you. They think it is today."

She asked, "How on Earth did you know all that?"

I explained to her that a lot of people were working for Lunar Prospector on the outside and that the Wisconsin support group had access to Sensenbrenner. Hence, my Wisconsin friends had informed me that Sensenbrenner's staff expected to see me today! She said she would straighten out the misunderstanding about the date.

Tom was in a tizzy. Dom had asked him to do the subcontract work, but did not realize he was going back to Houston in a couple of days and would not be back in Sunnyvale for at least two weeks. Hence there was no way Tom could do the subcontracts.

I calmed Tom down and made him understand he was not going to be responsible for something he couldn't do because he was not yet in Sunnyvale full time. Then Tom and I went to Dom and I pointed out the obvious fact that Tom was not going to be in Sunnyvale for the next couple of weeks and hence he could not possibly do the subcontract work for the Phase B effort in the next couple of weeks. Dom finally realized he was asking the impossible.

Dom then talked to Martha and they decided to have poor old Francisco and Richard do that work — I knew that wouldn't work either. More and more frequently I wondered about Dom.

On the lighter side, it was beginning to look like the DSN realized we would be using the LEOT network. I thought the tracking issue was beginning to get straightened out and I hoped by Monday or Tuesday of the following week we would be in a good position to have our tracking needs taken care of — without screwing up the budget.

We had our data archiving meeting with Ed Guinness, Ray Walker, and Chuck Antoine, which ran from 1:00 to 9:00 PM. The meeting went extremely well. Then we all had a gigantic supper at the Cattleman's Restaurant.

Thursday, May 11, 1995

We started a two-day meeting with various groups working on the ICDs (Interface Control Documents). The meeting went very well; we got about half way through the ICDs by late afternoon, essentially on schedule. Just before lunch, Gary Noreen from JPL gave a talk on the tracking system and said that JPL wanted to have us use one (!) 26 meter antenna and have about 15 minutes (!) of tracking per day! If we were dumb enough to accept that suggestion then, 1) we couldn't do the gravity experiment, 2) we

would have to put a recorder on Lunar Prospector, 3) we would have to put a computer on Lunar Prospector, 4) we would have to have automatic safe modes, 5) we would
have to increase the downlink rate by a factor of 100, and the list goes on and on. In
short, we would have to completely redesign Lunar Prospector, which we simply were
not going to do. Clearly, the LEOT option was the way to go and that was the end of it.

Dom had told Gary forcefully in the morning session that because of our very
tight schedule and budget we couldn't and wouldn't change our design. After lunch,
when Gary got up and tried to press the issue about our changing Lunar Prospector's
design to fit JPL's tracking model, Dom got mad as hell and threw him out of the meeting! Other than that, things went quite well.

In addition to the fireworks in the ICD meeting, we had the beginnings of more
serious fireworks outside the meeting. Shortly after NASA had announced that Lunar
Prospector had been chosen for flight, Martha Martin, the President of Spectrum Astro,
wrote us a letter about how happy Spectrum Astro was that we won, and that they were
equally happy about being part of the Lunar Prospector team. That puzzled us. Dom
had let them know in no uncertain terms that they were not part of our team and that
we were going to put "Requests for Proposals" and "Requests for Information" out to
potential subcontractors and they could compete like everyone else to become part of
our team. That really ticked Martha off and she then wrote a letter to Sam Araki (then
the President of LMSC) and said Spectrum Astro didn't understand why they were being
forced to re-compete since they were written into the proposal and hence were already
part of our team. We smelled lawsuit.

After the ICD meeting was done for the day, Dom, Bob Goldin, and I looked carefully through the proposal to see if we had somehow said they were part of our team.
We could not find anything like that anywhere. True, we found Spectrum Astro was
mentioned twice, once as a potential SDB and secondly, in the third volume, there was
a reference to them as having reviewed our budget. But we did not use any of their
materials or any of their estimates in the text about the C&DH. We could not find any
reference to them being part of our team — just "potential" subcontractors. We concluded they were not in the proposal regardless of what they claimed.

Dom found out they were claiming they were mentioned as part of our team in a
news conference, which was also false. We were going to meet with the lawyers on Friday to make sure we were clean and then they would take care of the situation. Spectrum Astro had tried to push and had ticked us off; any chance they had of working with
us was over.

Friday, May 12, 1995

Friday was the final day of the ICD meeting. The ICDs were done. The meeting
kind of slowed down and the people just drifted away. The most pleasing thing was that
David Curtis was really into the program — more so than I had ever seen from the
Berkeley guys. We really got things accomplished.

Don Damon from LLV2 came by in the morning. Their latest tactic was to say, "You
won the contract, but since we are LMSC too, it is automatically our money, too." What
a load of crap!

Dom said, "How did you get that?"

Damon replied, "We looked through the contract." Another lie — we said nothing in the proposal or contract about LLV2 being part of our effort. The launch was written in as a service purchased from LLV2. Dom told him flat out we were getting very con-

cerned about the way they were interacting with us, that they had been trying to snook-
er us, that we had very little trust in them, and that things had better change. Damon
knew his hand had been called and he said they would do things differently in the
future. But Dom made it again damn clear we were aware of their skullduggery and
Damon had better be sincere about their future interaction with us.

Dom, Chuck Rudiger, and I were going to see John Palochak, the LMSC lawyer, later
in the day because of the Spectrum Astro charges. Dom, Bob Goldin, and I checked everything again. We checked the video from the news conference, the NASA news release, and
the proposal. Everywhere Spectrum Astro was mentioned, it was clearly only as a potential vendor, never as a vendor. We checked everything we could get our hands on and
could not find any reference to Spectrum Astro being a team member. Bob Goldin was
going to write a letter for Sam Araki's signature that pointed those things out and that
there was neither a verbal nor a written team agreement between Spectrum Astro and us.
The real tragedy was, as Dom, Bob, and I were looking for answers, Dom blew up at Bob
Goldin. Dom felt insulted when Bob asked him "Well, did you say anything to Spectrum
Astro about a teaming arrangement?" just as a probing question to shake Dom's memory.

Dom got hopping mad and screamed at Bob, "Did you insult me? Don't you think
I know what I am doing?" Dom ranted and raved while Bob tried to apologize and tried
to convince Dom he was not trying to insult him. I could not believe what I was wit-
nessing. Dom was so damned sensitive and childish it was just unbelievable. Finally Bob
got Dom to calm down. Then we went to see Palochak and dumped the Spectrum Astro
thing in his lap.

After the meeting with Palochak, I started preparing for a trip to Washington, DC,
the following Monday, Tuesday, and Wednesday to discuss how we would track Lunar
Prospector with Headquarters, attend a LEOT meeting, and go to the Hill to talk with
congressional aides about Lunar Prospector. Gerry Grismore, Tim, and I sat down and
discussed the tracking. I began to feel all that was no big deal and that I could go to
Headquarters and successfully present our requirements. If we could just keep Dom
from exploding over those issues, I felt we would end up with LEOT being our tracking
system and the LEOT staff would work out any problems. I thought I could defend our
arguments about not modifying Lunar Prospector so we could use the DSN for periodic downlink sessions since that would just screw everything up. I didn't see that NASA
had any other choice. In any case, the Monday and Tuesday meetings were critical.

If I could get the tracking issue resolved and if we could make the LLV2 people
stop their shenanigans, we would be past our two biggest hurdles. We were getting the
budgeting done for our July 22 deadline and unless there were any big surprises in
costs, I thought we could find ways to work around everything else. Dom was pushing
the schedules to get deliveries of hardware by May the following year! Though the science teams were squawking, they had come up with workarounds. All in all, we were
moving along rapidly and even though Dom was setting a fast pace, he was also amazed
we were doing it. Lunar Prospector was doing well.

Sunday, May 14, through Thursday, May 18, 1995:
The Trip to Washington

On Sunday the 14th, I flew to Washington, DC. The flight was long and tiring. As
usual, I stayed with Pat and Julius and they had a nice chicken dinner waiting for me.
After dinner we chatted about Lunar Prospector, NASA, and everything else connected
with our world of space exploration.

Early Monday morning, I went to Headquarters and had good talks with Mark Saunders, Jurgen Rahe, Al Diaz, Joe Boyce, and Bill Piotrowski. Everybody was very pleased with Lunar Prospector's progress and they assured me they wanted to keep out of our way and just let us do it. I told them how well things were working with Ames being our partner and serving as the NASA headquarters representative. Of course, like us, Headquarters was concerned about the tracking issue. Mark and I briefed the rest of them on the potential LEOT solution and then we went to our LEOT meeting with Stanley Fishkind and Ron Klinger.

Stan and Ron basically said they wanted to take all the money we had allocated for tracking, add some of their own, and expand the LEOT to meet our needs. It would be a sweetheart deal — we would help finance expanding their system and they would give us more value by setting up the entire network. We still had to work out some of the details. First, I assured them we would make Lunar Prospector as compatible with their system as we could, but second, I reminded them they also had to accommodate us since we had relatively little maneuvering room in terms of changing the spacecraft.

Monday was a good day.

However, Monday night was not so good. It was freezing in Julius and Pat's house. They unknowingly had the air conditioning on and I got a sore throat.

Tuesday was kind of a day off. I went to the National Air and Space Museum and had some fun and relaxed in the morning. Then I saw Lori Graver at the National Space Society and had a nice chat with her.

Wednesday I met with Melissa Robins, Lockheed's congressional liaison. She crabbed because I went to NASA without having cleared it with her and crap like that — I was not impressed.

She and I went to the Hill and talked to several congressional aides. That went well, except no one on the Hill knew what was going on with the budget cuts. Everybody was trying to convince Sensenbrenner that Lunar Prospector was not a new start; rather Lunar Prospector was just a continuation of Discovery Program as a way for him to get around his earlier proclamation that there would be no new starts. It was a ticklish situation. Lunar Prospector was small potatoes; Congress and NASA had much bigger problems with the Space Station and EOS. There were signs Congress was playing EOS off against the Space Station and Lunar Prospector was just a small pawn in that political game of budgetary chess. No one really knew what was going on and NASA was having big problems since enormous cuts were being pushed. Congress wanted to cut $7 billion from NASA's budget — mass confusion!

There was a nice article in the *Washington Post* that included Lunar Prospector as the newest Discovery mission. It was a colored spread that surprised everyone. There was a nice advertisement, apparently put in by Lockheed, about lunar exploration leading up to manned bases. The theme was catching on.

Mark told me Monday about a LEOT tracking meeting set for Thursday he said we should attend. I changed my return flight to early Thursday evening so I could go to the meeting with him. The meeting turned out to be useless and boring, so Mark said, "Let's get out of here," and we did.

I went directly to National Airport in hopes of getting an earlier flight home and I got there at about 1:00 PM. There were huge rainstorms in St. Louis (where I had to change planes), and everything was backed up. There was a flight at 12:30 PM that still had not gotten off the ground. The agent said the flight was going to leave around 2:00 and I could get on it. That meant I would have a long layover in St. Louis, but there is no difference between waiting in Washington and waiting in St. Louis and each step closer to home was one less step to do — especially in bad weather. However, the flight didn't get to leave until about 3:30, after a huge rainstorm had passed through Washington.

Of course, the St. Louis airport was in chaos because of all the planes that were backed up and all the people in the waiting areas. As expected, the plane to San Jose was very late leaving, so I didn't arrive in San Jose until 11:30 PM. Rebecca picked me up and I got home at 1:00 AM. It was a very long and very hard day and, of course, my sore throat and cold made it even worse.

Friday, May 19, 1995

I went to work and told Dom the results of my trip, especially the LEOT tracking discussions. Dom agreed wholeheartedly with me that we should jump on the LEOT solution. I set up a meeting with Gerry Grismore and Tim Bridges for Monday morning to discuss the LEOT issues. With a tracking solution in sight, Dom was in a good mood.

While I was on travel, I had received an invitation from the National Academy of Science to talk about Lunar Prospector at Woods Hole on June 15. That was convenient since I had to go to NASA headquarters on the 14th for the Discovery Lessons Learned Meeting (how to make the next Discovery proposal and selection process better than the first one) and to give a talk on Lunar Prospector at the Aerospace States Association Meeting on June 16.

All in all it was a hard, but very good week. The LEOT tracking solution looked very good, but the launch vehicle issue was still a mess.

Monday, May 22, 1995

We had the status review in the morning. Jim Schirle, the thermal engineer, made several suggested changes to the spacecraft without understanding their implications. That kept happening because the engineers didn't understand the basic concept of the spacecraft and mission requirements. If I had been able to spend a couple of days explaining the entire mission to them in the beginning that would not have been happening, but Dom torpedoed my doing so, so I had to handle each of the engineer's questions one at a time. Other than that everything went pretty well.

Afterwards, Tim Bridges, Gerry Grismore, Dom, and I discussed what I had found out at Headquarters about the LEOT. We discussed the Loral transponder that was used on Clementine and that we were considering for use on Lunar Prospector. I had called Loral and gotten the information on the transponder. It was just $400,000 and satisfied all our needs, but Gerry could not quite commit himself to the transponder (or anything else as Dom and I were quickly learning). With that information, I was ready for a telecon at noon between Code O and Mark Saunders at Headquarters, and Bob Jackson and Scott Hubbard at Ames.

Dom hammered home the fact that LEOT needed to adapt to the spacecraft if at all possible and not the other way around. He did a good job, but was very brisk. Mark also had gotten it across to Code O that Lunar Prospector was at a stage where we really couldn't afford to change much. The burden had to fall on LEOT since it was still flexible. We thought we were all done, we had everything we needed and then, unfortunately, Scott piped up and reopened the whole issue by asking, "What's the schedule and cost?" Luckily our telephone was on mute, because Dom just fumed about Scott. Dom's behavior really began to annoy me. He was so childish. True, Scott should not have said anything, but Dom didn't have to act like a two-year-old. Dom began to calm himself down and we tried to get the conversation ended. Then Scott opened it all up again by asking another dumb question. Mark was happy, Code O was happy, we were happy, and then Scott had to do it again! Dom fumed some more and then worse came to worse when Scott said, "Maybe we should call Gary Noreen at JPL." Dom blew his stack. I tried to end the telecon, but I couldn't. Gary Noreen got on the line and then the discussion started to get dragged down into the technical details. Finally Dom got them to shut up by saying, correctly, that we really needed to have the technical discussions off line. That telecon was about the policies, overall management, and how we were going to do it, but not about technical details. The telecon finally concluded with everyone agreeing that LEOT was the way to go.

But Dom was still fuming. He grumbled, "Why did you have Scott in on the telecon?"

Well, I had to bring Scott in because he was the NASA Mission Manager! Nevertheless, I agreed with Dom that if Scott kept screwing things up that way, we would have to somehow minimize his involvement when we were trying to get things done. On the other hand, it was getting extremely annoying that Dom always had to holler at somebody about something. I answered, "Well, you remember I was the one who never wanted a damned NASA center involved at all."

Dom replied, "Well, it would have saved us a lot of trouble, but we really don't want to interact directly with Headquarters." That made Dom shut up, but nursing Dom was getting tiresome.

We had Martha's kickoff meeting for the budget effort in the afternoon. I talked about 45 minutes on the mission; that was the first time I had a real chance to do a much-needed tutorial on Lunar Prospector. Of course, Dom was bored stiff when I was talking. He wasn't interested in what I was saying; he just didn't care. If he was not talking, he was not happy and he would not listen to anybody else talk. After I finished, Dom got up and did the PHSL (Program Hardware and Software List). Then Dom and I both gave a pep talk about how critical Lunar Prospector was to NASA and Discovery. The meeting ended on a high note and both Dom and I were happy.

The thing that worried me was that Dom was really no better than the engineers were — none of them really understood how the spacecraft was to go together as a unit and Dom would not listen to me or even discuss things. Also Dom was no better than Gerry Grismore for making decisions. Dom was the pot calling the kettle black when he complained that Gerry Grismore could not make decisions. There were many things we could have just decided straight out and gotten them done. But, of course, I always had to do that offline by talking to the individual engineers rather than doing it in meetings. Dom just did not like to play second fiddle in any of the technical discussions we had when we were with the engineering staff. That was just something I would have to live with since I felt he was damned good and I couldn't get the job done at Lockheed without him.

Dom was going on vacation and I was looking forward to him being gone for the next several days so I could get a lot of work done. Hopefully I would be able to work through the structure issues with Tom Chinn, propulsion with Ron King (though propulsion was in pretty good shape), thermal with Jim Schirle, and the other subsystems with Gerry. Our biggest problems were still the tracking, the rocket, and the money. I thought if the LEOT issues would get resolved the way we wanted them to, if we could get the damned rocket straightened out, and if we would get our money in the fall from Congress, we would be doing fine. Three big "ifs," but we were moving ahead.

Tuesday, May 23, 1995

A slow day. We had a meeting about the PHSL and the budget that went very slowly. Gerry Grismore got all ticked off and stormed out of the place.

I had a great phone conversation with Jim Pagliasotti from the Colorado Governor's office about the Aerospace States Association meeting at which I was going to give a talk on Lunar Prospector. I suggested that Dom also give a talk, and Jim liked the idea. Jim said that he was 100% behind Lunar Prospector and wanted to get the Aerospace States Association behind it (which it already was). Anyway, I was really pleased with the extremely positive feedback I got from him and I assured him I was interested in helping the Aerospace States Association in every way I could.

Tim Bridges, Gerry Grismore, and I went over to talk to the antenna guys. They had a big biconic antenna already developed that I didn't really like. They said they could make a much smaller, 8 dB, helix-antenna that I thought would do nicely for Lunar Prospector. We also talked about the slotted phase array antenna proposed by OMNI, but the helix seemed to be the simplest and least expensive. Tim and I pushed for it.

Wednesday, May 24, 1995

Dom was on vacation. Since I was getting more and more concerned about Dom, I had a long talk with Bob Goldin about him since he is one of the few people, if not the only one, who seems to get along — or could put up — with Dom. We discussed Dom's extreme sensitivity, my need to work on the spacecraft design, and Dom's sensitivity about my doing so, even though it was my spacecraft. I also explained I was getting sick of having to walk on eggshells with Dom all the time. It was a good conversation, but as much as I respected and liked Dom, he was making things very difficult. There was enough to do without having to deal with his ego problems and his extreme sensitivity. Bob was well aware of the problems with Dom, but could only say if I wanted to work with him, I had to put up with him.

Tim Bridges was finally officially on the program (his paperwork took several weeks as usual). Tim's presence made a big difference; he was a pleasure to work with. I really like Tim and was overjoyed to have him working on Lunar Prospector.

I was getting concerned because the costs were escalating, so I talked to Martha Taylor. Dom wanted the budget exercise to use the high bids on things like the transponder, but I had a sneaking suspicion that we were going to come in a million dollars, or more, higher than we should. If so, we would eat up the contingency Martha said we had built in. I was not sure that was a good idea that early in the program. Martha said the budget we were putting in on the 22nd of June was just a budget proposal. It would be refined and become our final budget for delivery in September. Reassuring words, but I was still quite sure we were going to come in higher than our original $59 million and that could or would mean cancellation!

Thursday, May 25, 1995

It was a good day; I got a lot done.

I talked to Ron King about propulsion and I felt that it was in good shape. However, I was concerned about the drop of thrust as the fuel was used up and the tank pressure dropped. Ron pointed out that we might be able to get up to 50% more thrust from the engines by enlarging their orifices. He was going to check with Olin on that. I also wanted him to get started trying to get a waiver from Range Safety so we would not have to have a Propellant Isolation Valve (PIV) on Lunar Prospector and maybe even get permission for us to have a higher maximum tank pressure than usual. I did not want the PIV because it was heavy (0.33 kg), and technically it was not needed. By Range Safety rules, spacecraft engines must be doubly fault tolerant against inadvertent firing to protect personnel working on a fuelled spacecraft. That is usually accomplished by having a PIV which is nominally closed (so no fuel can flow to the engines) and having the engines nominally off. It would take two inadvertent commands or actions to accidentally fire an engine. In Lunar Prospector's case, an engine fire command load must be followed by an "Execute Command" before an engine could fire — so we did not technically need a 0.33 kg PIV, and I wanted to get rid of it. The reason why I wanted a higher maximum tank pressure was to increase the engine thrust, since the thrust is essentially linearly proportional to the pressure.

Al Tilley came over; Al is another engineer who I very much respect and enjoyed working with. Al and I were going to work on the mass properties together, so I started telling him about the spacecraft balance issues. Since Lunar Prospector was a spinner, it, and especially the instrument booms, had to be properly spin-balanced. All the engine thrust vectors had to be properly aligned with respect to the spacecraft's center-of-gravity (c.g.). The spacecraft's c.g., the centers of the fuel tanks, the c.g. of the fuel, and the tangential engines all had to lie in a plane that is perpendicular to the spacecraft's spin axis at all times during the mission. Unfortunately, we would not know exactly where the spacecraft's c.g. was until we were nearly finished building it. We would have to design the spacecraft to allow for shifts in the projected c.g. to minimize ballasting — I did not want Lunar Prospector to carry any more dead mass to the Moon in the form of lead ballast than absolutely necessary.

Al was not aware of most of those requirements. Yet another case of an engineer not understanding the spacecraft because Dom kept sabotaging my efforts to educate everyone all at once about the mission and spacecraft. I had to tell them one-at-a-time what they were doing wrong. Dom seemed to think they could just go blundering along and somehow end up with a functioning spacecraft.

Al and I did boom mass balance calculations taking into account the projected cable and instrument masses. It looked like the heaviest instrument, the GRS, was going to come in at about 6.6±0.1 kg. Since the NS/APS assembly was very light, we decided to make the APS more massive by increasing its casing's wall thickness (that would also increase its thermal inertia and hence keep its temperature more uniform) rather than just adding ballast to the boom to get it in balance with the GRS boom. The MAG/ER assembly was only a couple of kilos light, but we had no choice but to add a couple of kilos of lead ballast to it. In any case, the mass issue was coming along nicely.

Friday, May 26, 1995

Another a good day (maybe because Dom was on vacation). I got a lot of work done.

Gary Noreen called and wanted to come to Sunnyvale the next Tuesday with some Wallops Island engineers to discuss the tracking issues. That could be kind of awkward, since Dom would be back and he hated Gary, so I expected the meeting could or would go badly, but we had to have it.

Gerry Grismore and I had a great conversation about the spacecraft Command and Data Handling Unit (C&DH). I was impressed with Gerry and thought the C&DH

was coming along quite nicely. I began to understand that Gerry's trouble making decisions was mainly because of Dom and his poor way of dealing with Gerry and everyone else. Gerry and I were getting along nicely. We had a great conversation and he always seemed pleased when I worked with him, apparently because, unlike Dom, I was not confrontational and I tried to understand and accept his suggestions. The spacecraft uplink and downlink were going to have to be a little more complex than originally conceived, but that was necessary if we wanted to use LEOT.

Basically, what OMNI originally proposed would only have worked if we used a dedicated network with nobody else on it. Then we could have had direct uplink with no nodes and hence no delays caused by nodes. The commands, specifically the pulsed engine firing commands we uplinked would have executed immediately. However, by using LEOT and the NASA system, our commands would be switched through various available nodes, so the commands would not be uplinked immediately and our engine firing timing would be off. We would have to design the C&DH to use the sun crossings (once per spin period of 5 seconds), as measured by the sun sensor, for an internal spacecraft timing reference. That would be no big deal and would give us all the accuracy we needed for the engine firings.

Anyway, Gerry and I got everything laid out for Gary's meeting. I asked Gerry to make a very consistent and non-refutable story to present to Dom so we wouldn't have a confrontation between him and Gary. If Dom was as obstreperous as he was during the previous meeting with Gary, the coming meeting was going to be bad. Anyway Dom was really beginning to worry me.

The problem with Lunar Prospector at that point was we still did not have enough people on the program. Those we had were just doing it on the side and that was worrisome. Dom was not able to get people committed and we were not spending our money as fast as planned; in one sense that was good, but on the other hand, the work was not getting done. If we could just get over the humps of the staffing, the budget, the rocket, and the LEOT and then settle down to really work on the spacecraft, and if Dom would quit acting like a nitwit, Lunar Prospector would be a lot more fun. I was hoping by October we would be into construction (Phase C/D), things would be all smoothed out, and we would have all of those headaches behind us. My biggest concern was that we were just not getting the support from Lockheed we needed. On those sour notes, Friday ended and a nice long three-day weekend began, three days to forget all those problems and just relax with Rebecca.

Tuesday, May 30, 1995

I got back to work after the holiday and, happily, Dom was still not back!

Gary Noreen and another engineer from JPL and one from Wallops Island arrived for the LEOT meeting. Unfortunately, Tim Bridges was not in. Gerry Grismore and I met with them with Richard Lynch sitting in. The meeting went very well. Gerry gave a good discussion of the issues and we got a lot accomplished. It was clear LEOT could support us and we all agreed LEOT was our baseline. It was an excellent meeting and I was very relieved.

Richard and I had talked about other launch vehicles. Richard had found out that the Taurus could probably launch us with a big shroud and, of course, the MedLite could also launch us. They both cost about $25 million, so if the LLV2 continued to be a problem, we were certainly going to investigate Taurus and MedLite.

Wednesday, May 31, 1995

I talked with Woody about power since he had the power balance all screwed up. He had reported at the staff meeting that we needed 130 watts just to run the spacecraft bus, i.e., not considering any power to recharge the battery. I knew that 130 watts of bus power was way high, so something was wrong. Unfortunately, he was still using old numbers from the proposal and needed to get the new numbers from all the subsystems. If I could get some decent data out of Woody, I expected our total power (including the power needed to recharge the battery) would be down to my estimated 175 to 180 watts.

The same thing was going on with the mass. Al Tilley came up with 150 kg for the spacecraft, which was about 25 kg higher than it should be. I didn't know where in hell the guys were getting their numbers, but I was planning to sit down with Woody and Al and help them scrub them.

Jim Beffa and his antenna engineers gave us the cost estimates and data on the three antennas we were considering — the biconic, the helical, and the slotted phased array. Because they had already built biconic antennas and knew something about helical antennas, Jim felt confident about their estimates about the antennas. That was not the case for the slotted phased array antenna, since they had no experience with it at all. It looked like we might go with the biconic antenna since Jim had the most experience with them.

Thursday, June 1, 1995

I talked with David Putnam and Tom Chinn and they said the Astromast booms must have a 20 cm diameter to be stiff enough for the 3.5 meter lengths we needed. Then it dawned on me that if we used the Astromast, I could go back to the old configuration where the 1.2 meter long MAG extension boom was solidly mounted (perpendicular to the Astromast boom) on the ER/electronic unit instead of having the MAG extension boom hinge mounted to the ER/electronics unit at the end of the MAG/ER boom. That way the MAG boom extension would lay flush along the spacecraft when the Astromast was undeployed and we would need neither a hinge for the MAG extension boom nor to deploy the extension boom before deploying the main, Astromast booms. That would also remove a failure mode from the spacecraft, i.e., the failure of the MAG extension boom to deploy and hence the loss of the mission. I checked with Mario Acuña about that configuration and he said it was fine

Also, if I could do something similar with the NS and APS, I could get rid of the hinge between them on their boom. I called Bill and asked him if we could shove the NS right up next to the APS and he said, "No problem."

Thus our boom configuration became Astromast with no hinges and I probably saved several hundred thousands of dollars and two failure modes!

Friday, June 2, 1995

I got an email from Pat. She said the Senate had put Lunar Prospector in its budget and damned Stu Nozette was trying to get Congress to kill Lunar Prospector and Discovery. He hoped the following year more Republicans would be elected to Congress and he would then tell the new Congress he would do a cheaper mission than Lunar Prospector; what a back stabbing SOB. Stu should be run out of the business, along with anyone who works with him. Pat said we needed to get to the Hill fast, so Dom and I went and talked to Gus. Gus agreed and was actually going to start pushing for Lunar Prospector on the Hill. Since we would be in Washington the next week, Gus said he would try to set it up so we could talk to various people on Wednesday.

I spent the rest of the day working subsystems since everyone had made a mess of their subsystem masses. Al Tilley had a spacecraft mass of 157 kg! Woody still had changed nothing from the proposal, so he had made no progress. Jim Schirle's mass estimate for the thermal subsystem was over 9 kg, or 6 more than we had in the proposal! Gerry Grismore had totally screwed up — he gave the mass of the two transponders as 16.4 kg based on his incorrect assumption that in the proposal we meant the mass of one transponder was 8.2 kg. However, 8.2 kg was the total mass of both transponders, each of which was just 4.1 kg! Gerry had the equivalent of four transponders in the spacecraft! He did the same thing with C&DH, so all his estimates were double the real masses. Al had added considerable mass to the structures where it didn't belong. All in all, when I got done scrubbing the mistaken inputs with Al, the spacecraft mass was down to about 135 kg. There were 20 kg of mistakes! That was annoying and discouraging because when I left the guys alone, they just made mistake after mistake. Nevertheless, Tilley and the rest of the engineers were all fun to work with. The trouble was, nobody was spending any time on Lunar Prospector, they were all busy on other programs and we didn't have a lot of money to pay them.

Similarly, David Putnam had screwed up his calculations of the forces on the booms during deployment. He had used the wrong angular velocity and was a factor of 10 too high! I swore if I didn't watch the guys like a hawk, they just made mistake after mistake. I wondered how in the hell Lockheed ever built anything. I was amazed that we were making any progress at all.

On the positive side, Scott had Bob McMurray simulate the gamma-ray spectra we would get with the BGO detector, the old Apollo NaI detector, and the high-resolution (but very costly) germanium detector. The BGO simulated spectra looked distinctively better than the NaI spectra, but, of course, not as good as germanium spectra. Our BGO GRS was going to be much better than most people thought.

Tuesday, June 6, 1995

I had a good meeting with Jim Schirle about the thermal issues. Unfortunately, he had originally calculated all of the instrument temperatures with the old boom configuration, not knowing we had gone over to the Astromast. In the meantime he had redone the calculations and it turned out the GRS could get quite cold. In fact, Jim found it would have to be heated a little to keep it at $-40°$ C. That was good, because it meant we could accurately control the GRS's temperature using just a few watts.

Jim also said the nickel-hydrogen (NiH_2) battery needed to be quite cold, so it was going to be a problem to find a cold place for it in the spacecraft. We discussed the thermal environment on the shelf, where all the other units were to be, and noted that the temperature there was just perfect for a nickel-cadmium (NiCd) battery. Those facts, plus the facts that a NiH_2 battery has some bad magnetic properties and is heavy (it would have to be broken in two parts for mass balance purposes), pushed us in the direction of a NiCd battery. I was going to try to get rid of the NiH_2 battery and try to get Dom to agree with me.

Wednesday, June 7, 1995

I had a long talk with Tom Chinn about the mass of the structure and we got it down to where it should have been without too much difficulty. He still needed to check some things, but they would probably be OK.

Gus had me come to his staff meeting in order to congratulate me for being the runner up in the Nova Award for the division.

I had a long talk with Scott. Mark Saunders wanted to have a Project Manager, some damned trainee or whatever, back at Headquarters and we were going to stop that crap. We absolutely didn't need that. That's not what we proposed and it was just plain stupid since it would cost money and add needless bureaucracy. Headquarters was always fooling around, changing the rules, and doing something dumb.

Thursday, June 8, 1995: The Trip to Los Alamos

Francisco and I arrived at Los Alamos Thursday morning and had a good meeting with Bill, Bruce Barraclough, and others in Bill's group. The first item was the collapsing of the NS and APS into a single NS/APS assembly so they could both be mounted at the end of the boom without a hinge between them. The APS part of the housing was to be an 11 cm cube with the two 4x4 cm frames holding the two detectors mounted on five of the sides. The APS "cube" was the front end of an elongated rectangular box, the back part of which would have the two neutron detectors — the ^{3}He tubes — attached to two of its sides. No hinge — that was good.

We talked about dropping the GRS temperature another 10° to get another 1 percent better resolution. Bill said the little electronic boards on top of the photo-multiplier tubes might break at –50° C, so we decided to leave the operational temperature of the GRS at –40° C.

The power of the spectrometers came to 12.2 watts, just a tad under what was in the proposal. That was good.

The mass of the spectrometers came in about right. The unit for the common electronics in the spacecraft was 6.8 kilograms. The total mass of the instruments was basically the same as in the proposal.

Everything about the spectrometers seemed to be in pretty good shape and we had a good meeting.

Bill and his wife, Margrethe, had all of us over for a very lovely meal. A good ending to a good day.

Friday, June 9, 1995

Tom Chinn and Dom arrived for the second day of the meeting. Dom was in a good mood, but seemed to be wearing out. He and his wife came out for a long weekend and were staying at Santa Fe for some much needed R&R.

We went through the ICDs and resolved a lot of issues. The things that really concerned me were the dynamical and acoustical loads on the instruments during launch. We still didn't know anything about the LLV2 launch environment, so we could not define them for the instruments in the ICDs. The instruments would be sitting on the spacecraft, attached to its sides, and the spacecraft would be sitting on the Star-37 Trans-Lunar Injection (TLI) Stage. The entire spacecraft/TLI assembly would act as a big inverted pendulum whose launch environment would be very different from those of the LLV2 whose characteristics we did not know! Nevertheless, the science instruments were getting close to their final configurations and I was just going to freeze their designs — I had no other choice.

We discussed one more critical issue. Los Alamos still hadn't gotten any money. They were supposed to have received $20,000 a month, but hadn't. Fred DeFrank had given me a check to carry to Los Alamos. That was just a temporary solution, so we had to find out what in the hell was going on with Bill's money. Dom was annoyed, so was I.

I got home very late that night and I was very tired.

Monday, June 12, 1995

I got in really early and went through all the mail that had accumulated while I was in Los Alamos.

I checked with David Putnam to see if the angular acceleration on the booms exceeded the bending moment of the Astromasts when we did spin-up and spin-down maneuvers, but happily it didn't. The angular accelerations would be equivalent to 0.03 g or 0.04 g, about the same as the linear accelerations. That was fine. All we had to do was to be sure that there was no problem with the centrifugal force when we were deploying the booms, but, since we could deploy them as slowly as needed, I didn't see that would be a problem. Anyway it looked like the Astromast booms were going to be fine and we would not need any hinges on the booms.

I talked to Tim about the LEOT teleconference that had occurred while I was at Los Alamos. Tim told me that someone who was new to the project reopened all the old questions like, "Why don't you use the DSN?" and, "Why do you need continuous coverage?" I was sick of people who had no idea what we were doing and of having to readdress old issues every time we had a meeting. Worse, Tim got the impression they couldn't provide the big antennas they had promised and they were also fussing about using the tracking stations at Murdock, Poker Flats, and Wallops.

I thought, *this isn't going to work.* I called Frank Donovan. I asked him what was going on. I clarified and amplified all the points about the need for continuous tracking, not only for the gravity experiment, but also just as important for navigation. We couldn't just have good tracking for two months and then nothing. Anyway, Frank pretty much understood what we needed. Mark Saunders was also waiting impatiently for the final answers. When I was in DC, I was going to tell Mark to tell Wallops to get us three 8 m antennas, to set them up at the DSN stations, to quit fooling around, and to get the job done.

Dom and I talked about the budget. I got the impression that Dom had gotten the message across to Martha that we had to stay within our $63 million budget. Dom was still keeping the higher priced items, like the Motorola transponder, in the budget to insure we had reserves. I still thought that was a mistake and a waste of effort. I felt we should be getting down to the real numbers and not use fake stuff at that stage.

Dom was still rambling on about the damned NiH_2 battery. I hoped if he and I were on the same plane the next day, I could get it across to him that the NiH_2 battery just wasn't going to work so he would get off that kick.

Dom was very tired. He had had a good time in Santa Fe, but it was clear he was running out of steam. Tim Bridges also noticed that Dom was running out of gas.

Tim and I went over to Ames to talk to Jackson and Fred about the tracking system in general, LEOT specifically, and how we were going to set it up with Command

and Control Center at Lockheed and/or Ames. I thought we would do the high activity periods, i.e., the critical phases, with a full staff at a Lockheed Control Center and have Ames do the monitoring. That might be a way of minimizing the cost because Ames already had controllers over there. They ran the Pioneers and could do double duty. If we had two control centers, we could always do training on one when the other one was in use. I liked the idea of having all the critical phases done at Lockheed, that way Lockheed would get the publicity and Lunar Prospector would not look like a NASA mission. If we did everything over at Ames, the news media would most probably assume that Lunar Prospector was just another NASA mission.

Tuesday, June 13, through Sunday, June 18, 1995: The Trip to Washington and a Little Vacation

Rebecca and I left for Washington so I could give my talks to the Lessons Learned Meeting at Headquarters on the 14th, to the National Academy of Science at Woods Hole (MA) on the 15th, and to the ASA at Headquarters on Friday the 16th. Rebecca and I were going to spend two days with Pat and Julius in Washington. Rebecca and I flew out of San Jose at about 7:00 AM. She got off in St. Louis to see her daughter for two days and I flew on and got into Washington at about 5:00 PM.

Mark started the Lessons Learned Meeting and then Bill Boynton talked. Bill's talk was pretty good. He pointed out that everybody was crabbing that Lunar Prospector had no science value. He said nobody really understood what the missions NASA had selected were all about and, therefore, in the absence of knowledge, everyone was saying they were lousy. Hence, NASA needed to better inform the community about the new missions. Bill complimented me specifically because I had gotten a lot of my fact sheets out into the community while the other missions had not.

Chris Russell got up to talk. Chris was the PI for the Diana Lunar Orbiter Proposal and acted like a total egomaniac. His first two slides were all about him, all the papers he had written, all the missions he had flown, all the committees he was on, and how wonderful and great he was (he sounded just like Dom). The rest of his talk was just crabbing that he did not win and that if Discovery had been done right, he would have won. He insisted the RFP had requested proposals yielding the maximum science for $150 million. That was absolutely not true as Mark replied, but Chris retorted that Mark did not know what he was talking about (remember that Mark was responsible for the RFP and definitely knew what he and its other authors had written and meant)! Chris had made up his mind and would not listen to anyone.

When it was my turn, I said I felt Discovery had been done properly, not because I had won, but because I had been working toward the same goals for the previous five years. I also said I was tired of hearing everyone say that the RFP requested the maximum science for $150 million when the Dear Colleague Letters, the Discovery pamphlet, and the RFP all quite clearly stated that the average mission was to cost ⅓ to ½ of the maximum. But Chris and most of the community wouldn't listen.

I expressed my concerns that the proposal efforts had cost the community far too much money and what NASA wanted for a Phase A effort was far too much. I pointed out that the 28 proposals had cost the science and aerospace communities $15 to $20 million — or about as much money as the Lunar Prospector Spacecraft was going to cost! Was it not better to build spacecraft than to write expensive proposals?

Several aerospace industry representatives got up and said they too had the same concerns about the Discovery RFP process. It was far too costly, the community could not afford to do it, it was far too complex, and far too much was expected. The aerospace community also felt the scientists were expecting too much to be done on each mission. My good friend from our Viking days, Ben Clark from Martin Marietta in Denver, said they had tried in vain to get the scientists to stop having so many instruments. Ben said, "Every time we turned around, they would add more instruments and they were always two or three million dollars each." They had tried to get the spacecraft costs down, but the scientists wouldn't cut the science down, so the proposals all came in at about $150 million.

Russell retorted, "Well, science instruments all cost two or three million dollars, you can't do anything about it." I got sick of that and said Lunar Prospector's five instruments cost only $3.5 million altogether. If Lunar Prospector could get the instrument costs down to 10%, then everybody else could, too.

I flew off to Woods Hole and got there in the evening. The next day, Thursday, I had a lot of good conversations with Gene Shoemaker and Wes Huntress. Wes gave a 2-hour talk about NASA's reorganization, NASA's problems, and how NASA was trying to survive. He said that funding looked quite good for Discovery in the fall.

I took the opportunity to really tell the National Academy of Science people what Lunar Prospector was all about. I explained that most people thought because Lunar Prospector was inexpensive it wouldn't do good science. I went through the science very carefully and everybody realized how really good it was. I discussed the GRS in detail. One of the committee members was an expert in gamma-ray spectrometers and he agreed wholeheartedly that Lunar Prospector couldn't fly a germanium detector because Lunar Prospector was spin stabilized and because the costs would have doubled. He thought we were doing wonderfully and that made me feel very good.

I flew back to Washington that night and picked up Rebecca at National Airport. The next day we went to the ASA meeting and I gave my talk. I emphasized the commercial aspects of Lunar Prospector and where it could and should lead. Everybody in the ASA wanted to get behind Lunar Prospector. They were going to write a letter of support to NASA and the lieutenant governor of Colorado would be the representative of the ASA who would sign it. Hugh Pickens from Allied Signal came up and said he would try to get tracking network support for Lunar Prospector, so Rebecca and I had a discussion with him over lunch. It was clear I had really gotten everyone turned on about Lunar Prospector and, happily, about me, too.

I went up to see Mark and to tell him about Pickens's offer. When I walked into Mark's area, Bret Drake was sitting there with Mark! I made a joke about Bret being a spy for Bill Boynton (Bill had teamed up with JSC, so Bret was part of Bill's Lunar Polar Orbiter Team) and that Mark could not trust him. To which Mark replied, "Well, Bret is going to be my representative on Lunar Prospector." What a nice surprise! That was just great. We chatted about Bret's temporary (1 year) assignment to Headquarters and Lunar Prospector. I chastised Mark for not telling me that Bret was the one he was considering as his representative on Lunar Prospector. Likewise, Mark related that he had told Bret of all our concerns about a new face, a new interface, and the trouble they would cause. The kicker was that Mark simply did not know that Bret and I were good friends and had worked together in Houston, so we all had a good laugh about it and I was happy to have Bret on board.

Rebecca and I ended a great Friday by going to dinner with George French at a great Chinese restaurant and had a good time.

Then we spent a relaxing and interesting weekend with Julius and Pat. They took us to some of the interesting Washington sites and Rebecca and I took a boat ride down the Potomac River and toured George Washington's home at Monticello. We had a great weekend and flew back Sunday evening, and then Monday, Dom spoiled everything.

Chapter 2-11
Too Much of Dom

Monday, June 19, 1995: Reaching the Limit with Dom

I got in very early and went through my mail, telephone messages, and email. Happily, I had received a call from my old friend and ex-coworker Colin Jones, who was working for the European Space Agency in Holland. Colin congratulated me and wanted to know how it felt to be famous. It was really good to hear from Colin and I hoped we would see each other again.

I got a call from Dan Ujifusa at Lockheed in Cherry Hill, NJ. He wanted to set up a Lockheed commercial tracking network that Lunar Prospector could use. The first question I had for Dan was the same one I had asked Hugh Pickens at the ASA meeting three days earlier, "Could you get permission to use NASA S-band frequencies?" Dan did not know the answer. I then called Hugh to get his answer to that question, but he was not in, so I left a message saying I would call him later.

Tim Bridges had a telecon set up with the Wallops engineers. It turned out there was also a TOTS (Transportable Orbital Tracking Station) tracking system we could use, which was good, because we were then informed that LEOT had no radiometric capability to do the Doppler tracking and hence could not support Lunar Prospector! The Wallops team asked a lot of questions about what we absolutely needed for navigation and the DGE and what we could get along without having. I said, "Well, I have to talk to Alex." We got Alex on the phone. Alex said he only needed one 8-hour pass a day to get the gravity data around the Moon. Alex also got Jordan Ellis on the line and he told us the way Clementine did it and suggested we do the same. We all concluded we should get the DSN to track us 3 times a day for four hours at a time on the way to the Moon. We would only need the DSN for downlink and radiometrics until we got into lunar orbit, then we could use the TOTS, which would give us good radiometric and downlink tracking, for 8 hours a day for navigation and the DGE. Finally the LEOT stations could track us the remaining 16 hours per day delivering just the downlink data. Given that information and the money we had in hand for tracking, Tim and I decided that sounded like a reasonable mix of capabilities. Tim felt good about it because he had been raising those questions for a long time and I felt good we would have the DSN to at least get to the Moon.

Tim and I then went over to Ames to talk to Bob Jackson about that tracking solution. We called Frank Donovan and told him we three were ready to have the telecon the next day to go over what we thought was a reasonable solution. Finally, I felt we had a realistic solution to the tracking problem.

I called Hugh Pickens again and he thought he could put together a network for us. I still didn't think he could get permission from NASA to use the S-band frequencies, but he was going to see what he could do. I liked the possibility of having a non-NASA tracking alternative, either via Hugh or Dan Ujifusa.

Dom said he wanted to see me and I knew Dom was fussing — to put it mildly — about something. He said we had a lot of problems and needed to talk later.

I saw Dom at about 11:00 when I went to lunch with Tim. Dom came in with Bob Goldin for their mid-morning snack of coffee and donuts (I had already been at work for about 5 hours and Dom was just starting his mid-morning snack). We began to discuss the Lessons Learned meeting, but the conversation quickly took its usual course. Nobody at the meeting knew anything but Dom; everybody was wrong except Dom; no matter what was going on, only Dom knew how to do it right — and I was getting sick of it. He yapped on about his talk and how impressed the ASA was with him. He was always on a damned ego trip. He had no interest in hearing what was going on, either about the rest of the meetings, or with the tracking issues, or with the LLV2. I tried to tell him we had the whole ASA behind us and we had a hell of a lot of other support. He brushed that off by saying we were in very bad shape with the spacecraft and everything was all screwed up with the rocket. As always, Dom just clacked on and on instead of getting to all the work we needed to do. Why didn't he stop complaining and get off his dead ass and do something? Why did he just sit there and pontificate and say how wonderful he was and how impressed everyone was with him? I really thought Dom had finally gone completely over the hill and I was reaching the end of my rope with him.

I finished lunch, disgusted with Dom, and went back to work on real issues, one of which was the damned LLV2.

Don Davis from LLV2 came over about 12:30 PM. He said he had some questions about how we were going to do the mid-course maneuvers. That was strange because the mid-course maneuvers were not really of any concern to the launch team. He finally said that there was a 5% uncertainty in the amount of velocity the Star-37 TLI Stage delivered! If it were really that bad, that would mean that we would have a 160 m/sec uncertainty in the launch velocity. That would translate to a 970 m/sec mid-course maneuver 16 hours after launch. Lunar Prospector was only going to have fuel for a total ΔV capability of 1300 m/sec. I had allocated 90 m/sec of ΔV for the mid-course maneuvers based on the results of earlier lunar missions. If Don were correct, Lunar Prospector was in big trouble, but I was sure Don was full of it. I said, "I don't believe you. The Star-37 has been used on numerous missions and none of them had such large launch errors." But Don was adamant about the 5% uncertainty and continued to try to spread doom and gloom around the project under the guise of helpfully pointing out all our errors.

Richard Lynch later verified via Thiokol, who made the Star-37, that Don, like the rest of the LLV2 engineers, was full of crap. The Star-37 maximum errors were quoted at 0.5% and its typical error was only 0.3%. Numbers like that were exactly what I had assumed based on previous missions to the Moon. On that basis, I had assumed we would have a 10 to 15 meters per second launch error and that was how I had gotten my budget of 60 to 90 m/sec for the midcourse maneuvers. That SOB was trying to get us to believe the errors were a factor of ten higher than they really were. All the LLV2 bunch had done was to lie to us or to feed us wrong information because they did not know what they were talking about (The reader might be interested to know here that Lunar Prospector's launch error was just –9.6 m/sec or –0.3% and the total ΔV we used for the two midcourse maneuvers we made was 69.9 m/sec or 78% of what I had allotted. So much for Don Davis's BS).

Dom and I finally got together for the meeting he had wanted at about 4:00 PM. I was going to tell him what we had decided about the tracking network, but he didn't want to listen. He went into a big tirade about how concerned he was because, ". . . there was no engineering going on, the guys hadn't done their jobs and all they did was shitty engineering." He was clearly directing that at me since he didn't want me working with the engineers and he didn't want me interfering with "his" spacecraft. He didn't say that directly, but that is what he meant. We were moving towards a collision, which I wanted to avoid if at all possible, for the time being.

The conversation turned to other issues. Dom was very agitated, first of all because of the damned launch vehicle. Dom had believed Don Davis's crap about a 5%

error on the Star-37 burn. Further, the LLV1 was supposed to have launched earlier that month, but had been delayed to next month. We were just going to have to blackmail Lockheed to get the vehicle done. As Dom correctly said, the whole program could crash because of that launch vehicle alone. He was telling me nothing new, but I was glad to see him finally getting concerned about that problem.

I tried to get back to the business of the tracking network. Dom went into another tirade about how he didn't want to waste his time listening to that — what he was saying was that I was to keep out of it. The SOB — I was the PI, it was my mission and my spacecraft, and because of him, the engineers did not have a clue about how Lunar Prospector was to be done or how to accomplish it. I was getting really tired of Dom's insane behavior. I had kept my work with the engineers as quiet as possible in order to keep his damned ego from getting bruised, but it was getting clearer and clearer there was no way of working with the SOB.

Dom continued and said, "Well, these are engineers, they can't make a decision on the spacecraft. Ever since we have been working, the guys haven't done anything. Instead of taking the stuff (meaning my stuff) — well, you gotta do trade studies and we gotta get information to make decisions. That is not the way you do engineering." Such BS. All Dom did was to rattle on and get nothing done. He didn't want information to make decisions; he was doing his best to avoid making decisions and hated it when I made them.

It was becoming clear to me that Dom did not know how to manage people. I thought he did, but I was wrong. I also thought he at least knew how to work with the Lockheed system, but I was again wrong. I was beginning to realize that Dom simply couldn't work with people of any kind or within any system. I could work with those people. I was getting the work done. Dom did not like that and was saying, "Keep your nose out of it," i.e., keep my nose out of my own spacecraft. Neither Dom nor the engineers knew anything about the spacecraft or how it was to be operated and that was really bad. For example, Gerry Grismore, for whom I had a lot of respect, thought we were going to get the spacecraft trajectory information from the sun and infrared limb crossing sensors! They only provide spacecraft attitude data and have nothing to do with the orbital data. Gerry hadn't the slightest idea of how we were going to track the spacecraft. How in the world did Dom think he and the engineers could build Lunar Prospector when they had no idea how it even was to work? He is just nuts.

Though for completely different reasons, I agreed with Dom — what we had was shitty engineering, things were a mess right then, and we needed to get them straightened out. Bob Goldin came in Dom's office about then and Dom said, "Bob, we have to have these guys sit down and list their requirements." Crap, the requirements were there! I had brought the "Mission Requirements Document" (MRD) with me to Sunnyvale when we did the proposal in the fall. Dom had the MRD; it was Appendix II.B. of the proposal and both Dom's and my signatures were on its signature page. All that incompetent, arrogant ass had to do was to read the MRD and have the engineers read it. But there was no way that Dom would use my mission requirements for "his" spacecraft.

Dom started undermining Tim, probably because Tim worked too closely with me. He said, "You know, Tim is a retiree and he has the wrong mental attitude, and if he can't do the job, I have to get somebody else who can. Hy Plutchok can do it."

I knew Hy and I knew he knew nothing about tracking issues. I said to Dom, "I don't agree. It was Tim who was asking all the right questions and pointing us in the right direction. I think he is doing a good job."

Dom said, "Oh, you really do?"

I answered, "Yes, I do." He dropped that approach and tried another attack on Tim. Each time he did, I said, "I just don't agree. Tim is the one who is doing a good job."

Finally Dom gave up and we started discussing the tracking requirements Alex had given us earlier. He said, "Why do you need 8 hour passes, how come you can't do it in 5 hours? I think you would be able to do it without even having tracking if you just listened to your radio."

I thought, *he thinks he knows everything and he doesn't know crap*. Then he started asking a bunch of questions that were clearly his attempt to trip me up and show that I did not know what I was talking about. I thought, *OK, you SOB, you don't think I know anything, so you are giving me a pop quiz — let's go*. I answered every stinking question he asked and told him exactly why I came to those conclusions. It was interesting because he couldn't poke any holes in anything I said.

He finally gave up and said, "I know you know your stuff, you are an expert and all."

I thought, *then why don't you shut up; quit trying to prove I am not an expert and start listening to me*.

I saw there was no way I was going to get him to discuss the tracking issues. He was going to avoid discussing it at all costs. Dom was so afraid I knew more about the spacecraft and the mission than he did that he was sabotaging the whole effort. As I realized that, I said to him, "Since the guys don't know anything about the spacecraft, we are going to have to have a series of reviews on each subsystem starting Thursday."

I had to get him to have those reviews, to sit down and go through each subsystem piece by piece. It wasn't going to work if he kept telling me to butt out and let the engineers do the engineering. We were getting nowhere and Lunar Prospector was on a road to failure. I was very frustrated. We were at a point where Dom had to face the reality of his own incompetence and stop just protecting his damned ego or Lunar Prospector was finished.

Tuesday, June 20, 1995

Dom calmed down and stopped acting like a maniac after his Monday tirades. He seemed to be very happy and was actually working and not annoying me.

Things progressed on the tracking front. We talked on the phone with Allied Signal and that went well. Then we had a telecon with the LEOT team. They were moving forward, but they were backing down on LEOT's capabilities. Dan Ujifusa and a couple of other engineers from Cherry Hill visited us in the morning. They very much wanted to set up a commercial tracking network and wanted Lunar Prospector as a customer.

Thursday, June 22, 1995

The LLV2 was getting to be a bigger and bigger catastrophe. Damon and his band came over in the morning for a meeting and Dom cut them off. We were going to have a requirements review because they had not even looked at the requirements. They had done nothing except try to get out of their earlier commitments and make it look like we were to blame for the mess. Dom nailed them down and made them explain why they couldn't do what they had promised.

Damon tried to tell us that the Star-37 for Clementine was $12 million dollars plus $4 million extra for a destruct system and there had been all kinds of problems with the destruct system that took months and years to get resolved. Richard Lynch had gone over the Clementine Star-37 with Denver a couple weeks earlier, so we knew what

Damon was telling us was a pack of lies. First, the $12 million covered everything; there was no extra $4 million. Second, the reason the TLI Stage was so expensive was that it had solar cells on it; it was fully instrumented and was part of the experiment. It was not just the Star-37 TLI Stage — it was a little satellite.

I thought what they were doing with their lies about 5% Star-37 injection errors, $16 million Star-37s, and similar fabrications was to scare us into dumping them. Then they could walk away and say, "Gee, we were ready to do it, but you guys didn't know what you were doing and then you dumped us." They hoped that would get them off the hook and make Dom and me look like fools. If so, it would not work. Dom was forcing them to address the issues in exactly one week.

If we showed LLV2 couldn't do the job, then we could clearly say to Lockheed Corporate Management we had to have an alternative and then try to get on the Taurus. That was clearly a very a ticklish situation — asking Lockheed to let us use the competition's launch vehicle because Lockheed could not do the job, but we had to try or probably lose the mission. Unfortunately, Dom and I both thought Lockheed would rather accept the total failure of Lunar Prospector than admit the LLV2 was just not ready (and that turned out to be the case).

In terms of the budget stuff, Martha accepted that we had to be within the $63 million and she was working toward that amount. Actually, we were in good shape with the budget. We had over $6 million for contingency, $4 million we had put in there and then, because Peggy had screwed up the proposal budget by double booking the $2.3 million for tracking (she had booked it at $4.6 million), we had $2.3 million more than we thought. I thought we would be able to pull off the budget effort.

Friday, June 23, 1995

There was a review of the propulsion system at 10:00, but since nobody bothered to tell me about it, I missed it. However, essentially no one else was there, so it was rescheduled for 1:00 PM. We met, but again there weren't enough people to review propulsion, so we talked about the work Tom Chinn had done on structures. The spacecraft structure design was in pretty good shape, but there were a lot of questions about the shroud. Damon and his LLV2 band had told us during the proposal effort we could use the 3.05 m shroud they advertised. We just found out it didn't exist — the 3.05 m shroud was just another LLV2 lie. We had to try to figure out how to fit Lunar Prospector into the 2.34 m shroud! Since it wasn't big enough as it was, it seemed the only way for Lunar Prospector to fit was to have a 4-foot extension built onto the shroud. We had Richard Lynch write a memo to Damon so we could roast them over their own fire.

Richard told Dom and me that Damon and his band were trying to back out of the meeting set for the next Thursday. It was clear they were not capable of launching Lunar Prospector and I thought they were getting ready to bail out any way they could. We began talking about the Taurus and the Titan II. Nevertheless, Dom felt Sam Araki, LMMS's CEO, would never let LLV2 bail out on us (not because he cared about Lunar Prospector, but because it would look too bad for Lockheed), rather he would throw enough resources at them to get the job done. However, I was sure that even if Lockheed threw $10 million at that bunch of LLV2 boobs, they still could not do anything end up failing. Anyway, Dom did a good job of helping Damon and his bunch hang themselves, despite Dom's weird way of behaving.

Another point of aggravation: The previous week, when both Dom and I were in Washington, Steve Griffin took one of our Requests For Information and sent the damned thing out on the street! It was amazing he would do that behind our backs. Those guys (upper management bozos) were monkeying around in our program and not even knowing what they were doing, they are just stupid asses. It was clear I had to get out of Lockheed before they drove me crazy. The real problem stemmed from my being an employee of the company that I contracted to build my spacecraft. Lockheed simply wouldn't accept my being the PI and hence the manager of Lunar Prospector, despite what the NASA contract said, i.e., "All phases of the project will be performed by the contractor (Lockheed) under the direction of the Principal Investigator."

Tuesday, June 27, 1995

I finally sold my house in Houston, one less thing to be concerned about.

I talked to Mario Acuña about the magnetic problems with the nickel hydrogen battery and he said it would not interfere with the MAG measurements. I still wanted to dump the nickel hydrogen battery and use the nickel cadmium battery for thermal and mass reasons. I didn't know if I could convince Dom of that, but the next day I was going to see if I could interface with Dom on that, or any technical issues, without him blowing his stack.

Tim Bridges and I worked on the 15/15's (personnel time and charges) for mission operations and they came out quite reasonable, close to what we had estimated earlier. There were significant cost savings in having Ames take over most of the monitoring effort. Martha thought the other engineers were not going to do so well with their 15/15's since, other than defining their subsystems, they had done nothing about manufacturing.

Tom Polette was making another attempt to get LESC to hire me back and let me run Lunar Prospector from LESC, but the Houston bureaucrats just kept screwing it up. I decided I would have to talk to Jim Adamson again. If Jim were interested, he needed to get off his dead ass and do something, a requirement I doubted would ever be met.

Wednesday, June 28, 1995

Richard Lynch was at Thiokol and Orbital Sciences (Taurus) and had sent us a fax. Apparently Taurus could launch Lunar Prospector to TLI for about $23 million — great news. Richard would give us the details when he was back in Sunnyvale.

Thursday, June 29, 1995

I had a telecon with the Wallops guys in the morning. Basically they could get me two 8 meter TOTS antennas and a LEOT station, but they couldn't give me any decent Doppler for the gravity experiment. I checked with Alex and found out if we had one hour per day of Doppler from the DSN, we could do the DGE. We could get the navigation and DGE data if we could get a combination of the DSN, TOTS, and LEOT. The only trouble was the costs would be significantly greater than the $5 million we had for tracking, and that was absurd. Headquarters was going to have to make some contribution if we were going to be able to do the tracking that way and that seemed unlikely. The LESC tracking offer wasn't any better; they could provide us with uplink and downlink, but they couldn't give us Doppler.

I talked with Hugh Pickens from Allied Signal, and Hugh said he could set up a tracking network for us. He had a 10-meter dish at Goddard with full Doppler capability. That would give us 8 hours per day of tracking with at least the one-millimeter/second accuracy Alex needed for the DGS. He could also get two other stations around the world for uplink and downlink, giving us the full 24-hour tracking we needed. I asked, "Can you do it for the $2 million we have?"

Hugh said, "Yes." At last, it looked like we had a potential tracking system that would work.

Dom and I had a meeting with Sylvia and Scott to talk about the funding and other issues and we found out that Mark had changed his mind; he wanted us to get the tracking network! If so, then it would not be a government supplied capability.

The LLV2 guys came over for an afternoon meeting. Before we got started and before Dom came in, Don Davis started hollering at me. He was very angry with me. He said I had taken the letter they sent us on October 10, 1994, and used it in the proposal (Gee whiz, isn't that the reason I had asked them for a price quote on an LLV2 launch to TLI?). He said further, "The letter was unsigned and you didn't respond to it. The next thing we knew, you had won the contract and now you expect a launch to TLI for $25 million based on an unsigned letter, and blah, blah, blah." Then he accused me of tricking them and being unethical. I reminded Don I had the *signed letter* from a year earlier (a letter to LEI) for the same service (a launch to TLI) for $22 million and that it should have been clear to everybody (as it was clearly stated in both of their letters) that we (my spacecraft team and I) were not in the position to develop and integrate a solid stage into their rocket. He was full of shit. That was just the latest of their attempts to get out of launching Lunar Prospector. They were just a bunch of lying cheats.

Dom came in and we then got started. Dom just hammered the bastards down. He made them go through their proposal line by line and made them clarify each point. Then he said, "OK, but you guys realize that I am not saying OK, I agree; I am only saying OK, I understand what you are proposing. What you are proposing is virtually nothing. You want to sell us an LLV2 for $25 million, but you will not provide a Star-37 upper stage, you will not even provide a separation device, so you are just backsliding from what you knew we wanted over two years ago."

Then a snotty young kid from LLV2 budgeting said, "Well, you get the launch vehicle for $25 million and that's that."

Dom really lit into him and said, "You know this is not the way to conduct business. You come in here and arrogantly tell us that's all we are going to get, take it or leave it. You wouldn't do this to an outside customer and you're doing it to your own company guy. You better learn how to conduct yourself." Dom just nailed the bastards and then said, "If we choose to go with you guys, then we will get these issues resolved. Now, let's talk about the shroud."

Damon or Davis said, "Well, you guys said you could fly on the 92 inch (2.34 m) shroud. You said it was OK."

Both Dom and I said, "No, we told you we would look at it, and after we did, we told you we needed the 120-inch (3.05 m) shroud. We won't fit in the 92 (2.34 m)." I looked at old Don Davis and he just dropped his eyes. They knew they were lying.

I was very pleased with the way Dom had put them in their place and then he said, "Well, Sam Araki is going to have to decide how this is going to go and then we will see." Thus ended a very rancorous meeting.

Richard Lynch had returned from his trip to Thiokol and Orbital Sciences. He said the Taurus people were really good and could do the job. The Taurus shroud was big enough and they expected that Taurus would be flight-proven by the time we needed to use it. They had no other launches in our timeframe, so they could devote themselves totally to us. They had already integrated a Star-37 and they would do a launch to Translunar Injection (TLI) for $23 million ($2 million less than LLV2, if they launched us just to LEO, which was all they wanted to do). If I could get away with it, I wanted to dump the LLV2 and go with the Taurus.

Friday, June 30, through Tuesday, July 4, 1995: Vacation in Cascades

Rebecca and I took a much-needed vacation at the National Lava Beds Monument, Mount Lassen, and Mount Shasta in northern California, and the Cascades in Oregon and Washington. Though we had a good time camping, going through lava tunnels (I did anyway, Rebecca was not too excited about walking through big dark holes in the ground as she described lava tunnels and caves), and hiking around the volcanoes, the trip was overshadowed by the mounting problems with Dom. It was clear to me that Dom's behavior was putting the entire program in serious jeopardy and my concerns had grown as our trip progressed. Finally, I decided that I had no choice but to act, so I called Scott on Monday, the 3rd, and told him we needed to meet as soon as possible. We set up a meeting for the late afternoon of July 5, so Rebecca and I cut our vacation short and started for home, fast.

Wednesday July 5, 1995: Setting the Stage

I spent 2½ hours talking to Scott about the problems with Dom. We were both concerned because if Headquarters lost confidence in our team, they would cancel Lunar Prospector. Scott wanted specifics, so I told him about Dom's ignorance of the mission and the spacecraft, about Dom's telling me to shut up when I tried to discuss various issues, of his trying to keep me from talking to the engineers about the spacecraft, about his refusing to use — or even look at — all the work already done on the spacecraft and the mission planning, etc., etc., etc. Scott was amazed that, given our short time scale and lack of money, Dom would totally ignore all the work that was already completed. We went through several examples and we got into much more detail than I had intended. I told Scott I did not want to malign Dom and that I had the greatest respect for him (as did Scott). Regardless, Scott said he understood what was going on. He said, "I have the same problem with some of my managers because these older managers, like Dom, even though Dom believes in skunk works and all that stuff, he simply will not accept the fact that things are different. In the olden days, the Project Manager, be it a NASA, Lockheed, or any aerospace company person, had absolute control of every aspect of the mission. He told the scientists what they could and could not do. He told everyone what his or her limitations were. He controlled everything and that is what Dom is doing. Dom is refusing to accept the facts that you are the PI, that this is your mission, that you are in control, and that NASA has reversed these roles so he has to work for you." Scott said further, "I have the same exact problem, really serious problems, with some of the older guys who simply refuse to accept the fact that they no longer have absolute authority over every aspect of the mission and where the science is simply — hey you get what science I get you."

I then said, "Beyond all of that, Dom has just gone overboard. He rants and raves, swears and curses. When we are on telecons, Dom will mute us out and then just flip his lid and curse everyone out. 'You dumb sons of bitches, shut your fucking mouths, you stupid assholes, you don't know what the fuck you're saying.' Once he calms down, then he puts us back on line. That's intolerable." Independent of my statements, Scott said he had heard about Dom's blowup at Gary Noreen at the review meeting. We agreed all that was not only very embarrassing to everyone, but was destroying Lunar Prospector and could cause its complete collapse.

As far as Scott was concerned, I was the PI. I hired and fired whomever I wanted to. I was responsible to NASA for Lunar Prospector, not Dom, not Lockheed, not anyone else — even though Lockheed thought it was in charge since I was its employee. We agreed NASA had made a mistake in allowing in their rules for a PI to be an employee of the company that was hired to build the spacecraft. That class of PI had far too many built-in conflicts of interest to work, but somehow we had to make it work.

I told Scott the engineers were also very dissatisfied and would like me to be the Lockheed Project Manager, an impossibility, since Gus and Lockheed had insisted from the beginning that one of their own be Project Manager (was I not a Lockheed employee?). At that point Scott said, "In reality you are the Project Manager, you are acting as one."

Scott said Gus had talked to him several times and wanted to make sure everything was OK. Scott then asked me how I thought Gus would react. I said I wasn't sure since I really did not know him, or anyone at LMSC, very well. Scott said, "My general feeling about Lockheed is that they are a sleazy bunch of people and they lowball, they come in low and then charge a lot of money, and they are sloppy and they don't do good work."

I told Scott I agreed with him and added, "Dom knows these guys are a bunch of bozos and he has been fighting their incompetence every step of the way, but in the process, he has become one of them. The trouble is there is a fine line between a genius and a megalomaniac and I think Dom has slipped over that line. I really think Dom is nuts. If I thought the problem was me and not Dom, I would just shut up and leave."

With that, Scott asked, "What would happen if you just swallowed your pride and kept quiet?"

I answered, "Well, the first thing is I would absolutely lose control of the program and you would too. Dom would get a mission done, there is no question in my mind, but it wouldn't be the mission it was supposed to be. He would successfully get a spacecraft built and the science guys would deliver the instruments. But they would not get the science done the way they wanted to because Dom would do it the way he wanted. A mission would fly and it would be an apparent success."

Scott responded, "Then it would be just like the old missions where the science did not prevail and that is totally against Discovery. The whole purpose of Discovery is to prove the PI, a scientist, can be responsible for the mission. That would defeat the purpose of Lunar Prospector and the whole Discovery theme."

Scott said, "You have very concrete reasons for concern, beyond the personal issues. You are the PI and if you choose to fire Dom, we will have some explaining to do to Headquarters. But NASA gave you full responsibility for the mission, so Headquarters would have to accept your decision. If Dom and Lockheed don't like it, too bad, because Lockheed is committed contractually to you and to NASA."

We decided NASA could not side with Dom and have him do Lunar Prospector without me because I had too much external support and hence there would be a huge stink. Worse, Headquarters would then have to admit that the whole concept of Discovery didn't work. Scott's attitude was that what we needed to do could be done legally and that everything was on my side. Then Scott said, "Do you think Dom will — I know he's volatile — will he calm down and accept it."

I answered, "I don't know; he has said a couple of times it's my mission and I can do it the way I want. But he has also told me so many times how he holds grudges and gets even with people who cross him. I think this is going to be extremely difficult."

With that, we ended our conversation and I started to prepare for the next, very important day.

Thursday July 6, 1995: D-Day

I got to work at 5:00 AM. Dom showed up about 7:30 or 8:00 AM. I had left a note on his door telling him I wanted to see him in my office, ASAP. Instead of coming to see me, he monkeyed around for a long time. That annoyed me — I had asked to see him ASAP and I assumed he would stop by in a reasonable time, but not High-And-Mighty Dom Tenerelli! Finally, he condescended to come by. I said to come in and close the door. He came in and sat down. He could not have known what was about to happen, but he was smart enough to know I would not have asked to see him in my office if everything was OK. I knew from his defiant glare he resented my even asking to see him in my office.

I said, "I want to talk to you because I have some things that are concerning me. I want to make sure you and I are not working at crossed purposes and we are communicating." Then Dom knew for sure something was up since he hunched down in his chair in a very defensive way. I continued, "I am concerned that you told Richard he had to understand every aspect of the mission so he could do the mission planning and act as the interface between the mission and the spacecraft engineers. Those things are what I do and I have always done. You should know that. You and I divided up the tasks that way when we did the organization chart. I have certain things that are my responsibility and others are yours. I didn't want people taking on mission operation responsibilities. I have kept careful control of the documentation and the like since the earliest beginnings of Lunar Prospector. Nobody knows the mission like I do and nobody can learn about it, except from me. That is not the way I wanted to do it and I did not want duplicate activities going on and causing confusion." To my surprise, Dom was listening. I could tell he was listening, because for the first time I had ever spoken with him, he was silent and didn't babble.

I then said, "I brought a functional spacecraft design to Lockheed, not that it can't be improved, but it will do the job. I know that spacecraft. I worked on it for years. I laid it out and I reworked the design. I found things in the OMNI design that wouldn't work because they were used to designing spacecraft for geosynchronous orbit where there is plenty of maneuvering room, unlike low lunar orbit. Though I don't want to interfere with your part of the work, an army can't have two generals. I know the spacecraft; it's my spacecraft and my mission. I want to make sure you don't have a problem with my discussing the spacecraft with the guys."

Instead of addressing my statements, Dom floored me by saying, "Well, you know, your whole attitude is that it's my spacecraft. I did this and I did that. You never give any credit to Lockheed (meaning Dom) or to any of the work we are doing."

That was it. That fixed Dom's wagon as far as I was concerned. Yes, it was my spacecraft and my mission. I had brought a complete Phase B definition of the mission and spacecraft to Lockheed for the proposal effort and NASA had accepted our proposal with me, as PI, totally in charge of the program, so who in hell's mission and spacecraft was it if not mine! I answered Dom's charge by saying, "Well, I find your view of the situation very interesting."

Dom said, "Yeah, well Gus is really mad about that."

I said, "Except for you, nobody else has mentioned it."

He said, "Yeah, he's really mad. When we were watching your news conference, there was no mention of Lockheed and both Gus and I just got up and left."

I said, "I think that is a matter of perception."

Dom continued, "A lot of people have noticed you think that it's yours and nobody else has anything to do with it."

Though I did not say it, I thought, *Dom, there is no satisfying you or these other egotistical SOBs at Lockheed.* Rather I said, "First of all, what in hell did Lockheed do that was so great?"

Dom retorted, "Lockheed gave you money to keep Lunar Prospector going."

I answered, "Yeah, Gus did, but then he pulled it out from under me every time we made progress. In any case, I'm surprised you feel that way, but that's your perception. I have a different perception."

I made up my mind right then that it was irrelevant whether he thought I was giving him enough credit or not. He was not capable of listening to himself and how he continually says, "I'm the greatest. I'm the best engineer there is. I, I, I," that's all one heard from Dom, day in and day out.

We discussed the spacecraft, my working on it, and my working with the engineers. I said, "You know, I don't want to do it in a way that causes any problems, but I intend to do it. I know a lot about the spacecraft."

Dom began backing off and said, "Well, you know, that isn't the way you do it (i.e., engineer a spacecraft), you're really not causing trouble, but you could." Though Dom didn't like it, he was getting the message that I was going to do my job as the PI and run the program, the spacecraft, and everything. He knew at that point he couldn't stop me (after all, the NASA contract with Lockheed said I was in charge) and if he had any brains (which, by then, I was convinced he didn't), he would have recognized that I knew the mission and the spacecraft.

But Dom was not about to give up and said, "Well, the engineers have to do things a certain way."

I cut him off by saying, "Dom, I don't agree, I know that spacecraft and I know the things that have to be done to it, so why waste time and money?"

He said, "Well you gotta let the system work, you have to let the engineers do their trade studies."

I said, "I had a spacecraft that was flyable when I came here, so what is all the BS about trade studies?" Clearly Dom was trying to start from scratch because he didn't know the spacecraft and wanted to gain control of the program by doing so. I thought back to Scott's statements from the day before about the old time Project Managers who had absolute control of the projects and who refused to change over to the new way of doing business. Despite Dom's loud protests about lousy Lockheed management and the need to do everything in a "skunk works" mode with a minimum of bureaucracy, he is just one of those old time guys. He is pathetic.

Dom tried another tactic. He complained, "Well, I haven't seen any problems, but you know, the guys are hiding behind you. They're using you to keep away from me, they're hiding behind your skirts from me."

Hiding behind my skirts, what a joke. I said, "No, not true, if I thought anybody was doing that (not doing his job and then hiding from Dom behind me, not that I doubted the engineers did not want to see Dom) I would be the first one to come and tell you that something was wrong."

Dom said without any apparent anger, "If you don't like the way I am doing it, you can just get somebody else to do it. But, you know, my task as Project Manager is to deliver you a spacecraft and I am going to deliver you a spacecraft and it will work." Right then I knew the situation was exactly as Scott and I had thought. He considered that Lunar Prospector was exactly like every other program, regardless of what he said.

He considered that NASA was the customer, not me. There is no use trying to discuss anything different with him.

It wasn't worth discussing it any further; he had told me what I wanted to know. It was his way or he would quit. I did not want to lose Dom, since I did not trust Lockheed and I did not know anyone else there who I could trust to help me get Lunar Prospector done. As the old saying goes, "Better the devil you know than the devil you don't know." But I was tired of Dom trying to keep me from doing my job, I was tired of listening to him complain about everybody and everything, I was tired of having to feed his ego by having to constantly agree with him that he was the greatest engineer in the world and I was tired of trying to keep things going smoothly when he seemed to be fighting me every step of the way. It was my mission and my spacecraft. NASA had entrusted the success of the mission to me, not Dom, and not Lockheed. I hadn't worked for six years to have him take it away from me and screw it up just to satisfy his ego. I said most of that in as polite a way as possible and we agreed we would get the job done together and the meeting was over.

We had a useless document review that afternoon. The only thing interesting about it was that Dom never said one negative thing to me and never snapped at me as he had in the past. He was friendlier than he had ever been and even acknowledged he was getting direction from me! Dom clearly knew things had changed, but I was certain his newfound politeness was just a facade. The real test would come the following week when we were having a real meeting. But the marked change in Dom's behavior towards me told me I had made a serious mistake in trying to have him be my equal partner in Lunar Prospector. Previously, I had always told Dom that Lunar Prospector was our program; that I wanted to share it with him, but that was over. I thought Lunar Prospector would work only if our relationship was based on my being the PI of my program and that he was doing a job for me.

The review was a total waste of time. Bob Goldin put a new Mission Requirements Document (MRD) together. Since I had written the real MRD and the Mission Operations Document (MOD) years earlier, Bob's effort was a complete waste of time. Worse, what Bob had done was to take my MRD and MOD and reformatted them, tried to interpret them, and screwed them all up. 90% of Bob's "new" MRD was taken verbatim from my MRD and MOD and it was still a useless mess. Even worse, Bob used my MOD, not my MRD as the basis for his "new" MRD!

That was bad enough, but the thing that really made me mad was when we got into the magnetic experiment requirements. Dom said, "Well you know, we have to have magnetic cleanliness requirements."

I said, "Dom, I have the magnetic requirements, they are in my MRD, the ICD (Instrument Control Document), and of course, in the proposal," but he didn't believe me. I was really annoyed; once again it was clear Dom (and the rest of them) didn't know anything about the spacecraft and didn't know or read the information I had put in front of him months ago. I got the proposal, copied the page, marked it up and showed it to Dom.

He said, "Oh yeah, we did, oh yeah, I knew that, but we don't have all that in the ICD."

I said, "Yes we do, it's all in there, but I'll go check." We had spent considerable time on the ICD and Dom was so proud because he believed it was a perfect ICD — even though he didn't remember what was in it! I got the ICD and, of course, the magnetic cleanliness requirements were all in it. Dom didn't remember from one day to the next what we had done or agreed to. I had told him a dozen times we had magnetic cleanliness requirements. I had repeated it over and over and we had written them into the ICD and the dumb ass still didn't know it and his stupid people didn't know it. It was pathetic and hopeless. As far as I was concerned, Dom was just a dunce — a damned egotistical dunce.

Friday, July 7, 1995

Richard got some good news from Orbital Sciences; the Taurus people were ready to help us in any way they could. Of course, we couldn't go to a Taurus then but we could find out if it was capable of launching Lunar Prospector, and if it could, I would try to get off the damned LLV2 and onto the Taurus.

I talked to Bob Jackson about the tracking network and we were apparently getting two good proposals, one from NASA/Wallops Island and one from Allied Signal. Finally we had two good ways of doing the tracking that were within our budget — what a big relief.

Bob also said we had offers from both JPL and Goddard to do the navigation and he was leaning towards Goddard. Goddard's budget proposal was only $300,000, while JPL came in at $400,000. I also wanted Goddard for the job, not so much because their budget was less than JPL's, rather because Goddard had done Clementine's navigation and I did not trust JPL to hold to their budget. I said, "Yeah, let's go with Goddard." One more thing was decided.

Woody had supposedly done a trade study on the battery. I was not sure he had done a real study, but I really didn't care, since I believe most engineering trade studies are a waste of time anyway. Woody concluded we should use a nickel-hydrogen (NiH$_2$) battery rather than OMNI's baseline nickel-cadmium (NiCd) battery. Though the NiH$_2$ batteries have temperature problems (they have to be kept fairly cold and that would be hard to do if the battery was on the equipment shelf inside Lunar Prospector) and are heavy, Woody felt that the NiCds were even heavier — too heavy for Lunar Prospector. OMNI's mass data showed NiCds that were half as heavy as anything that Woody could find in the catalogues. The question I had was, how much do NiCds really weigh? I figured I would have to find that out myself and planned to call Wayne Stevens the following Monday to ask where OMNI got its mass data on NiCds.

As Woody, Jim Schirle (the thermal engineer), Dom, and I discussed the battery temperature issue (for both the NiH$_2$ battery, as well as for the NiCd — even the NiCds have to be kept cool, but not as cold as the NiH$_2$), Dom made the stupidest comments — comments that showed just how dumb he is and how little he understood the spacecraft design. He said, "Hey, you know, if that thing needs to be exposed to space (to cool it), which is the way Clementine did it, then we'll just cut a hole in the solar cell array and stick it out." However, the battery was not in the solar array area, it was on the equipment shelf next to the FOSAR ring (a radiating surface, that would be used to keep the electronic equipment and battery cool, mounted on the outside of — and at the bottom of — the outer drum of the spacecraft). The man had no idea what the spacecraft looked like or how it was to function — and he was supposed to be the Project Manager in charge of building it!

Dom's stupid comments reminded me forcefully of a similar display of his ignorance that had occurred a week earlier. We were discussing the layout of the fuel tanks and engines when he asked, "Why does it (the spacecraft) have to have the center mass at the center of the tanks and the plane where the (tangential) engines are, the fuel is going to float anyway. It's not going to be where it is supposed to be in those tanks." I pointed out to him that Lunar Prospector was a spinning spacecraft, so centrifugal force would, of course, force the fuel radially outward and hence to the "bottom" of the tanks! Having to explain that simple fact of basic physics and spacecraft design to Dom was annoying and pushed me to the point where I just didn't trust him at all.

Back to the battery mass and temperature issues: When I had laid out the positions of the electronic units on the equipment shelf, I put the heavy battery on the bottom, rather than the top of the equipment shelf and inside the launch adapter on the spin axis so it would not cause the spacecraft to be off balance. Then the engineers and Dom started to complain, "It (the battery) has to be cooler, it's too hot in the shelf area."

Since none of them had ever looked at my equipment shelf layout, I said, "Look, I put the damned thing in the adapter ring, because of the spin balance problems and if it has to be cool, that's the place to put it, because the sun never shines there. It would be in total darkness, so it would cool down. All you have to do is put a FOSAR sheet over it and you can control the temperature."

Interestingly, when I had made such comments in the past, Dom always said sharply, "Hey, let the engineers do the engineering." That time he shut up, but he ignored my comments. He tried to go on like he never heard me, but Jim and Woody heard me and we started discussing what I had said. Dom clearly did not like that turn of events and did not want to continue, so he got up and left. As he left, he said, "Well, have a good weekend guys," and went off in a huff.

Dom did not want to hear or acknowledge what I said because I knew more than he did about the mission, the spacecraft, and the engineering issues. I came to the conclusion that Dom was just covering his incompetence. He didn't know what he was doing, so he pretended he didn't hear the comments — he just ignored everything except what he said. When things started getting sticky for him, he changed the topic or started BSing or whatever to keep the conversation away from the real issues. I decided I would have to watch him closely the following week when we were to have review meetings to see what he did and how he reacted to my running my program. I was going to evaluate whether I thought he was capable of doing the mission, and right then, I didn't think he could. I planned to talk to Scott at the end of the following week and if things went the way I thought they would, I would tell Scott we would have to get rid of Dom — he just was not functioning. I was convinced Dom was just trying to get by on his ego and his reputation from the past.

Woody and Jim were also annoyed with Dom because he kept saying the Eagle Picher NiH$_2$ battery on Clementine "went through seven total discharge cycles and came right back and was working fine, no other battery can do that." First of all, it didn't do that. Dom had screwed up his facts and didn't understand what had gone on with Clementine. No battery can do what Dom said, not even a NiH$_2$ battery. To be sure, we asked another battery expert and he agreed that was the case. Dom had fixed ideas that were based on his prejudices and ignorance. I couldn't do the mission that way.

The workday ended on that sour note, but when I got home, I found a beautiful woman in red high heels and a pretty dress waiting for me — my mood changed immediately for the better.

Monday, July 10, 1995

We prepared for review meetings on Tuesday and Wednesday.

I had an archiving meeting that went really well. We discussed the various data products and got everything in order.

Dom was really quite nice all day, but I only saw him about three times for just two or three minutes because I was busy. He didn't go out of his way to talk to me and I did not go out of my way to speak to him. Though he was civil when I saw him, I thought how interesting it would be at the review meeting when I presented the Mission Profile. He still thought Richard was going to give it, but as I told him during our talk last Thursday, that was my business, so I was just waiting to see if he objected.

Scott called. He said he wanted to get together with Sylvia and me to discuss various issues. Scott had his own concerns about Dom that were independent of mine. It was clear from his cryptic comments he wanted to get with me independent of Dom so we could discuss the problems with Dom openly. Scott also assured me he was going to get Headquarters to talk to Gus to make Lockheed absolutely aware I was in charge of Lunar Prospector, what I said goes, that I was the one who was responsible to NASA for the mission, and there should be no confusion about who was running the program.

Tom Polette came in and we had a long talk about everything and he was excited about being at Sunnyvale, so ended a good day.

Tuesday, July 11, 1995: The Review

We had our first day of our review meeting and it went very well. It was a good meeting and we got a lot done.

Dom had changed remarkably; he didn't argue and he didn't try to stop me from doing anything. He was forced to listen. I gave my discussion of the Mission Profile and the objectives of the mission and he didn't say a word. If Dom kept on behaving himself, things could be OK.

Wednesday, July 12, 1995: The Review — Continued

The second day of our internal review meeting went very well. The negatives with the spacecraft were that its mass was far too high and the power was way too high. Those problems were mainly because the estimates of the thermal subsystem's power requirement and mass were quite high. We also found out the cost estimates were between $64 and $66 million and that might cause budgetary problems. But, in general, everything looked pretty good.

When Jim gave his estimates of the mass and power requirements for thermal, Dom whispered to me, "We will get the thermal mass and power down." But when I crabbed about the dry mass of the spacecraft being up 20 kilograms, he said, "Well, that's about 15%; that's what you would expect." That made me mad.

When we were writing the proposal Dom had said, "Oh man, we'll beat the mass down below 126 kg (the mass estimates we had come up with)." He had said the same thing about the power and all of the sudden he was saying the increases were normal! Why did he tell me during the proposal effort we would get the final mass and power requirements even lower and now he was telling me I had to expect increases like that?

If he had told me then, I would have said, "OK, if there is an expected 15% increase in the mass, I will raise everything up by that amount." I didn't like Lockheed and Dom's BS way of coming in low (low-balling the mass, power, and cost in order to win) for the proposal and then ending up with higher numbers when we won the contract. In my book, that happens only if you don't know what you are doing and/or you are dishonest.

The low-balling of our costs was still a sore spot between NASA and Lockheed and me. I was still mad that Dom and Lockheed had botched the proposal cost estimate (I still did not think they intentionally low-balled the costs, rather they just did a bad job of it), that NASA insisted that our uncertified estimate of $59 million was the real cost of the mission, and that NASA was trying to hold us to it. If Lunar Prospector did end up costing more, it would cause headaches, if it did not get Lunar Prospector canceled.

I was still concerned Dom was making a mistake in the way he was developing the new cost estimate. I knew he had buried cost reserves in the budget, like still booking the cost of the transponders based on the $2.4 million Motorola transponder we had proposed rather than the $0.8 million Allied Signal transponder we intended to use and things like that. I knew he was doing that because we would certainly have unexpected costs in other areas and he was trying to get some padding in there so we wouldn't over-run. But I was disappointed and annoyed to find out that was the way it is always done by aerospace companies.

Despite those concerns and the still unresolved issue of the tracking, I thought the review meeting was pretty good. I thought Lunar Prospector was going to succeed. That feeling was supported when we got word from Mark Saunders that Lunar Prospector and/or Discovery (we didn't know if Lunar Prospector was mentioned specifically or just Discovery) was in the new budget and Pat Dasch also sent a message saying we were OK. Everything indicated we were going to get Lunar Prospector's money in the fall. I really thought it was going to happen, even if our costs were $5 or 6 million higher than proposed (i.e., still within the 15% allowance). That might be hard for NASA to swallow, but since most NASA programs end up being a factor of two or three times more expensive than estimated, if Lunar Prospector came in even 15% higher, it would still be a bargain. I didn't like the idea of our budget coming in higher than we said, but the main thing was to get Lunar Prospector done successfully.

Finally, Dom was on his best behavior all day. He didn't say anything when we had a meeting with Sylvia and Scott after the review meeting was over. Dom did not try to dominate everyone or shout anyone down! Even Tom noticed the tremendous difference in Dom's behavior.

Thursday, July 13, 1995

Headquarters and Code O decided that Wallops would provide the tracking and it would be a government-supplied service. It would cost us the $2.2 million we had in our proposal. We still wouldn't know all the technical details for another month, but the tracking issue was finally resolved and out of our hair financially. That was the highlight of the day.

I became more concerned about Dom's indifferent attitude towards the continual increase in Lunar Prospector's estimated mass, power requirements, and cost as indicated by his comments to me during the review meeting and when he said to me, "If we don't make our launch date — so what, nobody is really going to care." With respect to the proposal estimates, the dry mass was up from 126 kg to 144 kg, the power was up from 180 w to 215 w and the cost was up from $59 million to $63 or $64 million. Dom was no longer saying, "Well, we'll get the power down, we'll get the mass down, and we'll make that thing even lighter and smaller."

He was not even trying to control the spacecraft's growth. Dom was clearly backing off from our goals and objectives and that reminded me of what Scott said when I was talking to him about Dom on July 5, "Lockheed has a history of coming in low and then charging more at the end." I was sure that was part of the problem, but I also was beginning to believe that Dom was just not up to the task of doing Lunar Prospector as we had proposed — despite all his arrogant blustering.

Somehow I had to get the spacecraft's mass, power, and cost back down where they were supposed to be, otherwise it would not be able to achieve the scientific and programmatic goals I had set and NASA had bought. Lunar Prospector had to be done within our budget and that was part of the problem — we didn't have the money to really work hard on the mass, power, and cost issues. In a certain sense, I did agree with Dom that the main thing was to get Lunar Prospector done successfully, even if it did cost $65 million and even if it did take a couple of extra months to build (instead of the proposed 22 months). That was still damned cheap and fast compared to the Discovery caps of $250 million and 36 months for Phase C/D. Nevertheless, I would just hate having to tell NASA that our programmatic goals had already started to erode.

Lockheed got some really bad news; Lockheed lost EOS, the whole program. There were only three companies still in the competition for that huge contract. I had been complaining that EOS was taking all the help and all I had was what was left and no more. I had worked on the EOS proposal earlier and Lockheed probably spent $10 to 20 million on that proposal and now they were out of it. It was a big loss for Lockheed, one with major and unforeseen consequences for Lunar Prospector.

Friday, July 14, 1995

Dom talked to Al Smith about Lunar Prospector's costs. He kept the meeting a secret from me, so I wasn't there! He told Al that our budget was $61.7 million, only $2.7 million higher that the $59 million in our proposal. I thought that was an acceptable number, so I didn't think we would be in too much trouble with Headquarters. However, I was very concerned that Dom was sneaking behind my back, having secret meetings with Lockheed's upper management, keeping me out of the budgetary discussions and who knows what else? Clearly Dom and Lockheed did not consider me in charge of Lunar Prospector!

Monday, July 17, 1995

I went over to Ames at 8:30 AM to talk with Scott and Sylvia. We had to talk about a press release we had prepared. Mark Saunders was upset because we had mentioned the original $59 million cost estimate in the press release. Since by then our cost (and, including Lockheed's $4 million fee, the price) was a few million more, he didn't want us repeating something that was no longer true. He was mad because we had said that Scott was a co-investigator as well as the NASA Mission Manager. We had thought his concerns about that were over, since Scott was not carrying out any of the responsibilities of a Co-I (Bob McMurray was to represent Scott until the mission flew, though Bob was doing essentially nothing), but they were not. Mark did not want Scott mentioned as a Co-I, period. Mark also did not want any mention of Lunar Prospector's role in developing a commercial lunar exploration capability. We addressed all those issues and also decided we would emphasize that Lunar Prospector was my, i.e., the PI's program, and not Lockheed's program, since Lockheed kept trying to say that Lockheed and not I was going back to the Moon. Scott and I changed the title to "Lunar Prospector Going Back to the Moon" and then started the press release with a discussion of my role as PI and buried Lockheed and Dom down under the part that described Ames's role in Lunar Prospector.

Scott said he and NASA were very concerned about the escalation of the costs, even though I had told him that our current cost estimate was only $61.7 million. However, that did not include the $2.2 million for the tracking and Ames's costs. When all that was added in, the final budget was about $66 million. Even though that was not much of an increase, under the environment that prevailed at Headquarters and on the Hill, it was not acceptable. What made it even worse was the fact that, earlier the cost of the rocket came out of a different part of the budget; that had been changed so it came out of Mark's Discovery budget. That really hurt and Mark was really sensitive about costs.

I asked if Mark was really mad about the things in the press release, which were really trivial, or was he really mad about the money. Sylvia said, "Well the trouble is he is upset about the money to begin with, so everything makes him annoyed now."

Then Scott asked me about the Taurus. He had heard it was about $6 million less than the LLV2 and he wanted to know if we were going to investigate the Taurus. I told Scott I had already started to do so and had decided I would write Dom a memo indicating that, because Lunar Prospector's cost had escalated well beyond what was acceptable to NASA, we had to determine if Orbital Sciences could offer us a less expensive launch vehicle.

NASA was not happy with the cost increase and I was not happy about two things. First, NASA kept changing the rules on us, e.g., the rocket costs had to come out of Mark's budget. Second, NASA expected us to give them the cost estimate during — not at the end of — Phase B (end of September) without our having had the time necessary to do the work. NASA conveniently forgot that they delayed us by one month because they didn't announce whom they selected until the end of February 1995, rather than in January 1995. NASA kept changing the rules and kept being behind schedule and then expected us to make up for their deficiencies. The budget we were putting together had to be the final budget. If we were going to have to escalate the costs, it had to be right then, because we couldn't come back later and say, "Gee, we were kidding, we are going to need an extra $3 million," because it wasn't going to be there. That was the time to fight the fight. If Lunar Prospector was really going to cost another $3 to $5 million, we had to tell NASA then. If they didn't like it, then they would have to cancel Lunar Prospector.

Bill Sjogren called up from JPL. He was upset that Ames gave the navigation contract to Goddard rather than to JPL. I said, "That was their decision. I gave them authority to choose the one they wanted and I back Ames's decision."

Bill asked, "Well, can't you change it?"

I answered, "No, I gave them the right to do it and I am not changing it."

That was pretty much the end of the day. I was tired and Tom was tired.

Tuesday, July 18, 1995

I didn't feel well and came home early, but before I did that, I left Dom the memo regarding our getting information on Taurus from Orbital Sciences. We would see what would happen when Dom got the memo, but he was gone for a couple of days. I would have to wait two days to find out how Lockheed would react.

One more issue arose before I went home; Woody said he needed another meter or so for extra solar cells. That worried Tom Chinn because if the spacecraft got taller, it would no longer fit in the rocket shroud, among other bad things. The power was out of control, as was the mass, and everything else. It was about time things started to settle down!

Wednesday, July 19, 1995

I got a message from Pat saying that Lunar Prospector was fully funded in the House version of the budget and was expected to be fully funded in the Senate version — so we would get our money in the fall! That was very, very good news — if we didn't get canceled first!

I went to tell Richard, Francisco, and Martha (the lady who was working on our budget) the good news. We were standing there talking while Richard was working on a memo about our using the Taurus. I read the memo and then we got into a conversation about writing an RFP for Taurus. Martha asked, "Why are you doing that?"

I answered, "Because the budget is too high, we need to get the budget down and Taurus is supposedly several million cheaper."

She said, "You can't do that right now, we are in the midst of it." What a load of bull. Martha had been saying for months that we should get off the damned LLV2. She didn't trust it, she didn't like it, and she was happy about us getting off. But she got angry or frustrated about our doing it at that time. She said, "I can't change the budget now."

I said, "I don't expect you to, but we are getting an estimate from another vendor."

She asked again, "Why are you doing that?"

I answered, "Because the budget is too high!"

She then said, "You are not supposed to know what the budget is yet because it has not been finalized." I guessed, according to Martha, Dom was not supposed to be telling us or me (damn it, I was the PI and I had no right to know what they were doing to my budget) what was going on in terms of our budget. Anyway, she got in a tizzy and flittered off. Clearly, something was amiss but I did not know what. Dom had told everybody about the budget and he had had budget meetings with Gus and with Al Smith (which I was never asked to or told about until they were over). I didn't know whether they were doing things they shouldn't do or whether Martha was just in a stupid tizzy.

The next thing I knew, Richard came and said that Martha had run off to Steve Griffin (Gus's deputy, but he was really Al Smith's spy sent to watch Gus and mess around in our business) and Steve had sent a memo to Dom and Steve Lowell (but, of course, not to the PI) that stated, "There will be no RFP's, under any circumstances, sent to any other launch vendor unless the LLV1 fails."

I thought, *well, he can go screw himself! That is my program, not his and not damned Lockheed's.*

It seemed to me that a big flap was brewing. There was to be a meeting between Dom and Steve, to which I was not invited! Then I was told there was a meeting set up with Al Smith the following week. I said, "I'm on travel next week." Then I asked, "Do you know who set it up?" and the answer was no. I suspected that Dom had set up another damned meeting behind my back when I was on travel, to be sure I wouldn't and couldn't attend. I didn't know what the hell was going on and I was getting tired of that crap. All of Lockheed's managers, anyone who had anything to do with Lunar Prospector, were doing all kinds of things behind my back. All I was getting was second hand information. I was really getting mad about all the hanky panky that was going on.

Late in the day I had a very interesting conversation with Steve Lowell, our subcontract guy whom Dom absolutely hated and whom I thought was nice and trustworthy. We decided it would be best to have our conversation "out of the office." Since Dom hated Steve, Dom could conceivably cause him trouble if he saw us talking and further, it was none of Dom's business with whom I talked to find out information, so we went for a walk. I told him I wanted to find out what the hell was going on. I wanted to know why Martha had gotten all-bent-out-of-shape when I discussed and/or questioned the budgetary stuff. Was I doing something wrong by asking or was Martha just not used to someone other than a Lockheed manager getting involved with the budget? Steve answered, "You can talk about the budget and stuff like that, it's just that this is not the way she is used to working and she gets very flighty under such circumstances." He continued, "Martha has been told a dozen times the budget can't be high and she just sort of stubbornly sticks to her way of doing things, regardless of what is required."

Steve then told me he hated Dom and thought he was a terrible manager. Steve was fully aware that Dom, as well as the rest of Lockheed management, just didn't want to accept that I was the customer. They were not used to having the customer being an employee of the company and they were just not prepared to deal with that. They wanted to keep to the old way of doing things, rather than the way Discovery was supposed to work. Steve suggested I talk to Al Smith (who I did not trust) to explain the situation to him. Steve said, "You have to get independent of these guys if you are going to have the control you are supposed to have as PI." Steve's opinion was that I had every right to ask for whatever I wanted or needed to get my job done. If Lockheed truly accepted that I was the customer, then they had to respond to my directives. I, of course, knew and believed all that, but it was very interesting and reassuring to hear Steve's perspective on it.

Thus ended another generally annoying day.

Thursday, July 20, 1995: Apollo 11 Anniversary

July 20, the 26th anniversary of the Apollo 11 lunar landing and the 18th anniversary of the landing of Viking 1 on Mars.

I talked to Dom as soon as he got in and I told him something was up. I told him about my conversation with Richard and Martha, how Martha had run off and told Steve Griffin and how Griffin had written an email memo to various people saying that no RFP was to go out unless the LLV1 launch, which was supposed to be the following week, failed. Dom was very annoyed. That was the third time Griffin had messed around with Lunar Prospector and Dom was livid. He ranted, "If that stuff keeps going on, I'm not going to do Lunar Prospector." I felt like saying, "Yippee!" But I then told him Lunar Prospector was to be fully funded according to the marked up budget. Then Dom went off to his meeting with Griffin.

I talked with Dom after his meeting with Griffin and he said Griffin was just representing Gus in his absence and Martha hadn't really done anything. I was more than a little bit suspicious about Dom's answer and I had more than a sneaking suspicion they were keeping as much as possible from me about the budget and who knew what else. Given Dom's high level of agitation before his meeting with Griffin, he was far calmer than I would have expected after the meeting. I was fairly certain they had agreed on something that was to my disadvantage. Of course, I had nothing to back up my suspicions, but I no longer trusted Dom in any way, shape, or manner.

Later, we got down to spacecraft engineering issues. It had dawned on me that, rather than having a radiating surface on the lower quarter of the solar array drum to keep the electronic units cool (they were all located near the bottom of the spacecraft), it would be better to remove the bottom thermal blanket from the spacecraft and let the electronics radiate their heat directly into space out the bottom of the spacecraft. That would allow us to make the spacecraft smaller, either make it shorter or decrease its diameter.

Also, Woody's solar array model was in error. He had calculated the solar array power output using the highest temperature when the spacecraft was right smack over the center of the Moon at full moon. That resulted in a low power output and hence the need for a larger than necessary solar array. Woody should have used the average solar array temperature integrated over an orbit to calculate the required (and hence smaller) solar array surface area.

I talked to Dom about both of those issues and he agreed with me. I didn't know whether he really understood what I was talking about or whether he was just covering up his ignorance about the spacecraft. Maybe he was much sharper than I had begun to think he was, but if so, then why didn't he see those things and/or why did he let those things slide? Whatever the case, Dom had a very peculiar way of managing and was a very strange person and getting stranger.

To top everything off, the LLV2 guys came in with their formal bid. It was $29 million! That was way above the $25 million they had quoted during the proposal effort and was way too high. They claimed it was high because we needed the 3.05 m shroud instead of the 2.34 m one they had. The basic LLV2 with the 2.34 m shroud was $22 million and they were willing to do the integration of the Trans-Lunar Injection (TLI) Stage for another $2.3 million. Without the bigger shroud, the launch vehicle was going to cost $24.3 million. They would charge us about a million dollars for the 3.05 m shroud, but the hitch was they wanted to charge us an extra $3.5 million to develop it! Interestingly, Mel Brashears, who was supposedly so supportive of Lunar Prospector and me, said to the LLV2 guys when they asked him if they had to eat the cost of the 3.05 m shroud development, "No, you are not going to swallow the $3.5 million, you charge them (Lunar Prospector) for that." If we couldn't get around that, it would kill Lunar Prospector! Brashears, just like the rest of the Lockheed managers, was an ass; when it came down to money and Lockheed profits, Lunar Prospector had no allies.

Dom asked me if we could do without the damned 3.05 m shroud, if we could scrunch the spacecraft down? I answered, "Based on what I told you earlier today about removing the radiator from the lower part of the solar array drum and letting the electronics radiate their heat out the bottom of the spacecraft, we could take about 30 cm off the height of the spacecraft and we could also make the drum diameter somewhat smaller. We could also put the instruments on top and have the booms up there (I also had another reason for doing that), so we could probably fit in a 2.34 m shroud."

At about the same time Richard came to us with news about the Taurus. It was only about $22 or $23 million for everything, TLI Stage and all. That was a big saving; but Dom flopped back and forth, knowing if we pursued the Taurus, we would open a big can of worms. There was no question if we tried to go on a Taurus, Lockheed would fight us tooth and nail, so Dom chickened out immediately and said, "The $22 million couldn't be a fixed price bid. Orbital Sciences would just back out and escalate the costs if we switched to the Taurus." I didn't believe that. Then he said, like a good company man, "Well, you know, we can go with LLV2 because they will be cheaper than they said they would be and blah, blah, blah."

I said, "Well, I would still like to find out what the real cost of the Taurus is." I pressed the issue more, but Dom just kept searching for excuses not to pursue it, not wanting to get in a fight with Lockheed over the Taurus.

Martha came into Dom's office and asked if I wanted to see the final budget. Dom said I could not see it; he wanted to review it alone! Annoying as that was, I didn't feel like fighting about it because I was sick and tired of him and of Lockheed's sneaking around behind my back. The budget problems would get handled when it was finished, nothing I said or did until then would do any good, so why waste my time and energy?

So ended another frustrating day.

Friday, July 21, 1995

Dom was bitchy as usual. First, he said he wasn't going to do anything about the high cost of the LLV2 or the Taurus. Then he got to the real point he was angry about. He had seen the press release and since he didn't get top billing, he was angry and insulted. At that point I was very, very close to saying, "Dom, tough luck." It was clear to me that if Dom didn't straighten up he was going to have to go. There was no way we could get Lunar Prospector done with him acting that way all the time.

Shortly after I left Dom still bitching and moaning, I got a call from the Lockheed PR guy who said there was going to be TV interview of me at 1:00 PM and he wanted to know if I wanted Dom there. Despite everything, Dom was still the Lunar Prospector Project Manager and I felt that he should be part of the interview.

I went to tell Dom about the interviews and found him talking with Woody. To show his disdain for me, he simply ignored my standing in his doorway and continued his conversation with Woody. He saved that special treatment for me; when I was talking with him and someone came in, Dom would always interrupt our conversation and ask, "What do you need? Will that take very long?" Finally, he condescended to speak to me and I told him about the interviews.

Then, I had a good laugh at Dom and his intense vanity. Being Friday, it was dress down day. For the first time ever, Dom had come in without a suit and tie on — the very day he was finally going to be on TV. He left work, drove home, and put a suit and tie on. Mr. Dandy could not be seen on TV in casual clothes!

We had three interviews for TV and I had a telephone interview with KCBS — the All News Radio Station. When the TV spots aired that evening, the first one was very good, the second was not so good and the third one was pretty bad.

After the interviews, I went over to see Scott. I told him Lockheed thought it was running the show and hence had totally ignored the memo I wrote to Dom requesting he get costing information on Taurus and then Griffin had bitched about my trying to get the Taurus information. Scott was trying to get it across to Lockheed that we had to keep the costs down and that Taurus was the answer. Gus was finally beginning to be sensitive to that. But it was clear that it was Scott and me versus Lockheed all the way.

When I got back to Lockheed, I found the LLV2 people had sent a stupid addendum to their proposal stating it would be a $2 million charge for any changes to the 2.34 m shroud, no matter how minor, needed to make it fit over Lunar Prospector! Then, to add insult to injury, they even had a clause saying if we interfered in any way with their development schedule, i.e., required modifications or information they did not already have, they would not deliver the rocket, period! We take what they wanted to give us under their conditions or we can go to hell — nice way to deal with a customer!

Dom and Frank said the LLV2 jerks were just throwing the opportunity to launch Lunar Prospector away. Our attitude was, *good, we don't want them, these guys are bad and hopefully the LLV1 will blow up on the 25ᵗʰ when they try to launch it. If it blows up and doesn't get into orbit, then that is the end of that and we can get on the Taurus. They don't know what they are doing; they are a bunch of idiots.*

In addition to all that, the LLV2 memo had really ticked me off for another reason. Because of their high costs, I had been forced to start looking at the Taurus and that made me the villain in Lockheed's eyes. That was highlighted when Steve Griffin called Dom and told Dom to tell me, "Lockheed is in the business of selling rockets, not having their competitors launch Lockheed satellites. Binder had better understand that, and blah, blah, blah."

Saturday, July 22, 1995

Tom, Rebecca, and I drove down the coastal highway, famous California 1, and had a really nice weekend ride. We enjoyed the beautiful scenery and Tom was so taken with it he said, "Boy, look at that place; we ought to have the Binder Lunar Exploration Institute here."

Tom's comment caused a little light bulb up in my head to go on. I said, "Wait a minute, we have the entire staff and administration of LEI in the car right here." I called a meeting of LEI to order. The thought dawned on me that the problems associated with my trying to run my program at Lockheed while being a Lockheed employee would be solved if I quit Lockheed and did Lunar Prospector through LEI.

Tom, Rebecca, and I talked about doing that. I wanted to talk to Scott, if possible, before I started my trip, to see if I could get a contract directly from Ames to LEI for Tom's and my time. We could even hire Tom Chinn and Tim Bridges and any other retiree who was working on subcontracts and have them be working on Lunar Prospector through LEI. That would completely divorce Tom and me from Lockheed and the "conflict of interest" problem. Then Lockheed would have to do what I said since I was the customer and not an employee. Further, I could get rid of Dom, which I was going to have to do anyway because he was getting to be intolerable.

We decided to pursue the idea. I would have to talk to Todd Greenwalt at Vinson & Elkins to make sure how we were going to do it was OK and to find out what we had to do to keep LEI as a Texas corporation. If that really worked out, and I thought it could, it would really resolve a lot of issues. There was risk for Tom and me, but it was worth it to us. I thought, *what a good thing it was that I kept LEI around and did not kill it as Lockheed had insisted. If it works, it would really fix those Lockheed bastards. We could get Taurus and do all the things we need to do. And best of all, Lunar Prospector would be done by LEI and not by Lockheed.*

Monday, July 24, through Friday, July 28, 1995: On Travel

Monday I flew to Albuquerque and then drove to Los Alamos. After arriving in the late afternoon, I had supper at Bill's, along with Ron Black from Southwest.

Tuesday, Woody and Gerry Grismore and the rest of us discussed instrument/ C&DH interface issues. I was a little disappointed. I had thought we would discuss pin assignments and things at that level of detail, but all we did was to decide who was going to take care of those issues, rather than actually resolving them. I felt the meeting was a waste of time. Anyway, the meeting didn't take very much time and we were done by noon. Bill and I went for a nice hike in the mountains and then we had a nice steak dinner.

I flew to Houston Wednesday. Tom and I worked on the archiving document during the afternoon.

The next morning, Thursday, I attended a meeting that Bill Beatty had set up. The LESC Cherry Hill people wanted to set up a tracking network and wanted to know from me what types of requirements a mission like Lunar Prospector would have.

I had a chance to talk to Bill Huffstetler before the meeting; unfortunately Bill was not going to be at the meeting. I always liked to see Bill whenever possible since he had done so much to make Lunar Prospector possible, so I was happy we had a little time to chat.

Bill Beatty headed the meeting; unfortunately, stupid Moe Miller was there and about a dozen other LESC guys. It was a great and very satisfying, two-hour meeting. They were very impressed with Lunar Prospector and clearly I knew much more about missions, tracking, and opportunities for commercialization and follow-on missions than they did and they were all very impressed (funny, except for Bill Beatty and Bill Huffstetler, they had all ignored me when I worked at LESC before Lunar Prospector). I went away from that meeting feeling extremely good and thought, if the meeting in the afternoon with Jim Adamson went that well, it would be silly for Tom and me not to rejoin LESC and work Lunar Prospector from there. I went in very confident and hyped up about that possibility at the 3:30 PM meeting, but I was disappointed.

Jim Adamson was very conservative about everything. In addition to Jim, Cyrus, Rich Lyons, and another guy, who I didn't know, were at the meeting and all except Jim were very positive about Lunar Prospector and the possibility of Tom and me returning to LESC. Though very interested, they did not fully understand the problems. I had laid it all out on the table for them — the conflict of interests as long as I worked for Lockheed, the trouble with Dom, the trouble with the rocket, and the possibility of my leaving Lockheed and doing Lunar Prospector through LEI.

Jim understood the problem that Project Managers, like Dom, expected to get the requirements from scientists and then tell the scientist to go to hell, i.e., "Keep out of my way and let me build it." Jim was willing to both support me in my PI role as the manager of Lunar Prospector and get me back to LESC, but he wanted to make sure I really had that authority (which contractually I did), so I was quite disappointed with his attitude. I thought he would be much more aggressive about the whole thing, but he was too cautious and I came away from the meeting with the attitude, *to hell with all of them, I will just pursue getting LEI started to do Lunar Prospector.*

I decided I would talk to Scott about my doing Lunar Prospector through LEI the following Monday or Tuesday, before I went to Wallops Island for the tracking network meeting. Also, I wanted to talk to Mark Smith before I left to see if he would be interested in working on Lunar Prospector as my Systems Engineer, but not as a Project Manager. I had no intention of giving him that authority if I were running Lunar Prospector out of LEI. I was sick of that crap. Then, when I got back from Wallops Island a week later, I would talk to Gus about the three main issues confronting Lunar Prospector and me; the LLV2 mess and hence my getting information on the Taurus (the stupid LLV1 hadn't gotten launched on the 25th, an actuator didn't work so they had had a two day hold to fix it, then they found that the actuator was corroded. As they were fooling around with the actuator, they found that the software was incorrectly programmed. Had they gotten down to T minus 72 seconds, the self-destruct system would have blown the rocket up! They ended up with a two-week delay. What a bunch of idiots), LMSC's accepting me as the PI and customer and hence stop vetoing things I wanted done, and last but not least, getting rid of Dom.

That was my plan. I did not want to do anything until the Technical Design Review was over in five weeks. But those issues had to be resolved before we went into C/D in October and I no longer saw how Dom could be part of Lunar Prospector. He was not going to change and I was sick of him. I was also sick of LMSC (nothing I could do about that — I was stuck with LMSC as my main contractor) and I was sick of Gus and the rest of the Lockheed bozos, both those at LMSC and those at LESC. If the change to LEI worked out, then Lockheed could kiss my behind. But a transition to LEI would certainly be a very delicate thing to accomplish and I couldn't afford to screw up Lunar Prospector under any circumstances. I had to do everything very carefully and make sure Headquarters was in agreement with what I wanted to do. If not, I was stuck in LMSC and/or Lunar Prospector was in deep trouble, if not dead.

Friday I flew home from Houston and was looking forward to a relaxing weekend with Rebecca.

Chapter 2-12
Lunar Prospector Facing Cancellation and the End of Dom

Monday, July 31, 1995:
Dom Hangs Himself and Lunar Prospector Nears Cancellation

When I got to work I had an email announcing that Gus was being replaced as the head of SSD (Space Systems Division). He was going to lead some Lockheed commercial effort and someone from outside of the company would replace him. The real story behind that change was, after Lockheed lost the EOS bid, NASA told Lockheed to get rid of Gus for botching the job, which everyone, including NASA, thought Lockheed would have easily won. I was both surprised and impressed that NASA had enough clout to force Lockheed to remove one of its managers. Perhaps I should not have been surprised. NASA and the big aerospace companies are so intertwined with each other they are more like one big, incestuous (and corrupt) family rather than a federal agency and independent, commercial companies.

Gus's leaving was both good and bad. It was bad at that point in time because we had to get so many critical things resolved and Gus was an integral part of the management of Lunar Prospector. It was good because it would get Gus, who I did not trust, out of my hair for good. I was hopeful his replacement would be more forthright and helpful.

After digesting the memo about Gus, I arranged the trip for the Wallops Island meeting on the tracking and then talked to Frank Donivan at Wallops about the meeting. According to Frank, everything had been worked out in some detail. Headquarters hadn't decided exactly how they wanted us to do the tracking, but they had two or three options they were considering.

I went to Ames to talk to Sylvia and Scott about Dom and how we might do the tracking, the costs of which might be as little as $500,000 or as much as the full $2.2 million we had budgeted. Finally it looked like the tracking issue would get solved.

While I was at Los Alamos and Houston, Dom had been thrashing around about the spacecraft design and had opened up all kinds of cans of worms. We were at the end of Phase B and should have had a complete design ready for construction (Phase C), but Dom was just beginning to do the trade studies needed to complete the spacecraft design! Richard and Francisco were told they had to write down all of the spacecraft requirements! I was outraged; first of all, I had written the Mission Requirements Document (MRD) years ago — the MRD had been part of the proposal! Dom was trying to start from scratch rather that use my requirements and the spacecraft design I came to Lockheed with had been the basis of our winning the program! What Dom was doing was absurd — clearly he was trying to push me aside and make Lunar Prospector his spacecraft by starting all over again. Though we had to do some redesigning to make Lunar Prospector fit into the 2.34 m shroud, there was no reason to have Francisco and Richard, neither of whom knew anything about the mission, redefine the mission requirements which I had defined at the beginning of the program years earlier. Dom is just plain nuts!

In Dom's thrashing around trying to get Lunar Prospector into the LLV2 shroud, he and the engineers had changed the design from having two tanks to three and from having six engines to eight for no apparent reason (except to add mass, cost, and complexity, and because they did not understand the basic design I had come to Lockheed with). They were making major changes to the spacecraft without my knowledge and I had no idea what the hell they were doing. Though in a certain sense, I didn't care. Dom could thrash around all he wanted, what he was doing meant nothing because I was going to fire him one way or another next week, period, end of the discussion.

I went to Ames to discuss with Scott what Dom had done. That only added fuel to a new fire that was already burning Scott up. A reporter from *Mercury*, the Journal of the Astronomical Society of the Pacific, had interviewed Dom. The result was an article on just Dom and Lunar Prospector. There was no mention of the PI in the main text; the only place my name appeared was in a little set of boxes showing the various Discovery Missions, their PIs and a few facts about them. Much worse from Scott's standpoint was the fact that NASA-Ames was not mentioned at all, though Scott, Sylvia, and Mark Saunders were mentioned in passing. That was it. Mark had seen the article and had angrily called Scott to demand to know, "What the hell is going on out there? Who in hell is running the program?" Mark just flipped his lid. Scott said he had tried to answer Mark, but Mark just interrupted him saying, "Lunar Prospector is about ready to be canceled because the costs are at $70 million and the technical design is no longer what was proposed. As always, Lockheed used the proposal to get its foot in the door and then changed the design and raised the price."

Scott said to me, "It was bad enough about the costs, but now Dom has done all that other stuff. What Dom is doing is simply taking over the program, or trying to at least. That is not what Headquarters wants and that is not what I want."

I told Scott my conclusions about Dom and what I had found out in Houston. I said, "The issue is not so much where I do Lunar Prospector from (i.e., stay at Lockheed or quit and do Lunar Prospector from LEI), the first issue is getting rid of Dom." We all agreed that had to happen. There was no changing Dom. He was running amok. I told Scott, "The spacecraft design has devolved instead of evolved. We had a decent design to begin with. Certainly, some things had to be refined, but the trade studies Dom is now making at that stage of the game are devolving instead of evolving the spacecraft — it is in much worse condition. Its mass is up. Its power is up. Dom has just totally screwed everything up. It all boils down to the fact that Dom will not listen to me or allow me to do anything. He has kept me from doing the things I needed to do to get that thing on track." Scott didn't know the depth of the mess because he hadn't followed the technical issues in detail. Nevertheless, Scott believed and trusted what I was saying, in part because he had seen how Dom had screwed up the costs and was bastardizing and subverting the concept of the PI and other such programmatic issues. I said to Scott, "I just do not see any way out of that except to get rid of Dom. He is doing a bad job on almost every front. He has done some good things, but we are right on the verge of being canceled; Lunar Prospector could be over in five weeks." We decided right then and there that there were several steps we needed to take ASAP.

First, as the NASA Mission Manager, Scott was going to make Lockheed understand that I was not only the PI, but also the customer and they had to do what I told them, period. If they accepted that, then I would remain at LMSC — but with the absolute authority I needed. If not, then I would go to LESC or LEI. In either place I would be outside LMSC's realm and they would have to do Lunar Prospector my way. One way or another LMSC was going to have to accept that I was running the program.

Second, Dom had to go. Dom was not doing his job. He was destroying a program that everyone said in the beginning was a sure winner. Because of Dom's arrogance, conceit, and ego, we were at the point of losing it. Scott was going to talk to Gus and find out if he should talk to him or someone higher up about getting rid of Dom. Scott was just going to lay it on the line by saying Lunar Prospector was in the process of being canceled if things didn't turn around and Dom was the problem.

Third, Lockheed had to accept we needed to consider going over to the Taurus and had to get information on it.

I didn't know how it would play out. Lockheed had a contract to fulfill, they had to do something or they were going to have to default. That would be a big embarrassment for Lockheed, as would our using a Taurus instead of an LLV2. I didn't care what Lockheed liked or didn't like; we were at the point where the program was going down the drain if we didn't bring it around. Scott and I knew it was going to be difficult. We were about to make major changes in the program, but we felt we could say to Headquarters, "Look, Phase B allowed us to shake out these problems. We have solved them and are ready to go into C/D. We know what we need to do and we can do it."

Interestingly, Scott had commented to Mark Saunders before Discovery got going that maybe it was a bad idea to have an industry PI for the first external Discovery Mission, since there would be built in conflicts of interest in such a case. Scott's prophecy turned out to be more than correct.

I went to talk with Mark Smith. I had seen Mark accidentally earlier and I told him I wanted to talk to him. Mark was the only person at LMSC I had any personal experience with (other than Dom) and had any trust in, so I wanted to see if he was interested in working on Lunar Prospector as my Systems Engineer. I was not interested in getting someone at Dom's level to replace him; I was concerned the same mess would happen all over again since I suspected that none of the Lockheed Project Managers would be willing to accept the fact that they could not run the show, and Scott agreed with my concern. What I needed was someone who would do the things I needed done, regardless of what Lockheed wanted, and someone who was willing to play second fiddle to me and not fight about it.

I went over to Mark's office at 1:00 PM. I not only wanted to talk to him about working on Lunar Prospector, but also because I wanted to get an independent assessment of Dom. Mark had been Dom's protégé and knew Dom as well as — or better than — anyone. I wanted to see if Mark thought my concerns about Dom were real or if I was the one who had gone bananas. Scott thought that was also a very good idea since it would give us an independent reading on whether the problem was just a personality problem between Dom and me or if we were dealing with a fundamental problem with Dom.

I told Mark what was happening and he was not at all surprised. He had expected everything I told him. He said, "Dom will not change. He is that way all the time. He can only work if he has absolute authority and he never listens to anyone. He believes he is the only person who is capable of anything in the company and everyone else is an idiot." Though he was not surprised, Mark was appalled at the things Dom had done and literally threw up his hands. Mark said, "Dom sees this as a brand new spacecraft, a brand new technology, a brand new line of missions and he sees him doing all that. He wants to make sure no one else is around to get any of the credit except Domenick. He is trying to push you out so he can run it and he will give you a spacecraft and then he will do that for other PIs — it will be all his show." Then Mark continued with, "There is no way Dom will not continue in his ways. There is nothing you can say to him; he has done that on every program. People hated him so badly on Hubble they would come to me and scream the man is nuts. Everything you have said about him, other people have come and said, and everyone says Dom is nuts." Thus, Mark confirmed everything Scott and I felt was going on with Dom.

I explained to Mark I wanted to get someone I trusted to replace Dom. I said, "As Dom's protégé, you learned many good things from him — because he does do good things — but you also understand his failings. The role I want you to play, if you take it, will be my second in command. You will not be the Project Manager; I will be the Project Manager and you will be my Chief Engineer or whatever title we choose. You will help me do these things and we will talk, but the decisions will be mine, not yours."

Mark had several concerns. The main one was that he thought Lockheed would never let him do it because he was too junior. I replied to that saying, "Don't worry about that. First of all, Lockheed has to accept this is my program, that I am the customer, and what I say goes. If I tell them I want you as my second in command, they don't have a choice in the matter. If they will not accept my being the Project Manager, the customer, and the person who runs that program without interference, then that program is lost. It is dead. We will lose it. There is just no question of that. If Lunar Prospector is going to go forward, it is going to go forward the way I want it to and the way Ames wants it, so don't worry about that," and Mark accepted that.

We discussed Mark's concern about the probability of success. I told him what had happened with the spacecraft design — that we had a good design, that we had to refine it and that Dom was trying to re-invent the mission requirements, five weeks before the technical design review! Mark was astounded at that, though he didn't know the worst of it, because I didn't know the worst of it (Richard told me later that afternoon that Francisco and he were charged with getting all the spacecraft requirements that night — such stupidity).

In the end, Mark was extremely interested in taking the job. He understood what we were up against. He knew we had a program that was a winner and that it should have easily gotten through the coming review and gone straight into Phase C/D without any questions. But because of Dom, we had a program that had a 50/50 chance of being canceled! Even if we didn't get canceled, we had to make up for Dom's stupidity and incompetence. I thought and hoped Mark would do it. I asked him to give me his answer the following Monday. In the meantime I asked him to suggest other people for the job in case he didn't want it, or if Lockheed wouldn't let him do it.

I left our meeting feeling very positive about everything. He wanted to talk to his management and alert them. I told him I did not want any rumors getting out, because I did not want Dom hearing about my replacing him from anyone but me. I told Mark I would appreciate him waiting until Scott and I had at least talked to Gus or whomever, but he could proceed with his management very cautiously and everything had to be done confidentially and absolutely on the quiet.

When I got back to building 107, Dom caught me and said he wanted to tell me what had happened at the Lunar Prospector budget meeting the previous week. He asked if I had a minute to talk with him and I answered, "No, I don't." It was interesting to note the change in his attitude since I was tending to ignore him — all of the sudden Dom was a little more attentive and a little more polite when I was around.

He asked, "Where were you last week?"

I doubted he had forgotten over the weekend that I was at Los Alamos and Houston; rather he wanted to find out what I had been up to. I answered curtly, "I was on travel," and I ignored his implied question about what I had done. Then I left to go to Ames again to discuss trajectory issues.

While at Ames I talked with Scott and Sylvia. It turned out Headquarters was going to look at the Taurus for us since Lockheed wouldn't; that was how serious the launch issue had become. Sylvia asked me for the technical data so Headquarters could get the information we needed on the Taurus and to find out if it really only cost $19 million (without the TLI stage).

When I returned to Lockheed, I told Richard to send Orbital Sciences an email using my name and my computer so he wouldn't get in trouble. Both Richard and Francisco knew something was up. They both were loyal to me and we worked well together, but they could not overtly cross Dom because he paid their wages, so they were caught in the middle.

As the day ended, I knew if we got rid of Dom at the beginning of the following week, I would have just five weeks to get Lunar Prospector back on track — so the next five weeks would be very tough. If I could get Mark Smith working on Lunar Prospector towards the end of the following week, and if I could get Tom Polette out to Sunnyvale early, I thought I could do it. I had told Mark about Tom and explained that the three of us plus Scott would manage Lunar Prospector — that it would be a team effort with me making the decisions. Mark liked that very much. I had also told Mark that Tom did not have any experience in spacecraft design and construction, but that he was very capable and I trusted him.

I was going to ask Tom to come out for the meeting in the middle of the following month and then come out permanently the week after that. In the meantime, I needed him to finally start learning about Lunar Prospector. If we were going to save Lunar Prospector, I couldn't afford to spend time bringing Tom up to speed after he got to Sunnyvale. I needed him not only to finish the archiving document without my help, but also to take over the Outreach Program, among other things. During the next five weeks I had to bring Mark up to speed, get the spacecraft design fixed up, and undo everything Dom had screwed up during the last three months. I badly needed Tom in Sunnyvale and for him to know what the spacecraft and mission were all about.

All in all, except for my having a slight sore throat and being very tired, I felt good — I felt that the day had marked a very important turning point for Lunar Prospector. As far as I was concerned, the stress and damage to the program caused by Dom was over. My decision to fire him was made; Scott and I just had to work out the delicate details with NASA and Lockheed management by the end of the week. My biggest concerns were making sure Lunar Prospector did not get canceled and getting the costs down. To insure that Dom did not hurt the program any more, I would just veto everything he tried to do during the rest of the week. My mood right then was that if Dom crossed me in anyway during the next few days, I would not wait for the discussions with Lockheed management and NASA Headquarters, I would just say, "Dom, I am the PI and you are no longer the Project Manager. You have nothing to do with the program any longer, end of story."

Tuesday, August 1, 1995

Scott came over at 10:00 AM and Dom and I had a meeting with Mike Griffin, Frank Martin, Fred DeFrank, and some other contract guys. Scott's official NASA job was to tell Lockheed that we were $10 million over budget and if we didn't get it down, the program would be canceled. The Lockheed side tried to minimize the danger of the high cost, but finally Scott got it across to them that there was no talking around the issue, so Lockheed agreed. They promised to get everything behind Lunar Prospector and get the job done.

Then I brought up some of my issues. I said I was concerned because of the conflict caused by my being a Lockheed employee while Lockheed was supposed to be working under my direction on my program. Frank said, "Yes, I was worried about that from the very beginning, but I didn't say anything." Then I gave some examples. As expected, Dom was very defensive about the whole thing, insisting it was Lockheed's problem and they had more to lose than I did if Lunar Prospector didn't work. Griffin said Lockheed would not take direction from me about the rocket or anything they felt would interfere with their interests, so basically my being the customer and the PI had no effect on them whatsoever. They all insisted I should remember that I work for Lockheed and blah, blah, blah. Lockheed clearly was giving lip service to the concept that I was the person responsible to NASA for the mission as was written in the Lockheed/NASA contract and they considered Lunar Prospector their mission, not mine.

I then pointed out that was the first time I had been in any of the budget meetings and that I had not been informed about a number of other important meetings. I said, "You guys can find Dom for these meetings, but you claim you can't find me? That's BS, Dom is usually a lot harder to find than I am. In fact, if Scott hadn't insisted I be at this meeting, I don't think you would have had me here." Despite my attempts to have those issues properly addressed, it was clear to me I was fighting a losing battle with Lockheed on those issues and decided to let them go for the time being.

We then got around to discussing how we could get the budget down. To Dom's credit, he had already started thinking about things that could reduce the mission costs. The meeting ended, but Dom and I continued to talk about how to get the costs down.

In the baseline design, all the major subsystems, i.e., the transponder (transmitter and receiver), the battery control unit, and the command and data handling unit (C&DH) had a primary unit and a secondary or back-up unit, as is standard spacecraft design practice. While that protects the spacecraft against failure, it doubles the cost of all those subsystems, doubles their masses, adds more cabling to the spacecraft, requires a C&DH with more command capability, and adds complexity to the mission operations. I had been toying with the idea of going "single-string" (having just one of everything) for a long time — long before I had decided to propose Lunar Prospector as a Discovery Mission. That would mean if anything failed, I would lose the mission. It would be risky (but less so than the risk of being canceled in a few weeks if we didn't get the costs down), but the hardware we were going to use was very reliable and had years, in some case even decades, of space flight heritage. Also, we had planned an extensive test program that would shake out any problems. I felt that we could — and should — go single-string. I said, "Look, Dom, what about going single-string?"

He just looked at me and said, "That's a hell of a good idea! You realize it's a risk. If you lose a component, you lose the spacecraft — that's what single-string means. It's like hanging on a cliff with one rope instead of two."

I answered, "Yes, of course, I know all that; but we are going to use flight proven hardware that's very reliable, so I think the risks are minimal." By not having back-up units, we could save $3 to $4 million, at least, so we decided to do it. Then we continued trying to find other cost saving ideas.

I then brought up the business of launching after the September 16, 1997, total lunar eclipse. Normally there are two (sometimes three) umbral lunar eclipses per year. But it just so happened that for a 22-month period between September 16, 1997, and July 28, 1999, there were no umbral (partial or total) lunar eclipses, just (short and mild) penumbral lunar eclipses — Mother Nature was being nice for a change. David Lozier had pointed that out to me once we seriously got looking at trajectory and mission operations issues at the start of our Phase B effort. Not knowing when (if ever) we would launch Lunar Prospector, I had written the proposal for the general case of Lunar Prospector having to endure the twice yearly, total eclipses of up to over five hours duration (over two hours in the umbra [no sunlight] and over three hours in the penumbra [partial sunlight]). That required that Lunar Prospector have a heavy, 15 amp-hr battery on board and a very hardy thermal control subsystem if it were to survive those long, cold eclipses. But if we could launch early in the 22-month period with only penumbral eclipses, Lunar Prospector would have to carry only a 5 amp-hr battery (⅓ as heavy as the 15 amp-hr battery — and less expensive) and the thermal subsystem could also be much less costly and heavy. Thus, if NASA allowed us to postpone the launching from June (the date in the proposal) to October 1997, we could save money, simplify the spacecraft, and reduce the mission risk.

Dom had also thought about compressing the test program by six months, which would save a lot of money. All in all, we concluded we could drop the price of Lunar Prospector by about $10 million, which would bring us right back where we needed to be. We realized that NASA might not accept all of our suggestions (especially about going single-string), but at least we could show we were making the effort to reduce the costs.

I was pleased because for the first time in a long time, Dom and I had a very good working session — if only he had been so cooperative and helpful all the time. Also for the first time, I saw we had a way out of the money crunch. We were making real suggestions and real progress.

Meanwhile, Richard was trying to get the stupid LLV2 mess straightened out. Unfortunately, sometimes Richard just did not understand things and made harebrained suggestions. He wanted to use Lunar Prospector's spin-up engine to spin-up the TLI Stage before it fired, instead of the TLI Stage having its own spin-up motors. First of all, I had never intended to have Lunar Prospector turned on until after or at the Spacecraft/TLI Stage separation, and I would never do anything with Lunar Prospector, especially fire its spin-up engine, until it had been completely checked-out. One just does not rely on a spacecraft to get itself launched, because if something is wrong with it, the mission is dead before it even gets started. Second, Lunar Prospector was to have only one spin-up (and one spin-down) tangential engine, so the spin maneuvers were to be done with unbalanced torques. That would make no difference to the spacecraft because the tangential engines were to be located in the plane perpendicular to the spin axis (Z-axis) containing the center of mass (CM) of the spacecraft. However, if we tried to spin-up with the entire Lunar Prospector/TLI Stage stack, the stack would wobble because the spin-up engine would be so far away from the CM of the entire stack — one just could not do the Lunar Prospector/TLI Stage spin-up that way. Third, I had no intention of using Lunar Prospector's precious fuel to spin-up the entire, heavy stack. I had better uses for that fuel.

No matter what I told Richard, he just wouldn't pay any attention and then he would want to do something else that just wouldn't work. His not listening to what I was telling him was beginning to annoy me. I decided I would have a little chat with Richard in the very near future.

Wednesday, August 2, through Friday, August 4, 1995:
The Tracking Meeting at Wallops

Tuesday night, before my morning flight to Wallops, I was frustrated with Dom and Lockheed management and was very concerned about the fate of Lunar Prospector.

I did not trust any Lockheed manager, period. As a result, I was annoyed and highly agitated and slept very little. I was very tired even before starting the long trip to Wallops.

Wednesday morning Tim Bridges and I flew from San Jose, CA, had a stopover at St. Louis, MO, where we had to sit on the runway for an hour because of weather, then we flew to Baltimore, MD, and finally took a little puddle jumper (which we barely caught, because our St. Louis/Baltimore flight was so late) to fly down to Salisbury, VA. Having been there before, Tim knew the drive from Salisbury to Wallops, so that made the final leg of the long trip easy.

Tim and I had a long discussion about Dom that lasted most of the trip. Tim said wholeheartedly that Dom had to go. Tim agreed that Dom was out of control. He was destroying the program. He would never listen. His ego always gets in the way. It was hopeless and if we didn't get rid of him, Lunar Prospector would fail. Tim said once he had had a friendly talk with Dom about how he acts and does things. Dom told Tim that even his kids told him the same thing, but Dom always just answers, "That's just the way I am." Then Tim told me once he questioned something Dom had said at a meeting and Dom immediately called him out of the meeting and angrily told him, "Don't you ever do that again." Tim agreed that Dom is nuts. I appreciated hearing that from Tim, whom I like and respect very much. Once again, someone else had independently confirmed everything I thought was going on with Dom, so my resolve to throw him out was strengthened even more.

When I got to my hotel, there was a message to call Frank Martin. I did, but he wasn't around. I reached him the next morning. Frank said Scott had told Gus about the serious budget situation and about the equally serious problems with Dom. Frank said we needed to talk as soon as I got back Monday. He was concerned that I hadn't gone to him and Gus; rather I had gone straight to Scott. Well, the bomb had been dropped and it looked like things were finally going to happen.

We had one hell of a good meeting. The tracking and DSN guys were great. Frank Donivan (GSFC), Gary Noreen (JPL), Mike Stewart (JPL), who was going to be the Tracking Manager for Lunar Prospector, and the rest of the guys at the meeting were extremely cooperative and wanted to do everything possible to help Lunar Prospector succeed. We had the kind of meeting that happens when I could tell the engineers about Lunar Prospector so they could fully understood the mission. I told them what we could and could not tolerate, we discussed all the details and I answered all their questions. Unlike just having a tracking requirements document sent from the scientists to the engineers and the latter having to work with the requirements as they are written — as is standard practice in the NASA/aerospace world — the engineers found out from me what variations were acceptable and what their significance was. I told them we had to have the cheapest solution possible that gave us at least 90% coverage for the mapping mission, with 100% for the first ten days plus extra coverage for both the orbital maintenance burns and the month needed for the gravity mapping. They said the cheapest possible solution might be as low as $500,000, if so, then we would save $1.7 million and that would be extremely important in helping us get the mission costs back down to $63 million.

That was the way to work a program like Lunar Prospector. Unfortunately, as long as Dom was involved, that was nearly impossible and we were faced with disaster. The tracking issues were being resolved because I had been successful in keeping Dom out of the picture.

The tracking team had worked out four main alternative tracking systems and several minor variations thereof. The first two alternatives were basically the same, depending on whether they set up an 8 meter TOTS (Transportable Orbital Tracking Station) antenna at Wallops or used the existing Wallops' 10 meter Redstone antenna. The global network would be Wallops plus 26 or 34 meter antenna coverage from the DSN (Deep Space Network) sites at Madrid, Spain, and Canberra, Australia. That would give us 90% coverage — most of it on the 26 or 34 meter antennas. We would also have nearly full DSN (including the Goldstone, CA, site) coverage during the first ten days of the mission and then enough time on the full DSN during the first month to get the high quality Doppler data we needed for the gravity mapping and the navigation.

The second two alternatives were based on Wallops using its Redstone antenna and having TOTS set up at both Madrid and Canberra. That would give us essentially full time coverage, 98%. As was the case for the first two alternatives, we would get enough 26 or 34 meter antenna coverage at all the DSN sites to do the gravity experiment and to cover the first ten days of the mission.

All those alternatives were totally acceptable to me and they were the alternatives approved by Headquarters at that time. However, there was some possibility that we could have complete 26 and/or 36 meter DSN coverage, but it would be only 85% or so. I didn't like 85% coverage; that would be too low. On the other hand, if we had those big antennas, than we would not have to worry about having the 9 dB gain antenna on the spacecraft. I wanted to use a helix-antenna for the medium gain antenna and since Lockheed already had a 6 dB helix-antenna design, we could use the exiting design without modification and we still had margin all over the place. That would be a great thing for the spacecraft budget since we would not have to spend a lot of money modifying the 6 dB antenna. Also, if we were completely supported by the big DSN stations, then there was a possibility of getting rid of the medium gain antenna altogether and just having the 0 dB Omni antenna on Lunar Prospector. That would save a lot of money and simplify the spacecraft considerably. However, if I went that route, then, if we didn't get complete DSN support for any reason, we would lose data.

Wallops Island meeting was extremely satisfying. I could work with those people and get things done. As far as I was concerned, the tracking was resolved and we were going to save a considerable amount of money.

Monday, August 7, 1995: The Big Day

I talked to Frank first thing in the morning before we went to the spacecraft review meeting. I told Frank of my concerns and Frank told me that Domenick had been complaining to him about what a rat I was, how I was never giving him enough credit, how I was causing trouble with the engineers, and blah, blah, blah. I told Frank that I needed to get rid of Dom because we clearly couldn't work together. I told Frank how Dom had totally disregarded all the information I brought to Lockheed about the spacecraft and mission, my requirements and operations documents (the MRD and MOD) and all the work I had done. I told him we had to get the damned LLV2 out of our hair if we were going to succeed and we had to get the budget down. Finally, I told Frank how Dom kept budgetary and other information from me, etc., etc., etc. We had to stop our discussion because of the review meeting, but I felt that everything had gone very well.

We went to the review meeting and I asked Frank to stay for the entire meeting and he did. Dom did not like Frank being there and nipped at him and tried to nip at me. Dom got up at the beginning of the meeting and said how he was running all the technical issues and any questions were to go only and directly to him. He said the engineers could talk to me only about science and none of that sat well with Frank. At one point, Frank made the comment that we had to keep the spacecraft the way we had defined it in the proposal and Dom just jumped all over Frank for saying that. When we had our first break, Frank said to me emphatically, "We have to finish our talk."

I responded just as emphatically, "Yes, we surely do."

After the meeting ended for the day, I went with Frank to his office. Our talk was short and sweet. Frank said he was going to can Dom (from Lunar Prospector, not from the company, unfortunately) and he was going to discuss it with upper management. He then said to me, "If you were an external PI, I would have fired Dom right on the spot, but it's a little more complex since you are a Lockheed employee."

The day ended perfectly.

Tuesday, August 8, 1995

The rest of the spacecraft review meeting went well, despite Dom's asinine behavior. However, the review was far too little and far too late, it should have happened months earlier.

Wednesday, August 9, 1995

Dom, Sylvia, Scott, and I had a meeting 10:30 AM. The meeting was worthless, Dom just pontificated about how the Technical Design Review in September was hardly more than a PhD exam, it would be no problem, we had nothing to worry about. In reality, I thought Dom was trying to convince himself he could bamboozle Jim Martin and the rest of the review team into believing that he, the great and infallible Domenick Tenerelli, would build the spacecraft without a hitch. It was just the same old Tenerelli, self-glorifying BS. I just about puked during the meeting.

Frank came and got Scott out of the meeting. Frank then gave Scott the word that Dom was to be thrown out as soon as possible. I didn't know who Lockheed would replace him with. That was a problem, but we would take care of that when we got there.

At Frank's suggestion, I wrote a memo to him about my concerns with the LLV2 and the need to go to a Taurus. In Frank's opinion, NASA would just have to tell Lockheed to use the Taurus and that would be the end of it. Frank took the memo to Steve Griffin and, as expected, Steve said, "No way." Steve was such an ass, but he was one Lockheed ass I didn't have to worry too much about.

I talked to Scott in the afternoon. We compared notes and made sure that everything was OK. Together we would get the job done — one-way or another.

Tom Polette had finally gotten the archiving document finished. We had to get a copy of it to Mark Saunders. The archiving document fully described our science data products and Mark wanted to know what he was buying.

I was extremely pleased that Dom was going to be fired. Unfortunately, it wouldn't happen until Friday, but it was better Friday than a week from then — every day counted in trying to save Lunar Prospector.

Thursday, August 10, 1995

I reviewed the archiving document and sent the draft copy over to Sylvia so she could send it off to Mark.

It was very quiet all day because Dom was gone.

Frank told me the three of us were going to sit down together at 7:00 AM Friday. I finally knew when I was going to fire Dom.

After talking to Frank, I finished writing the justification for moving the launch from June 1997 to early October 1997, just after the September 16 lunar eclipse. I took it over to Sylvia and then quickly returned to Lockheed since I was supposed to be in the Lockheed display area to show Congressmen Walker (then head of the Space Committee) and Burns and their entourage the Lunar Prospector model and describe the mission to them.

Gus was in charge of showing the Congressmen around Lockheed and to my surprise he was very complimentary and generous to me. He even told them I was the boss — his boss as a matter of fact — and the way I was running Lunar Prospector. Gus was running behind schedule, so after he explained all that, he said, "Well Alan, even though you are my boss, please hurry up and don't say too much." But Walker and Burns asked a lot of questions and were very interested and impressed with Lunar Prospector.

One of the aides stayed behind and talked to me for about three-quarters of an hour. When he asked if we had any problems, I had to lie like a rug. I said, "No." Obviously I wasn't go to tell a congressional aide all the crap that had gone on, but I also said "No," because I was getting very confident we were going to pull Lunar Prospector off since Dom was on the way out.

I then talked to Frank about who we were going to replace Dom with. He asked me if I had a preference, but since I hardly knew anyone at that managerial level except Dom, Gus, and Frank, I was at a loss (Mark Smith was, unfortunately, too junior). The only other person I even knew superficially was Dale Vaccarello, who was a really nice guy. He had worked on the EOS proposal, so I mentioned him. Frank said Dale was one of the guys he thought we should consider and the other guy was Tom Dougherty, who I didn't know at all. Knowing that Frank had some positive suggestions made me feel much more relaxed.

Later in the day I talked with Sylvia. She said Scott was having problems with the lady in Ames finances who was doing their end of the Lunar Prospector Budgeting and had to fire her. Both of us were having problems with the people who worked for us!

I was looking forward to the next day, Friday; it was going to be an interesting, important, and hard day. Getting rid of Dom was the first step in saving Lunar Prospector. After that, I felt that Headquarters really wanted Lunar Prospector to work, even though they had set a limit of $65 million for the project. They were not going to budge on that number and I felt they shouldn't. If Discovery was going to work, it was going to have to work within its predefined limits, i.e., no cost overruns. I also knew Scott and Sylvia were certainly on my side and Frank seemed to be. Gus certainly was, but that didn't make any difference since he was leaving very shortly. The only major problems I thought I had once we got rid of Dom were the launch vehicle, the costs, and Steve Griffin; but I was certain those things were going to turn around. I was getting much more relaxed about the whole situation; the imminent removal of Dom was the biggest step. I thought we were going to get through that mess, but it was going to be tight.

Chapter 2-13
Exit Dom, Enter Tom

Friday, August 11, 1995: D-DAY

I got up about 4:00 AM and went to work. After working a while, I decided to take my morning walk around Lockheed and then I fooled around until Frank finally came in. I asked Frank how it (firing Dom) was going to happen. I asked, "Do I do it?"

Frank answered, "Oh no, it's my job. Dom works for me, so it's my job to inform him that he's off the project. You have nothing to do with it, in fact you won't even be here when I tell Dom."

Surprised, I said, "Oh, OK."

Frank said, "I want you to meet Tom Dougherty, the man who I would like to suggest to replace Dom."

I said, "Fine."

Frank and I then went to the EOS area and found Dougherty in his office. My first impression of Dougherty, who is 10 to 15 cm taller than me, was that he looked like a chubby or stocky teddy bear. Frank and I sat down and we began to discuss the generalities of Lunar Prospector. My second impression, after we began to talk, was that — unlike Dom — I could talk openly and honestly with Dougherty. After about 15 minutes, Frank said, "I like what I am hearing." Then he asked, "Do I have a nod from you? If so, then I will go ahead and take care of Dom." I didn't understand exactly what he meant. Did he mean if I was satisfied with Dougherty, then Dom was out, if not, then would Dom not be fired right then? What difference did it make? Dom had to go and we could always look for other people if I didn't like Dougherty. The Lockheed way of doing things never made any sense to me in the past, so why should it right then?

Anyway, I felt comfortable with Dougherty and I wanted to get Dom out of the way as soon as possible, since I did not have any time to waste if I was going to be able to save Lunar Prospector, so I said, "I am fine with that." Frank left to fire Dom.

Dougherty and I got down to the details of what my job and responsibilities as PI were, what my experience working with engineers was and what Lunar Prospector and Discovery were all about. I explained the technical and budgetary mess Lunar Prospector was in and that we were slated for cancellation if things didn't improve rapidly. I told Dougherty that Dom had kept the budgetary information from me and had held meetings when I was on travel so I would miss them (it was even worse than that, after Dom was fired, Richard told me Dom had ordered him to take me off of the distribution lists and he and the other engineers were not to tell me anything unless I specifically asked! Dom had been hiding everything possible about the entire program from me. I was furious), and, of course, things like that were not to happen again. Of course, Dougherty agreed.

We discussed the rocket issue and he said he would do something about it. He thought Lockheed was totally wrong in not exploring the Taurus. He said he would find out unofficially what we needed to know about Taurus.

He also agreed, regardless of the errors, if we proposed a $63 million budget, we would have to stick to it.

I then explained in some detail the mission, the spacecraft, each subsystem, and my concept of keeping everything simple, i.e., KISS (Kept It Simple Stupid).

We discussed the personnel we had working on Lunar Prospector, what I thought about them, and where I thought there were problems. Interestingly enough, Dougherty agreed with the concerns I had about some of the engineers. He said he would make any absolutely necessary changes, but he also said, "We can't just change everybody we have a problem with." I agreed with him, we couldn't all of the sudden go in and make major personnel changes at that stage.

Finally, we discussed Dom and why I felt he had to be removed from the program. Dougherty agreed and explained he hated Dom. He said he had known Dom for 20-some years and disliked him very much. He complained about the way Dom treats people and his engineers.

I felt he acknowledged — at least he said — "You are the customer. You are the PI. It's your program; it's your spacecraft. I want to help and I want to make sure it works." I felt comfortable with Dougherty.

Frank came back and asked, "How are you guys doing?" Both Dougherty and I said that we felt comfortable with everything. I thought he was a likable person.

I told Frank I wanted to inform the guys, but again he said, "No, that's my job." Everything I had expected to do was actually Frank's job as a manager. The issue was an internal Lockheed problem and he had to handle it. Thus ended Dougherty's and my first meeting.

Frank said later that Dom had taken his removal from Lunar Prospector very badly and Dom said he was going to talk to me and to Steve Griffin about it. I anticipated him coming to me and saying something. As I told Frank, I was not interested in a confrontation, if Dom wants to talk to me, that was fine, I wished him no ill will, but if he got confrontational I would throw him out. Dom never showed up. Instead, immediately after Frank had fired Dom, he stormed off and called Ames. He wanted to know if NASA had him fired, and Sylvia — Dom couldn't reach Scott — had told him no, they were aware of the problem and had made it known to Lockheed, but no, Headquarters had not asked for his removal. In an attempt to force his way back on Lunar Prospector, Dom made a not so veiled threat to Sylvia by reminding her that her brother worked for Lockheed and implying that he could be fired if things did not turn around for Dom! Sylvia didn't take the veiled threat seriously, but it was telling of just how unscrupulous Dom is.

Frank and I called a meeting of the team at 10:30 AM and everybody came, wondering what the hell was going on. Frank told the group there were a lot of changes going on in the company. He said it was Gus's last day and explained that Al Smith wanted Lockheed to demonstrate it could work with a PI and they were going to do what they had to do to make sure Lunar Prospector was a success. The bottom line was that Lockheed wanted to be in a position to get other Discovery PIs to choose Lockheed as their industry partner. Then Frank said Dom was being reassigned to work on other programs. Frank did the whole thing very politely and added that he was there to help the program and had every confidence we would get the budget down and resolve the difficulties we found ourselves in. Then Frank emphasized again Lockheed was going to do everything to ensure that the program worked.

Frank then asked if I wanted to say anything and I did. I re-emphasized what Frank had said about NASA wanting Lunar Prospector to be a PI driven program and that was the way it had to be. I told them since I had worked with many of them, they already knew I had an open door policy and they could and should talk to me about anything they had questions about. I said I was very concerned about the cost overrun, but I was confident we could get the job done. I also said I was pleased that everybody in the room had done a good job. But, I made it damned clear that Lunar Prospector was my program, that I was the customer, and that it was a mistake for anybody to believe anything different.

I welcomed Dougherty, who had already been introduced by Frank, to the program and I said I was looking forward to us getting the job done. Then Dougherty said a few words about the same things.

Most of the guys were very, very happy to see Dom get thrown off Lunar Prospector — no one liked working for Dom (in fact, as soon as the word spread about Dom's removal from Lunar Prospector, engineers who would not work on the program earlier asked if they could work on it).

Frank opened up the meeting to questions and there were several. Someone asked if we were ever going to get offices in the same place. I said, "We are supposed to move into our own section and now is a good time to do it."

Dougherty said he would take care of it. I began to feel good about Dougherty, each question that was about something a Project Manager should do, he just stood right up and said, "I'll take care of it," or, "I'll find out about it." Dougherty seemed to be stepping up to those responsibilities and he asked everyone who they were and what they did if he didn't already know them.

When asked who he was and what he did, Richard said, "I'm the interface with LLV2 and I am getting sandbagged all the time. I get no answers from them. We are in big trouble." Dougherty said he wanted information on Taurus.

One of the comments the engineers made was that they had been floating without direction and they were worried. I replied, "I am going to narrow the design down to one in a couple of days and early next week we will have a meeting to review the spacecraft design and finalize it — things will now move ahead." All of a sudden, all the flopping around and misdirection were over.

The meeting ended and then Dougherty and I sat down with Tom Chinn so he could show us his proposed configuration for the structure of the spacecraft. One of the options to the design changes forced on us because we had to fit Lunar Prospector into the 2.34 m shroud was using a triangular prism load bearing structure based on the Iridium spacecraft module already developed by Lockheed. Tom Chinn had found that a triangular module made of graphite epoxy already existed. It was a structural test module used in the development of the defunct "Small-Sat" program Lockheed had started in order to have a standard bus for small satellites. Tom Chinn said, "We can't use that module, but the mold is already there, so we can just make another one like that. We might be able to save quite a lot of money by doing the spacecraft in that way."

We went through the concept and I pointed out a couple of errors in what he had drawn and then I said, "That is great, it looks good, let's go with it," and Dougherty agreed, so we had the basic structural design just like that — no more screwing around with endless trade studies.

Later Richard, Francisco, and I went to lunch together so I could talk to them. They were shaken, especially Richard. Francisco understood, but they were both kind of lost. Dom had been their mentor for some time and all of the sudden he was out. I needed to reassure them. Their first comment when we got in the car was, "Boy, we don't ever want you mad at us, you'll fire us." That comment told me that everyone knew what had really happened.

We had a good chat over a nice lunch. I explained as much as I felt I could and told them Lunar Prospector was in deep trouble. Francisco accepted the situation, but Richard, to my surprise, kept saying we can't do this or that about the budget and asked if we had time to fix everything. I answered, "No, there is no time. NASA is setting the rules and that is the end of it right now. We have to consider that we are canceled, all we can do is get ourselves back into the swing of things." I said further that I was mad as hell about how Dom had screwed up a winning program.

Richard said that Dougherty was not a strong leader and I said, "I don't want one."

He replied, "That's right, you are the leader; you don't need one." Then Richard added, "Dougherty is not technically very good."

I replied, "That's fine; I don't want someone who is technically good, I know how to do that. I just want someone who can do the bureaucratic management."

Francisco said, "My assessment is that Dom won't be here (at Lockheed) very much longer."

The biggest hurdle for Lunar Prospector had been eliminated. If we could get the budget down and get through the Technical Design Review in three and a half weeks, we would be OK. We knew we could do it. There were a lot of problems, but Dougherty was certainly stepping up to the batting plate and I felt very good about it. The day was an excellent day, very tiring and stressful, but nevertheless an excellent day.

Chapter 2-14
Trying to Save Lunar Prospector

Monday, August 14, 1995: Getting Back on Track

The first thing I did in the morning was to finish writing the justification for delaying the launch until after the September 1997 lunar eclipse to send to Headquarters and then I got started working on the Technical Design Review materials.

Martha was supposed to have come to talk to Dougherty and me about the budget. Instead, she avoided us all day, snuck off, and sat around in Dom's office for a couple of hours talking with him — so I figured that she was up to no good, and I was concerned.

Dougherty was doing a pretty good job of getting started on Lunar Prospector and getting things organized for the review; I was pleased with the progress he was making after less than one working day on the job. Despite the lack of help from Martha (or perhaps because of it), Dougherty thought he could get the budget down a few million dollars, but we still had to get it reduced by a total of $10 million.

Richard was hemming and hawing about staying on Lunar Prospector since Dom was out of the picture. Richard felt his star was hitched to Dom and if he stayed on Lunar Prospector, Dom would be mad at him and would dump him. Richard said he would make up his mind by Friday and would tell me then whether he would stay.

A bit later, after our meeting on the review preparations, I cornered Richard about his arguments that we could not have the tangential engines in the middle of the solar arrays (in order to have them in the plane perpendicular to the spin axis containing the spacecraft's center of mass) because that would cost an extra $100,000, a "fact" he claimed he got from Woody. When Woody got up in the meeting to talk about the power, I brought up the topic and Woody said, "The answer is no, it (putting the tangential engines in the middle of the solar array) has no effect whatsoever on the cost and Richard did not get the information from me."

When I cornered Richard about it, he said, "Well, it was my intuitive guess and blah, blah, blah." Once again, he had lied to me in order to have me accept one of his baseless and incorrect points of view.

That little incident, coupled with Dom's apparently putting the squeeze on him (I had noticed that Dom had had Francisco and Richard in his office before our meeting) made me conclude I would not encourage Richard to stay on the program. Richard's loyalties were clearly to Dom and he clearly thought Dom was buttering his bread. He also thought Dougherty couldn't do a good job and did not want to be part of a poorly run program. If he wanted to go, it was fine with me.

I decided to take complete charge of the spacecraft; Dougherty didn't mind since he wasn't technically oriented anyway. In order to have Lunar Prospector fit into the 2.34 m shroud, I inverted the spacecraft design, putting the instruments in the bottom and the equipment bay on top. I decided to go with the triangular, graphite-epoxy load-bearing structure from the Small-Sat program. By doing so we could use the existing molds for the parts (and thus save money) and the structure would quite nicely hold the three tanks we needed. I was not pleased about increasing the tanks from two to three, but since we might save money by launching from the Western Test Range at Vandenberg Air Force Base, we had to keep the option open of having more fuel on board Lunar Prospector and thus we would need a third tank. Everything about the final design seemed OK, but I sat down and went through it again and tidied it up a bit.

I was amazed that the engineers had no insight into the overall issues as we went through the redesign process to fit the spacecraft into the 2.34 m shroud. They just did their subsystem analyses without regard as to how their conclusions impacted the rest of the spacecraft — they just didn't see (or care?) how it all had to fit together.

The other thing that bothered me was, despite the fact that Lunar Prospector was in trouble, not one of those guys was willing to put in free overtime. When I said, "Well, there are more than 8 hours in a day."

They just said, "No way."

As Dom had said, "Engineers are 9 to 5 people — they are not professionals." I found that disgusting.

Thus ended the 14th. We had three weeks and one day to save the program.

Tuesday, August 15, 1995: The LLV1 Test Launch

Ed Guinness, Larry Lasher, and my Science Team had an archiving meeting all day, during which we got the draft archiving plan finished. Though it still had to be reviewed internally and externally, the draft was finished.

BIG NEWS, Richard called and said the LLV1 blew up on its maiden flight! As a result, I expected I could finally force Lockheed to let me get the information on a Taurus and then buy a Taurus to launch Lunar Prospector. I was relieved.

Good news, Dougherty found $12 million worth of overestimated costs in the Lunar Prospector budget! Even if the overestimates only amounted to $8 to $10 million, we would finally be in good budgetary shape, especially if we could dump the LLV2 and launch on a Taurus, since that would save another $3 million.

What a day. All of a sudden all the crisis issues of the past few months were gone. Dom was gone (though I was becoming increasingly concerned that Dom was sneaking around behind my back and talking to the engineers about Lunar Prospector. Richard said that was not the case, but I no longer trusted Richard to tell me the truth about Dom's activities), Dougherty and I were working well together, the LLV1 blew up, so I expected I could get on a Taurus and it looked like the budget could be easily brought back down to the $63 million NASA expected (demanded). We would see during the next few days how all that would fall out and, of course, we had to get through the Technical Design Review, a task that would be a lot easier once we truly had the budget and the LLV2 woes behind us.

Wednesday, August 16, 1995: Day One of the Final Internal Review

Among many other things, we discussed the budget, which we were going to get back down to $63 million, and the impact that the LLV1 failure had on our using the LLV2. Sylvia made some good suggestions on all topics and also said that Larry Lasher did not want to be the archiving deputy anymore, which was a relief because I wanted to get rid of him anyway. I was really pleased with Dougherty — he was doing a good job. All in all, the meeting went really well, but it was a very, very long day. However, by day's end, I was convinced that the spacecraft design was in reasonable shape and that Lunar Prospector was pretty much back on track. I strongly felt we were going to get through the Technical Design Review and into Phase C/D without any real trouble.

The only things I was still annoyed about were that the LLV2 mess had forced us to redesign the spacecraft (to fit into the 2.34 m shroud) and that Richard had told Dom (much earlier) and everyone else that if we launched out of the western test range, we could save $2 to $3 million — hence the Vandenberg option and the need for three fuel tanks instead of just two.

To be sure of that, I checked with the LLV2 guys and they said, "No, we won't save anything, just a little travel money." The whole damned permutation of the spacecraft design from two tanks to three tanks to allow us to launch from Vandenberg was unnecessary, but it was too late to change back to the two tank design and since I had decided to use the Small-Sat triangular module for the load bearing structure, three tanks were much easier to integrate into the triangular structure than two tanks. I decided to stay with the three-tank configuration.

However, I was really annoyed with Richard for once again shooting off his damned mouth without knowing what he was talking about. Because of Richard, we had wasted tremendous amounts of time and money. He had caused a similar problem with the dynamics guys by telling them they could use the spacecraft engines for active nutation control during the Trans-Lunar Injection (TLI) burn and/or correcting the Spacecraft/TLI Stage stack's attitude during the burn. Lunar Prospector was going to be turned off during the entire launch sequence and hence, it could do nothing during the TLI burn and even if it were turned on, it did not have the capability to do those things. Richard had just made it all up. I bawled him out and told him I would not tolerate him trying to sell baseless guesses as facts or just out-and-out lying any more to get things done the way he thought they should be done. I finished, for the time being, by saying we were going to have a serious talk about those things Friday.

Thursday, August 17, 1995: Day Two of the Final Internal Review

We carefully went through the spacecraft design and got a lot done. Dougherty did a good job.

Tom Polette, who had been working some archiving issues, came to me in a semi-panic. What Tom told me was disgusting and confirmed my suspicions that Dom was trying to continue to dominate the program behind the scenes. Dom had grabbed Tom for an hour and one-half and had proceeded to tell him I was doing everything wrong; I was destroying the spacecraft; I didn't know what I was doing; I was interfering with the engineers and confusing everybody; and that only he — Domenick Tenerelli — could do Lunar Prospector, so I had to be eliminated (Dom was so nutty that Tom was really concerned Dom might try to physically eliminate me — a concern I did not share, though I would have welcomed Dom trying to do so). Dom finished his tirade by telling Tom he was keeping a file on me for future use against me (shades of the KGB) and how he was continuing to run Lunar Prospector, making sure it was done right and we got through the Technical Design Review and that he would continue to run the program.

Tom was very shaken by all that and was fearful Dom would somehow hurt me (physically or professionally). I was both amused and annoyed — amused that Dom was clearly a full-blown nut case who lived in his own fantasy world where Domenick Tenerelli is KING, amused that Dom was so stupid he told my best friend and confidant all his BS (like Tom would not come straight to me and tell me what Dom was up to), and annoyed Dom was still hurting Lunar Prospector.

I decided right then and there to tell Frank ASAP that Domenick was undermining the program, undermining me, and trying to run the program even though he was fired. If Lockheed management had any balls, they would fire Dom, but they didn't, so I didn't think Dom would get fired — ever.

I went to Ames to talk to Bob Jackson and Mike Stewart (via telephone) because JPL no longer thought they could get Lunar Prospector the promised 90% tracking coverage using the Wallops/DSN option we had accepted. It looked like they were going to end up giving us a system we couldn't afford, so I said, "Look, we'll take the tracking system as it is, even if we only get 80% coverage, because we can't afford anything more expensive."

I got ticked-off at Richard again. We were talking to David Lozier about the trajectory presentation. Dave said he didn't want to give the presentation because he didn't know the mission well enough to do a good job. He said I should do it. I said, "Well, OK, I'll do it."

Richard piped up and said, "No, I want to present it."

I said, "No, I'll take care of it."

Richard retorted insistently, "No — I really want to do it."

That was enough, I said pointedly to Richard, "Richard, when I say something is going to happen, it's going to happen and you have to learn who is running this program and it is not you!" With that, the thought crossed my mind that Dom, in his attempt to continue to run Lunar Prospector behind Dougherty's and my back, was telling Richard what to do and trying to keep me out of the picture as much as possible.

Thus ended a very, very long and tiring day. Enough was enough, I was sick to death of Tenerelli and his backstabbing — he belonged in a nut house or a jail.

Friday, August 18, 1995

When Frank came in, I told him what Dom was up to. He sort of sloughed it off, saying Dom was trying to save face and blowing a lot of hot air; but he said if Dom was really doing what he told Tom and if he kept it up, he would be in big trouble. Then Frank said, "Dom has already finished his career, so it would make little difference." Then Frank added, "Dom really believes he is the only one who can do Lunar Prospector, but no matter, it's over for him, he is out, he has nothing to do it. I'll tell Dougherty about that — it's his business to take care of it and if that doesn't work, then I'll step in."

I said, "I'm sorry about that whole situation."

To which Frank replied, "You're not to blame. Dom did it to himself. There is no sympathy for Dom. Don't worry, Dougherty hates him and Tom won't put up with Dom if he is trying to do that." Frank made one more point and that was, "Dom will never ever be given another project manager job, he has screwed up too many. That was the last one."

I then went to talk to Dougherty and Dom was in his office! I didn't know if Dom was just leaving as I came or if he tried to get out fast when he saw me coming. In either case, we met at the door and Dom sort of scurried out like a cockroach. He just said, "Hi," and looked sheepish.

I suspected Dougherty had talked to Frank about Dom before I did, so I asked him and Dougherty replied in an understanding way, "Don't worry about it."

Tim Bridges, Gerry Grismore, and I had a 9:00 AM meeting with the antenna engineers to discuss the helic antenna. They showed us how it would look; it was the neatest damned little thing, a very clever little antenna — simple and elegant. I asked them for a formal confirmation of their bid — and that was that for the antenna!

At 11:00 AM, Dougherty and I went over to Ames to discuss a number of issues. First, Headquarters agreed to have us launch in October, so that issue was finished.

Second, Headquarters was concerned about the amount of data we were getting versus the percent of tracking coverage. I had discussed that with Scott and Sylvia to make sure everyone on our side understood my position that 80% coverage was still acceptable, but Headquarters wanted to make sure we would not lose any significant amounts of data.

Third, Headquarters had again complained about Scott being a Co-Investigator, so he was going to have Bob McMurray be an acting Co-I until we got to the point where he could step back in as a Co-I.

At 1:00 PM, David Lozier, Richard Lynch, the LLV2 engineers, and a girl named Amy who does trajectory analyses, discussed the October launch opportunities and we settled on October 9 for the launch date — my 58th birthday, what a birthday present that would be!

After the launch meeting, Richard and I had a long, very excellent talk. Richard listened and accepted what I said and understood I was not mad at him. He agreed he would have to know what he was talking about and not just make things up as needed to support his (wishful) thinking. He agreed he was in a trap because Dom was having him do things outside of Lunar Prospector, but he admitted he was working with Dom willingly. He said it wasn't Dom making him do all the dumb things (he was capable of doing the dumb things on his own). In the end, Richard understood that I was not going to fool around with him, the program was too tough for that, and I did not have the time to waste. He was to do what I said, when I said it, and not argue. If he really didn't think I was right, then he had to prove it by showing me real data and facts, not just stand around and argue. He accepted all that and did not try to worm out of it, which was his usual mode. I felt good about our conversation and Richard felt OK when we finished.

Interestingly, when we discussed Dom's role in Richard's activities, Richard seemed to agree with every assessment I had about Dom, i.e., that Dom was just incompetent — technically, managerially, and in every other way. Given Richard's loyalty to Dom, I was surprised at his view of Dom. Richard said all the engineers agreed that they hadn't known what they were to do, Dom had provided no direction — in short, he had just been flopping around as I had thought.

As part of our effort to get the budget back down where it belonged, I had asked my Co-Is to see what they could do to reduce their budgets. Alex was able to reduce his by $70,000 (from $270,000 to $200,000). Bill knocked off a $100,000 just in personnel costs alone and suggested we could get LANL to drop their 4.5% burden on the contract. If so, that would save another $60,000. Bill also thought he could squeeze out another $40,000, so he could probably save $160,000 to $200,000. Roughly, we were probably going to be able to save a quarter of a million dollars from Bill and Alex. If the MAG/ER Co-Is came back with similar savings, then we would have reduced the budget by about a half million dollars via the science team alone.

Bad news — I found out that Taurus might not be able to launch Lunar Prospector because it seemed to have less capability than Richard initially thought. Of course, the spacecraft had gotten heaver since we asked Orbital Sciences about Taurus's capabilities. That made me very angry, we had had a good spacecraft with a launch mass of only 233 kg, well within Taurus's launch capability. Then, under Dom's crappy leadership — and while I was away on travel and could not stop them — Dom and the engineers came up with a piece of crap that was heavy and required more fuel and an additional fuel tank, despite my having tried to hammer into those idiots, that the mass, power, and fuel were not to grow. By increasing the mass, they probably put Lunar Prospector out of the launch range of the Taurus, and, by doing so, they were eating up the launch margin on the LLV2! Under Dom's incompetent leadership, rather than refining it, they had just let the spacecraft design go to hell.

Regardless of what Taurus could do and the spacecraft design mess Dom had created, I was getting quite confident we were going to succeed and do it for about $65 million — we would get Lunar Prospector done one way or another. Basically, with Dom out of the picture, things were getting done correctly and people were working. I was enjoying myself. Despite the fact that I was very tired, Lunar Prospector was fun again.

Scott and Bob Jackson called because NASA had decided if we stayed with the Wallops/DSN option for tracking, they could only guarantee 70% coverage, a value that was getting too low for my tastes. The option NASA offered to bring the coverage back up to 85% just blew my mind. NASA would put one of the TOTS in Australia and that would cost $1 million or so. That concerned the hell out of me because I was faced with the option of either spending money I did not have or getting only 70% of the science — a low value that I might be able to justify because, except for the GRS, most of the other instrument mapping objectives could be achieved with 70% coverage or even less, but the GRS was the main experiment and reducing its data output would be a big change to the mission. It seemed everything was going backwards again, and that worried me. Either I accepted the 70% coverage, or added $1 million to the budget that we were working so hard to reduce to $65 million or less so we would not get canceled in a few weeks!

I was really not sure I could live with 70% coverage since that would really begin to compromise the science. I thought I could always pick up extra coverage during the extended mission (if NASA funded an extended mission), but then the extended mission objective would be lost or compromised. I could try to get the AMSAT group and/or various interested universities to build a secondary tracking network, but I couldn't rely on that at that point in time, so I would have to think the problem over during the weekend.

The problem with the tracking made me even angrier, since we might be too heavy for a Taurus. Since a Taurus was reportedly $2 to $3 million less than the LLV2, if I decided I could not live with only 70% tracking coverage, I would have the extra $1 million for the extra TOTS, if I launched on a Taurus. If we were stuck with the damned LLV2, then I wouldn't have the money for the extra TOTS. Sloppy engineering had put the program into a bad position.

Monday, August 21, 1995

I talked with Scott about the tracking problem and then I called Mike Stewart. Over the weekend I had decided I didn't want to spend the $1 million on the extra TOTS and I didn't want to make the spacecraft and mission operation more complex by — and have the added expense of — putting a recorder on Lunar Prospector so we could do periodic data dumps and hence do with less tracking coverage. If necessary, I would take the 70% coverage. The DSN said they would try to get me as much coverage as possible in the hopes of getting back to the 80–85% coverage, but I was still concerned about us ending up with gores (areas with no data) and doing a poor job of mapping the distributions of magnesium, calcium, and aluminum with the GRS if I was really stuck with only 70% tracking coverage.

I tried to get started preparing for the Technical Design Review, but since I had so many interruptions I had made just one whole viewgraph all day, so I decided I would have to work in the evening to get them done.

Richard told me Dom told him that he (Dom) was the technical leader of Lunar Prospector and I was JUST the science leader. Dom was really trying to steal the mission for his own purposes, the SOB.

Dougherty was still doing well. He was having a little bit of trouble accepting the fact that the job of the Project Manager was not what it used to be. That was apparent because he frequently would start to say, "That is what I want to do." And then all of a sudden he would realize what he was saying and would then hurriedly add, "If it's OK with you." He was learning, but it was still a big change from the way they did things earlier.

Tuesday, August 22, 1995

I had an interesting chat with Fred DeFrank since I had complained that Lockheed wouldn't drop its $4 million fee to help us get the budget down so we would not be canceled. Unfortunately, Lockheed would rather have no contract at all than to have less than a certain amount of fee, a fact I found stupid. We discussed the issue a little, a topic which led directly to the issue of the conflicts of interest brought about by my being the PI of Lunar Prospector and a Lockheed employee at the same time — and then Fred brought up Dom! Fred said it was obvious that Dom and I had diverging goals and the program had not been going well. Fred had always been a good supporter of Dom, but to my surprise he was not defending Dom. Fred said he could finally talk to me about the contracts, budgets, etc., but he couldn't before, because Dom had instructed him not to tell me anything about the program, the contracts, etc. There was yet another confirmation that Dom had done everything he could to isolate me from my own program. I was a little angry with everyone because none of them said or did anything to stop Dom from doing what he did. I really wondered if I couldn't do something to get Dom either fired or at least demoted because of his nearly destroying the program. In my mind he had acted illegally by hiding information from me I needed to be able to lead my program and he should have to pay for his crime.

The issue of the conflicts of interest between Lockheed and me was brought up again shortly after Fred and I were finished talking. Frank Martin came to see me. Frank had been talking to Noel Hinners (at Martin Marietta in Denver) and Noel said he and Headquarters had come to the conclusion that it was a mistake for NASA to allow for industry PIs. Clearly, people had recognized the problems associated with my being a Lockheed employee at the same time Lockheed was working for me. Frank asked me how I felt about the problem. He asked, "Do you want to go to another company or to a different part of that company?" I didn't want Frank to know what I was up to, so I told him I was thinking about that issue and would let him know what I would like to do a little later. He said he understood and we discussed the various conflicts a little further. As an example, Frank said point blank, "As PI, you shouldn't have to write three memos to get information on the Taurus."

I added the thought, "If I had been an external PI, I would have come to Lockheed weeks earlier and you would have gotten rid of Dom right then and there, rather than my having to go to Ames for help."

After our discussion ran its course, it looked to me like Frank and Lockheed were running scared. At least Frank had recognized Lockheed was getting a black eye because of its shoddy treatment of me — the Lunar Prospector PI. The question on their minds was, could Lockheed work with a PI or not — and if not, how would that affect future business?

I then got a very interesting piece of information from Scott and Bob McMurray about the GRS. It had always been a sore point with the lunar science community that we were flying a BGO GRS rather than a Germanium GRS, because the latter is much more sensitive and has much higher spectral resolution than the former. However, a Germanium GRS costs about $10 million and has to be cryogenically cooled (which cannot be done on a spin stabilized spacecraft like Lunar Prospector), whereas our BGO GRS costs less than a half million and works just fine at normal temperatures and on a spinner. When I wrote the proposal, I had assumed, based on what was in the literature, that our BGO GRS was perhaps twice as good as the Sodium Iodide GRS flown on Apollo 15 and 16. I made all my calculations on that basis and the results indicated we would get the uranium, thorium, and potassium mapped in about three months, and, at the other end of the list of elements, aluminum, calcium, and magnesium would take up to three years to map well.

At Scott's request, Bob McMurray did Monte Carlo simulations of the three types of GRS detectors and he found that if we could passively cool our BGO detector down to $-40°$ C, then we would be up to five times more sensitive than the Apollo Sodium Iodide GRS! That had several implications.

First, even if I could only get 70% tracking coverage and if I only had the 1 year nominal mission with no extended mission, we would still get all the data on all the elements we had initially proposed to get in 3 years of mapping. That relieved all the pressure about the tracking network and its coverage.

Second, we would get exquisite data from our GRS, data as good as a Germanium GRS could produce because no matter what spectrometer you use, you can't get better than 1% absolute abundances for the major elements because the regolith (lunar soil) is heterogeneous at the scale we are mapping from orbit. All of the sudden, our GRS could do everything one would want from a GRS. While our GRS would not be as fast as a Germanium GRS, that would not make any difference since we would get the job done in the time we had.

Third, since we would be able to map all the major elements, as well as uranium, thorium, and potassium, at less than 10% of the cost of a Germanium GRS, the complaints from the lunar science community should end and that would really help to sell our entire program.

Thursday, August 24, 1995

I got to work at 4:30 AM and got a lot of my charts done. At 10:00 AM we had our usual 9:00 AM meeting. I went through my charts, showing the changes in the spacecraft since the proposal. That went very well and we had a lot of good discussions about the engineering. Then, horrors, Al Tilley said, "Well the spacecraft is now 167 kg dry."

I was floored; then I hit the roof. I asked, "What the hell is going on here?" Then I said, "We have to look at that, that's 40 kg more, 33% more." Most of the mass increase was because of all the stupid stuff that went on when the extra tank was added behind my back while I was on travel. I had had to accept that because it was too late to do a redesign and change it all back to two tanks. If I had an extra two weeks, I could have straightened the mess out, but I did not have the two weeks. Nevertheless, after the Technical Design Review, the mass was going to come down — come hell or high water.

On the very positive side, Dougherty had gotten the budget down to the point where we were in fair shape.

Despite the mass mess, the meeting was a good one. The engineers and, I thought, Dougherty, were finally beginning to understand that I knew the spacecraft and mission from start to finish. Anyway, I noticed a big change in Dougherty during and after the meeting. I hoped I was correct.

The other thing I was supposed to do was to help with the "Earned Value" assessment; that is, did we accomplish what we said we were going to do in Phase B. Dougherty, Bob Goldin, Richard, Francisco, and I sat down with the proposal, the contract, and especially the "Statement of Work" in the contract and got busy. It soon became abundantly clear that Dom had gotten essentially none of the proposed tasks done! Clearly he had just been in his little la-la-land, doing only what he wanted to do, which was mainly trying to push me out of the program and playing his little ego games. With most of the tasks incomplete or not even started, NASA had paid Lockheed $1.7 million for essentially nothing and we had until the end of the month after the review to make up for Dom's incompetence. That really annoyed me. Lunar Prospector was my first spacecraft, so I had had to rely on Dom to correctly do the management within the Lockheed system and he totally botched it.

As we continued to uncover the mess Dom had created, I thought that Bob Goldin began to see that Dom hadn't done a damned thing during the past 5 or 6 months. Later I went and talked to him and he was appalled and mad that Dom had done nothing. Dom had screwed Lunar Prospector up so badly it was incredible.

When we were finished, I got a sandwich for lunch and then Tilley came over to my office. Richard, Tilley, a couple of the other engineers, and I sat down and tried to figure out what the hell was going on with the spacecraft's mass.

That was interrupted at about 1:40 PM when I got a phone call from Dougherty who said that I should get over to Gus's replacement's office since we (Dougherty, Frank, and I) were to give a presentation to him on Lunar Prospector. I immediately went over to his meeting room and met Mike Henshaw, who, like Dougherty, is a physically large man with a booming voice (typical of Lockheed managers). My first impression was that Mike was really a nice guy and he seemed to be technically quite well versed.

First of all, Frank introduced me to Mike and stated that I was the PI and hence I was the boss, it was my program, I was the customer. Then Frank repeated it all again and emphasized that while there was the natural tendency to treat NASA as the customer — I was the customer, not NASA. NASA was my customer, not Lockheed's. Later during the meeting, Mike said something about the NASA customer and Frank butted in, pointed to me and said, "No, that's the customer. Alan is the customer and we have to treat him as such. He is running that program, he is the customer and we have to satisfy him."

After Frank was done with his introduction of me, I went through the mission and spacecraft in detail. Then Dougherty started his spiel and Mike interrupted Dougherty to ask me, "What were the pacing items?"

I answered, "Well the launch vehicle, obviously, and the cost."

Mike said, "Well, you know this sounds like the kind of program you do for the future, not for the profit."

I responded, "Well, that's why I told the Business Council (when I asked Lockheed to be my industry partner for Lunar Prospector and to support my proposal effort) that we could build several of these things to go to the Moon and some to Mars, Venus, and near-Earth asteroids, as well as using the bus for small Earth satellites. That is the way it was meant to be."

Mike replied, "You know, the company shouldn't be squawking about the fee, we should cut the fee down or do it for free." Then Mike talked about the damned rocket. His attitude was the same, "We can't be screwing up this program. Who cares if the LLV launches it, the main thing is to get it done right." That was, of course, music to my ears and I really began to like that Mike Henshaw guy.

Frank, of whom I was getting a better and better opinion since Lunar Prospector had really got started, jumped in and just kept pushing. He said, "The PI has got be able to go to the company without any concern and say — I can't use that rocket." Frank was really pitching in and was very sensitive to all the issues. He said, "Lockheed wants to be able to have PIs like Alan, work with them, have the right relationship with them, and wants them to be happy." I was amazed! Things seemed to be getting better by the minute!

After the Henshaw meeting, Jim Schirle, the thermal engineer, came to my office with a couple of questions about the damned nickel-hydrogen battery that Dom had so loved. Nobody wanted it because it had to have a cooler environment than the spacecraft could easily provide, so Jim wanted to discuss the battery/thermal issue. We cornered Woody and discussed the battery question and I decided then and there that we were going to use a nickel-cadmium battery, period. According to Woody, the NiCd would be somewhat heavier than an equivalent nickel-hydrogen battery, but that was OK by me since, by launching after the September, 1997 lunar eclipse, we would only need a 7 amp-hr battery instead of a 15 amp-hr one. As a result, the total mass would be less than our baseline and the cost would go down. Using the NiCd would relieve the thermal requirements, so the trades were all going in the right direction.

I went back to my office and Al Tilley came over, so we went through the spacecraft's mass. I had finally gotten it through everyone's heads that I couldn't go to NASA and say, "Gee, guys, my spacecraft has gained 40 kg or 33%." They would immediately know we were in money trouble since money is usually proportional to the mass. The bigger the thing is, the more it costs. I also told them, "Look, I can't go into the review meeting and say my spacecraft is now 40 kg heavier, when all my charts show we are going single-string and made a lot of other changes to save mass. If I saved all that mass, how can I explain that Lunar Prospector's mass increased by 40 kilograms?" I finally got it across to the engineers that their usual attitude of, "Oh, it's just a kilogram more," wouldn't work on Lunar Prospector.

Since the mass was going in the wrong direction, we went through a straw-man exercise and got the mass down to 140 kilograms, with the intent of getting it down for real the next day.

Then there was the question of the ballast; I wanted less than 5 kg of it. I just couldn't get Tilley to understand that he couldn't have all the damned ballast he wanted. We just had to be very careful about the placement of subsystems in the spacecraft and put the damned thing together right so as to minimize the need for ballast. The Lockheed engineers were just too used to building their spacecraft rather sloppily and ballasting out their miscalculations. That works when mass and money are no problem, but neither was the case for Lunar Prospector. I needed careful engineering and that was that.

By the time Tilley and I got done, the afternoon was shot. It had been a long day and the mass issue had me ticked off. Nevertheless, things were getting better and better. First, I was pleased about Henshaw's attitude. Second, Dougherty was getting the budget in good shape and if we got together with Taurus, we would save another $3 million. If we could get the stupid company to drop a million or so off the fee, we would end up getting our real budget down to the desired $59 million (plus fee) and that would really look good. Third, I was enjoying working with Dougherty. When I told him he had to do the value earned evaluation because I did not know anything about it, he just laughed and said, "I dumped it on you and now you are dumping it right back on me. That's OK, you go take care of the mass thing, that's your problem." I thought I was getting the situation I wanted — Dougherty took care of the administration, budgetary, and schedule stuff and I built the spacecraft. I noticed Dougherty was consciously trying to change his old mindset — when we talked about the launch vehicle, he would start to say that he or Lockheed would decide about the choice of launch vehicles, but then he would correct himself and say, "We have to decide, that is Alan and I have to make that decision," or, "That's Alan's decision." We were making good progress on all fronts.

Friday, August 25, 1995

I got to work at about 4:30 AM and started working on the details of the mass problem. I found my little spreadsheet on the mass and balancing of the booms. I determined that by shortening the booms from 3.5 to 2.5 m, I was able to save about 1.8 kg. Then Francisco came in and we started looking up the information on the propellant tanks I had used earlier in the two-tank configuration when the spacecraft was smaller. I found that using three of those tanks, instead of the ones Ron King, the propulsion engineer, had selected, would save us 4 kg. It looked like that tank would work so we called Ron to get his opinion. Ron was about to go to a meeting and said that he would stop over and check it out at lunchtime.

I went over to Ames to talk to Scott and to sign something saying it was OK by me that, because Scott could not simultaneously be a Co-I and the NASA Mission Manager until later in the mission, Bob McMurray would be the acting Co-I for Scott until the appropriate time.

We talked about Dom and how things were going since we got rid of him. I told him about Frank's helpfulness and what he said the day before to Henshaw, what Henshaw had said about cutting the Lockheed fees and helping to get the rocket issue resolved, and that I was really pleased with the way that things had picked up after Dom was fired from Lunar Prospector. I said we were finding out that Dom really didn't do anything at all — he had just wasted our time and money. Scott said (towards the end of Dom) he and Sylvia had been getting very concerned about Dom's flippant attitude and his not getting any documentation to NASA. Scott also said he had (then) not understood why I didn't seem to know a lot of things. As he said, "I would call you up to ask you questions or to tell you something and you didn't know anything about what I was talking about. Now we know that Dom was hiding everything from you — just not giving you the needed information."

As we talked about Dom's screwing up the program, I thought about what I had told Scott when we first discussed the difficulties I was having with Dom back on July 5. When Scott had asked me if I stepped out of the way, would Dom be able to do the job, I had answered yes. I knew then my answer was totally wrong. Even with me around most of time, Dom had made a mess of the spacecraft and when I was away on travel for two weeks — though I thought Dom couldn't destroy the program in that short a time — he damned near did. As we talked, it became clear that, even before July 5, Scott (and NASA in general) had also had serious doubts about Dom. However, since I was the PI and I had chosen Dom as my Project Manager, Scott could not have easily told me to get rid of Dom. He was relieved when I broached the topic and I was pleased to find out we had all been on the same wavelength all the time — NASA was just as concerned about Dom as I was way back before July.

When I got back to my office, Al Tilley was there to discuss the mass issue. Those guys just killed me. I had told everyone much earlier that the way I wanted to balance the spacecraft in the Z direction (the spin axis), while A) minimizing the need for ballast, B) keeping the CG (Center of Gravity) fixed, and C) keeping the plane of the tangential engines going through CG, was to move the position of the booms up and down along the Z axis. When Al Tilley came up with his 163 or 164 kg dry mass, he hadn't done that. He left the booms and the tanks fixed where they were and just added 10 kg of damned, unnecessary ballast to balance the spacecraft (I was appalled that the engineers couldn't remember overnight what the hell I had told them to do), so I reminded Al of that. I also reminded him I wanted only one IR detector and one nutation damper (not two for redundancy — he forgot that we were going single-string), that I had reduced the mass of the science booms by shortening them by 50 cm and I had the guys arrange the equipment on the equipment shelf more symmetrically so it would be essentially in balance, thereby minimizing the need for spin ballast in the X and Y directions (the engineers were just used to, design wise, throwing the equipment on the spacecraft and then throw lead weights on it to balance the whole mess rather than taking the time to move the things around to get it fairly well balanced to begin with). Al went back to his office to recalculate the mass.

I got together with Tom Chinn to see what we could do about reducing the mass of the spacecraft structure and came up with only a 2 kg savings. Not much, so I began to think we weren't going to get the mass down to where I wanted it.

Richard came in and said, "It ain't going to work with the tanks!"

I had already talked to Ron King and Ron had said, "Yes, those tanks would work fine from the standpoint of draining and stuff like that, because they are the tanks I've used before."

I thought everything I had wanted to do with them would work, so I was surprised and disappointed when Richard continued with, "That isn't going to work because the damned tanks are supposed to be supported by the ends, not the middle, so they won't fit into the spacecraft structure."

That being the case, they wouldn't have fit into any of the other spacecraft designs, but nobody seemed to have known that. It appeared we were stuck with the heavier tanks and I said, "Crap, we're not going to get the spacecraft (mass) down enough." I was annoyed.

We began talking about how to mount the booms on the triangular load-bearing structure. Someone said something about the tanks and all of a sudden the tank solution dawned on me. I said, "We have a triangular structure, we'll just stick the boss of each tank right on the longeron at the apexes of the triangle!" I got up and drew it on the blackboard. That was the solution. It not only allowed us to use the smaller tanks I wanted and to save the 4 kg from the tanks, it took away a whole mess of mounting structures, so we saved nearly another 8 kg of the structure! Happy as I was about the solution, I was still ticked off that the engineers couldn't seem to come up with the solutions to the issues themselves.

Under my direct control and within the span of about an hour, we had the spacecraft's dry mass down by 25 kg, down to 137 kg (a value Al Tilley would check and refine in the next day or two)! When I was not in control of the spacecraft's design, its mass went up from about 140 to over 160 kg!

As a secondary result of that little exercise in tank placement and mass control, Richard finally began to understand that I knew my spacecraft and how to engineer it better than the engineers did. Nevertheless, Dougherty had still not caught on to that fact. I went and got Dougherty and we told him about the mass saving and the tank placement solution. He responded with, "Well, we will have to make sure it's right." Which was, of course, true in the abstract, but I knew I was right. Dougherty continued with, "You're really doing that (making the design changes) fly by wire and we have to have some control on that once we get through the TDR (Technical Design Review). We have to have a Change Control Board (CCB) to make sure everything is OK."

To which Richard replied, "Alan is the CCB."

A serious personnel problem was developing with Vu Ho, the structures engineer who was responsible for the booms. First, Vu (who is Vietnamese and, in my book, totally incompetent) and Tom Chinn (who is Chinese, absolutely competent and the overall spacecraft structures engineer) did not get along (some of us suspected that part of the problem was the age-old dislike the Vietnamese and Chinese have for each other) and were always at odds with each other on all structural issues. Second, Vu didn't understand what he was doing and was always coming up with stupid ideas. Given the absolute criticality of the boom design and their deployment after launch (no deployment would mean no mission), I had been getting worried about Vu's performance. That was heightened when Vu suggested, prior to deployment, the 1 m long MAG boom extension should not have a lock down mechanism — it should just hang there, free as a bird, during launch! What was he thinking! Lunar Prospector was going to undergo up to 12 g's of longitudinal acceleration and several g's of vibration during launch and Vu was telling me that the MAG boom extension would take that unconstrained! Even a kindergartener would know the boom wasn't going to take that. My opinion was that Vu was an idiot — young, stupid, and inexperienced. I decided that somehow, Vu would have to go as soon as we were through the TDR.

Somewhat later, I was reviewing the viewgraph illustrations being prepared for the TDR (as people finished their presentations, they taped copies of their viewgraphs on a very long wall in a hallway for everyone to look at). As Ron King and I were looking at the viewgraphs, Dougherty came by. He was still worried about the mass, the tanks, and the spacecraft in general. I went through everything I was doing, in part because I wanted his concurrence and because he was the damned Lockheed Project Manager. Hypothetically, he was the Project Engineer, but in reality I was the Project Engineer. I told him everything was fine, the tanks were properly mounted to the spacecraft's load bearing structure, and we would save 25 kg, etc., but he was still worried I was just doing all that on the fly. I felt like saying, "Damn it, Dom and your engineers screwed the spacecraft design up on the fly and now I am unscrewing it on the fly."

I said, "Ron, come here and shake-your-head-in-agreement-with-me at Tom."

Ron did and said, "The tanks and everything are fine." Then Ron put his arm on my shoulder and said (as he had before), "When I came back (on the project), the propulsion system was already designed, I didn't have to do anything. Alan did it all. He's your new propulsion guy." Dougherty seemed cautiously satisfied, but I suspected he was still suspicious of a scientist doing engineering.

It was late afternoon by that time and I had been trying since 9:00 in the morning, with little success, to get to work on my viewgraphs. During the entire day I had succeeded in typing just one lousy paragraph, the paragraph telling what Congress had written about Lunar Prospector in the Congressional Record. It was useless to try to get any of my work done during normal working hours. I decided I would just have to do my viewgraphs over the weekend.

On that note, I ended my long day's work and was satisfied that we were getting there. The guys were doing what I wanted them to do and that was the main thing.

Saturday, August 26, 1995

I went in to Lockheed to work on my presentation and to talk with Mark Smith, who had almost certainly decided to work on Lunar Prospector. As such, he was going to help with the TDR presentation. Interestingly, and as I expected, the minute Dom was out of the picture, Mark was in.

I got a fair amount of work done on the viewgraphs, though Richard, Dougherty, Bob Goldin, and essentially everyone else was in preparing for the TDR.

Dougherty was still concerned about the configuration of the tanks and had asked Tom Chinn to come in to discuss the issue. When Tom was done, Dougherty was satisfied that everything was OK the way I had changed it. As a result, I thought, but was not certain, that Dougherty was beginning to accept that I knew what I was doing. Only time would tell.

I had a nice long talk with Mark, who had some concerns about the way I ran things and how I was involved with all the details. I told Mark the most important fact was that I was the PI and the customer, even though Lockheed hadn't quite understood or accepted those facts. I said that I was getting along well with Dougherty, though, once in a while, he still lapsed back into the old way where the Project Manager ran the show, even though he was trying very hard to accept the fact that I ran the show. I said, "You seem to understand that, so I need your help to keep Lockheed and Dougherty from slipping back. You and everyone else have to understand that I know my spacecraft and my mission. I know what the requirements are and I know what the sensitivities are and you can't get that from a piece of paper." I had decided that the best way to make sure that Mark knew the rules was to have him help me enforce them. I thought and hoped that would work. Anyway, I really liked Mark and I thought he would be a great asset to the program.

Sunday, August 27, 1995

Sunday I worked at home on my viewgraphs and the Mission Profile with my little laptop computer, though Rebecca and I had to drive into Sunnyvale, because I had left something at work.

Monday, August 28, 1995

I finally finished all my viewgraphs, so I was ready for the TDR.

Bill's viewgraphs on the spectrometers arrived; they looked great and were put up on the wall. Except for the MAG/ER materials, we had essentially everything ready for the TDR. I started reviewing the materials, a big job since one whole wall was filled with over 600 viewgraphs.

We had several meetings during the day, at which I kept having a recurring problem with Bob Goldin. Bob had much earlier officially retired from Lockheed, but still worked essentially full time, was an excellent engineer, had a wealth of experience, and, as it turned out, was invaluable to the project. However, Bob was firmly rooted in the old way of doing everything; Bob just couldn't let go of the old concept of having reams and reams of documentation and excessive contingency and margin in the spacecraft design — all of which are a load of crap as far as I was concerned. I decided I would have to sit down with Bob in a day or two and have a long talk with him. I had to try to get him to accept that Lunar Prospector and Discovery were meant to find a better way of doing missions. For example, he (as well as Dougherty and the engineers) had to understand they could no longer calculate contingency and margin by adding the components, subsystem by subsystem, linearly, instead of taking the square root of the sums of their squares, as is the statistically correct way of doing it. The former resulted in the spacecraft getting bigger and bigger and ended up with something that is far more capable than is required. That worked when NASA had lots money and the aerospace community had nearly infinite resources, but those days were long gone. We were in an era when, due to the lack of money, one had to design the spacecrafts to work with a minimum of contingency and margin — and that was in part what Lunar Prospector and Discovery were all about.

At one of the meetings, I had to go through the ΔV budget again because Bob and the other engineers insisted we had to have contingency in the spacecraft's mass estimate. According to their way of thinking, its design mass was not 145 kg (Al's latest design number after our last scrubbing), but 165 kg because they wanted 20 kg of contingency. I said, "No, we are not doing it that way, because then what you do is have contingency on top of contingency." I couldn't get Bob to understand that, but I did succeed in making Dougherty give in.

I sat down with Dougherty and Ron King (Ron was beginning to understand what I was doing, while both Francisco and Richard had completely caught on) and explained it to them. Based on the spacecraft design, a dry mass of 145 kg and the 1400 m/sec of ΔV needed to support the one-year nominal mission and the planned two-year extended mission, I had calculated that I needed 138 kg of hydrazine fuel (and had selected the tanks based on that fuel load). If, as the design matured, the spacecraft got heavier, then, instead of redesigning (requiring more time and money), increasing the tank size (and mass), and adding more fuel (making it even heavier), I would just shorten the extended mission phase from two years to one year or whatever was required. If the spacecraft did grow to 165 kg dry mass, my calculations showed I would lose nearly one year of the extended mission. That's the way I had planned it, but the engineers just couldn't quite get used to that idea. Dougherty suggested I make a viewgraph showing the decrease in the mission duration as a function of increasing dry mass so the engineers (and, in reality, Dougherty himself) could understand the impact on the mission if we didn't keep the mass from growing. That proved to be a very useful tool in helping to keep the engineers on the straight and narrow path of mass control during the construction of the spacecraft.

Finally, Dougherty understood my way of doing things and, though it was very different from his and the engineers' way, he accepted it and didn't fight me on it. He said, "OK, I understand. You give me the marching orders, but in their (the engineers) minds the spacecraft is 165 not 145 kg, because they say there has to be 15% contingency at that point in the development, so the spacecraft is really 165."

I retorted, "Right now the numbers add up to 145 kg and though that may grow, there's a difference between your assuming it's going to grow and the possibility of it growing. My attitude is, if they know there's a 15% contingency, guess what, it's going to get used up because it's there. Look Tom, I held my science guys (the payload) to 21 kg, 1.8 kilobits/sec and 17 watts for the past six years. Go look for yourself at what they have in their viewgraphs on the wall. If I can stop them from growing by telling them if their instruments get over their allocations, they're off the mission, you can't tell me we can't make the engineers do the same thing. They're not used to doing things that way, but they can and will do it."

After our discussion, we walked the whole wall all morning and made some good changes to the entire presentation. I was pleased with how well the presentation was coming along and felt Dougherty was going a great job. Things were looking good for Lunar Prospector.

Tuesday, August 29, 1995

Three nice things happened during the day.

First of all, David Curtis got the MAG/ER materials in and they were beautiful. Dave was just raring to go.

Second, Bill called up and told me he had taken an old BGO detector, a little crummy crystal that had only 16% resolution at room temperature, cooled it down to minus 40°C while it was hooked up to our breadboard GRS electronics to see if everything was going to work. First of all, the breadboard electronics worked perfectly. Secondly, the resolution went from 16% to about 11% as the temperature decreased — a 30% increase in resolution. That meant if we got an 11% crystal (at room temperature), we would get 8% resolution with it cooled. We knew what we were doing was right. That was tremendous; we had known theoretically we could get 8% by passively cooling. But then, we had done it ourselves, so we knew we could get the 8%. We knew our electronics were going to work, at least for the GRS. But since the electronics for the NS and APS would be simpler than those for the GRS, we saw no problems. Our science was getting better and better and I thought we were going to do really well.

Third, after Bill's good news, Woody said something that was very nice. Woody had been very skeptical about my having Dom thrown out, so I was really pleased when he said to me, "That is really beginning to look good, I am really surprised we are coming along so well. Two weeks ago I really had my doubts."

I said, "Two weeks ago, I wouldn't have given you a nickel's worth of shit in a ten-cent bag for that program. If I hadn't made the change (fired Dom), we would have lost it."

Woody replied, "Yes, if you hadn't changed things around, that program would not have worked; we were going to lose it. I know how much you admire Dom and I certainly admire Dom, but we were going to lose it." Woody, who liked Dom, was also saying that we were losing it.

Thus, without exception, every person I had talked to and who had confided in me said the same thing, "We were losing it."

Though Dougherty and I were working very well together and he was getting somewhat used to my way of doing things, he still did not seem to completely understand that Discovery and Lunar Prospector were about determining if a scientist could lead an engineering group and make a spacecraft work on his terms, not their terms. That was reflected in Dougherty's viewgraphs showing the Change Control Board. Dougherty was clearly used to big programs where no one person understood the whole thing and hence where you couldn't change things like I did. You had to put it in a memo and the CCB had to see what the impacts of the change on the whole spacecraft were and on and on and on, in order to get anything changed. In the viewgraph, Dougherty showed some 6 or 7 people on the CCB! Hell, we were only going to have about 30 people working on the whole program, so I said to Dougherty, "No, the review board is you, Mark, and me. That's it. It doesn't need any more. More people means more confusion and nothing gets done." That was how it would be presented at the TDR.

Wednesday, August 30, 1995

I got most of my planned work done and spent most of the day just checking on various things. I thought we were in good shape for the review and I was looking forward to the long Labor Day break and the TDR, which was finally just a week away.

Thursday, August 31 through September 4, 1995: Long Labor Day Break

Rebecca and I spent a relaxing Labor Day break. First, we had a visit from two of Rebecca's Houston friends. The next day Tom (who had arrived from Houston for the weekend and for the TDR), Rebecca, and I went on a nice drive to Capitola and the following day we went to Roaring Camp to take the Red Wood Forest Train ride. We all had a good time and were relaxed and ready for the TDR.

Tuesday, September 5, 1995

One day to go. We had a meeting in the morning to have a final review of the viewgraphs and the presentations and basically just got everything ready to go. I was satisfied we had recovered from the mess Dom had made and was confident we would get through the TDR and start building Lunar Prospector. In any case, we would know in a couple of days.

Chapter 2-15
The NASA Technical Design Review — The Gate

Wednesday, September 6, 1995: The First Day of the TDR

To sum it up, the TDR went well. It was tough, it was grueling, but I knew we were successfully getting through it.

Things started off with Frank Martin giving a little introduction and then the NASA Review Team Leader, Jim Martin (no relation, but, among many other things, the much respected and capable Project Manager of the 1976 Viking Mars Lander Program on which I was a PI on the Lander Camera Team) told how he wanted to run the review and what he expected. Jim also said, "We are here to help you, not to get in your way. But our job is also to make sure NASA is not getting you into a situation that leads to nowhere." Jim, like me, clearly viewed NASA Headquarters as the enemy!

Scott got up and began to explain how Lunar Prospector was being administered and, to my surprise, Jim Martin jumped all over him, saying, "That's too much NASA control; Lunar Prospector is to be run by the PI and he doesn't need a lot of interference from you." Then Jim asked pointedly, "What's the working relationship? You say you have almost daily contact; are you over there (at Lockheed) sticking your nose in their business every day?"

I felt that was unfair because Scott had done a marvelous job of helping me fight Lockheed, especially concerning the problems with Dom, and I felt we were partners. I said, "No Jim, they're not intrusive at all, we work as partners." Jim still did not like what Scott was doing and made it quite clear that Discovery Missions were supposed to be the PI managed programs and NASA was supposed to keep its nose out of the PI's business (a position I, of course, agreed with 100%). Jim's (and my) view of Discovery was clearly different from NASA's and that was one of the bones of contention all day.

I got up and gave my overview of the mission. That went very well until I got to the Outreach and Education part (as required by NASA). Jim gave me holy hell about the Outreach part of the program. He said, "You are wasting your time and where is the money going to come from?"

I answered, "Well, the Outreach is totally privately funded, I have no money for it, all I am doing is offering them (the institution that wanted to do the Outreach and Education programs) information and they have to find their own resources."

Jim retorted, "Yes, but you're wasting your time doing that, you have better things to do."

I replied, "Well Jim, I'm sorry, but Discovery demands that we do that and I am only doing what is required." Scott jumped in to defend me saying that I was catching hell for something I had no control over.

When I discussed the tracking, Jim jumped all over me about us using the DSN. I explained that Headquarters had put me on the DSN and I had no choice in the matter. Jim was concerned about the cost of the DSN and said, "You're just double bookkeeping, it's going to cost somebody something." Jim just wouldn't believe that according to

Discovery rules, the DSN was free. I couldn't help it; those were the rules. Again, Jim had reamed me out about something that I had no control over.

When I talked about the spacecraft and instrument requirements, the spacecraft magnetic cleanliness issue came up and Jim raised hell about what I had said. He believed (essentially correctly) the magnetic cleanliness effort was always done wrong — most spacecraft are magnetically dirty because the engineers do not properly design the circuitry to avoid current loops and do not properly follow magnetic cleanliness procedures during construction because they are a pain in the butt. One of the worst cases in Jim's experience was Mars Observer, which was a magnetic mess. I explained what Mario had told me, i.e., that despite his having told everybody to follow the procedures in the past, no one ever did; but if I personally saw to it that Lockheed followed all of Mario's procedures, Lunar Prospector would be magnetically clean as a whistle. I told Jim I had promised Bob, Mario, and Lon that I would produce a clean spacecraft for them when I had refused to let them have a standard, second, inboard magnetometer to monitor the spacecraft generated magnetic fields, and I would keep my promise. That seemed to placate Jim, but then he didn't like it because I didn't have the magnetic cleanliness requirements on one particular chart, even though it was on the next one. The review team just hammered away on the magnetic cleanliness issue and, unfortunately, Mario was not there to set the record straight.

Finally, I got through the mission overview and I moved on to the changes we had made in the spacecraft design since the proposal effort. I explained I had made my decisions about the design changes based on whether they reduced the cost (a vital necessity or we would be canceled simply because our budget was too high), made the spacecraft simpler, and reduced the risk. Then Jim wanted to know exactly how we saved money and how we made the spacecraft simpler and how we reduced the risk in each case. Also, Jim didn't like my mission risk viewgraph, so I caught a lot of flak from him about the mission risk.

In attempting to answer his mission risk questions, I said, "Well, to me, making something less complicated and simpler lowers the risk." But the real problem in trying to answer Jim's many questions was that we had been trying to recover from the catastrophe caused by Dom in less than four weeks, so we simply didn't have all the back-up information needed to satisfy him, or anyone.

Questions about the costs came up over and over again and Jim wanted to have the costs discussion on the first day, rather than the next day as scheduled, so they could think about the budget overnight. Obviously cost was the main issue with risk being a close second.

Finally, my presentations were finished. It had been a very tough two hours and I was, to put it mildly, very tired. My grilling had been so tough that Tom Polette thought we were in big trouble. By the time I had finished, it was lunchtime, so we broke it off and went to the cafeteria.

After lunch Dougherty talked about management. He got chewed out a few times, but he handled it well and was very straightforward and very honest about what had happened with Dom and how we had recovered.

As the day wore on, it became clear that Dougherty's honesty, his and my capabilities, our straightforwardness, and Lunar Prospector's simplicity were saving our butts. Lunar Prospector was a simple program and they knew how straightforward and simple the spacecraft was. As I had said a hundred times before and a hundred time afterwards, Lunar Prospector's simplicity was its saving grace.

After they finished chewing Dougherty up a little bit more, it was my turn again. As I got up to give the science goals and science instrument overview, Jim (like all engineers) was sick of science and said, "What are you going to deliver? All I want to know is what you will deliver." I skipped most everything I had prepared and went directly to my viewgraphs showing deliverable and delivery schedule tables from the archiving document and Jim was happy. Then he said, "OK, now I know what you are delivering. Now I have to find out from your instrument guys if you can deliver that. I don't want to hear anymore about that from you."

It had been a very long, hard day. I was very tired and so, before Jim had time to change his mind, I quickly replied, "That's fine with me."

Bill got up first to begin the discussions about the three spectrometers and did a great job. Then one of the engineers from the Southwest Research Institute, where the spectrometer's common electronics unit was to be built, discussed the electronics, working his way down to the last thing I had asked them to do, i.e., put switches in the main unit to shut off any of the three instruments in the case of a failure. For some reason Jim didn't quite get the point and asked, "Do you have a provision to shut the instruments off in case they fail, one at a time?"

Ron Black, who headed the Southwest effort, answered, "Alan had asked us to make that change just a while back," and then proceeded to explain it to Jim's satisfaction.

David Curtis then went over the MAG/ER instrument package, without incident, in part, I was sure, because Jim was familiar with it since it flew on Mars Observer and Mars Global Surveyor. Having successful flight heritage does wonders at a review.

Mark Smith got up to talk about systems engineering and did a very bad job, so bad that the review committee decided that was a good time to have a break, so they could talk to Dougherty and me alone.

When we were alone, the committee pointed out how badly Mark had done, that some of his charts were wrong and he did not even know what his charts said. Jim flatly said to Dougherty, "You should consider replacing somebody who doesn't know their charts and has them wrong and doesn't know it."

Jim asked if Mark, like Dougherty himself, was new on the job. Instead of just saying the truth, which might have gotten Mark off the hook, Dougherty said, "Well, he has been on and off," a typical Lockheed managerial response instead of the truth. Dougherty's answer pleased neither Jim nor me.

By that time it was 4:00 PM, we reconvened the meeting and Dougherty started talking about the budget. It was touch and go because they were obviously trying to find out why we had had such a huge budget increase and why, in just a couple of weeks, Dougherty thought he could cut $8 million out of it.

Tom did a good job; the only real blunder he made was where his viewgraph showed only $100,000 for the propulsion subsystem — peanuts for propulsion as was obvious to everyone, and Dougherty had no idea where that low number came from. Also, he had skipped over the fact that we had gone from a four-tank configuration in the proposal, to two tanks and finally settled on three. I hadn't explained all that in my review of the spacecraft changes and Dougherty didn't discuss the fact that the current configuration was cheaper. The whole propulsion budget discussion was screwed-up, though the committee didn't seem to notice and I just hoped we wouldn't get caught with our pants down on that one.

In general, they grilled Dougherty until he was well done, but he gave satisfactory answers to all their questions about cash reserves and a number of other budgetary issues. The tough budget issue, which could have easily killed Lunar Prospector, went well.

It was after 5:00 PM and Jim chased everyone out except the review team, Dougherty, and me, and we had the private session.

Jim spoke first and said flat out, "Well, I'm convinced you guys can do it for the cost. Things are tight, there are some unresolved issues and you don't show enough reserve; but the way I see it, you might have up to $4 million reserves."

Astounded, Dougherty and I both asked, "Where?"

Jim answered, "Well you have $4 million of Lockheed fee they should be willing to put up. I can't conceive of Lockheed not helping out and making sure the mission goes well. It is in their best interest for them to forego the fee in that case and get that job done because if they don't, they will never get another Discovery Mission. As I said at the start of the meeting — if Lunar Prospector fails, Discovery fails. It is very important that the mission be done right. If we think Lunar Prospector could fail, then it is better for Discovery if we throw you out now and try to recover on the next mission rather than to have you fail down the line." Just like my getting rid of Dom, it was better to have done it early with time to recover, than later when it was too late.

One of the committee members took the floor and said he was impressed with both the program and what we had done and he was also convinced we could do it within budget. He had some concerns about our going single-string and then he went through his list of concerns. His comments would have seemed harsh had he not said in the beginning, "You guys are going to do it."

Then the budgetary guy on the committee, Paul Marshall, complimented the hell out of Lunar Prospector. He commented on the simplicity of the program, on my knowledge of the mission, and on how it really was a very, very good mission. I though, *well, when is he going to get to the criticisms?* He just went on and on and repeated, "I am convinced you can do it for the money, it's so simple and straight forward and elegant and blah, blah, blah," i.e., all the things I had been saying about Lunar Prospector from the beginning — but nice to hear from the committee. Then he said, "The thing that bothers me is that you (Dougherty) have been on that thing three and one-half weeks. I would like to know why it was necessary to change, why it was so bad you had to change? I would like to understand what was happening before that and why did the other project manager get replaced?"

Jim interrupted and said curtly, "He left."

The guy ask, "What do you mean, he left? Why did he leave?"

Jim said pointedly, "All you have to know is that he left and Tom Dougherty replaced him, period."

As Jim finished, I thought, *it shouldn't take a genius to figure out that we came in with a $73 million budget that was $8 to $9 million over proposal estimate and that somebody was at fault, and it wasn't me.* That's all they had to know to figure it out. They would also figure it out if they knew the damage Dom did to the spacecraft and mission that we are hiding from them.

Then Jim asked the other committee members for their comments, which were mainly about the budget, the reserves, and the risks. Each and every one of the members was very complimentary and had very nice things to say about the mission, Dougherty, and me. However, one of them said, "I want to make some very caustic remarks here, because everybody else had been so nice."

I thought, *oh no, here it comes.* Then he asked, "Why is Lockheed charging 200% overhead on the program? Why are they charging $4.4 million fee? It is absurd on a program like Discovery, that the company is doing that. They ought to get down and do the thing right."

I felt like clapping and yelling, "Yeah — go tell those bastards!"

The engineering side of the committee's remarks ended with those of Al Schallenmuller (a good friend of Jim's and a friend of mine from our Viking days and a great mission operations engineer). Al's comments were followed by those of the three science members of the committee, Joe Boyce, Al Metzger, and Roger Phillips, who had little to say about the science or instruments, they just commented on the costs.

Then it was back to Jim. He started his summary with the nicest compliments. He said, "The project has a superb Principal Investigator. Alan is an absolute advocate of science and knows his science business. He knows the engineering of the spacecraft and the mission planning better than anyone I have ever seen." I was absolutely floored and extremely flattered to hear Jim say that.

Jim then said, "Tom has demonstrated tremendous confidence for someone who has been on the program for only three weeks and clearly has done a marvelous job and has things well in hand."

Jim continued with, "Lockheed has two strong leaders of the program and I am convinced you will bring it to a successful end and you can do it within budget. There is enough reserve if Lockheed wakes up and realizes that this is an important mission, that it's necessary for Discovery and it's necessary for NASA."

Jim's last comment reminded me of what he had said at the beginning of the meeting in response to a statement Scott had made about the state of NASA. Jim said, "NASA — hell, it's collapsing totally. We're just watching it fall apart. The only hope that NASA has is Discovery. This is its only saving grace."

Jim continued, "You can do it. I have concerns, but you can do it. We will make our recommendation to Headquarters and it is going to be positive." I was stunned. Why did he say that after just the first day of the review? He should have waited for the whole damned review to be finished! Whatever — I was extremely pleased, Lunar Prospector was going forward — forward to the Moon.

Jim said, "With the exception of Mark Smith, everyone who presented did an excellent job and knew their business, knew what to do, and did a great job. You have the nucleus of a team that can absolutely do that mission. You demonstrated everything you had to convince us."

Then someone raised the critical question, "Can Lockheed, which is a big company, act like a small company and let you do your business and not get involved?" Dougherty and I wanted to answer yes, but Jim's rule for the private session was, "Keep your mouths shut and listen to what we say."

The session ended with Jim and the entire committee being extremely supportive. I kept wondering when those guys were going to give their caustic comments and when they were going to stop complimenting Lunar Prospector. Several of them kept commenting on how very simple the mission was and just marveled that we had no computer. One guy said, "You've gotten around the biggest problems on small satellites, no computer, no software, and then the house wiring! Small satellites always get into trouble with their computer, their flight software, and the wiring, and you have gotten around all these problems." Music to my ears — everything I had planned for all those years for Lunar Prospector and had said over and over again — its simplicity, its simple mission operations, it just goes to the Moon, spins, and takes data. That's all; it's just back to basics.

It was a very exhausting but exhilarating day. I was tired, but I knew that unless something dramatic happened the next day when we got into the subsystems, we had made it. Unless the subsystem engineers screwed up big-time, we were home free. We would get the money and start building Lunar Prospector. There were some concerns: Gerry Grismore always worried us and there were some sticky issues, like the launch vehicle, which we couldn't do much about.

None of that worried me much though, given Jim's summary remarks and his readiness to recommend to NASA that we proceed without hearing the subsystem presentations. Also, the committee members seemed to have softened their resistance to our going single-string. They knew the mission was tight, but they also knew it was a good mission and that I knew my business, my mission, my spacecraft, and my science, and that I had the very best science guys. I was convinced nothing would change and we would end up with a positive recommendation at the end of the review.

Despite all the good vibes, dark clouds were gathering on the horizon. Congress had failed to pass a budget and the Federal Government was getting ready to shut down on October 1 — the day we were to start phase C/D — and that would throw a monkey wrench into our works. If we had to wait around for two or three months without money, because Congress couldn't get its act together, we might not be able to keep our team together and that would have a very, very negative impact on the program. If it was not one thing, it was another.

Thursday, September 7, 1995:
The Last Day of the Review — SUCCESS AT LAST

Since we already knew we had gotten through the gate, the second day was actually kind of boring — everyone had lost his or her concentration. We discussed the subsystems and all the other issues all day.

Richard did a bad job. He was severely chastised for having said he couldn't find a vendor for the timer we needed on the TLI Stage to do the sequencing of the TLI burn, Lunar Prospector's turn-on, and its separation from the TLI Stage. When asked, he just said, "I couldn't find one, so I designed one."

Someone asked. "Well, did you really look (for a vendor)?"

Richard answered, "Well, no." He got caught in another lie.

The committee also didn't like Richard's idea of using the spacecraft's battery to run the TLI Stage timer anymore than I did.

They didn't like my having the spacecraft turned off during launch to insure that electrical arcing at the critical altitude (critical atmospheric pressure) or launch vibration induced electrical shorting wouldn't destroy Lunar Prospector's electrical system. I agreed I would rather have Lunar Prospector turned on before and during launch, then I would know it was on and OK; but until I was sure we did not have any potential arcing or vibration problems, I was going to play it safe and launch Lunar Prospector off and take the very small chance it would not turn on when commanded to do so.

The committee was really hot for the LLV2. They believed the way to do the mission was the way I had proposed it, i.e., have the whole program in-house at Lockheed, launch vehicle and all. They were not certain about the Taurus option, in part because they believed Lockheed would step up to the batting box and do the LLV2 right — all I could do was hope they were right.

They also made the suggestion that we again chastise Lockheed for having too high an overhead and for charging a fee on the program. They thought we would have plenty of reserve cash if Lockheed would just be reasonable about the allocation of the funds, i.e., not charging us for overhead, GNA, and all that sort of stuff.

Then there was concern about the real possibility of a Continuing Resolution that would shut the Government down and could totally screw us up.

The committee was mad at Headquarters about the way they were jerking me around about the tracking and the DSN and because Headquarters had made no provisions for getting an assigned frequency for the mission. Normally it takes about two years to get through the bureaucracy to get a frequency assigned to a mission, and we were supposed to be launching in two years. They wanted to know why NASA had not planned ahead if it wanted Discovery Missions to fly on such short time scales?

Finally the TDR was over and Jim and the committee confirmed that their recommendation to Headquarters would be for us to proceed to flight. Lunar Prospector had made it through the gate.

They still had to write their recommendations and send them to Headquarters and Headquarters had to agree, but there was no reason to believe it wouldn't. We would know officially in a couple of weeks, but as far as we were concerned, Phase B was over and we were starting Phase C/D the next day.

We were all tired. It had been a long two days, but a lot had been accomplished and a lot of good suggestions had been made about the spacecraft. The committee was going to let us go single-string, though they were nervous about it and wanted us to have as much internal redundancy in the electronic units as possible — but in terms of true backups, they realized the money was too tight, so they gave up arguing. They were still concerned about the fact that we would never have enough money. As they said, we should have had two or three million bucks to do a decent Phase B and we didn't have it, but that was the environment we all were in. The main thing was we had survived and Lunar Prospector would move on. With continued luck and perseverance, we would be launching in two years and a month.

In the end, they said they were all very impressed with the program and when we went around to shake hands and say goodbye, everyone, except Roger Phillips, said they were really looking forward to Lunar Prospector happening, that it was a good mission and there were a lot of good concepts in it. Lunar Prospector was the right mission — simple, straightforward, uncomplicated and ready to move on to construction, launch and flight.

PART THREE

Building
Lunar Prospector

September 8, 1995
through January 5, 1998

Chapter 3-1
Getting Ready for Phase C/D

Friday, September 8, 1995: The Day After the TDR

Well, we had made it through the TDR Gate and *psychologically*, we were in Phase C/D and ready to move ahead — assuming Congress did not shut down. If the government could not agree on a budget and did shut down, we would not get the money for Phase C/D, and Lunar Prospector would be in big trouble. Despite our psychological feelings, *bureaucratically*, we were still in Phase B until we got the go-ahead from Headquarters we expected by the end of the fiscal year (September 30). However, *in reality*, we still had to finish Phase B, i.e., finish designing the spacecraft, since Dom had wasted the $1.7 million we had had for Phase B and we had to do some clean up reporting on Phase B. Thus, at that point in the program — when we should have begun ordering parts — we still did not have a completely designed spacecraft! Annoying as that was, the fact that we had recovered from Dom's fiasco, saved the program, and were ready to move ahead, negated the annoyance and we were enthusiastically ready to press on towards construction, test, launch, and flight.

Friday, the day after the TDR, was a very busy day. I got in early and met first with Dan Swanson and another Lockheed engineer from West Windsor. We talked about a potential problem due to the nutation of the spacecraft/Trans-Lunar Injection (TLI) Stage stack. The Lunar Prospector/TLI Stage stack would be stable during the TLI burn, because the hot gas blasting from a solid fuel motor actually counters the tendency of a spinning (at 50 to 60 rpm) stack to cone or wobble. Once the burn ends, the self-damping effect stops and the stack begins to cone or nutate with an ever increasing angle of coning — just like a spinning top increases its wobble until it falls over.

The coning could become a problem because solid fuel rocket engines don't stop burning cleanly; little bits of residual solid fuel flare up after the "end of the burn" and these little burns or "burps" go on for a few minutes and add several m/sec of velocity to the stack. If the spacecraft and the TLI Stage were separated right at the end of the burn, there would be no coning problem, but since the typical separation velocity of a spacecraft and a TLI Stage is about 1 m/sec (due to the separation springs), the burping TLI Stage would quickly catch up with the spacecraft and ram it — not a good thing! On the other hand, if separation is delayed by about 5 minutes, until the TLI burping is finished, then the spinning spacecraft/TLI stack may start to cone — also not a good thing.

One solution to the problem the West Windsor engineers wanted to implement was to use the spacecraft's thrusters in an automatic mode to stop the nutation, a solution I was not excited about. I wanted Lunar Prospector to be completely turned off during the entire launch sequence and I also didn't want to use Lunar Prospector's precious fuel for nutation control at the very beginning of the mission.

We discussed other possibilities and I asked about the possibility of having the separation event immediately after the burn ended and using a yo-yo to immediately and completely despin the TLI Stage and cause it to tumble. That way, the chugging of the tumbling TLI Stage wouldn't make any difference, because it would not be moving in the direction of Lunar Prospector. I liked that solution; I was always trying to find the simplest solution to our engineering issues and the one that didn't cost much money. The West Windsor guys said it might work and they would get back to me about it.

Then we went to our 10:00 AM staff meeting and I had intended to tell the engineers the results of the TDR, and to hammer home the point that, as the PI, I was in charge of the project and at the same time I, not NASA, was Lockheed's customer. However, as the team came in, Dougherty was talking to one of the engineers and I waited for him to finish so I could start the meeting. But Dougherty just kept right on talking and then, all of a sudden, said to the group, "Well, we got through it (the TDR)," and then just kept on blabbing. Finally he finished and said to me, "Do you want to say anything else?" As I started saying something, he cut me off and said he wanted to get the meeting going and by then I was ticked off.

Clearly, Dougherty thought the TDR and the staff meetings were his meetings, not mine, despite everything that had been said by Jim Martin and the TDR Committee about the PI being in charge and being responsible for his mission. Despite all that, Dougherty was quickly reverting back to the old way of doing business, where the Project Manager was in charge. Clearly, I was going to have a battle on my hands trying to keep control of Lunar Prospector and I was going to have to keep on Dougherty all the time — a prospect I was not looking forward to.

The meeting got started and Dougherty began going through the action items for the engineers and then he said to me, "Well, I've got action items for you too, Binder." He said that in a pseudo-good natured way, but he was clearly trying to establish his dominance (and Lockheed's) over the project. His attempting to do so was not appropriate, but that was not going to stop him and Lockheed from trying to run the mission — Discovery or no Discovery (I should point out here that though Lockheed and Dougherty contractually worked for me, the engineers worked for Dougherty. NASA and Lockheed did expect Dougherty to run the meetings, but under my supervision — a structure I did not believe in, but that I was stuck with).

As far as I was concerned, Dougherty was not in charge and thus didn't assign action items to me, rather the reverse. I just sat back and waited to see what he was really up to. Interestingly, despite his blustering, he didn't have any "action items for me"; he just had several issues he didn't understand, one of which was related to the downlink data rate. At the TDR, Al Metzger had incorrectly thought the data rate of the science instruments was greater than the spacecraft downlink data rate and hence, we would not get all the data transmitted to Earth — a misconception that Dougherty had not understood during the TDR. He brought it up and I said, "That's not an issue."

He asked, "Are you sure?"

I answered, "Yes, it's a non-issue; the data rate is exactly what we need and what Al Metzger was saying is simply not correct."

He accepted what I said and added, "Well, OK, it's good to have the PI — that is the customer, right here to resolve these issues." It was too bad he didn't really believe what he had just said and it was also too bad he still did not understand that I knew what I was talking about, even though Jim Martin had made it very clear that I knew my spacecraft and my mission better than anyone he had ever seen.

As the meeting progressed, we went around the table to discuss various issues with each engineer. When we came to Woody, he said, "I recognized something during the TDR that we all have to understand and it is that this is not the old way of doing it. All we owe NASA is data and Alan is our customer — NASA is his customer, not ours. This is something new and everybody needs to remember it all the time. Also, the TDR Committee was not a review committee that came here to tell us what to do; it was an advisory panel. They can advise us, but we don't have to do it. What they were saying doesn't make any difference, because we don't have to satisfy them, we just have to satisfy Alan." I couldn't have said it better myself and the fact that Woody said it, rather than me, made it even more powerful.

I turned to Woody and said, "Thank you, and now I am going to reinforce what you said. Everybody has to remember that you are here to please me — not NASA, that I am your customer and what I want done is what's going to get done. I am here to deliver data to NASA and that is the chain of command."

Woody's comments really helped quite a lot. Later, I saw Woody as he was trying to sneak out of the meeting at about 3:00 PM. He said, "Hey, you caught me sneaking out." I again thanked him for what he had said and then he said, "I was afraid you were going to be mad at me for what I said."

I replied, "Hell no, Woody, that is exactly the problem, people forget how this is supposed to be done and you did me a big favor."

Woody said, "It's very hard to remember that this is a different program," and left.

In addition to Dougherty's action items, I had a few of my own. One very important item was Vu Ho's assertion that we needed only one release latch for the booms and that the science instruments did not have to be latched individually during launch. That was nonsense; science instruments have to be firmly locked or latched during launch or they could get damaged. As far as I was concerned, there had to be four latches, one each for the GRS, the APS/NS package, the MAG/ER package, and a common release latch that held all three booms secure until it was used to simultaneously release all three booms. When I brought up the latching issue, Dougherty said, "Right now the baseline (design) is one latch," and all the engineers just shook their heads in disbelief at Dougherty's stupidity. They all knew having one latch was just asking for trouble (I should point out here that Dougherty was just following the old standard engineering practice of keeping the baseline unchanged until the engineering question is resolved and then formally changing the baseline. However, the whole idea behind Discovery and Lunar Prospector was to get rid of the old, outdated, and ineffective practices, especially when the correct answer is staring you in the face. But I was soon to learn that Dougherty is no engineer, that he doesn't understand the simplest engineering concepts, and is incapable of letting go of the old way of doing engineering).

Then Dougherty brought up the launch issue. Unfortunately, the TDR Committee said I had better stay with the LLV2 and not go to a Taurus or some other launch vehicle. They used the same argument I had originally used, i.e., that it was a good idea to use a Lockheed launch vehicle, so all the elements of the program were Lockheed elements, and thus we would all work together as one big happy family to get the job done (what a mistaken idea that was). What the Committee did not know was how badly the LLV people were treating Lunar Prospector. Also, the Committee was concerned that Taurus had only one launch, so was an unproven launch vehicle. Though the LLV2 had never flown, the Committee's attitude was that a big and experienced company like Lockheed would get behind us and not let LLV fail us. However, I hadn't seen Lockheed get behind Lunar Prospector or the LLV in any substantial way, so I was concerned.

Both Dougherty and LLV's Damon said they believed the Committee had made the decision about the launch vehicle and the LLV2 was it. I was of the opinion that the Committee had only made a recommendation. Nevertheless, I thought, *OK, I want decisions to be made and not have everything just left hanging.* I agreed with Dougherty and Damon — with reservations. Then Dougherty said to Damon, "Though we still don't have all the (LLV) information, I've decided you're basically it." That was not Dougherty's decision to make, but rather than address that recurring problem and the launch vehicle issue right then, I decided to sit down with Dougherty the following Monday and discuss both issues with him.

There was another part of the launch vehicle issue that was of great concern and it was, "Who is going to be responsible for the TLI Stage, the LLV people or us?" Dougherty had correctly told Damon I wanted the LLV guys to do the TLI Stage and they still refused to do it.

Dougherty thought he was going to be able to make them build it. But, as I told Dougherty, I was having some second thoughts about that, because when Dom and I had discussed the issue with Al Smith, Al had said, "Don't let them do the injection stage, they don't know what the hell they are doing," a surprising vote of no confidence about the LLV Team from one of Lockheed's upper managers! The TLI Stage became an open issue until we could find out how much it would cost and resolve some other issues.

After the staff meeting was over, I went over to Ames to talk to Scott and Sylvia about Dougherty and some of the science issues. I said we were going to have to keep after Dougherty and Lockheed about how the mission was supposed to be run and then Sylvia pointed out the Committee had given mixed signals to Dougherty. Despite Jim Martin's making the point very clear and very often that I, the PI, was in charge of — and responsible for — Lunar Prospector, the committee members had all too often said to Dougherty, "You have to do this," or, "You have to do that." They too were prisoners of the past and kept falling back into the old mode where the Project Manager was in full charge, thereby reinforcing Dougherty's incorrect position of authority over the mission. I had not noticed that, so I was very impressed Sylvia had picked it up. Clearly, getting everyone to accept the Discovery idea that the PI — not the aerospace company Project Manager — was in charge was not going to happen overnight.

On the positive side, Dougherty is a good-natured guy and I didn't think he was trying to take control of the mission out of malice or selfishness as Dom had done. Rather, it was just the old way that he, Lockheed, and all the aerospace companies were used to! Also, I was impressed with Dougherty; he had done a marvelous job of getting ready for the TDR and during it. In the few short weeks that Dougherty had been on board, he had helped me save the program that Dom had nearly killed. Further, Dougherty was working very hard to get us on the path to Phase C/D. He was working after hours and at night at home and was really doing a good job. Despite his strong tendency to be an old-time Project Manager, he was taking on the responsibilities the job demanded and I was happy about the job he was doing.

Monday, September 11, and Tuesday, September 12, 1995: George French's Visit

Dougherty had taken a short vacation and wouldn't be back to work until Wednesday, so I had to postpone my management discussion with him a couple of days. As a result, Monday and Tuesday were both quiet days and I just tried to get caught up on a number of things I had to do.

Mark Smith, who had done such a bad job during the TDR, called Tuesday and told me that he did not want to be our System Engineer, so that ended that, to both his and my satisfaction.

George French had come to Sunnyvale to see me both about the educational program he was developing as part of Lunar Prospector and the future beyond the mission. I told George I hoped we could do commercial follow-on lunar missions using Lunar Prospector as a springboard and I wanted to change LEI into a for-profit company so we could do that. We talked about how that could be done, and, since he is a businessman, how he could help do it and be part of it. He said, "I think that with the right ideas, if Lunar Prospector is a success, if Congress passes a commercial space act, and if Lunar Prospector creates a lot of interest in renewed lunar exploration, we can find the investors and do it." George thought the possibilities were very exciting.

We then talked about the Aerospace States Association (ASA) and how it might be able to help with both Lunar Prospector and our future commercial lunar exploration plans, since the ASA was really founded to promote commercial space activities.

Finally George showed me the educational/outreach program he was developing for Lunar Prospector he called Moonlink and I thought it was marvelous. He was going to take care of all the educational aspects of Lunar Prospector, so I wouldn't have to worry about a thing — and that was great, I had enough to worry about as it was. One neat aspect of his program was it was for profit. I thought that was good because, if successful, George's venture would help show that one could make money doing lunar exploration. Part of his program was an interactive computer display, or kiosk, that he was going to develop and that he hoped to sell to museums and the like. The other part was an educational package about the Moon and the Lunar Prospector Mission he wanted to sell to schools and universities. George hoped to make a small amount of money, but if that was a problem (i.e., if NASA didn't want him to make money on a NASA supported mission), he said he would just change it into a non-profit venture. I said, "I'm for keeping it for-profit. We'll have to check with NASA to make sure it is legal. But, after all, Lockheed is going to make money on the mission, so why can't you?"

Finally, we finished our very productive meeting and then George wanted to go to dinner. George loves sushi. Though I am not much of a cooked fish eater, let alone a raw fish eater, I promised him that I would try sushi with him. We found a sushi bar and I had my first and — I guarantee — my last sushi, though I must admit, dinner was an interesting experience, to put it mildly. While we ate, we talked about the University of Wisconsin lunar rover proposal and why it lost — it came in 28th out of 28 proposals!

Wednesday, September 13, 1995: Trouble with Vu

Dougherty was back from his vacation and was into work bright and early. I talked to him about the need for clarity about who was running the program, i.e., that he worked for me as *my* Project Manager — not *the* Project Manager, and the fact that I knew and understood my spacecraft and mission, while he did not. I told him I would certainly take his counsel and advice, but that I would make the decisions, not him. He agreed and said, "You're the boss, I'll do whatever you want. If you don't want me to work on spacecraft, I won't."

I said, "No, that's not my point, I just want to make sure I maintain authority over the project. I've had enough of Project Managers like Dom." Thus ended a very good conversation and then we went to our weekly spacecraft subsystems review meeting with the engineers.

The subsystems review meeting lasted a couple of hours. In general, the meeting went well, but I was very concerned about Vu Ho, who was the Responsible Engineer for the all too critical science instrument booms.

One of the problems with Vu started when we decided to use a paraffin actuator to release the booms rather than explosive- or pyro-devices which, of course, produce shockwaves that go through the spacecraft when they are detonated (we had to use three pyro-bolt cutters to release the spacecraft from the TLI Stage after the TLI burn, and that was bad enough). A paraffin actuator is a nifty little device with a piston at one end of a paraffin filled chamber with a little heater wrapped around it. When I was ready to release the booms during the mission or testing, I would send a command to turn on that heater. After several 10's of seconds, the paraffin would melt. When the paraffin melted, its volume would increase dramatically and it would force the piston out of the chamber and the end of the piston would trip the release mechanism that would start the boom deployment sequence. Thus, unlike pyro-release devices, paraffin actuators produce no shockwave that could damage the spacecraft.

Unfortunately, Vu could not understand that two or more paraffin actuators would not trigger simultaneously the way pyro-devices do (the reason is that the heating time for each actuator is, of course, a little different from all others). Since the successful deployment of three booms on a spinning spacecraft requires that all three booms be released absolutely simultaneously, there can be only one paraffin actuator that starts the boom release sequence and not three (i.e., one for each boom) as Vu maintained. No one could make him understand that and that worried me to no end. Vu apparently thought that, since explosive bolts or pyro-bolt cutters can be activated simultaneously by a single electrical triggering event, turning on the heaters of three paraffin actuators with a single command would cause all three actuators to heat up and trigger exactly at the same time — but that is just not the case.

Also, Vu simply could not understand that the heavy instruments (their masses were expected to be up to 6½ kg) had to be latched securely to the spacecraft's structure to prevent them from doing damage to themselves and to the spacecraft as a result of the violently shaking during launch. Thus, though he was responsible for the critical science instrument booms, he had no idea about how to properly design them (do you remember the New Business Council had said I would need the best that Lockheed had to offer if Lunar Prospector was going to be successful in August 1994 [Part One]? And what did they give me to work with? Vu).

Finally, Vu made a big to-do about the separation of the spacecraft from the TLI Stage. The spacecraft and TLI Stage were to be securely held together by three pyro-bolts during launch. Vu was greatly concerned about the possibility of a "hung corner" during the spacecraft/TLI separation event. A hung corner could occur if, for some strange and improbable reason, one of the three pyro-bolts detonated a fraction of a second after the other two. Such an unlikely event would cause the spacecraft to tilt with respect to the TLI Stage and then the bolt in question could jam in its housing and the spacecraft could be left hanging on the TLI Stage by one corner. I asked Vu, "What's the probability of the bolt hanging up if one of the pyros fires later?"

Vu answered, "I don't know, but it's small."

I said, "If it's small, then it's too small to worry about."

Not to be dissuaded, Vu said, "But if you get a hung corner, you'll lose the mission."

I asked Woody, "What's the probability of a pyro firing late?"

He answered, "Basically zero; pyros are the most reliable of all space hardware and they have been fired thousands and thousands of time without failure or firing late."

I said to Vu, "If pyros always fire on-time and if a hung corner would only occur very infrequently, even if a pyro failed to fire on-time, then the chances of us having a hung corner is astronomically small and we don't have to worry about it." Nevertheless, Vu rattled on about the dangers of a hung corner and Dougherty, who I was convinced by that time has no understanding of engineering at all, said he would have some dynamics engineers look into the problem — a complete waste of time and resources as far as I was concerned, but it is the Lockheed way.

Later in the afternoon, I went to talk to Frank, who was really getting behind Lunar Prospector and then Frank, Steve Griffin, and I had a telecon with Mike Henshaw. In part, because of the Continuing Resolution the Federal Government was working under until it could resolve the budget issue, Henshaw wanted Lockheed to give us $12 million of pre-contract money (basically a loan). That way, we could keep going even if the government did shut down for a while — Henshaw wanted Lockheed to give us every bit of support we needed. As always, Steve Griffin was against any idea that would help Lunar Prospector and he didn't want us to do anything except minimize the impact the mission might have on Lockheed, so he was against us getting pre-contract money from Lockheed. While Henshaw thought Lunar Prospector was important to Lockheed, Steve was just a pain in the butt and I was getting sick of him. Despite Griffin, I left the telecon thinking we were going to end up getting the pre-contract money so we could start Phase C/D on time on October 1 and then really get into high gear on Lunar Prospector.

Wednesday was a very good day. My meeting with Dougherty went well and, except for Vu, the subsystem meeting went well. The telecon with Henshaw gave me a good feeling that he was really behind Lunar Prospector and he would get us the support and money we needed to get going in October.

Also, as planned if we got through the TDR, Tom (to keep the three Toms — Tom Dougherty, Tom Polette, and Tom Chinn — who were working on the project straight, I will refer to Tom Dougherty as Dougherty [except in direct quote where I have to write Tom, when Dougherty is being referred to as will be clear from the text], Tom Polette as Tom and Tom Chinn as Tom Chinn from here on out) was making arrangements to come out to Sunnyvale full time, starting October 1, to help me run the project. I was very much looking forward to having my good friend and trusted companion working at my side.

Thursday, September 14, and Friday, September 15, 1995: More Design Discussions

I spent the last two days of the week dealing with a number of issues, some small and some large.

I talked to Dave Curtis at Berkeley about the latching of the 1.2 m long, MAG extension boom that was to be mounted on the top of the MAG/ER electronics unit (the Data Processing Unit or DPU) at the end of the main MAG/ER boom. Both he and Vu had independently come up with the idea that we did not have to latch the MAG and its boom extension to the spacecraft, rather we could just let it be firmly seated in a saddle mounted at the top of the solar array drum. I liked the idea (sometimes, but not often, Vu did come up with a good idea) for two reasons. First, if the MAG was not latched, then there would be one less latch to have to release and second, there would be one less point of failure in the critical boom deployment sequence. Second, I was certain that, because the mass of the MAG and its little boom extension was only about ½ kg, they could be safely constrained during launch due to the springiness of the boom extension, if it was leveraged firmly into the saddle — nice and simple, the way I like things.

I talked to Dougherty about LLV and Taurus. I was really dissatisfied with the LLV team and getting more distrustful of them every day. I told Dougherty I was going to talk to Orbital Sciences about our getting a Taurus launch and, to my surprise, he agreed I had better do so. He, too, was getting worried about the LLV crowd. I was pleased with that and pleased we were getting along so well.

The West Windsor guys got back to me regarding the potential problem of the nutation of the spacecraft/TLI stack after the end of the TLI burn. They agreed that active damping was not required to solve the potential problem if, as I had suggested, we put a yo-yo mechanism on the TLI Stage that would be deployed immediately after its separation from the spacecraft at the end of the TLI burn. They agreed the TLI Stage would quickly start to tumble and that would eliminate the danger of a collision between the TLI Stage and the spacecraft caused by the burping of the TLI Stage. That took care of that problem.

There was the problem of the damping of the boom deployment. If left unconstrained, the Astromast booms, which we had chosen for the 2.5 m long science instrument booms, would spring out in a fraction of a second. The result of such a fast deployment would most certainly be that the centrifugal force acting on the heavy science packages at the ends of the three booms, and the momentum of the packages themselves, would cause the booms to break. Thus, boom deployment had to be retarded so it took several minutes rather than a fraction of a second. We quickly decided to add a viscous damper to the deployment mechanism. The only question remaining was, "What kind of viscous damper?" and Vu started looking into that.

One major problem was that the engineers were still trying to figure out how to make Lunar Prospector 99.9% reliable, like all other NASA spacecraft (that was the reason that Vu kept hollering about his hung corner). I kept telling them that I didn't want or need that kind of reliability. The idea of the project had always been to keep Lunar Prospector simple and cheap and a 99.9% reliable spacecraft is anything but simple and cheap. Not only was I not interested in that kind of reliability, the Discovery Program was asking for only 95% reliability, or as Goldin had said, "If one out of twenty Discovery Missions (5%) doesn't fail, then we are spending too much money on them." I knew it was difficult for Dougherty and the engineers to get used to the Discovery way and my way of doing the mission, but we (the space exploration community) could not do the missions "Faster, Better, Cheaper" if we kept doing them the old way. The guys were catching on, but it was a slow process.

Next was a question about the infrared (IR) limb-crossing detector. Dougherty didn't have a clue as to how it was supposed to work for the Moon, since he was only used to the IR limb-detectors flown on Earth orbiting satellites (and I was certain he did not understand how those detectors worked either). I explained to him that the IR limb-detectors of Earth satellites detect the very bright carbon dioxide (CO_2) emission lines at 15 microns; that the CO_2 lines are emitted from the Earth's upper atmosphere and form a bright, very narrow band just above the Earth's horizon; and that the IR detector locks on to that bright band, thereby providing the spacecraft with a horizon reference.

I explained to him that, because the Moon has no atmosphere and hence no CO_2 emission lines, we would use a broadband IR detector that would detect the times when the detector swept onto — and off of — the lunar disk by measuring the timing of the abrupt increase — and abrupt decrease — of its output signal during each 5 second spin period of the spacecraft. After explaining that to Dougherty, I decided I had better talk to Barnes, the manufacturer of IR limb-detectors, myself to make sure they knew what I needed.

Saturday, September 16, and Sunday, September 17, 1995

Rebecca and I had a great weekend camping at Henry Coe State Park, which is just a 45-minute drive up into the mountains near Gilroy where we had our home. We had some good hikes, I had some good observing with one of my telescopes, and we wore ourselves out.

Chapter 3-2
Phase C/D Draft Letters

Monday, September 18, 1995:
Jim Martin's Draft Letter to Headquarters

Jim Martin sent a draft letter regarding the results of TDR to Headquarters. With that as a "go signal," we started trying to get money from Headquarters to start Phase C/D or, at least, to get Wes Huntress to confirm that we would get the money from NASA. If Wes did that, then we could show Lockheed that, even if the government did shut down, we would eventually get the money and, hopefully, Lockheed would give us pre-contract money so we could get started on Phase C/D. If not, and if the government did shut down and hence, we received no money, we would be in big trouble. Thus, the big questions were, "When would we get money; how much money would we get, and from whom?" We hoped we would know the answers to those critical questions within a week.

Tom Chinn found that the GRS didn't need to have a support structure for its thermal-shield; rather we could mount the thermal shield directly on the graphite epoxy structure of the GRS itself. That meant the GRS's mass would drop by 0.8 kg, which in turn would result in a total mass decrease of the spacecraft by three times that amount or 2.4 kg, since the mass of each of the other two instrument packages would also be reduced by 0.8 kg. The reason is that all three science booms and their instruments had to be balanced if Lunar Prospector was to spin properly. Since the GRS was the heaviest of the three instrument packages, the NS/APS and MAG/ER packages had to be ballasted to make them as heavy as the GRS. A decrease in the GRS's mass automatically resulted in the same decrease in the ballast masses attached to the other two packages. Thus, Tom Chinn's work very nicely helped me keep the spacecraft's mass down — keeping a spacecraft's mass down is a constant battle that all spacecraft developers face, the same constant battle most of us face as we try to keep our own weight down!

We had a communications/tracking meeting at Ames about our getting a radio frequency assigned for Lunar Prospector's transponder and Bob Jackson said he would take care it. That sticky issue was out of my hair. However, I still needed to have a meeting with the Code O guys to discuss the tracking issues, so I called Headquarters to try to get a meeting set up, but I could not get a firm date from them. Thus the tracking of Lunar Prospector was still unresolved.

We got the report Dougherty asked for from Ed Boesiger concerning Vu's "hung corner" to-do and, as I had expected, the whole effort was a total waste of time. All the report said was, "Well, you could have a problem with a hung corner, so maybe you should use a Marmen clamp instead of explosive bolts. But to really get a definitive answer, we need $70,000 to do a complete analysis of the issue." $70,000 worth of analysis and/or a Marmen clamp that costs $100,000 vs. three bolts that cost about $17,000! What a bunch of BS.

The only real question that needed to be answered was, "What is the probability that we would have a hung corner if one of the bolts did not fire properly?" and they clearly didn't know. Typical of engineers, they just thought of what could go wrong and started fussing about it instead of determining whether it was a high or low probability issue. Ed Boesiger and his engineers were just a waste of time and money. We had a five-page report, based on a week's worth of effort, that said absolutely nothing we didn't already know — a total waste of our money! Worse, they asked for a meeting with us on Tuesday to present their results — what results! I crabbed at Dougherty about the report and the meeting on what was from the beginning a dead issue, and he sort of agreed it was all a waste of time and resources — his admission did not make me any happier.

Also, I called Joe Boyce to discuss the comments he had on the draft of the Archiving Document I had sent him. As I thought, all of Joe's negative comments were really from Roger Phillips, while Joe himself, like everyone else, was completely satisfied with what we were planning. I answered all of Roger's questions and Joe was ready for me to finish the Archiving Document and send it around for signature.

Tuesday, September 19, 1995:
Improving the GRS and the End of the Hung Corner Issue

Bill had gotten together with Bicron, the manufacturer of the BGO crystal we were going to use as the detector in the GRS. It turned out their best BGO crystals have a spectral resolution at room temperature of 10.5%, or about 1% better than we thought — great news. If we got a really good crystal, we might get 7% resolution at $-40°$ C and that would be tremendous.

At 11:30 AM Ed Boesiger and his idiots came over for the useless hung corner meeting and I didn't waste anytime listening to their useless analysis. Right off the bat, I asked him the real question, "What is the probability of a hung corner?" and, of course, he didn't know. However, he immediately started rattling on about us being on the safe side by using a ($100,000) Marmen clamp instead of the ($17,000) bolts. I said no to that and explained what Woody had told me about the reliability of explosive bolts and hence that the probability of us having a hung corner was astronomically small, so I was not worried about it.

Ed said, "Gee, do you want to take the chance when all you can save is $30,000?"

I answered, "It's much more than $30,000, the cost difference between the bolts and the clamp is over $80,000 and you want to do a $70,000 study, but yes, even $30,000 is important to us. Also, you have to add to those costs the cost of us designing and building a new load-bearing structure for the spacecraft bus since our bus can't accommodate a Marmen clamp." Then I asked him again about the frequency of hung corners and he said he didn't know, but finally admitted it is an unlikely failure mode and I said, "Fine, then we aren't going to bother with it."

Not willing to concede defeat, Ed complained, "This isn't the way we do programs!"

I replied, "That's the whole point of Discovery. NASA can't afford to solve problems the way it's usually done and that's what we are trying to prove with Lunar Prospector." That finally shut Boesiger up and ended the hung corner BS. That whole waste of time and effort confirmed my opinion of Boesiger, i.e., he is an idiot.

One good thing to come out of that abortive meeting; I learned exactly how explosive bolts really work and it's really quite neat. When they explode, the nut securing the bolt is blown apart and the explosion blows the bolt right out of the casing (like a bullet) and into a bolt catcher. Thus, as far as I could see, there is no way a bolt could get hung up unless the thing doesn't work properly and I was told they work properly all the time. I just didn't see any problem.

After that useless meeting, we received information from Thiokol regarding my suggestion that we use a yo-yo to cause the TLI Stage to tumble so it wouldn't ram into the spacecraft after separation. Thiokol said, "We use a yo (just one yo, not a yo-yo pair, as I had thought) all the time to get injection stages to tumble." Thiokol also said the chugging of an injection stage lasts, at most, two minutes and produces 5 to 10 Newtons of thrust. In Lunar Prospector's case, that would mean the TLI Stage would accelerate up to a velocity of about 10 m/sec, which is quite a bit. Thiokol already knew how to take care of the problem, so another "major issue" disappeared just like that.

I talked to Dougherty about the Taurus and we decided to write an RFP for it to Orbital Sciences whether Lockheed liked it or not. Happily, Henshaw was going to be in Sunnyvale the following week (he still worked out of West Windsor and came to the west coast every week or two for a few days), so we were going to have him OK the RFP, since he was the only one who was really in favor of what we were doing.

I was really concerned about the launch vehicle issue, and, because Lockheed was not really supporting Lunar Prospector the way it needed to be supported if we were going to be successful, I started to think more about quitting Lockheed and running the mission from LEI. I decided to start exploring that option with Dougherty and NASA and to make my decision based on how the critical launch issue was resolved.

Tuesday was a good day. We got rid of the hung corner red herring; we were going to get 7 or 8% resolution out of the GRS and that would be fantastic; and Thiokol put the nail in the coffin of the nutation/TLI ramming issue.

Wednesday, September 20, 1995: Keeping the Mass Down

Al Tilley's calculated mass of spacecraft had gone up again because the masses of the graphite epoxy structural elements had gone up. Tom Chinn and I got together to see if we could reduce the mass of the spacecraft's structures. I suggested that we do away with the top shelf where the battery, transponder, and the other electronic units were to be mounted and just mount them right on the upper lip of the triangular load-bearing structure — all we would have to do to allow that was to widen the lip just a little. I figured that would save a kilogram or so. Then, if we could do away with the side panels and just put in supports to handle the stresses, we might be able to knock another six to eight kilograms off the spacecraft's mass and get it back down where it belonged. Tom said he would check out my suggestions to see if they would work (in the end, we didn't use them). It was a continual battle trying to keep the spacecraft's mass down and I wondered what mass we would end up with when Lunar Prospector was finally built.

We found out that Mark Saunders was going to try to get us $11 million to get started on C/D, but we needed more than that. I don't get NASA at all. You lay out a budget and funding profile in your contract, NASA agrees to it, and then later, when you need the money, NASA says, "Well we won't give it to you." So how in the hell are you supposed to stay on schedule, which is what NASA insists you do?

Dougherty still wanted to stay with the LLV2 and he was going to try to use the Taurus (that cost less than the LLV2) as leverage to force the LLV people to cut their price to $22 million. That was fine, but I still didn't want to be on an LLV2. I did not trust the LLV gang and I did not trust the numbers they were giving us, especially their numbers for the LLV2's lift capability. The whole launch vehicle issue was very ticklish because Lockheed was not going to let me dump the LLV2 and use a Taurus very easily.

Thursday, September 21, 1995

I finished making the changes to the Archiving Document and sent it off for sig-natures first thing in the morning.

Dougherty came in my office to talk to me. Things were getting much better because Dougherty had begun to act the way he should, i.e., he came and cleared things with me before he did them. He wanted to tell me that the Lunar Prospector Team was finally going to get a permanent work area! Dougherty and I were getting adjacent offices and the cubicles of all of our team members would be all around us. Finally, we were getting organized — workspace-wise.

I received the data on the Taurus from Orbital Sciences and they indicated they were very interested in launching Lunar Prospector, and I was going to do everything I could to make it happen. I decided to make a trip to DC to visit Orbital Sciences so we could discuss launching Lunar Prospector on a Taurus, regardless of what Lockheed (remember, I was still an employee of that damned company) said I could and could not do.

Friday, September 22, 1995

Dougherty had been at Gus's going-away party, where he had a conversation with the Lockheed lady who hires people. She told him a lot of people were interested in working on Lunar Prospector and they thought it was a great program.

I found out that Steve Griffin had stopped our RFP's for spacecraft components from being sent to outside vendors. He wanted Lockheed to do everything, regard-less of how much it cost us! I was really ticked off. Griffin didn't care about Lunar Prospector; all he cared about was Lockheed. He had even fixed it so we couldn't get outside bids on our solar arrays. I decided right then and there that, when I saw Hen-shaw the following week, I was going to raise hell and ask him to get Griffin out of our hair. Steve had interfered with Lunar Prospector too many times and enough was enough.

Jim Schirle told me his management was trying to take him off Lunar Prospector, but he told them he wanted to stay on the project and they should find somebody else to do the other work. He also said at least five guys he knew wanted to get on Lunar Prospector after Tenerelli had been removed from the project. Nobody wanted to work for the bastard.

Monday, September 25, 1995: Wes's Draft Letter

Monday was a slow day because we had no money, so I went over to Ames to talk with Scott and Sylvia, since Scott had been at Headquarters the previous week. Scott had the draft of the letter Wes was preparing regarding the recommendations of the TDR committee. Scott couldn't legally show it to me, so he sort of read it to me and it contained a lot of nice things. Interestingly, it didn't say a word about NASA waiting for congressional approval for the money for Phase C/D. It was still questionable whether we were going to have to wait for the money. Even if we didn't get the money on time, we would officially be in Phase C/D when we got Wes's letter, and that ought to be good enough for Lockheed. I was going to find out the next day how our request for pre-con-tract money was proceeding.

When I got back from Ames, I talked to Frank and Dougherty about Steve Griffin. Dougherty said Griffin's interference was probably his fault because he had not moved fast enough on the issues Griffin was messing up for us. I was glad Dougherty admitted that, it gave me the feeling that I could trust him.

We started to talk about the rocket and Dougherty said, "The direction I'm going in is LLV2."

I said, "That's fine, but the direction I'm going in is Taurus. We've had nothing but trouble with them (the LLV2 staff) and they have just fed us BS. I want an RFP or an RFI (Request for Information, because it is quicker than an RFP) from Orbital." Interestingly, Frank agreed with everything I said!

Frank added, "You can get more information on your trip than we could ever get from an RFI or an RFP. As PI, you are the boss and you can go there as a free agent," i.e., Lockheed couldn't stop me. Happily, at least Frank considered that, as PI, I was outside the company and not a regular employee.

Because I move much faster than Dougherty does and we frequently were going in slightly different directions, Dougherty said in a humorous, but negative tone, "I sure like the way you work."

I retorted, "It doesn't sound quite like you do."

Frank said, "It doesn't matter whether he likes what you are doing or not, he does what you want him to do." Frank's statement made me feel good, because I didn't think he would have said that if he thought I was screwing up and I was ecstatic that Frank was really pushing to have the mission done the way Discovery and I wanted it done. If Lunar Prospector worked under my direction, then Discovery could work, and that was critical for NASA.

After that very satisfying meeting, I worked on a propellant usage spreadsheet that would accurately show how much propellant was going to be used during all the burns of the mission, taking into consideration all the inefficiencies of the burns and the expected engine performances.

Tuesday, September 26, 1995: Still No Money

I got in fairly early and continued working on the propellant usage program.

I got a message from Dougherty; Lockheed had said no to our request for pre-contract money, because they hadn't received any word from Headquarters that we were going to proceed into Phase C/D. That prompted Dougherty to really start worrying about either getting a no-money-extension of Phase B from NASA that would contractually allow us to continue to charge money to the contract (money that would be paid when NASA finally sent the money) and keep us working, or to find some other way to get C/D started.

Dougherty wanted an immediate meeting with Scott and Sylvia, so we just got up and went over to Ames at 7:45 AM and found Scott and Sylvia. Scott called Cathcart, Ames's contract guy, to his office and we all sat down and discussed the serious situation. Despite the urgency of our money situation, all Scott, Sylvia, Dougherty, and Cathcart did was to talk around the issue of getting something done quickly (after all, Phase C/D was supposed to start in just five days, on October 1). They talked about doing something later in the day or on the next day. Finally, I had had enough and I asked, "Can't we get Wes's letter now or can't you (Scott) write a letter giving Lockheed the information it needs so they might give us the pre-contract money we need? Or, why don't we call Mark Saunders right now and get something started," so we called Mark and got his OK for Scott to write a letter to Lockheed. Happily, shortly thereafter, Scott wrote the letter and we finally got things moving forward again.

That whole episode drove home to me the fact that Dougherty has a tendency to let things slide, while my mode of operations is based on my mottoes, *"There is no time like the present."* And, *"If I wanted it tomorrow, I'd ask for it tomorrow."* I don't want to wait for something to be done; I want to get it done and get it behind me. I was sure Dougherty was not used to that mode of operation.

Sylvia called later in the morning and said she had Scott's letter. I went to Ames and got it and then Dougherty took it to the appropriate Lockheed official. We were back on track and we hoped to get pre-contract money by the end of the week.

Sylvia had also arranged it so we got the no-money-extension. Even though no money was available right then, we could legally move ahead and Lockheed would be reimbursed for the money it spent keeping us on track.

I had invited the lead OMNI guys, Wayne, Asif Ansari, and Mike Chobotov to come to Lockheed to determine how they might become involved in Lunar Prospector. Only Mike Chobotov and a guy from his new company showed up and I spent the rest of the morning bringing them up to date and talking with them. Then we went to a Mexican restaurant for lunch.

When we got back, I took them to see Dougherty and they explained what they were doing and how they could help us. The OMNI guys are really good engineers and I wished I was doing Lunar Prospector with OMNI, not Lockheed. Mike wanted to do some work on a subcontract through his company in Santa Rosa, CA, and pointed out that they were only an hour of travel time from Sunnyvale, so that would work well. Wayne called from Boston and described his situation and said Asif was on travel and hence, could not make our meeting. Asif still lived in LA and he was available if we wanted to hire him.

Dougherty recognized that the OMNI guys are good just from listening to them. Nevertheless, his position was that Lockheed had all the capabilities we needed, so we didn't need the OMNI guys. However, as we had already found out, we couldn't always get our hands on the Lockheed engineers because they had other jobs. We did have a need for their help and I suggested to Dougherty, after they left, that we hire Asif as our Systems Engineer, since Mark Smith had bombed on us. If Asif were our Systems Engineer, he could very nicely interface with the other OMNI guys. Then I added, "But, Tom, my attitude is, even though I am the PI and you are the Project Manager, I'm not going to tell you who to hire. I might make suggestions, but the engineering team you put together is your engineering team. I think that is the right way to do this." Given the numerous discussions that had occurred about my role as PI vs. Lockheed's and Dougherty's roles working for me, I thought my statement surprised him, but I didn't see how we could efficiently work together any other way.

Tom called to get the information Lockheed Houston needed to finish his paperwork so he could get out to Sunnyvale fulltime by October 1. I quickly got the information and I was told that, with any luck, the paperwork would be ready by the next day.

All in all, it was a good day.

Wednesday, September 27, 1995

I planned my trip to Washington for the following week to see about our Phase C/D money and to go see Orbital Sciences.

I asked Frank about my raise (we all got raises at the beginning of the new fiscal year); he said he couldn't discuss that with me, but that I would find out when I got my paycheck! Such Lockheed nonsense! I was really tired of Lockheed's BS and the thought of doing the mission from LEI seemed better and better every passing day.

Tom's paperwork got straightened out. He was going to get $80,000. The minute we got the Phase C/D money, he could start driving to Sunnyvale! I was very happy I was able to get a decent wage for him, but I was annoyed that I was only making $10,000 more than he was, but thought, *that's life!*

Thursday, September 28, 1995

An article about Lunar Prospector and me, entitled *Space Ace, The $65 million man*, appeared in the *Sunnyvale Sun*; it was a really great article and extremely accurate, with the exception of reporting I was four years younger than I was. It was great PR, so I got copies of it for Henshaw and Scott, both of whom were going to be at an 11:30 AM meeting.

The meeting with Henshaw went well. He was very impressed with Lunar Prospector and Scott really did a good job of presenting the NASA side to him. Scott went through all the things NASA was concerned about: the cost, the budget, the rocket, and pointed out that, all of a sudden, Lunar Prospector was a hot item at Headquarters — as I had found out earlier in the day when I talked to John Gruener.

John had called because Goldin had told JSC he wanted to get man back on the Moon in just six years! Goldin told JSC to do it for $100 million per year (!), and to land two-men crews on the Moon in a vehicle that had a longer surface stay-time than the maximum three-day stay-time of Apollo. As soon as Goldin had made those statements, his entourage of lackeys ran down to Mark Sanders and asked, "What's Lunar Prospector going to do? It's going to be the precursor to this new manned program. Is it going to give us the data we need? Is it going to tell us the place to put the men down?"

Just like that, as Scott said, "Lunar Prospector is right back up on the 9th floor (where the NASA Administrator's office is located at Headquarters)." All of a sudden, Lunar Prospector was an extremely important mission — it was going to be the beginning of putting Americans back on the Moon in six years! Despite all the hullabaloo and despite my wanting man back on the Moon; I didn't think it would happen. But, if it did, then good old Lunar Prospector was going to do what I had always wanted it to do — lead the way for man to go back to the Moon. All of a sudden, Lunar Prospector was the hottest little program at Headquarters and that made Henshaw sit up and take notice.

Jim Burke, whom I had invited to come up and see me, arrived at about 1:30 PM. Jim and I had a nice lunch and then I brought him up to date on the entire program. Then we had a long talk with Dougherty and he really liked Jim. Dougherty asked for Jim's opinion about the LLV2 vs. Taurus issue. Dougherty told Jim, "I want to stay with the LLV2 because it's an inter-company deal, so I think I can work Lockheed management to do it right. It has a softer ride than Taurus (not true), but it does have some problems. The LLV1 (not the LLV2) has had one complete flight (that failed) and will have another two before we fly. But there is the $3 million difference in the price tag (between LLV2 and Taurus)."

Jim's opinion was, "Go with whoever you trust the most." Well, I trusted Orbital Sciences and Dougherty trusted Lockheed.

After Jim had gone, Dougherty and I decided, despite his being very nervous about my wanting to talk to Orbital Sciences, that we would both go to Orbital Sciences and then to Denver (after the merger with Martin Marietta, the LLV program had been moved from Sunnyvale to Denver) to talk to each group. Then we would compare the details of the two launch vehicles, since Dougherty didn't know much about either one of them. It was an interesting discussion because it was the first time Dougherty and I sat down and compared notes on the issue.

I called Wayne to ask about Asif and Wayne said, "Asif is better than Mike (Chobotov). Mike has charisma and is very brilliant, but is also very stubborn. He is only wrong 10% of the time, but he refuses to recognize when he is wrong. In contrast, Asif is very steady." I decided to ask Asif if he wanted to join my team. When I called him, he was more than willing to join us.

Friday, September 29, 1995

I made the arrangements for my trip to Headquarters and to meet with Orbital Sciences.

I went to see Scott and I found out that Mark Saunders had Wes write in his letter, telling us to proceed with Phase C/D, that we were to get only $62.8 million, instead of the $65 million we had agreed on! That was BS. It was just one of Mark's little games he was playing to try to cut our budget. It was counterproductive and it would waste a lot of time. Scott told Mark he was just causing trouble and wasting effort. Scott also said we would quickly be right back to the $65 million and Mark said, "I know, but I wanted it in the letter, so I had Wes do it." What was the matter with him? He was just making a mess for no real reason!

I also broached the topic with Scott about my quitting Lockheed and doing the mission from LEI. I told Scott, besides the personal advantages to me, my going over to LEI would save a significant amount of money on Tom's and my salaries because LEI's overhead would be very small compared to Lockheed's and it would remove the conflict of interests caused by my working for the company I hired to build my spacecraft. Scott agreed that my being in LEI would certainly clarify the chain of command issue. He said that my going to LEI was contractually possible, and agreed there might be some advantages to the project, which was, of course, NASA's main concern.

Chapter 3-3
Trying to Get a Taurus

Sunday, October 1, through Thursday, October 5, 1995:
The JSC and DC Trip

I flew to Washington on Sunday, October 1, the day we were supposed to have officially started Phase C/D — but didn't!

I met with Bret and then with Mark early Monday morning. Mark told me about his cutting our budget to $62.8 million, so, as I had planned, I tried to make him understand that was a serious mistake and would only hurt the mission. However, Mark was adamant and wouldn't change his mind, but he said he would hold the $2 million in reserve and if we really needed it, we would get it later. His basic reason was that, based on his previous experience, he did not trust Lockheed and he was certain Lockheed had padded the budget. Though I don't trust Lockheed either, I knew our budget had absolutely no fat in it — a fact Mark simply would not believe. We were going to be short by $2 million, which was stupid, but that was what we had to live with.

That discussion was a good lead-in for me to bring up my possibly leaving Lockheed and going to LEI. I discussed the conflicts of interest caused by my being an employee of the company that I had hired to build and launch my spacecraft, e.g., Lockheed paying lip service to my being in charge of Lunar Prospector and Lockheed trying to stop me from getting information on the Taurus. Mark was not against my moving to LEI, but he was not excited about it either.

Mark and I went to meet with the Code O guys at 11:00 AM to discuss their tracking options. I told them I wanted the one that gave me 85% coverage. If the coverage got as low as 70%, that would be acceptable but that was the lowest I could go. I added that I really wanted 90% coverage and they said that might be achievable.

One of the Code O guys brought up the question of our putting a recorder on Lunar Prospector to store several orbits worth of data and then to download it just a couple of times a day and I said, "No! The spacecraft is designed to have a low data rate, no computer, and to be controlled from the ground. The addition of a recorder would mean a complete redesign of the spacecraft with a higher data rate and hence, a despun, high gain antenna, a new C&DH unit, higher power requirements, and more command capability. All that would mean that Lunar Prospector would no longer be a simple, low-cost spacecraft. It would become much more complex and we would need a lot more mission operations capability. That alone would cost roughly an extra million dollars a year for the extra personnel needed to do the commanding of the recorder to record and then to playback, instead of Lunar Prospector just down-linking the data all the time as it is designed to do. While we probably have $100,000 for a recorder, we have neither the time for a redesign nor the extra several million dollars that the redesigned spacecraft would cost. If that question had been brought up six months earlier, we might have been able to discuss it, but now, it's far too late to do so. Even six months ago, I would have resisted adding a recorder, because it changes a very simple concept into a much more complex one than Lunar Prospector was ever meant to be." They accepted all that and that ended that discussion (or so I thought).

I brought up the possibility of us developing a secondary network of small antennas built by AMSAT and various universities I had been talking to. Code O loved the idea and said they would like to help build it by giving the various groups grants or small contracts and they would want to use the secondary network after Lunar Prospector was done with it. That worked out very well.

After noon, and without having had any time for lunch, because the Code O meeting lasted so long, I took the NASA bus to Goddard to meet my Goddard Navigation Team for the very first time. I had a good time talking about our trajectory with the celestial mechanic's guys and then I went back to Pat and Julius's apartment, where Julius had prepared his delicious meatloaf for dinner.

The next morning I drove out to Orbital Sciences (near Dulles International Airport to the west of DC) and that was incredible. The meeting with the Orbital engineers and managers was a delight. They knew it was unlikely that I could force Lockheed to accept a Taurus launch, but they were willing to spend considerable time and money to get me all the information I needed to try to do so. They would have just loved to take the launch of Lunar Prospector away from LLV, their biggest competitor.

We went through the capabilities of the various versions of the Taurus that were under development and it was clear the version with stretched first and second stages (built longer than normal) could get Lunar Prospector and its TLI Stage into Low Earth Orbit (LEO). Better yet, if I could keep Lunar Prospector's mass below 300 kg, we could use the regular version of the Taurus that had already flown. In addition, they could spin up the Spacecraft/TLI Stage stack to the required 60 rpm. They didn't have to use a launch pad, they could just launch from a concrete slab, i.e., from NASA's Wallops facility on the Virginia coast just 180 km from Orbital Sciences Headquarters. They had already used "yos" to tumble injection stages. They were willing to do everything, including the TLI Stage (they would even eat the TLI Stage development costs since they needed one anyway for geostationary transfer orbit missions). The cost was $20 million for the basic vehicle and a couple million for the TLI Stage.

Since their vehicle had flown, they had all the launch environment data, from which it was clear that the Taurus launch environment was better than what LLV had predicted for the LLV2. I was impressed with the Taurus and with the cooperation and interest I was getting from Orbital Sciences, in contrast to the stonewalling and downright deception I had to deal with from the LLV crowd. Taurus could do everything I wanted and even more (the spin up and the yo), so I thought, *I am going to end up on a Taurus come hell or high water*, and then I told them I wanted them to launch Lunar Prospector and I would do everything possible to make it happen.

I drove back to Pat and Julius's and took them out for a steak dinner. When we got to the restaurant, Pat and I went in and got a table while Julius parked his ancient VW van. Since Pat is 16 years younger than Julius and I am 7 years younger than him, Pat and I pretended to be a couple and I said to the hostess, "My father, a tall, elderly gentleman, is parking the car," and asked, "Would you show him to our table when he comes in?"

The hostess bought it hook, line and sinker; when she showed Julius to our table, she said very politely, "Here is your father," and both Pat and I had a good laugh at Julius, who knew he had been had.

The next morning, I drove to Thiokol, which is closer to Baltimore than to DC. We discussed the burping or after-burning of the TLI Stage. Their after-burn data were very old because they had been using stabilized injection stages with active nutation control for some time. As our discussions continued, they convinced me we should have retrorockets on the TLI Stage, instead of a yo, to be sure there would be no post-separation collision. The retrorockets would help produce a clean separation, they would burn cleanly (they produced no residue to degrade the solar array or the thermal blankets' thermal properties) and they would also be off axis so they would cause the TLI stage to tumble. My meeting with Thiokol was also very productive.

I flew home on Thursday and got home at about 11:30 AM. I was tired from the long trip, so I stayed home and rested during the afternoon.

Friday, October 6, 1995

I called Kent Joosten, an ex-coworker of mine in the old advanced mission-planning group at JSC, to find out what they were doing to support Goldin's "back to the Moon by 2001" directive. Kent filled me in and said they wanted me to keep them informed about Lunar Prospector's progress and wanted to get my input to their planning efforts.

When Dougherty came in, I told him what I had found out at Orbital Sciences. Despite his being a loyal company man, Dougherty basically agreed that Taurus was the way to go, but he still was concerned about Lockheed's reaction to my wanting a Taurus instead of the LLV2. He wanted to go see Henshaw to discuss it and it was clear he didn't want me there when he did, but that was not going to happen.

Tom arrived Thursday to start working full time and was relaxing before beginning work on Monday. Everything was beginning to look very good.

Monday, October 9, 1995: My 56th Birthday

If everything went as planned, we were two years from launch and counting.

Dougherty was still trying to have the meeting about the LLV2 and the Taurus with Henshaw, but without me. He came in while Richard and I were talking about the meeting and told Richard he should be prepared for the meeting by Wednesday. I asked, "Do you know what time we are going to meet with him?"

Instead of answering my question, he said, "Richard is going to present it," and implied that only he and Richard were going to go.

I said, "No, we are all going to go," and that was that.

Dougherty went out and stuck his head in later and said, "4:00 PM Wednesday," he should have known he couldn't get away with that BS.

Somewhat later, we met with the LLV2 people; those guys knew nothing about what was going on and they were non-cooperative — the worst of the bunch was Don Davis, who I was learning to hate. Dougherty really laid it on to them about getting us the information we needed in three weeks, while they wanted three months to get it to us. Dougherty started putting the pressure on them by saying, "Taurus is a serious competitor."

That prompted Don Davis to ask, "Well, can it (Taurus) really do the job?"

I turned to him and said, "Yes, it can do the job."

Davis started backtracking and said, "I don't know for sure if we can do the job, so how do they know if they can do it?" Then Dougherty twisted their tails some more to get them to cooperate and to do their job right, but I was determined that LLV was not going to mess up my mission with a bad launch.

Things like that LLV meeting and Dougherty's wanting to meet with Henshaw behind my back further increased my desire to quit Lockheed and run the mission from LEI. I started to check on the formalities we had to go through so LEI, a Texas Corporation, could operate in California. I found that once we got the paperwork submitted, it would take four to six weeks to process them. Tom and I decided we would drive up to the California State Office in San Francisco to get the forms Thursday and get everything started.

Monday was also Tom's first day at work after coming out to Sunnyvale permanently and it was great to have him on my side.

Tuesday, October 10, 1995: The Real Kick-Off Meeting

Tuesday was the day I finally got to have a proper Kick-Off Meeting about Lunar Prospector — the kind of meeting I should have had with the engineers at the very beginning of the Phase B activities.

However, the meeting did not start the way I wanted it to. First, I thought more engineers would be there, since I thought Dougherty had already hired everybody we needed — but that was not the case! Second, I was annoyed because almost everyone showed up late — and that had to stop. I was tired of the engineers wasting everyone's time by always being late for meetings. Third, slowly but surely, several of the younger engineers (who always think they know everything) just drifted out of the meeting — Dougherty had told them they really didn't have to attend because he thought they knew most of what I was going to say anyway — that was a load of BS. None of them, not one — and especially Dougherty — knew what I needed them to know about the mission, the programmatics, and the spacecraft. There was little I could do about the guys leaving, since Dougherty had already screwed that up. Nevertheless, all the older (and wiser) guys Dougherty had hired were very interested, listened very intently and stayed for the whole meeting. Despite the fact that many of the guys left early, I was happy to have gone through everything in detail and I made it once again very clear how the project was going to be run, how it was set up, that I was the customer, and that they were answerable to me — not to Lockheed and not to NASA. It was amazing how hard it was to try to get them to understand and accept that!

After the meeting, Tom told me that, at the beginning of the meeting, the guys were smiling and snickering as if to say, "Ho hum, here goes the crazy scientist trying to tell us engineers how to do our business," and then, as the meeting continued, the smiles faded away, they began to look very serious, they began to ask questions and they began to find out that I knew how to build my spacecraft and do my mission and that they didn't. I was relieved when Tom told me that, since it meant I was finally getting it through to them that Lunar Prospector was not going to be "business as usual," with big schedule slips, big cost overruns, and expensive "fixes" to cover up poor engineering.

Besides the managerial and technical issues I discussed, and since I believe that one does his or her best work when they are enjoying what they are doing, I told everyone, *"Lunar Prospector is supposed to be an interesting and fun program to work on. If you are not having fun, then go find another program to work on that is fun."* Though I doubted that the engineers understood what I meant right then, they certainly did later on.

It was a long meeting; it started at 9:00 AM and ended at 4:00 PM. The nice part was that Dougherty was there all the time and he too finally began to understand that I knew what I was doing. Also, Dougherty had asked Dale Vaccarello to be the Systems Engineer and Dale was also at the meeting, which was really great. He asked a lot of good questions and he said, "Boy, this is exciting; I'm really excited to work on it." Dale's reaction made my day very worthwhile.

Sylvia called after the meeting and said NASA was not giving us the $5 million we needed to keep us going and they didn't know when they would, or even if they would! They had started to screw us around again! However, she said we did get $2.3 million of pre-contract money from Lockheed, so we were OK for the time being.

I was sick of their jerking us around like that and I was going to raise hell about it — Discovery was supposed to be "Faster, Better, Cheaper," and all Headquarters did was make it next to impossible for us to proceed on schedule.

After we finished talking, I called Mark and Bret and really laid it on them about NASA getting our money to us. They said our money request had been sent to the congressional office, it would be about a week before that office could get anything done about it and send it to Congress, then it would be another week before Congress could get anything done, and blah, blah, blah. Nothing like a big government bureaucracy to keep things moving right along — at a snail's pace.

Sylvia also reminded me to get her our proposed LEI budget so Tom and I could get out of Lockheed and into LEI. I had earlier promised Scott and Sylvia I would give them something in a week and then I had forgotten about it. Tom said he would take care of it and started working on the budget.

Wednesday, October 11, 1995:
A Meeting with Henshaw and a Very Good Day

First thing in the morning, I called Joe Padavano, the Taurus Program Manager at Orbital Sciences, about the information package on the Taurus that had come and I asked him a number of questions.

Shortly after that, Dougherty and I went over to Ames to talk to Sylvia about the advantages and disadvantages of Tom and my quitting Lockheed and running the mission from LEI. I told Sylvia that if Tom and I went to LEI, "I wanted to make absolutely sure that nothing we did would be questionable."

To which Dougherty laughingly asked, "Ha, ha, are you going to get a Lincoln Continental for a company car?"

Sylvia, trying to sidestep Dougherty's inane comment, answered, "Well, a car is very questionable."

In a futile effort to politely shut Dougherty up, I said jokingly, "Tom, don't say such things, NASA will believe you."

After that Dougherty nonsense, we seriously discussed all the issues about how I would do the mission from LEI and Sylvia really began to accept the idea. She asked the important question about how my role as PI would change if I no longer worked for Lockheed and I answered, "There would be no difference whatsoever in my position. I would work in the same office at Lockheed and Tom (Dougherty) and I would work together just as we do now. Don't forget, NASA expects that most of its Discovery PIs would be university or private institute space scientists, not industry PIs, so we are just changing my title from Industry PI to Institute PI and nothing else," and Dougherty agreed. Then she asked if we would need an Ames Project Manager to be the interface between LEI and Lockheed and I said, "No, I will be the interface, just as I am now; we don't need anybody in between us. The project will be run just the way it is now, because, in reality, I am the Project Manager."

Sylvia said, "You know what you should do? You should officially be the Project Manager as well as the PI and Dougherty should (just) be the Lockheed Project Manager."

I said, "That's exactly the way it's being run now — I am, in reality, the Project Manager. It's just that Lockheed won't allow me to officially have that role, because I am not a Project Manager according to their definition. But your suggestion is great, because I can be the Project Manager at LEI and Lockheed can't do anything about it if you guys (NASA Ames) define it that way if I go to LEI."

We discussed the various government regulations about funding, contracts, and the like, so Dougherty and I would understand what the government would and would not allow us to do if we changed the contract so I was managing the project from LEI and not from Lockheed. I again said to Sylvia, "I'm relying on you to tell me if there is anything questionable, anything that could even be questionable, about what we are doing, and if there is, I don't want to do it." With that, we discussed LEI's corporate structure. I explained that I was LEI's Corporate Board President, Tom was its Vice President and my wife was its Secretary-Treasurer, i.e., the minimum number of Board members a Board can have. I said, "Rebecca is going to be the Executive Secretary. She is a fully qualified legal secretary."

Sylvia responded with, "That's fine."

Because of Dougherty's stupid remark, I added, "Don't worry, there won't be a company car. Tom and I've already found out from the IRS what is allowable and what is not for a non-profit, tax-exempt corporation — and a car is not allowed."

The discussion lasted over an hour and a half and I really got the feeling that Scott, Sylvia, and Headquarters — and even Dougherty — were warming up to the LEI option. Then Sylvia said something I really liked, "In cases where a scientist is the Project Manager and the PI, NASA and the government can make you a *de facto* civil servant. You're not paid as a civil servant and you're not a NASA employee as such, but you are given the authority over the project and you are treated as a civil servant, even though you are not. It empowers you as a civil servant and you're acting for the government." Then she added, "But Scott might not allow that because he resists anything that could infringe on his authority." Her last remark about Scott seemed out of context, so I didn't pay much attention to it (but I should have).

My immediate reaction to her saying that I could be a *de facto* civil servant was that I would have Lockheed by the balls. I thought, *Man-oh-man, if they can do that, it would just be incredible. I would be PI, Project Manager, and a government official. I could really take full control of the mission and Lockheed couldn't stop me from getting a Taurus or doing the mission right,* but I kept those joyous thoughts to myself.

Our next topic was the LLV2 and Taurus issue. Sylvia said Headquarters was concerned the government regulations might not let us just buy a LLV2 or a Taurus launch. We might have to ask for bids from all the launch vehicle vendors and that decision depended on whether the launch vehicle had already been sold as a commercial vehicle — more red tape! Sylvia then told Dougherty that Headquarters was also putting the pressure on for us to dump LLV2 and go with Taurus (music to my ears). Very annoyed, Dougherty said, "I don't care what Headquarters says or what Alan says, I am going to decide what rocket we go on."

Before I could say a word, Sylvia immediately said, "You better remember that Alan is the customer and what Alan says goes, Alan is running this show."

Dougherty backtracked and said, "Yeah, I meant Alan and me."

Dougherty and I went back to Lockheed for the 10:00 AM, weekly subsystem meeting. Again, nobody was there on time and I was ticked off. I found Dougherty (who was also late) and said, "I'm getting annoyed that the engineers show up when they damn well please. These meetings are going to start and end on time, or else," and Dougherty agreed and said he, too, was getting annoyed. I felt like telling Dougherty, "If those guys don't start coming to meetings on time, they're fired," but didn't — that was probably going too far. Nevertheless, they had to realize that we had a very short time schedule and a very limited budget (they were used to big budgets and schedules that could slip) and those guys were wasting both time and money. The engineers make about $50/hour, which translates to over $150/hour, considering Lockheed's overhead. There were about 15 guys at each meeting and if a couple of them were late by just 15 minutes, then the rest of us would be wasting about $600 every meeting waiting for them to saunter in. We had at least three meetings per week, so every week we were throwing away $2000 or about $100,000 per year and I was tired of going to the meeting room and finding no one there.

When everyone finally got there, Dougherty mildly told the guys to be on time in the future and then we got started. As usual, most of the engineers were unprepared for the meeting, another behavioral pattern that was beginning to annoy me, so the meeting was largely a waste of time (and money). Because they were not prepared, we got into a big, useless discussion about the various documents and engineering drawings that had to be done and that dragged on and on. Like me, Dougherty was getting rather annoyed with the engineers and then he got dragged out to a Henshaw meeting. In his absence, Dale Vaccarello took over the meeting. Unlike Dougherty who did keep control of meetings, but who didn't want to accept that he worked for me, Dale did not run meetings well, but totally accepted that I was in charge and that he was subordinate to me; even better, he actually listened to what I said! However, since the engineers didn't have the information we needed and we were just wasting time, Dale said, "Why don't we just call this off right now and have everybody go back and get prepared and we'll start again after lunch." We broke up and Tom and I went to lunch.

As Tom and I were leaving the cafeteria, Henshaw was there and said, "Hi, Alan, how are you doing?"

I answered, "OK."

He said, "I understand from Dougherty that we have a problem with the rocket. This is a very delicate issue, a political issue, though I understand there are some technical things, but it is really a political issue, so we'll have to go see Al Smith about it."

I said, "Fine, we are going to see you at 4:00 PM anyway, so we can discuss it then."

He said, "OK."

Tom and I went to the meeting room at 1:00 PM and nobody was there! Dale came in and I said to him, "Tom told the guys this morning they had better start being on time. This has to stop; these guys are either going to start coming to these meetings on time or they're getting fired. They're not taking this seriously; they're not prepared; they aren't doing anything. I want people who are dedicated to this program and who don't waste my time." I was really ticked off at how the engineers acted and how Lockheed ran its programs.

Finally the guys drifted in and I had to take charge. Dale is a good guy and I like him, but he is no leader. I took charge and ran the damned meeting and told the guys that what they were doing was not acceptable.

To top off a very bad meeting, Vu Ho kept interrupting and raising objections to things he didn't have a clue about. He would not listen and insisted that everything had to be done the way it had always been done. I said, "No Vu, that's not the way I want it. Listen to me, that is not the way I want it. This is Lunar Prospector and it is not gong to get done the old way; we are going to do it my way." The guy is useless and I decided to tell Dougherty to get rid of him before he totally screwed up the booms and other things he was unfortunately responsible for.

Dougherty came by, poked his head in the meeting and told me our launch vehicle meeting with Henshaw had been postponed, but that we were going to meet with him in a few minutes, at 3:30 PM, for a debriefing. Henshaw had had lunch with the Ames managers and said he wanted to talk to us about the things the Ames guys had discussed over lunch and that he really didn't understand about the program. I said, "OK, at 3:30," and turned back to the meeting. Dougherty disappeared and then I said, "Keep going after I leave and we will start again tomorrow at 8:00." Right then, Frank came by and dragged me out of that meeting to go to Henshaw's meeting.

Later, Tom said, "The minute you left, the meeting just collapsed. Nothing got done," and I wasn't a bit surprised, but I was concerned and disgusted.

Frank and I went to Henshaw's office and sat down. Fred DeFrank was there and, of course, Dougherty. Steve Griffin was not there and that was fine with me. Finally, Henshaw came in and he said he didn't understand what Ames was talking about when they brought up the $59 million, the $63 million, and the $65 million budgets for the program. Frank started to explain the evolution and resolution of the fee and budget mess.

Just as Frank got started, Henshaw looked at me in a very friendly way and said in a joking way, "We ought to be careful here, the customer is sitting right here, but that's all right, you're a good customer." Well, I was glad he accepted the fact that I was the customer, but it appeared that he and Frank were the only two managers in Lockheed that did. I suspected he was told that by Ames during the Ames lunch.

Frank continued and said, "Well you know, we screwed up here. We know the difference between price and cost and we thought they meant price where they meant cost. That is our error, but we had the total price information in the proposal."

Henshaw joked, "Somebody is going to get in trouble about this, that's a $4 million discrepancy." Then he added, "But Alan doesn't need to worry about it because he is the customer and he has customer immunity, even though he is a Lockheed employee."

Finally Frank finished explaining that mess and then we talked about the $62.8 million budget and how the program was going to be handled. Henshaw said, "If $62.8 million is what they (NASA) say, then that is what we are going to do it for, even if we have to eat into the $4 million profit and that's fine because we are not doing this mission for profit. We should be doing this one for no fee anyway." I liked his attitude and I surely wished the rest of Lockheed felt that way, if they did, my life would have been a lot easier.

Henshaw looked at me and said, "What about the rocket business?"

Remembering that Dougherty had said earlier that he was going to have that discussion with Al Smith on Friday, I realized Frank and Dougherty got caught with their pants down — they hadn't expected the rocket would be brought up. Nevertheless, I was going to capitalize on the golden opportunity and I said, "Well, I am the offending party here, so I'll discuss it. I'm very concerned about the launch vehicle and the stonewalling we're getting from LLV. They won't do the TLI Stage, they won't give us the information on the launch environment we need to finalize the spacecraft design, and they want additional money to get us those data, data that one normally gets from a launch vendor as part of the package. I've had a meeting with Orbital Sciences and it appears that Taurus has a softer ride than the LLV2. Taurus's cost, with a TLI Stage that they will take responsibility for, is $3 million less than the LLV2 costs, without the TLI Stage!"

In an attempt to undermine what I was saying, Dougherty ticked me off by interrupting and charging, "Your cost numbers aren't right!" which was a load of BS.

I said, "Not true, the costs are directly from Orbital Sciences. Besides, we don't have good numbers from the LLV guys, but everything they have given us says $25 million just for the LLV2."

Dougherty was doing everything he could to keep the LLV2 looking better than the Taurus, even though it wasn't — but what do facts mean to a Lockheed manager when they get in the way of company profits?

Frank was trying to stay on the LLV2 side of the fence, but he was nervous about it. He wasn't going to let me jump off the LLV2 if he could help it and said, "Well, aren't you guys preparing to go on an LLV2? It's a rougher ride (than a Taurus), but you're building it (the spacecraft) for that aren't you?"

I answered, "Yes we are, but if we didn't have to, we could have a lighter spacecraft and there would be other savings. Also, being on the LLV2 is a higher risk."

Henshaw said, "I know we had a launch failure, but we have two more launches before you go."

I said, "No, you don't. Those are LLV1s and I am the first on an LLV2 and that is not an LLV1!"

Then I again brought up the cost difference, "Taurus is $20 million for the basic rocket and $2.8 million for the TLI Stage, while for the LLV2, it's $22 million, plus $3.5 million (if they built the TLI Stage at all). And that's a $3 million difference."

Frank said, "That can be taken care of and the other things really don't make any difference."

I replied, "Maybe not to Lockheed, but they make a difference to me, Frank." Then I added, "Taurus can spin the Spacecraft/TLI Stage stack up to 60 rpm and point it in the right direction (for the burn) and LLV2 can't do either of those things right now. LLV wants another $600,000 for a spin table and another $600,000 for improvements and modifications of the OAM (Orbit Adjust Module), which is a new development. Otherwise we go with the existing spin-up rocket concept (little rockets on the sides of the TLI Stage that would spin-up the stack immediately after separation and just before the TLI burn), which is much less accurate and endangers the whole thing. There is another half a million dollars difference."

Frank was trying to stop me, but I just went on and said, "I spent all day last Tuesday with Orbital Sciences and I was very impressed. I made a list comparing all the issues: cost, launch environment, spin-up, and all the other things. For example, the LLV2 has to launch from Pad 46 that is being modified and might not be ready when we need it. If it's not ready, then we have a slip in schedule. Taurus can launch from Pad 17 or 46, and in fact, it needs neither one, it can launch from a concrete slab, so Taurus is totally independent of the availability of launch pads down there (at the Cape). When you compare the LLV2 and the Taurus on my list, every single item and every single characteristic is clearly better on the Taurus."

At that point, Henshaw was getting red in the face and he interrupted, saying, "You're the customer and you're dissatisfied with the LLV2. Is it true that what you're telling me is that you do not want to be on an LLV2, you want a Taurus?"

I answered, "That is exactly correct." Henshaw jumped up in a huff and stormed out of the room, saying, "That's all I want to know," as he left.

I didn't know exactly why he stormed out, but storm out he did and he didn't come back. I assumed that he either stormed out to start raising hell with LLV or he stormed out because I was the customer and I was dissatisfied. I didn't know which, but I turned around and looked at Dougherty, Frank, and Fred and they were stone silent and scared to death — I had just told the vice president, the head of our entire division, that I didn't want to be on Lockheed's lousy rocket. I said, "Well, this was a good meeting," thinking it was an absolutely perfect meeting. I had finally been able to get the LLV2 issue on the table without Dougherty or Frank acting as a filter and putting a Lockheed spin on it.

Frank was the only one to say a word. He said, "You're going to have to go in there and tell them (Lockheed upper management) that NASA has the same concerns about the launch vehicle as you. If you're going to go against this company, it's a big political issue and it is very difficult; you're going to have to have arguments that are fail proof. You're going to have to also remind them that you're on the first LLV2." That reminded me that the TDR committee had said, "We don't like it that you are the first on an LLV2 and we do not like it that you are first on the refurbished pad," important points to remember for the upcoming battle. Nevertheless, I was pleased that Frank was trying to help me, even though I had forced open the LLV2/Taurus can of worms.

After that excellent meeting was over, I talked to Tim Bridges and told him about my possibly going to LEI. I said that if I did, he could join LEI if he wanted to and do his work (remember he was officially retired from Lockheed and did not work directly for the company anymore) on the mission as an LEI employee. Tim loved the idea. I was also going to give Tom Chinn the same option after he retired.

Thursday, October 12, 1995: Subsystem Review Day

I talked to Dougherty as soon as he got to work and found out that my discussion with Henshaw had caused a flurry of activity. Dougherty said he had to spend most of the day with LLV and then had a meeting with Al Smith to discuss the situation.

Shortly thereafter, we started the subsystem meeting and most of the guys weren't there and the ones that were there were late again. That had to change. Other than that, the review went quite well.

Frank asked me to come to his office. He told me we got the NASA contract for Phases C/D and E negotiated, without the rocket in it — that was the way to do it, since the rocket was an open issue. Anyway, the contract was almost done — it only had to be signed, and I could hardly believe it. Then Frank said he told Al Smith that, because they had treated a customer very badly and because there were serious questions about the launch vehicle, they had a good chance of losing the launch vehicle. I was really pleased with Frank; he was working hard to find the best way to get what we needed to be successful.

The rest of the day was spent getting ready for Friday's meeting with Al Smith. The meeting was set for 8:30 AM. Dougherty was going to discuss the differences between the LLV2 and the Taurus, as we understood them (they were afraid to let me to do it, since I would have given them the straight facts, while Dougherty was going to slant it towards the LLV2 the best he could), and hence, the need for us to get an AO out so we could get the real data on those two rockets, make a valid comparison and know exactly what we were doing. Lockheed was going to have to bring the LLV2 price down to be competitive with the Taurus. I felt the situation was very good and I was looking forward to the meeting.

I called Asif to ask him to come to Sunnyvale to discuss his joining Lockheed or LEI. Unfortunately, his house in Northridge (near LA) was badly damaged by the Northridge Earthquake and he was trying to get it fixed. He couldn't meet with me right then.

Chapter 3-4
LLV2 or Nothing, Power Problems, and a Second Fee Crisis

Friday, October 13, 1995: The Al Smith Meeting

The meeting with Al Smith started at 8:30 AM. Henshaw, his deputy, Frank, Dougherty, Mike Griffin (who didn't say one peep), the President of LLV (who was sitting right behind me along the wall), and I were there.

Al Smith was not there and while we were waiting for him, Henshaw got on the phone and called someone at LLV. It was one of the most interesting conversations I had ever heard. Henshaw started off being really nice and asked, "We're friends and have been working together for a long time and we help each other out, right?" Then he suddenly attacked, "God damn it, I want you to get on this Lunar Prospector thing. Are you going to help me on this or are you going to keep screwing it up? If you don't get this straightened out, I'm going to kick your ass." After that outburst, he became friendly again, "Now, we're going to remain friends and we're going to work together on this problem, aren't we?" Then, another attack, "But by God, if you screw this up . . . ." He just kept swinging back and forth, playing the "good cop, bad cop" game all by himself. I guessed that when the guy did not answer exactly the way Henshaw wanted, he let him have it. It was very interesting.

Al Smith finally came in and, right off the bat, chewed everybody out for signing the $2.3 million pre-contract while he was gone. He said, "That's just lost money, because NASA always screws us. I hope you guys are all prepared to mortgage your houses to pay back Lockheed for signing the pre-contract," and they all laughed a little uncomfortably. Then he asked Frank if the pre-contract was OK.

Frank answered, "Yes, we're going to get our money back."

Al Smith responded, "Well, OK, I don't like this, but you guys should have put in the evaluation of whether we are going to lose the $2.3 million as a medium risk, not low risk."

Frank again said, "We're OK." Then Al Smith ended that part of the meeting with, "You guys aren't going to get any more (pre-contract money)," and I thought, *oh crap*.

Then it was Dougherty's turn; he went through the launch vehicle issues and said that the PI and NASA were concerned and wanted to investigate the Taurus.

Al's first questions were, "Who is responsible for the rocket?" and, "Does Lockheed have the choice of the rocket?"

Dougherty answered, "I'm going to make the choice, but I'm not certain my PI is going to agree with it or allow it."

Henshaw asked, "What is written in the contract?"

I answered, "What is written in contract is that the PI is solely responsible for all aspects of the program."

Al Smith asked me pointedly, "Who are you responsible to?" and answered the question himself, "You have responsibilities to both Lockheed, as a Lockheed employee, and to NASA, and there is a balance between those responsibilities."

I responded, "I'm fully aware of that, but my main concern is getting this mission done right, because that is what is good for everybody involved."

Al Smith asked threateningly, "Who pays your wages?"

Frank intervened with, "He gets his money from the contract he brought in, but he's paid through us. I sign his time card; so technically he is a Lockheed employee."

Since that didn't lead to any real leverage against me, Al let it go by saying, "Well, that's a secondary issue anyway."

Al Smith made it very clear that we were not going to go on a Taurus by saying to me, "The only reason we're doing Lunar Prospector is that I want to sell LLVs and I am not going to let you ride on some other rocket, because that would show other potential customers that LLVs are not good vehicles."

I retorted, "This goes beyond selling LLVs; I'm trying to prove that Discovery and 'Faster, Better, Cheaper' work and to make sure that we (Lockheed) have a full package, not just the LLV, but a spacecraft, Mission Ops — a whole mission capability to sell. If I'm successful, there will be other Discovery missions and a new line of business for Lockheed. I'm not going to do that if I'm at the bottom of the Atlantic Ocean. I want to be assured that, if I am on an LLV2, I am going to get all the support I need. "

Al Smith just didn't understand that; to him, he was just selling a rocket to a one-shot deal and advertising the LLVs via that launch. In stark contrast to him, Henshaw understood what I was trying to do. (Frank later said, "Henshaw is 110% behind you and understands that you're not selling a rocket, you're selling a whole mission concept. He says this is the future.")

I said, "Let me explain my viewpoint on the LLV problem. I originally came here and asked for an LLV2 because Lockheed is a big company with a lot of capabilities and has built hundreds of rockets, but then we got nowhere with LLV. True, Orbital Sciences is a small company without much of a record and they don't have the resources to match Lockheed's. You say they can't do the job and Lockheed can. To me that's just rhetoric; you can say that, but where is the proof?"

Al Smith retorted, "We are capable of backing this and getting you the appropriate launch, better than they (Orbital Sciences) can because if we get into trouble, we have more resources."

I countered with, "Sure, as I said, I know Lockheed has a lot of resources; why do you think I asked for the LLV in the first place? But, to date, LLV hasn't performed in anything close to a satisfactory way, while Orbital Sciences has given me what I wanted to know."

Al Smith said, "We are not in the business of having Taurus take business away from us and getting the credit for a mission like this. If LLV1 were to fail again, then obviously, we would have to reconsider this, but not before then."

I said, "That's fine from your standpoint, but the only problem is that we have a 22 month Phase C/D and we are launching in two years. I can't wait until next summer to find out if the next LLV1 flies or not."

That stopped Al Smith cold; he fumbled around and said, "Well, you know, things can be done faster if they have to," which was a big load of BS. Nevertheless, it was clear he was not going to allow me to go on a Taurus. He didn't say that right out, but it was clear I was fighting a losing battle against a very big company that was not going to let its small competitor steal the launch of a highly visible mission, even if it meant that mission might fail on the LLV2!

Henshaw said, "Well, OK, tell us exactly what your concerns are about LLV."

I said, "As Tom showed in the list of things, LLV2 is marginal on a number of issues: there is no margin on the size of the shroud; the (LLV2) environment may be worse (than Taurus), the cost is of great concern, because we are very tightly constrained on money. These things are of concern to me, because each one of them could make Lunar Prospector fail. I realize if you guys really get behind this, these issues can be resolved. But, what really concerns me is that I proposed an LLV2 launch and a Lockheed built spacecraft, because I felt that was the best combination — that I would have in-house support for both legs of the mission and then I came here and I found I am getting absolutely no support from one of the legs. I have no information and I have had no cooperation whatsoever from LLV."

The LLV President sitting behind me said, "That's over. You will get the cooperation you need. There are other issues, technical issues, but you will get full cooperation from LLV and the people who are giving you problems will be removed. We will get the people you need."

I said, "Well, that's all fine and good, but I want to see it happen."

Then Al Smith asked if there was anything else I wanted to tell them. I said, "Yes, the other thing is the cost, we are very tight, so $25 to $26 million would be very difficult for us."

He said, "We are going to discuss that, but since you are the customer, we would appreciate it if you would leave the room." Since it was clear that I had no choice, I did. What a bunch of two-faced asses. When it was to their advantage, I was the customer and when not, I was their employee — what a bunch of BS. Lockheed managers simply have no scruples, period.

To top that off, Al Smith said, just as I was about to leave, "The other thing you can do for us is to make sure the NASA money comes, because we will all be fired if we don't get it pretty soon."

I thought, *good, the sooner you're all fired, the better*, but answered, "I'll do my best," and walked out.

I went over to Ames to tell Sylvia what had happened. I told her I had succeeded in waking Lockheed up and making them address the launch vehicle problems and that I was not supposed to talk to Orbital Sciences — which I had already done anyway. Since there had been no resolution of the technical and cost issues, they were going to talk about those things in my absence, and that made me feel uncomfortable. I also told her Taurus only needed 16 months to get ready for a launch; so I didn't have to have a Taurus right then — I had 8 months before it would be too late to call up Orbital and say, "I need a launch."

I told Sylvia, "As far as I am concerned, I'm ready to go to LEI. I want out of Lockheed. I am sick of being a customer when it pleases them and an employee when it's to their advantage. There is just no way I can win because, as an employee, they make it clear that I have to do things the way they want or I will get nothing at all. As far as I'm concerned, my going to LEI is a closed issue."

When the Al Smith meeting was over, I found Dougherty, who was quite pleased! He said, "We really did good! We really have them where we want them."

I was skeptical about that and asked, "What happened after I left?"

He answered, "Well, they are sticking to the $25 million."

I said, "That worries me, Tom, then we have no reserves at all."

He said, "I know. Also they (LLV) are not sure they can do the TLI Stage."

I said, "Well crap, you know we can't do it. This stuff makes me very concerned."

He said, "Well, me too."

I said, "Tom, you know that even though they don't want us going on a Taurus now, it takes Taurus as little as 16 months to prepare for a launch, 22 months is what they want, but they can do it in as little as 16. If things don't improve, even if they (LLV) are cooperative, if I don't feel like they are going to be able to give us a ride, then we still have time, the door isn't closed."

He said, "I am really glad to know that, because I am worried too."

I said, "Good, then we are on the same wavelength."

Dougherty and I had a nice talk and he was much more cordial and friendly than he had ever been. He had apparently come to recognize that I understand launch vehicles, because he said, "I want you to be in on all the technical discussions and you make sure those guys (LLV) understand what you need and what you want and how you need it done. I'm going to have those guys come down Tuesday and Wednesday of next week."

I said, "Fine."

He said, "I really need you to find the problems with the launch vehicle."

I said, "And you have to realize I need the same thing from you." It was comical to a point how sometimes he recognized I was in charge and sometimes he thought he was — force of habit, I guessed.

I went to see Frank and Frank said, "You really did well. You were totally professional and you impressed the hell out of those guys." Frank related that the day before he had been over at LLV and had raised holy hell. He told them, "You're screwing the customer and you're doing it to the wrong guy. You should be out there kissing his ass, making sure he gets what he wants because this guy is going to go out in the community with a successful mission and sell more LLV2s for you than anybody you can think of." He said, "They've caught hell from everybody and they know they screwed up. They're going to be over here wining and dining you. Take every bit of it; they're going to be kissing your ass."

That was nice to hear, but I wanted to see results, not hear promises — I had enough promises from Lockheed, like the New Business Council's famous, "Lockheed is going to have to give you all the support you need and the best engineers we have," and what did I get, the Vu Ho's of the company and the LLV bozos.

I said, "That's nice to hear, but I'm still concerned they haven't resolved the money issue, and they haven't resolved the TLI Stage issue, and all the other stuff, but I am happy we got their attention."

Frank said, "Yeah, I understand; nevertheless it was a great meeting, but it's too bad all this had to happen. They treated you very badly and they're paying the price for it." Frank said further that after I left the meeting, they asked him and Dougherty about the people I had interfaced with and all those guys were going to be removed, not fired from the company, but just removed from LLV onto something else. That was good news and I asked if Don Davis was going to go, and Frank said, "Yep, they're getting rid of him too." How nice, we wouldn't have to interface with those guys again — they were out of the picture.

Frank and I had a very pleasing conversation and just as I was getting ready to leave, Frank got a call from Mark Saunders. Frank said, "Really, that's great!" and I knew we had our money! Despite what Mark and Bret had told me Tuesday, Congress had quickly gotten word back to NASA that Lunar Prospector was to be funded in the interim for $10 million. The $10 million was a stopgap measure until Congress could finally pass a budget and they could get us all our money. Frank immediately tried to call Al Smith and left a message with his secretary saying, "You can stop getting me fired, NASA just came through; we got our $10 million!"

That was great news, but there was a little more background to it. Because the government still did not have a budget and was therefore operating under a continuing resolution, NASA's hands were tied when it came to sending out money for new programs. Because of that, I had called George French a week or so earlier and asked him to try to get Congressman Sensenbrenner to somehow get us our much-needed money before we shut down. As a result, Congress quickly directed NASA to give us our money and to tell us to get started on Phase C/D, despite the continuing resolution and the shut down — unbelievable, but true.

I called Orbital Sciences to tell Joe Padavano what had happened at Al Smith's meeting. He said he wasn't surprised. I said, "Joe, this isn't over yet, because the issues that concern me have not been resolved. Lockheed is going to address them and I will have to wait and see if they do anything. But, since you are able to launch with just a 16 months' notice, I have 6 to 8 months of time during which I can still switch over to Orbital Sciences. I want to keep in contact with you about this," and Joe agreed.

Monday, October 16, 1995: Subsystem Review Day

The subsystem review went pretty well. Dougherty was getting a little too boisterous, thinking he was running the show, so I would again have to step on him a little bit and very soon (that clearly was going to be a continuous battle).

Woody wasn't doing a good job on the power in general and then a power issue came up because of the cutouts (areas on the solar array drum where the booms and the tangential engines were to be mounted). The solar array drum was designed to be 1.25 m tall and 1.32 m in diameter and that was just enough to give Woody the 5.2 m^2 of surface area he needed for a solar array made of inexpensive silicon (Si) solar cells, but it left no room for cutouts. The cutouts removed 0.2 m^2 of area, if not a little more, which meant the drum would have to be taller to provide enough power, but then the spacecraft wouldn't fit in the rocket's shroud! The only apparent solution to the problem was to use expensive gallium arsenide (GaAs) cells that would only require 3.75 m^2 of surface area. But Woody objected, not just because of the cost, but also because GaAs cells were heavier than Si cells.

Somehow Woody's statement didn't equate with me; though GaAs cells are slightly heavier than Si cells, we would need fewer of the former. I went with Woody to his office to get the data on the cells and found that the array would be a 1 or 2 kg lighter if we used the GaAs cells, and we could even make the solar drum shorter by 3 to 5 cm in height — and that would help us fit into the small LLV2 shroud. Basically, because of the shroud problem, we were going to have to use GaAs cells anyway. I was annoyed that Woody hadn't done that correctly and wondered why I always had to go with him, and the other engineers, to dig out the correct answers. I guessed they were just used to throwing money and mass at a problem, rather than finding a good solution.

Similarly, I was a little annoyed with Irv Benard, who had replaced Ron King as our Propulsion Engineer. Irv still didn't have the information we needed about the fuel tanks I wanted to use and he wouldn't even call up the vendor to find out where it was. I asked myself, "Why can't he just make a call and find out about these tanks?"

Vu was still Vu, but other than those things, the reviews went pretty well and the guys were more or less on time.

I was tired during the review; I had slept badly because I had woken up in the middle of the night because of a nightmare. I had dreamt that a big fish was trying to eat a little fish and I jumped in the water to stop the big fish from eating the little fish. When I woke up, I decided the big fish was Lockheed and the little fish was LEI and/or Lunar Prospector. Freud was right!

Early in the afternoon, I went to Ames and talked to Scott about us getting money. The $10 million was at Ames, so it was just a matter of getting it transferred to Lockheed, but Ames's Cathcart was hemming and hawing and slowing the process down. I said we had to have the money right then, Lockheed wasn't going to give us any more pre-contract money, especially when they knew the money was literally right across the street and why should they, when all that had to be done was to get it through the Ames bureaucracy. I said, "I'm putting my PI hat on, and since NASA expects us to do everything on time, NASA better get the money to us on time, and you're already late."

I called Asif about his starting to work on the mission and if I still could get him to come to Sunnyvale. I was getting more and more disappointed in Asif and if he didn't get there pretty soon, I was just going to tell him not to bother. He was supposed to be the Systems Engineer and he was not even there.

Dougherty said that Lockheed in Denver was going to send six guys down on the 30th to review our spacecraft and tell us how we were doing! At first, I said, "That's fine, let them come on down; it's good to have people look over your shoulder." But then I thought, *I'm not about to have a bunch of bozos, who know nothing about my spacecraft and mission, come down and try to tell me what to do.* I told him, "On second thought, no," and I politely explained why.

He said, "I wasn't even thinking of having you at that meeting."

To which I replied, "Tom, if there is such a meeting, I'm going to be at it." That was it. As soon as I turned my back, Dougherty thought he was running the show. It was still the same old battle and would always be so; Lockheed and its Project Managers were always going to try to take over Lunar Prospector, but they could go to hell. I thought, *I'll be so glad when I am out of Lockheed.*

Wednesday, October 18, 1995:
A Meeting with the New LLV Denver Team

I had meetings with the engineers from AEC (Able Engineering Company) in Santa Barbara, CA, the company that we were considering hiring to build the science instrument booms. I gave them a pep talk and we discussed the technical issues. That meeting went very well; they were enthusiastic about the mission and they impressed me.

I had to go to a meeting at 1:00 PM at Ames with the LLV guys from Denver. Richard had been in Denver the week before and those guys had really gotten their butts chewed out, so they came down to kiss up to me. We talked with Dave Lozier and Ken Galal, my Ames Navigation Team guys, about the launch and the launch trajectory. We gave LLV most of the technical information, and then the LLV guys and I went back to Lockheed for the meeting Dougherty had set up about the launch vehicle issues that concerned me.

At that meeting I told the Denver guys, "I'm very disappointed, at best, with what I have gotten so far. I've been lied to. I've been ignored. Even though you guys are not the ones at fault, you are starting on the negative side of the equation. You have to build up my trust to the point where I believe you can do the job . . . . Remember, I can get a Taurus as late as 16 months before launch . . . your costs are far too high, we have no money in reserves and if we went to Taurus, we would have an extra $3 million . . . . Lunar Prospector is important to everybody and it can't fail. You had better do a good job . . . . I am not a happy customer and you have your work cut out for you . . . . NASA and I are not happy about being the first launch on a LLV2, but there is nothing we can do about that and . . . ." When I was finished with my stern lecture, they all agreed and said they would do everything possible to get my trust back and to provide me with a successful launch. Well, I would see how they performed. I was still more impressed with Orbital Sciences, but maybe the Denver guys were good. If nothing else was accomplished at the meeting, Denver certainly knew they had a very ticked off customer and something had better be done about it.

Thursday, October 19, 1995: Staff Meeting Day

We went over the various subsystems. Woody still hadn't done a damn thing. We had told him we had to use GaAs solar cells, but he still resisted. I asked, "If you don't like it, then what is the answer?"

Woody said, "Well, maybe you could get better silicon cells."

I replied, "Fine, where's the information? We have to make a decision here, because we don't have enough surface area and we can't expand the panels."

I was getting more concerned about Asif; he had simply not responded to my request that he finally start working on the mission. I decided to call him the next day and tell him if he couldn't get to Sunnyvale by Monday, he should just forget it because we were moving ahead and we couldn't wait for him. I was more than a little disappointed in him.

I started bringing Tom up to speed on the instruments and spacecraft. He had a lot to learn, but I thought he could do it.

Dougherty told me in the afternoon that NASA was fussing about the Lockheed fee again. NASA had said, "No science (a failed mission), no fee," and everybody agreed. Then NASA added, "No fee if you run over the budget."

Lockheed replied, "Hell no, we are not going to go into this mission with a deficit." Once again, I could see Mark Saunders's fingerprints all over that brewing mess and I was getting ticked off about it. Both NASA and Lockheed had made mistakes, but we had to pay for all of them. Sure the money was tight, but what NASA was doing was financially squeezing Lunar Prospector to death with its stupid little games. We needed the money (it was still at Ames) and if they didn't get us the $10 million in one week, Lockheed was going to shut Lunar Prospector down!

Once again, Lunar Prospector was being screwed up because of NASA's brinkmanship, bluffing, and posturing. First Mark took the $2 million away; and then he and NASA hit us again with the fee business. Every time we turned around, NASA screwed us. Apparently, NASA wanted to make up for all the sins of the past 20 years by making Lunar Prospector pay all their old debts and show the community, "Hey, we are serious about all this stuff."

Friday, October 20, 1995: The Second Fee Crisis

Scott came over at 8:30 AM and said the fee problem wasn't going to go away. He, Cathcart, Frank, Bob Garner (Dougherty's budget guy), Fred DeFrank, Dougherty, and I had a meeting. I started it by saying, "I don't know anything about this, but this better get done fast, so we can keep Lunar Prospector going."

Frank said, "This issue is just a load of BS; this company cannot accept a situation where it cannot make a fee. It just won't do it. We aren't kidding." We discussed the problem for about an hour and one-half. Dougherty charged NASA with acting in bad faith, and I agreed with him.

Scott, who of course was following NASA party line, said, "It's the budget constraints, . . . that's the rule . . . That is the way Goldin wants it . . . NASA is tired of aerospace companies jacking up the price and NASA wants to make sure that an example is set."

I said, "I don't see any advantage in destroying the program to make a point and cutting your nose off to spite your (NASA's) face. If you kill Lunar Prospector, I will be unhappy, Lockheed probably won't care and might even be relieved, but, sure as hell, destroying the first real Discovery mission isn't going to do NASA any good." Finally, after considerable gnashing of teeth, but without anyone getting angry, we had something that was about halfway acceptable to everyone.

I wasn't extremely sympathetic to Lockheed (I never am), but I understood they had to have some profit. Also, I could not understand why Headquarters didn't realize that killing Lunar Prospector and making an example of it over a small budgetary issue would only hurt everyone involved and probably destroy the Discovery Program. If NASA's attitude was, *we would rather kill the program than let you go a nickel over budget*, especially when their own rules allowed up to a 15% overrun, then Discovery wasn't going to work.

After everyone left, Tom, Francisco, and Richard took me out for a belated birthday lunch; we went Mexican.

When we got back, there was once again bad news. Frank and Dougherty had gone to see Henshaw, thinking they had a solution to the fee issues that he would buy, but his answer was a loud, "NO." Henshaw had bought the fact Lockheed was going to have to eat the $5 million development on the TLI Stage, which was bad enough, but he was ticked off (as I was) about the $2 million Mark had ripped off. On top of losing the $2 million, Lockheed would not get any fee if the mission failed, and Henshaw considered that was the equivalent to having two penalties. He said, "No, we've already put $7 million into this mission and now you expect me to not get any fee? The answer is no."

Everybody agreed there should be no fee if there were no science. However, if we got the science, but there was an overrun, NASA was saying, "For every dollar you overrun, we will take a dollar off the fee." That would mean, if Lockheed had a $4.4 million overrun and I flew a perfect mission, Lockheed would get zip out of it. While I didn't care if Lockheed made a penny, Lockheed is not in the business to not make money.

The line was drawn in the sand, and Lockheed was not kidding. I immediately trouped over to Ames while Frank called up Wes Huntress to get him to settle the mess. I told Scott the answer was no and that Lockheed was getting ready to shut Lunar Prospector down in four working days, on the 27th. Scott knew very well that I did not sympathize with Lockheed, but it was unreasonable to ask them to take a bath on the mission.

I told Scott, "We've had Henshaw's total support up until now and now he is saying, piss on it. All that NASA has accomplished is to create ill will in the company; first by making Al Smith mad that we had to ask for, and got, pre-contract money, and now we are losing Henshaw's support over the fee question and Lockheed doesn't care. Either NASA blinks or there isn't going to be a Lunar Prospector Mission. As far as I'm concerned, I can't run a program where every five minutes the rules change. This time NASA has just pushed us too far."

Scott began to realize the danger the mission was in and he called Frank to make sure I had understood everything correctly. Frank said, "Yes, that is exactly our position." Scott promised he would have an answer from Headquarters by 3:00 PM. I excused myself and went back to Lockheed.

I found Frank and Dougherty and I told them what I had said to Scott. Frank thanked me very nicely for backing Lockheed. Frank added, "You did a hell of a good job of negotiating. I don't know why you say you can't negotiate, you just laid it on the line and said that's it and didn't blink, then they blinked." Nice words to hear, but Headquarters had not yet blinked.

Frank and I agreed that if NASA pulled the plug on Lunar Prospector, we were going straight to Congress with a position paper exposing NASA. We both felt that Lockheed had bent over backwards to get a workable contract, that Lockheed had admitted its mistakes, that NASA had also made mistakes, but that we had to pay for all the mistakes and that was what we would tell Congress.

About 5:00 PM I got a call from Scott. He said he had talked to Headquarters and basically, what it boiled down to was that Mark was still trying to put the screws to us and Wes Huntress told him, "No!"

Even after Headquarters had decided on a solution that they thought might be acceptable, Mark had still said, "No, No, No." It was all Mark, and I was getting tired of his obstructionism.

But Headquarters had an agreement they thought was acceptable to Lockheed. Scott called Lockheed, they discussed it, and Lockheed said, "Yes, that would be acceptable." *The solution was exactly what we started out with in the contract!*

That whole mess was caused simply because NASA, probably just Mark, wanted to change the contract to Lockheed's disadvantage. I thanked Scott for the good job he had done and then I complained bitterly to him about Mark. I said, "This whole thing was just a bunch of crap. All the difficulties we have had have been caused by Mark trying to screw Lockheed and that's unacceptable."

Scott said, "Well, then I've got good news for you. Mark is being reassigned, he will just take care of the AOs and somebody else will be managing the Discovery Program." Scott was right, that was good news.

I also complained that I was tired of Headquarters getting involved in all those issues; according to our contract, I was supposed to be dealing with Scott, not with Headquarters. Happily, Wes seemed to be of the same opinion, because as Scott said, "Wes did not call Frank back, rather he called me, so I could handle it."

I said, "I realize that, but I still think I'm going to complain to the appropriate people at Headquarters because of all this BS — this is supposed to be a cooperative arrangement, not an adversarial one."

Thus ended a long, hard, tiring, and annoying day — a wasted day, because Mark wanted to screw Lockheed and in the process, Lunar Prospector. However, the way seemed clear for us to get our money and officially start Phase C/D within a few days.

Chapter 3-5
Officially Starting Phase C/D

Monday, October 23, through Thursday, October 26, 1995

First of all, I had the flu and I didn't feel well the whole week. I was sick enough that I had to stay home Wednesday. Other than that, the week was fairly good.

The main event was, we finally got official word from Ames that we were to start Phase C/D and would receive $5 million out of the $10 million that was at Ames. The fact that we got just half of the available money was an amazing demonstration of how bad bureaucracies and bureaucrats are. Cathcart just didn't want to do the contract during the week, because he was looking forward to taking a vacation! Before he left, he did a provisional contract for $5 million to keep us going in just FIVE MINUTES! Damn it, the fat SOB could have done that 10 days earlier when the $10 million was sent to Ames. That was very annoying.

We had meetings about the spacecraft all week. Monday's subsystem review went well, except for a couple of things. When I looked at the diagram that was being used for the Finite Element Model to determine the effects of vibrations and stresses during launch, the engineer had the point masses that represented the fuel and the fuel tanks, i.e., over half of the spacecraft's mass, in the wrong places. He had them at about 0.7 spacecraft radii from the spacecraft's spin axis and I was sure they were at about 0.4 spacecraft radii. I asked the guy how he got his numbers and he said he just took the drawing and measured it with a ruler, since the drawing did not have dimensions on it. Sure enough, he had made a mistake and the tank point masses were not properly placed in his model. I told Vu and all the other guys to get a list of coordinates of all the spacecraft components and get them on all the drawings.

Similarly, I found an error in Al Tilley's placement of the fuel and the tanks in his calculations of the spacecraft's moments of inertia! He had misread their coordinates! When he corrected that, the moment of inertia with respect to the spin axis dropped a little bit, but still was 7% higher than for the other two axes. However, that was too close to the stability limit for comfort. In order to be a stable spinner, the moment of inertia with respect to the spin axis must be at least 5% greater than those of the other axes. We were going to have to watch the moment of inertia ratio like hawks.

I was disturbed that the engineers were making such fundamental mistakes, but pleased I was finding the errors. It was becoming very clear that I was going to have to check everything myself if I wanted to be sure Lunar Prospector was designed and built properly.

Woody and I had finished modeling the power usage during the lunar eclipses and we found we only needed a 7 amp-hr battery for the worst eclipse Lunar Prospector would have to endure. Since that eclipse wouldn't occur until after the main mission was over and we were in the extended mission, we could even use a 5 or 6 amp-hr battery, if we could find one in that range. I called and left a message for Wayne Stevens to get the data on the less massive batteries OMNI had in their original design of Lunar Prospector.

Also, I gave up on Asif. He had sent a fax indicating he could only work three days a week on Lunar Prospector, because he wanted to spend time working at another company. I thought, *to hell with it*, and let him know I was no longer interested in having him work on Lunar Prospector.

Most of the week was filled with meetings, one way or the other. We had a meeting on the launch environments, our normal staff meeting on Tuesday, and a meeting with the TLI Stage engineers to see how that was going. I set up and/or prepared for a meeting with my Spectrometer Group at Los Alamos, one at JSC to talk with Kent and my other friends in the old Lunar/Mars planning office, a meeting in Omaha with Julius and his Space Grant Consortium to discuss the Lunar Prospector Outreach Program, and finally one where I was to give a talk in San Diego.

The Florida Space Authority called and asked me to come to the Cape and give a talk on Lunar Prospector, but I postponed that one for two months because I was not going to go there after having been on travel for the previous two weeks.

Friday, October 27, 1995

I still felt really bad because of the flu, but I went to work anyway. Tom (who had settled in Gilroy; we took turns driving to work together) drove us into work, while I slept in the car.

Dougherty and I went to Ames to talk with Sylvia and Scott. Dougherty had gone through our budget in great detail and found that we had just $200,000 of reserves or 0.3% of the total budget. We discussed how we would manage to get by with essentially no reserves (remember the $2 million Mark had taken away from us?). Dougherty said that despite the lack of any significant amount of reserves, Lunar Prospector was doable, but it was going to be tough. I was very pleased with Dougherty's performance in the budget arena; he is very good at that.

We discussed personnel and Dougherty told Scott he had brought Dale Vaccarello on board, but Scott didn't know Dale. Dougherty gave him some background information on Dale and said he was already farther into the engineering details than he was, which was more than true. Dougherty didn't understand the engineering, period. Happily that meant he was staying out of my hair, which was really good. However, Dale did understand the engineering and was doing a really good job. I was pleased about that and I told Scott so.

Tom called Asif about the battery OMNI had planned to use and then made calls to the battery vendors to get the details. As I expected, Tom was doing the things I needed to have done and was doing what the engineers were not doing. Also he was beginning to pick up on the engineering very nicely and he really began helping me keep track of the critical issues, mainly the power and the mass. Thus, Tom was really beginning to function as my deputy and I remained very confident that, together, we were going to be able to pull off the mission, despite Lockheed and NASA. I was pleased.

I got the information from Tom Chinn I needed about the masses of the various graphite epoxy structural elements of the spacecraft and I did my version of the spacecraft's mass property tally. I found the calculated mass would be at my goal of 290 kg, if we could get the battery down to 4.6 kg. I was pleased and optimistic that I could keep the mass down, despite the tendency of spacecraft to get heavier than calculated as they are actually built.

The TLI Stage guys came from Denver for a meeting at 1:00 PM. Happily, the meeting went perfectly. They had done a good job and gave us a decent presentation about the TLI Stage. They still didn't know the cost of the stage, but Dougherty told them the total cost of the LLV2 and TLI Stage had to be $25 million or less. Other than that, Dougherty pretty much kept quiet and the Denver guys discussed the TLI Stage details with me.

Since Bill Feldman had warned me that if the helium gas used to pressurize the fuel tanks in the LLV2's Orbit Adjustment Module and in Lunar Prospector were to get into the GRS detector, it would be degraded, I warned the Denver engineers about the helium problem.

By quitting time, I was satisfied that it had been good day, even though I felt crummy — in addition to the flu, I had somehow broken a rib. I was really looking forward to recuperating during the weekend.

Monday, October 30, 1995: Subsystem Review Day

Not all of the guys were at the meeting, and those that were didn't show up on time! Dougherty didn't seem to care — maybe he was used to it, but I did care.

We had a big discussion with the structure engineers about the mounting of the instruments on the booms. It turned out the instruments were all to be mounted with the bolts coming in from behind the boom tip plates (on which the instruments were to be mounted). That meant that anytime there was a problem during integration and test, we would have to deploy the booms to be able to get in there to unbolt the instruments. However, the booms were not meant to be deployed more than a couple of times (one or two test deployments plus the final deployment in space). To avoid overstressing the booms and their deployment mechanism before launch, we were trying to find ways around that serious problem.

We also discussed how we would fill the fuel tanks. Normally, each tank has a fill valve and a drain valve, but I wanted to do away with all the extra plumbing and valves and just have one fill valve for all three tanks, thereby saving both mass and money, as well as keeping the propulsion system simple. My solution for loading the three tanks equally was to put the helium pressurant in first and then force the fuel into the tanks via a common fill line and fill valve. If we ever needed to drain the tanks, the helium pressurant would blow the fuel back out the fill line. There was no need for a separate drain system. Even though what I suggested worked on paper, Irv was concerned we would end up with different amounts of fuel in each of the three tanks. Though we needed to work the issue more, I really wanted to have just one fill line and one fill valve, so we proceeded with that idea.

Woody said we needed a 9 amp-hr battery. That worried me because it would be fairly massive and I saw no reason for having more than a 5 amp-hr battery based on the eclipsed data we had worked through a week earlier. Later, I looked at Woody's information. One company, Eagle Picher, had a 9 amp-hr battery that cost about $370,000 and had a mass of 11 kg — far too heavy. South Company had a 7 amp-hr battery that was much cheaper, about $100,000, and had a mass of only 9 kg — I thought we might use that one. But Eagle Picher also had a 4.8 amp-hr battery whose capacity was actually 5.4 amp-hr and whose mass was only 6 kg! That sounded even better, but we didn't have its price information. Also, the average Depth Of Discharge (DOD) of that small a battery during the maximum nighttime pass of 47 minutes would be about 60%, which was high, but probably OK for a one year mission. Nevertheless, we were going to check to see if a 60% DOD was OK before we went to the 4.8 amp-hr battery. Assuming it was, the choice of the battery really came down to two things. If we could get the 7 amp-hr, South Company battery for $100,000, we would probably buy it and take the 3 kg hit in the mass. But if it turned out the 4.8 amp-hr Eagle Picher battery didn't cost too much more than $100,000, we would go with that battery. There was just no reason to have more than a 5 amp-hr battery, and if I could get the cost and mass down, I would be very happy.

Monday was a good day, except my broken rib hurt all day.

Tuesday, October 31, 1995

As a result of the merger between Lockheed and Martin Marietta, the Martin part of the new combined leadership decided that Lockheed didn't know how to conduct successful programs. Even though I agreed that Lockheed didn't know what it was doing, Martin's saying so was an extreme case of "the kettle calling the pot black." Regardless, a Martin team went around trying to tell the managers of the different Lock-heed facilities how to be successful. As a Lockheed manager, Dougherty had to endure that BS and had been asked to talk about Lunar Prospector. Of course, he asked me to be there at about 11:00 AM to back him up in case there were questions (gee, as a Lock-heed manager, wasn't he supposed to know all the answers?). When I got there at 11:00, a guy from Gravity Probe B (a Stanford University mission being done with Lockheed) was babbling and he kept babbling until about 12:15 PM! By the time Dougherty was on and then talked for 40 minutes, I had spent over two hours getting nothing accomplished and that kind of shot the day.

To make the day even worse, I was in useless meetings all the rest of the day. Tom and I tried to get information for the command and downlink lists from Gerry Grismore, who had been on vacation and had done nothing. Tom had called Eagle Picher and South Company to get the information on the batteries and he gave Woody that information. Of course, Woody did nothing with it and still hadn't done anything on the power in general. An annoying day!

Wednesday, November 1, 1995: The Able Boom Meeting

The Able Engineering guys flew up from Santa Barbara for a 9:40 AM meeting to discuss the design of the booms. We had decided to have them build the booms and they were getting ready to start construction and needed to get a contract signed. Hot damn, Lunar Prospector hardware was finally going from the paper stage to the metal, plastic, and nuts and bolts stage — Phase C/D was getting real!

I started the meeting with a pep talk. I first told the Able guys that we had gotten $10 million and were officially starting phase C/D — because Congress had directed NASA to get us the money, so we could get started even though the government was operating on a continuing resolution. I wanted them to know that Lunar Prospector was very important to Congress. Then I said, "You are not contractors, you guys are part of our team," and they really liked that.

After the pep talk, I told them we were concerned about the mounting of the instruments on the booms that we had pondered over during the previous subsystem review meeting.

They started their presentation. They had devised a very neat latching mechanism that would allow the instruments to be securely latched during launch and would still allow all three booms to be released simultaneously (so much for Vu's nonsense). The mechanism had a central unit that held the release mechanism, the viscous damper, and the reel that held three lanyards which connected the booms to the viscous damper (so the viscous damper could slow down the boom deployment), and had three spindly arms that extended to — and would be bolted to — the sides of the spacecraft where booms were located, so we called the device the "Spider."

Given the Spider's absolute criticality to the mission, we discussed and worked it over in great detail. As part of the discussion, we also talked about how the Spider was going to be mounted to the three aluminum-mounting plates that carried the three canisters that held the three undeployed booms on the sides of the spacecraft. I pointed out that we had to tie the Spider directly to those plates as a unit. We couldn't mount the Spider and the plates independently on the graphite epoxy load-bearing structure, because the graphite epoxy surfaces are not flat, machined surfaces. Hence, we wouldn't be able to get the exact alignment we would need for the whole thing to work properly. We discussed the issue for some time and decided that the Spider, the plates, and the canisters had to be constructed and mounted into the spacecraft as an integrated unit, otherwise there was no way we could get everything properly aligned.

I was really impressed with their work; they had designed everything really well. The only trouble was, the entire mechanism was heavy. It appeared the whole thing would have a mass of some 5 or 6 kg — a real hit when I was continually fighting to keep the mass of the spacecraft down. But there was nothing I could do about it; the Spider was far too important for me to worry about its mass (but worry I did). Regardless of that, we had a very good meeting and by the time we finalized most of the design, it was lunchtime.

After a nice lunch in our cafeteria, we went back to the meeting and worked through the rest of the issues.

Able had a budget guy with them and he said towards the end of the meeting that they were going to have to charge a lot more money than they had originally proposed, because we were asking them to do more than we originally asked. Able's original estimate was $325,000 and the budget guy implied that there was maybe half a million dollars worth of work to be done. Vu said, "If you go up to a half million dollars, we'll have to reconsider, because we haven't got that kind of money." For once, Vu was right and I backed him up.

Bob Crawford, Able's Senior Vice President, said they had to go or they would miss their airplane. I said, "Thanks for coming. I really appreciate your interest and capabilities, especially because the booms are the second most critical part of the mission. The launch vehicle will either kill us or get us on to our translunar trajectory. Then the next most important thing is the booms — if they don't deploy, the mission is over" (if the booms didn't deploy, Lunar Prospector would become an unstable spinner when we used up fuel during the long lunar orbit insertion burns and it would start to tumble. We would then lose control of it and lose the mission even before Lunar Prospector had reached its final 100 km altitude, mapping orbit).

They knew how critical their work was and how important the mission was. Bob said to me, as he pointed to the budget guy, "I don't care what he says, we are going to get it done for what you can afford. We're not going to charge you a half million bucks. Do you understand what I am saying?"

I answered, "Yes, I hear you," and thought, *great, they want to help us and though that doesn't mean they won't have to charge more than the $325,000, they will do their best to cut costs and give us the best booms they possibly can.* I was very pleased about that.

Dougherty came by and told me that LLV was again trying to have us put a computer in my spacecraft and having the spacecraft control the TLI Stage. I just about flipped. I was really ticked off.

I found Richard, who was by then our Launch Vehicle Engineer and who should have taken care of that, and chewed him out royally. I told him he should have told the LLV guys that was not acceptable — it had never been an option. Richard defensively said he had told them that, he had redlined it out of their proposal, but they kept putting it back in. Then he said they wanted to get an estimate of how much it would cost us to add a computer. Richard, in an attempt to try to make that option appear so costly that LLV would just automatically throw it out, said it would be an $11 million impact and a three-month schedule slip — that was pure nonsense, the spacecraft was only $14 million to start with! I gave him hell for doing that because, as I said, "I'm not interested in giving them a bunch of fictitious numbers (one of Richard's favorite pastimes) which, when they check them out, are found to be high by a factor of three or four or more. It makes us look stupid when we get caught (and it was always easy to catch Richard's fabrications). LLV will say these are our options, here is what they cost and we'll do this one — and we will be the ones left holding the bag. This is simply not an option; it is as simple as that. I am the Principal Investigator and this is not acceptable to me, period. It never has been and never will be. We have a spacecraft designed and we are going into construction with it as designed."

Richard said, "OK, OK, I'll tell them and say if they have any questions, they should ask you."

I said, "That's correct; now they're in trouble again, it's the same old LLV crap."

Richard said, "They're just trying to get out of doing the TLI Stage." Same old LLV song — just a different verse. I was again ticked off at LLV and even more determined to get a Taurus.

Apparently, I was getting through to the engineers that I meant business, because Tom, Richard, and Francisco all said that when I came down the hall, everybody ducked in hopes I wouldn't see them.

November 1 was a long, hard, tiring, but fruitful day, except for LLV. I was so tired that I was even looking forward to the trip to Omaha, Houston, and Los Alamos, just to get away from Lockheed for a few days, and I could hardly wait until Rebecca and I went to Disneyland for a real vacation.

Thursday, November 2, 1995: Staff Meeting Day

First thing in the morning, I talked to Dougherty about the battery because he wanted us to decide which battery we wanted so we could get it ordered. Dougherty asked me why Woody had not gotten us the information. I said, "Because Woody is doing nothing, he's just procrastinating."

Dougherty said, "I'm not sure we want a battery that small," but I disagreed. Since he didn't understand anything about the power issues and, like the rest of the engineers, just wanted something with lots of margin to be on the safe side, instead of just getting one that satisfied the requirements, he had nothing to say about it as far as I was concerned. But we still needed the data on the various available batteries, and Dougherty wanted to give Woody more time to get it.

I replied, "Since it's a matter of just getting vendor information, Tom can take care of that. I know Woody doesn't really want Tom to do it, but Tom will quickly dig up the information on the temperature sensitivity of the various batteries, the number of (charge-discharge) cycles they can take, and their costs." With that, Dougherty began to understand I was taking the engineering assignments away from some of the engineers because they were not doing the work, and I was having Tom do it. That way I was getting things done.

Interestingly, I had a discussion with Dale Vaccarello about the cost and mass savings we would have by using the 4.8 amp-hr battery instead of a 9 amp-hr battery and Dale understood the entire logic. Dale was clearly way ahead of Dougherty on all the technical issues and I was beginning to wish that Dale were my Lockheed Project Manager and not Dougherty. In addition, Dale was getting just as frustrated as I was about the damned engineers not getting anything done.

We had our staff meeting from 8:00 to 10:00 AM and the stupid Martin committee that had been running around trying to tell Lockheed how to run their programs came to our staff meeting so it could go through their 47 rules on how to run successful meetings! Dougherty started the meeting and began babbling. It was clear from what he said he again thought he was in charge of the mission. I didn't feel he was doing it maliciously, rather he was just so used to running programs he just slid right back into the old role of the "in total control" Project Manager. Since Lockheed really wanted him to do so, the only resistance against him doing so was from Ames and me. Short of an all out war, the situation was never going to change.

The stupid committee members soon started their asinine, kindergarten discussion of their 47 points and I just got up and left, as did Tom and Sylvia. Then Tom and I talked to Sylvia about our going to LEI while we waited for those numskulls to finish. That was one of the stupidest things I had seen, a committee spending all week, wasting two hours of my time on Tuesday and then wasting my whole team's time on their nonsense! I could not believe how childish and silly their presentation was — at least what I heard of it.

After that, at about 11:00 AM, we started our real staff meeting. I got a sandwich from the cafeteria and ate lunch during the meeting. One major issue was, of course, the 4.8 amp-hr Eagle Picher battery or something similar, and hopefully, something cheaper.

Irv Bernard said he was concerned because the LLV2 launch environment was so bad that the vibrations could force the engine valves in Lunar Prospector's engines to open and the engines would fire — during launch! Clearly, such engine firings could destroy the vehicles! We were probably going to have to put a Propellant Isolation Valve (PIV) in the spacecraft to keep the engines from firing during launch. The LLV2 issue was getting absurd; its launch environment made it beyond useless and I was getting more ticked off about it.

Irv had some other propulsion items, none of which was critical. The main one was the alignment of the engines; because the engines we were going to use have right angle nozzles, they couldn't be mounted on the spacecraft very accurately. We would have to align each engine after it was mounted to get its thrust vector pointed in the right direction.

We got Able's new cost estimate for the booms and it was $440,000. We couldn't afford that, so something had to give, but budget issues were Dougherty's problem and I knew he would take care of it.

Friday, November 3, through Tuesday, November 7, 1995: The Trip to Omaha, Houston, and Los Alamos

I left for Omaha on Friday about noon and got there that evening. The Space Grant Consortium Meeting started the next morning. I talked about the mission, about the downlink requirements, and about the possibility of setting up a small worldwide tracking network with Code O's help. Several of the Consortium universities, as well as others in Japan, Spain, Argentina, and a number of other countries, were very interested in setting up stations. That meeting went very well.

I flew to Houston. I had dinner with John and Barbara Gruener on Sunday. George French had offered John a job with Moonlink in Green Bay, WI, and I thought that was great. John was interested, but he was very cautious and nervous. Barbara was much more aggressive about having him talk to George French, in part, because her family is in the Green Bay area.

Monday I talked to John Connolly and a few of the guys in Building 31 at JSC. They had a very good scheme for getting man back to the Moon by 2001. They proposed using existing equipment or that which was already under development. Their lander would put a crew of four on the Moon for a six-day stay. They would use a Russian tug to get the lander on the way to the Moon and have a fuel tank depot in LEO, where the tug would be refueled and launched with the lander as a second stage. The tug/lander stack would use the tug to get into a highly elliptical Earth orbit. The tug and lander would then separate and the tug would swing back to the LEO fuel depot and refuel for another flight, while the lander would execute a small burn that would put it onto its translunar trajectory. The Lander would then land on the Moon, stay the six days, and then return to Earth, where it would do an aerobraking maneuver and then dock with the tug at the fuel depot to get ready for another mission. It was a good plan and I hoped that it would get man back to the Moon — soon.

I flew off to the last stop on my trip — Los Alamos.

Woody, Alex Kochergin (who was working with Gerry Grismore on the C&DH), Tom Chinn, and Dougherty had come from Sunnyvale for the Critical Design Review (CDR) for the NS and APS and for a discussion of the GRS's graphite epoxy housing and, of course, Bill Feldman and his technical crew were all in attendance. There were a lot of issues, like the venting of gases from the instruments, the launch environment, the thermal modeling Lockheed was supposed to have done, that were not very well defined. Despite those deficiencies, the CDR went well.

Bill said the LLV2 launch environment was so bad that the photomultiplier tubes in the GRS could be destroyed or, at least, their gains would change during the horrific launch vibrations! Bill had flown the same photomultiplier tubes at normal launch loads without a problem. He said, "I've also run tests at high enough g loads to change the gain. A gain change means that the photomultiplier tubes were shaken in their housing so much that their internal components shifted — and the LLV2 g loads are even higher than what I tested, so I'm really worried about the tubes breaking."

The whole mess with the damned launch vehicle was getting sickening. What Bill had just told us, coupled with what Irv told us the previous Thursday about the engines firing during launch, just put the frosting on the cake. The LLV2 was useless and I had to find a way to get on a Taurus or potentially lose the spacecraft during launch!

Friday, while I was on the trip, Woody and Dougherty had tried to sneak the 9 amp-hr battery back into the spacecraft design, but Tom stopped them. Without Tom watching my back, I would have lost ground every time I went on a trip! Instead of doing good engineering, the guys were just doubling or tripling their margins to cover their incompetence. I thought that was what was going on with the LLV2, too — if so, then maybe the launch environment wasn't as bad as reported — I hoped so, because I doubted I would succeed in getting a Taurus.

Wednesday, November 8, 1995

After what I had learned during the previous several days, I was greatly concerned about the launch environment. Even Dougherty came back from the meeting at Los

Alamos saying, "We can't handle this environment; it will destroy all the science instruments. Either LLV gets the damned environment down, one way or another, or something is going to have to give."

Richard and I talked about the launch environment and then we had a telecon
with the LLV people about it. The result was that we concluded we would have to do
our own model of the launch environment (why in hell were we paying LLV, if we had
to do all of their work). Richard and I found out what was needed to be done to get a
first order approximation of the launch environment for our immediate needs.

Tom got the information on the battery from Eagle Picher. It turned out they
didn't really have a 22 cell, 4.8 amp-hr battery, but they could easily build one for us and
it probably would have a mass of 6 to 6½ kg. Also, they suggested we might use a Magnum battery that would be cheaper than a super-NiCd battery, but they had never built
one of them before. As far as I was concerned, the battery issue was getting solved.

I was getting concerned about personnel; Dougherty kept forgetting who was the
PI and who was the customer. Gerry Grismore wrote another one of his nasty letters
condemning the program and me, Woody was doing nothing, and Richard kept spending part of his time working with Dom to keep on his good side. I decided to tell
Dougherty to get rid of them and get some people to work on the program who knew
what they were doing and who would work for the program, not against it! All that
Lockheed crap was getting tiring.

Thursday, November 9, 1995

I talked to Scott and he said that Mark was getting more and more bizarre. First,
regarding my going to LEI, Mark said he didn't think there was any conflict of interests
between Lockheed and me! Scott thought that was just absurd and I wondered how far
Mark had his head up his ass. Despite his not seeing any conflict of interests, he had no
objection to my being in LEI, if we had a memorandum of agreement between all three
parties. Then Mark had told Scott he saw no reason why the PIs should run Discovery
missions! He thought the programs should be run by JPL, in the old way — he just did-
n't think PIs could run programs! He was crazy as hell. He was just going back to the
old mode of doing things. Scott and I were both incensed. I told Scott, "This is another reason why I should get out of Lockheed and get into LEI, because if they start screwing around and have JPL run this, it will destroy the program. If Headquarters tries to
pull this stunt off, I'll go to Congress and tell them to stop NASA from destroying Discovery before it ever gets started."

Mark's change in attitude about Discovery was very disturbing. It was really stupid that he was beginning to question the whole concept of Discovery and the role of
the PI. He didn't understand that if I weren't running Lunar Prospector, Lockheed
would have already run it into the ground.

Friday, November 10, through Monday, November 13, 1995:
Disneyland and the San Diego Meeting

Friday morning, before Rebecca and I left for Disneyland and the San Diego meeting, we had our staff meeting that had been postponed from Thursday. There were no
critical items, except the battery, and that was going to be addressed afterwards in a
meeting between Tom, Woody, some Lockheed battery engineers, and me.

The battery engineers saw nothing wrong with my having a 4.8 amp-hr battery, though they were concerned about the voltage drop of the batteries as they discharged. They suggested that instead of using the standard 22 cells (the basis for the standard 28 v DC spacecraft power system) we use 24 cells — no big deal. They were going to check that out and try to put the whole battery issue to bed very quickly. I hoped they would get us the information by Tuesday so we could get the battery issue settled and the battery ordered.

Rebecca and I flew to LA and took the Disneyland bus to Disneyland, where we stayed in the Disneyland Hotel for two days and had a great time.

Then we went to San Diego for a meeting hosted by Mike Simon at International Space Enterprises, and I gave my talk on Lunar Prospector Monday.

Before I did, a young woman from the European Space Agency talked about their plans to have a lunar lander with a rover. As usual, there was nothing to it; just the usual studies and I couldn't understand why they had picked a complicated lander/rover mission as their first lunar mission, instead of something simpler. It was pathetic; there was no rhyme or reason to what they were doing. When I asked her about that, she said, "It's basically that we want to learn how to do missions and we have to do something we can do." Clearly they did not have a coordinated plan. As I knew from spending a decade in Germany, the Europeans simply do not understand lunar science or how to focus a program. Rebecca found the young lady's talk unusually boring and very disappointing. I didn't think the Europeans would get beyond the paper study stage of that idea.

George French was at the meeting and he said that Moonlink was going extremely well. I talked to him about hiring John Gruener to work on Moonlink and I said John would do a good job for him.

Rebecca and I flew back to the Bay Area and I stopped at Ames and Lockheed to see what was happening before we drove home to Gilroy.

While at Ames, Scott said the government had reached a budgetary deadlock and was getting ready to shut down. If it did shut down, they (meaning Scott and Sylvia, but in reality, all government personnel in general) might or might not be furloughed for some indefinite length of time. We had the $10 million and that would keep us going for a while, but if a shut down went on too long, we would run out of money. No one had any idea of what to expect. The politicians — the President and the Republican leadership — were getting together to try to get the budget issue settled, but so what?

Tuesday, November 14, 1995

The Government shut down, but other than that, Tuesday was a fairly good day.

We had a battery meeting. Woody got everyone there at 4:00 PM and the battery engineers agreed with me that the 4.8 super-NiCd battery could do the job; the only question was the cost. We decided to put out a RFP to get the required information on the Magnum and the super-NiCd batteries.

I talked to Dougherty again about Woody and Gerry Grismore and told him they were still not performing. They were responsible for two of the major spacecraft subsystems and if they continued to fail to do their jobs, the mission would also fail. They had to go and be replaced by good engineers, but Dougherty was very reluctant to get rid of people. I didn't know why. However, as a result of my crabbing about Gerry, Dougherty actually had a talk with him, but I wondered if it did any good.

Wednesday, November 15, 1995: Clinton and Lewinsky

The government shut down had no immediate effect on our operations; Scott and Sylvia were furloughed, but were still working on Lunar Prospector when needed. Though the government was shut down, Clinton and one of his staff, a young, flirtatious, White House intern by the name of Monica Lewinsky, were busy. While my staff and I were busy trying to get America back to the Moon, Clinton and Lewinsky were busy starting their illicit sexual tryst that should have led to Clinton's removal from office. Though that unfortunately did not happen, Clinton and Lewinsky disgraced the Presidency, distracted the nation from essentially all other issues for months on end, and led to an interesting little episode for Lunar Prospector over two years later.

Tom and I worked on a computer model of the spacecraft and Francisco wanted to help, because he was tired of doing BS and wanted to do something more interesting — I was pleased that he did.

Gerry came to my office, after having been chewed out by Dougherty for not doing anything, and gave me the command list I had been asking for — minus Woody's power commands, of course.

After lunch, Dougherty told me he had just found out the LLV2's environment was even worse than we thought (you ask, how was that possible?)! The problem was a 50 to 60 Hz, high amplitude vibration, a so called "pipe organ effect," that occurs during a 120 Castor motor burn (the 1st and 2nd stages of the LLV2 are Castor 120 solid fuel motors), a phenomenon I already knew about, but didn't know how bad it really was. The pipe organ effect starts at the ignition of a Castor 120 with a large amplitude at about 50 Hz and, as the burn continues, the frequency sweeps up to 60 Hz and the amplitude drops. Dougherty found out about it, not from the LLV crew, but from the engineers working on Lockheed's Commercial Remote Sensing Satellite or CRSS, that was also to be launched on an LLV2. The CRSS engineers were having major problems because some of that spacecraft's main components had fundamental frequencies in the 50 to 60 Hz range. Unfortunately, we didn't yet know what the fundamental frequencies of Lunar Prospector's components were, so we didn't know how much of a problem we had, but the situation looked really bad. For the first time Dougherty admitted, "If that can't be solved, we are going to have to have a serious look at Taurus." I was extremely pleased he was beginning to look out for Lunar Prospector and not just pandering to Lockheed.

He also surprised me by telling me he had asked for replacements for Gerry and Woody, but said it wouldn't happen very fast. I was surprised and pleased that he was responding to what I had asked him to do and that he was chewing out the guys when they didn't do what I wanted them to do.

Tom and I talked with Bill Feldman and Dave Curtis about the instrument command lists and I told them their money was on its way to them — so they were solvent again.

When Bill gave me the commands for the spectrometers, he told me the GRS and NS did not need to be turned off during burns. I had assumed that, since the GRS and NS have high voltage supplies that could arc and destroy the instruments if they were exposed to low-pressure gasses, the spectrometers should be shut off when we did burns. But that would not be necessary, because, as Bill said, GRS and NS would be encased in thermal shields that would keep the engine exhaust gasses out. That was great; it simplified all the operational procedures. I started reworking the Mission Profile and the Mission Operations Document (MOD) to reflect the changes in the GRS and NS operations.

Thus ended one of the best days I had had on Lunar Prospector. Tom was doing his work better and better. Everything was going smoother and smoother and for the first time in a long time, I wasn't exhausted when I finally got home. I felt that if everything kept getting better that way, we were going to have a successful mission.

Chapter 3-6
Pushing For A Taurus

Thursday, November 16, 1995: Staff Meeting Day

I initially got to work at 5:00 AM, somewhat earlier than usual, since Tom, who didn't get started as early in the morning as I did, was going to drive in independently of me. But, when I arrived, Tom called and said his car had broken down! I had to drive all the way back to Gilroy to pick him up — so much for an early start on the day.

We had our usual Thursday staff meeting in the morning. We went through a number of issues, none of which were problems, and Dougherty said he felt the program was really beginning to roll, as did I.

After hearing about the pipe organ effect, the possible destruction of the GRS, and the need to add a PIV to the propulsion system to ensure that Lunar Prospector's engines didn't fire during launch, Dougherty was finally beginning to get concerned enough about the launch environment that he was willing to go to Orbital Sciences and talk about a Taurus. Since Dougherty probably had to go to an award meeting at Headquarters on December 5, I said, "Well, why don't we go to Orbital then. You're beginning to agree that we need to look at Taurus, so let's just go. Even if the award meeting is canceled, let's go."

Dougherty said, "All right."

I immediately called Orbital and talked to Chris McKelvey, since Joe Padavano was on travel. I told her we wanted to talk with them about a ride on a Taurus and that the issues were the environment, the TLI Stage, and the $23 million price tag. Chris, who knew both how strongly I felt about getting on a Taurus and that their real job was to convince Dougherty to go for the Taurus, was more than happy to set up the meeting. She said, "We'll roll out the red carpet for you, all you have to do is to fly into Dulles."

I started to set up the trip. I decided I would stop off in Houston on the way to DC, since Goldin had been at JSC a few days earlier to review the "back to the Moon plans" that Kent and my other friends were developing and I wanted to keep my finger in that pot. Also, I didn't think I would stay with Pat and Julius, because Orbital Sciences is near Dulles and it would be easier to fly into Dulles and stay at a hotel near Orbital Sciences.

I was very pleased that Dougherty was waking up to reality. But, as he had said to me, "You're always moving too fast for me. You're always way out ahead of me. I'm much slower at deciding these things." I thought that was what was going on; he was conservative to n^{th} degree, while I pushed ahead. Regardless of the reason, we were working better and better together and I was pleased and relieved that we could start seriously discussing Taurus.

Friday, November 17, 1995

It was a good day. Most people were gone, so Tom and I got to work undisturbed. We got all the LEI paperwork taken care and sent it off to Todd Greenwalt. I called Todd to tell him that the LEI paperwork was on its way and that I expected to be in Houston on December 5 or 6 and I would stop by to see him.

I finished changing the Mission Profile and the MOD to reflect the facts that Bill did not want the GRS and NS high voltages ever turned off once I had turned them on, and that the MAG/ER commands could be ganged together in a computer load. Also, after Gerry Grismore, Tom, and I had talked about uplink commands, I got the bright idea that we should fix the C&DH software so when I sent the Execute Command to fire the engines, the engine catalyst bed heaters (or cat-bed heaters), that had to be turned on about 30 minutes before a burn so the catalyst was hot, would automatically turn off. That would mean there would be fewer commands sent during a burn sequence, so I asked Gerry to make that change in the C&DH. All that made Mission Operations even simpler — KISS, just the way I like things.

As we went through the propulsion commands, it became clear to me that Tom still didn't know anything about the spacecraft engines. He didn't know how burns would be made, what a Vector Burn is, what an axial engine burn is, how a reorientation maneuver is performed, or anything else. I went through all that with him and tried to figure out how to get him to learn those things, as well as everything else about the spacecraft and mission in general. He was doing a really good job on the bureaucratic issues, the reports and the like, but if he didn't start understanding the spacecraft, it was going to get very serious very quickly. He had to know the spacecraft and mission inside and out, or would not be able to function as my deputy and second in command, and that concerned me.

Scott called and I told him Dougherty had finally woken up to the fact that we have a rocket that might destroy our spacecraft and that we ought to seriously consider getting a Taurus. Scott said he called to tell me, "If you are running out of money, I can quasi-legally make sure you get the other $5 million — even though Ames is officially shut down."

I replied, "The $5 million we have will last us well into December, so it is not critical right now, but it's nice to know."

It had been a good day; in fact, the whole week had been the best week we had ever had on Lunar Prospector since I came to Sunnyvale; everything was working quite well.

Monday, November 20, 1995: Subsystem Review Day

Dougherty was in New York City; he had just gotten remarried and was spending the week showing his new wife his old hometown, so things were quite peaceful.

We had subsystem reviews all morning. As usual, Gerry didn't have his work done; he was always very defensive and very uncooperative. We discussed the 4.8 amp-hr battery and the remaining question was, "How low can the voltage safely go?"

Tom was sick and went home right after we got all the subsystem reviews done.

Tuesday, November 21, 1995

Tom was still sick and stayed home, so I got in very early.

I checked the voltage requirements of everything in the spacecraft. All of the subsystems and the science instruments were designed to function perfectly down to 22 v, would work down to 20 v, and would begin to work poorly only when the voltage was below 20 v. The low voltage question was answered and the answer was, "No problem."

I called Mario Acuña about the latching mechanisms on the ends of the booms, since Able wanted to make the tip plates and the entire mechanism out of stainless steel. As Mario confirmed, and as I was quite certain, stainless steel could not be used since it would mess up the magnetic measurements. Everything had to be made of plastic and titanium, even the springs had to be made of something that was not magnetic. I called Able later and verified what I had told them during our previous meeting regarding the exclusive use of non-magnetic material in the boom mechanisms.

I had a meeting with Scott and Sylvia at 8:00 AM and we discussed the growing concerns about the rocket and the status of the Phase C/D/E contract, which Scott said was almost ready for signature.

While I was at Ames, I stopped by to talk to Bob Jackson about the telecon we were having the next day at 10:00 AM. We were going to choose the S-band frequency for the mission.

In addition to everything else, my appointment calendar was filling up: December 14 — MAG/ER TDR at Berkeley; December 15 — Congressional aide visit at Ames and Lockheed; then the following week, Dougherty and my trip to Orbital Sciences with a stop in Houston; the TDR for the spectrometers common electronic unit (or SES, Spectrometer Electronic System) at Southwest Research Institute in San Antonio, TX; and Vu wanted me to go down to Santa Barbara in a couple of weeks to talk to Able Engineering about the booms.

I received an email from an Air Force cadet at the Air Force Academy in Colorado Springs. His aerospace engineering class project was going to build and launch a small lunar spacecraft called "Blue Moon" and he wanted to inquire about a possible payload for their mission. I called to find out more about what they were up to. When I reached the cadet, he said they wanted to fly a neutron spectrometer by the Moon to see if there was water ice at the South Pole. I asked him to send me the details of the spacecraft and mission so I could understand what they were capable of doing, but I said I doubted they could look for polar water ice using the spacecraft and mission he described. Since that was the case, I would try to convince them to make Blue Moon into a relay satellite for us or to do something else useful. Since I needed to see Eagle Picher in Colorado Springs about the battery anyway, I decided I would go to the Air Force Academy, give a talk on Lunar Prospector if they wanted me to, try to convince them to do something useful with Blue Moon, and see Eagle Picher.

It was a very busy day the whole day, setting up meetings and trips, going to meetings, and checking with everybody about the voltages. I was running from morning until night, but I got a lot done, so it was another satisfying day.

Wednesday, November 22, 1995

Two major events occurred on Wednesday. First, Bob Jackson and I had the telecon to select our mission frequency. There were three S-band frequencies, 2273, 2273.5 and 2275 megaHz, available during the time of the mission. From the data we had been given by the Air Force, the 2273 and 2275 megaHz bands would have interference problems because of the Cluster and Wind satellites, respectively. One of them was located at the Lagrange Point between the Earth and the Sun and the other was out in geomagnetic tail. Once per month each of them would screw-up our communications for a couple of hours and we would lose some of the best data from the MAG/ER. There were also some short period interference problems caused by satellites in LEO, but they would not bother us for two reasons. First, because all our data would be downlinked twice; if we lost a few minutes of data due to interference from a LEO satellite, we would get it during the second downlink 53 minutes later. Second, we expected to have the secondary network of university-built tracking stations. Thus any LEO satellite that was in view of one such station would not be visible at the same time from some of the other stations, so at least one of those stations would receive clean signals from Lunar Prospector. Also, in addition to the interference from Wind, Air Force satellites were screwing up the 2275 megaHz band, so it was definitely out.

I thought we would select the 2273.5 megaHz band, since it had no problems due to Wind, Cluster, or the Air Force, but someone raised a question about possible interference from another Air Force satellite. Bob called the Air Force and asked them what was going on at 2273.5 megaHz. They said they had a satellite transmitting with the carrier at 2272.5 megaHz and with a sub-carrier at 2273.5 megaHz — so they didn't want us at 2273.5 megaHz! That left only the 2273 megaHz. As far as I was concerned 2273 megaHz was it and we would have to accept the little bit of interference from Cluster. Also, since Cluster's primary mission would be over by the time we flew, it was of even less concern.

We had another battery meeting to discuss the low voltage issue. Jim Schirle, the two battery engineers, Woody, and I were supposed to be at the meeting at 3:30 PM. I was annoyed that it was so late in the day, because I had wanted to leave early to start the Thanksgiving break a little early. When we finally got started, only one battery engineer had shown up — but happily the one that had made the worst case calculations for us that showed the battery voltage would never get below 24 v, even after two or three years of 60% DOD. Since I had found that all of the spacecraft's subsystems and the science instruments would function down to 20 v, it wouldn't hurt anything even if the battery voltage dropped somewhat below 20 v; all the concerns about low voltages were unfounded. But as usual, Woody was afraid to make the obvious decision to go with the 4.8 amp-hr, 22 cell battery and was mumbling something about the battery to Jim to get his support. I knew Jim was balking because he had to make some thermal calculations for the battery and design a battery radiator, which were not big jobs. I was really annoyed at Woody and Jim because they just wouldn't make decisions, even when there was no problem! I was getting tired of the overly cautious engineers slowing everything down.

Thursday, November 23, through Sunday, November 26, 1995: The Thanksgiving Break

Rebecca and I had a great Thanksgiving. We went to Clint Eastwood's Mission Ranch Resort Restaurant in Carmel, which is less than an hour's drive from Gilroy. The resort is beautiful and the turkey and all the fix'ins were excellent, though each plate held enough food for three people. After eating, we drove around Carmel and saw the Carmel Mission.

We spent Friday, Saturday, and Sunday recovering from all the turkey and just relaxed and had a good time.

Monday, November 27, 1995: Subsystem Review Day

The subsystem reviews went very well. Things were going quite smoothly. The battery issue was decided as far as I was concerned, though Woody was still flopping around about it.

I set up my trip to go to Washington and then to Houston, and I decided to stop in Phoenix to pay a courtesy call on Spectrum Astro; they were in the midst of finalizing the C&DH design they were building for us and I wanted to make sure they were happy campers, especially since Dom had really ticked them off after we had been selected for flight (see Part Two).

I looked at the material I had been sent about Blue Moon and I called the Air Force cadet. I told him Blue Moon could neither do neutron spectrometer mapping nor Doppler gravity mapping, it simply didn't have the mass and the power to do those things. However, they could carry a magnetometer and go into a high altitude orbit, from which they could monitor the solar magnetic field, and that would allow us to do a better job of interpreting our MAG data collected in our 100 km altitude orbit. I had called Mario earlier and, knowing the value of having solar magnetic field data to go along with the lunar MAG data, he was more than happy to provide Blue Moon with a magnetometer, if necessary, for free. The cadet thought that would be fine.

I told him about my trip to Colorado Springs and my willingness to go to the Academy to talk with them and to give a seminar on Lunar Prospector. He was happy with my suggestion and said he would talk with his professor about my offer. I asked who his professor was and he answered, "Dr. Humble."

I was astounded and asked, "You mean Ron Humble?"

He said, "Yes, do you know him?"

I answered, "Yes, Ron and I are old friends, we worked together at Lockheed in Houston and he was on the original Lunar Prospector Team. What is Ron's number?"

I called Ron and we had a good chat and were both happy that we might be working together again. What a nice surprise — it really is a small world after all!

Tuesday, November 28, 1995

Tom had been having trouble with his post-polio problems. When I picked him up to drive to work, he still wasn't feeling very well. I said he should stay home until he was better, but he said, "No, I'm OK; I can't stay home forever," so I drove us to work. Just after we had arrived, Tom got so bad I had to drive him back down to Gilroy and take him to the hospital where he got some medication and a shot. Then I took him home and drove back to work.

Dougherty was getting even more concerned about the LLV2, especially when he heard from Denver they wanted $5 to $9 million for the TLI Stage! That just wasn't going to fly. Upon hearing that, I talked with Frank and he said the same thing, "If Lockheed doesn't get competitive, then we will go to Taurus."

Chris called up and told me that *Aviation Week* had called Orbital Sciences because they had heard that Taurus was the backup to LLV2 and *Aviation Week* wanted to print it. She wanted to know what I wanted her to tell them. We both had the same idea and that was, "We know nothing about that, but if called upon to launch Lunar Prospector, Taurus can do the job." That way the cat would not be completely out of the bag and yet Orbital Sciences would get credit for saying Taurus could do it.

Irv talked to me about the engines. Happily, because the valves in the engines would be horizontal the way the engines were to be mounted on the spacecraft, they would not be affected by the launch vibrations as much as he thought. The reason is that the main launch vibrations are axial and not horizontal. The possibility of the engines firing during launch was minimal to nonexistent, even if the launch environment was as bad as we thought.

However, we still might need a PIV, because of launch pad safety rules. The rule was, there had to be two actions to cause an engine to fire to protect workers at the pad from getting hurt by inadvertent engine firings. We thought we had solved that requirement earlier, because two commands were required to fire an engine, the first being the firing instruction(s) and the second being the "Execute" command. Then Irv came up with a bright idea and said, "Hey, the spacecraft is not powered up anytime it's on the pad, so the engines can't fire. We don't have to get around that rule; the pad safety people will probably accept that more than anything else we think of." I hoped he was correct — I didn't want to have a 1 kg PIV in the spacecraft for no real reason.

Dougherty and I talked to Sylvia about the LLV and we all agreed if Lockheed didn't start getting it done right and start getting the costs down to $25 million or less, we would go to a Taurus.

We had a meeting about the tracking issues and the frequency allocation. At first I thought it was going to be a messy meeting, but it turned out we just dotted i's and crossed t's. We were requesting the 2273 megaHz frequency; we had to because it was the only one left and the only one with an existing crystal! NASA had to agree with us, because if they didn't, they were going to have to accept the cost and schedule impacts. Normally, it takes two years to get a frequency assignment, but that schedule had to be circumvented and NASA had to find a way of doing it. Even so, since we had to order the crystal right then to stay on schedule, if the international committee did not approve our use of the 2273 megaHz frequency, Lunar Prospector would be sunk — a risk we had no choice but to accept.

We discussed the tracking. I told them about my helping with Blue Moon and that, as a result, I got the idea of trying to get the Air Force to return the favor by helping us track Lunar Prospector. In particular, since the TLI burn was going to occur over Africa and since the spacecraft would not be visible from the DSN tracking station in Canberra, Australia, until some 20 minutes after the TLI burn and separation, I wanted the Air Force to use its tracking airplane during the TLI burn and to use their tracking station on the Seychelles Islands in the Indian Ocean to track us during those first critical 20 minutes of the mission.

Sylvia said Mark wanted Bret to go to the Taurus meeting with Dougherty and me so I called Bret later to talk about that and about my idea of getting Air Force tracking. I told Bret I had mixed feelings about him being at the Taurus meeting. I thought his attending the meeting was a good idea from the standpoint it would strengthen my hand with Orbital Sciences by showing that NASA was supporting my efforts to go on a Taurus. But I was concerned Orbital might then think it was a done deal and that would be very bad, especially if Lockheed caught wind of it. I had talked to Joe Padavano earlier and he agreed the whole situation was very delicate. Bret said he would talk to Mark.

I called Bret right back because I forgot something else and he said Mark wanted to talk to me. I called Mark, who liked the idea of us getting Air Force tracking and he added that a friend of his at the Naval Academy in Annapolis had a 12 meter antenna and he wanted to help track Lunar Prospector.

Interestingly, the Annapolis antenna was one of those the Air Force Academy cadets were going to use for Blue Moon! Since Annapolis is not far from Wallops Island, where the TOTS antenna is located and since TOTS was costing us $400,000, if we could get the Annapolis antenna integrated into our network and get rid of TOTS, we would save the $400,000! Also if Blue Moon had money to pay Mario to build their magnetometer, then I might be able to get them to go in with us and split the costs of building both magnetometer packages. That way we would both save money and basically get two for the price of one, since the cost of building two identical systems is only a little more than just building one. I didn't know if all that would work out, but if it did, we might be able to save $500,000 and I was sure going to try.

I updated the spacecraft mass calculations and found we were still 4 to 5 kg over the 153 kg I had as a goal for the dry (no fuel) mass of the spacecraft. I wanted to have a look at the mass of the spacecraft structure to see if we could push it down any and I was fairly confident I would eventually get the mass down below my goal. In any case, I was pleased the mass was certainly not growing the way it would have if the engineers were allowed to do what they normally did, but I had to watch them like a hawk.

At 2:30 PM I left for Stanford, where I was going to give a colloquium hosted by the Gravity Probe B Mission Team. My talk on Lunar Prospector was well received and afterwards, they told me all about Gravity Probe B and showed me some of their amazingly precise equipment that was going to test part of Einstein's theory. I thought Gravity Probe B was very interesting and they thought Lunar Prospector was neat.

All in all, it was a very productive day, but, because of the colloquium, I got home quite late, at about 8:00 PM.

Thursday, November 30, 1995: Staff Meeting Day

Nothing much of significance happened. We had a staff meeting that ate up most of the morning and then I spent the afternoon at the Lockheed facilities in Palo Alto where I gave another talk on Lunar Prospector.

Friday, December 1, 1995: Preston and the Lawrence Livermore Labs

Preston had invited me to give a talk at Lawrence Livermore Labs. Rebecca and I drove over there and spent all day at Lawrence Livermore. I gave the Lunar Prospector talk and then talked with Preston Carter and his staff about Clementine 2 and the other things they were doing over there. We saw the incredible laser facilities that were being used to study nuclear fusion. Like Gravity Probe B, that was all very interesting and it was great to see Preston again.

Monday, December 4, 1995: The Final Decision on the Battery

We had subsystem reviews all morning. There were several interesting things. First, Dougherty thought we were going to have to build the TLI Stage, which I did not want to do. Richard said it would cost $4 million if we did it, and that was a million more than we could afford. As far as I was concerned, I was going to get a Taurus if it was the last thing I did.

I talked to Scott and Sylvia at Ames. According to Scott, Goldin told the Houston crew if they could keep the "Man Back on the Moon" idea within the budget constraints he had leveled on them, he was going to make an announcement in three or four months about NASA's going back to the Moon! That was very positive news and made my efforts to make sure JSC kept Lunar Prospector at the very top of their viewgraph charts very worthwhile.

I told Scott I was really concerned about our getting the contract signed because the whole thing with the rocket was coming to a head. I said, "It's clear Denver isn't going to do the LLV2 for anything we can afford and they're going to be $7 to $9 million higher than Orbital Sciences if they do the TLI Stage, which they didn't want to do anyway. Dougherty is under the delusion that we are going to have to do it and Richard said it will cost us $4 million."

Scott understood I wanted the contract signed before we raised hell about the rocket and went to a Taurus, because I was very concerned Lockheed would just say, "Well, if we don't use the LLV2, then we are not going to build the spacecraft." We simply had to have Lockheed under contract to build the spacecraft before all hell broke loose. Scott agreed and said they were trying to get the contract finished.

Also, Scott said NASA would not let the launch get all screwed up and would force Lockheed to have a Launch Vehicle Review, which was exactly what I wanted. While Dougherty and I were gone for the rest of the week, Scott was going to meet with Henshaw and the rest of them at Lockheed and tell them NASA was not at all happy about the LLV2 and they want to review the whole issue.

I called Joe Padavano and told him I really wanted to get on his Taurus, that they had to do a damned good job of selling it to Dougherty when we visited them and that the Taurus had to be for $23 million. He asked me, "Should we prepare a bid and a fixed fee price?"

I answered, "Yes. If you can have it ready when we get there and just hand it to us when we walk in, then we would have the evidence we need." That was great; but the whole thing was as dicey as hell and I wished I were already in LEI, so I had more leverage to force the issue and get on a Taurus.

Regarding LEI, I called Todd Greenwalt; he had all the LEI paperwork finished and he had been waiting to get the last bit of information from some other lawyer. He said he would Fed-Ex the package off to the State of California and a copy to me very shortly. If it came the next day (while I was winging my way to DC), Tom could start bugging California on Wednesday and make sure they got our paperwork processed ASAP.

I worked on the spacecraft's mass a little more and I thought we were going to be able to keep it just about where I had hoped — at 143 kg, plus or minus a few kilograms — hopefully on the minus side.

The bid for the battery came in and it was only $109,000 — we had expected it would be two or three times that! That was just for the 22 battery cells; we still had to make the mounting and that would increase the costs a bit, but the total cost would be a lot less than we had planned! We were considering buying the Magnum rather than the Super-NiCd, because Eagle Picher was trying to get people to start flying the newer Magnum. The Magnum cost $103,000 vs. the $109,000 for the super-NiCd. I thought, *to hell with that; that's stupid, why should we go with an unproven battery to save $6,000.* Eagle Picher blew that one. I said to Dougherty, "Just forget it," and he agreed and we finally ordered the battery.

Also, Dougherty had been over to the production center talking about having them build our solar array and they suggested we use slightly substandard cells to cut the cost. That was what I had suggested way back in the beginning, so Dougherty felt pretty positive about the idea and thought we could get a decent price out of those guys.

A good day also ended on a very positive note; the final design of Lunar Prospector was moving right along and soon we could start building it.

Tuesday, December 5, through, Friday, December 8, 1995:
Orbital Sciences, JSC, and Spectrum Astro

I went to Lockheed to work Tuesday morning and ran around doing all kinds of things I had to do before I left for the San Jose Airport at 10:00 AM to fly to Dulles.

Wednesday morning Dougherty and I drove the few kilometers from our hotel near Dulles to Orbital Sciences, but Dougherty got lost despite the short drive. We had an excellent meeting. When we were finished, Dougherty understood that Taurus was quite capable of launching us and Orbital Sciences would do it for $23 million — TLI Stage and all. There were no unanswered questions and no serious problems.

Dougherty flew back to California and I flew to Houston to spend Thursday talking to the guys at JSC about getting man back to the Moon. Unfortunately, they told me Goldin wanted to have it done even more cheaply than they thought possible and I agreed with them.

Friday morning I flew to Phoenix to go to Spectrum Astro. I had a nice meeting with them. I gave them my standard subcontractor pep talk about Lunar Prospector and how important it was for both Discovery and helping to get man back to the Moon. I told them about my backing in Congress, in the Aerospace States Association, in the National Space Society and the like and they were very impressed. I told them I expected to leave Lockheed and go to LEI soon and then I would be able to do follow-on missions on my own. As such, I was looking for small companies like theirs to work with me on such missions. They were impressed and very eager and I certainly won them over as team players on Lunar Prospector. I achieved that goal (and negated the bad impression they had gotten because of Dom), and, in a certain sense, that was the best part of the whole trip.

I called Tom back at the ranch to see what had gotten screwed up in my absence and, true to form, something had; the mass of the solar array drum had doubled in the couple of days that I was gone. However, Tom (who I had authorized to sign for me, in my absence when I was on travel) would not sign off on that change, nor would Woody, nor Bob Goldin, nor Al Tilley, so Dougherty couldn't get it accepted (apparently the guys were learning I was serious about keeping the mass down). I didn't believe the mass had really doubled, so when I got back to work Monday I was going to kick some butt.

Happily, as Tom also said, everybody knew Dougherty and I had been to Orbital Sciences and that put a lot of pressure on Denver to find a way of getting the LLV2 plus the TLI Stage for $23 million, even if they had to use part of their profits from the launch vehicle to cover the TLI costs. My going to Taurus the first time and having Dougherty go with me the second time had the right effect. Though I still hoped I would get a Taurus, if Denver dropped the price to $23 million and did the TLI Stage, I would not have a leg to stand on in the fight with Lockheed about the LLV2. However, that would change if Goldin insisted on his rule that you can't launch a NASA spacecraft on a launch vehicle that had not been used at least once. If applied, that rule would eliminate the LLV2 and open the door to Taurus that had already had a launch with nearly the configuration I would use and they had another Taurus launch or two planned with my configuration before I was to fly. Taurus was not out of the picture; the next few weeks were going to be interesting.

Monday, December 11, 1995: Subsystem Review Day

Tom did really well; he was beginning to show his stuff, though he still didn't know Lunar Prospector very well. Nevertheless, he showed he knew a lot about drawings and how to get things done and he really was beginning to act like my deputy. I was very pleased.

Two things happened during the Subsystem Review meeting. First, the big mass increase in the solar array drum was totally erroneous. For some reason, Al Tilley had gotten the drawings totally screwed up in making his mass estimates. Though we didn't know the full answer to that question right then, he and I were going to straighten it out. Then we discussed the mass of the material used to fill the honeycomb at the edges of the shelves and panels to keep the edges from being damaged. The filling material would add a lot of mass, so the issue was, could we just use tape to protect the edges, rather than using the heavy filling. Tom Chinn said that using tape was the "common practice" way of protecting the honeycomb edges. I said, "However, common practice does not mean it's necessary." I thought the edging was really a matter of neatness, but in space, neatness doesn't count.

There was a big to-do about the stiffness of the booms. Vu had worked the issue with another engineer whom I didn't know, but who is an expert in such things, and brought up the stiffness problem. I said, "We are talking about a maximum acceleration of only 0.3 m/sec^2, or just 0.03 g's."

Vu said, "Oh, the guy used 0.3 g's in his calculations!"

I said, "If that's the case, and we had better verify it, then he is wrong by a factor of 10!" It was, and he was. There was no problem whatsoever and I was ticked off at the damned engineers who kept making stupid mistakes and who just could not do anything right.

After that, Dougherty and I gave Frank a debriefing about our meeting with Orbital Sciences in preparation for a meeting with Henshaw the next day. I presented my arguments for buying a Taurus for $23 million. I said the only thing I would accept at the next day's meeting was to be on the Taurus for $23 or have LLV build the TLI Stage and have a total launch cost of $23 million. We had a long discussion and Frank's attitude was that I had reasonable arguments for being on a Taurus and that the availability of the LLV2 launch pad at the Cape was also an important issue. Also, he wasn't convinced when Dougherty said we should build the TLI Stage. Frank thought it should be built by the people who (supposedly) knew how to build it. Frank made Dougherty swallow the fact that I was the PI and since I was the PI, he (Frank) believed if I wanted to go to a Taurus, it was my decision. Even so, we would have to fight the battle with Henshaw the next day and then we would have to go fight it again with Al Smith, but I was sticking to my guns, and, as PI, it was my choice — or so I hoped.

Frank also felt we should go directly to Headquarters, get an OK from Wes Huntress and make sure there were no hidden agendas at Headquarters we didn't know about and that could cause us all kinds of trouble. I said, "OK, I'll go directly from San Antonio (the meeting at Southwest) to Headquarters and meet you and Tom (Dougherty) there, and that was where we left it.

We went over to Ames at 3:00 PM and spent 1½ hours talking with Scott and Sylvia about the arguments, pro and con, for the LLV2 and Taurus. There were lots of issues, like, if I chose the Taurus and it failed, would Lockheed lose all of its fee? I felt that it shouldn't; it should at least get $2 million, since, if we got no data because of a Taurus failure, it would not be Lockheed's fault.

Scott said he did not feel comfortable with us building the TLI Stage either; he thought it was a bad idea and that the LLV people ought to build it. I also argued if Denver said it would cost them $8 or more million to build the TLI Stage and Taurus said it would cost $6 or $7 million (though they were willing to swallow the costs), then how in the hell could we build the stage for just $3 million? I didn't believe it. There was something wrong there.

In the end, we were all prepared for the Henshaw meeting that I hoped would put an end to the launch vehicle question or at least be the beginning of the end.

Tuesday, December 12, 1995: Henshaw and the Rocket

We met with Henshaw. I said I wanted a Taurus and I gave all of my reasons. We discussed my reasons in detail. I said, "If Lockheed would build the TLI Stage and if they would get the cost down, I would consider staying on the LLV2."

He, of course, wanted me to stay on the LLV2 and promised that if I did, Lockheed would do its part. He said he did not feel that Orbital Sciences had the pedigree and the reliability that Lockheed did, which you would expect a Lockheed manager to say! However, he concluded, "But, if you don't have confidence in LLV and want a Taurus, I'll agree with your decision."

We also talked about the TLI Stage and Henshaw agreed with Frank and me that we should not build it; rather the people who knew how to build it should build it. Dougherty had investigated having Thiokol do the TLI Stage and I agreed that would work. We all agreed there was no way that Denver could do the stage, if nothing else, because they wanted $8 million for it and that was absurd.

In the end, Henshaw was very sympathetic to my position and I firmly believed Henshaw was fully behind me. We all left the Henshaw meeting happy and we agreed we were going to find out if NASA had any hidden agendas.

I went to Ames and told Scott what had happened and he promised me he would call Headquarters and try to find out what was going on from their standpoint. We didn't want to make a decision and then find out that Headquarters had different ideas, especially since they had called Orbital Sciences about the Taurus a week earlier and there were some discussions going on with Lockheed about the LLVs.

After the meeting, we finalized our request for the tracking and the frequency allocation. Slowly but surely, we were getting everything done so we could really start Phase C/D — the construction and testing of the spacecraft.

Just before I left work to go home, I got a call from Scott. He said Headquarters had no preference between a Taurus and an LLV2 as far as the technical issues were concerned, but the rule that you cannot launch a NASA mission on a vehicle that had never flown before was in force! As Scott said, "Goldin will not let his favorite Discovery Mission fly on an unproven vehicle."

The die was cast. I could walk in Henshaw's office the next day and say that my decision about the launch vehicle had to be OK'ed by Goldin and he would not allow me to be on a vehicle that had not been proven. The LLV2 was out. That gave Lockheed a graceful exit because they could say, "We haven't had a launch, so we can't launch him," and it got me off the launch vehicle hook. Boy was I happy and relieved!

In a day full of good things, the nicest thing was that Preston Carter sent me an email in which he wrote that everyone enjoyed my talk at Lawrence Livermore Labs and that what I had said had a great impact on their management. Management decided they didn't want to fly Clementine 2 the way Clementine 1 was done. Clementine 1 was just a bunch of sensors with no science objectives — it was just a test of military hardware. After hearing my talk about how I was doing Lunar Prospector, they decided they were going to have science play the major role in their mission and, "we should do it the way Dr. Binder is doing Lunar Prospector and how he has it organized." That was really important stuff. Preston thanked me for helping to get Clementine 2 on a better track. I was extremely flattered and taken aback by that. It sure helped make my day.

As I drove home, I thought about the events of the last two days. Clearly they marked the real beginning of Lockheed's accepting my PI-ship as Discovery meant it to be. The Discovery concept was working. I was very pleased and couldn't have been happier.

Wednesday, December 13, 1995: Lockheed's Deceit Unveiled

Early in the morning I went in and told Dougherty and Frank what Scott had told me. They immediately started yapping because, all of a sudden, the LLV2 was out. I quickly realized the discussions of the previous two days had been a subterfuge! Lockheed had no intention of ever allowing me to launch on anything but LLV2! Nevertheless, I was amused as I listened to Frank and Dougherty bemoan their predicament. The chips were down and they were making nonsensical arguments as they flailed around trying to find ways of forestalling the inevitable: "If you can't launch on something that hasn't launched before, the program could get canceled . . . . Taurus hasn't really flown exactly in Alan's configuration either . . . there is no proven TLI Stage," and on and on.

They called Henshaw and it turned out Lockheed's Sam Araki (I thought Sam had retired, so I assumed, like stupid Moe Miller in Houston, Sam stayed around as a high priced consultant sucking up Lockheed's profits to supplement his golden parachute instead of letting the real workers make an extra dollar) was going to meet with Goldin in two hours to discuss the LLV2 issue. Henshaw warned Sam about what had happened to prepare him for Goldin and I smelled a rat.

We were supposed to hear something back in a couple of hours. In fact, we heard nothing from Sam all day. It was obvious to me that the launch vehicle decision was just a political issue between big, powerful Lockheed and big, powerful NASA. It had nothing to do with my PI-ship, or with which launch vehicle was better, or with the success of the mission. Lockheed was simply not going to allow its competitor to launch Lunar Prospector. I realized I had no choice in the matter and all I could do was hope for the best. The issue had nothing to do with programmatics; it was strictly about who was kissing whose butt at Headquarters. Nevertheless, the fact that we heard nothing from Sam suggested to me that the meeting didn't go the way Lockheed wanted — so maybe there was some hope after all, but I thought, *what a stinking business this is!*

We had our weekly staff meeting and a number of issues came up and one was most interesting. Jim Beffa, whose group was building our antennas, said the gain of the Omni antenna at its null point (out the back of the spacecraft, or in the –Z direction or at 180°) was very, very low. The gain in the +Z direction (0°, or the front of the spacecraft) down to the X-Y plane (90°) was normal at about 0 dB and it decreased only a little bit more by 120°. But by 130°, the gain was –10 dB and it might be close to zero at 180°. That worried me because right after launch, before we reoriented the spacecraft to put the Earth in the medium gain antenna's pattern, we would be looking right up the bottom of the spacecraft. Thus we might not be able to command the spacecraft. Tim Bridges and I had thought there might be as much as a –20 to –30 dB loss in the –Z direction, a loss that would be easily made up for because of the nearness of the spacecraft to the Earth. However, what Jim showed us looked serious and I brought up the possibility of having a patch antenna on the bottom of the spacecraft. We discussed my suggestion.

After the meeting, I made some calculations to determine what gain was required when we were looking straight up the bottom of the spacecraft. The results depended on the exact antenna pattern, so I asked Jim to get me those data for the Omni antenna. I found that, right after launch, when we were still near the Earth, we would have a +40 to +50 dB gain because of the spacecraft's closeness to Earth, and if the null point's loss was not more than –30 to –35 dB, we would be OK. Otherwise, we would have to have a patch antenna.

Jim asked whether the switching between the patch antenna and the Omni would be automatic or commanded. I hadn't decided that, but I thought I could command the switch because there seemed to be enough overlap between the patch antenna, which had a 160° degree field of view (FOV), and the Omni that had a 240° FOV.

Jim asked what would we do if the switching were commanded, rather than automatic, and, after we were in lunar orbit, the spacecraft got into an orientation where we were again looking at the Omni's null point. I answered, "First, I can't imagine how a stable spinner like Lunar Prospector could get in such an orientation without our being so dumb that we command a series of major screw-ups. Second, if we were that dumb, all we would have to do is to wait a few days until we would move back into the good part of the pattern as a result of the Moon's orbital motion around the Earth. I can deal with the command switching under all circumstances."

I talked with Irv about the maximum pressure in the tanks. If possible, I wanted 450 psi in the tanks at the beginning of the mission. Since the thrust of the engines is essentially directly proportional to the feed pressure and since the tank pressure drops as the fuel is used up, I wanted a high initial thrust level so I would still have a reasonable thrust level at the end of the mission when the pressure was around 125 psi. However, to my great disappointment, Irv thought that anything over 450 psi might damage the valves. Since the pressure is dependent on the tank temperature, if we tanked up at 450 psi and the temperature in the shroud before or during launch got higher than 50° C, the pressure would get high enough to damage the engines. I was going to have to settle for a somewhat lower initial pressure, about 400 psi, and lower thrust levels than I wanted.

Then there was a new concern about the booms; the torques on them during reorientation maneuvers appeared to be more than they could handle. Either we would have to beef the booms up, which would have been a big deal, or find another solution. One obvious solution was to do the reorientation maneuvers with just one engine rather than using two coupled engines, but that resulted in the problem of adding unwanted ΔV to the spacecraft during the maneuvers. We started to look for other solutions. In any case, I was worried about that problem.

By afternoon we had still heard nothing about the launch vehicle meeting between Goldin and Sam Araki. Scott called Mark and Bret and found out three interesting things.

First, Mark was beginning to feel that he was no longer part of the program and thought his superiors were beginning to dislike him. I wasn't surprised, because I believed that Mark had been making some serious mistakes in his dealings with us.

Second, and to my great surprise, Mark thought we should be on a Taurus for many of the same reasons that I did!

Third, from what Scott found out, it appeared that the choice of my launch vehicle was going to be an upper level NASA decision, there might even have to be an executive meeting called to make the decision — I hoped that was not the case.

Scott was getting all the information about the costs, the merits, the heritage, and all the other things about both LLV2 and Taurus and simply giving it to Headquarters. As always, when one looked at all that information, one chose the Taurus. But what we were dealing with was that the big kid on the block didn't want the new kid on the block to get into the business and Lockheed is a very big kid. Despite that and despite all the slings and arrows I had gotten from all the Lockheed people about what a rotten company Orbital Sciences is and how they would leave me in the lurch, Lockheed continually left me in the lurch and the Taurus was the better launch vehicle, period.

Scott was preparing the best viewgraph presentation he could so Headquarters would know what the real issues were and what the data really were, so Lockheed couldn't snow NASA. Clearly, the launch issue was going to drag on and there was nothing I could do about it; it was not my decision and had never been. Also, it was not Scott's decision and it was not Wes's decision — it was Goldin's decision. As a result, it was clear there was no reason for me to go to Headquarters to plead my case for a Taurus.

I was able to finalize my trip and I was just going to go to San Antonio for the meeting at Southwest and then get my butt back to Sunnyvale as fast as I could.

Thus ended a long, complex, and frustrating day.

Thursday, December 14, 1995: MAG/ER CDR at Berkeley

We spent all day up at Berkeley, doing the design review of the MAG/ER system. It was a very good meeting.

Mario Acuña was there and we went over the magnetic cleanliness issues and they were in good shape.

Finally we got to the main issue, the MAG extension boom release mechanism. Vu had devised a complex device with a yolk, a capture wire, a cord spring to hold the capture wire, and a couple of other things all made of stainless steel. Mario said, "You can't use stainless steel," and I told Vu his device was far too complicated. As usual, Vu did not understand what we were saying and just stood there, saying it had to be done his way. That was especially stupid because the Berkeley instrument mechanical engineer, Paul Turin, had already suggested using a device they had used over and over on many spacecraft — a simple little wire cutter with two little pyros you could hold in your hand when they were fired and we began discussing that. Vu and Woody loudly complained that the cut wire would catch on something and foil the deployment.

I said, "That's ridiculous, the spacecraft is rotating at 30 rpm (at deployment) and centrifugal force will throw the damned boom outwards with an acceleration of more than 28 m/sec^2, so that tiny wire is not going to stop the deployment," a statement of simple physics they both refused to accept.

Woody tried to counter with, "But we don't have pyro-circuits (in the spacecraft) and adding them will impact the C&DH system."

Paul said, "We don't need a pyro-circuit, just a command that sends a 5 amp current to the wire-cutters for 10 milliseconds."

I immediately asked Alex if adding such a command to the C&DH would have any impact on it and he said, "No, none at all. Besides, the C&DH design is not complete and there is no difference between that command and the one we will use for the paraffin actuators in the boom release mechanism."

Vu, and to a lesser extent, Woody, continued to object and I said, "No. This is what we are using. There is nothing to it. It has flown and it's proven. They have all the parts; they will build it and give it to us and we will install it. End of story."

Woody said, "Well, this will have to go through CCB (the Change Control Board we used to officially accept changes in the spacecraft design)."

I was within a hair's breath of saying, "We just had a CCB." I was sick of those overly cautious engineers.

Other than the boom release nonsense, the CDR went very well and Mario and the Berkeley boys got the OK to start building the hardware.

When we got back to Lockheed from Berkeley in the late afternoon, there was still no word from Sam Araki about his rocket meeting with Goldin.

Chapter 3-7
The Rocket Mess Continues

Friday, December 15, 1995

I got to work very early after not sleeping very much — I was too aggravated about the rocket nonsense to sleep.

I talked to Frank when he came in. We had heard nothing from Araki because the idiot was at a damned retreat! I told Frank we had to have a decision, one way or the other, but we agreed we couldn't make the decision until we knew what the rules were. I said I was getting more than a little annoyed. Frank said he didn't blame me.

I went over to Ames to meet James Paul, a Congressional aide, but I went over early so I could talk to Scott and Sylvia about the rocket. They hadn't found out anything from Headquarters, so we were still in the dark. Scott agreed the decision was a political issue and was completely out of our hands. I had resigned myself to that fact and was no longer frustrated, except by the fact we still didn't have a decision from Headquarters.

James Paul was supposed to have arrived at 9:00 AM and was supposed to have been picked up by an Ames PR guy who was supposed to bring him to Scott's office, but he didn't show up. At about 9:10, James called from the reception center and said no one had met him to let him in the gate! Scott was hopping mad — James was a Congressman's aide and one doesn't treat Congressman's aides like that. Scott called the PR guy's boss and asked why the guy wasn't there. Apparently they had gotten the date confused or something, we never did find out exactly what happened. We waited for another 20 minutes and Scott called again, but nobody knew where James was. Then we figured out they had sent him — without an escort — to the wrong building! Sylvia and Scott's secretary went looking for him and finally, about 25 minutes later, James arrived. The guy who should have picked James up came in and apologized and correctly said, "I'm in big trouble."

We had a good talk about Discovery and Lunar Prospector. James knew I was very enthusiastic about Discovery, and he also thought Discovery and Lunar Prospector were the best things since motherhood and apple pie. Then he asked Scott a question that just amazed me, "How is Discovery going to work in general? Scientists generally don't know how to engineer things and don't know how to run programs, not like Alan does. How are you going to find scientists to actually do Discovery missions? There aren't that many guys like him." I was floored — I didn't know James from Adam and I didn't think he knew me. How did a Congressman's aide know all that? Though I was very flattered, I was very curious to know why he said it. Then I thought, *George (French) knows all these guys, maybe George set him up?*

Scott gave his answer to Jim's question and then, when I had again gathered my wits, I said, "It has always disturbed me that in space science, engineers run the program and scientists don't. In astronomy, which is my background, in physics, and in all the other sciences, scientists always run the big programs — engineers never run them. This is the only field in which the knowledgeable people do not run their own programs. For thirty some years, space scientists have reduced data and built instruments, but have never had the full responsibility of a mission. One of the things I want to do with Discovery is to get the point across that scientists need to run the programs. I think that is the way it should be."

James asked, "Well, how are they going to learn?"

I answered, "Well, I had to learn. Seven years ago I didn't know how to do all of this stuff and I learned it. There are many good scientists out there who are certainly capable of learning it and becoming competent to run missions." Then I explained what I had experienced when I was working on MAUDEE. "Right away, I saw that Killeen was not running the show and I knew that was a formula for disaster. If he wasn't going to run it, it wasn't going to work. Remember — MAUDEE came in 14th out of the 28 proposals!" Then because it was so late, James left and I went back to Lockheed.

It was almost noon, so I got a sandwich from the cafeteria. Then I tried to find Dougherty and Frank to see what in hell was going on, but they weren't around.

At 1:00 PM, we had a meeting regarding the launch loads on the spacecraft that we had some of the local Lockheed engineers calculate. The engineers' models were just crazy. They had calculated the 99th percentile worst cases! If we accepted that crap in the absence of reliable data on the LLV2, we would have to redesign the entire spacecraft! It really made me mad because I knew we would end up with a 185 kg spacecraft if we did that. I was not going to let them build a spacecraft that satisfied the 99th percentile worst case, when we only had the funds for — and as Discovery required — a 95th percentile spacecraft. However, that to-do lasted just a couple of hours. It was just over-engineering and over-conservatism. When an angry PI confronted them, they backed down and presented reasonable results. I was sure if we just built the spacecraft the way we had been designing it, it would be fine.

It was a long day, but the high point was what James Paul had said.

Monday, December 18, through Thursday, December 21, 1995: San Antonio and Southwest

Monday morning, before we left for San Antonio for the review of the spectrometers' SES unit, we had our weekly subsystem review meeting.

Dougherty, who didn't have a clue about the engineering involved, was concerned about Berkeley's simple release mechanism for the MAG extension boom. Both he and Vu were still worried about the cut wires mysteriously catching on something and preventing the MAG extension boom or the main booms from deploying. I simply couldn't get them to understand that centrifugal force would prevent that from happening. I concluded they were both idiots who never passed a high school level physics course. Dougherty wanted to make sure that the Berkeley device would work and thus wanted them to write a document that would prove that their device would work! The fact that he could understand neither the simple engineering involved, nor the fact that they had successfully flown that mechanism on several other spacecraft, plus the fact that he would not listen to me was getting on my nerves. I really felt I was dealing with an idiot.

We left to fly to San Antonio at about noon, but the flights were late because it was raining in Dallas. Then the plane had some instrument problems; so we sat there for some time and then, for some strange reason, they de-iced the plane — in San Jose! We finally took off and, though it was cloudy most of the way, there were some breaks in the clouds and I had a gorgeous view of the Grand Canyon as we flew right over it. We arrived in Dallas late, but all the other flights had been delayed, too. As a result, we made the flight that was to take us on the little hop down to San Antonio. But again, we had instrument problems; then we had to de-ice! All that took about an hour, so we didn't get to our hotel until after 11:00 PM.

Despite the flight problems, we had a good meeting the next day at Southwest Research. There were no problems with the design of the SES, just a lot of details; so they were ready to start building it.

After the meeting was finished, I flew to Houston to talk to John Gruener and the mission planning guys at JSC on Wednesday, and then flew back to California on Thursday.

Friday, December 22, 1995: The Last Working Day of 1995

We had our weekly staff meeting and Dougherty was huffing and puffing about everything. The big news was about the Araki — Goldin meeting and I wanted to know why they hadn't relayed us the information a week earlier. Apparently, Goldin didn't care about the rocket! Sam told him about the two (LLV1) launches for Lewis & Clark, and Goldin had said they were good enough and he had no objections to us flying on an LLV2. There was nothing I could do. Despite Taurus being better and cheaper than the LLV2, since NASA wouldn't push it, there was no way I was going to get a Taurus. Nevertheless, Dougherty promised he was going to push LLV to knock $2 million off the price of the LLV2.

Saturday, December 23 through Saturday, December 30, 1995: The Christmas Break

Since Lockheed closes its doors between Christmas and New Year's Day, I had a nice long break from Lockheed, its engineers, and NASA. After Christmas Day, Rebecca and I took a little road trip that started at 8:00 AM on Friday the 29th. We drove to Santa Barbara where we enjoyed the waterfront area, had a nice dinner, and stayed the night. Saturday morning we drove to Long Beach, where we toured the Queen Mary and had lunch in one of its restaurants. Then we drove back to Gilroy and arrived at 8:00 PM Saturday night.

Sunday, New Year's Eve Day, and Monday, New Year's Day, 1995/1996

As 1995 ended and 1996 began, I thought back over the year. One year earlier, Rebecca and I had been waiting impatiently for news about the Discovery mission selection, not knowing if I would have a future in my profession or not. Then I had received the best news possible — Lunar Prospector had been selected for flight. That good news had been followed by the fee and Dom crises, both of which could have led to the mission's cancellation. Then, Dougherty had replaced Dom and we got through the TDR with flying colors, despite having been on the brink of disaster just a few weeks earlier. As soon as the TDR was successfully behind us, the government had shut down and then we had the money crisis and another fee crisis, followed by the Taurus/LLV2 issue. Man, it had been a bumpy, but a great year. Somehow Lunar Prospector and I had survived all that and we were well on our way towards actual construction. Furthermore, I expected that in a year, when 1996 ended, we would be nearing the end of construction and getting ready for test and finally the launch in October of 1997. I was looking forward to an exciting 1996, but fully aware that many battles with Dougherty, Lockheed, and NASA were hiding in the bushes.

Tuesday, January 2, 1996: The Rocket Mess Continues

Though I had gotten completely rested up during the holidays, within an hour of being back at work — I felt like I hadn't rested at all!

The main issue that concerned me was, of course, the launch vehicle. Because of the government shut down, Scott and Sylvia were working at home — illegally; they would get fined $5,000 if they were caught — on the contract and launch vehicle issues. Scott called me from his home and asked me to have Dougherty send him a letter stating that if the launch vehicle issue was not fully resolved and if the contract was not signed by January 8, there would be significant costs and schedule impacts to the program. Scott needed the letter to give him every bit of leverage he could possibly get in order to get the contract done, despite the government shut down.

I passed Scott's request on to Dougherty, but then I began to worry that Lockheed might take the letter as an excuse to jack up the price and start screwing everything up again.

I received a timely email from James Paul. He wanted to know what effects the delays caused by the government shut down were having on Lunar Prospector. I immediately called James and told him the same things Dougherty was writing in his letter, as well as my concerns about the letter. James said he would do his best to get what Scott needed to have done, so he could work on the contract, and that was to have Congress declare Lunar Prospector a critical government activity. Then NASA could tell Scott, Sylvia, and the Ames contract person to go back to work in order to finish the contract and to get us more money. Since we only had $10 million to begin with, we would be running out of money by the end of January.

I called George French, told him the same thing, and asked him to call Congressman Sensenbrenner. George said he would call as soon as he could, but since he was leaving for a meeting, it would be the next day before he could make the call.

After I got all that going, I told Dougherty what I had done and he was relieved.

I called Joe Padavano at Orbital Sciences and told him we were apparently stuck on an LLV2 because Headquarters, i.e. Goldin, was not going to enforce the no-first-launch-rule in Lunar Prospector's case. Joe was not surprised; he knew I was fighting an uphill battle. Then he said he had heard that Lockheed was going to launch an LLV in March 1997 as demonstration. I said, "That's news to me; but who knows what is going on?"

Joe answered, "I think I do."

Apparently, because of all the failures of small launch vehicles or MedLite vehicles that had occurred over the last year, a committee was being formed to set the standards for the launches of NASA spacecraft on small vehicles. Joe thought if those standards were applied to Lunar Prospector, it would have to be launched on a Taurus — which would be fine with me. He said, because Taurus is a MedLite, they were in on all of the discussions about forming the committee. Joe also thought the person forming the committee wanted Lunar Prospector in the MedLite category. If that were the case, then Lunar Prospector would have to fly on a Taurus. Though Joe didn't say that, the implication was clear.

What concerned me was, with all the backroom hanky-panky going on, NASA was not giving us any directives. We were completely out of the picture and in the dark. I was really concerned that we might be going down the road on the LLV2 and then, in two or three months, the committee might come and say, "We have just put Lunar Prospector in this class of missions and it can't fly on an LLV2."

If they pulled the rug out from under us like that, then what would we do? If that happened, there would certainly be a major schedule slip and a major a cost impact. Then NASA would say, as they always do, "You'll just have to make it up somehow or get canceled."

Immediately after talking with Joe, I called Scott and told him what I had just learned. I said, "Scott, I can't risk forcing the decision on the LLV2, only to be told two or three months down the road that the rules have changed and I can no longer be on an LLV. I need to have some answers from Headquarters. I don't give a damn how we get them; I have to know what is going on. I still have another four weeks before Taurus would start having problems launching me."

Scott shared my concerns. Since we had only heard via Araki that Goldin had said, "Hey, no problem, just launch on the LLV2," Scott and I no longer trusted that information. Scott said he would try to find out from Headquarters what the real situation was. Scott also began to agree with me that the letter Dougherty was writing might open Pandora's box and result in Lockheed's taking advantage of the situation to raise the price and slip the schedule.

I thought, *the whole damned rocket issue is a stinking mess. We don't know what NASA is doing and NASA doesn't know what it is doing either.* I said to Scott, "What concerns me is the left hand at Headquarters doesn't seem to know what the right hand is doing. Code XL (responsible for launch vehicles) is doing all the rocket stuff and Code S is doing Lunar Prospector and neither of them have the foggiest notion of what the hell the other one is doing. When XL gets all its rules and regulations set up, I am going to be sitting here with no rocket and a slipped schedule." I was getting more and more concerned and more and more frustrated.

To top everything off, I went to set up a meeting with Henshaw during the following week and was informed that Frank had to come along. Frank would not allow any of his people to see Henshaw alone. It all started when, after asking Arthurine (Frank's secretary) to set up the meeting, she asked, "Are you going to bring anyone else along? I have to inform Jo (Henshaw's secretary) about the number of people, because Jo has this rule that you can't come to a meeting with more people than you set up the meeting for."

I felt like saying, "You stupid twit, you're all crazy here with your stupid little rules and regulations!" but I said, "It'll be just me." Then she told me about Frank's rule and that did not please me one little bit either!

Arthurine must have noticed my annoyance, but mistakenly assumed a different cause, because about two minutes later she came waltzing back in my office. She said, "Maybe I didn't explain it properly. I just wanted to make sure you understood that this is Jo's rule."

I said I understood and then I remembered I had seen Arthurine catch hell from Jo, as Frank, Dougherty, and I were going to see Henshaw. I didn't know what the big to-do was all about, but Jo said very angrily to Arthurine, "I'm the senior secretary around here and I'm the one who sets the rules and you are not supposed to do anything like this. You've overstepped your bounds," and Jo turned and stomped out.

Arthurine — in her sexy spike high-heels and sexy short skirt — literally ran after Jo trying to explain by saying, "I was only doing what I'd been told to do by Frank!" — but to no avail!

Even the Lockheed secretaries had their little empires — man, I wanted to be out of that company and into LEI so bad. I was totally fed up with all that petty Lockheed crap. As we drove home that evening, I told Tom, "As soon as I'm in LEI, I am going to inform Jo and those other idiots that I am not a Lockheed employee, that I don't work for Frank, that Henshaw and the rest of them all work for me, and that I am the customer. If I want to see Henshaw, I will see him when I want to and with whomever I want and I don't give a damn about their damned rules. I'm fed up." Clearly, the first working day of 1996 had been a long and frustrating day — not a good way to start the New Year.

Wednesday, January 3, 1996:
The Congressman Brown Letter to Goldin

James Paul called and said he had written a letter for Congressman Brown, the leading Democrat on the Science Committee, on my behalf, in the hopes that Brown would sign the letter and send it to Goldin. Sure enough he had signed it and had sent it on to Goldin. Goldin had a letter from the Congressional Committee saying it was concerned that Lunar Prospector was being held up because of the government shut down. If that continued, among other things, we would not get the rocket negotiated by the 8th and that would result in cost overruns and schedule slips. Thus the committee wanted Goldin to authorize Scott and the other people involved at Ames to do the necessary work to get Lunar Prospector back on track.

Interestingly, as James explained to me, Goldin worked for the President, not for Congress. The President was the one who shut Congress down and while Congress could make its requests, Goldin didn't have to do what Congress asked, but he most probably would.

Regardless, Brown had written a letter of support for Lunar Prospector on my behalf and Dougherty and Frank were awed about the letter and the fact that I could get political support like that, something they could not do.

I called Scott and told him about the Brown letter; clearly Scott was relieved that he and Sylvia would soon be able to legally work on Lunar Prospector again.

Thursday, January 4, 1996: Staff Meeting Day

We had the staff meeting all morning and got a lot done. We were moving right along getting the spacecraft design finalized and moving towards construction

Though Dougherty was a dunce when it came to technical issues and remembering that he worked for me and not the other way around, he was doing a magnificent job of managing the staff and tending to the money issues. When I told him that (not the part about him being a technical dunce), he said, "I don't do all that, Bob (Garner) takes care of the money and my other people do all the other things." Despite his modesty, he was doing the things I needed him to do — managing the money, the schedules, and the Lockheed personnel — beautifully.

As luck would have it, just after I had complimented him, Maryann Williamson (a very nice and competent lady on Dougherty's support staff, who did our contracts and purchase orders and sent them on up the Lockheed chain for processing — and who Lockheed treats as badly as they did me because she is a woman in a man's world of engineering) came to tell us she had just found out the purchase order for the battery, that we thought had been sent out in early December, didn't get sent out because there was a computer breakdown and the order had sat around Lockheed for a month!

Dougherty was livid and said, "This is an intolerable screw-up. Somebody is going to get in trouble about this. This has a serious impact on our program."

The screw-up was really serious. The battery was one of our critical "long lead items," i.e., pieces of equipment that usually require up to two years to get, and we needed it in less than a year — so even a month's delay was serious. Nevertheless, despite being annoyed about the purchase order, I was pleased that Dougherty was going to raise hell about the screw-up. He was seeing to it that things were getting done — a difficult task in a big company like Lockheed. Also, despite his frequent relapses, he was generally respectful of my being the PI and the other issues I was concerned about. He was doing his best to adjust to the new and unorthodox situation of having a (shudder) scientist run the program and not an engineer, so I tended to overlook his frequent lapses. The main thing was, together, we were getting a very difficult job done and both of us were pleased about that.

Right after that, about ten of us had a meeting about the instability of the booms due to the pulse burns of both reorientation and Vector Burns. Dougherty wasn't there, which was good when we were doing something technical. However, Dan Swanson, who is a young, very competent, dynamics engineer we were hiring from East Windsor, was there and added greatly to the meeting.

I had the engineers tell me everything they knew about the problem. Basically, the problem was that the booms had a resonance period of about a tenth of a second and that resonance mode would be excited the way we were planning to do the reorientation maneuvers or reors. The booms could tear off or, at least break during a reor.

I opened the discussion with my earlier thought about just using one engine instead of two to do the reors. We quickly determined that would cut the force down by about 40%. Then I asked about changing the boom lengths in order to change their fundamental frequency and hence to lessen the stress on them. Then I brought up the fact that engines don't turn on and off immediately, rather, they gradually build up and lose thrust over a period of 20 to 30 milliseconds. The slow buildup and decay of the thrust causes the real pulse to be much milder than the square wave pulse form the engineers had used in their calculations. Added to that was the fact that engines do not reach their full thrust levels during each short pulse, so that makes the pulses even more mild.

By that point, we had enough information about the problem and I said, "OK, after we're through here, take these changes and run them through the models so we can see where we are."

I was a little put out that the engineers didn't know enough to take into consideration all the real factors. I thought maybe it was just the difference in the way scientists and engineers think and work, but it disturbed me. Similarly, I was annoyed because the engineers couldn't answer my question about the effect of decreasing the lengths of the booms on their fundamental resonance frequency — I had asked if it was dependent on the length linearly or squared and they didn't know. They should know those fundamentals and should have been able to say one way or the other without having to look it up.

We talked about the poor stability of the spacecraft before the deployment of the booms. I said, "I'm considering (taking the risk of) deploying the booms automatically immediately after separation."

Dan said, "That is the way to do it."

Trusting Dan, I said, "OK, that's it, we will deploy them automatically." The pre-boom-deployment stability issue was resolved and perhaps the quasi-related patch antenna issue.

Because we had decided to have the booms deployed automatically right after separation, the need for a patch antenna on the bottom of the spacecraft diminished considerably. As long as I was planning to command the deployment of the booms, it was critical that I had good communications during the critical period right after launch and separation, so I would need the patch antenna. However, if the booms were deployed automatically, then there would be nothing that was critical to be done during that period of time and I wouldn't need a patch antenna. I called Jim Beffa and asked him to come over and discuss my idea about dropping the patch antenna. He did, we did, and we got rid of the idea of adding a patch antenna.

I got a call from a guy named Steve Ingles at the Marshall Space Flight Center in Huntsville, AL, who was going to a meeting in Japan on January 15; the Japanese wanted him to present information on Lunar Prospector at the meeting. I said I would send him a package of viewgraphs. I also told him to tell the Japanese I was most interested in cooperating with them in any way we could because their spacecraft, Lunar Prospector, possibly Blue Moon, and eventually WIND would all be either orbiting or near the Moon during the same time.

Thus ended a very good day.

Friday, January 5, 1996

Another good day. We had the CDR of the spacecraft structure and the guys had done a great job, but the mass had gone up. That was largely because we had reduced the number of cutouts in the solar panels to maximize the surface area for the solar cells. That in turn meant that we had to add more support structure, so the damned thing got heavier, by 7 kg! That concerned me — and Dougherty too, as matter of fact; I had finally convinced Dougherty that mass was our big enemy. Based on my propellant usage model, I showed Dougherty that every kilogram of extra spacecraft mass cut one month off the mission's lifetime in lunar orbit. That was a simple enough metric that even he could understand it. Every time an engineer wanted to add mass to the spacecraft, I would say, "No, that will cut the mission by so many months," and Dougherty was quick to pick up on my refrain. The 7 kg increase meant 7 months less time in orbit (from a maximum of 36 months, if we were to stay in the 100 km altitude orbit during the hoped for extended mission). I hoped we would eventually cut the mass increase down some, but some of it was clearly there to stay.

Worse, Dougherty was convinced that, as a result of the launch dynamics data that were starting to come in, we would have to add structure to make the spacecraft stronger and that would also increase the mass of the structure. That was not good news, but the guys did a very good job, so we signed off on the drawings. Then it hit me — within six months, we were going to start getting pieces of the spacecraft and begin to put them together to build it!

I got the viewgraphs ready for Steve Ingles so he could give a talk about Lunar Prospector in Japan.

The government was going back to work the following Monday, so we hoped we were going to get the rocket issue finally resolved.

The only thing that went wrong was Tom called the State of California and those bozos wouldn't do anything with our paperwork for at least sixty days. Before they would even start, our request had to go to a committee that wouldn't even look at it for sixty days and no one knew how long it would take them to process the papers, once they got them back from the damned committee. I was really annoyed; that was going to delay us getting into LEI by up to three months or more. The more we had to deal with the State of California, the clearer it was that California is a crappy state. Rebecca, Tom, and I were going to be very, very happy when we could leave California and never see it — in terms of living in it — again! As far as we were concerned, the sooner California fell in to the Pacific Ocean, the better — that is, of, course, after Lunar Prospector was done.

Monday, January 8, 1996: Subsystem Review Day

The review went pretty well, though Dougherty was in his huffing and puffing mode, which I was getting tired of.

I released Version 4.0 of the Mission Profile at the review meeting and discussed the Mission Operations Document. Both of which were getting simple and simpler as the spacecraft got simpler, and because I was planning to have the booms automatically deployed.

I was annoyed with Woody, who could never decide anything and hence was fussing about the Power Control Assembly (PCA). He said the (so-called) Lockheed Center of Excellence engineers didn't want to build the assembly Woody had suggested, they wanted to do something different. During the review, we decided maybe the latter would be OK.

But, later, when no one was around, Dougherty told me there was another way we could do the PCA. That was to have it put in the C&DH unit and let Spectrum Astro do the whole thing — so there would be only one electronics unit instead of two. I liked that solution; it would reduce the mass and simplify the entire system — the C&DH would just be a slightly bigger box with one or two more cards in it. I also thought it would be to our advantage to give the PCA job to a company — Spectrum Astro — that knew what it was doing. I found it very interesting that Dougherty, a loyal company man, was ready to pull work out of Lockheed and give it to the competition! He was just waiting for the necessary ammunition to back his case and the incompetence of the Lockheed Center of Excellence was providing him with an example of what he needed. Thus, it would be interesting to see how the PCA issue would be resolved.

In addition to Woody's PCA issue, I brought up the solar array changes that had added 7 kg to the spacecraft's mass, half of which was due to the need for extra support brackets, and part of which was due to the thickness of the surface layers on the honeycomb. Dougherty was sufficiently sensitive about the mass increase that he raised hell with Woody about it, too. Woody, never one to resolve an issue, said we would need to re-look at the issue. I told Woody that Tom Chinn thought we would save 3 kg if we went back to the original design in which the solar panels were attached directly to the load-bearing structure rather than being supported by long brackets. Tom Chinn also said that in the original design, the boom cutouts were at the panel's edges rather than in the middle of the bottom parts of the panels and hence that the panels would be stronger.

Later, we found out from the Lockheed solar panel engineers that there was no cost impact if we designed the panels the way Tom Chinn suggested. It would have been stupid for us to have more massive solar panels, just because of a more favorable cutout pattern for the solar cells. My mind was made up. I didn't care what Woody said, unless he found something catastrophically wrong with the older design, we were going to use it and save the mass.

Tom Chinn came up with a different way of covering the honeycomb panels. Instead of using two independent crisscrossing layers of graphite epoxy fiber to cover the aluminum honeycomb, Tom suggested we use single layer with a three-pattern weave to do the job, a technique that would save us quite a bit of mass, but would maintain the strength of the panels. We might be able to get the mass of the solar array knocked back down to its original value, and that would be great.

Tom called the stupid state of California again. They changed the filing fee for LEI from $500 to $800 and we were supposed to pay the fee in advance — even though, as a non-profit, tax-exempt corporation, we might not have to pay it at all. Clearly, the process of filing was going to take forever and I was beginning to worry they would decide we were a non-profit, but not a California tax-exempt corporation, despite the fact that LEI was a federal tax-exempt corporation. Tom was trying to sort out what they were doing, but he had to deal with some idiot who didn't know anything and that was driving us nuts. What a frustrating mess!

I talked to Scott about the rocket since he was doing a good job of informing Headquarters about the relative merits of the LLV2 and Taurus. I reminded Scott that, because of the 50 to 60 Hz pipe organ effect in both the Castor 120 first and second stages of the LLV2, its environment was a hell of lot worse than Taurus's. The Taurus had just one Castor 12 stage way down at the bottom of the stack and that stack consisted of the Castor 120 and then the second, third, and fourth stages, none of which have the 50 Hz buzz, and all of which would drastically attenuate the buzz of the first stage Castor 120.

Richard said he wasn't getting answers from Thiokol about the TLI Stage. They kept saying they would fax or email the information we needed, but it never came! He was getting worried, as was I. I went to see Richard to find out if there was any news from Thiokol and found him talking with one of the LLV engineers. I asked, "How is my rocket coming?"

He simply said, "We can do it."

I replied, "That's not a very good answer," and I began to wonder if they were just screwing around again and suddenly I felt tired.

I was getting tired of the engineers not being able to make decisions and the resulting waste of time and money. To be sure, things were getting done — albeit slowly, but I was frustrated with the engineers and frustrated with the California bureaucracy.

Tuesday, January 9, 1996

Twenty-one months to launch and counting!

The LLV2 — Taurus issue again dominated the day. It was obvious that Dougherty was getting really worried and I was convinced he was scared of the LLV2, but being a company man, he couldn't or wouldn't do much about it. LLV still hadn't gotten us any information; they hadn't been doing anything. It was the same old song, just the third or fourth verse. Thiokol hadn't given us information on the TLI Stage either. I saw the same old crap we had been dealing with ever since we got stuck in the LLV mess.

On the positive side, we were going to end up with the old, lighter solar array panel design. Woody had no arguments against us using the old design and Dougherty was very well aware that I was not going to lose six or seven months of mission's lifetime just for Woody's lousy heavy panels. Of course, Dougherty had to go through all of the useless Lockheed protocols before he would formally accept us returning to the old design. That was just some of the Lockheed nonsense I just had to put up with, so I did.

Late in the afternoon, I flew to Colorado Springs for my meetings at the Air Force Academy and Eagle Picher.

Chapter 3-8
Blue Moon, Boom Problems, and More Rocket Mess

Wednesday, January 10, through Saturday, January 13, 1996:
Ron Humble, Blue Moon, the Air Force Academy, the Garden
of the Gods, Eagle Picher, and Los Alamos

Ron came to my hotel where we had breakfast and talked about his engineering research, Blue Moon, and Lunar Prospector before we went to the Academy. He was doing some impressive work on hybrid engines that interested me greatly. The reason for my interest is that while one can obtain oxygen and metals from lunar rocks, there is virtually no hydrogen on the Moon. Thus, it is important to develop rocket engines that burn powdered metal and lunar oxygen or LOX, as it is called in the business of lunar resource utilization. Ron's work on metal burning hybrid engines is very important for the future development of the Moon.

He told me he had a 50/50 chance of getting the money he needed to do Blue Moon. It all depended on Pete Worden and I thought I could help Ron convince Pete to support Blue Moon. Pete had been a member of the National Space Counsel when Lunar Prospector got started, and Gregg Maryniak had gotten Pete to support Lunar Prospector. Since Pete knew of me and of Lunar Prospector, I thought we could close the loop by hitching Blue Moon to Lunar Prospector and get Pete to fund Blue Moon. As Ron explained, Blue Moon was to be a very simple spacecraft that, as I had already concluded, couldn't do the dual gravity experiment with us, but it could easily carry a magnetometer. It was well worth pursuing and trying to get the necessary funding from Pete and the Air Force.

Once at the Academy, I gave a technical talk to Ron's morning class, then a much more politically oriented talk about the Blue Moon/Lunar Prospector connection and the seeking of funds for Blue Moon at a brown bag luncheon that was attended by all the upper-echelon people in Ron's department. The second in command of the Aerospace Department was at the luncheon and he agreed, saying, "Yes, let's go try to do it (Blue Moon)." After lunch, I talked to the head of the Aerospace Department, since he had been unable to come to the brown bag lunch, and I told him I thought I could help them get Blue Moon funded. All the rubbing of elbows with the department bigwigs was good for Ron and I was pleased to be of some use to my good old friend. Then, during the afternoon, I gave a technical talk to a double class and finally, the Blue Moon class began. That was when we actually sat down and discussed Blue Moon and Lunar Prospector in full detail. It was a very, very good day and Ron and I had a great time.

Since Ron and I had completed everything we wanted to do the day before and since I wasn't going to talk to Eagle Picher until 2:00 in the afternoon, I had some time on my hands. I spent the morning walking around the beautiful "Garden of the Gods" park. I had been there when my mother, father, brother, and I were on a family vacation when I was about 12 years old and I wanted to see its beautiful rock formations again. While there, I had lunch at the park's new Visitors Center. It was really nice and I greatly enjoyed the morning.

When I got to Eagle Picher, they weren't prepared for my visit and I had to cool my heels as I waited for Lee Dolly to get back from lunch. When he finally got back and we got started, there were 12 to 15 people at my pep talk, mainly the managers and their secretaries, rather than the actual workers to whom I really wanted to speak. Nevertheless, I gave them the full blown political talk about Lunar Prospector and how it could lead to new programs. By the time I was finished, they were all very impressed. Then we had a technical discussion about the battery and I explained how I chose the battery size and how we were building the entire power subsystem. We had quite a good discussion, so I was very pleased and felt that Eagle Picher would see to it that they built us the best battery possible and would get it to us within the very short time frame we needed it. When I left Eagle Picher, I felt that I had accomplished my mission.

Eagle Picher is very near the Colorado Springs Airport, so I just needed a little time to catch the little bitsy MESA airplane that took me to Albuquerque that evening. The flight down to Albuquerque, along the front range of the Rocky Mountains, was very impressive and by the time I arrived, it was late, so I stayed at the Albuquerque Radisson Hotel near the airport, rather than driving up to Los Alamos.

Friday morning I drove up to Los Alamos to see Bill. We talked about the spectrometers and the mass of the GRS and several other hardware issues. Then we talked about the data we were going to get and how we should run both the extended mission and the data analysis part of the program. Regarding the extended mission, we discussed my plan to put the spacecraft into three successive sets of elliptical orbits with their respective periselene altitudes of about 10 km situated over each of the poles and then over the equator. The first two sets of orbits would give us high-resolution maps of the supposed polar water ice deposits and the equator passes would give us enhanced gravity and magnetic data.

Carle Pieters (a prominent lunar scientist who does multispectral studies of the Moon's mineralogical composition, and who was an investigator on the Clementine mission) was also at Los Alamos and we talked with her about Lunar Prospector and follow-on missions. I tried to make her understand what Lunar Prospector was all about programmatically and that missions could be done inexpensively. She kind of caught on, but Lunar Prospector was still a big leap for most scientists who were used to the NASA way of doing business. She was certainly interested in what I was trying to prove and was slowly becoming convinced of the importance of it — and she was impressed with Lunar Prospector.

As I left Los Alamos Saturday morning to start my trip home, I felt the entire trip was one of my better ones. Everything turned out better than I had hoped and I was very pleased. I had a good start with the Air Force; I thought we could do some interesting things together and I was pleased about the prospects of working with Ron again.

Monday, January 15, 1996:
Nothing Catastrophic — Except the Booms Will Break

We had the weekly sub-system review and nothing catastrophic turned up — except the booms were going to fall off. It turned out that once the engineers finished their modeling of the boom resonance problem, it was much worse than we thought. Able Engineering was coming to Sunnyvale for a meeting to discuss the deployment mechanism the following Wednesday, so we could also discuss the boom resonance issue with them at that time. Unfortunately, when Vu had arranged for Able to come, he didn't have enough

sense to inform them about the boom resonance problem that was by far the most pressing issue. I was disgusted with Vu and really wanted Dougherty to replace him. We then
informed Able about the resonance issue and set up the meeting so we would discuss the
deployment mechanism at 10:00 AM and then, at 1:00 PM, get everybody involved in trying to understand the very serious problem of the dynamics of the booms.

The only other thing that was worthwhile during the day was a meeting we had
with Woody and an engineer from the Center of Excellence about the Power Control
Assembly (PCA). The question remained as to whether it should go into the C&DH unit
or be in an independent electronics unit. It turned out that the Center of Excellence
had a complete PCA unit they had developed for a different program that would fit our
needs with minor modifications. The guy said we would only need about half of the
boards that their PCA unit had and its mass (with all the boards) was about 5½ kg.
5½ kg was far more than I liked, but our version of the PCA would only be about 4 kg.
However, that was still a lot more mass (3 kg) than the one-kilogram it would cost us if
we put the boards in to the C&DH unit. Nevertheless, Woody argued the C&HD unit
would suffer electrical interference and thermal problems if we put the PCA boards in
it. The reason is that all the power used by the spacecraft, up to some 200 w, would run
through the PCA boards and some of that power would be dissipated as heat in the
boards. All that power and heat do not belong in a sensitive C&DH unit. Woody had a
good point, but we needed to get more information to know if he was right, so we postponed the final discussion until the next day. Despite Woody's worthy concerns, I still
thought we would end up having Spectrum Astro put its PCA boards in the C&DH unit
and save mass.

Regarding one of my favorite topics — saving mass — since we had gone back to
the old solar panels, and if we could keep the PCA down to just 2 kilograms, we would
end up with a spacecraft dry mass just about 3 kilograms over my goal value. Not bad!

Tuesday, January 16, 1996

Paul Turin, the Berkeley engineer who was making the release mechanism for the
MAG extension boom came for what turned out to be a useless meeting. The mechanism was going to work, any idiot could see that, but Dougherty had gotten Ed Boesiger
and his people over to review it. Vu, of course, did a lousy job. He didn't understand
what was going on, he doesn't understand English very well, so he didn't understand
the questions. I again talked to Dougherty about getting rid of him since we had to have
someone who knew what he or she was doing — the booms were too damned important to have some idiot like Vu being responsible for them.

Gerry Grismore had looked at the PCA unit and was of the opinion it could and
should go in the C&DH unit, for which he was the responsible engineer. Though Gerry
was a pain at times, I always felt he knew what he was doing, so I trusted his opinion
on the PCA issue and hoped that would be the end of it — it was, we later decided to
put the PCA boards in the C&DH.

Wednesday, January 17, 1996

I talked to Dan Swanson early in the morning about the boom problem. We came
to the conclusion that we might have to replace all six 22 Newton engines with 4.4 Newton engines with which we would do the reors and the Vector Burns. Then we would

have to add two 22 Newton engines at the bottom of the spacecraft to do the big LOI burns, otherwise, we were apparently in trouble with the booms. I did not like that solution at all, it added considerable complexity to the spacecraft, but there didn't seem to be anything I could do about it.

We spent all morning and part of the afternoon with the Able engineers discussing the boom release mechanism. There were new concerns about the shaking or chattering of the latching pins that were to secure the instruments and their booms during launch. Unfortunately, the pins could not be too tight or they would not be able to disengage and release the booms — so there would be some chatter during launch. I was very concerned about that because it would amplify the g loads caused by the rocket's vibrations and the spectrometers, and the MAG/ER just couldn't take any more of that.

On top of that, Able brought up the problem of "the snap." When the booms reached the end of their deployment, there would be a final, sharp snap as the booms locked into place. That snap would put pretty good rotationally induced g loads on the instruments. We had a lot of discussion about the deployment, how to get the pins unlatched, the chatter, the snap, and how we would put the booms back in their undeployed, launch configuration after we had done the deployment testing — a task that was not going to be easy. The snap and the chatter were two big concerns.

With only about an hour left before Able had to go, we discussed the business of the boom stability problem and Able said they would look into the strengthening the booms.

It was a long, tiring, all-day meeting day and I was glad to go home to Rebecca.

Thursday, January 18, 1996: Staff Meeting Day

We had our usual staff meeting and we went through all the systems — there were no new surprises. We finished off the discussion of the engine configuration with the six 4.4 Newton engines and the two 22 Newton engines. It would work and would save the booms from collapsing, but it didn't give me that much thrust to play with and that concerned me.

Other than that, I set up my pep talk visits to the tank manufacturer (PSI in the LA area), the transponder manufacturer (Loral in the San Diego area), and the boom manufacturer (Able Engineering in the Santa Barbara area) for the following week.

Friday, January 19, 1996

I talked to Gerry about the engine firing commands and a suggestion he had made earlier about having an automatic reor (to reorient the spacecraft from its launch orientation to its trans-lunar coast orientation) right after the boom deployment as part of the initiation sequence. His idea had quite a bit of merit, but I was getting worried about doing anything automatically, including deploying the booms.

Frank told me that Dougherty presented a Lunar Prospector progress report at Al Smith's staff meeting. Al, who had been very concerned about how much we were trying to do for so little money and on such a short time scale said, "Well, I owe you a nickel, you're getting the job done."

Frank also said that everyone at the meeting was very pleased with Lunar Prospector and that he had told them, "This is a great lesson about the importance of having the PI in there working daily with the engineers. This is the way to do this stuff and

Lockheed has to understand that. This is really going well because of the intimate contact the PI has with the engineers." I was very pleased about that and I hoped that, besides Frank, the rest of them would finally realize what it meant to have a good PI leading the effort who knew what in hell he was doing.

Monday, January 22, 1996: Subsystem Review Day

Nothing spectacular happened all day, just routine stuff — just the way I liked it.

However, I did call Wes Huntress at Headquarters to give him an update on the program and his only concern was, of course, the rocket. Wes reiterated that the reason Headquarters went with the LLV2 was because of Lockheed's track record and because I had proposed the LLV2 in the Discovery proposal. But he admitted that he too was nervous and said NASA might make Lockheed have a test launch. Other than that, he knew everything was going well with the spacecraft.

Tuesday, January 23, 1996

I wrote a formal letter to NASA expressing my concerns about A) the launch vehicle, B) our small budget reserves, and C) the S-band frequency assignment that Jim Martin had discussed in his TDR letter to NASA telling NASA that Lunar Prospector should proceed into Phase C/D. I wrote that I had investigated the Taurus, which I found was a better rocket than the LLV2, and that I had recommended we switch to the Taurus, a recommendation NASA had chosen to ignore. Though the letter would not change NASA's support of the LLV2, I wanted it on record that I was not happy with the decision.

While I was writing the letter, the LLV people were in Dougherty's office (next to mine) pulling the same old crap as usual; LLV wanted to charge more money than we had and didn't want to start work on the vehicle until they had a contract. It was the same old crap, just a different bunch of idiots pulling the same old crap. Dougherty went to Henshaw and told him LLV was giving us the same old crap again. Henshaw immediately called up the head of LLV in Denver and asked gruffly, "What's going on here," and got the usual BS answer. Clearly, we were going to have trouble with LLV all the time. I had made a terrible mistake in initially choosing that damned rocket, but there was nothing I could do about it then.

Tom Chinn, Tom, and I drove to Sacramento to visit the small company that was going to make the graphite epoxy housing for the GRS. When we got there, we found out they still hadn't gotten the contract! That really ticked me off and then they said they required 18 weeks to do the job — despite our having indicated that we needed it by the end of February. They were supposed to have started it in early January, but the contract had obviously gotten all screwed up and the people that screwed up were at Lockheed! In an effort to save the situation, I explained that we needed the housing in just five weeks and I gave my pep talk about Lunar Prospector and tried to pump them up. They listened politely, but they didn't show the enthusiasm the other vendors had shown. Lunar Prospector and the GRS housing meant nothing to them and they weren't going to put in the extra effort needed to help us. Disappointing as that was, it was a good thing we drove over there and discovered the problem. I thought if they didn't care about the mission, maybe they would respond to more money. I asked them to figure out what the cost impacts were and to let us know ASAP because we needed the housing and we could not wait.

We got back to Lockheed at about 5:00 PM. I saw Dougherty and told him about the situation with the GRS housing and then we talked about the rocket. Dougherty was going to kick some Lockheed butt about both issues. However, as Tom and I drove home, I said to Tom, "If we ever get launched on that damned LLV, it will be a miracle."

Wednesday, January 24, and Thursday, January 25, 1996: The Vendor PR Trip

I flew down to San Diego early Wednesday and visited Loral, where our transponder was being built, during the morning. Twelve to fifteen of Loral's leading people attended my talk. They were very pleased I came, and after I finished my pep talk, they were excited about Lunar Prospector. I was then given a tour of their facilities and shown various transponders in various stages of their two-year development. They told me that since we were on such a short time scale and because Lunar Prospector was so important, they were simply taking one of the transponders they were making for the Iridium program out of the Iridium assembly line and using it for us! And, of course, they were starting a new one for Iridium. Wow, my PR talk sure had the desired effect at Loral!

I drove up to PSI (Pressure Systems Inc.). PSI was also very happy I came to talk to them and there were fifteen to twenty high-level people at my talk. They said I was the first PI, or Project Manager, or anyone else associated with a mission who ever came to tell them about the spacecraft and mission they were building fuel tanks for. I was surprised at that and they were very impressed that I thought enough of them to come and tell them about my mission. They said they had an all hands meeting every month and asked me to come down and talk to all the workers. I said I would do that and that at the end of the mission — I would come and tell them the results. To say the least, they were very pleased and I knew I was going to get my three tanks on time and in the best possible condition.

After the talk, they showed me their facilities, which were very interesting. They explained that tanks start out as two hemispherical castings of pure titanium whose walls are nearly three centimeters thick. PSI has huge, computer driven lathes that turn the castings into the tanks, whose walls are just a few millimeters thick! They explained how it is done in detail, showed me every step in the process, and how they cure the tanks to make them as strong as possible. The highlight of the very interesting tour was when my guide said, "You know, maybe the castings for your tanks came in today? Let's go look." Sure enough, there they were, eight hemispherical castings (six to make my three tanks plus two spares), sitting on a wooden platform. Boy-o-boy, I saw my tanks in their raw form; that was really neat. He said they would start turning the castings down the next day, so I was basically right there at the beginning of the first stage of turning the raw castings into the my tanks. I was elated about that.

I drove up to Santa Barbara and stayed in the same hotel that Rebecca and I had stayed in over New Year's. I went to the same restaurant for a piece of pie where Rebecca and I had had supper; I had eaten supper earlier at a Sizzler Steak House on the road because I had gotten tired of driving and wanted to rest.

That night I called Tom to see what was going on back at the farm and he told me that the little 4.4 Newton engines weren't going to work — they couldn't stand the launch environment. I was relieved in a way, because those engines have such low thrust levels that I was concerned about conducting maneuvers towards the end of the mission when the tank pressure, and hence, the thrust levels were so low. I was glad to be back to the 22 Newton engines and was certain we would find a way to deal with the boom resonance issue.

When I got to Able Thursday morning, I talked to Jeff Harvey, the lead engineer on our booms, and asked him if there was any way they could strengthen the booms. He answered they could put extra battens in the booms, thereby decreasing the space between the battens (L) by a factor of two. Since a boom's stiffness goes up inversely with L^2, the booms would be four times stiffer. That sounded good to me, it would make the booms a little bit heavier and it would cost us a little more money, but it would take us out of the deep-doggy-do-do we were in with the boom resonance problem. I was very pleased about that, but Bob Crawford wanted to think about Jeff's suggestion for another day or so and suggested we might also make the booms with four longerons (square cross-section) instead of three (triangular cross-section). Bob wanted to think about the various options within the limited mass and money constraints they had to work with.

With that underway, I went to the little Santa Barbara Airport to fly home, but the plane I was to take home had mechanical trouble. I had to take a later flight and instead of getting in at 2:15 PM, which would have allowed me to get to Lockheed and try to resolve some of the issues before I went home, I wouldn't make it to Lockheed in time to do so. I called Dan Swanson, who was by then permanently in Sunnyvale, from the airport and told him what I had found out about the booms.

I finally arrived at San Jose at 5:00 PM and Tom picked me up at the airport. He said that the engineers were in a tizzy, jumping back and forth between the 4.4 and 22 Newton engines, since they had found out that the little engines could survive the launch environment, and that we were to have a meeting very early the next morning, before I left for Phoenix, to resolve the issue.

I was annoyed because the engineers always seemed to get half-assed information; we would make a decision based on that information and then they would get some more information and we would have to reverse ourselves over and over again! Why couldn't they get things straight the first time? Tom added that the guys were grumping because of all the changes. I thought, "Well, tough luck! Get it right the first time guys and we won't have to continually make changes because of your stupidity."

I decided that at the next day's meeting, I was going to stay with the 22 Newton engines come hell or high water. I just did not trust trying to do the end of the mission, especially our planned low altitude mapping, with such low thrust levels.

Tom told me that the little company Tom Chinn, he, and I had visited on Tuesday called Dougherty and said they couldn't get to our GRS housing for another nine weeks and it would cost another $15,000 to get it done. I said, "Tough luck guys! We'll have the housing done at Lockheed."

Friday, January 26, through Friday, February 2, 1996: The Big Trip — Spectrum Astro, a Wedding, and the Cape

I had been invited to give a seminar to a group of organizations at the Cape Kennedy Space Center on the 29th, and Rebecca's nephew, Mark Whitebread, was getting married in El Paso on the 27th. Rebecca and I decided to make a vacation/business trip out of it and spend a couple of days at Epcot Center and Disney World in Orlando. Also, I decided I would stop off in Phoenix on the way for a brief visit to Spectrum Astro to see how the C&DH was coming along, especially since we had decided to put the PCA in the C&DH and let Spectrum Astro do the whole thing.

Because of the efforts that were being made by Able to strengthen the booms, the planned meeting about the 4.4 vs. the 22 Newton engines had been canceled — if, as we suspected, Able could strengthen the booms, we could forget the 4.4 Newton engines — which we later did. After spending a couple of hours at Lockheed, Tom drove me to the San Jose Airport for my flight to Phoenix. Since I was going to spend just a few hours at Spectrum Astro, Rebecca was going to take a later flight and meet me at the Phoenix Airport, and then we would fly on to El Paso for the Wedding.

When I got to the airport for my 9:30 AM flight, it was postponed until 11:20! I got to Spectrum Astro late and we discussed the C&DH unit and their integrated power control unit that consisted of only one board that was going to be added to the C&DH. I was very impressed and happy with that solution. It kept the mass down and simplified the spacecraft — two of my favorite things.

I met Rebecca at the airport in Phoenix and we flew on to El Paso for Mark's Saturday wedding.

The next day, Sunday the 28th, we flew to Orlando and drove over to the Cape.

Monday morning, I gave my seminar to the Cape Kennedy Group, Florida Business Roundtable, Space Port Florida, Space Grant University, and I forget who else. My talk was enthusiastically received (what do you expect from a Cape crowd?) and afterwards an attractive young lady came up and introduced herself as Karen Ramos.

Karen was the lead engineer building the Space Port Florida Launch Pad 46 — my launch pad — and she was hyped up about Lunar Prospector. She took Rebecca and me over to see Pad 46, which was fascinating to see, and then took us to meet the Navy Captain who ran that pad (it was still a Navy facility that was being shared with Space Port Florida) and his second in command. I briefly told them about Lunar Prospector and they were duly impressed.

Rebecca and I stayed at the Cape Tuesday and enjoyed seeing the various launch pads, but we were a little disappointed in the tourist tour of the Cape we took. Late in the afternoon, we drove back to Orlando to spend two and a half days at Epcot and Disney World and finally flew home on Friday, February 2.

Tom took care of things at work while I was gone, and, of course, several things had happened.

Able had reported that the booms would be fine with just three longerons and with double battens on only the first half of their 2.5 m lengths. That would increase the mass by only about ½ of a kilogram, so I was very pleased.

Based on that information, the engineers had finalized the propulsion system design, using the original six, 22 Newton engines, in a way that helped meet the stability requirements of the redesigned booms. That was done mainly by moving the A1, A2, A3, and A4 engines close to the spin axis of the spacecraft and canting them slightly, decreasing their lever arms and thereby decreasing the torque produced on the booms during the reors.

The real problem was with the stupid LLV jerks who wanted more money! They wanted one million dollars instead of half million dollars for the adapter between the LLV2 and the Thiokol TLI Stage and Dougherty blew his stack. Tom said that Dougherty and I were to meet with the head of LLV on Tuesday. I was mad as hell about the whole damned rocket mess. I was certain we were going to lose the mission because of that stupid rocket, unless we were damned careful. I wished to hell I was on a Taurus.

Despite the continuing LLV mess, Rebecca and I had a nice vacation. When we got home, the local newspaper, *Country News* had come out with a nice article on the mission.

Monday, February 5, 1996:
Subsystem Review Day and the Unending Rocket Mess

For the first time ever, software was on the subsystem review agenda, and, much to Dougherty's annoyance, Tom brought up several issues the engineers were confused about. Dougherty tried to belittle Tom in an effort to stop him from bringing those issues up, but Tom stood his ground and it was an interesting confrontation. It was clear from Dougherty's snippy and snotty comments and actions that he resented Tom's representing me in my absence. While Dougherty was forced (some of the time) to accept that, as PI, I was in charge, he was not about to listen to Tom, who was merely my deputy in Dougherty's eyes. I swore, at times like that, Dougherty had the mentality of a two-year-old.

Gerry Grismore complained, justifiably, to Dougherty that we were always rehashing the same issues over and over again. As Gerry said, "We had the appropriate layouts and diagrams in our TDR, so why do we always have to start over again? Why don't we start from where we were and just modify?" (See, I was not the only one who was frustrated with the Lockheed way.)

I found the confrontation between Gerry and Dougherty amusing (I was tired of being the only one to complain to Dougherty), so I let them battle on for a while. Then I finally said, "I agree with Gerry's and Tom's concerns. Nobody seems to have any of this stuff straight." Dougherty didn't win that one and he wasn't winning many such battles anymore.

We went through the rest of the subsystems and found nothing monumental until we got to — you guessed it — the rocket.

Thiokol was coming to Lockheed for their TLI review Wednesday and Dougherty was getting very concerned they might not know what they were doing, a concern that I very much doubted was valid. Nevertheless, Bob Goldin said, "Well, you know, we are basically doing most of the work on the TLI Stage, so why don't we just go ahead and build it?" I didn't like that suggestion one bit; I was certain that Thiokol knew what they were doing and I was just as certain we didn't. Also, I was certain they could do the TLI Stage cheaper than we could. Denver said it would cost $8 to $12 million. Orbital Sciences said it would cost them $6 million. Thiokol said they could do it for $4 million, so how could we do it for $3 million or less, never having done it before and knowing nothing about doing it? It was the same old problem — the people who knew the least about the issue always think they can easily do it and do it for less money. Unfortunately, Richard Lynch was one of the biggest sinners in that category.

I let that conversation go on a little while, then, when I was sufficiently annoyed, I said, "Look, we have gone over this again and again. I told LLV I wanted a launch to TLI and they backed off to the point where we had to consider doing the TLI Stage ourselves. That didn't work out, so then we talked to Lockheed in Denver and they backed off and now we've talked to Thiokol and, if you're right, they are backing off. We can't get anybody to do the TLI Stage and every time we come back to the damned point where somebody here says we will do it for less money than the experts. That's BS. OK, if Thiokol doesn't want to build the timer (that would start the TLI burn and separation sequence), we will take the responsibility for the timer, but not for the entire TLI Stage. I'm sick and tired of this damned LLV stuff. I wanted a launch to TLI. I proposed a launch to TLI and LLV has been backsliding ever since the proposal was submitted. As Richard said earlier, LLV does not want to have anything to do with the TLI Stage, because they don't care if it works or not. They only want to launch us to LEO to show that their damned rocket works and they don't give a damn about what happens to us beyond that. I wanted LLV to be responsible for the entire launch vehicle, including the TLI Stage, even though Thiokol is going to build it. Our job is to build the spacecraft, not the damned rocket."

Sylvia agreed and Dougherty sat there like a wet puppy and everyone else was very, very quiet. Then I said, "You know, as far as I am concerned, this company is going to have to stand up and take responsibility for the launch vehicle because that is what I proposed and the company agreed to it."

Dougherty, in an attempt to make me back down, said something about my trying to outguess the experts and I said, "Tom, for seven years I have made the right decisions on this program or we wouldn't be here now," and that shut him up.

After that, Woody gave a very good discussion about the efficiencies of the different solar cells and concluded we could save $300,000 to $400,000 by using cheap, but adequate silica cells — $300,000 to $400,000 we desperately needed since we were back down to zero reserves again.

Interestingly, as we were discussing the LEI issue with Sylvia after the meeting in my office, and as I called Scott on the phone, she said to Tom, "You know, he has to get out of this company!" It was clear I had to get out of Lockheed and if I couldn't do it through LEI, I was going to see if I could go to Ames as Sylvia had told me before.

Tom called California about our paperwork again. They wanted us to pay the $800 and then we could start doing business while they processed our papers and determined our California tax status. I told Tom, "We're not going to quit Lockheed and start LEI assuming everything will be OK, only to find out in sixty days that LEI is going to be taxed and then you and I will not have jobs." My attitude was that we would start working in LEI only when the State of California had given us the correct approval and if California didn't, we were staying put in Lockheed, like it or not.

Chapter 3-9
Doing the Launch Vehicle Two-Step

Tuesday, February 6, 1996: NASA's Vacillations

What a day! I talked to Sylvia early in the morning. Though I was supposed to have been kept in the dark, Sylvia told me an amazing tale of NASA indecision. She found out that NASA had decided, within a month after I had raised the LLV2 vs. Taurus issue, that they were going to enforce the requirement that a new launch vehicle had to have been previously launched before it could be used to launch a NASA spacecraft. But they never informed me of that decision. Then they decided against the "no-first-launch" rule — so I could go on an LLV2. Then they changed the rules again and I could not launch on an LLV2 unless Lockheed had a demonstration launch. The launch vehicle merry-go-round just kept going round and around. Apparently, if NASA wanted a demonstration launch, they did realize they would have to pay for it — but where was NASA going to get $25 million for a demonstration launch for a program that costs just $63 million! And, a demonstration launch would mean that Lunar Prospector would be delayed by months — a delay that would also cost significant amounts of money.

All that BS would disappear if they would just allow me to go on a Taurus. But Sylvia said NASA was also concerned whether Taurus fit the description of a previously flown vehicle, since the version I would use had a slightly different configuration than the one used on the first Taurus launch. They were looking at putting me on a Delta with another payload! And that would cost considerable amounts of money because of all the interfacing issues with the Delta and the other payload!

Basically, what NASA was doing would end up increasing the cost of Lunar Prospector by at least several millions of dollars and causing significant delays, which would, in turn, increase the cost again. Every day was just a waste of effort, a waste of time, and a waste of money. NASA just can't ever get its act together and make a decision about anything — and they wonder why they have huge cost overruns and delays!

When I got back from Ames, Dougherty and I had a meeting with Buddy Nelson, Lockheed's PR guy. Buddy is a really nice guy who knows his trade very, very well, and he and I quickly developed a collegial friendship based on mutual respect. Buddy was impressed with Lunar Prospector and said he would do his very best to get us the best PR possible. As we discussed the various aspects of Lunar Prospector PR, Dougherty kept trying to tell me how to do my part — the main part — of the PR job. Finally, out of frustration, Buddy told Dougherty, "You don't have to worry about Alan, he does his job and does it right."

After finishing the discussion about our part of the PR campaign, we discussed George French's Moonlink program as well as George's and Congress's interest in having a kiosk like Lunar Prospector computer/educational display. Dougherty's first reaction was, "Lockheed can't have anything to do with something like that."

I said, "It's part of the Outreach Program. My data and everything are going out immediately on the Internet and everyone has a right to use it in any way they want. If George and Congress want Internet kiosks, that's good for Lunar Prospector and good for Lockheed." Buddy loved the idea, but Dougherty — always the company man —

remained cool to the idea, despite Congress's interest in the education aspects of the program.

After talking with Buddy, I found out that, while I was over at Ames talking to Sylvia, Eric Sterner, an aide to Congressman Sensenbrenner, had called and wanted to talk to me about the display, but ended up talking to Dougherty, who told him Lockheed wouldn't allow the kiosks to be made (talk about being dumb)! That caused a flap and I had to call George to straighten the mess out and make sure he and Congress understood they were not dealing with Dougherty and Lockheed, rather they were dealing with Lunar Prospector and me.

Dougherty and I went back over to see Sylvia and she said NASA had decided to get rid of the 26 meter tracking network, so they didn't know how they were going track Lunar Prospector anymore! Headquarters also said we should put a recorder on Lunar Prospector and download data just once or twice a day to minimize our tracking requirements! Crap, we had been through all of that before; what in hell was the matter with Headquarters that they could not understand or remember anything about the mission? I was annoyed and said to Sylvia, "Look, we're already building Lunar Prospector and it's far too late to add a recorder. If we did that now, the impact would be enormous, because we would have to have more power and we would have to have more mission controllers to run the spacecraft. Lunar Prospector was not meant to be flown that way. We have been through this before, for Pete's sake. We would be forced back into Phase B and we are already four months into C/D! That's idiotic."

Bob Jackson was also at the meeting and he said, "What we should do is make them get you two more TOTS stations, rather than just have the one that is already at Wallops, and put them at Canberra and Madrid. That would cost about $4 million." That was a good suggestion and I hoped NASA would do it.

Despite Bob's good suggestion, I was really annoyed with Headquarters. NASA had changed two rules in one day — one for the launch vehicle and one for the tracking. If they insisted on their new rules it would add $10 to $15 million, or even more, to Lunar Prospector and there would be delays. I hoped we would survive NASA's stupidity, but we would only do so if they gave us the extra money needed to make up for their indecision.

Dougherty was also ticked off about the rocket and said that one month ago he had told them, "If you're going to make us launch on a launch vehicle with a previous history, tell me now, because I (he meant he and I, of course) have to make a decision and I cannot make it next month or there will be cost and schedule impacts. If you try to tell me in a month, that's too late and I (he meant we, of course) am staying on the LLV2 and that's it."

Since Dougherty and I were both fired up, I added (referring mainly to the tracking issue), "They kept making me change horses in the middle of the stream and there was nothing I could do about it. But now, they're shooting the horse that I am on. That's fine if they want to do that, but they have to pay for the dead horse."

Dougherty and I went back to Lockheed just shaking our heads. Could NASA screw-up Lunar Prospector any worse? I was afraid of the answer.

Wednesday, February 7, 1996

I talked to Eric Sterner to take care of the snafu Dougherty caused by saying no to the display on Lunar Prospector that George French and Sensenbrenner wanted. Then I told Dougherty of my conversation with Eric and his reaction was really amusing. He had been bitching and bitching about George trying to use Lunar Prospector for his own benefit (as if Lockheed wasn't going to make $4 million off of Lunar Prospector) and, after I had talked to Eric and smoothed everything out, Dougherty said, "Well, that's really a good idea, I am glad it worked out." I thought, *how two-faced can you get?*

Scott called from Headquarters and said NASA had decided it was going to enforce the rule that a NASA payload couldn't fly on a rocket that had not flown before. I could not be on an LLV2 because if I were, Lockheed would have to have a demonstration launch and that would mean a delay of the program and additional costs. NASA was not going to accept the delays and certainly not the extra costs, so I was going to have to be on a Taurus, though there were a couple questions that had to be resolved. However, it sounded like they finally decided to get their act together and that was the end of that damned LLV2; at least I hoped it was the final decision.

However, the whole tracking issue was still up in the air. As Scott said, "The whole tracking issue is a lot more fuzzy and if they fool around any more, you're going to have to go to Washington and fight the battle." He said Mark wanted to use the $2 million saved by going on the Taurus to pay for the extra tracking.

I told Scott, "That's nonsense, every time we get a penny of reserves, he finds a way of taking it away from us. I am going to tell him to go to hell on this one."

Regardless of the tracking issue, unless something intervened, I was going on a Taurus and I was quite happy about that.

Thursday, February 8, 1996: — Or So I thought

I called Bret Drake at Headquarters as soon as I got into the office in the early morning to find out what the deal was with the Taurus and found it was still a continually changing situation. The first thing Bret said was, at that moment, I could fly on a standard Taurus, but there was an issue with the 2.34 m shroud I needed because Orbital Sciences was not going to get it developed until later. I knew that was incorrect, but I couldn't prove it at that point. However, Bret continued, saying Headquarters felt they could get McDonald Douglas to help Orbital Sciences with the shroud and get it validated. Then I could launch on a standard Taurus. However, I knew the standard Taurus could barely do the job and I would have to accept a non-apsoidal TLI burn rather than having the burn start from a circular parking orbit. I needed the more capable XL Prime Taurus configuration with the stretch second stage to be able to do the TLI burn from a circular orbit, but it didn't look like NASA would allow that because that version had not flown! I said to Bret, "OK, fine, there is a usable option using the standard Taurus."

Bret said, "The LLV2 would be fine, if Lockheed would fly a demonstration flight."

I said to Bret, "That's absurd. I would have to wait months for a demo and the delay would increase the costs. Then there would also be the costs of the demo itself and you're telling me that I can't have any additional money. You're tying both of my hands behind my back and telling me to do the job. I just can't, you have to accept that."

Bret retorted, "You proposed a mission with a certain budget and it's not our fault that some of the things haven't worked out."

I shot back, "That's not true. I proposed a mission under a certain set of rules and you guys keep changing the rules."

Bret said, "Well, it's not my fault."

I said, "I know that Bret. It's not you; I realize you're just saying what you're told to say, but NASA has to realize this is a major impact and there are going to be major cost impacts." Then I added, "I need to know what the full story is on the Taurus shroud." He said he would check on that and call me back. When he called back, he said NASA was OK with the shroud issue. I said, "Fine, I'll try to talk to you later."

Dougherty came by, so I told him what had happened regarding the launch vehicle and the tracking. Dougherty said he knew something was up about the launch because he had heard it too. That was interesting because, of course, he hadn't told me anything about NASA's flip-flopping — it was very clear Lockheed considered that the launch vehicle issue was none of my business. Then Dougherty said, "Well, I'm not changing anything (with regard to the LLV2) until we get something official," and I agreed. Unfortunately, we also knew then that it might be another two months before NASA officially signed off on the rocket. In the meantime, we were charging ahead, developing the spacecraft and spending about $1 million a month — without knowing what rocket we had to interface with — we had to, but it was a risky thing to have to do.

I called Orbital Sciences and talked to Joe Padavano. Joe told me they were launching a standard Taurus in November with the big shroud. As I was certain, Orbital did have the big shroud and Bret was wrong about that — there was no shroud issue. Also, the November launch was using the Castor 120 and not the original Peacekeeper for the first stage and so, except for not having the stretched second stage, that Taurus would have the same configuration as the one I would need. It began to look to Joe and me that NASA might accept that and let me go on the Taurus. However, the situation was totally fluid — the rules changed literally by the minute. As I had told Bret earlier, "Two months ago the time-scale for NASA to change its mind was a month; two weeks ago, it was a week; and now it's down to a minute. The rules are even changing during a single conversation and that's really stupid."

I also asked Joe about how Orbital Sciences would get the long lead items on time if NASA let me jump to the Taurus. One such item was the Castor 120, which took a long time to get. Joe said if Lockheed had already bought the two they needed for my LLV2, then Orbital Sciences would be able to buy one of them from Lockheed, since Lockheed would not be able to use it for me. The second issue was the Star-37, but again, since Thiokol was making one for us, Orbital could just take it over. Those issues were not problems and Joe was certain they could get a Taurus ready for me in sixteen months. He was hopeful it would work out that way, and so was I. Joe knew where my heart was, but he also knew it was a very ticklish situation.

I thought about saying to Joe, "Look, since you are launching in November, why don't you just slip in the stretched second stage and then that launch configuration would be exactly like mine." It would cost Orbital Sciences $20,000, but it would demonstrate they could fly Lunar Prospector without any questions. I decided I would make that suggestion the next time we talked.

Dougherty and I went over to Ames to talk to Sylvia and I went through a number of issues, one of which was my great concern about the schedule. Because Lockheed's CRSS was supposed to launch on an LLV2 in December of 1997, NASA was considering having me wait until CRSS launched, thus demonstrating the reliability of LLV2 to launch a NASA payload (however, Lockheed wanted Lunar Prospector to go first for the same reason — to demonstrate that the LLV2 would reliably launch CRSS! Some vote of confidence for the LLV2). Sounded good, but I knew from my engineering friends working on CRSS that it was way behind schedule and would never make the December 1997 launch — a fact Lockheed was hiding from its nervous investors and NASA. I explained that and added that waiting for a CRSS launch would kill us. Though

I didn't know when CRSS would be ready to fly, it was certainly going to be delayed at least a year (the first CRSS launch attempt was on April 27, 1999 — a 17 month slip).

I said, "There is no way I can keep my science and engineering teams together for a year after the spacecraft is built. What am I supposed to do, tell NASA we have to pay my team to just stand around doing nothing for a full year? That would be a big cost impact and NASA would just say, 'We won't do that; they can work on other programs until we need them for the mission. Then we will just rehire them on this job.'" However, as every idiot knows from numerous historical examples, that just would not happen; when people leave a program, they are gone for good, period.

Besides the major personnel problem, I brought up the problem that the spacecraft would have to be stored for a year and we would have to take it out of storage, retest it and recheck it out — all of which would cost money and increase the risk of failure.

There was the issue of the mission window defined by the total lunar eclipse in September 1997 and the partial, umbral eclipse in July 1999. Since the spacecraft was no longer designed to survive umbral eclipses, I could not fly the mission if we were delayed too long waiting for CRSS. I told Sylvia and Dougherty that the latest I could launch and avoid an eclipse during the one-year nominal mission was late April 1998. If CRSS were delayed even as little as three or four months, an April 1998 launch of Lunar Prospector would be next to impossible, considering the time it would take for the LLV2 launch crew to prepare my rocket for launch at the Cape on the east coast after having just launched CRSS from Vandenberg on the west coast. The real story was even worse. If, as NASA expected, I was to have an extended mission with a six-months duration, then I could launch no later than January 1998. There was no way in hell that CRSS was going to be launched in December 1997. I had to keep to my October 1997 launch schedule if I was going to have a chance of completing my full mission and the extended mission with a couple of months to spare to account for possible launch delays due to weather or technical problems of my own.

Even if CRSS were to launch in December 1997 and assuming the impossible, i.e., the LLV2 launch crew could get my LLV2 ready for a east coast launch in less than two months, there would certainly be a two to three month verification period during which the engineers would look at the CRSS launch data to know if everything went as planned. If it didn't, then there would be some months of time required for fixes. I could not expect to get launched until well into 1998, assuming that CRSS launched on schedule — an impossibility and a Lockheed lie.

After I was done, Sylvia knew the whole launch vehicle mess was getting to be a total fiasco that had to be resolved. She was going to write a letter to Headquarters stating the impacts of the delays on the mission and the costs per month due to the delays, impressing on them the fact that we had to know the answer soon, or else!

We turned to the unresolved tracking issue. Sylvia said NASA was considering turning the 26 m stations over to a commercial company who we would have to pay to track us — with money we didn't have! Before NASA had started monkeying around with the 26 m tracking network, we were supposed to have some 70 m and 34 m antenna time, along with the one TOTS. That would get me something like 50% coverage. I still needed 25 to 50% coverage on the 26 m net to fill out my tracking requirement. As long as NASA had the 26 m net, then NASA would pay the $14 million to itself to track Lunar Prospector — so the $14 million was just funny money. But if NASA sold the 26 m net to a commercial vendor, the $14 million of funny money would have to be paid out in real dollars. That was the dumbest thing in the world — that is, the dumbest thing except for the rocket mess.

All of that was very aggravating, I had spent a lot of time getting the tracking issue resolved before and I would have to do it all over again.

Another thing that was annoying was people at Headquarters kept saying Lunar Prospector was the perfect model for everything. In the case of tracking, Code O said Lunar Prospector was the perfect example of how to show the value of the commercialization of the DSN. Fine, then where was the money? They wanted to use Lunar Prospector as a showcase, but they wouldn't give me the money to do it. My attitude was, *if Code O wants to have us do this as the model, then Code O should just go ahead, pay for it, shut up, and let me get on with my mission.*

I called Bret again and he said NASA wouldn't direct me to go on a Taurus. I said, "Bret, this is ridiculous. Lockheed will not do this without a directive from NASA and you're not going to direct it? How in the hell am I supposed to get on a launch vehicle? Taurus is the only one I might be able to fly on. This is idiotic. Why can't NASA just stand up, take on some responsibility and resolve this mess before it kills Lunar Prospector?" But what could Bret say?

Ironically, right after talking to Bret, I got a call from Leonard Davis from *Space News* who wanted to catch up on Lunar Prospector. He had heard some of the launch vehicle rumors. I was as careful as I could be, but I told him what was going on.

Thus ended a very tough and disappointing day.

Friday, February 9, 1996

Given Thursday's frustrations with NASA's indecision about the rocket and the tracking, I slept very poorly and woke up a little after 1:00 AM. I left for work very early and got there about 3:45 AM PST or 6:45 PM EST.

Shortly thereafter, I called Joe Padavano, hoping he might be at work by 7:00 AM EST (he was), and I asked him if they could do their November launch with the stretched version of the second stage to provide exactly the demonstration of the Taurus we needed. He said he had thought of the same thing and didn't know if they could or not, but he was going to investigate it. That sounded very good. I told him I thought I was very close to getting a Taurus, though I would have to launch on a standard Taurus. According to our earlier conversations, if the spacecraft's mass were 300 kg as I had told him, we would have to use a non-apsoidal trajectory, which would be hard to get exactly right. I told Joe the spacecraft's mass was holding at about 290 kg and asked him if the standard Taurus could do the TLI burn from a circular parking orbit if I kept the mass at that level. He was very enthusiastic about the possibility and left a message for me later in the day saying they could launch up to 302 kg with the Star-37 from a circular orbit and they thought that they might even have some more margin they could use! Man, that was great news and consistent with what they had told me in the beginning, i.e., they always had a 30 kg built-in margin and there was possibly some more margin beyond that. That would easily put me over the top, and if worse came to worse and the spacecraft grew well over 300 kg, I could take a few kg of fuel out and I would certainly do that to be on the Taurus.

I called and told that to Bret and Bret thought that was very good.

I took a critical look at our mass estimates to make sure they were what I thought they were. It turned out that Tilley's and my estimates were only about 6 kg apart, mine being more optimistic and his being less optimistic, but we were holding between 290 and 300 kg (nearly two years later, Lunar Prospector's fully fuelled launch mass was 296 kg). I thought those numbers would hold until the LLV2 environment caught up with us. That was the nice thing about the Taurus, we wouldn't have to change the spacecraft to accommodate Taurus's launch environment, so I could relatively easily keep the launch mass within the limits of, perhaps, even the standard Taurus. With the launch mass numbers Joe and I were discussing, I felt very confident we would win the Taurus vs. LLV2 battle.

Because of the CRSS-first-launch-bugaboo, I sat down and re-looked at the lunar eclipse data and my mission window to be absolutely certain that what I had told Dougherty and Sylvia was correct. It was.

Later Dougherty and I talked about the CRSS issue and he admitted two things that were no surprise. First, Lockheed was not going to hurry with CRSS. Second, Lockheed didn't give a damn about Lunar Prospector — it had a very low priority. Lockheed wanted it to work, but they were not going to do anything to help us that might cost them money. CRSS was a very big program and we were way down at the bottom of the totem pole. Though I knew all that, it was nice to have him admit it and what followed was a very serious talk.

Sometimes Dougherty was not a company man and that was one of those times. He said, "Don't compromise your mission. You need those 18 months (of orbital mapping time). You shouldn't even start considering not doing it (not fighting for my October launch before CRSS)." It was a fair and open conversation and he acknowledged it looked bad for LLV2 and that Taurus was my best bet. Since he really knew CRSS would not be launched in December, Dougherty said, "If the launch rule applies and since Lunar Prospector has to launch no later than January 1998, I'm going to start trying to make management understand that we have to go on a Taurus." That would work out since Orbital only needed sixteen months to prepare for a launch that was still twenty months away. Dougherty was worried that the delivery of a Castor 120 and the TLI motor could make it twenty months, but I told him what Joe and I had talked about, i.e., that Lockheed could just sell one of our Castor 120s and our Star-37 to Orbital Sciences and that issue would go away. We had sixteen months plus four months of margin. Even if NASA, as expected, took up to two more months to get the order out in an official document, we still had a two-month cushion.

Though Dougherty was often a pain in my butt, I really appreciated our conversation and it strengthened my hope that, though Dougherty was a company man, when the chips were down, he would back me in my quest for success.

Sylvia came over after lunch and we re-discussed the issues. We had just found out that Araki was going to have lunch with Goldin on Sunday. Araki had sent a message saying if the no-first-launch-rule stuck, we would have to wait until CRSS's December launch. But, apparently Araki understood if there were any CRSS delays (which there would certainly be — and were) then waiting on CRSS wasn't going to work. It was up to Araki to try to convince Goldin not to apply the rule if Lockheed wanted to keep me on the LLV2. I didn't think he had a snowball's chance in hell of convincing Goldin, nor did Dougherty. We still didn't have a launch vehicle, in part because we did not know for sure (though Joe and I were pretty sure) if Lunar Prospector could get launched on a standard Taurus from a circular parking orbit, and in part, because we were all skeptical about a non-apsoidal launch, but mainly because Headquarters didn't know what in hell it was doing.

Later in the afternoon I went over to Ames and talked to Dave Lozier about the non-apsoidal launch. Dave said he would call Orbital Sciences and discuss it to see if it would work or not. I was sure it could work, but I thought it would be very restrictive.

We had a review of the power system, which went well, followed by a discussion of the redundancy in the thermal subsystem. I wanted to minimize the latter's mass, in part by eliminating all of its redundancy — the rest of the spacecraft was single string, so why not have a single string thermal subsystem? Jim Schirle promised he would do that. But Dougherty wanted to keep its redundancy because, as he said, "the little bitsy thermostats and wire heaters tend to fail and they have a trivial amount of mass."

Based on what Jim had in his parts list, I thought we could save a kilogram if we went single string. Jim said that was a very optimistic number and the mass of the subsystem wouldn't be as much as he had indicated. However, they knew what I was after — I had to keep the spacecraft from getting any heavier than 290 kilograms so I could get on a standard Taurus. Nevertheless, Dougherty said again, "I want the redundancy."

I said, "Well, I don't."

He said, "You have to understand that these parts do tend to fail and there is really no mass."

I said, "Well, OK, I'll compromise if there really is no significant mass impact."

Always trying to get the last word in, Dougherty said jokingly, "Good; Alan, you just gotta get in step with me."

I said, "No, Tom, you gotta get in step with me."

By the time I started home, it had been a long (more than 12 hours), but very good day. My hopes were up that I was going to end up on a Taurus, and, as Dougherty said, we were rolling on the spacecraft — things were really moving. He really felt confident about the spacecraft, which was nice to hear because he had been involved with many spacecraft.

Sunday, February 11, through Wednesday, February 14, 1996: A Long Trip, Seattle — JPL — Denver

Irv and I flew to Seattle, WA, to visit Olin where our six little engines were being made. It was a clear day and on the way up we flew directly over all the Cascade volcanoes from Mount Lassen to Mount St. Helens. To my great — and I mean great — consternation, I was on the wrong side of the plane and didn't get to see hardly anything. I was really ticked off and was determined to sit on the correct side of the plane the next time we went to Olin.

I gave my Lunar Prospector pep talk to the Olin staff on Monday. They were very excited about the mission and thought it was great that I came to tell them about it. As was the case with all the other vendors, Olin had never had a PI visit them before.

Then we had a really good meeting about the engines. We got a lot done because I was right there and could answer their questions on the spot, rather than have Irv bring questions back to me at Lockheed and then send the answers back to Olin. They were very happy to know what the Mission Profile was, so they could understand how the engines would be used. For example, I told them I would be doing three LOI burns of about 30 minute duration each, and they told me no one had ever burned their 22 Newton engines for such long periods. They would look into it and see if their engines could take such long burns (they could).

Similarly, I explained that we were using a simple blow-down propulsion system with an initial tank pressure of about 400 psi and a final pressure of about 120 psi. They then told us that at pressures lower than about 150 psi, the thrust of the engines begin to "sine," that is, the thrust begins to fluctuate with a frequency of about 20 Hz and with an amplitude of up to 50%, starting about 20 seconds into a long burn! That was of concern and we would have to find out what the sineing of the thrust would do to the dynamics of the spacecraft.

Because I was concerned about the low thrust levels during most of the mapping phase of the mission when the tank pressure would be below 200 psi, Irv had told me that Olin could enlarge the fuel injection orifices of the engines and thereby increase the thrust of the engines by up to 50%. I asked Olin about that and the answer was yes, they could do that, but the sineing of the engine thrust would begin at pressure above 200 psi. I asked them to send me the data on the sineing so we could evaluate its effect on the spacecraft.

And finally, putting the icing on the cake, I got an accurate value for the engine masses — just 4.4 kg total! That entire exchange of information went very well and the Olin staff said, "Boy, this is the way to get things done in a few hours, rather than resolving the issues by memos and phone calls over several weeks. We know right now what you need and we can get busy on it." It was a very, very good meeting.

Monday night I flew to LA for a tracking meeting at JPL on Tuesday. It was a general meeting JPL had a couple of times a year so everybody could talk about his or her mission and resolve tracking conflicts. The 26 m net was discussed, since everyone had heard NASA was either going to commercialize it or take it out of the net. However, it was not only going to be taken out of the net, NASA was going to destroy it! That was stupid, why didn't they just give it to a vendor and let them use it? I quickly decided that the best thing for me to do, even though I was going to get time on the 34 and 70 m dishes, was to try to get the Air Force to give me tracking time in exchange for my helping with Blue Moon. Other than that, the meeting was a waste of my time.

I flew on to Denver that night and got in quite late.

Dougherty, Sylvia, and I had an excellent kick-off meeting with the LLV people on Wednesday. Of course, we were all very concerned about the no-first-launch-rule. Dougherty was quite good about everything, and, when introducing me, he pointed out that it was my program! I got up and emphasized that, "I am your customer, not NASA. NASA is my customer and this is my mission, not a NASA mission." Then I proceeded to tell them about all the LLV2 and TLI Stage issues I was concerned about.

To my surprise, we had a very good meeting. But another scary thing became very clear: The time required to get permission for a launch from the Cape is such that we were already behind schedule! We had to get moving or else. Other than that, I got it across to LLV that, because of my mission window of 22 months, I couldn't have anymore than a 4-month delay from my October launch or I would start losing mission duration. Though the meeting was fruitful, it didn't change anything; we still didn't know what launch vehicle I was going on.

Thursday, February 15, 1996

I got up very early in the morning to go to the Denver Airport to catch my 6:40 AM flight home. I was very tired, I had slept only two and a half hours that night and I had not slept much during the whole trip because of all the aggravation about the rocket and the tracking. I flew from Denver to Phoenix and then on to San Jose where I arrived about 10:30 AM. I got to Lockheed in time for my usual early lunch.

After lunch and after talking to Frank about the various issues, I went to Ames to talk to Scott about my trip to Headquarters to discuss the burning launch vehicle issue and nothing else. Frank wanted Dougherty to go with me and give a general update on the mission, but Scott and I agreed that would be a waste of time. The meeting had to be a one-issue meeting and though Dougherty and Frank thought that the no-first-

launch issue was just going to fade away, I didn't think it was going to go away as quickly as those guys thought.

When I got back to Lockheed, I found out that, while I was on my trip, the idiots
had again brought up the dead issue of the coning of the Spacecraft/TLI Stage stack during and after the TLI burn and hence, the need to have active nutation damping on the
TLI Stage. I blew my top at Richard about that. It was stupid. Dan Swanson and Richard
had found that a Star-48 could have as much as 5 kg of slag (molten aluminum) build
up during its burn and it could cause significant coning if it all lodged in one place in
the engine. So what? We were using the much smaller Star-37 that could only have, at
most, a couple of tenths of a kilogram of slag and that little bit of slag couldn't cause
any big problem. Also, Thiokol had flown numerous Star-37s and Star-48s and I had
never heard of a slag/coning problem destroying a mission. I understand that the engineers are supposed to look for all potential failure modes, an absolute necessity if one
wants to have a successful mission, but one has to be able to properly access the reality of the potential problem. But, as usual — especially when I was gone — some of the
guys ran off, half-baked, making dire predictions about some pseudo-problem and
screwing everything up.

Beyond the direct flap caused by the bogus coning concern, Woody was worried
because he wanted to have an extension of the solar panels at the bottom of the spacecraft to get more power. If we did that and there were more than 10° of coning when
the TLI Stage and the spacecraft separated, that solar array extension would be damaged. I was annoyed, the guys were always screwing something up — between them,
NASA, and Lockheed, it was almost enough to drive me to drink.

By the time I got home from the trip and from Lockheed, I was exhausted. It had
been a very, very tiring trip. A lot had been accomplished at Denver, even more at Olin,
and I had gotten a better understanding of what was going on with the tracking, but I
was tired and glad to be home with Rebecca.

Friday, February 16, 1996

I called Bret in the morning to find out what had happened about my launch vehicle at Headquarters during my trip. Basically, there was nothing new.

We had our staff meeting — a day late since Dougherty and I had both been in
Denver — and it was mainly the design review for the spacecraft structure, which was
in really great shape.

There were several other issues, such as Woody wanting to add his 15 cm skirt at
the bottom for the solar array I didn't like. When he chose silicon solar cells over the
more efficient (but more costly) GaAs solar cells, he chose standard, but very inefficient
ones instead of looking at the new Japanese (Sharp), 17% efficiency, silicon cells. Even
Dougherty realized that was a bad decision and nobody wanted the skirt, except Woody.
Woody, Dougherty, and I sat down after the review meeting and discussed it and decided that Woody needed to look into getting the Sharp cells. They cost $100,000 more
than the American silicon cells (which is still a lot less than the GaAs cells), so it was not
a trivial matter to choose the Sharp cells over the American cells, despite their greater
efficiency.

Then there was the coning. I politely pointed out that the issue was a load of BS.
Interestingly, though he didn't understand it, Dougherty tended to agree with me!

The other good thing that happened was that Tom and I found out we were
accepted as a non-profit, tax-exempt corporation in California. We were going to move

ahead rapidly with our getting into LEI. Hopefully, we would be out of Lockheed by the end of the month.

Later, Frank, Dougherty, and I went over to Ames to talk to Scott about the launch vehicle problem that was really threatening the whole mission. We just couldn't wait for two or three more months for NASA to make up its mind — that would kill Lunar Prospector. Frank and I agreed we had to force Headquarters to make a decision right then, one way or the other. Scott and Dougherty thought we should just charge ahead with the LLV2 and by the time NASA made up its mind, it would be too late to change what we were doing. But that was just not the way to do it; if we did and Headquarters disagreed in a few months, we would be in deep trouble. In the end, we all agreed I should go to Headquarters the following week and try to get a waiver of the no-first-launch-rule.

By the time I set up my trip to DC, Frank had caught wind of the fact that I was going to see James Paul and Eric Sterner from the House Science Committee, so he insisted I call Michelle and have her accompany me. That really ticked me off; I really resented having to put up with her and to be babysat by her — all because I was still a damned Lockheed employee. I could hardly wait to get out of Lockheed, if for no other reason, then I would never have to put up with her again.

Monday, February 19, 1996: Subsystem Review Day

I slept only a few hours, got up at 1:00 AM, and went to work at 3:00 AM. It was a long day. I was getting ready to go on the trip to Washington, Houston, and San Antonio the next day.

The main topic of our subsystem review was Woody's unpopular 15 cm extension of the solar panels. Even though I didn't believe that coning at separation was a real problem and hence that damage to Woody's extension would occur, the skirt could cause problems for the A1 and A2 engines. The engines were down there behind the skirt, so they would be in permanent shade and they would get really cold. Thus their heaters would require a lot of extra power, or worse, the hydrazine fuel could freeze with potentially catastrophic results. And, of course, the skirt would add mass and complexity. As we discussed all that, Dougherty was initially huffing and puffing, but then got reasonable very quickly.

Later, Jim Schirle checked and found that the engines probably wouldn't freeze, though, as expected, more power was going to be used down there to keep the A1 and A2 engines warm. They should be OK, but I was not 100% certain of that.

When I said I really wanted to see if we could do away with the skirt, we again talked about using GaAs cells. The trouble was they cost $300,000. Since Tom and I were getting ready to go into LEI, that was going to save the project about $350,000 and hence, that would pay for the GaAs cells. Also, based on my power balance model, I began to feel confident that we needed only 5 to 7 cm of skirt to generate enough power using the basic American silicon cells. Woody still didn't want to consider the Sharp cells that had 17% efficiency (vs. 14% for the American cells) because they were new and unknown. Anyway, it seemed like we had a reasonable solution with a 5 cm skirt. Also, a 5 cm extension of the solar array wouldn't be damaged at separation, even if the bogus coning got up to 50°.

Still regarding the bogus coning, we talked about putting little graphite epoxy bumpers next to the A1 and A2 engines to protect them and that made everyone happy — just in case.

At the end of the subsystem review meeting, I felt we were doing pretty well, especially since we were going to stay with the cheaper silicon cells and a short skirt (men generally like short skirts).

However, during the meeting it became apparent to me that there was something very important I did not understand about the shadowing of the solar array by the booms and science instruments. I went to Woody's office after the meeting and had him explain the effects of the shadowing to me. I had been under the misconception that the amount of power lost by shadowing was simply proportional to the geometric area being shadowed. Not true — as Woody explained, the solar cells, each of which produces about 1.5 v, are arranged in series in strings of about 20 cells each to get the voltage up to 28 v, no surprise there. Then the strings are added together in parallel to get the required current, and hence the wattage, up to the levels needed. Again no surprise there — just first year physics. However, when a shadow falls on even one cell in a string, the entire string shuts off — and that was the big surprise for me! The power loss is far larger than simple geometric consideration would indicate. Thus, the effects of shadowing in my power model were well underestimated! I was very happy to finally know that, but I was also very perturbed that Woody had not explained it to me at least a year earlier. After all, we had discussed both his and my power modeling innumerable times over the past year and a half. Why didn't he point out that I did not properly understand such a critically important part of the power equation? Well, at least I knew about it before my ignorance caused any serious trouble.

Regardless of the cause of Woody's lapse in my education, we turned to the serious problem at hand — getting the power modeling right before we ended up building Lunar Prospector with far too little solar array area. As we did, it was apparent to me that Woody himself had not correctly thought through the problem of shadowing on a spinning spacecraft and hence, had not done his job correctly! We went through a quick exercise to roughly determine the order of magnitude of the shadowing problem, i.e., to find out just how deep we were in the doggy-do-do, and it was considerable.

The way I was planning to fly Lunar Prospector was to have the spin axis perpendicular to the plane of Moon's orbit around the Earth. That way the Earth would always be in the middle of the radiation pattern of the medium gain antenna and, since the Moon's orbital inclination is only 5° with respect to the ecliptic, the Sun's rays would strike the surface of the solar array drum within no more than a 5° angle. Hence, we would have a negligible, maximum loss of solar power of only 0.4% compared to that if the spin axis of the spacecraft were perpendicular to the ecliptic, as would normally be the case. Given that geometry, the shadows of the instruments (as they crossed the solar array drum during each 5-second rotation of Lunar Prospector) would move up and down the drum as the Earth, Moon, and spacecraft all together went around the Sun each year. That is, the spacecraft would have yearly seasons just like the Earth, where the noonday Sun is high in the summer sky and low in the winter sky, respectively.

Since the booms were to be mounted towards the bottom of the spacecraft, Woody wanted to have two sets of solar cells, one covering the upper half — and one covering the lower half — of the solar drum. That way, the shadowing would affect only half of the strings. That was a great idea and it would minimize the effects of the MAG/ER and NS/APS instrument packages, but unfortunately the upper part of the GRS's large shadow would still fall on the upper part of the array during the spacecraft's "+Z summer." We went through some rough calculations and found we had a 10 to 15% loss of power due to the instrument's shadows during the worst case of spacecraft "+Z summer." Given that, I thought we would have to use the expensive GaAs solar cells.

I got ticked off at Michelle. Because of Frank, I had to call her and tell her I was going to go see James Paul and Eric Sterner and she was supposed to accompany me. When I did, she said haughtily, "You have overstepped your bounds, I am supposed to arrange all such liaisons." I told her politely she could kiss my butt.

Tuesday, February 20, through Saturday February 24, 1996: DC and Houston

The long trip was planned to start by my flying to DC Tuesday, then I would go to JSC on Friday and/or Saturday, and finally, I would fly over to Southwest Research in San Antonio to give them their pep talk on Monday the 26th. The trip got cut short because Tom called when I was at JSC and told me that I had to get back because of the damned rocket. Here is what happened.

I flew to Washington on the 20th, but I was very, very late getting there. First of all, when I changed planes in St. Louis, we got in the airplane and then we sat in it for an hour while they fixed the brakes! Then, when we finally got in the air and were halfway to National Airport, an airplane had run off the end of the runway at National, so they diverted us to Dulles. Then I had to take a damned bus to National and finally, got to Pat and Julius's very late, but Julius's had his usual, delicious meatloaf dinner waiting for me!

I rented a car Wednesday morning and drove out to Orbital Sciences to talk with them. They felt pretty confident that they had a good shot at launching Lunar Prospector; NASA had been inquiring about a Taurus for me and were even considering letting me use the XL Prime configuration, even though the stretched second stage was untested. Orbital said the XL Prime Taurus could launch up to 315 kg to the Moon with a TLI burn from a circular orbit, so I had to keep the mass down.

I, too, felt that Orbital had a good shot at launching me and I certainly wanted them to do so. The only fly in the ointment was, if the new rules apply, they would have to have the new Iso 9,000 validation along with Goddard Space Flight Center oversight, both of which would increase the costs from the $23 million we were talking about by some unknown amount. Nevertheless, I still felt my best shot was the Taurus, because it would let me get launched on time — if nothing else.

I drove back to downtown Washington and had a little time to spare. I went to the Aerospace Museum, I had a quick lunch, and finally went to see Bret. We discussed my finally getting into LEI since our paperwork had been accepted by California. Bret said Mark had changed his tune and no longer wanted me to go to LEI because he believed I would no longer have any control over Lockheed. Mark was getting to be a big pain in the butt; he was making the program as hard as possible.

We talked about the meeting I wanted so I could discuss the rocket issue and Bret said he was setting it up for the next day. Since I had nothing to do until then, I spent the rest of the afternoon at the National History Museum looking at the dinosaurs and other Paleozoic and Mesozoic fossils. I was a little disappointed; instead of having a nice timeline, starting with the Precambrian and going systematically through time to the present, the displays were sort of a hodgepodge. They have absolutely beautiful fossils, but in my opinion, it was not a good display.

I took Pat and Julius out to dinner to a restaurant not far from their home and had an expensive, but, in my estimation, not a very good meal.

I called Bret early Thursday morning and he said the meeting was set for 1:00 PM, so that meant I could fly to Houston on my original schedule. I went over to the American History Museum and walked around there, had lunch at the Air and Space Museum, and then toddled back to Headquarters for the meeting.

Ken Ledbetter, Bill Piotrowski, Mark, Bret, Scott, and I were at the meeting. We all sat down and talked about the whole rocket mess. I explained the situation and emphasized that part of the problem was, though NASA could tell me that the choice of the launch vehicle was mine to make, Lockheed simply would not do what I told them to do. As far as Lockheed was concerned, I was a Lockheed employee and they didn't care one bit that I was the PI and the customer. I was the customer and the PI only when it was to their advantage and when it was not, I was simply an employee and, as such, I was supposed to keep my mouth shut. I told them that having an Industry PI was a rotten idea and that they shouldn't have allowed it. I hoped Mark was paying attention, but, of course, he wasn't.

We went around and around about the various possibilities, like slipping the launch, reconfiguring the spacecraft, and blah, blah, blah, and it became clear they really wanted me on the LLV2, although they didn't really want to say so. I pointed out that all those options cost money and time and they said, as always, "Well, you can't have any more money."

Finally I said, "Look, if you guys tell me that I can't fly on a vehicle that hasn't been flown before and don't give me a way of leveraging Lockheed to make them let me go on a Taurus, then Lockheed is just going to do what it has done from the beginning. They'll say, sure, you can launch on a Taurus, just get NASA to direct us to do it. And, of course, you won't do that. It's not going to work. You have me in a box and there is nothing I can do. Lockheed will not cooperate. Either you give me a way out or we are at a stalemate and I have no launch vehicle, period."

Mark then said, "Well, the only thing you can do is duck."

A stupid, remark to which I replied, "I can't duck. I'm the Principal Investigator and this is my responsibility. I have to somehow make sure this happens." Mark didn't make any further comments and I thought, *if they expect me to roll over and drop dead and just let their stupidity destroy this mission, they're out of their minds.*

Finally, they decided to write a formal letter to me saying that NASA recognized there was a problem and asking me what my options were. Then NASA would answer my reply by formally giving me a directive based on my options. I said, "That is the only possible solution," mission accomplished — at least I hoped so, but I had been around NASA too long to believe it before I saw it in writing.

I left Headquarters, went to National Airport, flew to Dallas, then to Houston, and finally flopped into my bed in my hotel room.

I went to see John Connolly and Kent Joosten at JSC Friday morning. They said Clinton wanted to get man back to the Moon in an attempt to emulate Kennedy, since Kennedy was Clinton's hero, so he, Clinton, could end his administration in 2001 with man back on the Moon. It was really a presidential program and the key was that Clinton thought he was going to be re-elected, then he could have his place in history (what he got after being re-elected was several Lewinskies from Monica, impeached, but — unfortunately — not kicked out of office). That was the thrust of it and that gave me a lot of power to push for the things I really needed to get done at Lockheed. Goldin was, of course, trying to make it happen (the man on the Moon thing, not the Lewinskies).

We talked about the way they were proposing to do it. They were going to use the Space Station as a fuel depot, where various vendors (mainly the Russians using the Proton) would store the fuel for the missions. They would use the aerobraking vehicle JSC had begun developing much earlier for the Space Exploration Initiative to take man between the Space Station and low lunar orbit. They would use a simple lander, the kind the Air Force had thought about in the Apollo days that carried a two-man crew that just stood on a platform with no structure around them. That thing would land the crew on the Moon, where they would live in either a habitat or a rover that had been put down earlier. The crew would stay six days and then they would return to the Space Station using the lander and the aerobraking vehicle. Eventually there would be a more reusable lander, longer stay times, and the like.

The guys knew about my rocket problem and when they said they had a telecon with Goldin every two weeks, I said, "Look, get it into Goldin's head that I have to launch. If I am going to get you guys the data you need in time to do you any good, I have to launch and stay on schedule. You guys can help force the issue with the rocket." They said they were going to push like hell to help me get a launch vehicle.

I got a message from Tom saying I had to get back to Lockheed ASAP because Scott already had a draft of the letter Headquarters was going to formally send me through Scott, and that Frank and Dougherty had blown up. They said they were not going to present the launch options (they forgot the letter was written to me, not them) and Scott had to say, "Yes you are, you are going to give us the options." I needed to forget my PR visit to Southwest Monday and get home ASAP, which I started getting ready to do.

I was annoyed with NASA and Lockheed. NASA continued to play its stupid game of "let's jerk Lunar Prospector around" while insisting there be no resulting cost impacts and I was again going to have fight with stupid Lockheed about the rocket. Despite Dougherty's kind words two weeks earlier about my getting a Taurus if I needed it, when it looked like NASA was really going to put me on a Taurus, he and Frank changed their tunes — as they did back in mid-December when the no-first-launch-rule was first brought up.

After receiving his message, I called Tom to see what had happened. He told me that, according to Dougherty, if we delayed the mission until after CRSS, assuming that CRSS got off in March (everybody agreed it was going to slip from December 1997 to at least March, despite what Lockheed told its investors), the delay to March would cost $650,000 and $75,000 for every month beyond that until we launched! That would be about $1 million! And I would lose the extended mission, and perhaps part of the nominal mission. If NASA then said, "delay and reconfigure the spacecraft for eclipses," that would mean having a 15 amp-hr battery, more solar cells, etc., which would cost another two million dollars, or more!

The numbers Dougherty had ginned up about the LLV2 were fine and showed that delaying the mission was not a "no cost impact" solution. But what really ticked me off was that Dougherty said it would cost $10 million if we went to a Taurus! That was pure, unadulterated BS; going to a Taurus was a positive cost impact of up to $3 million, because it was cheaper than the LLV2! In fact, I had asked Dougherty a couple of weeks earlier how much we would have to spend making the transition to a Taurus and he had said, "Only a few hundred thousand dollars, if we jumped over to a Taurus right now." He was lying by at least a factor of 10, if not a factor of 20, or even more.

It was clear to me that what Lockheed (and even NASA) was doing was loading the dice, so that no matter what happened, I would have to stay on the LLV2. I was really mad. Lockheed was going to keep me off a Taurus even though it was cheaper and a better rocket, if it was the last thing they did. They didn't give a crap about the mission; they just wanted to advertise their damned rocket. I had to get out of that foul company as fast as I could.

I immediately called Scott and told him that Dougherty and Frank were making it look like going to the Taurus would be prohibitively expensive and that was a bald-faced lie.

I got a flight home on Sunday (I don't remember what I did Saturday, I was too mad to remember, but I probably spent it with John Gruener) and I was very frustrated, very annoyed, and not looking forward to going to work Monday. Somehow the battle had to be fought to a successful end — I was not going to let Lockheed and NASA's stupidity destroy Lunar Prospector. The fact that Lunar Prospector was not only a key mission in Discovery, but had also become a key mission in the President's "Return Man to the Moon Program" was the only leverage I had in the battle. I really hated Lockheed and NASA (and I still do).

Monday, February 26, 1996: The Rocket Mess Gets Worse and Worse

The main topic during the subsystem review was not the spacecraft, but the damned launch vehicle. Dougherty had a series of viewgraphs about the well-proven Delta vehicles used by NASA. The Delta-lite would cost $15 to 25 million more than the LLV2 or the Taurus, but still significantly less than the standard Delta. If NASA put us on a Delta-lite, that would be OK — if they paid for it. We might have been able to afford to go on the bigger Delta-2 by sharing the launch with another payload, but there was no easy way we could co-manifest with a normal Earth satellite. As usual, Dougherty presented the case for the Taurus as negatively as he could.

We went through the "wait for CRSS and modify the spacecraft" option — again. Why we had to go over the same ground over and over again was a mystery to me. Maybe Dougherty, Lockheed, and NASA thought if they discussed a non-solution often enough, Mother Nature would get tired of it and change the laws of physics to accommodate their desires! We discussed the impact of modifying the spacecraft for eclipses: the bigger battery, hence a bigger solar array, hence more mass, hence more fuel, hence bigger tanks, hence new structure, hence no longer fitting in the LLV2 shroud, and on and on. Not only all that, but the changes would mean we would have to throw away what was already being built, e.g., the tanks. A child could see what NASA and Dougherty could not see — it would not work. Finally, Dougherty did realize that was not an option.

I said we had to put in the option of us getting a waiver of the no-first-launch-rule. We went around and around on that. It was hopeless — NASA would not let me on the LLV2 and Lockheed would not let me off of it!

Frank, Dougherty, Sylvia, and I then had a meeting with Scott at 3:00 PM and we went through the whole mess again.

Frank had seen Ledbetter at some review and they had talked. Ledbetter reiterated that there was no extra money, so we had to find an option that cost nothing. That option was Taurus, but NASA would not direct Lockheed to let me use a Taurus, so it was an untenable situation.

Frank made excuses for Ledbetter, saying he was new at his position, but I found that excuse very shallow, especially when Ledbetter wanted us to wait for CRSS because he naïvely believed that waiting would cost nothing and he was even going to send us a letter telling us to preserve the extended mission option at the same time!

Annoyed as I was that Ledbetter was sufficiently ignorant (or stupid) that he could not understand that delaying for CRSS meant expensive spacecraft modifications, costly storage, team disintegration, etc., Lockheed was still lying to NASA and telling them that CRSS was launching in December, 1997. Ledbetter was not only naïve, but was also being misled. Regardless of who at NASA was naïve and/or stupid and who at Lockheed was lying, both NASA and Lockheed were being unrealistic about the whole thing. The way I felt right then was there was a very good chance that Lunar Prospector was going to fail because of the rocket issue.

On top of all the NASA nonsense, Richard told me that LLV was still not cooperating. They never had and they never would. I talked to Dougherty and told him I was really concerned that LLV was pulling the same old tricks they had pulled in the past. I was even more convinced if I were stuck on an LLV, Lunar Prospector was going to fail and there was nothing I could do about it, because NASA was tying my hands.

Richard thought LLV was failing us because of its move from Sunnyvale to Denver and because it had lost half of its staff. He thought LLV was just not capable of doing the job and they knew it, but they didn't have the guts to say so. They jacked the price up, hoping to make the LLV2 as unattractive as possible so we would dump them. That was just what we had believed when Damon was running the LLV show in Sunnyvale during the Phase B effort. I agreed with Richard's opinions completely.

I got a call from a guy named George Collins from the Bob Jones University (I had never heard of the Bob Jones University before, so I didn't know it is a fundamentalist Christian University) in South Carolina who had read the *Country News* article about Lunar Prospector. George told me that a teacher by the name of Dick Seeley teaches high school level physics at a remote learning center called BJ Link at the Bob Jones University. George asked if I would do a half hour video for Dick's class and then talk for an hour via telephone with his students so they could ask me questions. I said yes, it was another good outreach opportunity.

I had a good conversation with Frank who believed that the rocket issue had to be addressed by Wes. Frank maintained that Lockheed didn't care about the mission (which I knew), but if it was directed to use a Taurus, Lockheed might agree, but on the other hand, Lockheed was quite capable of just dumping Lunar Prospector before using a competitor's rocket. Frank also said that if Lunar Prospector started going into the red, Lockheed would fire him. I was dealing with a big company that didn't give a damn about anybody or anything, except its profits, period.

Tuesday, February 27, 1996

Despite getting no sleep because of the frustrations, I actually did some work! I worked on the shadowing of the solar cells by the instruments that Woody had done all wrong — he had not taken into account the cosine effect on the shadowing correctly. I calculated that we would have about 18% shadowing, so we were either going to have to use GaAs cells or extend the solar array 10 cm at the top and at the bottom of the spacecraft.

The spacecraft mass was also creeping up. The booms and their release assembly all came in a little heavier because of the changes we had made so they could be released automatically while the spacecraft was still rotating at 60 rpm.

I also called Larry Price, the head of LLV in Denver, and bawled him out because LLV was not doing what it was supposed to, but I doubted it did any good.

Other than those few things, Dougherty and I went around in circles about reconfiguring the spacecraft to fly after CRSS. No matter how you looked at it, it was a can of worms — very, very costly worms. The thing that really bothered me was that Headquarters just kept saying, "Why don't you just make these little changes and fly after CRSS?" You would think NASA had never build a spacecraft before — there are no such things as a little change on the spacecraft at the point we were at in Phase C/D, period. We would have to start over again. Why didn't NASA get it?

Wednesday, February 28, 1996

I stayed home since Tom and I had a meeting with Dorothy Van Fossen, whose company, DataMate, we were going to hire to do LEI's bookkeeping. We got a lot done at DataMate, so Dorothy could move ahead setting up our bookkeeping. We talked to an agent who could handle the LEI 401(k) and retirement accounts. Then we talked to the young lady we were going to use as LEI's travel agent. We got a lot done in preparation for getting LEI up and running.

Chapter 3-10
The End of Taurus

Thursday, February 29, 1996: Leap Year Day and Staff Meeting Day

We had our staff meeting and discussed a number of issues, one of which was what we would have to do to modify the spacecraft to survive the eclipses in case NASA made us wait for CRSS, and the other was, of course, the spacecraft's mass, since I intended to keep the Taurus option open.

Since the size of the battery was the starting point for modifying the spacecraft to survive eclipses, we discussed changing the battery from the 4.8 amp-hr NiCd battery we were going to use to a 15 amp-hr nickel hydrogen battery if we had to go that way. Regarding the mass increase, I had been carrying 5 kg for the 4.8 amp-hr battery I had gotten from the catalogue, plus some mass for the battery support structure, while Woody and Al Tilley had been conservatively carrying 8½ kg. For some unknown reason, Woody felt the 15 amp-hr battery would be only a couple of kilograms heavier, but in reality it had to be at least a 5 kilogram hit. Since my mass tally for the spacecraft was 290 kg, the bigger battery would make it at least 295 kg and I thought it would more likely creep up to 300 kg, due to the battery and its structure alone — and that was at the top of Taurus's range.

When we got done discussing the modifications needed to survive the eclipses, we found they would cost an extra $3 million or so, money NASA said they would not give us! I was impressed at how well Dougherty did in estimating the cost impacts — that was where he shined.

I got a call in the morning from one of the managers at Loral I had met when I gave Loral their pep talk in January. I had told Loral that if there were any problems they should call me, so he did. He said they still didn't have the specifications and the contract needed to start work on our transponder! I immediately talked to Dougherty and he said the transponder had been one of the lower priority items! I was astounded since it was one of the long lead items and the only hope we had of getting it on time was, as Loral had said it would do, to have Loral take a half finished transponder off their Iridium production line and turn it into ours. I said, "Tom, if they don't get the damned thing going, they're not going to be able to get it to us on time." I was annoyed that he sort of poo-poo'd the urgency of the situation.

But he said, "We'll get it done and get it out today." I called the Loral guy back and told him the specs and contract were supposed to be sent via Fed-Ex no later than the next day and if he didn't have it by Monday, he should call me again. Dougherty took those things a little too lightly, so I was not going to fool around with him anymore.

Tom and I went over to Ames to talk to Dave Lozier about some trajectory and orbital issues. During the discussion, Dave mentioned that two days earlier he discovered that if we launched on October 9 as planned, we would reach the Moon when it was at one of its nodes. I said, "That's great. That means when we go into orbit I can orient the spacecraft so the shadowing on the solar array is minimized. Then I'll do a 180° reor six months later, that I have to do anyway for the GRS, and that will minimize the shadowing for the next six months." By doing so, there would never be any shadowing on the upper part of the solar array, so none of its strings would cut out. That was great and it would make Woody happy, too.

By then it was noon and we had to go to a going away luncheon for Vu. The Gods had smiled down on me from Mount Olympus. Vu, a Vietnamese, had decided to take a year off and go back to visit his homeland. He had told us the good news a few days earlier, so we were taking him out to lunch. Thankfully, but no thanks to Dougherty and Lockheed, the worst engineer in our group and the one who was responsible for the most critical subsystem was leaving the project for good, hopefully to be replaced with someone who knew what he was doing. I was delighted and thankful to be going to Vu's going away luncheon.

I went to see Sylvia after the luncheon to find out what was new from Headquarters about the rocket. As I had known earlier, NASA was going to have GSFC watch over Taurus and that would add to Taurus's cost. Well, believe it or not, NASA had added $6 million worth of oversight onto a $23 million launch vehicle — that was criminal, a 25% increase in cost! I was surprised that Orbital Sciences held still while they were being raped, but I supposed NASA had enough power to force them to keep quite while they were being violated. Thus, a Taurus would cost $29 million, so I could no longer afford it. What a clean way of getting rid of the issue, just force the price up so I couldn't go on a Taurus and then neither Lockheed nor NASA would have to listen to me ask for the cheaper and better launch vehicle any more! Regardless of what I thought, I could read the handwriting on the wall, so I said to Sylvia, "Well then, to hell with it (the Taurus)."

Sylvia then said that she, Scott, and some other officials at Ames had a dry run for our videocon about the rocket with Piotrowski and Bret set for the next day. As far as I was concerned, the whole thing was a Lockheed/Headquarters set up because it all came down to the following: Both the Delta, and, due to NASA's shenanigans, the Taurus were too costly. I was going to be stuck on an LLV2 (which Lockheed had nothing to do with, of course).

Other than that, we were going to be asked to do the simplest, no cost option to keep us on schedule.

Our first option was to ask for a waiver of the no-first-launch-rule right then, so we could just proceed full speed ahead towards our October 1997 launch. We expected a negative response to that request.

The second option was, "OK, don't give us the waiver now, but wait until LLV1's next launch in the summer and if it works, then revisit the issue and give us a waiver then." By then we would be building the spacecraft without the capability to survive the eclipses. If we got the wavier then, we would be able to launch in October with no cost impact. We thought they might buy that, but it was doubtful.

Third — wait for CRSS to launch and modify the spacecraft for the eclipses. That would be a $3 to 4 million hit and a delay of an unknown number of months with a corresponding hit of $75,000 per month.

The fourth option was to do nothing to the spacecraft, wait for CRSS to launch, have a shorter mission and take the hit scientifically.

Sylvia asked me what I felt about the four options and what it would really mean if my mission were curtailed in any way. I replied, "I do not want to modify the spacecraft; we need to leave it as it is. If we start changing the spacecraft, we'll find that the costs are going to escalate dramatically. Things are never as simple as you think when you start something like that. If we buy a bigger battery, then we have to change the solar array and all of a sudden there are a lot of other things we will have to modify — the whole thing will just snowball. If we have to wait for CRSS and it blows up, then we have to wait for another LLV2 to launch. Then we could just end up waiting and waiting. That could go on for a year or more. I didn't want that at all. The only thing to do is get a waiver and keep on schedule for an October launch, period."

Sylvia said, "Headquarters isn't really asking many questions about modifying the spacecraft. They just don't have the money for that. I think they are going to end up telling you to leave the spacecraft as it is, wait for CRSS and just cut your mission short (i.e., fly the spacecraft until the July 1999 eclipse killed it) and get less science."

I thought about it and said, "If I have no choice, I would take that option." Then, since I trusted Sylvia, I told her why I would be willing to accept that miserable option — "I don't want to have to start modifying the spacecraft. That would jeopardize the mission more than anything, because it would be like little Brer Rabbit and the Tar Baby — it would be an unending mess. If I agree to wait for CRSS, then NASA won't make us mess with the spacecraft (for which there was no money anyway). But, the minute I get into LEI and I am free of Lockheed, I'll go to the Hill, to the National Space Society, and to the Aerospace States Association and get everybody to raise hell and force NASA to let me launch on October 9 on an untested LLV2. The whole Clinton manned Moon program is based on flying men back to the Moon on untested or nearly untested vehicles. If Clinton and NASA are willing to risk men's lives on the minimum type of a manned mission my JSC friends are talking about, then NASA will have to let me launch a $20 million satellite on an untested vehicle," or so I hoped.

Friday, March 1, 1996: The Launch Vehicle Videocon

We had our videocon and it was the highlight of the day, but everything else was slow and boring. I talked to Dougherty when he got in and told him what I had told Sylvia the day before. He especially liked my idea of getting political support after I was in LEI to make NASA let us launch on the LLV2 in October.

Frank and I talked, but I didn't tell Frank my whole plan, I just said I did not want to modify the spacecraft and, if necessary, I would go after CRSS. He was happy with that.

Finally, after what seemed like a very long morning, we got around to the videocon. Dyle Palmer, the new Deputy Director of Ames, Scott, Sylvia, Richard, Dougherty, and I were on our end of the line and Bret, Earle Huckins, Ledbetter, and Piotrowski were on the other end.

Scott did a marvelous job leading the videocon. He had the series of viewgraphs we had prepared showing the entire history of the LLV2 issue. Using them, he pointed out I had described my logic for my selection of the LLV2 in the original Discovery proposal and I had stated that there were to be two LLV launches prior to my launch (though I did not say they were LLV1 and not LLV2 launches, just two LLV launches) and NASA had accepted that when they chose Lunar Prospector for flight. Then, we had clearly discussed the fact that Lunar Prospector's launch was to be the first launch of an LLV2 at the TDR just six months earlier and Jim Martin had pointed out to Headquarters in his TDR letter that that was something to be addressed. And again NASA had accepted it without a word of concern, and NASA Headquarters, knowing full well that I was going to be the first on the LLV2, told Ames to proceed with the negotiations for the Phase C/D contract. When the issue again came up during December at the start of the negotiations for the rocket, Headquarters verified that the LLV2 first launch was OK. Then, when we finally got around to negotiating the contract in January, after the shut down, the furloughs, and the catastrophic DC snow storms, and after we had heard the rumor about the possible no-first-launch-rule, we brought up the issue again and Headquarters was still OK with LLV2. We proceeded and then, a month after we had started getting the rocket contract done, Headquarters decided we couldn't launch on an LLV2! There it was in a nutshell, the whole history of NASA saying OK, OK, OK, OK and then NOT OK!

Scott went through the various options with other launch vehicles and pointed out the Taurus, because NASA had jacked up its price to $29 million, and Delta-lite were too expensive for us. Thus, the only option we had was to stay on an LLV2. Then he said, "The questions: Are we allowed a waiver or do we have to go after CRSS? If we have to go after CRSS, are we required to modify the spacecraft to survive the eclipses which we are not now configured to do?" Simple and well put.

First of all, Earl apologized for the mess they had caused and said, "You guys have been doing a marvelous job and we can hardly believe you've come as far as you have on Lunar Prospector. We've thrown you a bad curve and we don't expect you to pay for the damages. If we choose another rocket, we will pay the costs, because you're not at fault." That was the first admission that the mess was not our fault and we wouldn't be held responsible for cost increases. That was very good. Then Earl reemphasized how well we had done and how well the presentation was done. He noted, "You've done your homework; you've found every bit of information we needed in a very short time. It's clear to us what the options are and what we can and cannot do."

I talked about the science and explained that I did not want to modify the spacecraft and that I clearly wanted a waiver. I said, "I proposed a simple, straightforward mission with good science and we were proceeding well along towards that goal." I then proceeded to tell them all the reasons why I did not want to modify the spacecraft. I said, "I will risk losing science before I will do that (modify the spacecraft)." I went through the loss of science caused by waiting for CRSS and shortening the mission. I ended my discussion by saying, "I would prefer losing the extended mission and even shortening the primary mission to nine, or even six months rather than to risk losing the whole mission by trying to change the spacecraft at this late date."

Someone from Headquarters asked some questions of Dougherty, who, typically, didn't understand the difference between an LLV1 and LLV2, so Richard explained that, "An LLV2 just has one more Castor 120, but other than that, it's just an LLV1 stuck on top of a second Castor 120."

Scott went through the four options Sylvia and I had discussed the day before. Earl asked, "Is that your order of preference?"

I answered, "No, my preferences are one and four. We really don't want the other two."

Someone said, "You're making this very easy for us. We can't give you a waiver, because, first of all, *there is no rule to waiver*, though we all think there probably will be that rule." The whole issue might go away and they realized we wanted to preserve the option of keeping everything on track as it was. Since I wanted to preserve my October 1997 launch date and my spacecraft by choosing options one and four, if they didn't put the rule in place, then we would have lost nothing. Happily, we were on the right track.

We all agreed that if the LLV1 launches of the Lewis & Clark satellites were successful in June and July, we would have a launch vehicle that NASA could rely on, even though the LLV2 hadn't flown — but as Richard had indicated, LLV2 is just an LLV1 on top of a second Castor 120. We left it that way and they said they would write a memorandum indicating that we would use options one and four.

As we ended the videocon, the headquarters contingency was again very complimentary and said they were very pleased about how fast we were doing the mission and that we were staying within our budget. They repeated that the rocket issue was an unfortunate situation they had forced upon us and we had responded very well to it. We won in many ways. First, because it was the first time Headquarters people really listened to the Lunar Prospector team rather than just to Scott and/or me when we were at Headquarters. Second, the Ames administrators who were responsible to NASA for Lunar Prospector were there and they stood behind us and said, "Let them launch. If not, then don't make them modify the spacecraft and screw things up." Happily, everybody agreed the biggest mistake in the world would be to start changing the spacecraft, which was my biggest worry. Third, we won because we clearly demonstrated we knew what we were doing. All that strengthened Scott's hand as being the real NASA Project Manager for the mission and not someone at Headquarters, i.e., the way we proposed the program. The videocon was a success and we could get back to working on the real issues.

I got a call from Bill Feldman, who said the next time I visited Los Alamos, all three spectrometers (but not the SES that was being done at Southwest) would be done, though the GRS would not be fully assembled! He had already put together all the mechanical parts of the NS/APS unit and they fit together perfectly. All he had to do was the final assembly of the NS/APS. That was basically the same story for the GRS. I told Bill that Tom and I had been over to Lockheed's manufacturing area the day before to inspect the graphite epoxy housing for the GRS that was nearly done. It would soon be ready to be shipped to Los Alamos and he could assemble the GRS. All of a sudden, we had three instruments that were nearly done!

I then called Dave Curtis at Berkeley and the MAG/ER package was also coming along nicely. Tom and I decided to drive up to Berkeley the following week, just for the fun of it, to see all the MAG/ER pieces. We were moving along like gangbusters.

My next two major tasks were 1) to solve the tracking issue with the help of the Air Force and/or force NASA to stand up to its tracking commitments and 2) to get Tom and me into LEI.

The day resulted in a victory that culminated nearly four weeks of frustration with Headquarters.

Monday, March 4, 1996: Subsystem Review Day

The various subsystems were fine, just the way I liked things.

Chapter 3-11
Completing the Spacecraft Design

Tuesday, March 5, 1996: Completion of Lunar Prospector's Design

I had not slept well (as was beginning to be a habit) and neither had Tom, so we were both tired when we drove to work; despite that, it was a very good day.

I made a lot of calls to various people during the morning, the most important of which was a call to Air Force Captain Bryan Hays, who was Pete Worden's assistant of some kind. He said they were quite interested in helping to track Lunar Prospector and we discussed some of the details, e.g., the Air Force has 10 meter antennas that are big enough to do the job, if they had decent transmitters and receivers and I told him about the connection between Blue Moon and Lunar Prospector. I was very pleased with the conversation and I decided to fly up to Colorado Springs to see Bryan the following Wednesday and also to see Ron Humble.

I then called George French and told him what was going on and said, "Once we get into LEI, I have got to hit the political scene to get Lunar Prospector launched on time. I'll need your help on that." I could always rely on George.

Tom, Tim Bridges, Alex Kochergin, Kim Foster, and I went up to the Lockheed facilities at Palo Alto to talk with Bill Jacobsen and his crew about the software they were developing for our Mission Operations Center at Ames. That went extremely well.

When we got back, I checked with Dougherty and we decided to use the GaAs cells with 1.22 m long panels — so we were back where we were about a month earlier in the solar array design. The GaAs solar array would cost us $300,000 that we didn't have, but Dougherty would somehow find the money and we were back on track with the basic spacecraft design. With that decision finally made, *the spacecraft's configuration was essentially finished*, so we had reached a major milestone in Lunar Prospector's development and I was pleased about that.

Irv and I talked about how we were going to fuel the spacecraft. I didn't think that we needed a fill valve for each tank or that we had to fill each of the tanks, one at a time, though Irv thought we would. I was of the opinion that we could very carefully fill all three tanks simultaneously through one fill-line and fill-valve and that we could monitor the filling to insure that all three tanks had the same amount of fuel by suspending the spacecraft from three spring scales that were attached to its three lift points (the three attachment points we would use to pick the spacecraft up so we could lift it when we needed to, i.e., to mount it on the launch vehicle). As long as the weight was equal on all three scales, the tanks had to contain equal amounts of fuel. We would have to do the filling very, very carefully and monitor the tank pressure carefully, but I was sure we could fill the tanks that way.

The best part of a very good day occurred when Jim Beffa from the antenna division came over with the prototype of the medium gain helic antenna and it was just beautiful. The helic antenna had a gain of 8.7 dB; we had expected 6 dB and hoped for 9 dB, so they were very close to the best possible performance with a 10° x 360° field of view (FOV) with just a 3 dB drop-off at the edge of the FOV. It was a joy to see that elegant, simple, little helic antenna; I was really pleased.

Everything was coming together, though I was still concerned about the launch vehicle. If I could have just gotten some sleep, everything would have been great. That was the only problem Tom and I seemed to be having.

Wednesday, March 6, 1996

Tom and I drove to Berkeley to look at the structural pieces of the ER that were finished. It was great to see the pieces Dave Curtis was soon going to assemble. Though Mario was too far way to visit, the MAG and the MAG/ER common electronics were also coming along very well. Soon all five instruments would be fully assembled and their testing would begin.

Tom and I went back to Lockheed for a little while, but we soon left for Gilroy and our respective homes early, because we were both very tired. Though we had begun to sleep better, we were still tired.

Thursday, March 7, 1996: SSI Tries to Cash In

The staff meeting went well, all the subsystems were well defined, so the spacecraft design was in very good shape.

Tom and I went over to look at the GRS housing again. It was basically finished and almost ready to be shipped to Bill Feldman.

I talked to Dave Lozier at Ames and asked him to find out from our navigation guys at GSFC how quickly they could determine our post-launch trajectory. Since the amount of fuel needed to correct the launch errors increase very rapidly with time after launch, I wanted to make my first midcourse maneuvers (MCM) as soon as possible. Usually, the first MCM is made 16 hours after launch and the ΔV required is 5.3 times the launch ΔV error. Thus, if the launch error ΔV were 10 m/sec, then the 1st MCM ΔV at 16 hours would be 53 m/sec! If the 1st MCM were performed at 4 hours, the ΔV would be just 35 m/sec. Thus I wanted to do the 1st MCM as early as I could to save as much fuel as possible and that depended solely on how soon after launch the nav team could determine our launch errors and calculate the 1st MCM ΔV requirements. Dave said that he would discuss that with GSFC right a way.

Then, at the very end of the day, came a real zinger. Frank told me that Betty Graber from Space Studies Institute (SSI) had written Lockheed saying Lockheed was using SSI's spacecraft design for Lunar Prospector and therefore Lockheed had to pay SSI for its use of the design. I was not surprised, since I had assumed SSI would eventually get around to trying a stunt like that, though they didn't have a leg to stand on.

The reader may recall that SSI had paid OMNI $65,000 of the $75,000 due OMNI for the Phase B Spacecraft Design study that we, the SSI and LEI Consortium, had OMNI do from December 1989 through June 1990 (Part One). However, SSI did not own the rights to the design, OMNI kept the design as its property and gave SSI a license to use the design to build one spacecraft, which, of course, they didn't do. Also, a clause in the SSI-OMNI contract I was unaware of, or had forgotten, was that if SSI failed to pay the full $75,000, SSI lost its license — which was the case.

The reader might also remember that, before I started the Lunar Prospector Discovery proposal effort, OMNI sold the spacecraft design rights to LEI for $1.00, with the caveat that if LEI ever used the design, OMNI would get an additional $99,999 — which they did (Part Two). Also, as part of the deal to have Lockheed be my industry partner for Lunar Prospector, LEI would give Lockheed the rights to the spacecraft design — which it did (Part Two).

I explained all that to Frank and I told him I would ask Wayne Stevens to write SSI a letter telling them that, due to the non-payment of the full $75,000, SSI had defaulted and hence, lost their license to build one spacecraft using the design. I did so and Wayne was more than willing to write the letter, in part, because SSI had stiffed OMNI.

Also, when Frank told me about the SSI letter, he said the Lockheed lawyers were already looking into what was almost certainly a frivolous and baseless (if not illegal) attempt to get money from Lockheed and the Lockheed lawyers were not worried about SSI's petty scam. However, he was happy I was also going to help sink SSI's ship.

Nevertheless, SSI was doing what all bums do when somebody makes a success out of something; they try to get some money out of it somehow. SSI's underhanded attempt to swindle Lockheed really ticked me off, in part, because Betty Graber had called me after we had won and wanted to make sure that I gave SSI full credit for their part in the development of Lunar Prospector. I said I always did and I would continue to do so — and I did. In addition to that, I was embarrassed for having been involved with an organization that would stoop to a petty swindle like that. It was bad enough to have been associated with SSI in the beginning, but to have SSI try such a cheap trick was way over the line. I swore I would never again give credit to SSI for their part in the program, but I did anyway, even though SSI did not deserve it.

Friday, March 8, 1996: Propulsion Subsystem Review

We reviewed the propulsion sub-system to determine what we were going to do about the sineing of the engine thrust. I was uncomfortable about having the sineing start at tank pressures as high as 200 psi, since that would mean that the sineing would start during the second of the three, long LOI burns. That was just too critical a phase of the mission to have to deal with the unknown effects of the sineing on the spacecraft. I decided against having Olin enlarge the orifices of the engines and stuck with the lower thrust levels. However, since I wanted to get the thrust up as high as I could, and since Olin had determined that the engine valves could handle 450 psi without damage, we decided to have the initial tank pressure at 450 psi.

With that decision behind us, the spacecraft's design was pretty much frozen, except for a few little items like the question about how we were going to be sure the tanks were properly filled. Also, there were some range safety issues like — would range safety allow us to have a tank pressure as high as 450 psi (at that pressure, the tanks are nice little bombs filled with very nasty hydrazine)? Would Range safety make us put in two PIV's (propellant isolation valves) on the fuel lines to ensure the engines could not fire when workmen were on the pad, despite our having fulfilled the range safety requirement that two actions were required to fire an engine (we had three, first the spacecraft had to be turned on; second, an engine firing command load had to be transmitted to the spacecraft; and three, the Execute Command had to be sent to the spacecraft)? I did not want the PIV's, since they are heavy (about a kilogram each) and they added complexity to my simple spacecraft. And would Range safety make us have a destruct system for the TLI Stage if our launch trajectory took us over Africa?

Also, when Woody and I were calculating the shadowing of the booms and the instruments on the solar array, we forgot to take into account the small shadows of the two tangential engines, but by going to GaAs cells, those small shadows had a negligible effect. All in all, the spacecraft design was in very good shape. But, as everyone knows, once we began to put the spacecraft together, there would always be some small changes and fixes made as we discovered the inevitable weaknesses in the design and when we started the testing process.

Because of SSI's attempt to get money for Lunar Prospector's design, Frank asked me to talk to John Palochak, the Lockheed lawyer who was looking into the issue. I explained the situation to John (John was aware of the previous history, since it was he who did the legal work when I transferred the rights of the spacecraft design from LEI to Lockheed). John agreed we were on the legally correct side of the question and he agreed with my plan to have Wayne Stevens drop the boom on SSI. I told John I would get him all the necessary information by Monday, so he could answer SSI's letter.

Interestingly, when I talked to Frank about my meeting with John, he pointed out to me that if I were in LEI, I wouldn't have the Lockheed lawyers to help protect me. I was not sure whether Frank was giving me a friendly and concerned warning about my supposed legal vulnerability if I went over to LEI or if he was trying to dissuade me from doing so. His comment did not really sound negative, so I took it as friendly warning, but since SSI's attempted swindle was directed at Lockheed, I doubted I would have any problems with SSI.

I made my travel plans to visit the Falcon Air Force facilities near Colorado Springs to talk about the Air Force helping to track Lunar Prospector.

Finally, I went home early because Rebecca and I were driving down the coast to San Simeon to spend the weekend there and to see the Hearst Castle.

Monday, March 11, 1996

Irv and I talked about the fuelling of the tanks and I was certain we could do it properly with the system just the way it was designed, without having the tanks interconnected as Irv wanted to insure that all three tanks were loaded equally. I didn't think we needed to waste our time and money on that; as long as we loaded the tanks slowly until the fuel inlets were covered with fuel, after that the pressure in each tank would keep them filling equally.

I talked to Captain Hays at Falcon to get the details of our meeting on Wednesday. He didn't see any technical problem with their tracking Lunar Prospector, it was just a matter of how much time was available and that would be handled at the Blue Cube, the Air Force Satellite Tracking Center that is located at Lockheed about two blocks from Building 107 where I worked!

Tuesday, March 12, 1996: A Video and Trouble for LEI

George Collins from BJ Link came to make the video for Dick Seeley's physics class. He was staying at the Leavesley Inn in Gilroy, so I went over there, found him, and he followed me up to Sunnyvale in a driving rain. We got to Lockheed at about 6:00 AM and worked to about 8:00 AM doing the videos.

George explained what BJ Link does and his involvement with it. He is an Air Force retiree and his job is to go around recruiting small schools for their remote learning program. It was on his last trip through Gilroy that he happened to read about Lunar Prospector in the *Country News* and then he called me. At that time, BJ Link served 74 schools all over the United States. They not only teach physics remotely, but also French, Spanish, and some math courses. It sounded like a good program and via it I would be able to reach a wide audience for the Outreach part of the project.

I explained the importance of our Outreach Program to him and said I would like to consider having Dick Seeley be one of my high school team members. He thought that would be a great idea. I also said the next time I was out in that direction, I would stop by BJ Link (I still did not know that Bob Jones University is a fundamentalist Christian University, but, despite my being an absolute atheist, that would not have made any difference. I firmly believe everyone has a right to his own opinion and if I could help educate the BJ Link students and open the world of space exploration to them, I would be happy to do so — regardless of their religious beliefs).

I told him about the commercial aspects of future lunar exploration and he said that one of their supporters, a millionaire, lives near Langley, VA. The guy is heavily into communication satellites and had set up the communications for Desert Storm! George said he would be happy to introduce me to that guy and maybe it would lead to some support for my commercial missions. That was pregnant with possibility.

Tom and I went over to Ames to talk to Sylvia and Scott about our getting into LEI and I was very disappointed because they were exhausted from the endless tussles with Headquarters — Sylvia was at the end of her rope, as was Scott. For the first time, they began to put up every excuse in the world as to why our going to LEI wouldn't work. It would take time and they didn't have much time. They had other issues that were more important, and on and on. I was surprised and not very happy about their change of attitude; it was suddenly clear that they were going to make it very difficult for Tom and me to go to LEI. I immediately thought of what my mentor, Dr. G.P. Kuiper, always said, "Ninety percent of the people are trained to say NO." Though they were both down in the dumps about everything and didn't want to deal with LEI, I was not willing to drop it.

I was not going to do anything that could damage Lunar Prospector, but on the other hand, I was not going to allow all the things I had worked for just to go down the drain. I was really quite ticked off. As I said to Tom, "It's days like this I would just like to quit, just walk in and say that all I do is fight Lockheed, all I do is fight NASA, and now I have to fight this. I quit." I was really tired of the constant battles. In my anger and frustration, I said, "If I had the resources, I would just walk off and leave the whole bunch." Tom was even more upset about it because he always takes things at their very worst and saw our future crumbling.

At 10:00 AM, we had a telecon with Headquarters to discuss the tracking. We went through all the issues again. Of course, NASA did not know what it was going to do about the tracking; they didn't know what their options were; and blah, blah, blah. We said that until Headquarters knew what their options were, there was nothing we could say or do that was going to change anything. I hoped the Air Force could get me out of the tracking mess that NASA had created.

I got out of that stupid meeting and Tom and I had a quick bite of lunch before I left to catch my airplane to Las Vegas. I slept on the flight to Las Vegas, where I changed planes to fly on to Colorado Springs, where I arrived at about 6:30 PM. It was brisk and nice when I arrived there. I started to drive to the hotel and then I realized I had made a mistake; I had reserved a room at the Radisson up in the North. I didn't know the Air Force Base was right next to the airport or I would have stayed at the Radisson South, but that was then irrelevant. On the way up north, I began to get hungry and I had a taste for spareribs. I started to look for a Tony Roma's, without any luck, but I did find a Black Eyed Pea and happily, they had barbecued baby back ribs and then, so did I. I ate more than I thought I would and really enjoyed those ribs. Then I drove on to the hotel and tried to get a decent night's sleep.

Wednesday, March 13, 1996: The Air Force Connection

The meeting at Falcon was scheduled for 10:00 AM. As usual, I got up early, found a Dunkin Donut for breakfast and then drove down the road towards Falcon. Since I had some time to kill, I just drove on further east to see what the country was like east of the Rockies — it is flat prairie land. Finally, I drove back to Falcon, got badged, and then had a hell of a time finding a parking place. You would think with all the prairie around Falcon, they would have enough parking space! I had to park as far away as possible from the building where the meeting was to be held and still be in the state of Colorado!

After parking, I walked to Building 200 and a Captain Damon Feldman was there to meet me. He explained how to get through the little glass security entrance room into the building: I was to put my identity card in a slot, then I had to punch in a randomized code of numbers and then I thought he said to punch star, but when I tried, the screen said to punch pound. I kept punching the damned thing as the guards were watching and a camera was taking pictures of me. The guards finally got tired of watching me trying to do it right (I guess they figured if I couldn't figure out how to get in, I couldn't do much harm once I was in — actually Captain Damon told them to let me in), and they let me in the door.

Lo and behold, they took me right up to Pete Worden's office where Pete was waiting for me. I was amazed; nobody, but nobody gets to see Pete. He was the head of the entire Air Force Satellite Program. During the days of the first President Bush Administration, Pete was on the National Space Council and, as a result of SSI's connections, he had given his verbal support to Lunar Prospector. I had met Pete after Lunar Prospector had been selected for flight at a meeting in Pasadena, CA, and we chatted about the mission. Pete is a very nice, no nonsense guy and I have a great deal of respect for him. Pete had been responsible for getting the Clementine mission done and was behind having the Air Force try to do Clementine 2. When I had asked for a meeting at Falcon, I had not asked to see Pete, but Pete wanted to see me and I was very surprised and very pleased at that.

I told Pete the spacecraft development was well advanced, we had started building it, the instruments were being assembled, parts from the vendors were coming in, we were going to have it assembled in a few months, and we would start testing in September. I explained to him the fiasco with the launch vehicle and our hope that NASA would back off and let us launch on schedule after the hoped for successful launches of Lewis & Clark. I said if Lewis and/or Clark went into the drink, my mission was going to be compromised. He said he could help to make sure I got the launch when I wanted it. Boy, was I happy to hear him say that.

Then I brought up the tracking. Pete immediately said, "Well, I can help track you, and I'll do it free. I also have people who have nothing to do and if you are running out of money during Mission Ops, I'll get you money and help you do Mission Ops." I was absolutely floored by his offer and, after I picked my teeth up off the table, put them back in my mouth, and closed the latter, we discussed some of the details,

After finishing the Lunar Prospector part of the meeting, I brought up Blue Moon. I explained I could get a magnetometer for Blue Moon and I needed to be sure that we both launched at about the same time. I said it was imperative that Lunar Prospector and Blue Moon were in lunar orbit simultaneously, because the Blue Moon magnetometer would just be getting calibration data for me on the solar wind magnetic field, it was not getting stand-alone science data. Pete thought that was great.

Pete asked how Blue Moon was getting done and I used his question to get as many brownie points for both Preston Carter and Ron as I possibly could. I told Pete what Ron had told me and that I had talked to Preston, who was also involved with Blue Moon. I said further that it was Preston who told me to give him (Pete) a call about tracking. Preston worked on contract at Lawrence Livermore for Pete, but Preston seldom got to see Pete. Pete asked why Ron and Preston hadn't talked to him about Blue Moon. I said I didn't know, but I said I expected they would do so very soon (the minute I got to the Academy, I was going to make sure Ron started making plans to get his butt down to Falcon, since I had just opened the door for him to talk to Pete).

Pete then asked, "Who is funding Blue Moon?"

I answered, "I thought you were."

He said, "Well, maybe I am for all I know, but I need to talk to Ron about it." Again, good news for Ron!

We discussed how he could build the case for having the Air Force support both Lunar Prospector and Blue Moon. He had to make it sound useful to the Air Force. I said, "Well, since we are carrying a magnetometer, an electron reflectometer, and an alpha particle spectrometer, we will be getting information on space weather (i.e., on the solar wind and solar storms) and the Air Force is surely interested in that from the standpoint of communications." Pete agreed that was useful data for the Air Force and he could use it to justify the tracking. Finally, he said he would have Captain Feldman prepare a letter that acknowledged our meeting, the cooperative nature of the Lunar Prospector and Blue Moon Projects, and the fact that he would like to help do Lunar Prospector's tracking.

I left Falcon a very happy man and drove to the Air Force Academy and found Ron's building. Ron was out to lunch. When he returned, I briefed him on my meeting with Pete. Ron was quite happy about the results of the meeting, but he did not know quite what to do about seeing Pete. I said, "Damn it, get your butt out there and do it. I opened the door for you, now get in there and talk to him." He said he would.

Gil Moore, who was Ron's boss and head of part of the Aerospace Department, came by Ron's office. Gil had been sick with the flu when I was at the Academy in January, so he really wanted to meet me. Later, after Gil's class, the three of us sat down and discussed Blue Moon. Gil wanted to fly a camera as part of the deal with the French to get a free piggyback ride on the Ariane. Ron was not really interested in doing that, so there was a little tug of war between Gil and Ron about what the payload was going to be. I said I didn't care, as long as there was a magnetometer on board that only weighed a couple of kilograms and required only a couple of watts. The main question was whether Ron could design the spacecraft, get it built, and be ready for launch in 18 to 20 months. Ron wanted Blue Moon to be a simple spinner, which was the right idea, but he didn't even have the fundamental design done. He had to get his butt in gear. All in all, it was a good meeting and I left the Academy feeling very happy at about 5:00 PM, figuring I had more than enough time to get to the airport and have a bite to eat.

When I got to the airport, I just had a hot dog because I wasn't very hungry. Then I found out my 7:15 flight wasn't going to arrive until 8:30 and it would not be loading until about 8:45! I had to wait around the airport doing nothing and unfortunately, I didn't get home until well after midnight. Nevertheless, it was a very fruitful trip.

Thursday, March 14, 1996: Back at Lockheed

I got up at about 6:30 AM and called Tom, who had not yet left for work, so we drove in together. When we got there, the staff meeting had started. I whispered to Dougherty that things had gone well at Falcon and that I would explain it all during the meeting. Dougherty didn't know what to make of my success with the Air Force. As Tom said, by the look on Dougherty's face, what I told him just bowled him over.

After the staff meeting, Kim Foster, Tim Maloney, Irv, Dougherty, Tom, and I had a meeting on how we were going to load the propellant tanks. During my absence, Irv had convinced Dougherty that we needed a second set of propellant lines connecting the three tanks so the helium pressurant could equilibrate, which was simply not necessary. I went through the simple physics of the situation and ended by saying, "We are going to do it the way I want to do it, because it is the right way. The other way (Irv's way) is no different except we would have to add more fuel lines and that would mean we would have to re-qualify the tanks because we would have to have another hole in the tanks and that's a load of crap. The base line is that we are pressurizing first, then we get the spacecraft exactly level, then we feed the fuel in very slowly and keep tabs on the process by weighing the spacecraft at the three lift points."

Kim, who was responsible for Test and Integration and launch preparations, wanted to ask the fuelling team if there were any problems with my method. I said, "Look, don't give those guys any options because they will just say, 'no we can't do that because it's not the way we usually do it' (usually they load the fuel and then pressurize). I don't give a damn what they usually do, the physics is correct and it will work for our spacecraft. This is Discovery and not 'the usual way' and they are just going to have to get used to it." As usual, I won and Dougherty lost (21 months later, we loaded 137 kg of hydrazine equally into the three tanks in exactly the way I wanted to do it without a hitch and in a fraction of the time that we had allotted for fuelling).

Sylvia came over to my office and I told her about my success with the Air Force. Happily, she appeared well rested and I said I wanted to talk to Scott about the Air Force tracking and about the letters I had received from teachers in Gilroy who wanted to do volunteer work on Lunar Prospector, something Lockheed was dead set against. I said, "I'll be dammed if I want all this volunteer Outreach stuff to go to hell just because I am stuck in Lockheed. But I'm not going to bust my butt if you guys don't let me get out of Lockheed (and go to LEI). I'm just going to let the whole damned Outreach Program fall by the wayside, except for what George French is doing. It's a battle I don't have the time and energy to fight, so I'll just do the absolute minimum required and NASA will suffer. And, frankly, I don't care." I was really getting tired of all the crap I had to put up with from Lockheed and NASA. I had all those people who wanted to help me; everyplace I went, people wanted to give me resources and volunteered to help. Pete Worden was willing to give me a tracking network and controllers and was willing to help pressure NASA to let me launch in October 1997. Then, when I told Lockheed or NASA about those things, both sides dumped on me.

When I got done ranting, Sylvia seemed a lot more positive about LEI and she said she had been looking into some of the issues. She said they had had similar cases before where PIs had changed their affiliations in the middle of programs, though the cases were not of the magnitude of Lunar Prospector. It could be done.

I had a very interesting talk with Frank. First of all, Frank said SSI was making more noise and we had to get that issue straightened out. I said I would call Wayne and make sure he had written his letter to SSI and had sent it off.

I told Frank about my meeting with Pete Worden and he was fairly impressed, but said, "I don't like Pete; we've clashed in the past." Then he laughed and said, "It would be funny if you ended up doing this in the Blue Cube and it became the Alan Binder Blue Cube." He thought that possibility was just uproariously funny!

Frank said something I could use to help leverage my going over to LEI. I had said how pleased I was with the way things were going and he said, "This is going well and you are doing a great job. You're helping build the company (Lockheed) up and its reputation."

I said, "Yes, I'm very pleased."

He asked, "What do you want to do when this is over."

I answered, " I want to do follow-on missions."

He then asked, "How old are you?"

I answered, "I am 56."

He said, "Wow, you'll be about 60 then; you can retire if you want to or you'll probably want to go someplace else."

That was a very interesting statement; there was no hint of any interest about Lockheed wanting me to stay on after Lunar Prospector. I was immediately reminded of what I had told Scott just three days earlier and that was, "Lockheed doesn't give a damn about me or Lunar Prospector, they're just using me and the minute this is over, I'll be shoved out the door," a statement of fact that Frank had just inadvertently confirmed. Lockheed might just as well have given me my severance check right then and said, "The minute this thing is over, you're fired!" But Lockheed treats all the workers like trash. All the upper management wants is money for themselves and their company. They don't care about the workers, period.

That reminded me of what Scott said in response to my statement on Tuesday and that was, "Oh no, they really like you. When I talk to them, they praise you to high heaven."

I felt like saying, "Sure, that's what they say to your face. But, if I am so damned valuable, why doesn't Frank give me a $25,000 raise to bring my wages up to what had been written in the original Discovery proposal?" I knew I would die of old age before that would happen.

Friday, March 15, 1996

We had the subsystem review for software. We went through the Oasis program we had bought to run Mission Operations. Bill Jacobsen pointed out to me that Oasis had sequences in it I could use to set up standard procedures that are repetitive; for example, I could use them for the periodic Orbital Maintenance Burns. That was great. However, the thing that worried Tom and me was that they were spending all the money for software development and we also needed them to make the spacecraft computer model. At that point, the software engineers were talking about developing just a static model that would be useless for training. Somehow I had to have a dynamic model so we could properly train to run the spacecraft.

When the mail came, I got a copy of Wayne's letter to SSI. He did a good job of blowing SSI out of the water. He wrote that he understood that SSI was bothering one of OMNI's clients by saying the client was using SSI's spacecraft design without paying SSI for its use. He then quoted the various paragraphs in the contract that clearly stated that SSI only had a license to build one spacecraft and that OMNI had retained all rights to the design. Then he asked that SSI call Lockheed and apologize for interfering with their work. Finally, he reminded SSI that they owed $10,000 to OMNI and that any further delay in the payment of the $10,000 would result in their losing the license to build a spacecraft in accordance with the contract. Talk about shooting yourself in the foot — well, SSI deserved what they got.

The day ended with Tom and me going to Francisco's bachelor dinner — he and his Rebecca were getting married!

Saturday, March 16, and Sunday, March 17, 1996

Rebecca and I went to the movies Saturday and I got a terrible headache that stayed with me all the rest of the day. The headache turned out to be the beginning of the flu, so I postponed going to the Lunar and Planetary Science Conference on Sunday. Sunday I just stayed in bed. Happily, my flu was of the 24-hour variety, so I was feeling better by Sunday night.

Chapter 3-12
Where Can We Buy
Some Solar Cells?

Monday, March 18, through Saturday, March 23, 1996:
The Lunar and Planetary Science Conference and Los Alamos

Because of the flu, I didn't leave for the Lunar and Planetary Science Conference until Monday. I got there in the afternoon, registered, and heard a talk or two. As I talked to various colleagues, it was clear a lot of people were beginning to realize Lunar Prospector was an awfully good mission and we were going to produce a tremendous amount of good data — that was very gratifying.

However, just as was the case at the previous conference, it was clear from the talks that most lunar scientists had done little to advance the field in the last twenty years. Apollo was nearly a quarter of a century behind us and we needed new data, the data Lunar Prospector was going to provide, and much more, if lunar science was going to advance.

Bill Feldman gave his talk on the GRS late Friday morning and everybody was very interested and there were numerous questions. It was clear we had accomplished what we wanted to, i.e., show the community that the GRS was a lot better than people originally thought.

I called Tom to see what was happening back at Lockheed and he gave me some good news and some bad news. It turned out we could not buy any GaAs solar cells — there were just none available! The whole question about the solar array had opened up again and that really annoyed me. Other than that, things were kind of OK.

I went to Los Alamos with Bill. All the pieces of all three spectrometers were there and they were just beautiful. The GRS graphite epoxy housing, which Lockheed had sent to Los Alamos earlier, was all drilled and ready to go. Bill was going to take the BGO crystal back to Bicron, because he thought the crystal might have to be trimmed a little to fit properly in its housing.

To my surprise, Bill had built a backup set of all the mechanical parts of the NS/APS. We could use them for the spacecraft mockup to see if the engineers could remove the nitrogen purge lines and things like that without damaging the real spectrometers; so they would be useful even if Bill didn't need them to replace any broken parts.

When I got home, Rebecca and I looked at Comet Hale Bopp with one of my telescopes. It was just incredible. It was moving like a bat out of hell and you could see its motion in a few seconds and when it was near a star, you could actually see it moving. We had a good time and the next morning we got up and looked at it again. Its tail was about 10° long and it was really spectacular.

Monday, March 25, 1996: Subsystem Reviews Day

Over the weekend, Tom had told me Richard said there is no flame bucket at Pad 42 (at the Cape), so the launch environment would be much worse than we thought. The reason is that at ignition and during liftoff, an enormous amount of acoustical energy is reflected off the pad right back up the rocket, enough energy to damage the space-craft and the rocket unless it is buffered. The acoustic effect is bad enough with a flame bucket that directs the flame and hence, a lot of the acoustic energy away from the bottom of the rocket and pad, but without a flame bucket, the acoustic energy was murder. When Tom told me that, I thought, *crap, there goes my spacecraft.*

When we got to work Monday, it turned out there had been some confusion about the environmental data LLV had given us. LLV had given us the correct data for a Pad 42 launch that really does have a flame bucket. However, the LLV engineer who gave Richard the data thought Pad 42 doesn't have a flame bucket (which it does) and the West Coast pad does (which it does not). He thought he had given us the West Coast — instead of the East Coast — environmental data. Logically Richard concluded that the East Coast launch environment was a lot worse than for the West Coast. Finally, Richard and the engineer determined that we had the correct East Coast data all along. That whole flap was totally unnecessary.

I told the software guys at the subsystem review meeting that Bill Feldman had all his spectrometer software done and he could give it to them right away. I said further that I would check with Dave Curtis to see what the status of the MAG/ER software was.

We talked about what we were going to do about the solar array, since we could not buy the GaAs cells. I asked, "Why can't we find some solar cells in this company? This company supposedly uses more solar cells than all other companies combined. Are you telling me you can't find a measly five square meters worth of GaAs cells and what about Martin Marietta?"

Woody answered, "Oh gee, those are good ideas. I guess I'll look into them." With that stupefying answer, I thought, *why can't these idiots do this by themselves? Why do I have to tell them everything? Why do I have to put the pressure on them, that's Dougherty's job?*

We discussed trying to get the new 17% silicon cells from Sharp in Japan. If we could, then we would be OK.

Woody harped about wanting his damned 5 or 6 cm solar array extension. I said he was not going to get it, I would be damned if we were going to change all that again.

After that we talked about the rocket and for the first time I got really angry. Richard had been on a telecon with LLV and heard someone saying in the background that they might not have even ordered the damned rocket stages for Lunar Prospector and CRSS! If that were the case, we were in big trouble.

In addition to that bombshell, Richard wasn't getting any support from LLV for the launch trajectory work. He was doing it himself, using our people and our resources because he couldn't get through the LLV bureaucracy maze — we were doing LLV's work for them! Dougherty said to Richard, "No, you can't have those people, we are spending too much money. This is work Denver is supposed to do and I'll take care of it."

By that time I was really mad and despite the fact that Sylvia and the three ladies on our staff were there, I said, "This is the same shit I've gotten from LLV every time. This is the fourth time they've come up with nothing."

Dougherty quickly said, "Don't go making trouble. You're just going to make a fool of yourself."

I said, "I've had nothing but trouble with them, they've never come through and this is the fourth time." Dougherty was trying his best to stop me and that just made me really blow my top. I slammed my fist down on the table and said, "This is the same shit, this fucking rocket is no damned good and I get this crap every time. This is the fourth time and I am going to raise hell about it." Dougherty decided he had better back down and everybody else just kept very quiet except Sylvia, who basically said the same things I said, but not quite as vehemently as I did. I was disgusted and pissed.

As it turned out, Larry Price was going to be in Sunnyvale on Wednesday and Dougherty didn't want me to raise hell with Larry, but I was definitely going to do so.

To make thing worse, Mark Saunders had gotten into the act. He had been reading Scott's reports and was always bitching. He wrote an email to Scott complaining about Lockheed not having any financial reserves (remember, Mark took $2 million from us just for fun), charging that Lockheed was hiding information from NASA and demanding that Lunar Prospector be canceled.

Sylvia said she had never seen Scott madder. He and Mark had a one-on-one and Scott reamed Mark out and told him in no uncertain terms who in hell was running the program — and it wasn't Mark.

Scott then sent Mark an email that basically said, "If you think Lockheed is trying to somehow sneak around and bilk the program and hide things, then you better tell me where you are getting this information because we are not seeing it. We are monitoring everything and we have had access to everything. Also, if you think Ames is hiding anything and is not doing its job of monitoring the program, you tell me and tell us to quit." It was blunt and to the point — I liked it.

I decided I had to write a letter to Huntress and say, "Lunar Prospector, as everyone knows, is in good shape, we (Lockheed) are doing our job, and we (Lockheed) have intimate contact with Ames at all times. We (Ames and Lockheed) visit back and forth a couple of times a day, so everything is completely open and above board. The only real management problem we have is Mark Saunders. Every single technical problem we have is amplified and made worse by Mark. Mark has blown all of the issues that we have had with the launch vehicle and the tracking out of proportion. He has consistently caused problems for the program and I want him removed from it."

Tuesday, March 26, 1996: LEI Postponed

The main event of the day was a talk I had with Scott about LEI. Scott had decided he didn't want me to go to LEI. He thought it might be impossible to do, or at a minimum, would cost a great deal of effort — two or three months of fiddling around with contracts, lawyers, and everything else — and detract from the real work at hand. He was also concerned I might have to spend too much time running the company and not doing mission work.

We talked about several alternatives. One was whether it might be possible for me to subcontract to Lockheed. I didn't want to do that, but I would rather do that than nothing at all.

Secondly, I could stay with Lockheed, but get LEI started on the side. He suggested that because he realized the value of the Outreach Program and the value of having LEI become a real entity to do follow-on missions. He thought that maybe LEI could get a $100,000 contract from Ames to work on the Outreach, and that would get LEI started. Scott really wanted to see LEI get started. He just thought it was the wrong time to do it. There was already too much turmoil, Lunar Prospector was at a critical phase, LEI was too big a mess to try to tackle when he was trying to get the Ames situation figured out (Ames was always the first NASA center to be considered for closure) and he was concerned about the big blowup he had just had with Mark.

Scott had a series of good reasons for postponing my going to LEI and I had to respect them and agreed that the time was not necessarily ripe to start LEI. Nevertheless, I was annoyed because staying at Lockheed made getting Lunar Prospector done right much more difficult to do. I was screwed and stuck at Lockheed. I thought, *well, we'll just have to make the best of it and hope that in the end we have a good mission and then I can get LEI started one way or another.*

When I got back to Lockheed, Tom and I had a very good discussion with Gerry Grismore about the Spacecraft/TLI Stage separation, reorientation maneuvers, attitude determination, and the attitude sensors. Dougherty was also present, but didn't understand a thing Gerry and I discussed. How could a Project Manager be so dumb? Tom loved watching Dougherty just sit there, not having even the slightest idea about what we were discussing — he is such a dunce. Despite the fact that Dougherty didn't have a clue as to what was going on, it was a very, very good meeting and I was very pleased that Gerry understood how I was going to run the spacecraft and I understood how Gerry was building the C&DH to satisfy my operational needs.

Wednesday, March 27, 1996

I got the letter from Pete Worden. I took a copy over to Scott and he informed Headquarters about the letter. Obviously Headquarters might not want me to work with the Air Force, since NASA doesn't like the Air Force, but I did not care. If I had free tracking from the Air Force, then Headquarters would probably match it so they would not look bad. It was going to be interesting to see what would happen about the NASA tracking after they saw the letter.

Sylvia, Dougherty, and I had a meeting, and, to my utter amusement, Dougherty tried his usual huffing and puffing. He tried to make Sylvia believe that at the meeting the day before, when Gerry and I were discussing the reorientation maneuvers and the C&DH issues, he was on top of the situation by saying, "We (he and Gerry) explained it all to Alan," and, "Alan got all upset about the rocket and I had to calm him down." Sylvia and I just looked at each other, knowing he was full of BS.

Tom and I then went for an early lunch because we were both starving and tired. When we got back, Dougherty was telling Sylvia about the Lunar Prospector logo he had done (behind my back), how he had designed it, and blah, blah, blah. When he had it done the first time, NASA was not on it; just Lockheed (how dumb can you get?) and NASA made him change it. When Tom and I appeared, Dougherty said, "I have a task for you."

I replied, "Oh, I can see the BS starting already."

He laughed the way he always did when I called his bluff and said, "The logo is in my office, you should go look at it," so I did. I thought it was pretty good, though it needed a couple of changes that Buddy Nelson could take care of.

Dougherty and I had a serious discussion when there was no one around for him to try to impress. He admitted again that he was very concerned about the rocket and that we had no working relationship with LLV, period. Since we both agreed on those two points, we changed topics.

Dougherty said I shouldn't worry about the solar array because he was confident that we would be able to buy the 17% Sharp cells and, even if that were not the case, we wouldn't be building the solar array until the very end of the program because, as he said, "You don't put the solar panels on the spacecraft until after most of the testing is finished." The reason is that the cells are fragile and tend to break during testing. You put a few dummy cells on the panels to see if the real cells will survive the loads and then put the real cells on the panels after the majority of the testing is finished. If worse came to worse, we could have bought the solar cells very late in the program.

Scott called and wanted to talk to me privately, so I went over to Ames. He said he had been giving some thought to my desire to have LEI become a commercial vendor for NASA and he agreed that would be a good thing, because it was what NASA wanted to happen. It had dawned on him that Ames and NASA in general had supported commercial activities, so he wanted to have us talk to the commercial division (Code C) and get some seed money to start LEI on the road towards a commercial venture. He said he wanted LEI to exist and become an asset to NASA, but not at the expense of Lunar Prospector. I told him his suggestion was great.

When I got back to Lockheed, I told Tom what Scott had suggested and Tom was very happy and relieved. Tom was as worried as I was that all our efforts weren't going to pan out. That was certainly one of the factors why neither one of us had been sleeping well. After that, I actually started getting some work done!

In the late afternoon, Dougherty said Sylvia wanted to talk to me, so I called her. She told me some very good news: Mark was being transferred to NASA Langley in Virginia in three to four weeks and would be out of our hair! Headquarters had removed him as the head of Discovery and had assigned him other Discovery tasks. I was happy, Scott was happy, and Sylvia was happy. We were soon going to be rid of Mark and I didn't have to write a letter to Headquarters to get rid of him or do anything. That was a great ending to a good day.

Friday, March 29, 1996

Friday was a quiet day. I spent most of it working on the new version of the Mission Profile.

Monday, April 1, 1996: Subsystem Review day

I received a copy of the Lockheed Martin Annual Report and though it contained discussions of Lockheed's involvement with Stardust, Mars Global Surveyor, the other Mars programs, and the Hubble Telescope, there was not a peep in it about Lunar Prospector! I was not pleased about that and pointed it out to Frank who just sloughed it off, as I expected. As I knew all too well, Lockheed did not give a damn about Lunar Prospector.

At the subsystem review we found that the software effort was way behind schedule. That was the case because their equipment hadn't arrived and that was because Lockheed hadn't ordered it properly! Regardless of the cause, Dougherty was on Bill Jacobsen's case about the delay.

I tried to get Woody to start designing the battery structure, with little success. He had an estimated mass of a kilogram for the structure and since we were going to freeze the spacecraft configuration at the end of this month, I wanted everything as accurate as possible.

Woody and Dougherty had been poking around for solar cells and they thought they had a way of getting the GaAs or the 17% Sharp cells, so that was coming along.

The rocket was a mess — as usual. The rocket's Critical Design Review had been postponed by nearly six months and was reset for August! That really made you believe LLV was getting nowhere! Dougherty and Frank put a good face on it and said they were not concerned about the delay, because they believed Lockheed would come through in the end. I said I would believe it when I saw it.

Then there was a major problem with Pad 46. We were told that the service tower could only stand winds up to 55 km/hr and it would have to be pulled back from the rocket if the winds got higher than that — and 55 km/hr is not much of a wind. Worse, without protection, the rocket would fall over at wind speeds greater than about 70 km/hr! Remember, we were going to launch during hurricane season and it would take 8 days to de-stack the spacecraft and rocket — so I really begin to wonder how we were going to get the mission launched before the rocket blew over!

Beyond all that, everything was OK!

I talked to Frank about my getting into LEI on a Lockheed subcontract and as far as he and Henshaw were concerned, that was fine. They had no objections, but, of course, they didn't want to do anything that might hurt Lockheed (they weren't concerned about hurting me). Regardless of what I did about LEI and Lockheed, Frank assured me that everybody thought very highly of me and blah, blah, blah. That might have been true, but so what?

I went over to talk to Sylvia and Scott again and to my disappointment, they were again blowing cold on LEI. I thought Scott was again blowing the whole thing out of proportion. He was concerned that Headquarters had to be informed about what was going on, so Wes wouldn't find out in the newspaper that I was in LEI. He was also worried about the PR effects of my leaving Lockheed and asked me what would I say if *Aviation Week* or *Space News* asked me why I went to LEI. I said my reply would be, "Hey, I did this for seven years in LEI and I would have like to have done the whole mission back into LEI. However, that was not possible when we did the proposal, but now the possibility exists again, so I am going into LEI." I didn't think they would stop me from going to LEI, but I wished they were a little more enthusiastic about it.

One thing happened that I thought was very interesting. Dale Vaccarello (who is very good and who I wished was the Project Manager instead of Dougherty, because he was always very cooperative and always wanted to get things done) and I were talking between meetings. Dale said the problem was, "This is a can't-do-group instead of a can-do-group. They always say, we can't do this, we can't do that, we can't do anything, instead of saying — we will find a way."

I thought about Dale's statement and it was very true. At Lockheed, the response was always, "We can't do it this way or we can't do it that way." It is a big company that doesn't try to solve the problem; it tries to avoid them!

Captain Feldman sent me an email indicating that Pete Worden was moving my request for Air Force support right along, so the Air Force was responding nicely.

Tuesday, April 2, 1996

As Tom and I drove to work, we talked about getting things ready to get into LEI. A couple of things we had to do were to get the budget and work statement fixed up. Then I said, "We have to look at the old agreements between SSI and LEI to make sure they can't get their hooks into us the way they are trying to do with Lockheed. I don't trust them," (later, I got my old LEI files out and decided there was enough wiggle room in our old agreements that, knowing how greedy SSI is, they would try to get money from LEI if they couldn't get anything from Lockheed).

Then I remembered the legal advice Art Dula had given us when we were starting LEI back in September 1989, i.e., after achieving LEI's goals, we should dissolve LEI, because all the people who were involved in the beginning would try to horn in on LEI and get some benefits from it. Similarly, I thought about what the guy with the teleflorist computer business, that Mick and I had had lunch with, who had said, "Once you are successful, everybody tries to sue you."

We decided the best thing to do was to kill LEI and start a new company. Of course, my old Lunar Resources Institute was still on the books in Texas and it still had a tax number, so we could simply use that. The more we talked about it, the more that seemed to be the correct thing to do. Otherwise, if we got LEI going again and SSI tried to horn in on us, they could cause us a whole lot of trouble and tie us up in litigation and we didn't need that. We didn't have the time or the money to survive that.

When we got to work, I called George French and he agreed that the best thing to do was to kill LEI and start over. We talked about setting up a new company in Arizona (since I wanted to get back to Tucson after Lunar Prospector), or in Texas with Todd Greenwalt's (Vinson & Elkins) help again, or in Wisconsin where George is. No matter where we set up the new company, it would take time, but it would be clean. George was more than happy to help and said he would be happy to do most of the work. George also said he was going to be in California and we could meet on the 22nd to discuss setting up the new company.

Interestingly, my sweet wife was enthusiastic about the idea of forming a new company, while I was disappointed to have to dump LEI after all the work that had gone into it, but I knew it was necessary.

Shortly after my phone call with George, we had a great, three and a half hour meeting on the propellant loading issue. It was confirmed that the way I wanted to load the propellant could be done. However, TC Noble, our Safety Engineer, said he was very concerned that range safety would not let us have the tank pressure as high as 450 psi without having a way of lowering it in an emergency. He said, "You might have to add extra plumbing in there to keep the gas (the helium pressurant) independent of the fuel." That would mean adding another fill and drain valve and having another hole in each tank, which would mean that the tanks would have to be re-qualified. As far as I was concerned, that had to be avoided at all costs.

Somewhat later, I went to see Dougherty (who had not been at the meeting) and I asked him if Irv had told him about the potential problem with range safety. He said, "Oh yeah, that's all fixed. Irv told me that the PIV we have in there would take care of it."

I said, "I don't get that, how in hell can a PIV have anything to do with the pressure safety problem?"

Dougherty said, "Oh, no, it's all taken care of."

I said, "Well, I'll have to talk to Irv, because I don't see how that PIV has a damned thing to do with it." Just then Irv came by and I said, "Irv, I don't get this at all. I don't see how that PIV can satisfy range safety. We are talking about the pressure in the tanks that has to be released before we can de-tank in an emergency."

Irv also said, "No, it's OK."

I said, "Well, you have to explain it to me, because I sure don't see it." Irv said he had to go do something and would be right back to explain it to me.

Richard came in and said everything was OK, which I still did not believe. While we were waiting for Irv to come back, Richard, Tom, and I walked into my office and I drew the tanks and fuel lines on the blackboard and put the PIV in where they wanted it and just then Irv came in. I said to Irv, "I don't get it, this cannot have anything to do with the pressure problem."

Irv looked at the blackboard and said, "Oh my God, you're right, we snookered ourselves into something incorrect."

I said, "That's right, this doesn't do it."

I then said, "Look, the main thing is that we can't go in and put more lines in there for the pressurant plus another fill and drain valve. If we did, then we would have to put another soda straw in each tank and it goes on and on. If we put a PIV down by the fill and drain valve, that does the trick. The one up at the top has nothing to do with it (the pressurant), so we don't need the damn thing."

Irv said, "You're absolutely right."

I said, "Get Dougherty in here." Then we explained it to Dougherty — or, at least, tried to.

Irv is very good, but it was annoying that I all too frequently had to identify the problems and/or their solutions. I didn't blame Irv *per se* in that case. I thought what had happened was that Richard, who always shot his mouth off before he knew what he was talking about, had said something about the PIV at the top of the spacecraft and everybody said, "Yeah, that PIV will do it," without thinking it through. Dougherty never knew enough to even know what we were talking about, so he was no help on technical matters. The engineers should have been thinking the issues through, but they weren't and that concerned me. If I hadn't followed that issue up, we would have ended up with a configuration that did not resolve the range safety issue.

Later, Al Tilley, Dougherty, some of the other guys, and I discussed getting ready to drill the boltholes in the load-bearing structure for the tanks in about four weeks. That was a critical step, because it fixed the location of the center of gravity (cg) of the spacecraft. Once those holes were drilled, all the errors we had in the spacecraft's mass distribution would have to be compensated for by adding ballast at the appropriate places on the spacecraft to keep its cg exactly on the spin axis (Z axis) and in X-Y plane defined by the centers of the three tanks. For every kilogram of unbalanced hardware mass at the top of the spacecraft, we would have to add a kilogram of ballast at the bottom and I did not want to carry several kilos of lead to the Moon. Until we drilled those holes for the tank bolts, we would continue to balance everything out on paper, but in four weeks, that was over.

I got a call from Dick Seeley, the BJ Link physics teacher. He was going to show his students the video and send me a copy of it in a week or so. He asked if I could do the phone Q&A session with the students during the week of the 22nd and I said yes. Then I asked him about being a teacher Co-I. He was interested and said we would have to talk about it.

I worked on a draft of the new Mission Profile and finally Tom and I drove home.

Wednesday, April 3, 1996

I finished the Mission Profile and got it distributed to everyone.

I talked to Dan Swanson about the nutation damper. Dan explained to me that nutation damping occurs in one of two modes depending on the nutation angle. When the nutation angle is large, the damping is relatively fast and the nutation angle decreases on a several hour timescale. Then, when the nutation angle reached a critical angle called γ^*, usually 2 to 3°, the damping mode changes and the damping rate decreases dramatically, so it takes several hours to damp the remaining nutation down to zero.

Dan was working on the design of the nutation damper to get the nutation damped as fast as possible and to keep γ^* as small as possible. He said the best we could do was to use a 25 cm diameter nutation ring damper and that would damp an initial nutation angle of 35° down to γ^* in several hours. That meant if the nutation was too large right after launch, we couldn't deploy the booms until several hours after launch and that our first reor maneuver would be very sloppy. The fact that we could not deploy the booms until the nutation had damped down also meant we could not automatically deploy the booms right after separation — so that was out! Dan also said that that 25 cm nutation damper had a mass of just 1.1 kg — very nice.

Given what Dan had just explained to me, I had to change the Mission Profile. I would have to turn the instruments on early, do the first reor while we were still near the Earth, then deploy the booms after the nutation had damped out, and finally do the first mid-course maneuver. Things were getting very interesting because I was finally getting hard data on how the spacecraft would operate, so I could accurately define the Mission Profile, i.e., the mission was getting more and more real.

Woody told me we were going to be able to get the solar cells either from the Japanese — they were pretty confident they would be able to get their new 17% cells on the market by the time we needed them — or GaAs cells from one specific vendor. Someone had talked to the Lockheed President and he would see about getting us the GaAs cells.

Hopefully, we would get the GaAs cells, because Woody was worried about the power and said we needed every bit we could get. He thought, because of the shadowing, even the difference between 17 and 18% cells was significant. I would like to have the GaAs cells because of the higher power and also because the spacecraft would be warmer on the inside than with silicon cells. However, because the GaAs cells are heavier than silicon cells, we would have to take that mass hit.

Though there were still issues to be resolved, and there would be many more to be resolved before Lunar Prospector was completely built, we had reached a point in our work where it was clear we were getting there. I was confident I would at least get a good primary mission out of the spacecraft, so I was pleased.

I talked to Sylvia and told her that Tom and I were going to kill LEI, then revive my old Lunar Resources Institute and the reason for our doing so, i.e., to protect ourselves from SSI. It was clear it would be several months before we could move to the Lunar Resources Institute and that was fine with Sylvia and Scott. We all felt that most of the major issues, the tracking and the LLV1 Lewis & Clark launches, were going to be behind us in a few months, so our going to the Lunar Resources Institute would not be a burden to anyone by that time. Also, Sylvia said, "Happily, Mark is fading to nothing." I was very pleased about all of that.

Thursday, April 4, 1996: Staff Meeting Day

Both Sylvia and Scott were there for the staff meeting. Sylvia said to me, "Gee, Dougherty acts differently when Scott is here." As Sylvia noted, when there was an audience, Dougherty always tried to bully Sylvia and treat her with as much disrespect as he could get away with; he did the same to me — but even more so, and he treated Tom quite poorly. All of that was his childish attempt to keep control of a project he had little competence to manage. As far as Sylvia and I are concerned, Dougherty is an idiot.

We went through every issue during the staff meeting. We were somewhat behind schedule in a number of areas, but nothing was extremely critical.

The biggest problem for the spacecraft was still the solar array. We still hadn't found a vendor for the solar cells. Woody had talked to the vendor for the GaAs cells and we could not get them, period. We knew we had better be able to get the Sharp cells, or we were in trouble and, even if we did, we were going to be low on power for two reasons.

First, the way the solar array engineers had laid out the solar array, the strings above the boom canisters were going to extend down from the top half of the array into the bottom half and therefore, the instruments would periodically shadow them. We wouldn't get as much power from the top half of the array as we had thought. Second, the strings were wider than we thought when Woody and I did the shadowing loss calculations, so the shadowing was worse than we thought. Thus, the power had again become a critical issue — no question about it. I was just hoping the power contingency and the undedicated margin in Woody's calculations would get us over the hump. He and I were going to fully discuss the power crunch later in the day.

Then there was a small problem with the GRS. A couple of the graphite epoxy GRS housing pieces had to be done over and they had to undergo mechanical testing to see if they were OK. That was not of great concern, but nevertheless it caused a little slip in the schedule and I was always concerned about schedule slips — big and small.

There was also a problem with the booms. The side panels on which the boom canisters were to be mounted were going to flex because of the launch loads, so the boom canisters would move up and down. That would be OK except for the fact the MAG extension boom was going to be held securely at the top by the capture wires. Clearly, we couldn't have one end constrained and the other end moving around. We started looking for a solution. I suggested we put a 2 to 3 cm, loose sleeve around the boom extension where the capture wires were located and have the capture wires hold onto the sleeve. That way the boom could move up and down, but still be constrained from moving left and right as well as back and forth. Somebody suggested we use a bearing surface, but that would be a lot of work and expense for virtually nothing. The sleeve idea was a lot simpler

Dougherty, who, as usual, did not understand what was going on, said, "We have a problem here," just after the engineers had all agreed on a solution to another issue.

Not being able to resist tweaking Dougherty, I asked in all, innocence, "Gee, Tom, am I not supposed to trust your engineers?"

My comment ticked Gerry Grismore off and he said softly from the back of the room, "He (me) only believes or accepts the stuff he already believes," actually, a very true statement!

I went through my new Mission Profile and got a lot of good comments from the engineers. Most of the comments were related to adding more detail so the profile would be more understandable for them. We didn't need all that detail for Mission Ops, because I knew how to run the spacecraft, so would Tom and Dan Swanson by the time we launched. But it was good to have those things clarified so when the engineers went through the Mission Profile, they could fully understand it, and I could get good feedback from them.

Dougherty wanted all the recovery and emergency modes put in the Mission Profile — a good suggestion — so I explained to him that they were all in the Mission Operations Document. I said I would just code each emergency procedure with its paragraph number and add its code in another column of the profile and he agreed.

As the meeting broke up, I thought about the characters I was dealing with: Dougherty never understood anything and was always confrontational; Gerry was very good, but usually confrontational; I liked Woody a lot and despite his inability to make a decision, he usually had a lot of good ideas and made good comments; the rest of the guys were fine; but the best person around was Dale Vaccarello. Dale was always helpful; was always looking for the best solution and always tried to be friendly. Unlike Dougherty, Dale has no ego problem. I like Dale a lot; he is the kind of guy I would like to have in the Lunar Resources Institute.

I talked to Swanson and an engineer named Ho about the flat spin calculations Dan and she were trying to finish. Dan had been concerned that if at launch, the moment of inertia with respect to the spin (Z) axis were not large enough compared to the moments of inertia with respect to the X and Y axes of the spacecraft, and if the nutation were large enough at separation, the spacecraft would not be a stable spinner and could go into a flat spin. If that happened, there was no way we could recover and the spacecraft would be lost. Dan and Ho didn't think there was a serious problem, but they were still checking it out and I agreed with them.

Then there was a second problem caused by the nutation. If the nutation angle were too large when we deployed the booms, the booms would flop up and down violently because they would be like limp spaghetti until they were fully deployed, then they would be stiff. Thus, at the very beginning of the deployment sequence, the MAG could smack into the spacecraft and break some solar cells and/or damage itself. The way to get around that problem was to wait for the nutation to damp down to a couple of degrees and then to deploy the booms. Dan said that, since he finally knew the nutation damper's characteristics, it would take 2 to 4 hours for the nutation to damp down to something acceptable, basically to get down to the γ^* amplitude. If the spacecraft were a stable spinner in its stowed configuration — and we had to make sure that it would be — we would just have to wait for the nutation to damp out before I deployed the booms to insure they did not flop around and cause the MAG to damage itself or the solar array during the deployment.

I was very pleased with Dan; he and I worked together very well, he is very bright and gets the necessary information quickly. However, I had to get him to understand we were not doing a 99.9% mission, rather that Lunar Prospector was to be a 95% mission, done in the Discovery style for a very small amount of money.

Chapter 3-13
A Simple Change
Makes Major Differences

Friday, April 5, 1996:
A Major Improvement to the Power Problem and More

I talked to Woody about the solar array. It looked like the best we could do was to get the 17% Japanese cells, but since the strings were wide, we were going to lose a lot of power due to shadowing, so we needed to get it back somehow. Woody was most concerned about the shadowing on those few strings in the upper panel that were to extend down into the lower half of the array. I asked him, "Why do we have to run those strings all the way down to the canisters, since we will lose power when they are shadowed? Wouldn't it be better just to keep them just above the shadow line, so we wouldn't lose the power?" Woody said he had thought of that and that he had also thought about laying the array out with smaller cells so the strings would be narrower, which would also reduce the effects of the shadowing.

Then, because I had also had the problem of the banging of the MAG into the solar array as the booms deployed on my mind, it suddenly dawned on me that I could solve three problems with one simple solution!

First, if the MAG extension boom were hinged, instead of being solidly mounted perpendicular to the main boom, then when the capture wires were cut, it would rotate about 100° and lock in position straight out from the main boom, so the shadows of the MAG and its extension boom would no longer fall on the upper half of the solar array. As a result, we would gain about 5% in power! Woody liked that very much since it pushed us over the power hump that he and I were so worried about, and the 17% Sharp cells would do just fine.

Second, when the main booms were deployed, the MAG extension boom would be nowhere near the solar array, so it could not bang into the array and I could deploy the booms as soon after separation as I wanted — as long as the nutation were not too large.

Third, and this point was very important, when the MAG extension boom deployed, the rotation rate of the spacecraft would decrease, the spacecraft's attitude would change, the nutation would increase, and the magnetic field would appear to rotate by 100°, four changes that we would easily detect. Thus, for the first time I had four certain ways of knowing if the MAG extension boom had been properly deployed before I deployed the main booms! Man, was I happy.

I immediately tried to call Bob Lin and Dave Curtis to see if they would agree to my changing the MAG extension boom configuration, but neither of them was there! Nevertheless, I knew there was nothing wrong with the change I was suggesting; in fact, it would put the MAG another 1.2 m from the spacecraft and that would reduce the effects of the spacecraft's magnetic fields on the measurements by a factor of three! I also knew they had a hinge mechanism they had developed for the WIND spacecraft (and probably others), and I was sure we could use the same hinge for Lunar Prospector, so we would not have to develop and validate the hinge.

That simple change in the MAG extension boom configuration would have such dramatic effects on the simplicity of the spacecraft, on the safety of the mission and on Mission Ops, I decided I was just going to tell Dougherty Monday we were not going to waste time talking about it, we were just going to do it.

I then talked to Bill Feldman about several things. The first was getting the spectrometer turn-on sequence right. I wanted to first turn on the SES and then turn on each spectrometer, one at a time, rather than having all four of the units ganged together so they all went on at once. That way, if something was wrong with one of the four units, I could stop the turn-on sequence and we could determine what was wrong and what to do about it. Bill and Ron Black, who was building the SES at the Southwest institute, finally agreed.

It had been a very, very good day. I was especially pleased (more like ecstatic) about the effects of changing the MAG extension boom configuration would have on the entire spacecraft and mission. And, in general, I was quite pleased with the way things were going. Being Friday, and since Rebecca was visiting her daughter in St. Louis, Tom and I left work at about 2:30 and went down to San Juan Batista and had a nice dinner.

Monday, April 8, 1996: Subsystem Review day

Everything went quite smoothly; there were no big issues. I told the guys about the MAG extension boom change and that Tom and I were going to go to Berkeley the next day to check it out with Bob and Dave. Woody was trying to get the Sharp solar cells. The battery mass was lower than Woody thought and a bit higher than I thought. I was using 221 grams per cell and they were 235 according to the vendor's specifications. Still, my number was a kilogram or so less than Woody had. The final battery mass was going to be about 5.17 kg. I was trying to make everybody get as accurate mass numbers for their subsystems as possible, so we could get the best possible cg for the spacecraft before we drilled the holes for the tanks. I was pleased with the battery mass number.

Some weeks earlier, we had asked the Lockheed Model Shop to take our Lunar Prospector engineering drawings and build an accurate, full scale engineering model of the spacecraft we could use to check out engineering changes to the design and for PR purposes. The model was coming along nicely and one of the modelers brought over the propellant tanks and the antenna complex of the model and they were beautiful.

Sylvia came by and said that Mark and Headquarters had called Scott to complain about my comments that were to appear in the April 8–14, 1996 issue of *Space News* (I didn't know what was printed, since the issue had not yet appeared, but NASA had seen the article already), so I went over to see Scott. As usual, Headquarters and Scott were all bent out of shape over two things I had said to Leonard Davis. I had told Leonard we were hoping to be able to launch on time after successful Lewis & Clark launches or something like that. Leonard had quoted me as saying, after a three-paragraph discussion of the LLV2 issue, "Everything will be tested out in the Lewis & Clark launches. We believe that we will then be able to proceed towards our early October launch date for Lunar Prospector." "We" was meant to be Scott, Sylvia, Lockheed, and me, but not NASA in general. That was a fairly accurate quote, but Wes's deputy was concerned we had misunderstood their directive.

The other point that concerned NASA was that I had said that my main goal was to prove that "Faster, Better, Cheaper" worked and that getting good science was necessary for proving that. Headquarters did not like that at all, because they said Lunar

Prospector's main goal was getting good science data. Well, they should have read their own goals for Discovery, because if they did, they would have learned that determining how to do missions "Faster, Better, Cheaper" was one of its main goals. As a scientist, clearly I wanted to get good science data, but still my main programmatic goal was to prove that the "Faster, Better, Cheaper" concept worked — that was always the main goal of Lunar Prospector, from its very beginning. Despite the fact that NASA was upset about the article, my attitude was, *no matter what I say, somebody is going to be upset.* As far as I was concerned, NASA could go to hell, which I told Scott in a polite form.

Tuesday, April 9, 1996

Eighteen months to launch!

Tom and I went up to Berkeley to talk to Dave Curtis and Paul Turin about having the MAG extension boom deploy outward to avoid having it smack against the solar array during deployment and to keep it from shadowing the upper part of the solar array. They said there was no problem building the MAG/ER package that way, using the same type of hinge that they had built before. Happily, they had not yet cut hardware on the structure, though they had it all planned, so we would only lose about two man months of time and money to make the change.

Tom and I drove back down to Lockheed and dealt with a concern I had with the GRS. Because the GRS was going to extend down about 8 cm below the bottom of the spacecraft, I was concerned it might get bumped during separation. We checked and found out that the standoffs between the TLI Stage and the spacecraft were 15 cm tall to allow room for the A1 and A2 engines. Also, the three standoffs were 120° apart, so we wouldn't have any problem with the GRS getting hit during separation.

I planned my trip to the Cape on Tuesday, flying there the following Monday, and then flying up to Baltimore to give a talk at the Applied Physics Laboratory (APL) on Wednesday, and finally visiting Los Alamos on Thursday.

Wednesday, April 10, 1996

Dave Curtis sent me the design for changing the MAG extension boom. The boom was to be mounted on a little stand above the MAG/ER DPU (the Data Procession Unit, i.e., their common electronics unit) and when released, it would just flop out. I showed it to Dougherty, who happily finally understood its very positive impact on the spacecraft and mission, so he wasn't concerned about the extra time and money. That was a relief, because I was worried about the costs. Despite my other concerns and aggravation with Dougherty, when it came to the money, he shined.

I found out that the meeting at the Cape was postponed until May 7! That was too bad; I would have to make two trips to the east coast instead of just one big one.

Dougherty, Tom, and I sat down during the morning and went over a number of issues. Dougherty was really decent for a change and, for the first time, Tom got to see him when he was not in his huffing and puffing, showoff mode, rather just sitting down and talking seriously with me. He also treated Tom with respect for the first time.

I talked with Alex about the C&DH and the commands. I wanted to be sure that I had a delayed command capability, so I could do out-of-sight-commanding when the spacecraft was behind the Moon and/or in the dark, since some of our commanding relied on the sun sensor for timing.

Dan told me the nutation period was about 12 seconds after boom deployment and that was great.

As Tom and I drove home, we both had had a good day. Everything was going well.

Thursday, April 11, 1996: Staff Meeting Day

We went through all the subsystems and I discussed with the engineers the new way we were going to mount the MAG extension boom and why. Then we had a big, long discussion about the possibility that the launch vibrations could cause the GRS to hit the solar array drum. I did not see any problem except that the engineers were just chasing their own shadows.

Steve Honodel, our replacement for Vu (happily, Steve seemed to know what he was doing), pointed out the fact that it was very hard to reach the three latching pins on each of the tip plates of the booms to reset them after we deployed them for testing.

We also found that the detector head of the ER protruded into the maximum dynamic envelope of the shroud (the maximum distance the shroud walls could swing inwards due to launch vibrations), which is a no-no. However, the dynamic envelope we had been given by LLV did not allow for the fact there are struts that extend into the payload area. As such, there are places between the struts where the dynamic envelope is further out and we could make sure the ER was in one of those places. It was a matter of getting the right information, which we didn't have.

Though the staff meeting was very fruitful, I was concerned that, because Dougherty is so slow, so dull, it took him forever to understand any of the issues. I was absolutely stunned that he could not understand that, when the capture wires holding the MAG extension boom were cut, the centrifugal force of the spinning spacecraft would put almost 3 g of radial acceleration on the extension boom and it would rapidly swing radially outwards. Dougherty simply did not understand the simple high school physics that would cause it to deploy! He just isn't capable of understanding even the simplest concepts. We spent an hour and a half discussing the issue with Steve and Dougherty, when a half an hour should have sufficed. He is just slow.

Richard, Francisco, Tom, and I had a late lunch. Francisco had just gotten back from his wedding and honeymoon!

We got the first indications from the coupled load analysis, which LLV had just sent us, that the launch environment was not as bad as we had been told! One peculiar thing was there would be an 8 g load on one tank and only a 1 g load on the other two! It was weird that they were so different. However, if the trend with the coupled load analysis continued, we might not have such a bad environment as we had feared, and that would be great.

Friday, April 12, 1996

I worked on the Mission Profile to get it on a spreadsheet as the guys had suggested during the review several days earlier. I finally got it switched over with Tom's help.

I had a very interesting meeting with the alignment engineers on how the spacecraft would be aligned, the tools they used to do the alignment, how they would get all the surfaces parallel and how they would get the booms properly aligned. It was very, very interesting and informative.

We talked to Paul Turin and Dave Curtis about the way we needed to mount the MAG extension boom on the DPU. Also, they told me I was going to have to de-spin the spacecraft from its launch spin rate of 60 rpm to about 40 rpm before I deployed the MAG extension boom. That would keep the centrifugal and coriolis forces small enough so the extension boom would not be damaged. We also decided we didn't have to have a breaking device to stop the boom at the end of its deployment swing, it could just oscillate back and forth against some damping springs until it came to rest and that would be OK.

I started recalculating the spacecraft's fuel usage based on the new configuration of the engines we had decided on at the beginning of February to help solve the boom stability problem during reorientation maneuvers. That was necessary before I could work on the next version of the Mission Profile.

Monday, April 15, 1996: Subsystem Review Day

Woody still hadn't heard anything about the availability of the Sharp solar cells. The coupled load analysis looked like the environment was only 30 to 40% as bad as we had thought, so we all gave a very tentative sigh of relief. The IR limb-crossing detector had a longer response time than Dan thought it would have, so that was causing some modeling problems. That was not serious, but the IR sensor was not going to be as good as I had hoped in terms of giving us the data we needed to determine the roll angle, but it would be OK. The software was getting started slowly. And that was about it — things were good.

Tuesday, April 16, and Wednesday, April 17, 1996: A Wasted Trip to APL

I was at the IAA (International Aeronautics Association) meeting at APL (Applied Physics Laboratory) at John Hopkins University in Maryland. It was a wasted two-day trip as far as I was concerned. My talk was just 15 minutes long, which was far too short to say anything useful about Lunar Prospector.

There were several papers presented of the type I have heard over and over again from the Americans, Europeans, and others. It was the same old type of meeting about a lot of wanna-be missions that were going nowhere except into the wastepaper basket. Not only was my talk too short, but it was also right after lunch, so half of the people hadn't returned from lunch and those there were not interested in Lunar Prospector. They were just at the meeting to hear themselves talk about their own pet projects.

The only good thing about the meeting was that Jim McCurry was there. Jim and I had worked in the same section at Lockheed in Houston and I always had a lot of respect for him. He had left Houston, was in Huntsville and was about to move to LLV in Denver! Having heard my talk, he wondered why I was so annoyed with LLV, so I told him the whole history. I was sure he would go back to Denver and spread the word that I was still not happy with them.

It was a long trip for nothing and I decided not to go to the COSPAR meeting in Europe. Why should I fly all across the Atlantic for a lousy half hour talk to the same dis-interested people? It wasn't worth the time or money.

Thursday, April 18, 1996: Staff Meeting Day

The solar cells still hadn't been ordered from Sharp, although the Lockheed Center of Excellence said they would be happy to get us the cells.

Dougherty was his usual stupid self. Tom had set up a meeting for me in a small meeting room used for customers and Dougherty made a big deal about the room being too small and that Tom should have reserved the Pic Room. He then tried to tell me who I needed to have at my meeting — the man is such an idiot. I just kept telling him, "Hey, I don't pay attention to you and you know it," but that never stopped him.

As Tom said, "He has no shame and no conscience."

Dougherty asked why we didn't have engine redundancy for spin-up and spin-down maneuvers — which he didn't understand anyway. Two or three months earlier, we had gone through that issue because in the OMNI spacecraft design, the axial engines were tilted $3°$ in order to provide backup ways to do spin-up and spin-down maneuvers. The structure guys had crabbed about the $3°$ tilt because it made it harder to put the spacecraft together. Since Irv had told me that the engines were essentially fail proof, I said, "OK, to hell with the tilt."

When Dougherty asked his question, I answered, "That's a dead issue. We talked about it in great detail a couple months ago and we all agreed we're not going to have redundancy for spin maneuvers."

He said, "Well maybe it should be reopened."

I said, "I don't want it reopened." Then he implied that he might reopen it. I was really getting tired of his overbearing ways, especially since he is so incredibly stupid, so I said, "Tom, this has already been decided. You are so far behind the curve, it's not even funny." Even that didn't shut him up, he just continued. The man has no class, no conscience, no shame and he is just a flipping idiot. He did some things fairly well — like managing the money, but other than that, he is just pathetic.

Friday, April 19, 1996

I finished the propellant usage program in the morning and it turned out that my program and the one Dan Swanson had done gave the same answers, as they should have because it's just physics, after all. However, since our approaches and the ways we had set our programs up were different, the fact that we got the same answer meant that neither of us had made any mistake in our programs.

Al Tilley came by in the afternoon and said the latest data on the moments of inertia of the spacecraft indicate that we had a bowling ball again, i.e., the pre-boom deployment moments of inertia with respect to the X, Y, and Z axes (Ix, Iy, and Iz, respectively) were close to being the same, so the spacecraft would be unstable. That was very serious. We could not fly an unstable spinner because we could not control it and it could go into a deadly flat spin right after launch — well before I could deploy the booms, after which it would be a stable spinner. Al, Dan, Steve Honodel, and I tried to figure out what we could do to get Iz at least 1.07 times greater than Ix and Iy (the factor of 1.07 being the lowest stability limit we would feel comfortable with).

Independent of the bowling ball issue, we had to move the boom canisters out 4 cm to give Steve the access he needed to be able to reset the latch pins after testing and to make sure that the instruments didn't bang on the solar panels during launch. That would also help the moment of inertia problem a teeny bit. Then we talked about moving the canisters up 3 to 5 cm. Moving them higher would help even more with Iz, but then the instruments would start shadowing the upper solar array panel and decrease our power and I couldn't have that.

I remembered that Woody and I had talked about making the upper array shorter to minimize the shadowing effects of the tangential engines. If we did that, then we could move the canisters up a bit further. We thought about moving the SES, the C&DH, and the transponder from the equipment shelf to the side panels of the load-bearing structure down in the plane of the cg. However, we didn't know if the side panels would handle the stresses caused by those relatively heavy units during launch, but if the panels could, that would really help the moment of inertia problem.

I suggested that we despin to 2 or 3 rpm immediately after separation and then, even if the nutation were fairly big, we could still deploy the booms, stabilize the spacecraft, and then figure out what in the hell to do next.

Somehow we had to solve that very serious problem.

Dougherty believed the problem might go away, because he couldn't understand why the calculated moments of inertia had changed so much in just a few weeks.

Despite the lack of an immediate solution to the problem, I was confident we would find a way around the moment of inertia crisis.

I started to get a bad case of the flu — just in time to spoil the weekend!

Monday, April 22, 1996: A Day Filled with Meetings

Marcie Smith (Marcie, a young Ames engineer, had been put on the project by Scott to help me with Missions Ops) and I had a meeting with the software guys, Bill Jacobsen and Norm Bennett, from Palo Alto, about the Mission Operations software. Ed Guinness and his crew came to Lockheed for an Archiving meeting. George French, David Troup, and John Gruener also came to Lockheed to discuss their Outreach activities. George had more resources than I did for Outreach, so we were going to make sure his crew did things we could use in Mission Ops.

After work, George, Tom, Rebecca, and I had a dinner meeting and decided to dump the Lunar Resources Institute idea and start fresh with a new, Arizona based company, the Lunar Research Institute (LRI). We talked to a lawyer from Tucson, a friend of George's, who was going to help us get LRI started.

My flu was worse. Everybody had it, and even Rebecca caught it.

Tuesday, April 23, 1996

I felt crummy, but I went to work anyway, because I had the telephone Q&A session with the BJ Link students and it went quite well. There were some technical difficulties and the questions were OK, but nothing really great. However, I finally caught on that I was dealing with fundamentalist Christians when one of the young ladies asked me, "Are you a Christian? And how many of your co-workers are Christians? And do you discuss religion at work?"

I answered, "No, I am not a Christian, and no, we do not discuss religion at work."

Dick stepped in, recognizing that the student had entered into dangerous ground from their standpoint and said, "You should not ask Dr. Binder personal questions."

I talked with Al Tilley about the moment of inertia problem and we thought we could solve it by moving one or two of the electronic units off the equipment shelf, probably the SES and the C&DH, since the transponder and the battery had to stay up there to properly radiate their excess heat into space. In addition, if we moved the boom canisters and the engine tanks up 2 or 3 cm, we thought we would be OK. Anyway we were working on that.

I still had not heard a word about the damned solar cells from Woody, so I asked him what was going on? He answered that he had heard nothing because the damned Center of Excellence had done nothing. I was going to raise hell about that with Dougherty the next day.

I finished the propellant usage model, and, as expected, we could save a lot of fuel by having an early mid-course maneuver.

All in all, things were OK. I would feel a lot better when we had the moment of inertia and the solar cell issues resolved. But I couldn't complain too much because everybody was sick. Tom had the flu and half the guys at work had it.

Wednesday, April 24, 1996: The Solar Cells at Last

I felt lousy all day. Tom was home sick and nearly everybody else was sick with what we had.

I worked on the propellant model all day, and Al Tilley worked on the moment of inertia all day. He calculated that we could get a moment of inertia ratio of 1.08 to 1.09 if we moved the boom canisters up by 2.5 cm, moved the tanks down (not up as we thought) by 2.5 cm and moved C&DH to the side panel. It turned out the side panels were about 1½ kg lighter than he had thought and that actually helped, surprisingly enough. The trouble was, because of the weird triangular shape of the load-bearing structure, you couldn't really get a feeling for the moment of inertia. It was not something you could do intuitively, as would have been the case if the structure were cylindrical or something like that. Anyway, both Al and I wanted to err on the side of having a very high ratio, because it was a very critical issue. We better damn well have a good ratio; otherwise, we would end up in big trouble.

When I was about ready to leave, Woody finally got the word from the Japanese that they would be able to get us our solar cells! What a relief. Apparently, they would cost about what we had expected, $300,000, and the cells wouldn't be delivered as soon as we would have liked them, but soon enough so it wouldn't cause us any problem.

I was still concerned about the power because of the shadowing, and I was going to talk to Woody about that the next day. Also the power usage of the C&DH was high, as I expected, because we had put the power control unit in the C&DH unit. I also suspected that the IR Limb Crossing Sensor might take more power, because it had a lot more electronics than we had originally thought. If that were really the case, I could shut it off most of the time, because the spacecraft's attitude wouldn't change between maneuvers.

By the end of the day I was feeling better and I hoped I would be over the flu by the next day.

Chapter 3-14
Moving Towards Assembly

Thursday, April 25, 1996: Staff Meeting Day

Several things came up at the staff meeting. Woody and Al Tilley brought everyone up to speed on the purchase of the Sharp solar cells and the progress we had made on the moment of inertia problem, respectively. Mass-wise, the mass of the Sharp cells was 3 kg less than we had assumed. The mass of the booms went up a little because the tip plates' masses went up and we had added the double battens. But over all, the spacecraft's mass went down. I was sure it would come back up a little if we had to add stiffeners and other things after we did the testing. Nevertheless, we had the mass under control. The only thing that really concerned me was an increase in the power usage by the heaters. I was a little worried about the amount of power we would be getting from the solar array.

During the afternoon, I finished modifying the propellant usage model to make it a little bit more accurate and I found some errors in the way I set up the spreadsheet. That was in good shape.

Irv found out that the centrifugal force caused by a spinning spacecraft tends to stop the formation of vortices in the fuel as it flows out of the tanks when the engines are fired. He was going to check that out completely, and if verified, then we wouldn't have to put cuneiform vortex suppressors in the tanks. Apparently, when TRW had the tanks made the first time over a decade earlier, they did a detailed investigation of the formation of vortices in the tanks and found if the outlets from the tanks are offset from the exact bottom of the tanks by about 10°, vortices do not form! I thought that was really neat and it explained why the tank outlets were offset 8°, a fact that had been a minor mystery to Irv and me ever since we had seen the tank specifications months earlier.

I started modifying the Mission Profile to account for what we had learned about deploying the booms, having the first MCM 4 hours after launch, and the other things we had changed since I had finished the previous version of the profile.

All in all the day was a very good day. Lunar Prospector's design was settling down quite nicely. I didn't have to travel the following week and I was finally getting over the flu.

Friday, April 26, 1996

Dougherty wasn't around, which was nice — he was on vacation.

At Dougherty's insistence, Tom, Steve Honodel, another Lockheed boom engineer, and I went up to Berkeley to review the MAG extension boom to insure it would deploy properly. The trip and the review were a waste of time. The Berkeley guys knew what they were doing — far better than the Lockheed engineers did. But since Dougherty doesn't understand even the simplest thing, he always had to have several people check everything out. On the other hand, given the criticality of that piece of hardware, I agreed to the review. But as expected, it was a waste of time, except that Paul told me he had fixed the MAG extension boom so it could be deployed at 48 rpm. That was great. I would only have to de-spin the spacecraft from 60 rpm to 48 rpm rather than to 30 rpm.

When we got back to Lockheed, Irv pointed out that the Spacecraft/TLI Stage stack would spin up from its initial 60 rpm rate during the TLI burn, since the Star-37's fuel is further from the spin axis of the stack than the exhaust is as it comes out the nozzle. As a result, because of the conservation of angular momentum, the stack has to spin up. What I won by Paul's fixing the MAG extension boom so it could be deployed at 48 rpm, I lost because of the TLI burn spin-up effect — well, you win a few and lose a few.

I started working on the Mission Profile again, but decided I would work on it during the weekend, since I was just going to relax and try to get over the flu.

I also talked to Gerry Grismore, who said the C&DH unit was going to come in a little lighter than expected; so most everything was coming in light. The only things that were coming in heavy were the boom tip plates and the booms — about a kilogram heavy. It was beginning to look like all the other subsystems were going to be a total of about 5 kg light, so like anyone watching his own weight — I was very happy with the results of the spacecraft's diet!

The interesting news of the day was non-technical. Per the Lunar Prospector contract with NASA, Lockheed was to get a portion of its $4 million fee each quarter. The exact quarterly amount depended on NASA's evaluation of the work done during the quarter, e.g., if NASA were disappointed, Lockheed might get 70% of the maximum amount of fee; if NASA were happy, but not completely so, then Lockheed might get 90% — a typical award fee value for aerospace contracts with NASA. Interestingly, Lockheed was awarded 100% of its potential Lunar Prospector fee for the first quarter of Phase C/D and *that was the first time Lockheed had ever gotten a 100% fee award!* I was very pleased, not for Lockheed, but because it showed that when a program is run by a scientist who knows what he is doing and not by an engineer or a bureaucrat, the program moves forward as it should, and even NASA had recognized that. That was a very good piece of news at the end of another good day for Lunar Prospector.

Monday, April 29, 1996: Subsystem Review Day

Tim Bridges and I were appalled because Bill Jacobsen and his software guys didn't understand how you run a spacecraft of any kind, and didn't know you have to have real-time data on the sun angle, the spin rate, the nutation, engine temperatures, and things like that to do operations. Those data are not hard to get, but neither the software engineers nor Dougherty understood that.

We spent quite a bit of time discussing that because Dougherty kept hollering, "Mission Ops wasn't planned that way. We don't have the money for that," until I finally began to get it across to him that I had to have certain data in real-time or I simply could not run the spacecraft and that it had been planned that way.

To prove that, I said, "I'll show you in the original proposal where it is clearly described as being part of Mission Ops."

Tim Bridges agreed and said, "This is done all the time. You have to have these things to do operations."

Dougherty asked, "Well, what do you mean exactly?"

I answered, "For example, when we come off the TLI Stage, we have to be able to see what the solar equatorial angle is as a function of time so we can see when the nutation is small enough to deploy the booms."

Dougherty got excited because he thought I was trying to change the way the spacecraft was run. He did not understand that what I had described were normal command sequences and that I just had to be able to monitor the systems so I could decide in real-time if and when I could do critical things with the spacecraft. I gave another example that even an idiot could understand; I said, "If I start an engine burn and something goes wrong, I'll have to stop the burn. If I don't have the capability to monitor the engine parameters, I won't know I have a problem and that I need to shut the engines off, so we could lose the spacecraft."

Despite that simple explanation, Dougherty, who always thought I didn't know what I was talking about because I am a scientist and not an engineer, asked Dan Swanson, who is a very good engineer, if he agreed with me and Dan said, "Of course, I do."

Tim and I won in the end, but I was really disappointed that the Palo Alto guys didn't even know the most fundamental things about running a spacecraft. All of that was a colossal waste of time and it was very aggravating.

Al Tilley showed up and we started to talk about the spacecraft's mass. I thought we were going to come in 3 to 4 kilograms lighter than we were calculating at that point, or just under 290 kg; nevertheless I was still using 295 kg for my calculations at that time (the final launch mass was 296 kg). It was conceivable that the final dry mass might even be less than 150 kg; I would have loved that, since that was one of my goals. But I didn't really believe the spacecraft was going to be that light. Al and I spent most of the afternoon working on the mass calculations.

Dougherty started yapping again about the emergency procedures. I said, "Dougherty, they (the emergency procedures) are all in the proposal. I had one whole appendix just on the emergency procedures."

He said, "Well, I guess I'll have to read the proposal sometime," duh, yaha!

In addition to Dougherty's usual display of stupidity, two other amusing things happened during the day. First, after lunch, I stepped into a TLI Stage meeting for a couple of minutes. As I walked in, Dougherty was saying "Because we got a 100% award fee this quarter, Mike Henshaw came and congratulated us (Dougherty and Frank) and said this has never happened before. Nobody has ever gotten a 100% award fee from NASA before, so he (Mike) is going to take the whole crew out for lunch this week or next week." I found it very amusing that Henshaw didn't come to me and say anything, but I was fully aware that as far as Lockheed management was concerned, I did not exist.

Woody came by late in the afternoon to tell me that, though we were going to get the Sharp cells, the damned Lockheed solar array manufacturer guy, George Pack, was trying to screw us. George told Woody we had to use the solar cell layout he had given us, despite the fact that we had shown him it was not good because it didn't properly take into consideration the shadowing. He and his group had dragged their heels in getting the layout information to us, so they were a month or two behind schedule. They hadn't made any effort to get it done and then, all of a sudden, they said we had to do it their way and they had to have the contract right away. We found Dougherty, who understood the problem, which surprised me.

Regardless of my surprise, Dougherty said, "Well, tell you (Woody) what, you get this worked out and then Wednesday you get George over, and Alan, you put on your PI hat and then you make them do it right." Earlier in the day, Sylvia had asked about parking to make sure she was not parking in somebody's place because there were still a lot of old names on the parking slots. Dougherty had said to her, "You're our customer; I'll get you a parking spot."

Hearing that, I just could not resist tweaking him, I said very innocently, "Well, gee Tom, since I'm your real customer and she's my customer, you ought to get me one, too." He immediately said, "Oh, no, no, no, I can't do that, I won't do that."

With that earlier little spiel in mind and because I could not resist tweaking him again, I said, "Gee, Tom, I can't do that, because I don't have a parking space." Dougherty was not amused.

Tuesday, April 30, 1996

I worked most of the day with Tilley on the spacecraft's mass calculations. We compared our calculations for balancing the three booms and our individual results agreed, so we were both confident we were in good shape there. Al's fuelled mass for the spacecraft was about 290 kg, again in agreement with mine. We were convinced the mass had really come down some and would come down some more, because the upper and lower shelves of the load-bearing structure were coming in light. As such, I was confident that the 290 kg number was getting fairly solid.

Dan Swanson and I sat down and went over all the equations in our propellant usage models. We found some small discrepancies that we corrected and since Dan's and my models agreed on everything, both of us were confident our models were correct.

Tilley came by to talk with Dan and me about the moments of inertia calculations. The critical ratio had again come down from about 1.07 to only a little over 1.03! Though we really wanted a ratio of 1.07, we could get away with 1.03, but it just could not be below that. We thought if the top and bottom shelves came in light, as expected, that would help raise the ratio back up near 1.07. If not, since the spacecraft's mass was down a few kilograms, I could sacrifice those savings and have Al put a few kilograms of ballast at the appropriate places along the intermediate axes of the moments of inertia to get the 1.07 ratio. I would hate to have to do that, because every kilogram counted, but we had to have a stable spacecraft.

As was the case the day before, Dougherty provided two amusing displays of stupidity and managerial incompetence.

First, as a follow-up to our conversation the day before when Woody, Dougherty, and I were discussing the problem with the solar array manufacturer, Dougherty came to me and floored me. He asked, "Can you make sure that Woody gets that stuff done with the manufacturing center and make sure he gets everything ordered?" I found his request amusing; he was supposed to be the Project Manager and the manager of the Lockheed engineers. Lockheed had denied me that responsibility and almost everyday he huffed and puffed as he tried to maintain his Project Manager authority. But when it came to actually putting pressure on someone in Lockheed to do what he or she was supposed to do, Dougherty always shied away from his real responsibility and, in that case, asked me to do his job! It was one thing for me to have to manage all the technical effort (which I loved doing), but it was more than amusing to me for him to want me to put the heat on the manufacturing center! There was just no way in the world I could do that; the personnel over there were no more willing to accept my authority as the PI than were Dougherty, Frank, Henshaw, or any other Lockheed manager.

Second, in response to Dougherty bitching the day before about the emergency procedures, I had copied them from the proposal and had given them to him. Somewhat later, as I walked by his office and, much to my utter amazement, he said, "Can you help me a minute?" He was actually reading the emergency procedures! He continued, saying, "It's easier to ask you questions that to try and figure them out myself."

Dougherty was confused because, when I wrote the emergency procedures, long before we did the proposal, the spacecraft had a backup unit for each piece of hardware. According to what I wrote in the proposal, the first corrective step to take if a subsystem gave out was to switch to its backup unit. Since we had gone single string before the TDR, there were no longer any backup units to switch to. Strangely, I had to explain to him that, since I had not yet updated the emergency procedures to account for the fact that there were no longer any backup units in the spacecraft, those procedures were incorrect. He said, "This is the kind of stuff I was worried we didn't have."

I responded, "Well, there it is, though I do have to update it and remove all the procedures that are related to the nonexistent backups. Nevertheless, the rest of the procedures are still all valid."

I called Scott, because the full-scale engineering model of the spacecraft was finished and I wanted him to come over for some PR pictures of it and us, but he said he couldn't. Then he noticed that my voice was very hoarse and I said, "Yeah, I've had the flu."

He said, "I thought I hadn't seen you around."

I said, "No, I've been working, it's just that I've been so busy I just haven't gotten over to Ames much."

He said, "Yeah, things are really moving." And I thought, *yes, and everybody knows it. Lunar Prospector is really moving. We are going to make this baby and fly it.*

It was a very good day. I got a lot done and as I told Tom on the way home, "I got about half of the stuff done I wanted to do, but it was a good day, because I got, at least, half of it done." I usually only got a quarter of the stuff done I wanted to do!

Wednesday, May 1, 1996

Al Tilley had left a note on my desk that I found when I got to work. He had found that the solar panels data had been incorrectly entered into his program. When he corrected that error, Iz was 1.07 times Ix and Iy, so we did have a good stable spacecraft! Also, the mass had come down to 288 kg and the cg was right where we wanted it. Man, those were great pieces of news. Nevertheless, I was still going to let the cg float until we had to drill the holes for the tanks in a few days. We had to have the best possible value for the cg when we did that. I really thought our mass calculations were getting very accurate. The only thing that would add some mass would be if testing showed we needed to add some stiffeners to the structure and Dougherty and Al were pretty sure that would be the case.

The PR people came over and Dougherty and I were photographed in front of the beautiful new spacecraft-engineering model.

Tom, Dan Swanson, and I went over to the graphite epoxy shop because the side panels and most all of the various brackets of the spacecraft were finished. Man, it was great to see that beautiful hardware. The cutouts for the tanks and the boom canisters in the side panels had been cut out and I asked Pat McCormick, who ran the shop, not to discard the cutout pieces so we could have them cut up to make souvenirs for everybody who worked on the spacecraft.

I finished some additions to my propellant usage program and Dan checked it against the additions that he had made to his model and they agreed, so we had two independent programs that were in good shape. They both showed, if the spacecraft's fuelled mass remained at 288 kg, we would have enough fuel for 3½ years of operations in the 100-km altitude nominal orbit. We were certainly going to lose some of that, but the mission was in great shape from the standpoint of the spacecraft's fuel.

We found out one thing that was kind of screwy: the tip plates on two of the booms had resonance frequencies in the 40 to 50 Hz range — right in the range of the pipe organ effect of the Castor 120 rocket stages! Able suggested that they add a kilo-gram of mass to them to change the frequency. What they forgot was that I would have to add the same amount of mass to the other tip plate and I was not going to take a 3 kg mass hit, even though the mass was down. Also, I didn't believe that result, I believed that when the tip plates were connected to the instruments and the booms were in their canisters, the resonance frequencies would not be in the 40 to 50 Hz range. But that was to be a topic for the next day's staff meeting.

I worked on the Mission Profile and I added in the power usage associated with each command, so the profile was getting to be quite detailed. I hoped I would soon find enough time to get it finished and then I could start updating the Mission Opera-tions Document.

Finally, I set my trip up to go to the Cape and to BJ Link for the following week.

Thursday, May 2, 1996: Subsystem Review Day

The luncheon that Henshaw had promised us for getting the 100% fee was set for the following Thursday, when I was on travel, of course. I doubted that was intention-al, but Dougherty did know I would be gone all that week.

We finalized the spacecraft design and how we were going to put it together. Then we took a final look at every aspect of the spacecraft and its construction.

George Pack came over to talk to Woody and me. He convinced us that the best way to get the most power was to extend the long strings from the upper section down into the lower sections, because the effects of the shadowing on those longer strings wasn't too bad. Then he asked if we could move the tangential engines a little so he would need only three sizes of solar cells instead of four. By doing so, he said we save $100,000, which I thought was probably a very high number. But he said there would be cost savings because the manufacturer wouldn't have to manufacture four types of cells and his staff would need only three special tools, instead of four, to mount the solar cells on the pan-els. We assumed he was correct and since we had little money, we certainly wanted to min-imize the cost of the solar panels, regardless of how much or how little the savings were.

Woody, Tom Chinn, Dan, and I began to look for a way that we could move the tangential engines without messing everything else up. When we looked at the space-craft-engineering model, we immediately saw we could achieve the desired geometry for the solar cells by just flipping the existing, tangential engine brackets 180° and put-ting a bevel on them, so the engines would be mounted at a right angle to the brackets. Tom Chinn made the engineering drawing of the new design and we found it would work if we put in some spacers to move the engines out about 1.2 cm. As luck would have it, Jim Schirle wanted some thermal isolators in there anyway, so the spacers would help with the thermal environment of the engines! Thus we had a good solution that allowed us to use just three types of solar cells and to improve the thermal balance of the system at the same time!

Given the significant cost saving by having fewer solar cells sizes in the array and because the solar panel design used one type of big cells and two types of narrow cells, I asked George Pack, "Why can't we change the design so we just use one type of the narrow cells instead of two?" He answered he didn't know if that would work. George called somewhat later in the day and said my idea would work, so we needed only two types of cells, one large and the other small, and that would save us over $100,000.

We finalized those solar array design changes, changes that were minor because the manufacturing center had not yet started fabricating the arrays, so they were only paper changes. Had they already started fabrication, we could not have made the changes.

Tilley got the spacecraft's mass down another couple of kilograms, to 286 or 287 kg, which was great, and the moments of inertia were fine. The TLI Stage was getting heavy, but it was just at the beginning of its development, so I was not worried about it. Nevertheless, we were just about at the maximum lift capability of the LLV2, so we had to keep close watch on the combined mass of the spacecraft and the TLI Stage.

Noel Hinners from Lockheed Martin in Denver called because George French had been there talking about our Outreach Program. George wanted to do a Marslink, patterned after Moonlink, for Mars Global Surveyor and Noel wanted my opinion about that. I told him George had done a great job with Moonlink and I highly recommended they do a Marslink with George. Then Noel said the next time I came up to see the LLV crew, they would like me to give a talk on Lunar Prospector. I said I would do that and that I was going to be there on Friday, so, if they could arrange a talk that quickly, I would be glad to do it then.

Friday, May 3, 1996

The LLV crew was in Sunnyvale for a review of the LLV2 Interface Control Document. They ticked me off because they did the same thing they had always done. They insisted they were just launching us into lower Earth orbit and they were not responsible in any way for the TLI Stage or the interface between it and the LLV2! They had also paid no attention, whatsoever, to the injection point information that Dave Lozier had given them for the 93° azimuth launch trajectory we had to use for safety reasons. Dave's TLI point was over the ocean just west of the bulge in West Africa and the dummies from LLV had the injection point over South Africa! As I had said numerous times before, the damned LLV crew was just going to put us into Earth orbit and they didn't even care if we were at the injection point or not. They just didn't give a damn about Lunar Prospector, just their damned rocket.

Richard was sitting next to me, so I reached over and wrote in his notebook, "Why aren't we on a Taurus?"

He wrote next to it, "We sure as hell tried." He was as frustrated with LLV as I was.

During the morning break I said to Sylvia, "Sylvia, it's the same old crap as always, I have a TLI Stage that is an orphan," and I continued to crab about LLV, so she raised hell about it too.

Of course, Dougherty didn't like my crabbing at LLV, so he was in there, kissing ass, trying to persuade LLV to do it right, like a good company man. He didn't like me ranting and raving at LLV and, as usual, when he had an audience to show off to, he said, "Now Alan, don't start making trouble." Then the minute we were alone in my office, he came on like a little puppy dog and said, "I'm trying to get them to do it right."

Monday, May 6, 1996: Subsystem Review Day

The review lasted most of the day and it was very boring, because nothing was going wrong with the spacecraft — we were very happy to be bored stiff.

Dave Lozier was upset because the stupid jerks at LLV would not do what they were supposed to. He felt they ignored his work, never paid attention to what he said at meetings and never answered his inquires (guess what David, those were the same complaints Richard and I had). The situation was so bad that Sylvia came over to discuss it with Dougherty and me; even Dougherty had to agree that something had to be done about it.

We had a telecon with LLV at 2:00 PM about the issue. Dougherty started out by saying, "Some events have upset the customer."

One of the LLV guys asked, "Do you mean the PI customer or the Ames customer?"

Dougherty answered, "The PI customer is always pissed off at you guys."

I said quietly to Dougherty, "That's telling them, Tom."

Dougherty continued with, "No, this time it's the Ames customer that is upset about the disconnect." We discussed the problem, but I didn't think LLV took it seriously.

Tom Chinn, Tom, and I went over to the graphite epoxy fabrication shop to inspect (really to admire) the trimmed up load-bearing structure, the equipment shelf and the bottom panel that were finished and they were beautiful. Since the side panels had been finished a week earlier, all the pieces of the load-bearing structure were finished and ready for assembly. Unfortunately, the technicians were not going to start putting it together for another week. The parts weren't even going to be taken over to the assembly facilities until Wednesday of the following week! We were going to lose ten days before getting the structure put together for the static test — for no apparent reason and I did not like that schedule slip.

Dougherty, Bob Garner, Tom, and I were talking about the command and downlink lists I had been working on and Dougherty, who never understood anything I did, said, "Tom, you ought to do that for Alan and explain what they are and make a nice table out of it." He added, "It has to be real simple, so the dumbest of us, like me, can understand it."

Bob, Dougherty's faithful sidekick, said, "Yeah, it will have to be in monosyllable words."

Dougherty laughed and said, "Yeah." The trouble was, it was true.

Sylvia brought over a letter from Code O that said they were not going to support Lunar Prospector, so we had to find our own way of getting Lunar Prospector tracked! I was glad I had the Air Force!

Tuesday, May 7, 1996

Because of the Code O letter, I called the Air Force and was told how to proceed and that the arrangements for the tracking had to go through Ames, not through Lockheed. I said if it would help, I would go up to Falcon on the 10th to help push the tracking request along.

I talked to Sylvia. We grumped about Lockheed, Dougherty, and the fact that NASA was already saying they were never going to let another mission be managed the way we were managing Lunar Prospector. Despite the facts that we were on schedule, on budget, that everything was going very well, and that everybody at Headquarters was amazed at our success to date, they weren't going to do it our way again! Though Headquarters did not say why they wouldn't do it our way again, I was certain there were two reasons for their stupid attitude. First, they didn't want scientists running missions. Second, Headquarters simply did not like not having total control of the missions, and in our case, they had given that control to Ames, Lockheed, and me. Despite our success, they were willing to kill the goose that was laying the golden egg, just so they could keep themselves on top of the heap.

I said to Sylvia, "Fine, we will get this done and we will do it right. We will get it done at cost and on schedule. Then I will tell Congress that NASA destroyed the concept of Discovery after we proved it worked. If they don't let scientists run the programs and instead let JPL and other NASA places run them, they won't work," (the reader might wish to look ahead at my testimony to the House Committee on Space Science in Appendix E-2, also see www.lunar-research-institute.org).

Wednesday, May 8, 1996

I had a good day and got a lot done, maybe because Dougherty was still on a trip. There were no meetings, so I got to work almost all day on the Mission Profile and on a power usage spreadsheet for the computer model of the spacecraft Dan Swanson and I were writing for training purposes. I also talked to Woody about solar cells. I had a good day, because I was able to work for a change.

Thursday, May 9, 1996: Subsystem Review Day

Dougherty was back from his trip and in his absence, the Lockheed/Lunar Prospector coffee cups had been delivered and I had given the cups to the staff. Apparently Dougherty had told Garner he wanted to give the cups out at the Henshaw luncheon that had been postponed until that day. When Dougherty came to work, he said something about his cups and I said, "Gee, I'm the PI, so they are my cups and I already gave them out." I thought that little spiel was very funny, but Dougherty didn't.

We had the final review of the spacecraft's drawings. The only things that were outstanding were a few issues regarding the instruments, mainly the APS. For most purposes, the LLV2's third stage, the Orbit Adjustment Module, and the LLV2's payload (Lunar Prospector and the TLI Stage) would be in space when the shroud was ejected. However, there is still enough tenuous atmosphere at that altitude that we had to worry about the free molecular heating. Basically, a delicate surface could get hot enough to be damaged by the free molecular heating. In the case of Lunar Prospector, we had a potential problem with just one item: the very thin and delicate light shields covering the detectors of the APS. We were trying to design a little mechanical shield to protect the upper surface (+Z side) of the APS during the free molecular heating phase after the shroud popped.

We started talking about the shake test of the booms down at Able and I said, "I assume we are going down to watch the tests."

Dougherty said, "They don't need any spectators."

I said, "I have news for you, Tom, this is my spacecraft and those are my booms and I am going down to watch the tests."

At the end of the meeting, I mentioned that Lunar Prospector was 17 months from launch and I thanked everybody for helping build my little spacecraft. Dougherty said something about it being a Lockheed spacecraft and complained about the science payload. I said, "No, this is my spacecraft, it is my mission, and I am getting tired of this BS. Also Tom, one of these days you are going to have to realize that this spacecraft was designed to take instruments to the Moon and that is why we are building it and not for Lockheed." I stayed on his case all day, reminding him about whose mission it was, whose spacecraft it was, and whose cups they were.

I talked to the Air Force and they were going to proceed with their tracking Lunar Prospector. The Air Force would have to make some modifications to its stations in order to track us, but that was really up to Pete Worden. I set up a meeting at Falcon on June 10 for Tim Bridges, Marcie Smith, and me. The meeting was to be at the end of my trip to Los Alamos and Albuquerque. I was fairly optimistic about the Air Force tracking us, but everyone else was not quite as optimistic as I was.

Everyone went to Henshaw's pizza lunch. Dougherty got up and made a little speech and nobody clapped at all. Then he said, "Alan, do you want to say anything?" but before I could say a word, he added, "No, OK, that's good." Despite his insult, I stood up and I again thanked everybody for doing a great job building my little spacecraft and all the engineers clapped. Then Frank got up and said blah, blah, blah and the guys applauded a little bit — but it really stood out that nobody applauded for Dougherty. Then we had the big pizza award luncheon!

Richard told me he got a job with Orbital Sciences and would be leaving Lockheed very soon!

We called LLV for a telecon at 2:00 PM. Richard said after we had reviewed the LLV2 Interface Control Document, the chief engineer on the LLV2 was ticked off to high heaven at his staff. He was mad because the document was sloppy, because it was less than 50% finished instead of being at least 90% finished by the time of the review, because they had ticked me off again, and because Sylvia had just raised holy hell with them. All of the sudden, everyone was really getting sensitive to the fact that LLV was not treating Lunar Prospector properly, and their higher management was raising holy hell. It was about time.

Chapter 3-15
The C&DH Turns On

Friday, May 10, 1996

Dougherty told me that Larry Price was coming down for a meeting. He said he didn't want to exclude me from the meeting (which was not true), but he wanted to sit down with Richard, Larry, and John Uselman (who had been assigned by LLV to be the interface between them and us, and who was a source of many of our problems with LLV) to try and straighten out the communications mess before I dealt with Larry. Dougherty was really getting on their case. Everybody was getting on their case. I said that would be OK.

I got a lot done on the propellant usage model and added in the effects of the drops in the pressure due to the lines, the PIV, and the filters; so the model was getting very accurate. Then I started work on version 4.3 of the Mission Profile.

Dougherty came in my office and said, "Guess what!"

I said, "Well, now what?"

He said, "The C&DH works!" (Dougherty was speaking about the engineering model — the C&DH was the only electronics unit for which we built an engineering test model, all the other units were built directly as flight units.)

I said, "Great." Then I went to Gerry to congratulate him. I said, "Gerry, I heard that we've got a C&DH that works. I want to thank you personally for giving me a good C&DH."

I thought he was secretly pleased, but Gerry, being Gerry, didn't like to be complimented and said, "Yeah, it works, but it still has bugs in it. It will only take one command and then it won't do anymore, but at least it works." Even if Gerry did not want to be complimented, he had just made a big step forward.

The spacecraft assembly was expected to start the following week. The parts were going to be transferred over to the assembly area for the static tests on Wednesday, unfortunately, about a week late, but that was not too bad. The instruments were a little behind schedule. Bill was in the process of testing the GRS housing; if that went well, he would start its final assembly. The changes we made to the MAG extension boom configuration had slowed things up for the MAG/ER. And we had to fool around with a mechanical way of shielding the APS. I expected that the science instruments would be finished in a couple of months, so we would be just a little bit behind schedule, but not enough to worry about.

Sunday, May 12, 1996

I talked to Bill Feldman about the shake test they had done Friday on the GRS housing. They took it up to 12½ g's and the photomultiplier tubes were fine. Bill said that during one of the tests, there was a change in the resonance frequency from about 90 Hz down to 50 Hz, which indicated that something must have cracked. They were going to dismantle the housing and see what in hell had happened to it. I didn't like the sound of that, but we would soon find out what had happened.

Twelve and one-half g's is a lot of g's, but that was what we had to deal with because of that stupid launch vehicle. Actually, it was worse than that; Bill said the LLV2 loads were supposed to go up to 25 g's and, as he said, "There is no way the GRS can take that."

I also told Bill we might have problems with the light filters or foils on the APS detectors due to the free molecular heating after the shroud popped off. I wanted him to really look into getting rid of those damned, delicate aluminized films and deposit the aluminum filter directly on the detectors the way it was done during the Apollo missions. He was going to check that out. I hoped it would work, because it would save us a lot of fooling around trying to design a little shield for the APS.

Monday, May 13, 1996: Subsystem Review Day

Bill called and said the GRS housing seemed to be OK and they thought the change in the resonance frequency had occurred because one of the phenolic spacers around one of the eight bolts that held the GRS to the shaker (and eventually to its boom) had been loose. We decided to replace the spacers with two bars with four bolt holes each to hold the GRS on its tip plate. Anyway, Bill was going to send the housing back to Lockheed so we could x-ray it to see if it was OK. If it was OK, then Bill was going to put the GRS together with the improved mounting configuration.

We also talked about the APS foils some more. Jim Schirle was worried that the rapid heating and cooling caused by the constant changing from full sunlight to darkness during every 5-second spin period and during the 118-minute day/night orbital cycle would quickly destroy the thin little light filters. Bill still wanted to use the foils and he said he would do some tests in a thermal solar simulator and a vacuum chamber to see if the foils would be OK.

Then there were problems with the software and with the dynamic spacecraft computer model. The main problems were that the software guys didn't understand that the model wasn't as big a deal as they thought it was and I didn't think they were very competent. Regardless, we had to have the spacecraft model to train on and I would get it done one way or another.

We had a meeting with the LLV guys; John Uselman did not understand that they had to do the trajectory up to the TLI injection point, but we finally got that hammered out. The other problem was that he didn't understand what Richard and I were talking about when we said there was only about ten minutes between the LLV2's third stage burnout and our TLI burn, so there was not much time for the Orbit Adjust Module to do its thing and I was worried about that.

Also, we were back down to zero money reserves.

Tuesday, May 14, 1996

We had a meeting about the computer model of the spacecraft that lasted most of the day and, of course, Bill Jacobsen and his software guys weren't prepared to do anything but a static model and hardly even that. I really didn't expect that the Lockheed software people would do anything useful. Dan Swanson and I discussed our dynamic model needs and Dan did a good job of discussing his requirements.

Dougherty was in a Gold-team meeting, so we didn't have to put up with him. However, Jacobsen had been whining to Dougherty about the amount of work I expected from him and his team, so I expected Dougherty would "try to straighten me out" the next day. I was hoping he would try.

Wednesday, May 15, 1996: Spectrum Astro Site Visit

Dougherty, Sylvia, Scott, Tom, and I flew to Phoenix to visit Spectrum Astro for an on-site-review of the C&DH, mainly because Scott wanted to start seeing hardware. We were there for just a couple of hours for the Dog and Pony Show. It went quite well and Dougherty behaved himself (well, pretty much).

Gerry Grismore called us while we were over there and said they had just gotten the C&DH engineering model to work completely successfully and miraculously on the very day it was scheduled to be fully operational! That was great news and it made Spectrum Astro really happy to hear it while we were there. They were a little bit behind schedule on the construction of the C&DH flight unit, but they probably would be able to make the time up because they could use some of the breadboard boards for the C&DH.

The trip was not very useful, but necessary and tiring.

Wednesday, May 16, 1996: Staff Meeting Day

We discussed the GRS housing and apparently there was nothing wrong with it. We believed that when Bill and his crew did the tests on the first two axes, the housing was correctly tightened down on the test equipment, but since they couldn't get a torque wrench in there, they used a different tool, so there was a question about the amount of torque that was applied to the bolts. Then, when they were going to test the third axis, the technician who had set it up to test the first two axes left, and somebody else mounted it. As a result, we didn't think the bolts were properly torqued down, especially because one of them was loose after the test. That would explain the sudden shift in the fundamental frequency of about 90 Hz to 50 Hz. Even so, we were going to have the housing looked at with a thermal probe to see if it was OK.

Also, when Bill had dismantled the GRS, the rubber cushioning material that lined the cup holding the BGO crystal had deformed and Bill was going to ask Bicron to take a look at that material.

We looked at the results of a stress test we had done on the inserts that would be mounted in the graphite epoxy covered honeycomb of the side panels where we would fasten the boom canisters to the panels. The inserts were in bad shape and had torn loose. As we were inspecting them, Dougherty made some comment about how important the test was, so I said, "Gee, Tom, if I remember correctly, you are the one who said we didn't need to do this test." He laughed. He is an idiot. But, as a result of the test, we concluded we would have to strengthen the side panels in the areas around the canisters by putting a double layer of graphite epoxy there, and we would also put double inserts in there.

Frank told me something very nice. He said when Henshaw's people first came to Sunnyvale and we gave them our overview of Lunar Prospector, the consensus of opinion (behind our backs) was there was no way in hell we could do the program as fast and as cheaply as we said. Then, a day or so ago, one of those guys told Frank he was amazed at what we had been doing. They would have never believed that one could do a program the way we were doing it and they could never have done it back in East Windsor. Well, that was a very nice compliment.

Friday, May 17, 1996

Dougherty and I went over to Ames for a meeting with Scott about the Outreach Program. Scott was fussing because George French was going to make money on it. I said, "For Pete's sake Scott, it's a good Outreach Program and it's privately funded, what is the problem?" I was getting annoyed with Scott; NASA kept saying it wanted to commercialize some of its activities and as soon as you start to do it, they wet their pants.

I found out what the length of the fuel lines beyond the PIV was going to be and calculated that we would have about 120 cubic centimeters of volume in those lines. I calculated that when I opened the PIV after launch, there would be a 1 psi drop in the tank pressure. That was too small of a drop for me to detect in the telemetry, since the resolution of the pressure transducer was two or three times that. That was too bad, since it would have been nice if I could have detected that pressure drop and I would have known if the PIV was open and not have to find that out when I tried to fire the engines for the first time!

I went home early to give an Outreach Talk at a local school. I had been asked to give a talk at Career Day at one of the local grade schools for 4th, 5th, and 6th graders. I gave two presentations to the kids and they were very bright and they had very good questions. I was very impressed.

The librarian said she had written a letter to me in care of Gene Beley and it had come back. She had read the article in the *Country News* and she wanted to know if I would give a talk to her gifted class of 66 students. I said I would do it the following Wednesday morning.

Monday, May 20, 1996: Trouble with the Software Staff

I went up to Berkeley with Scott for a site visit. We looked at all the hardware they were beginning to assemble. Unfortunately, they had burned up one of the transformers in the ER, but they were fixing that. Scott, Bob Lin, Dave Curtis, Paul Turin, and I had a good session.

One thing of particular interest was that Bob, who was very impressed at how well Lunar Prospector was working with a PI in charge and with a minimum of bureaucracy and reporting, wanted to know if Lockheed was going to continue doing missions like that. We discussed the issue and I said the PI had to take full responsibility for the mission and be in residence at Lockheed for it to work. Scott had pretty much the same opinion as I had on those key requirements. As to what Lockheed would do — I didn't have a clue.

I went to Palo Alto to talk to Bill Jacobsen, who is an absolute can't-do-guy instead of a can-do-guy, about the command and telemetry list I had been working on and that I had gotten straightened out. He knew nothing about the commands and telemetry and couldn't do anything about them and wanted to make sure that we didn't have too much work for him and his crew! He was really just as useless as hell! I was very disappointed and I would have to talk to Alex about the software mess.

Tom had also had a long talk with Jacobsen and also found out that he was useless. Tom went to Dougherty and he too said that Jacobsen is not the one to do anything. Why in hell didn't he get someone who would actually do some work?

I drove back to Lockheed, but Alex had gone home and hardly anyone else was there. Dougherty, Richard, and a number of the other engineers had gone to the Cape for the Critical Design Review of Pad 46.

I found Kim Foster and talked with him, because we were getting ready to start the static test of the load-bearing structure, though we were unfortunately about two weeks behind schedule. I told Kim I wanted to be involved with all of the tests and he said, "Of course, I assumed you would." As far as I was concerned, the best way I had of really knowing my spacecraft was to pay attention to all the tests.

There was one troubling thing; I was beginning to think that Tom was never going to know the spacecraft and the mission well enough to serve as my deputy during the flight phase. Tom was in the midst of getting a divorce and starting a new relationship with our scheduler, Shelley Louis, and as a result of both, he was not able to concentrate on learning all the things he had to know cold to fly the spacecraft. I hoped that after his divorce and after his personal life got more settled, he would be able to concentrate on the job ahead. I valued Tom's friendship and help immensely and wanted to have him be part of the mission through to its very end. Other than that concern, Tom was doing an excellent job in every way, so I was not displeased, just concerned about his future.

Finally, everybody had gone home, so I went home and finished working on the C&DH lists.

Tuesday, May 21, 1996

A quiet day, Dougherty was gone. Actually most of our people were gone on travel or were involved in a review of another Lockheed program. Because it was so quiet, I got a lot of work done on the command and downlink lists.

Wednesday, May 22, 1996:
Headquarters Reopens the Launch Issue — Again

I gave a talk to a local grade school's gifted class of 4th, 5th, and 6th graders in the morning. It was amazing how much the kids knew; they even knew things from the earliest day of the space program, nearly three decades before they were even born! Every one of their questions was good. For example, one kid wanted to know if it was true that NASA had studied how to use atomic bombs to launch rockets; that was true, it was the Orion Program. They wanted to know if I thought that there was life on Mars and one asked if the Space Station was going to be any good — I answered, maybe to the first question and no to the second. I had a lot of fun with the kids.

I got to work at about 10:00 AM and immediately talked to Alex about the software issues. As a result, we got the commands straightened out and then I put them into the new version of the Mission Profile. With that done and with the commands straightened out, I started to work on the Mission Operations Document.

Tom came by and said Shelley told him we were getting behind schedule, which I already knew, but Shelley had it in black and white on her tracking schedule. The load-bearing structure was supposed to have been fully assembled and ready for static testing over two weeks earlier and its assembly was still slipping!

I talked to Dougherty about the slip and he said, "What slip?" I didn't know if he was trying to hide the slip, which would have been stupid because he knew I knew the truth, or if he was just playing games. At first, I thought it was a little bit of both. But he was very submissive during our short discussion, so I suspected he was probably trying to hide the obvious; the guy amazed me at times.

Sylvia called. The idiots at Headquarters had started on the launch vehicle again. Karen Poniatowski, who is largely responsible for launch vehicles at Headquarters and who hates Lockheed, said she wanted to have the contract rewritten to include a no-first-launch-clause and we had to wait for the CRSS launch. Then Headquarters crabbed about the tracking issue and insisted there be no reduction in the amount of science data obtained. In other words, they wanted to fix it so we could not get launched on time, that we would have inadequate tracking, thus making it impossible to get all the science — and then they were going to complain about the lack of science! As far I was concerned, the main requirement for working at Headquarters was to be a certified idiot!

The closer the LLV2 got to being fully developed, the smaller its calculated lift capability became (as anyone with more than two brain cells rattling around in their head should know from the previous several decades of rocketry — by then, it looked like the LLV2 would be less capable than the Taurus). As a result, Karen Poniatowski had said, "Maybe we should launch you guys on a Taurus."

That appropriately ticked Scott off and he said, "No way. You are not going to put us on a Taurus at this stage of the game." What a bunch of idiots!

Tom and I went over and saw the guys who were setting up the alignment tool for Lunar Prospector, but they hadn't started the alignment yet. It was amazing to see exactly how they were going to make all the measurements and do the alignment. Things were moving, but we were still behind schedule by a couple weeks.

Thursday, May 23, through Monday, May 27, 1996 (Memorial Day): JSC and the New York NSS Meeting

I left San Jose at about noon on Thursday and flew to Houston.

Friday I talked to John Connolly and Kent Joosten. They seemed to be on track with their plans to get man back to the Moon by 2001. The first mission was to go to the crater Aristarchus instead of an equatorial site. They had convinced Goldin not to go to the Poles to look for the water ice that Lunar Prospector was supposed to find right away, but to have an unmanned mission, perhaps the LunaCorp rover, do a polar ice mission first. LunaCorp had apparently gotten the promise of a launch from Mitsubishi, so if NASA could provide the instruments for the rover, then LunaCorp would be ready to go! If so, it would be the first commercial lunar mission — it sounded good to me.

I then flew on to New York, which I think is a rotten place, and gave my talk at the National Space Society meeting. The crowd at my talk was not very big; most of the people were interested in the space commercialization and space tourism talks. I was a little disappointed because the attendees were more interested in futuristic talks about how they might get into space rather than about a real mission.

George French was there and we talked about how things were going, the problems with NASA vacillating about the launch vehicle and the tracking.

I flew home on Sunday. It was a very tiring trip. Monday, Memorial Day, I just stayed home and rested up.

Tuesday, May 28, 1996

With Richard leaving, we needed to find someone to take his place as our Launch Vehicle Engineer, and Dougherty had suggested that Francisco take on the job. Despite my liking Francisco and respecting his intelligence very much, I was very skeptical about his ability to handle that very important job. Despite Richard's shortcomings, he is aggressive and had not let LLV run him over. In contrast, I was concerned that LLV would bulldoze Francisco, who has a mild temperament. I told Dougherty that Francisco was just not going to be able to handle LLV. Scott and Sylvia felt the same way.

Later, Sylvia and I started discussing an upcoming review meeting for Headquarters and I suggested we have it at Ames. I told Sylvia I didn't want Dougherty to talk about any of the technical issues since he didn't know anything about them. She seemed to agree.

Later, Dougherty got involved with the conversation and said to me, "Make sure you get the science stuff done right. Make sure that you know everything that is going on and that you know what the problems are." That series of stupid comments was the result of some combination of A) his stupidity, B) his thinking that he is smarter than everybody else, C) his trying to be funny, and D) his just being an idiot. As usual, I just ignored him. The guy has sawdust for brains.

I called Bill a couple of times because I couldn't find Warren Hoskins to see if the tests on the GRS housing had gone well or not and to verify that Bill could start the final assembly of the GRS. That was frustrating — that should have been nailed down a couple of days earlier.

Bill and I also talked about the APS foils he had tested to see if they could stand the heat cycling Jim Schirle was worried about. Bill and I had incorrectly thought Jim was worried about the thermal effects of the 5-second spin period, but Jim's main concern was the thermal effects of the 118-minute day/night cycle. Schirle wanted Bill to do a 48-day/night-cycle test that would be equivalent to about 4 days in orbit.

We talked a little bit about possible ways of shielding the APS foils from the free molecular heating, without resolving the issue. Since protecting the APS was an instrument issue and not a critical spacecraft issue, I wanted him to take the lead on that problem and solve it.

Wednesday, May 29, 1996

Dougherty, Sylvia, Scott, and I had a meeting over at Ames to discuss the upcoming meeting with a few of the Headquarters guys on June 20. I was sick of Dougherty's stupidity and arrogance and I didn't want him to screw it up by trying and failing to explain the technical issues. The only things I wanted him to talk about were the schedule, the costs, and Lockheed management.

I was going to discuss the science data and objectives to try to finally get the Headquarters managers, who didn't really understand much of anything, to understand them and then discuss the spacecraft, the mission, and Mission Ops. I wanted Marcie to talk a little about Mission Ops, too. The main thing was to keep Dougherty from sticking his big foot in his big mouth as much as possible.

Scott wanted to have some of the subsystem engineers talk, but I thought that was a waste of time. The meeting was not supposed to be a big Headquarters review, though Dougherty, Scott, and Sylvia kept moving it in that direction.

Dougherty, of course, was trying to keep me completely out of the launch vehicle issue and he didn't want me at the LLV2 review meeting on the 19th in Denver. He wanted Larry Price to talk with just Sylvia and him. I had had enough of that and was going to tell Sylvia and Scott that there would be no more secret meetings between them, Dougherty, and LLV.

I went over to see what was going on with the spacecraft. The technicians were getting further behind! Jeff told me the three brackets (or "feet" as we called them) that were the attachment points between the spacecraft and the TLI Stage and that held the explosive bolts and the bolt catchers, were incorrectly designed and incorrectly made of aluminum. Jeff said the feet should have had recessed conical alignment points in their upper surfaces to allow exact repositioning of the spacecraft every time it was removed from the TLI Stage. Instead they were flat with cylindrical (explosive) bolt holes. He also pointed out that the aluminum would quickly score with use, so the feet should have been made out of stainless steel. As a result, they had lost the alignment they had been working on! They would have to start all over again after the feet were modified to have — at least — stainless steel bushings put in them.

All that worried me because there were a lot of little errors like those, so we were getting further and further behind. We were a good month behind schedule at that point. That had to be discussed at the staff meeting the next day.

All of that was very tiring. I am convinced that most Project Managers are incompetent. They are just big bags of wind who found out they were not very good at engineering and decided to work their way into management where they could make lots of money without having to really do anything except shoot off their big mouths (characteristically, most NASA and Lockheed managers I know are physically large men with booming voices, who can just shout down their opposition — being right has nothing to do with it, they just have to be big, loud, and ready to protect themselves and their companies — at all cost). Since the managers are technically incompetent and can't manage (they have no training as managers, just as incompetent engineers), they form a self-preserving managerial clique in which everyone looks out after the other guys. Their philosophy seems to be, "If you don't tell on me, I won't tell on you and we will all make out like bandits." They just sit there, loudly huffing and puffing and faking their way through the programs on the backs of a few competent engineers. Under their management, spacecrafts are developed and built by a hit and miss process, just like the process a ping pong ball goes through when one throws it into the top of a wide mouthed funnel. It just bounces around in the funnel until it loses enough energy to fall through the hole at the bottom. The bounces represent the trial and error way they attempt to solve the problems and each bounce represents wasted time and money.

Using that ping pong ball and funnel analogy, I decided the way programs had to be run (the way I was trying to run Lunar Prospector) was to have a small group of competent people sit down and figure out what to do and just do it — or in the ping pong ball analogy — take the ball, carefully align it over the exit hole of the funnel and drop it straight thought the hole without having it touch the sides of the funnel. In contrast, the aerospace and NASA managers just throw the ball into the funnel and let it bounce around until it finally gets out the bottom and that is just pathetic. If the American aerospace industry and NASA doesn't change, everything is just going to continue to get worse.

Chapter 3-16
Getting Way Behind Schedule

Thursday, May 30, 1996: Staff Meeting Day

There were several issues; one was the problem with the aluminum feet Jeff had told me would score when we mounted and dismounted the spacecraft. We had a big discussion about that. We decided we would take the risk and leave them the way they were, making sure they were always protected as best we could and have Jeff build the new tools he needed to get the alignment done the way the feet were.

We talked about the top of the triangular load-bearing structure, which was not very flat. We could leave it that way and just screw the top shelf down onto it, but that would deform the structure and destroy the accurate alignment Jeff and his guys were in the process of very carefully doing. That would also put additional stresses on the structure and would not be good for the spacecraft during launch. That was out.

We considered putting aluminum shims in between the shelf and the top of the structure at every bolt connection, which would be perfect, except it would take a lot of work.

The third alternative was just to shim the structure with aluminum shims until the top was flat at the points where the three vertical longerons connected to the top of the load-bearing structure, and then put liquid shim in everywhere else. We decided that was the best solution, since we were going to glue the top shelf to the structure anyway, as well as bolt it down.

Jim Schirle had a problem with the antennas getting too cold, so we discussed it. Later in the afternoon, Jim Beffa and one of his engineers came over and Schirle, Beffa, his guy, and I discussed the antenna thermal problem. Schirle suggested we add a 6 watt heater (6 watts — that's enough to roast a pig with an apple in its mouth) to the antennas, but Beffa was vehemently against the idea (the heaters would add electronic noise to the antenna's signals) and we decided Schirle would use foam insulation to keep them warm.

Dougherty went with Ralph Fullerton, our Quality Assurance Engineer, to Goddard to pester Mario and Mario didn't like that at all. Dougherty didn't even know what the MAG and the MAG/ER DPU were or what they did, so how was he going to inspect them? He really wanted to go to Goddard to try to show Mario that he, Dougherty, was in charge and that Mario had better acknowledge that. Since Mario is much smarter, more competent, and more experienced than Dougherty, just how smart was it for Dougherty to go to Goddard and try to show Mario up?

I went over to Ames to talk with Sylvia about a number of things. First was our concern about the Launch Vehicle Engineer because we didn't think Francisco could handle the job. Then I told her I was sick and tired of Dougherty keeping me in the dark about the rocket issues and that there were going to be no more telecons or telephone conversations without me involved. She agreed. Finally, regarding the review for the Headquarters wienies on the 20th or 21st, I said I was going to review most of the issues because, in addition to the fact that Dougherty didn't understand any of the technical issues, I wanted to make it clear to the Headquarters guys that Lunar Prospector was my program, not NASA's, and certainly not Lockheed's. Again, Sylvia understood and agreed.

Friday, May 31, 1996

Dougherty was gone. Tom was gone. I set up my weeklong trip to Los Alamos and Denver. I was going to stay with my good friends, David and Laurie Weaver, in Albuquerque, attend the *Space 96 Conference,* and just drive up to Los Alamos to see Bill. Then I would fly on to Colorado to see Pete Worden and Ron Humble in Colorado Springs, and then to Denver to give my talk at Lockheed Denver and to take my tour at the Denver facilities.

Other than that, I didn't get much done all day; it was just one of those days where I didn't get anything done and I was concerned because the static test was still slipping.

Sunday, June 2, through Friday, June 7, 1996:
Another Trip — Albuquerque, Colorado Springs, and Denver

I flew to Albuquerque on Sunday and met John Gruener who was there for the *Space 96 Conference* and who was staying with this mother and stepdad as usual. As planned, John and I drove to the Malpais lava flows at Grants, NM, one of my favorite volcanic regions since my graduate student days in the 60s and, since I introduced John to the Malpais a few years earlier, one of his too. We hiked around a sandstone bluff at the edge of the flow a little bit, trying to get down to the flow, but couldn't find a way down. Then we hiked down the Indian Trail a little bit and finally went to our motel rooms and slept. The next morning we hiked on the lava flows and went over to the lava tunnels on their west side and explored them. We had a great time.

While John and I were tromping around the lava fields Monday, Tom was back in Houston getting his divorce. With that finally behind him, I hoped he would be able to settle down and start learning all the things he had to know if he was going to be able to be my second in command during Mission Operations. Given the importance of his doing so, I was going to really push him hard to concentrate on the operational phase of the mission.

John and I drove back to Albuquerque and I went to the Weavers where I was going to spend the night. We — John, the Weavers, several of our JSC friends and ex-coworkers, and I — all went to a baseball game.

Early Tuesday morning I saw on the TV news that the Ariane V blew up, taking with it 4 cluster satellites — a half a billion-dollar fireball! That was the first launch of an Ariane V and I was very worried that its failure was going to make NASA even more nervous about first launches in general and my launch on the first LLV2 specifically. I was quite certain NASA would stop me from launching on October 9 and make me wait for CRSS.

After that bad news, I drove up to Los Alamos to see Bill. We went over to watch the technicians assemble the NS/APS unit and we got some neat pictures of it being put together. It was being assembled for its tests, after which it would be taken apart, inspected, and then reassembled for flight. Nevertheless, there it was and it was beautiful.

We went through the spectrometer command list and straightened them out. For example, I had forgotten that we had a back up high voltage supply in the GRS, so I had to add extra commands to allow us to switch between the high voltage supplies and then there was another command that was missing. We got all that straightened out and then we called Ron Black at Southwest Research to verify all the command and downlink data.

After that, I drove back down to Albuquerque and took Dave and Laurie out for a nice dinner. We chatted about Lunar Prospector, the space program, and Dave's work. David had just got a job at Vinson & Elkins in Houston and Laurie was pregnant with their third child.

Wednesday, I went to the *Space 96 Meeting* and gave my talk. There weren't as many people at the meeting, perhaps half as many as in the past. Things were getting slow in the space business. Everybody liked my talk.

A young lady reporter for the UPI interviewed me. She said she had heard a lot of talks during the past few days, but I was the only one who was really enthusiastic about what I was doing. She wanted to get a personal interview and find out why I was so excited about Lunar Prospector. She wanted to know my history and how I got into space exploration. I told her my history in the business.

A day or two later, Rebecca saw on the TV news, "Scientist Alan Binder from Gilroy is building a spacecraft to go to the Moon." I suspected that the UPI article had appeared in several papers and San Francisco's Channel 4 had picked it up.

I also met Alan Hale of Hale-Bopp comet fame at the meeting.

That evening I flew up to Colorado Springs.

I met Ron Humble for breakfast Thursday morning and then we met with Brian Lomnis to talk about the tracking issues and Blue Moon. Like Lunar Prospector, Blue Moon was a very good demonstration of the use of simple technology. For example, Ron was using Windows, DOS, and a commercial computer in his spacecraft! What Ron was doing was very neat. We were trying hard to get his mission going and I was going to try to set up a meeting with Pete Warden in two weeks to get him behind Blue Moon.

After that, Ron and I had lunch and then I drove down to Eagle Picher. The visit to Eagle Picher was a total waste of time. They had not even started building the batteries, because we did not need them at that point in time. They were planning to start in a couple of months. I gave them some PR materials and left.

Then I went to see the Seven Falls, which I had seen on a family vacation when I was a little kid. It was really nice seeing them again.

The next morning, I drove up to Denver and met with Larry Price and John Uselman. I first sat down with Larry and told him about my many concerns and annoyances and the fact that we had an adversarial, rather than a can-do, relationship with them. I said I had not had much time to spend on the rocket issues because I was trying to get my spacecraft built the way I wanted it built. However, since the spacecraft was in construction and because Richard wasn't going to be there any longer, I was going to spend more time on the rocket. I also told him that Dougherty is full of crap and is technically incompetent, that I was not pleased with the way things were going and that I was their customer, not NASA. Larry said, "Gee, that's strange, because Tom always refers to you as the customer."

I said, "Well, he may say that to you, but he surely doesn't say it to me." Then Larry added that he always thought Dougherty was his customer and I was Dougherty's customer. I said, "Well, Lockheed treats me as the customer when it's to their advantage and like their employee the rest of the time."

I then started to tell him about the Al Smith meeting and he said, "Yeah, I know about Al Smith telling you that you had better remember you are a Lockheed employee and therefore, you couldn't do what you wanted with the rocket."

I reminded him of the meeting that he, Dougherty, Uselman, and Richard had about building a team and that it hadn't worked. Larry said he remembered that meeting and said, "Well, you know, we really didn't mean to exclude you, but we just felt it was a Lockheed employee thing and we didn't want to wash our dirty laundry in front of you."

I immediately said, "Wait a minute, remember, I am a Lockheed employee." Then he began to see what I meant about my being the customer or an employee when it was convenient for them.

As expected, he (pretended to?) agreed with every one of my complaints and he said he didn't want to make excuses, but then tried to explain why some of those things had occurred.

After Larry and I finished our discussion, John Uselman showed me the Titan, Centaur, and Atlas rockets and their facilities. After that, he and I had lunch and John queried me about a number of the same issues Larry and I had discussed. I told him the same things I had told Larry and he agreed with me, especially about the fact that Dougherty knows absolutely nothing about technical issues. I felt pretty good about that.

I flew home and Rebecca picked me up at 10:30 PM; we got home just after midnight on Saturday morning. It was a very, very good trip. I had accomplished a lot and I was especially pleased about my meetings with Larry Price and John Uselman.

Monday, June 10, 1996: NASA is Ticked Off

As Tom and I drove to work, he told me that NASA was mad at me about the interview that I had with the young lady from the UPI in Albuquerque. When we got to work, I got a copy of it. The reporter misquoted me as saying, since I wanted to go to the Moon but Lunar Prospector was too small for that, I would cut my finger off and send it to the Moon in the spacecraft and that really ticked NASA off. In reality, she had said that as a joke after I had said I had unsuccessfully applied to be an Apollo astronaut and still wanted to go to the Moon. I had laughed at her joke and thought nothing of it.

Headquarters also had a cow because I had told her what I had told my engineers, i.e., "Lunar Prospector is supposed to be an interesting and fun program to work on. If you are not having fun, then go find another program to work on that is fun." The reporter had distorted that into, "If people didn't like working on my program, they should quit." In addition she had several other errors in the article; they included the wrong launch date, my incorrect age at launch, her incorrectly describing the spacecraft as cone shaped, and her incorrectly saying that we were going to take pictures of the Moon.

I was not particularly disturbed by her numerous errors and misquotes (in all the years I have been in this business, I have essentially never seen an article without those types of errors), but I was ticked off at Headquarters for reacting badly to the article. One would think that after 40 some years of seeing misquotes and news media errors that the NASA wienies would have enough brains to know that reporters essentially always mess up interviews and press releases. But no, they are so afraid of their own shadows they wet their pants at every error. They make me sick and because I was mad at their stupidity, I was going to see Scott as soon as our weekly subsystem review was over.

The main issue at the review was the fact that we were about six weeks behind schedule in putting the spacecraft together. Dougherty denied that and justified his denial by the sleight of hand trick of just changing the schedule so it appeared that we were only two weeks behind! Nevertheless, the spacecraft was supposed to have been done six weeks earlier.

As soon as the review was over, I went to see Scott. Both he and Sylvia were annoyed about the news report because Headquarters had raised hell about the interview. I told them about the interview and all the errors and misquotes that the reporter had made and I said I was annoyed with NASA because the whole thing was ridiculous. I said, "I can't change the fact that they (reporters) are going to make mistakes and they are going to distort what I say." Scott countered by implying that maybe I should con-sider not saying much to reporters. That annoyed me and I said, "I'm not going to go out there and say nothing. I am supposed to go out there and generate interest in these (Discovery) missions and help promote NASA and that is what I am doing and the peo-ple like what I do. There are all those people out there behind Lunar Prospector and if I don't say anything, we will lose them."

Scott said arrogantly, "Well they're not the ones who are paying for it, NASA is pay-ing for it."

I said, "Scott, that is simply not true, these are taxpayers, they are the ones that are paying for it and they are interested in it."

He said haughtily, "They are only paying indirectly, it's NASA money."

I said, "Crap, it is their money and their mission. You know Scott, you should real-ize that because of the work I have done all these years on Lunar Prospector and because Lunar Prospector was a grassroots effort for most of those years, people are very interested in the mission and in what I am doing to get it done," and that sort of ended the combative part of our discussion.

The trouble was that Scott and Sylvia were scared to death of Headquarters, just like all the rest of the NASA wienies. They think Headquarters is omnipotent and they are always worried about every little thing that could get them in trouble with the mighty Gods in Washington. Nevertheless, Scott realized that neither he nor Headquar-ters were going to intimidate me, so he lightened up (or just changed tactics to save face) and said he actually found the whole thing intrinsically funny and he was just annoyed because Headquarters was annoyed. Then he tried to make a joke out of it by saying, "Let me see your hands and count your fingers," which I thought was as stupid as the UPI reporter's original remark.

He got a little serious again and said that because Headquarters was so sensitive, I should be careful. I said, "Scott, there is no way I can be careful. Let's get real about this. The only articles that have been error free are the ones I have had a chance to check before they were published and that is the truth." As far as I was concerned, tough luck!

I told Scott about my discussions with the Air Force and with Larry and John at Denver. Regarding the latter, I said I had told Larry the problem was that they were not performing and Scott asked me if Larry had given me any promises about how that would be corrected and I said no. I said, "Basically, Larry said they would get the job done and they wanted to support the mission; but he said nothing concrete. He was just waltzing around the issues, so I told him the damned rocket is nowhere near where it is supposed to be at this time."

I then told Scott we were six weeks behind schedule and Dougherty was trying, in vain, to hide that from me by claiming we were only two weeks behind, i.e., he kept changing the schedule! I gave Scott several more examples of those types of problems and Sylvia backed me up, though she seemed reluctant to do so and that surprised me.

Scott said, "Well, we have these problems and we have to really find out what is going on," which indicated to me he thought I might just be grumping about little things.

I said, "Fine, let's go find out what is going on."

He said, "What we need to do is to get all the principals in a room and see who is the liar."

I answered, "The liar is Dougherty. I think what Dougherty is doing is trying to protect himself, the company, and the $4 million fee. Dougherty does not want to have that fee start going away because there is a rule in Lockheed that if you don't get 90% or more of the fee two times in row, they replace you as Project Manager."

We talked about those issues some more and Scott indicated that NASA was on his case, so he was worried about his own career and blah, blah, blah. I was annoyed by his reluctant attitude, but I was dealing with two big organizations with hidden agendas and there was not much I could do about it; but he had been warned about the problems, whether he wanted to believe me or not.

I then said to him, "I've been able to keep the spacecraft in good shape because I know the spacecraft and the mission, but now we are getting into Test and Integration and these are not areas where I have a lot of experience, so I am not going to be able to contain those bastards as well as I would like."

We talked about the upcoming Headquarters review that Dougherty, Scott, and Sylvia were setting up as a much bigger meeting than was necessary and much bigger than I wanted. But, if they wanted a big Dog and Pony Show, I was not going to fight with them about it.

Scott showed me the meeting schedule and they just put me down to discuss the science and Dougherty was down for the spacecraft. I said, "No way. Dougherty doesn't know the spacecraft and the engineers don't know the spacecraft, they only know their subsystems. No one but me knows the integrated spacecraft and I am going to give that." They couldn't say no, but they were not happy about it, because they wanted to show Headquarters that we were a wonderful team just chock full of brilliant people. I said, "Scott, if you have Dougherty and some of those guys get up there, Headquarters is going to find out they don't know anything about this spacecraft."

Scott retorted, "Ledbetter knows Dougherty very well. He worked with him on Hubble and thinks he did a great job." Headquarters thought Dougherty was a genius Project Manager, who in reality doesn't know enough engineering to pound sand in a rat hole and what Scott saw was Lockheed's façade. Scott either didn't know enough to look behind the façade or did not care to and all he wanted was for us to get along. The fact that Scott had said to Sylvia somewhat earlier, "I wish that Tom and Alan didn't dislike each other so much," evidenced that. It was the same old story, I was in a lion's den and I was told I should just get along with the lion.

Still wishing I would just do the science and leave the spacecraft to Dougherty, Scott said that Piotrowski had said, "We (NASA) are not going to get much science out of this program, so we are going to have to decide whether we want to cancel it or not." That ticked me off and it was typical of Headquarters, since they are always in the mode of, "We don't understand what is going on, so we will cancel you." They don't understand science, they don't understand anything; they are just stupid engineers and stupid bureaucrats.

I said, "If they try to do that, I will go to Congress." That was the one thing that really worried Scott and NASA — that I would go to Congress and raise hell.

After I got back from Ames, I went over to see the spacecraft since Dougherty said, "They better have that thing ready by Friday." Well, when I got over to the assembly area, it was clear they were not going to have it ready by Friday and we would be lucky if they had it finished by a week from Friday. That meant we were about two months behind schedule and it was getting to be serious.

Tuesday, June 11, 1996

The main event of the day was that I had a long, two-hour chat with Dougherty in the morning. Then the whole team had a going-away pizza lunch for Richard and that sort of shot the rest of day.

I told Dougherty I wanted to talk with him, so we sat down and I started by telling him how things went on my trip. I figured the best way to get most of my points across to him without being confrontational was to tell him what I had told Larry Price, since he needed to know that anyway.

I went over the high points of my discussions with Larry and John, about their not performing, their not understanding that I was their customer and not Dougherty or NASA and that I was going to spend more time on the rocket since the spacecraft was entering its construction and testing phase and since Richard was leaving.

When I mentioned Richard, Dougherty said he was mad because Richard had come to him a month earlier and wanted to be the Responsible Engineer for the TLI Stage and Dougherty had somewhat reluctantly yielded to his wish. Dougherty felt betrayed because Richard had up and quit just a month later. That was certainly a valid criticism.

I explained what I had told Larry in detail about my concerns and their lack of performance and Dougherty said, "Boy that's good."

I said, "I accepted your viewpoint that, because you are a loyal Lockheed employee and I'm not, you could get the rocket mess solved by working through the company. But Tom, that is obviously not working and I think I understand the reason why. I've noticed that no matter how many times you've tried to make LLV do their work, it's only after Sylvia has raised hell that they start to react. They are sensitive to NASA, who they think is their customer. Since they are customer sensitive, I'm going to have to make them understand that I am their customer and then maybe they will listen to me instead of Sylvia." Dougherty was not so dense that he didn't get the connection that I was also his customer, so he had also better listen to me. Nevertheless, he agreed, but with little enthusiasm. I knew he did not agree with the concept that I was his customer, but what could he say, I had him trapped.

I started discussing the rocket by saying, "As you know yourself, this rocket is going to kill us if we don't get it straight."

He said, "That is a very good point." Interestingly, every time he said, "That is a very good point," he wrote down what I had said in a little notebook!

I said, "I told you before that I am convinced that you and Larry are correct. This company does have the resources necessary to get the rocket done right if it is convinced that we are in trouble. The problem is, Tom, that, given Lunar Prospector's very short development time, by the time Lockheed finally realizes we are in trouble — probably about three minutes before launch — and they throw us $10 million, what good will it do? They have to recognize we are in trouble now if they are going to make the corrections in time." He said, "That is a very good point," and he wrote it down!

After that, we discussed each of the issues about the launch vehicle and the program. I told him I felt that the spacecraft was in good shape and I said, "I know, Tom, every time I say the spacecraft is in good shape, you jump all over me and say, wait until we get into test. Despite your doubts, I am smart enough to know we will have some problems, but this is still a hell of a good, simple little spacecraft. I ask you, hasn't this gone smoother than any other program you have ever worked on?"

He smiled and said, "Yeah, this has really been pretty smooth." Then he laughed again and said, "I don't want to be too optimistic, because I know how bad things can go at times," and that was a very good answer.

Then we got to the more touchy parts. I said, "I understand you were ticked off about my not wanting you to interface with the instrument guys. I'm really not in favor of you getting involved with the instruments. I don't see any reason for your doing that. I picked these guys because they are the best there are for building these instruments and you really don't know anything about the instruments, so I see no reason for your involvement with them." He got a little huffy at that, which was OK. I said, "If you have a beef with me, I would rather you tell me; don't take it out on Tom (which was exactly what Dougherty liked to do). I don't mind you being ticked at me, since I get ticked at you."

He laughed and said the same thing. Then he defended himself by saying, "I want to do these things (talk with the science guys) because I know how things can go wrong. We are making changes to the instruments — like the change in the (MAG extension) boom and these are all critical issues. My experience tells me these are things that I have to look at."

I said, "Well OK, but here's the problem; I told you when we first started working together that I needed you for budget, interfacing with Lockheed, and scheduling, and I know the rest of it, except for Test and Integration."

He got a little mad again and said, "Well, if you only want me for budget and stuff, then I can leave right now. I'll leave Garner and the other people and they can do those things — you don't need me."

I said, "No, I am not interested in you leaving. The purpose of my comments is to understand what we need to get done and to make sure you and I are on the same page."

He made a fair comment, "You fuss about the rocket more than I do and I fuss about the science instruments more than you do. I am really concerned because we have made these changes at the end (of the development) and this is where, from my experience, things really get screwed up."

I said, "Well, that's a valid point and I don't want to get to the point where I say to you I don't want something and you say you want it and then I say, it's my mission and I'm going to do it my way."

He said, "I don't think we'll ever come to that."

I said, "I hope we don't and I don't want to. In the past we've done this very well. Remember when I wanted to have the 5 amp-hr battery and you guys were all turning cartwheels over that? Then we worked it through and we have a 5 amp-hr battery. I could have said I am the PI and that's my battery and I want it that way, but I don't like doing things that way. As I told you in the beginning, I don't want to make a mistake. Going through the process of discussing the issue is the way to avoiding making a mistake."

He said, "Yes, I agree wholeheartedly."

Then we talked about personnel. He said he just could not get the people he wanted and I said we had been doing OK with what we had, but I was disappointed that we couldn't get better people in some cases and I mentioned I was not impressed with Steve Honodel. Then I saw something in his expression and I said, "Wait a minute, do you think Steve is not very good, too?"

He said, "Well, he's doing OK. He's not the best, but he has done some pretty good analysis and the point is that anyone is better Vu." I could not disagree with the latter point!

I had asked him about the budget and, amazingly, he had found some way of getting some reserves again. Every time we spent our reserves, he found a way of getting some back. I said, "You've been doing a damned good job on that and I really appreciate it," and I added jokingly, "But tell me the truth, how do you get the money? Do you run drugs or something on the weekends to keep us solvent?" and he just laughed.

Then we talked about the scheduling. He said, "Yes, we are four to six weeks behind."

I asked, "What in hell are we going to do about it? This worries me a lot."

He answered, "Part of the problem is the things that are causing the slips are tests that were inserted into the program after we had gotten started and after we had laid out our original schedule (the engineers, mainly Bob Goldin, had convinced him we needed the extra tests). We are behind and we have to take care of it. I think we can make it up here and there." I really did not believe him, since we had yet to do the extra tests and we were still at least six weeks behind in construction.

As we neared the end of our two-hour conversation, Dougherty said he had told Tom that he (Dougherty) and I ought to have talks every week after the subsystem reviews. We both agreed that was a good idea and I said it would have been a good thing if we had started doing that much earlier. However, he agreed with me that we just didn't have the time earlier; we were just too damned busy.

Finally, we talked about the NASA flap over the UPI interview and he thought the whole thing was foolish and that Sylvia had gotten hysterical about it and I agreed with him. Then I added that both Scott and Sylvia were very worried about their jobs because Ames was on the verge of being closed. Any criticisms from Headquarters is a big deal to them. As I had noticed, Scott and Sylvia were getting very nervous.

After our little chat ended, I felt it was time well spent and I hoped we both had learned how to work better with each other. It turned out we had the same concerns about the personnel, the schedule slips, the rocket, and all the other things I had been worried about. Unfortunately, during the various meetings we had with the engineers, Sylvia, Scott, and everyone else, he put on his managerial façade of huffing, puffing, hollering, ranting, raving, and intimidating people. However, when we got together behind closed doors, that façade disappeared and he was much more reasonable.

Wednesday, June 12, 1996

Dougherty and I meet with Scott, Sylvia, and Frank at Lockheed to discuss our progress. Dougherty had managed to save some money (if he didn't run drugs, maybe he robbed banks on the weekends? No matter how he did it, he was very good at keeping the money flowing), so we had enough for five extra months. Thus, the schedule slips weren't so bad because we had three or four months between the completion of the final pre-launch tests and our October launch. As long as we did not run out of money, we could tolerate a slip of a couple of months.

We got our Headquarters Review Meeting set up for the following Wednesday. Despite my objections, Scott had insisted that Dougherty review the spacecraft, so we discussed what we needed to say and that worked out pretty well. I thought my talk with Dougherty the day before had helped a lot, at least things were smoother.

We went over to show Scott, Sylvia, and Frank the spacecraft and the pieces that were yet to be mounted on it. It was beautiful and getting more so all the time.

Thursday, June 13, 1996: Staff Meeting Day

Since everything with the spacecraft was basically OK, we mainly discussed the preparations for the NASA review. Dougherty asked if I was going to mention Blue Moon and said he didn't think I ought to do that. I said, "Well, I'm going to. NASA knows all about it since I've already talked to them about it." Happily, the staff meetings were getting very dull, because nothing was really wrong with the spacecraft and that was very good.

The only semi-serious issue was that the so-called Production Center still had not finished the long boom cables for Bill Feldman. They were supposed to have been finished weeks earlier, but nobody had ever bothered to tell the two ladies who were making them they could work overtime and on weekends to finish the cables on time. That was really stupid. Everything we had done in the Lockheed Production Center was late!

I spent the rest of the day with Jack McCommons from Thiokol, John Uselman and Roger McNamara from LLV, Irv Benard, Richard, and Francisco (who was going to replace Richard as our LLV interface, despite our concerns) in a TLI Stage Tiger Team meeting. Basically the TLI Stage seemed to be in good shape. Thiokol had built a proof model of the casing for the TLI Stage and expected to start building the flight model soon. Dougherty and I had talked about saving money and time by just using the proof model, so I made that suggestion and Dougherty backed me up.

Towards the end of the meeting, we talked about the effects of free molecular heating on the APS. I explained what was going on and what we were concerned about. John Uselman and Roger McNamara claimed they had never heard about the APS problem! Such idiots, when we had the Interface Control Document (ICD) meeting four or five weeks earlier, I discussed the whole thing with them and it was clearly described in the ICD.

After the Tiger Team meeting was over, I took the guys over to the assembly area and showed them the spacecraft. They really liked it.

A little later, I crabbed at Dougherty about LLV's not knowing about the APS-free molecular heating problem, but he just tried to pooh-pooh the fact that they didn't remember or know anything about it, while to me, it was just one more example of the LLV crew not paying attention to anything we said.

Friday, June 14, 1996

I talked to Dougherty and said I was disappointed that there wasn't more interaction at the Tiger Team meeting. Irv said the same thing and I felt like asking Irv, "Why didn't you ask any questions?" Dougherty said that Thiokol and Richard were in sync, but he thought that John and Roger were not there to listen, but to talk.

I told Dougherty I was glad we were on the same page about using the proof model for the TLI Stage casing rather than having Thiokol build another one for flight. He said, "Well, you blew my plan of not letting them know about that."

I replied, "Well, you didn't tell me that was a state secret. If we can use it, we will; if we can't, we won't."

I went to Ames to talk to Dave Lozier and Ken Galal about the new translunar trajectory we were refining. We had finalized our three Lunar Orbit Insertion (LOI) burn sequence: The first one was going to result in a 12-hour orbit, the second one in a 3½ hour orbit and the final burn would put us into the 118-minute, circular orbit. They were working on the details and the trajectory was getting more refined all the time.

Beyond that, I went over and looked at the spacecraft and the technicians were getting ready to put the modified feet on it (despite our initial decision to leave the feet the way they were, we did have to put stainless steel bushings in them as Jeff had wanted), but they were still way behind.

It was Richard's last day, so I took him to Taco Bell for lunch and then to Baskin Robbins for ice cream. We had a nice chat and I wished him well.

Since he was leaving Lockheed and Dom could no longer do him any harm, I asked him what had happened when I had gotten rid of Dom. He confirmed that Dom had been having meetings when I was not there, had kept me uninformed, and told the engineers not to talk to me.

I asked him what else Dom did. Richard answered that Dom had told them not only not to ask me questions and not to tell me anything, but also that he would give anybody holy hell who did. Richard said Dom had royally chewed Woody out because Woody had said, "Well Alan wants it done this way."

Dom just blew up and said, "It doesn't make any difference what Alan wants, I'm the Project Manager and it has to be done my way. Alan has nothing to say and don't ever listen to him again; he has nothing to say about this!"

Upon hearing that, I was convinced that Dom is totally crazy and I wanted to strangle the scrawny little bastard. It had been even worse than I thought and unfortunately, I could see some of that in Dougherty.

When I came back from lunch, Dougherty was still with John Uselman and they called me in to discuss the launch windows. Because of its simplicity, the LLV2 has to have a separate program for each launch date and they each cost $250,000. We couldn't afford to have launch programs for more than a couple of potential launch dates. Also, the launch windows were at most a few minutes in duration, maybe as little as one minute and certainly no more than ten minutes. Basically, we had to have an on time launch or we would miss the Moon. I didn't think that was a problem because we could put enough holds in the countdown to make sure we would be ready to go on time. I said, "Look, if we can only afford two launch programs, then it would probably be best to have one in October and one in November. The angle between the Moon and the Sun/Earth line is only 30° on October 9 and it decreases 12° per day; so, if we slip from the 9th to the 10th or 11th, that means we wouldn't be able to get good determines of our attitude because our points of reference would all be on a line." Dougherty didn't understand any of that, so I had to explain it several times and that was sort of the end of that. It would have been nice to have had a Project Manager who did not desperately need a brain transplant.

Jim Schirle came to me and said he was really sorry, but he thought he had made a serious mistake in the thermal calculations of the spacecraft and the GRS! He needed to check some more to be sure, but he wanted Dougherty and me to know that the thermal stuff could all be wrong. Boy, that was a shock!

After that fiasco, I talked to Woody, who had finally gotten the boom cables for Bill from the Production Center, at least the ones that were critical. Anything we had Lockheed do internally was always weeks late; in contrast, the things we had done outside were always done on time. Lockheed is the most pathetic damned company in the world.

Monday, June 17, 1996: Subsystem Review Day

Scott was at Lockheed for part of the review, which was good. There was some muck-up in the C&DH. Gerry made a mistake, but it wasn't his fault. When he looked up the ways that NASA could set up the uplink and downlink, the document showed there were various options one could use, so Gerry picked the one that was most favorable for us and it turned out NASA could not do that one! What the hell is the use of a NASA document if it is incorrect? He had to change the C&DH slightly. It didn't sound like too big of a deal, but it did impact the schedule.

Unfortunately, Jim Schirle was not there to elaborate on his possibly having screwed up the thermal calculations, so we didn't know what in hell was going on there.

We found out that the only Headquarters people who were coming Friday were Piotrowski and Ledbetter and they were only going to be around until 1:00 PM. That meant I could get home early enough so Rebecca and I could go camping!

We had a telecon with John Uselman, and to my amazement, Dougherty brought up a question about transporting the fully fuelled spacecraft from the processing facilities to the launch pad. The question was, won't the fuel flow from one tank to the other when we go over the bridges on the way to the launch complex?

I had raised this question way back at the kickoff meeting and I had asked for data on the issue. They got it for us; we looked at it and there was no problem whatsoever — it was a dead issue. When Dougherty brought it up, I said, "Whoa, wait a minute, that's a question I asked several months ago. We got the data and there is no problem. Why bring this up again? This is a dead issue."

Sylvia said, "Yeah, we dealt with this earlier, I even saw the data myself." Then Kim Foster said the same thing.

I said, "Tom, this disturbs me. I would like to know who in hell is asking questions that have been resolved a long time ago," and that put Dougherty in his place.

Bill Jacobsen was squawking about the need to correct the bit errors in the data archiving for the Level 0 data. Dougherty said, "We are just going to give them the integrated data stream."

I said, "Look, this stuff has been defined and we have a contract with NASA that clearly defines what Level 0 is and that it is to be bit error corrected, as well as being broken up according to science instrument."

Upon hearing that, Dougherty said, "Do you mean you are going to have to separate this stuff by instrument? We are not going to do that?"

I answered, "Yes, we are."

Dougherty would not believe it, so Tom got the contract and gave it to Bill Jacobsen and Dougherty and said, "Here it is and that is exactly what is in here. We are supposed to bit error correct the data and break it down according to science instruments." Jacobsen was so useless it wasn't even funny.

One nice thing that happened was that Ken Galal got me the spacecraft ephemeris so I could redo the Mission Profile. Unfortunately, he only had the solar occultation data and not the Earth occultation data in the ephemeris and there seemed to be a discrepancy between his numbers and Dave Lozier's, but it was a start.

Dougherty, Irv, Francisco, Sylvia, and I flew to Denver after work, and to save money, Lockheed had a limo take us up to the San Francisco Airport. In the process, I ended up paying for it (that didn't make any difference, since the money came out of the contract anyway), though according to Lockheed travel rules, we were supposed to pay individually. Then the limo driver forgot to give me my corporate credit card back (when he picked us up the next night, he gave it back to me), and Francisco ripped his pants in the airplane.

Wednesday, June 19, 1996: The LLV2 Specification Review

The review was very boring. I talked to Roger McNamara to get the data on the free molecular heating, and it turned out they could keep the shroud on long enough to get the heating down to 1.5×10^5 ergs/cm^2/sec. That was low enough it should not cause a problem for the APS, since Jim thought the APS foils could handle 3×10^5 ergs/cm^2/sec. That solved that problem in a most convenient way. Other than that, the meeting was a waste of time.

However, I was still bothered about the review for Ledbetter and Piotrowski, since I did not want Dougherty trying to explain any technical issues. My concern had heightened because, as Dougherty was preparing for his talk on the spacecraft, he kept asking me questions about the viewgraphs the subsystem engineers had made for him. I had to explain every single item to him, and then he promptly forgot it or confused it with another item — it was pathetic! I told Sylvia during a break in the meeting that Dougherty could not explain any of the technical issues, but she said Scott wanted it that way in order to show Headquarters we had some depth — that more than just one person (me) knew the spacecraft. I thought that was stupid of Scott; Dougherty was just going to screw it up and give the impression that we had no depth at all. I said to Sylvia, who I thought had begun to get nervous when she heard that Dougherty had to ask me to explain what was on each of the viewgraphs, "I disagree, we need to discuss this in the meeting tomorrow."

We flew home and got into the San Jose Airport at 11:00 PM.

A Major Thermal Modeling Error

Thursday, June 20, 1996: Jim's Thermal Modeling Screw Up

Jim Schirle called and explained that the program he had been using to calculate the thermal models of the spacecraft and the instruments had been for the Earth instead of the Moon! Our thermal engineering was all screwed up. The problem was, when he had gotten the program from the thermal engineers who had used it to make the thermal calculation during the proposal effort, they forgot to tell him there is a place in the code where he had to switch it from making calculations for Earth orbiting satellites to making calculations for lunar orbiting satellites. When Jim got the program, it was set up for Earth satellites, not for a lunar satellite. Since Jim did not know that, all his calculations were for the Earth, so were wrong!

My first reaction was that a scientist always checks out a program before he uses it, so why don't engineers! But it was too late to play Monday quarterback and I was just glad Jim had the guts to come to Dougherty and me and to say, "I screwed up big time, but I'll fix it as quickly as I can."

That won my total respect for Jim, since, "To err is human; to hide it is a catastrophe."

The correct thermal calculation showed the temperature of GRS was going to be way above the –40° C we wanted, but Jim thought he could get it back down close to –40° C. Also the temperatures of the various electronic units on the equipment shelf during the 118-minute day/night orbital cycle varied far too much, i.e., got too hot and then too cold, but Jim had a great idea about how to solve that problem. Instead of having a thermal blanket on the top and on the bottom of the spacecraft, he was just going to blanket the inside of the solar panel, leave the top and the bottom of the spacecraft open, and blanket each electronic unit separately. The blankets on the solar panels would help keep the solar array cooler and hence, help keep the array's power output high (the efficiency of solar cells drops with increasing temperature). It was too bad we had to have a catastrophe in his calculations to come up with that neat idea.

In addition to the major thermal problem, and to my dismay, Tom and Shelley had absconded together. She was going to live with Tom and start her divorce! She had left a note for her husband telling him he would get a divorce summons the next day. I was concerned because Tom's traumatic divorce had been finalized just 17 days earlier and he was getting emotionally involved in a second divorce that was going to be as difficult as his.

I was concerned for my close friend and confidant, who, according to my assessment, was nowhere near ready to start a serious relationship, let alone to live with someone with whom he had never even had a date and share her divorce trials and tribulations. I was also concerned because I knew right then and there that Tom had thrown away any chance he had to learn enough about the mission to help me during Mission Ops. He had been too distracted to do so during his divorce and he would be too distracted to do so during Shelley's divorce. If I were correct, and I had no doubts about that, I had no idea of how I could justify keeping Tom on the project after construction and testing were finished — and that made me sad.

Tom and Shelley were not around all day, which was fine with everyone.

Dougherty was working diligently on his viewgraphs and I gave him credit for that.

Scott came over and we talked about the earned value system, which was still a big deal because it would determine how much fee Lockheed would get. We ran out of time and never got around to discussing my concerns about Dougherty screwing up the spacecraft part of the presentation, so I just let it drop.

As a result, I decided I would take as much time as I could discussing the science objectives and then, when I showed Ledbetter and Piotrowski the spacecraft engineering model, I would tell them all the pertinent technical information and then just let Dougherty wallow through his part during what little time remained.

I was really concerned Dougherty was going to blow it and I really thought Scott was being extremely stupid, but it was too late to do anything about it. Again, to his credit, Dougherty was sitting in his office like a little schoolboy trying vainly to understand his homework.

However, my concerns increased dramatically and I was floored when Dougherty asked Irv, "What's this ΔV stuff? Is it like thrust?" Irv tried to explain to him that ΔV is a change in the velocity of the spacecraft and not the engine thrust and then Dougherty asked, "Is anybody going to understand what that means?"

Irv answered, "Yes."

Dougherty asked him, "Who wants this GHP stuff in the tanks?" — GHP stands for Gaseous Helium Pressurant and, of course, he didn't know that. That display of total ignorance was followed by, "What are these valves and this stuff here and why do we have two of these filters?" I was appalled. He didn't have a clue about the spacecraft — he did not even know which end of it was up!

I received an invitation from Olin to fly up to Seattle to take possession of our six beautiful little engines. Their official delivery date was July 26 and Olin wanted to throw a little party and have me give a talk to the troops who built the engines. Irv and I made plans to go up there and help celebrate our engines.

The assembly of the spacecraft structure just kept slipping, but we were told it should definitely be done by the following week, so we could finally do the static tests. Dougherty finally got ticked off about the delays and he finally started doing what was necessary to get us back on track.

Friday, June 21, 1996: The Headquarters Review

Ledbetter and Piotrowski were late by about fifteen minutes. Then, instead of just saying hello and welcome, Frank took about twenty minutes to blab about Lockheed. That put us way behind schedule, which I was very happy about.

Interestingly, after Scott talked about what Ames was doing, Ledbetter and Piotrowski criticized Scott for having too much oversight and said he should leave us alone and let us do our job!

After that, I got up and discussed the science and pointed out that the Discovery review committee had selected Lunar Prospector because it had the best science value per dollar, as well as being well advanced in its development. I explained that, as Mark Saunders had told us during our debriefing, we had good science, but not excellent science because we were so inexpensive. The only way I could have better science was to have more on it, which would have raised the cost and then we would not have had the best science value per dollar.

I said, since being selected for flight, we had increased our scientific output by at least fifty percent because we had gotten smarter and I explained how we had enlarged the GRS's anti-coincident shield and had it borated so it could measure the fast neutron flux. As a result, we had two neutron spectrometers instead of just one as proposed. Ledbetter said, "You're telling me this didn't raise the cost at all, no impact at all."

I answered, "Yes, that's right." Then Scott helped hammer the point home that none of the changes we had made had caused any cost or schedule impacts. I showed them in detail what we would be getting from the primary and the extended missions. The science discussion went very well, took a long time, and they were quite happy with it.

Finally, I took them over to the full-scale engineering model and described it in great detail; I described the batteries, the helix antenna, the electronics units, and all the major details to make sure I totally preempted Dougherty and took as much time as possible.

When Dougherty finally got up, we were happily running very, very late. He did a very good job discussing the schedule. He explained we were behind schedule by five weeks, partly because we had inserted several additional tests (not true) and partly because the alignment had taken longer than we had anticipated; but he made sure they understood that the launch date was not in danger because we had a 4-month period between our scheduled June completion date and the October launch date. When we changed the launch date, we did not change the schedule. Time was not a constraint, but money was and he explained that he had worked very hard and had gotten a month's worth of money in reserve. As Dougherty explained, even though we were a little behind schedule, we had the money to make it up and we have plenty of time to do so, so it wouldn't affect the launch schedule. As I expected, Dougherty did a great job of explaining the management issues.

Unfortunately, Dougherty then got to the spacecraft and, happily, he only had enough time to talk about the mass — always a major issue in spacecraft development. He showed the curve of the mass as a function of development time, explaining how we had kept it down and gave me credit for continually hammering it down. Then he said he was quite astounded at how much mission time we would lose for every kilogram of extra mass the spacecraft had (having made Dougherty understand and remember that simple relationship between loss of mission duration as a function of increasing spacecraft mass was one of my greatest achievements during construction — given Dougherty's dullness).

So far so good, but then he screwed up. He said, "We are very concerned about this moment of the major and minor axis thing."

I thought, *crap, now he's done it!*

He said, "We're not stable and blah, blah, blah."

He was screwing it all up so badly I interrupted and said, "We are a stable spinner after we deploy the booms. Our concern is the short period between separation from TLI Stage and the deployment of the booms. Right now, we are quasi-stable during that period, but we want to make sure that when we are finished, the spacecraft is stable during that short period."

My explanation got us out of that mess and then he got us right back into trouble when he tried to explain about the mission duration and the ΔV reserve. I had to explain that I had enough fuel for two extra years of nominal mapping, but that I would use that reserve in just six months of low altitude, extended mission mapping.

All in all, and despite Dougherty's brilliant grasp of the technical issues, the review went well.

We went over to the construction area and showed them the real thing and they were very impressed. I said, "I really think we have done a marvelous job when you remember it has only been eight months since we got started (with Phase C/D)." Piotrowski and Ledbetter were really quite impressed and pleased.

We went back to Building 107 and had lunch.

After lunch, Larry Price talked about the LLV2 and did a pretty good job. Happily, Mike Henshaw came to the review at that point. He was really enthusiastic and put Larry in his place a couple of times and said, "I'm on your (Lunar Prospector's) side and patted Dougherty on the shoulder, not your (LLVs) side, I want this thing (Lunar Prospector) to work."

Larry tried to rescue LLV by saying, "Clearly my sentiments are with the mission and LLV is not the enemy." The launch vehicle part also went well.

We discussed the schedule slip and Ledbetter was very vocal about wanting to make sure we got launched on time. He said, "We are going to have a battle on our hands because Goldin is concerned about first launches," but clearly Ledbetter was on our side. He said he was going to do everything he could to help us get launched. I felt very good about that.

By then it was 1:00 PM and Ledbetter and Piotrowski left. Everybody felt the review had gone very well. The interesting thing to me was that Henshaw still thought that Dougherty was running the show, which was both amusing and annoying to me. They were never going to learn. Anyway, I was pleased with the whole affair.

Right after Ledbetter and Piotrowski left, I went home and Rebecca and I drove up to the Henry Coe Park for our weekend camping trip, which turned out to be a fiasco because loud people kept us awake all night, both nights.

Monday, June 24, 1996

Tom, Tim Bridges, the software guys from Palo Alto, and I went down to JPL for a meeting on tracking and its associated software. It was a long meeting. We got a lot done. The highlight was that we would not uplink using TOTS because it was going to be hard to get the correct formats. It was a good meeting.

Tuesday, June 25, 1996

When we got back, the spacecraft still wasn't assembled for the dynamic tests and wouldn't be assembled for another week. That was getting ridiculous. Other than that, I just got a lot of work done.

Wednesday, June 26, 1996

I went to part of an LLV1 review and was bored to death. I went back to my office to get some work done on the Mission Profile using the new ephemeris data. Then I was told that Cassini, NASA's $3.5 billion mission to Saturn, might want our launch dates and guess who would win if they did!

I talked to Jim Schirle about his new thermal modeling and then to Bill about the new GRS temperatures Jim had calculated. Bill was not too worried as long as the GRS temperature did not get higher than $-30°$ C, because we would then only lose ½% to ¾% in resolution. However, Bill was concerned that the gain was going to vary as the temperature of the GRS varied as a function of the β angle (the angle between the plane of the spacecraft's orbit and the vector to the sun, β varies from $0°$ to $90°$ and back to $0°$ twice a year) as Jim's calculation showed it would. However, we could determine the gain from the position of the boron line in the spectra. Our main concern was to get the best resolution possible by keeping the GRS as cold as possible.

There were several ways to get the GRS as cold as possible. One was to make the housing more conductive so the heat could get out. Or, we could put some heat straps on the housing to conduct the heat out. However, Jim was skeptical about all of that and since he thought it would get down to –30° C, we decided that was probably OK.

Dougherty and I met with Scott and Sylvia to discuss the thermal issues and the schedule. Scott said Piotrowski and Ledbetter wanted to come out every three months for a one or two hour, informal review. They liked what they had seen and they just wanted to keep up to date on our rapid progress. Also, they thought we had overdone our review — they really just wanted a look around the place (I had been right all along).

Thursday, June 27, 1996: Staff Meeting Day

Tom and I went over to see the spacecraft and it was still not done. They were supposedly going to get it done by the next day, but I would believe it when I saw it.

Dougherty said he just didn't have the people to work on it — he had asked for more help from Lockheed, but he didn't get any. That was BS. The pieces had been just sitting over there for two months! The whole thing was ridiculous.

During the staff meeting, Steve Honodel said the booms would take about eleven minutes to deploy and that surprised me. However, not surprisingly, the deployment was very nonlinear, the booms would go out fast in the beginning and then really slow down.

Other than those things, not much was going on. Since I was very tired, I went home relatively early and went to bed.

Friday, June 28, 1996

We had a dry run for a meeting about the TLI Stage destruct system during the morning and it was pathetic. John Uselman ran the meeting and it was clear to everyone the meeting was going nowhere. When Francisco presented his material, it was clear he didn't have a clue as to what in hell was going on — he just presented a few viewgraphs showing the components of the destruct system. Francisco just did not have what it took to do the job. I knew it and everybody else knew it.

That was it. I had to have a talk with Dougherty and tell him to replace both of them or things were going to be bad. We could not have Uselman running the TLI Stage, and more importantly, the LLV2. We had to have somebody that represented our interests, not LLV's. And Francisco was just totally out of his element. He was just a little lost sheep in a pack of wolves.

I had been over to see the spacecraft in the morning and found that all the tank bolt holes had been drilled and it was ready for assembly. I went over again late in the afternoon and the technicians were assembling the mass simulator for the tanks and the inverted tripod that supported the tanks (during the static and shake testing, blocks of aluminum were used to simulate the tanks and electronic units, rather than having to wait for the real equipment, as well as running the risk of damaging any of it during the testing). Everything was supposed to be finished and taken over to the static test area by 10:00 AM the next day — I hoped that it would be there on time.

Tim Maloney, a really bright young engineer, a really great guy to work with, and the engineer who was responsible for herding the spacecraft through assembly, test, and shipping, was there and insisted the spacecraft would be done on time; but they still had a lot of work to do.

Scott had arranged a meeting with several old, very experienced Ames engineers who had worked on the Pioneer Missions, to discuss whether we needed to do dynamics testing before we went into the full test program. If we did, that would put us another month behind schedule. As a way out of that schedule problem, Tom asked Dougherty why he didn't get more people to work on the testing. Dougherty got huffy with Tom (he disliked Tom even more than he disliked me) because he had apparently tried to get some extra personnel, but the damned company wouldn't give us anybody. Lockheed just would not help us, despite what Henshaw and everyone else had promised me.

Dougherty explained the schedule problem to the Ames engineers and everybody sort of agreed that it was a waste of time to do a dynamics test. Nevertheless, the Ames engineers wanted us to do the other tests with the tanks filled with alcohol or water to properly simulate the fuel in the tanks and hence, do the tests right. That presented some serious problems, but we took their advice under consideration.

Dougherty brought up the issue of the GRS's temperature and said we were trying to fiddle with the temperature of the spacecraft to get the GRS colder! The idiot thought the spacecraft's temperature controlled the temperature of the GRS. The one thing had nothing to do with the other! He just did not understand anything and it was very embarrassing when he demonstrated how little he knew at such meetings.

Monday, July 1, 1996: Subsystem Review Day

I went to the static test area to see the spacecraft and it was beautiful. The technicians were putting on the stress gauges and the hydraulic presses. It was really neat to see the spacecraft structure standing there on a big platform with a red light flashing and signs on it saying "Valuable Flight Hardware, Do Not Touch."

The main topic at the subsystem review was that I had a message from Mario Acuña that indicated the solar array design was all screwed up in terms of its magnetic properties. I hadn't been able to get back to him to find out exactly what was wrong, but apparently the back-wiring was wrong (in order to cancel out the magnetic fields generated by the current flowing through the solar cell strings on the front of the panels, current is run through wires strung on the back side of the panels that are anti-parallel to the currents on the front). We didn't have the back-wiring diagram; so we did not know exactly what the problem was, but we would have to get it straightened out.

Jim reported that we could keep the end-of-life GRS temperature down to $-30°$ C at the hottest times during the mission, i.e., when we were at β around $0°$, which would be OK. We had to worry about setting the set-point (in order to keep a spectrometer at a stable temperature, one designs it so it would naturally be colder than the desired temperature — i.e., the set-point temperature — and then add heaters that turn on when the temperature drops to the set-point and then turn off when the temperature gets a degree or two above the set-point). I needed Jim to get me the GRS's expected temperature as a function of the β angle, so Bill and I could decide what the set-point temperature should be.

I talked to Dougherty about Francisco and the rocket. Dougherty somewhat agreed with my concerns, but he still thought that LLV was cooperating. However, Irv said he thought that LLV was trying to slip out of some of our critical agreements, like providing a nitrogen purge for the science instruments and providing access for measuring the pressure in the tanks during transportation and while the rocket and spacecraft were on the pad before launch. It was not just me, but Dougherty was never one to rock the (sinking) boat.

I made the suggestion that Tom and I start spending one day per week over at Missions Ops at Ames and have office space over there so we could start concentrating on Mission Ops issues. The Ops stuff had to get moving. There were a lot of open issues; how we would command the spacecraft was one, but, of course, those things were just dragging along, so I felt if I were at Ames, it would accelerate that work.

Tuesday, July 2, 1996

I worked on the launch date constraints. Dougherty was the same old jerk as always.

Wednesday, July 3, 1996

We straightened out the solar array design errors that Mario was worried about.

Tom took some pictures of the spacecraft in the test area and we got bawled out for having a camera in a secure area (a military satellite was in the next test bay).

The Long Fourth of July Weekend, 1996

Rebecca and I just stayed around home and relaxed.

Monday, July 8, 1996: Subsystem Review Day

First thing in the morning, Tom and I went to see the spacecraft in the huge steel structure that made up part of the static test set up. The spacecraft had a lot of test equipment attached to it. With all the strain gauges, hydraulic presses, wiring, and other things attached to it, it looked like a patient in an intensive care unit.

As we looked at the static test set up, Tom said, "Is this the thing we shake it on?" The week before Tom and I had seen the dynamic test equipment — the shaker — and he had confused the two, despite our going over there every day. Tom was still distracted, not concentrating, and didn't remember anything about the test and assembly activities. Tom was doing a great job in every other way of helping me, but he was just not getting on board with the program and I was disappointed and concerned.

We went back to Building 107 for the subsystem review meeting. We began seriously discussing how we were going to command the spacecraft and I voiced my opinion that I didn't need to be able to send a series of commands in each uplink block, rather I just needed one command per block, i.e., direct commanding. Unless there was some reason the science instruments needed to have series of commands sent up in one block, I didn't see any reason for changing the C&DH and making the commanding more complex. I said I would check with my science guys to see if they needed to send series of command in a block to the instruments. Gerry was happy with that.

Based on the information available, we decided we wouldn't use the Store-and-Forward mode (in Store-and-Forward, a block with a command or a series of commands is sent to an uplink station with a time tag indicating when the block is to be uplinked to the spacecraft and then the block is *stored* in the computer at the station until it is time to *forward* it to the spacecraft). We didn't want two methods of commanding and Gerry didn't believe that Store-and-Forward commanding would work with our C&DH, so we would just stick with the direct commanding.

We discussed filling the tanks with water for the tests. Nobody was happy with that idea, but it appeared we really needed to do it.

After lunch, Tim Bridges told me we could use Store-and-Forward and get the commanding done the way I wanted to. Tim said, "If you put zeros in for the delay time in Store-and-Forward, it is the same as direct commanding. We would have to get our command system to shake hands with JPL's command system (get them properly linked up) to get the process started. But once it was started, you could send as many commands as you needed to, one at a time, and just put zeros in when you didn't want to use the true Store-and-Forward mode." I liked Tim's suggestion. I would have two command modes and still have just one set of software and that would be the end of it. I agreed we would use that system if my science guys said it would be OK for the instrument commanding, but I saw no reason why it wouldn't be.

Dan Swanson had been pulled off working on Lunar Prospector to help write a proposal for a spacecraft called IMAGE, which was based on Lunar Prospector (IMAGE was a mission being run by the scientists at the Southwest Research Institute in San Antonio, TX, the same place where Davis Black was building the SES for the spectrometers). I said I was getting very concerned because my people kept being pulled off to do other things. Unfortunately, Tom made a stupid comment about that being Tenerelli's doing and that ticked Dougherty off. Dougherty snapped at him, as usual.

To make matters worse for Tom, Dougherty had read Tom's minutes about a meeting we had had at JPL and a telecon, and Tom had screwed up some of the information. He just didn't understand what was going on and was not paying attention. Then Marcie explained to Dougherty what had gone on at JPL and during the telecon and made a fool of Tom.

Dougherty read through the action item list Tom had written up, but Tom did not remember what was on the list and did not know what the status of each action item was. Dougherty very cleverly made a fool of Tom again and then gave him faint praise for writing up the action list, but patronizingly told Tom that he had to follow-up the action items properly. Tom was very upset because he got his fingers slapped again and again, but I had no sympathy for him. I had told him to concentrate on the project and to learn what he had to learn in order to be able to continue helping me run the mission, but Tom was too wrapped up in the trauma of his own divorce, and in Shelley and her messy divorce to concentrate on Lunar Prospector.

As a result, I reluctantly accepted the fact that Tom was never going to know enough about the spacecraft and the mission so I could trust him with the responsibility of being my second in command, i.e., the Deputy Mission Director, during the mission. That post was clearly going to have to be filled by Dan Swanson, who had already proven to me I could trust him to operate the spacecraft in my absence. Thus, I saw dark clouds forming on Tom's Lunar Prospector horizon and there was nothing more I could say to Tom to make him any more aware of the problems facing him in the very near future.

Tuesday, July 9, 1996

Dougherty was reasonable all day and I wished he were that way all the time; it would have made life a lot easier.

Tom arrived at work (since Shelley had moved in with Tom, he and I no longer drove in together, so I had even less time to teach him the things he absolutely needed to know to do his job) upset because of Dougherty and I had to calm him down.

I talked to Brian Landis at Falcon and he told me the Air Force could do the downlink very easily. At a minimum, I could get extra downlink time, or even do all the downlinking of the data using the Air Force and just do the uplink commanding through the DSN, since I would have to do so little commanding. All of the critical commanding I needed to do would occur during the week between launch and getting the spacecraft settled down into its mapping orbit and we were going to be on the DSN 100% of the time during that period anyway. After that, I would have to command mainly when we did the periodic orbital maintenance burns and I could get a day for commanding from the DSN when I needed to do those burns. I was really happy that I was going to be able to patch together a good downlink capability via the Air Force.

Other than that, I called Bill, who was visiting JPL, and talked to him about my discussion with Jim Schirle concerning the cooling of the GRS and him getting me the thermal data for different β angles. It looked like we could easily get the GRS temperature down to $-30°$ C and maybe even $-35°$ C. When I got all the β angle data, I would be able to figure it all out. Also, Bob McMurray at Ames had calculated that the GRS would have 8.4% resolution at $-30°$ C. We expected, at best, 7.8%. We were not going to lose too much resolution by not being able to get down to $-40°$ C. When we had all the thermal data, McMurray, Scott, Bill, and I would decide what the set-point temperature of the GRS would be.

Bill and I talked about the APS light filters or foils and the fact that, because of the large increase in the spacecraft's velocity due to the TLI burn, the free molecular heating was going to be 3×10^5 ergs/cm^2/sec right after the TLI burn. Thus, the free molecular heating wouldn't be any lower than that no matter when we released the shroud. I told Bill we would have to have some little covers over the foils or he would have to deposit the filters directly on the detectors, because we just couldn't fool around any longer with that issue. He said he would find out from Bicron if we could deposit the filters on the detectors — at least on the upper two.

I asked Bill about the rubber material that was around the BGO crystal that had deformed during his tests. It turned out the batch of rubber that Bicron had used for us had been improperly cured. It had been cured at 220 to 230° C instead of at 100° C, so Bill had taken care of that. I asked him to send us a piece of the rubber so we could check it out.

The APS foil issue was getting resolved, the GRS temperature business was being resolved, and the NS was fine.

Finally I asked Bill if there was any reason for him to do multiple commands and the answer was no.

I called Dave Curtis and asked him the same question regarding the MAG/ER commanding and his answer was also no. Nevertheless, he said that being able to do multiple commands would be convenient if he wanted to reprogram the DPU, but I said I did not want him to reprogram it after launch anyway. In any case, his uplink loads would only be a couple hundred words. That would be doable; it would just take a long time.

Having a multiple-command compatibility was a dead issue; we were going to send one command at a time, and we were going to use Store-and-Forward, and that was the end of it. I told Tim Bridges the issue was resolved. Then Tim told Gerry we were going to use Store-and-Forward and Gerry blew up. Tim tried to explain that it made no difference whatsoever for the C&DH. But Gerry fussed around and finally Tim calmed him down.

We had a telecon about the Ground Segment and tracking. Half of the guys weren't on line again. The Green Bay guys had forgotten about it and when I talked to George French about their absence from the telecon, he felt badly and said the appropriate things to his people.

Things were beginning to pick up speed. Tom, Tim Bridges, and I were getting offices over at Ames, so we could spend a day a week over there concentrating on the Ground Segment. That was really the problem, not being able to concentrate on it; so I needed to get over there and kick some butt.

Wednesday, July 10, 1996

Jim Schirle brought the temperature versus β angle data I needed for the GRS and I got those issues resolved. I thought we could get a good stable thermal environment with the temperature varying only a couple of degrees when β was near 0° with the set point set at −35° C and lose just ½% in resolution. If we set the set point at −40° C, then there would be several degrees of variation when β was near 0°, which was not acceptable. I thought that the issue was resolved.

I talked to Sylvia about things in general. I said Dougherty had been an ass the previous week, but had been really nice and cooperative since then. She noticed it too. She said she did the same things I did, i.e., we got what we needed to have done eventually, but we just had to waste a lot of time fooling around with the idiot to get it done. If he were always as nice as he had been during the previous three days, the project would have been fun for all of us.

Tom and I went to see the spacecraft at the end of the day. It was nearly wired up, they just had to put the reflectometer on it. We would most certainly start the static test Friday.

Thursday, July 11, 1996: Finally Ready for Static Testing

We reviewed the Mission Profile and the engineers had a lot of good suggestions, nothing serious, the suggestion just made it easier for everyone to understand it.

I talked to Scott, Bill, and Bob McMurray and we all agreed to set the GRS set point at −35° C. That would still give us about 8% or maybe 8.1% resolution and the GRS's temperature would be stable all the time, i.e., not vary by more that a degree or two. The dead band of the heater circuit was only 1¼° C, which was great.

We also decided to put the light filter coatings directly on the APS detectors, thereby getting rid of those damned films and getting around the free molecular heating problem.

The spacecraft was finally set up for the static tests and the tests were going to start the next day. The spacecraft was beautifully wired up; it had hydraulic presses and motion detectors on it and even acoustic sensors, little microphones, so we could listen to it. Hopefully we would not hear it break (remember, that structure was flight hardware. If it broke or cracked, we would be in serious trouble). We were going to do the static tests on Friday, Saturday, Monday, and Tuesday. We planned to be finished with the static tests by Wednesday.

Everything was finally moving rapidly forward and everything was going amazingly well. On top of all that, Dougherty had been a human being for a full week!

Chapter 3-18
Static Testing

Friday, July 12, 1996: Static Testing

Early in the morning, I finished working on a table showing that the best launch date was October 9, 1997, and that the other launch dates in that time frame were less favorable.

When Tom got into work, we went over to look at the spacecraft and they were not quite ready to start the static tests. We went back to building 107 until they were ready.

I called Bill about the thermal control of the GRS and about having Bicron evaporate the light filters onto the APS detectors. He had already talked to Bicron and they were willing to do it.

Tom and I had a meeting about the software and the Ground Segment at Ames. Our offices at Ames would be ready in two weeks, so I would be spending at least every Tuesday over there. We also had an excellent meeting about how we were going to do the commanding via Store-and-Forward and about several other issues. It was really a very good meeting.

We went back to 107, had a really quick lunch, after which we went to see what was happening with the spacecraft. When we got over there, they had had some trouble with some of the sensors, so they hadn't gotten started as early as they had expected. Nevertheless, by the time we got there, the technicians had already run a test up to the 50% load level and everything seemed fine. Then they got set up to run it up to 100% load.

They were making three types of measurements, using three different types of sensors. One type measured the strain to see how the structure was being strained or deformed by the applied stresses.

The second one actually measured the deflection and the instruments showed that at the 50% load level, the side panel bent about 6 mm, or about what it should have moved at full load! We were surprised about that, but it was deforming linearly, which was fine, as long as it did not break!

The third measurement was acoustic, where the little microphones on it would pick up the noise if the structure started to break, or crack, or snap, indicating if any damage was occurring.

They finished the 100% load test, which went well, and then they started the final, 115% load test. When they started the first 115% test — we could hardly believe it, but we could actually see the side panel bend about a centimeter, which was also what the instrument recorded. We still could not believe it, so Tim Maloney got some paper and we taped one piece to the test stand so it stuck out towards another piece of paper that we taped on the side panel of the spacecraft and which stuck out far enough so the two pieces of paper were 1 cm apart. The first test had been a push test and the one they were about to do was the pull test. If the side panel deformed the 1 cm we had seen during the push test, the two pieces of paper would just touch at the 115% load. They started the pull test and sure enough, at 115% load, the two pieces of paper touched as the panel bowed out 1 cm — we were amazed!

As is standard procedure, they dropped back to 100% load and started to take it back up to the 115% load — and we heard a loud POP! We all looked at each other with very worried looks on our faces — something gave somewhere. There was no indication from the strain gauge measurements that anything was wrong. The measurements all showed linear deformation, just the way you want it. There was nothing in the deflection measurements to indicate there was any failure, but there was that POP! We had to find out what had happened! Clearly, whatever it was, it was minor, but something did break or did something.

The next test, set for the next day, was to be another test to push the structure from the bottom up. That was not as severe a test as what we had just finished, so we expected everything would be OK, but we were never sure of that.

We had to find out what popped during the test and repair it. Also, the 1-cm deflection worried us; if the side panels deflected inwards that much during launch, they would hit the tanks. Those tanks would be under very high pressure and the side panels could not bang into them, so we would have to put some stiffeners on the side panels. The neat thing was that the basic triangular structure was rock solid. Its deflection was much less than predicted — only the side panels were bending.

I left the static test area at about 4:30 PM and walked back to 107 where I saw Dougherty. He was just leaving so we just talked about the test.

I found out Lockheed was going behind my back again. I had found out Monday that Dan Swanson was working on the IMAGE proposal with Tenerelli, and then that Tim Bridges was also doing so (I couldn't say anything about Tim; as a retired employee, he was only working halftime on Lunar Prospector — so if he wanted to work more, that was his business). A short time earlier, I had caught Francisco working on the proposal and right then, I found out Gerry Grismore was also working on it. I wanted to talk to Dougherty or Frank about that, but they were gone. I called Scott and Sylvia. They were also concerned because Frank had promised them that our personnel were never going to be taken away from us. Lockheed was always robbing Peter to pay Paul. It is the dumbest damned company I ever saw.

Nevertheless, I had a very good week. Dougherty was pleasant, cooperative, and listened to what I said all week!

Monday, July 15, 1996: Static Testing and Subsystem Review

The test engineers did the static tests with the forces acting vertically and then horizontally along the tank bosses (the attachment points of the tanks to the load-bearing structure) and the tank structure. Those tests went perfectly, there were no problems whatsoever.

During the subsystem review, everyone pretty much agreed that the POP we heard during Friday's test on the side panel was just due to slippage of the panel since there was a lot of movement on it. Regardless, we had to stiffen the panels by adding T or U brackets to them. Tom Chinn thought when installed, the Spider for the boom release mechanism would help to stiffen the panels, but I didn't think that was going to do a whole lot. We all agreed we needed the T or U brackets. They wouldn't add much mass, a half a kilogram at most.

Though we all thought the POP was not due to anything serious, the engineers were going to take the structure apart and X-ray and thermal probe it to make sure there was no structural damage. If there were no damage, then we would proceed to put the spacecraft together. If there were damage, well —.

In order to protect the solar cells from radiation damage due to the Van Allen Belts and solar flares, they needed to be covered with cover glasses and when the solar array engineers told us that, they also said, because Lunar Prospector was going to go around the Moon and not be protected by the Earth's magnetic field, we needed thick cover glasses that would add more than 3 kg of mass to the spacecraft. I did not like that and I asked, "Since our mission is only going to last a year, can't we use thinner cover slides with less of a mass penalty?" so they said they would find out. I still hadn't heard anything about that, and, as usual, Woody was not pushing the bozos over at the Center of Excellence. I was not going to put up with adding 3 kg of mass for no real reason — that was absurd. The guys over there were just not willing to put in the extra effort to get it right, they were too used to the old way of throwing money and mass at a problem, rather than doing some careful engineering.

We talked about the Ground Segment and the Store-and-Forward mode. Dougherty didn't want us to use Store-and-Forward (he never wanted what he could not understand), because our glorious computer guys didn't want to integrate it into our software. They complained it was such a big program (which it wasn't — anything that had over two lines of code was big to them)! I explained to Dougherty that when I had to fire the engines in the pulse mode to do an orbital maintenance burn (OMB) in the dark, I needed Store-and-Forward to get the phasing correct since we would not have a sun pulse to do that. Since, statistically speaking, 40% of my OMBs would be in the dark, if I did not have Store-and-Forward, I could not do the burns at the aposelene or periselene to conserve fuel. Rather, I would have to do the OMBs at the nodes and that would take twice as much fuel for every set of burns. If nature conspired against me and all of my OMBs were in the dark, I would have to do all the OMBs as nodal burns and I would use twice as much fuel. Thus, instead of having enough fuel for a three-year mission, I would have only enough for a year and one-half mission. That finally shut Dougherty up.

Gerry, Alex, and Woody were going to Spectrum Astro for the final review of the C&DH, so we were trying to finalize everything for the Ground Segment, which interfaced totally with the C&DH. As Gerry said, the initialization sequence and everything else had to be finalized very soon so the C&DH could be finished. Thus, I was in the process of finishing the initialization sequence.

I was concerned about getting the spacecraft reoriented as soon as possible after the TLI burn so the Earth would be in the optimum part of the spacecraft's antenna pattern, rather than having the butt of the spacecraft, and hence, the worst part of the OMNI antenna pattern, pointing at Earth. I had decided to put the PIV open command in the initialization sequence. Also, I was going to have the convolutional encoder turned off because, in case the Air Force did track us right after the TLI burn, I wanted to be able to communicate with Lunar Prospector using the Air Force station in the Seychelles Islands in the Indian Ocean, and that station did not have a convolutional decoder. Alex had added both of those commands to the initialization sequence.

However, when I was walking back from watching the final static test, I thought, *crap, if the PIV is opened automatically and something is wrong with the engines — one of the valves had somehow gotten open or if there is a leak, an engine could be firing for 33 minutes before I could do anything about it (before the spacecraft rose over the Goldstone station in California and I could start commanding the spacecraft)!* I immediately talked to Irv about that and he agreed it was a mistake to open the PIV during the initialization sequence. I called Spectrum Astro, since Alex and Gerry were in the airplane on their way to Phoenix, and told Spectrum Astro to make sure that Alex took the PIV open command out of the sequence.

Tuesday, July 16, through Friday, July 19, 1996: A Trip to the Cape

Tuesday morning I flew off to the Cape for the meeting about the destruct system on the TLI Stage and it took most of the day to get there, via St. Louis. Irv, Francisco, and TC Noble were already there. The four of us met and had a great dinner. The weather was hot and muggy.

The meeting on Wednesday went quite well. Basically, we learned that we were going to have to have a destruct system whether we liked it or not. The Range Safety engineers talked about their needing breakup models of the spacecraft, so they would know how big the pieces would be that could rain down on Florida, if the rocket went in the wrong direction and was blown up over land. They were also worried about the little spin up motors!

TC, who had been there for several days, was boiling mad because our glorious LLV2 friend Uselman hadn't given the Range Safety crew the information they needed. For example, they asked Uselman how much fuel was on board the spacecraft and Uselman said that he had no idea, even though TC had told him 137 kg! That was about the 20th time that Uselman had said he did not have information we had given him. He is totally incompetent. He either forgot or didn't write it down or ignored whatever we told him and he always claimed we hadn't given him the information to cover up his stupidity. TC was really mad because the Range Safety guys were taking it out on Lunar Prospector, because they were not getting any cooperation from LLV2 (what was new about that). I had never seen TC so mad.

Unfortunately, I did not know the meeting was scheduled for just the morning. If I had known that, I would have gone to Disney World in the afternoon and had my hotel in Orlando, but of course, it was too late for that, so I went to the Space Center and looked around.

The next morning I got up and tried to fly home. I got in the airplane at 8:20 AM and it took off, but it didn't go anywhere. About an hour into the flight, the pilot said we were circling Orlando because they could not pressurize the cabin. He said further that we were either going to go back to Orlando or on to Atlanta to get it fixed. They decided after another 20 minutes to fly to Atlanta, so we flew slow and low to Atlanta, got it fixed after an hour and finally after 6 hours of being in the airplane, I got to St. Louis, where, of course, I had missed my connection and had to wait until 5:00 PM to get another flight. It was a long, hard day.

I also found out on the trip that more and more of my guys were working on the damned IMAGE proposal with Tenerelli, so I decided it was time to raise hell.

Monday, July 22, 1996: We Pass the Static Test

When I got to work in the morning, I found out that Tenerelli had been yanked off of the proposal (no surprise there) and they told Dougherty to finish the damned thing. My entire damned crew was working on the damned IMAGE proposal and I was furious. I wanted to talk to Frank about that, but he was not around. I went over to Ames and told Scott that everybody was off working on the IMAGE proposal, including Dougherty, and Scott was furious, too!

When I got back to Lockheed, I went over to see where the spacecraft was. I finally found it over in the fabrication shop and it was still sitting there on the transporter. It had been sitting there for two damned days. Nothing had happened. I was doubly ticked off.

I found Tim Maloney and asked him why in hell nothing had been done on the spacecraft? He answered that the technicians were supposed to have worked on it, but they were held up because they didn't have the drill patterns. I asked why in hell weren't the patterns made when we were in static testing? He said they had started to, but, but, but, —. Once again things were done in series instead of in parallel and we were just wasting time.

I went looking for Dougherty, who wasn't around, and Frank, who still wasn't around. I asked where Frank was and Arthurine said I could see him at about 1:00 PM.

I got a report on the static tests from Thang Nguyen, our Structural Analysis Engineer. Clearly, we were going to have to strengthen the side panels so they didn't flex so much. That would cost 1 to 1½ kg. The popping was almost certainly due to metal slipping on metal, probably the bolts. There was some slight deformation around the upper two inserts, but you could just barely see the deformation if you looked tangentially along the spacecraft. Anyway, Thang said that was OK because it had not damaged anything and everything else was perfect! That was great news; we had just gotten through our first test hurdle!

Thang said he had found the reason his strain model of the panels was incorrect. In his model, he had assumed the side panels were continuously secured all along their edges, and, of course, individual bolts secured them. When he corrected the model for that, it predicted the strain would be 1 cm, which was almost exactly what we had measured. That was understood and we had passed the static tests.

Thang said they had done an ultrasound test on the structure and found that nothing was delaminated, cracked, or broken in any way and that they were going to do one more test to make sure that everything was OK. If it was OK, then we were ready to move on.

I finally saw Frank at about 1:30 PM. He asked, "Are we behind schedule, is this (everybody working on the IMAGE proposal) causing any trouble?"

I said, "Yes, it is causing trouble and yes, we are way behind schedule."

He said, "Well, let's get Tom Dougherty in here and find out what is going on."

I said, "I'm concerned and annoyed about this. I should have been asked or at least told what was happening."

Frank said, "Well, we didn't have to tell you anything. These are my people and they work for Tom and not for you. But, I agree we should have told you." He asked if I had told Scott, because Scott had called him.

I answered, "Yes, of course I did."

He asked, "Why didn't you tell me first."

I answered, "Because you weren't around and I got to Scott first. Besides, NASA and Ames are my customers and not Lockheed, so why shouldn't I go to Ames first?"

I tried to get my concerns across to him, concerns that were obvious to anyone, but he just dodged the issue. Basically it was the same old story, Lockheed came first and Lunar Prospector came in a distant second and I didn't have any right to bitch. Like all Lockheed managers, Frank just shouted (figuratively speaking) me down. There was no reason or logic behind their taking my staff away when we were behind schedule, except that it was "in the best interests of the company," period.

Frank called Dougherty in and he answered Frank's question by saying, "Well, last week, of course, it didn't cause any problem; but this week, yes, people were not working on Lunar Prospector that should have been."

Frank said, "Well, should we shut the proposal down?" which I knew Frank would not do under any circumstances.

Dougherty said, "No, we're going to get it done on the weekend."

I sat down with Dougherty after we left Frank's office and I told him about TC's concerns that LLV and Uselman were causing a great deal of trouble with Range Safety at the Cape and Francisco's lack of being able to handle LLV. Dougherty said he had somebody to take over Francisco's place (that never happened).

We talked about Mario's concerns about the back wiring of the solar panels. Mario said if they did the back wiring right, the spacecraft would be magnetically clean.

We got a snotty email from George Pack saying the Goddard scientists obviously learned their physics from a course called "Physics for Poets," since they did not know what they were doing and if we did what Mario wanted to have done, it would cost a few hundred thousand dollars more and cause a three month delay — that was pure BS. We talked about that and Dougherty got a little miffed and said, "He (George) is one of the best in the business."

I said, "There is nobody better than Mario; Mario is the world's expert in magnetics. Besides, Mario is the customer (through me) and George is an ass." Dougherty then sort of whined, "I don't know, who am I to believe?"

I answered, "Mario."

TC came by and told Dougherty about the way LLV was ticking off Range Safety and about the bad job LLV was doing.

Tuesday, July 23, 1996

I worked all day defining the launch windows in case Cassini chased us out of our October 9 launch date.

I looked at the spacecraft. The technicians had all the brackets done that were needed to strengthen the panels and they were getting ready to mount them, but they were as slow as molasses in January (despite it being July).

Chapter 3-19
The Delivery of the Engines and the Tanks

Wednesday, July 24, 1996

I received the test data on our six engines from Olin and they looked very good. The engines all had higher ISP than we had specified and somewhat better thrust than we had hoped. Two of them were really well matched for the long burns, so I tentatively was going to use them as the A1&A2 engines. Then I paired up the other four engines and tentatively selected the A3&A4 and the T1&T2 pairs.

Bill, Scott, Bob McMurray, and I talked about the APS light filters. Bill was going to test the foils for a thousand cycles, mimicking the spin period, and if they held up, we would use them, because it turned out that depositing the filters on the detectors was a tricky job.

Thursday, July 25, 1996: Getting My Engines

I flew up to Seattle with Irv and his wife to attended the ceremony that Olin had set up to give me my engines. The ceremony was fun and then Olin had a nice picnic for everyone.

As I flew back that evening, I had a great view of the Cascade Volcanoes. I had a really good day.

Friday, July 26, 1996

I got a lot of little things done. I finished making changes to the launch window study based on revised data Ken Galal gave me. But basically, I just got a lot of stuff cleaned off my desk.

Monday, July 29, 1996: Subsystem Review Day

I talked to Irv about the engines, since I had worked on their test data all weekend and the engines seemed to fall into two groups of three each. He said the orifices of the first three were bored at a different time than those of the latter three, so the differences I saw in the data were apparently real, though not significant. But, since I wanted to really understand those engines, I wanted to have an explanation for any variations, no matter how small. We asked Olin to send us the data they had on some water tests they did, in which they forced water through the orifices. Those data would allow us to determine if there were systematic differences between the engines and allow us to make the final selection of the engines for the A1&A2, A3&A4 and T1&T2 pairs.

Dan reported that the IR Limb Crossing Sensor had apparently degraded during testing. The detector is hydroscopic, so it degrades when exposed to the moisture in the air, but can be restored by heating it and baking out the adsorbed water. They were going to take the detector out, bake out the adsorbed water, put it back in, and seal the sensor. Then they would fix it so that, during launch, when the atmospheric pressure had dropped below 300 millibars, a spring would open a little door and expose the detector to the vacuum of space and that would suck out any adsorbed water and the sensor would be fine after that.

Nothing happened to the spacecraft for the last several days. Tom Chinn was also concerned about that, so Dougherty was going to see why no progress had been made.

Tuesday, July 30, 1996

For the first time Tom and I spent the day at Ames in our new offices. It was fun; it was nice being away from Lockheed. We had our Ground Segment telecon and it went a little bit better than the previous one.

The spacecraft was still just sitting over there in the shop while the technicians just piddled around on it.

Wednesday, July 31, and Thursday, August 1, 1996: The LLV2 Meeting at Headquarters

It took all day Wednesday to fly to Washington. Julius and Pat thought I was coming in the previous night, so they were surprised to see me when I did arrive. We had a nice dinner at a Mexican restaurant.

The meeting was about the LLV2, and Wes, Earle Huckins, and the LLV Chief Engineer, Buzz, were there, and Buzz gave most of the presentation. Wes was in and out because his secretary kept calling him out of the meeting.

When Buzz showed the configuration of the LLV2 with Lunar Prospector on it, Wes said, "Wait a minute, that's just an LLV1 with a booster, isn't it?"

Buzz said, "Yes."

And Wes said, "Gee, that's completely different than I thought. We thought it was two LLVs stacked on top of each other. This is a whole different story. This is something we are used to. We used to do sounding rockets like that, just put a booster on them."

Right then and there, Buzz and I knew he had made our point. It was clear they had not understood what the LLV2 was in comparison to the LLV1, but finally they did — after nearly a year!

Buzz had a viewgraph comparing an LLV1 with an LLV2. It showed, for example, that during the first stage burn, the LLV1 has about 27,000 Newtons/m^2 of dynamical pressure at max Q and a maximum acceleration of about 6.7 g's, while during the first stage burn of the LLV2, because it has a bigger load, the maximum acceleration is only 1.9 g's and the dynamical pressure at max Q is only about 7,000 Newtons/m^2. All the launch loads are more favorable for the LLV2 than for the LLV1. That impressed them and Wes understood. He pointed to Earl and said, "That's the guy you gotta please, if he is happy, then I am happy." Both of them agreed that the difference between an LLV1 and an LLV2 wasn't as big as they thought — LLV2 really just had a booster stage. However, they made it clear that their comments were just "off the cuff" and that everything had to be properly evaluated at Headquarters.

With those remarks, and if Lewis & Clark were successfully launched, I thought we would be able to pull off our launch on the first LLV2. As Wes said, "It's not a real big change and we are going to lose too much science if we delay things (for CRSS)."

Even though I didn't have to say a word, other than just pleasantries, it was a perfect meeting. We had made several steps forward regarding our LLV2 launch.

I flew home and had a great time looking at the geology. We flew right over Mono Lake; I saw the silisic volcanics all the way down from the little one up near Mono Lake down to Glass Mountain. It was beautiful from the air. I saw a caldera somewhere in, I thought, Utah, as well as sand dunes, deflation depressions, rivers, and just tons of geology all the way home. Also, there were two big forest fires on the west side of the Sierras. I had a really good time flying home.

Friday, August 2, 1996

Sylvia called and wanted me to come over to Ames because they were fussing about a number of Outreach Program issues.

First, Scott was concerned that the science data would be presented to the public before it was put into the archives and that was a load of BS. After all, it is the taxpayer's data, and nobody could do anything with the data in its raw form, anyway.

Second, George French wanted exclusive rights to do his part of the Outreach and I agreed we couldn't give him that.

Third, Scott didn't want the Outreach computer used to send the data to my Co-Is at their home institutions.

Fourth, Scott didn't want the slow scan TV camera in Mission Ops to be controlled by the Outreach people. He wanted it to be controlled by NASA, so my attempts to get the TV part of the program paid for by Outreach would not work, which was stupid.

Of all that nonsense, the thing that annoyed me most was that NASA was concerned about having the data presented to the public in real-time. They were so afraid somebody might misinterpret the data! They were undoing all the good George and I were accomplishing by having the Outreach Program engage the public in the mission and let students get to the data for their education. I decided I would make my concerns known at the appropriate time. Stupid NASA always undoes the good things it does by excluding the public for fear that some of those "unwashed ignoramuses" might actually learn something and question NASA's role in space.

Regarding the LLV2 meeting at Headquarters of the day before, Scott said everything looked good in the morning, but by the afternoon, Headquarters was worried about the Lewis & Clark LLV1 launches. They said there was a lot of political pressure on the Agency and they couldn't have a failure, and blah, blah, blah. NASA's timidity overwhelmed the brave stand Wes had taken on the LLV2 in just a few hours!

The issues were: Goldin didn't want to have a first launch mission; NASA didn't want us interfering with Cassini; and NASA didn't want us launching and failing just one month before they were to start putting the Space Station together in November (no problem there, the Russians launched the first element of the Space Station on November 20, 1998 — one year later than planned). In other words, NASA was concerned that a Lunar Prospector launch failure might reflect badly on NASA's ability to carry out the Cassini and Space Station programs and that was just more NASA BS to me. I said to Scott, "What it boils down to is, if they start getting conservative on us — as they are doing — we'll have to put the spacecraft in a big baggy, because they'll tell us to store it for several months and wait until a more opportune time. Then the science mission will go to hell because I'll have less than a six-month mission instead of a real mission, and Lunar Prospector will end up in the Smithsonian (the Air and Space Museum) instead of flying. They will just start slipping us and then they will say, because the costs are going up and you can't even do a six-month mission, we are canceling you — and then it's off to the museum with Lunar Prospector." I was really ticked off.

Dan Swanson had looked at the engine misalignment problem and the fact that we wouldn't know where the engine thrust vectors were pointing to anything better than 1°. He was concerned that we might have sufficient uncoupled torques to cause the spacecraft to spin-down completely or spin-up really fast during the long LOI burns. Thus, we thought we might have to spend a lot of fuel and time making the spacecraft do what I wanted it to do, because we were not going to get those engines lined up as accurately as I had expected.

I talked to Tim Maloney and he said that he was trying to figure out why nothing was happening with the spacecraft!

Monday, August 5, 1996: Subsystem Review Day

The C&DH had reprogrammed itself at the end of a test and nobody could figure out how or why! Gerry said it might have had something to do with the test set up, but nobody knew for sure. Scary — I had a haunted C&DH!

Able Engineering was going to start testing the booms the following week, and if everything went well, they would deliver the booms to us the following week for installation on the spacecraft.

The fuel tanks were coming in on Friday.

There was still not a whole hell of a lot of work being done on the spacecraft's structure and I was getting more and more concerned about that. The technicians said they would be done with it by the end of the week. If so, they would really have to hustle.

The cost of the system to keep the TLI Stage from colliding with the spacecraft after separation went up from $30,000 to nearly $200,000, so we were looking at alternatives. Irv and Dougherty suggested using the spacecraft engines to do that automatically, but the engines didn't have enough thrust to insure that the spacecraft could get away from the TLI Stage, so the stage could still bang into us. Also, I was not willing to have those engines fire automatically when the spacecraft was going to be out of communications for more than 33 minutes. If they didn't turn off after the 30 to 40 seconds they would have to be on to have a fighting chance to get the spacecraft away from the TLI Stage, then my spacecraft would use up a lot of its fuel, totally screw-up our translunar trajectory, and the mission would be lost. We had to have a different solution. Dougherty said we had the money to cover the anti-collision device if necessary, but clearly we didn't want to spend $200,000 on it if we didn't have to. Also, Francisco, Irv, and Dougherty were going to try to find out why the cost had jumped so much.

Irv and I got the additional information from Olin we wanted on the engines and Olin agreed that the systematic differences that I had found between the engines were real, but they were not sure what caused them. We were trying to understand the new data. I was of the opinion that, since the systematic differences were real, I would stick with the engine pairing I had already made and we could start getting them put on the spacecraft, especially since the tanks were being delivered in a few days.

I was getting concerned and annoyed because Scott was getting more and more conservative about everything since he had finally been given total (NASA) responsibility for the mission. There were two issues that Scott was fussing about. One was the duration of the launch window (which was essentially zero) and the second was the possibility of a delay until LLV2 had launched CRSS. I still maintained that if they made us wait for CRSS, we were going to end up never flying.

In order to placate Scott's worries about having to wait for CRSS, Dougherty had again brought up the possibility of putting a bigger battery in Lunar Prospector so we could survive the lunar eclipses. That was a load of crap, as it always had been, and it was an even bigger load of crap at that point in time since the spacecraft structure had been put together and the center of gravity was frozen in May when we drilled the structure for the tank boss bolts. If we added a 10 kg battery at the top of the spacecraft, we would have to add 10 kg's to the bottom of the spacecraft to keep the cg where the tanks were. Also, since we already had the wiring diagrams and everything else completed, we would have to do all that over again. Dougherty was talking about essentially rebuilding the spacecraft — though he was too dumb to know that. His suggestion was just pure nonsense.

I talked to John Gruener about the Outreach Program George was developing and the fact that Scott and NASA didn't want us releasing the data to the teachers and the students right away. John said they had been having the teachers who were attending the Huntsville Space Camp run their Moonlink simulation and the teachers were just going wild about it. I said that one way we could avoid the problem, since NASA was mainly concerned about somebody interpreting or misinterpreting the NS data about the water ice (at that time, we thought that the NS data could possibly be crudely interpreted by the man on the street) was to keep the NS data from the public and release the rest of the data in real-time. However, I did not like doing that because all the data belonged to the United States public, not to NASA and not to us.

We talked about how the different schools that were going to subscribe to Moonlink would pick their areas of study on the Moon. There are sixteen hundred 5° x 5° resolution elements on the Moon's surface. I suggested that John and the rest of the Moonlink crew could just start assigning them to classes at the equator and by the time they got near the poles, where the water ice might be found, there wouldn't be that many classes left to assign areas to. John said, "No, the teachers want to pick their own areas."

I asked, "Well, what if there is overlap?"

He answered, "Some of them want that. For example, a Japanese school and an American school want to have the same area so they can have a 'hands across the ocean' experience." I thought that was tremendous and that the idiots at NASA were just throwing away a golden educational and outreach opportunity if they didn't let us release the data in real-time. There just had to be a way to get around those idiots.

Tuesday, August 6, 1996

I got in at 5:30 AM and documented all the arguments against putting a bigger battery in the spacecraft — just in case I needed to present them to NASA.

Tom and I went over to Ames for a telecon with the Palo Alto software guys on the Ground Segment and that went well.

Some progress had been made getting the spacecraft put together, but it was damned slow.

I worked on the command and downlink lists that we were getting ready to finalize.

Wednesday, August 7, 1996

Nothing much happened all day, so I got to work on the command and downlink lists most of the day.

Thursday, August 8, 1996: Subsystem Review Day

Gerry and Spectrum Astro found out what was wrong with the C&DH and just had to replace one component.

The IR Limb Crossing Sensor was finished being modified to take care of the adsorbed water problem.

The engines were in, the tanks were coming in the next day or Monday, and the spacecraft was slowly getting put together, but it was still taking forever.

Scott said we couldn't give George exclusive rights to do the Outreach Educational Program, because he had no contract to do so (no surprise there). Scott suggested that we could put out a RFP for the Education and Outreach Program and have people bid on it. If George won, then he would have the exclusive rights to do it.

I called George and told him what Scott had told me. George was very unhappy, he was concerned that if he put a half million dollars into developing the text and the computer programs and sent them out to the schools, anybody could duplicate the whole thing and then compete with him. I understood George's concerns, but I didn't know what he was going to do about the problem. I was disappointed that Scott and NASA were screwing up the Outreach Program.

Friday, August 9, 1996: Fourteen Months to Launch?

We reviewed the launch constraints and decided we would probably move our launch date back to October 8 to get out of Cassini's way. However, Scott was concerned about Cassini pushing our launch date around willy-nilly, so he was pushing for us to go two weeks earlier, i.e., to launch well before the Cassini launch window even opened.

The other problem was that the weather at the Cape gets worse the further you get into October and November, so we wanted to get data on past weather scrubs as a function of time to try to understand that problem.

I was beginning to get a suspicion that our picking a launch date was going to be a lot bigger problem than I had hoped.

Irv, Dan, and I finalized the selection of the engine pairs and their assignment. We ended up putting the engines on the spacecraft pretty much the way I thought we would based on my earlier assessment of the Olin data.

The tanks arrived and they were beautiful. We had all the components of the propulsion system in house!

I showed Lunar Prospector to a group of visiting teachers and that was fun.

I went through the Mission Profile and added in all the hexadecimal (base 16) numbers for all the commands that Gerry gave me. When I issued a command, it would be uplinked to the spacecraft as a hexadecimal number the spacecraft could read, then the C&DH would check the number against its library of hexadecimal commands and verify it and then send it back down to Earth where it would appear on my command console screen. I would then cross check the hexadecimal number against the number

I had sent up to the spacecraft to insure that nothing had gotten garbled during the uplink. If the two hexadecimal numbers were the same, I would then have the Execute Command sent to the spacecraft. Those hexadecimal numbers were a very important addition to the Mission Profile.

Tom and I got the documents for LRI notarized and we were hopeful we could get into LRI in the not-too-distant future.

Finally, I went over to look at the spacecraft and they were getting it done as slowly as molasses.

Then I went home and Rebecca and I got ready to leave on our vacation the next day.

Saturday, August 10, through Sunday Afternoon, August 18, 1996: A Cascades Vacation

Rebecca and I left on our vacation Saturday morning. We went to Mt. St. Helens, Crater Lake, Mt. Lassen, and several other places in the Cascades. We relaxed and had a great time.

Chapter 3-20
A Major Power Crisis

Late Sunday, August 18, 1996: A Hot Solar Array

I talked with Tom after we got back from our vacation and he told me that Jim Schirle's thermal calculations were still screwed up and that Jim found that the temperature of the solar array was probably going to be higher than we thought. That meant the voltages and amperages would be lower than we expected and that got the battery people and George Pack all worked up. They had said we had to have the higher voltages; otherwise the battery would not completely charge up after the maximum nighttime passes of 47 minutes. George wanted to add more solar cells. Another possibility was using solar cell cover glasses that reflect the red and infrared solar radiation. That would keep the solar array cool and probably take care of the problem, but, in any case, they wanted to double the battery size, i.e., have a 9 amp-hr battery.

As usual, they just ignored the impacts on the spacecraft that doubling the battery would cause. The battery mass would increase by 5 kg and, since we already had the spacecraft structure built and the holes drilled for the tanks, we would have to balance that mass out. We would first have to ballast it out in the XY plane and that would add another 5 kg. Then we would have to balance out both the battery and the added ballast in the $-Z$ direction by adding another 10 kg of ballast at the bottom of the spacecraft. I would have to take a 20 kg hit on the spacecraft's mass and there was no way in hell I would allow that.

Also as usual, the Lockheed engineers were overly conservative and were running scared — it was always easiest to throw money and mass at a problem, rather than fix it right. As Tom had correctly told them, "Hey, if necessary, we can shut the science instruments off if we get in a position where the battery is getting depleted. We are not increasing the battery, no way." Tom had defended my position in my absence and I was very pleased. Happily, Dougherty was gone during that episode, so he had not added to the problem.

Then, to my surprise, Tom said that Dale Vaccarello jumped on the side of George Pack and said, "Alan can't dictate what goes on in the spacecraft; this is a NASA problem, they are the real customer." That really surprised me because Dale had always been one of the few Lockheed guys who reminded everybody that I was the customer.

Anyway, good old Woody jumped in and replied, "That's a bunch of BS. Alan can dictate anything he wants. He's the only person who knows everything about this spacecraft. He's the only person I have ever worked with who works with all the engineers on every detail and who has solved all the serious problems, made the hard decisions, and is willing to stand up and say, yes — I was wrong, when he is wrong."

Then Jim Schirle jumped on the bandwagon and said, "Yeah, he has worked with everyone of us engineers. He knows what is going on and he can make these decisions. It's his decision and if he wants to dictate, he will dictate." I would have liked to have heard all that; but hearing Tom relate it to me was good enough. Too bad Dougherty was not around to hear it.

With that assault from Woody and Jim, George and Dale backed down and Tom said, "You aren't going to make any decisions about this until Alan is back." Tom had used all the right reasoning and had held his ground and I was very pleased and proud of him.

Tom also said that Sylvia had got ticked off at him. She had asked him to get some photographs and PR information about the instruments for Goldin and I had told him to tell her, "OK, but if it interferes with Bill or Dave (Curtis) getting the instruments delivered on time, we are not going to do it." Sylvia jumped all over Tom about that and said it had to be done, because she had made a commitment to Goldin. I was not very happy to hear about that because it was interfering with the real work. While PR is very important, it cannot take precedence over the primary work.

Monday, August 19, 1996: Battery and Power Problems

Happily, Dougherty was still on vacation. He would be back the next day and we would then have the weekly subsystem review.

The main event of the day was, of course, the power problem. I went through the fuel usage program and, as expected, if we added 20 kg of battery and ballast, it would cut over a year off the mission. That was the solid information I would use if it came to a knockdown and drag-out fight over the battery issue.

Woody came in and we discussed the issue and the whole issue of a bigger battery was dead. Woody killed it himself when he said, "It's stupid, you don't solve a solar array problem by having a bigger battery." Woody killed it and I was pleased about that.

We discussed the solar array problem, which was that the array was going to be too hot around β zero. Then the array wouldn't produce enough voltage to charge the battery. We discussed the ins and outs of that and there were two questions, "Would the voltage be high enough to charge the battery once it gets nearly full and would there be enough power to do it?"

Regarding the first issue, if we didn't have 33 or 34 volts, we could only get a 90 to 95% charge level on the battery. But what difference would that make? As far as I was concerned, as long as we didn't totally discharge the battery during the 47-minute nighttime part of the orbit and as long as the battery charged back up to the 90 to 95% level each time — that would be OK. It would not be the way we would want to do it, but it would work and it had to work only around β zero.

Regarding the power issue, at such high temperatures, there would not be enough power to charge the battery. However, like all Lockheed engineering models, Woody's models had been the worst-case models and not the real-case models. All of Woody's models had always been based on the highest temperatures generated exactly at the subsolar point with β exactly equal to zero, i.e., when the spacecraft would be above the hottest part of the Moon (the solar array's temperature strongly depends on the temperature of that part of the Moon's surface the spacecraft is flying over at that moment).

When Woody told me that the fuss was based on the worst-case temperature model, I said, "Yeah, but the Moon is cooler everywhere else. You need to generate the real-case model using the integrated effect of the solar array temperature over the sun-lit part of the orbit. The result has to be that there is more power (and higher voltages) in the real-case than in the worst-case models." Woody said he would generate the real-case models and we asked Jim Schirle to generate the thermal data over an entire orbit so Woody could integrate the power profile over the entire orbit.

There was the possibility of using the red reflecting cover glasses and Woody and I were hoping they might drop the temperature of the array by 10 to 15° C, but it turned out that the cover glasses would drop it only 5° C. They would cost about $30,000, but that was a small price to pay for 5° C we were certainly going to need.

The other thing was that the colored glasses are 0.1 mm thick, instead of 0.2 mm like the clear glass covers and that would mean that there would be more breakage of the glasses during the construction of the solar array. Strangely enough, George Pack said, "Oh, we can handle that." Those guys changed their stories to fit whichever direction they want to go in! Woody and I decided to get the 0.1 mm cover glasses, in part, because they were already being made for another Lockheed program, so we could just have the manufacturer increase that existing order to cover our needs. Also, if we wanted to use the 0.2 mm cover glasses, that would have been a new order and would have caused a 3 to 4 month delay. We couldn't fool around like that; we had to get the solar array construction going.

Given the need for more power and a little higher voltage, Woody really wanted his 5 cm extension of solar array. As we had discussed in the past, if we added the 5 cm to the bottom of the array, it could be damaged during separation and there would be more shadowing by the instruments down there. Also, according to Jim Schirle, the upper part of the array was going to be cooler than the lower part, since Jim was not going to have a thermal shield covering the top of the spacecraft, and hence, the solar array heat could radiate from the inside of the drum. If we had to add the 5 cm skirt, it would be better to do so at the top.

I was fighting to keep from having any extra solar array surface because we had already started making the panels, and if we changed their size, we would have to start all over again. Also, I believed that when Woody finished with his real-case calculations, we would find that the power and voltage shortages had disappeared, i.e., we were chasing a ghost.

Al Tilley said we needed to add a couple of kilograms on the upper part of the spacecraft anyway, so the top would be the place to put the 5 cm extension from the standpoint of the mass properties. If I had to add mass, I might as well add useful mass.

However, countering that positive argument was the negative argument concerning the critical moment of inertia ratio of 1.07. We had already added the little thermal cap to the Omni antenna to keep it warm and that had decreased our critical moment of inertia ratio. Enlarging the solar array in the +Z direction would make that ratio even lower.

Jim Beffa said if we extend the solar array upward, it would degrade the pattern of the medium gain antenna. He had already pointed out that the A3 and A4 engine mounts caused a 2 dB ripple in the antenna pattern and that if we extended the solar array by 5 cm, it would decrease the gain of the antenna from just under 9 dB to as little as 6 dB. Worse, it would shift the plane of the antenna's pattern from 90°, i.e., from the XY plane, to something significantly less than that — and we couldn't have that! If we were going to extend the solar array at the top, we were going to have to raise the antenna off the shelf by 5 to 7 cm. That, of course, would increase the mass and lower the moment of inertia ratio below 1.07, and we couldn't have that either.

Then there was the problem that so many parts were already finished, besides the panels. They would have to be modified if we extended the array upwards. We would have to have a cutout in the panel for the MAG, because the place where the MAG extension boom bracket was to fasten to the spacecraft's structure would be below the top of the solar panel extension and that could not be changed — it was already glued and screwed on to the structure. The same thing held for the bracket for the Sun Sensor and IR Limb Crossing Sensor (thought it was not yet mounted to the structure).

Despite Woody thinking he desperately needed the solar array extension, there were numerous problems with that idea. I hoped and expected Woody's final model would show there was no power problem. Regardless of the final outcome, Jim Schirle felt very badly about screwing up the thermal models and causing so many problems.

I went to Ames and talked to Scott about a number of issues. I crabbed about my being the PI, but not really having the responsibility I was supposed to have at either NASA or Lockheed (a constant complaint on my part, but one I was very serious about, because I absolutely believe that science programs should be run by scientists, not by engineers or bureaucrats). We talked about Sylvia being miffed because she didn't get her pictures and her chewing out Tom. We talked about the battery and the launch.

Basically, I was trying to tell Scott that we were doing well, but I wanted to make sure we would do better in terms of demonstrating that the PIs should run the missions.

Also, I told him, despite the fact that Dougherty was technically incompetent, he was doing a marvelous job of keeping us financially solvent, keeping us more or less on schedule, and that he was doing the best he could with the personnel we had and the fact that Lockheed kept taking our people away, e.g., to work on the IMAGE Proposal. I was very concerned about the last point because Lockheed had won the IMAGE contract and I was sure that was going to cause us trouble.

Tuesday, August 20, 1996

Woody and I worked on the power problem all morning. Woody was getting all the data together and we would be able to make the final analysis in a day or two.

Dougherty spent most of his time with the people from Southwest Research Institute who were at Lockheed to kick off the work on IMAGE. That ticked me off because, as I feared, Lockheed was putting a lot of my team on the IMAGE team and Dougherty had to do a lot of the management, because Dale couldn't really do it.

I talked to Sylvia and said, "This isn't going to work, they (my staff) are just going to go off and do IMAGE. This is a load of crap. Lockheed won't do anything about it until we start missing deadlines. Lockheed is just screwing Lunar Prospector because they always want the next one. They don't care about Lunar Prospector and that has me concerned."

After that, Woody and I talked about the power again. We decided to get Woody his 5 cm extension, if necessary, by putting half of it on top and half on the bottom. That way, we would mitigate all the problems caused by having the extension only at the top. I hoped we would be able to get that issue laid to rest at last.

I talked to Beffa about the effect of adding less than 2.5 cm to the top of the solar panels on the antenna patters and he said we would lose about 1 dB if we did not raise the antenna. That was not too bad, so I hoped we would soon get the entire issue resolved, but we went around and around on it all day.

JPL sent us a program for Mission Ops and we discussed it late in the afternoon. We were certainly going to use it, but we still had to check on a number of interface issues.

A few days earlier, after Bob Lin had found out we would have to add ballast to the MAG/ER to get the science instrument booms balanced, he asked if he could add an ion probe to the MAG/ER to study the lunar exosphere and I said a resounding, "NO." Bob had argued that the ion probe had a mass of about 1 kg, far less than the amount of ballast we would have to add, so it would be better to use that mass to get more science. He said it would cost nothing and would require no extra power or extra downlink capability. Thus, it was free — so why not add it to the payload. Well, despite Bob's assurances, there is not only no such thing as a free lunch (or launch as we say in our business), but there is also no such thing as a free science instrument and certainly not one that has a zero impact on the payload and spacecraft. I remained by my NO.

However, since Bob can't understand the word NO (maybe "No," is like the Clintonian word "is" and has different meanings depending on who is using it?), he called me again to argue about adding the ion probe to the MAG/ER. That annoyed me — he really would not take no for an answer and was oblivious to the fact that only an idiot would OK the addition of an untested piece of equipment to a spacecraft so late in a program. There was no reasoning with him, so finally I just said, "No, and I mean No."

Beyond that, the spacecraft still had not moved one centimeter towards the test area. They were still fiddling around with it in the shop.

Wednesday, August 21, 1996

George French called at about 9:00 AM. He had calmed down and wanted to make sure we would do the Outreach. I told him, "I'm ticked off at NASA about this and you have to realize something, NASA is stupid. NASA just doesn't know how to do anything right." I had to tell him that about three times and then he started to believe it. I asked, "Do you understand now why I have tried to stay as far away from NASA as I can?"

Though he was still a little worried about not having exclusive rights to do the Outreach, he realized he was way ahead of anyone else and said, "I have put a lot of money in this and nobody is going to catch me."

Nevertheless, we still had to be sure NASA would let him do Moonlink, so I asked, "Have you talked to (Congressman) Sensenbrenner or anybody."

He answered, "No, but I have enough contacts to get something done."

I said, "If we have to, we'll play that (political) card, but we will get this done."

Then we talked about getting LRI going and I told him how far we had come in getting LRI set up.

I was very pleased at the end because George was upbeat when we finished, even though he had been very downbeat when he called.

Tom and I went over to Ames. Marcie wanted me to talk to the troops over there because they didn't understand how Lunar Prospector was going to be run in terms of commanding and maneuvers. I went through all that in great detail. It was a lot of fun and lasted about two hours. It was fun being over there with people who wanted to work, who wanted to get things done, and who weren't combative — both Tom and I really enjoyed it.

When we got back to Lockheed, the spacecraft had finally been taken over to the test area, so we went over to see it.

Woody was still working on the data to figure out what we had to do about our power problem.

Al Tilley came over and indicated that we probably should put the 5 cm extension of the solar array at the top of the spacecraft. By doing so, it wouldn't have much of a mass hit and though the moment of inertia ratio would come down a little bit, it would not be enough to hurt. Damn, I was getting tired of those 5 cm!

To my great surprise, Dougherty came in my office, sat down, and did what he should have been doing all along — he asked me how everything was going and how we needed to proceed. He seemed to really understand that I knew what was going on. As I answered his questions, he again wrote little notes about what we needed to do, who he needed to talk to, and the like. We had a really decent conversation — a conversation between a PI and his Project Manager. If he had been doing that during the entire year, we would have been a lot further along. It was a very pleasant conversation because he was not trying to be the big shot; he was just trying to understand what was going on. I was surprised, I never knew what the Lockheed idiots were going to do, but that was nice.

I thought our mass wasn't going to grow at all because the tanks came in 1.6 kg light — hurray! Everything had been coming in light and even though we had to beef up the side panels and a couple of other things, I thought we were going to maintain the 290 kg of mass. I didn't think it was going to be much more than a kilogram either way, which was really fantastic and would be 5 kg less than I was modeling.

Thursday, August 22, 1996

Mario was in town, so I showed him the spacecraft. For some strange reason Mario had sent the MAG to us, instead of Berkeley. Why he sent it to us was a mystery to me and, of course, it got lost in Lockheed! Tom finally found it, it had been sent to the wrong place. We had the completed MAG!

Friday, August 23, 1996

Not a lot happened during the day. We sent the MAG to Berkeley where it belonged and where it should have been all the time. We discussed the Ground Segment. Actually, it was a very uneventful day — the kind of day that I needed a lot more of!

Monday, August 26, and Tuesday, August 27, 1996: LLV2 Review in Denver

The review was long and boring. Dougherty did pretty well. He is pretty good at hammering at things.

The big issues were related to the fixes that were made after the LLV1 test launch failure. There were two causes for the failure and two fixes.

First, unlike other solid fuel rocket designs, the Lockheed idiots had designed the LLVs to dump the hydraulic fluid that is used to move the engine bell to steer the rocket instead of containing it and thus saving a little weight. As a result, the hydraulic fluid caught on fire (now who would have expected that, considering that a flammable fluid was dumped into the flaming rocket exhaust?) and that caused the control lines to burn through! As a result, an embarrassed Lockheed had added a hydraulic fluid capture tank to the first stage of the LLV1s and LLV2s. However, in their infinite wisdom they decided not to put a capture in the second stage of the LLV2s because, "Gee, it (the second stage burn) will be higher up in the atmosphere and it shouldn't catch on fire." When we heard that, everybody just raised serious hell and LLV quickly said that they would add a capture tank to the second stage, too.

The second problem was that the same idiots did not protect the avionics package from electrical arcing at the critical altitude, so when the LLV1 test vehicle reached the critical altitude, electrical arcing occurred and the avionics were destroyed. Not only was the rocket uncontrollable because the control lines were burned up, the rocket's brains got electrically fried. Well, clearly they were going to build the avionics with the proper arc protection.

Though they had fixed those two problems, the fact that there were problems to begin with disturbed everyone. Both of those issues had been understood and resolved decades earlier when rocketry was in its infancy, so why were these supposedly great Lockheed rocket engineers making kindergarten mistakes? Part of the answer was that they had done most of the design by analysis, i.e., on a computer, but did very little testing. The moral of that sad story is, "You can't fly a paper rocket. You have to test the components to see whether they are going to work." All that LLV stupidity made me a little nervous.

Then Dougherty just raised hell when we found out that LLV was not going to test the new avionics in a thermal-vacuum chamber to see if their arc-suppressant system really worked! Would they ever learn?

After that, we found out that there was no way that we could launch during the October 9 time frame. Cassini wanted the 6th, 7th, and 8th and the Range had screwed up our paperwork requesting the October 9 and 10 launch dates. As a result, the Air Force was planning a launch on the 10th or 11th, so all that just wiped us out. Also, Cassini might jump to the 15th, or even to a different date. There was no way we would know what Cassini was going to do.

We looked at the data and I said, "OK, let's do it on the 24th or 25th of September, with the backup dates a month later, or possibly on the 9th — if it gets freed up, we could still keep the 9th." That seemed to be OK with everybody. Then we found out the DOD had a launch planned for September 25! The only dates that were free were in late October or early November, but by then we would be getting close to the supposed CRSS launch in December. I was concerned that NASA would just say, "Well, just wait for CRSS," but CRSS didn't want to fly first either. Also, the late October to early November dates were getting close to the supposed launch of the first Space Station component and they were still within the six-week long Cassini launch window. What a bunch of BS, all the big guys on the block were kicking little Lunar Prospector out of the way.

I said, "Look, enough is enough, I'm digging in my heels. We are going to request the 24th and we were going to fight for it. The Range screwed up by not processing our paperwork the way they were supposed to and that is part of the reason this fiasco occurred. We did everything right and the Range screwed up, so why should we suffer?" Then we re-discussed the launch dates and I again said that we should go for September 24 and 25, while keeping October 9 open and everybody agreed.

Then the damned LLV guys said that each launch trajectory (we needed a new one for each launch date) cost quarter of a million dollars. We couldn't afford that and Dougherty was really ticked off.

Wednesday, August 28, 1996

Woody was still trying to properly model the spacecraft's power budget and Dan and I talked about how we could pulse fire the tangential engines in the dark. Dan was skeptical, but I thought it would work.

Scott said when he talked to Headquarters about our launch date problems they said, "You guys will all be heroes if you get out of the way of Cassini." We had two things going for us; one was that we were doing NASA a favor by getting out of the way of Cassini. Two, since the Range had screwed up by improperly assigning the launch dates, we lost the 9th of October and they knew that it was their fault, not ours. The Range was going to have to help us by moving the DOD launch out of our way on September 24 or 25. At least, that was what I hoped.

Thursday, August 29, 1996: Staff Meeting Day

Woody was still struggling with the modeling of the thermal effects on the power over an entire orbit.

Frank called me into his office and I brought him up to date. He asked me about my future plans. I told him a little bit about LRI, but I didn't go into much detail because I didn't really want him to know too much about LRI.

Then he congratulated me on helping Lockheed win IMAGE, since it was my success with Lunar Prospector that helped convince Southwest to choose Lockheed. I said, "Well, I am pleased, because, as you remember two years ago when we were asking the New Business Council to have Lockheed become my Industry Partner, I told them Lunar Prospector would lead to follow-on business like this." He was pleased and sounded sincere.

Scott and I talked about the Outreach Program again and Scott not only didn't want the science data going out before it was edited, he didn't want the engineering data going out to the public either! I said, "There is no harm in having the engineering data go out." But Scott said Dougherty was concerned because of what NASA and Lockheed had experienced with Hubble Telescope's initial screw-up. That was just plain stupid. Scott and NASA were gutting the Outreach Program because they wanted to deny the public access to the scientific and engineering data in real-time. I argued, "The public doesn't care about seeing the stuff if it's two days old. They want to see what Lunar Prospector is doing right then. What are they (the public) going to do that could possibly harm us? Nobody is going to know enough about the spacecraft to know if the voltages are wrong or if the temperatures are wrong."

However, the fear that Scott and NASA had concerning the possibility that taxpayers might find out just what NASA is doing with their money paralyzes them. It was really pathetic; NASA always screws up PR because of its fear of having the public be involved with the missions in even the slightest way. They always say "We can't tell anybody about this, they might do something with it that would embarrass us."

Well, my opinion is, "They paid for it; they ought to be able to look at the data." I was so disgusted I just washed my hands of it.

Friday, August 30, 1996

Woody was in the midst of the model calculations and it looked like we were going to be 10% low on power because of the thermal effects. I said, "Well, have you considered the energy we will get from moonshine, the moon's albedo is 7%, so that gives us another 7% of power." Also, Woody's calculations were made for the end of a 3-year mission and hence, after the solar cells had been degraded due to solar cosmic ray events and assuming we had lost one string of solar cells. However, the spacecraft had to last only for the 1-year nominal mission and there was no real reason to assume that we would lose a string. I felt confident we would be OK, but man it would be close. I asked Woody to continue his work, taking into consideration the moonshine, leaving off the degradation, and keeping the lost string.

Bill got the data about the GRS resolution vs. temperature and it turned out it was very insensitive to temperatures in the $-25°$ to $-35°$ C range. Since we couldn't cool down $-40°$ C, our resolution wasn't going to be as good as we had hoped.

Our next big test was going to be the pyro-shock test, in which the shock caused by the firing of the explosive bolts was going to be measured at several points on the spacecraft's structure. That test was scheduled for the following Wednesday and the shake-test for the booms at Point Mugu (about 70 km down the coast from Able Engineering, right near Oxnard, CA) was also scheduled for Wednesday. I wanted to see both tests, but if they really occurred on the same day, I would fly down to Point Mugu with Bob Goldin to see the much more critical boom test.

Chapter 3-21
Drop Test, Pyro Tests, and Boom Shake Test

Saturday, August 31, 1996: Rebecca and the Drop Test

Rebecca and I went up to Lockheed because I forgot the charger for my laptop. While we were there, I wanted to show Rebecca the spacecraft. We went over to the test area and, to my surprise, the engineers were getting ready to do the first two drop tests of the TLI Stage casing to see how high it was going to bounce during the separation tests. We needed to know that since we did not want it to bounce back up and hit the spacecraft during the pyro-separation test, in which we were going to test the separation of the spacecraft from the TLI Stage by suspending the spacecraft and attached empty TLI Stage casing 10 and 20 cm above a foam pad, firing the explosive bolts, and letting the casing fall on to the foam. We watched the drop tests from 10 cm and 20 cm. It was really neat. I was especially pleased that Rebecca got to see the tests. Right after the drop tests were finished, the guys started getting things ready for the pyro-shock test.

Labor Day Weekend, 1996

Rebecca and I just relaxed and had a peaceful, long Labor Day weekend.

Tuesday, September 3, 1996

Happily, Dougherty was still on his long Labor Day weekend vacation, but it was still a hectic day.

The pyro-shock test was still scheduled for Wednesday, but the shake test for the booms slipped until the following Monday.

We did a drop test from 40 cm.

Woody and I worked on the power calculations, but he still hadn't gotten all the information we needed to finalize the models. Nevertheless, we thought we were going to be OK, but it was going to be nip and tuck.

Wednesday, September 4, 1996:
The First Signs of Scott Becoming an Ass

We had a test readiness review for the pyro-shock test since the explosive bolts had been put in from the top, instead of the bottom, for the test. I was concerned that, as a result, we would be using longer bolts for the test than we would use for the flight. I asked, "Why don't we just use long bolts for the flight too? Then we would exactly duplicate the flight configuration during this test?" We discussed that and Dale Vaccarello agreed.

Bob Goldin said, "Let's have Thang look at it." Thang did and found it didn't make any difference. We could go with the long bolts for the test and the short ones for flight.

Then we had a concern about firing the two squibs (the actual firing mechanisms that causes each bolt to explode). The first one was supposed to blow the bolt, the second one was a backup and they were supposed to fire 10 milli-seconds apart to minimize the explosive shock to the spacecraft. The trouble was, we didn't have a costly test timer to conduct the test, so we were going to have to ask another program for one.

Woody made an interesting suggestion. He argued, "Since we're testing the shock effect and then the separation itself, but not the squib firing sequence, why don't we just forget the redundancy and fire the squibs singly (actually three at a time, one for each bolt)? If we have the spacecraft and the casing sitting on the foam, the casing can't fall away from the spacecraft. If one of the squibs doesn't work and the casing hangs up, it can't fall anyway, so it wouldn't put any stress on the spacecraft." That was a good idea.

However, in the meantime, one of the technicians found a test timer and we had to sign a form that said if we wrecked it, we would pay for it. Well, one of the technicians wired it backward and when they tested it, they wrecked it! We were probably going to have to do the tests the way Woody had suggested and we had to figure out who was going to pay for the wrecked timer, since we didn't wreck it, the test crew did. What a mess.

Scott called and wanted me to come to Ames because Karen Poniatowski was giving us trouble about our launching before CRSS. It turned out that of all the people in the world, she was NASA's interface with the Cape. If LLV in Denver did not succeed in getting our launch date, we would have to go through her to get it. Scott had called her and smooth talked her, saying that we all agreed the issue would be resolved in March (after the Lewis & Clark launches), but that we needed to have a date to work towards. We just could not proceed without having a target launch date. She understood and agreed.

I reminded Scott that I had suggested a couple of weeks earlier, "We should invite her for a site visit. Show her how wonderful Lunar Prospector is, how much data we are going to get and what bad things will happen to the mission if we have to wait for CRSS. We should get her on our side, rather than just letting her stay in Washington snipping at us." My though was, *it's easy for her to have some intermediary deliver the bad news to us, but it is a lot harder to have to stand there, look us in the eyes, and tell us that we can't launch just because she says so*. Scott had begun that process and it seemed to be working.

Also Scott assigned Lisa Chu-Thielbar, a really nice and competent lady, to do all our NASA PR work. Lisa had, under Scott's direction, made a one-page handout. It had pictures of Lunar Prospector, a short description of the mission, and the key personnel.

The key personnel started with Scott as NASA Project Office Manager and then Sylvia as his Deputy, followed by me as the PI and then Dougherty as the Lockheed Project Manager. I said, "I don't like the personnel listed this way; it looks like I am subordinate to NASA and that is not the way Discovery is supposed to be. I don't mind you (Scott) and me being equal — put side by side, but I don't like it written as if I am subordinate to you."

Scott, who had just been promoted and had become somewhat uppity, looked at me and said arrogantly, "You are answerable to me."

I said, "This is not the way Discovery is supposed to be and I am not happy about the decay of the role of the PI, not only in Lunar Prospector, but in the Discovery program in general."

He said, even more condescendingly, "I can just cancel this if I want to," which was a stupid and self-serving thing to say, since, by the rules of Discovery (at least the original rules, rules NASA kept changing to suit their whims), the PI was charged with canceling his or her mission if it was not going to be able to meet its objectives, budget, or schedule. It was then that I realized that Scott's promotion had gone to his head, as the old saying says, "Power corrupts and absolute power corrupts absolutely."

Then Scott said, a little fearful he had overdone it, "I hope this isn't something you are going to run to a Congressman about."

I said, "No, it's not that important." But I was not pleased; Scott was no longer the Scott Hubbard I had asked to be my partner in the mission two years earlier; Scott had become an arrogant, self-serving SOB, just the way Tenerelli had done during the Phase B effort!

Later in the day, Scott called to tell me we were probably going to have to go to Headquarters towards the end of the month. Then he apologized for his statements earlier in the day, saying, "I really kind of overstepped my bounds there. You've worked as hard as I have to get this where it is; we are equals in this." I thought, *give me a break. I've worked on this for eight damned years and you have been involved for just two. I'm over there at Lockheed everyday working with the engineers to make sure every detail is right and you're over here sitting on your fat ass, letting Sylvia do all the work while you take all the credit.* But I kept my big mouth shut and since he was apologizing, I accepted his apology.

Then he said, "It's you and me against the princes of darkness surrounding us" (which was true in the beginning).

I said, "I've felt that way — that it was you, Sylvia, and me against Lockheed and NASA. I hope that it will continue that way" (though I had begun to have some serious doubts about that).

I was disappointed to see what was happening. Scott had been promoted, probably because of Lunar Prospector, and he probably believed he had to make it work because his career was on the line. If Lunar Prospector failed, he probably thought his career was over. If he believed that, and I am sure he did, that was BS. History has shown over and over that as long as you are out there being gutsy, you win. The minute you get conservative, you lose. Scott was getting conservative and was doing his best to take control of the mission, just like Tenerelli before him. I was very disappointed in him.

Thursday, September 5, 1996: The Pyro-Shock Test

Woody and I finished working on the power calculations. I had reduced the power requirements to a very simple equation and I was sure we were going to be OK. Woody had a huge, complex spreadsheet that gave the same answer, but considered every detail. We both thought we were going to make it — but by the skin of our teeth.

First of all, the power requirements of every unit had come in lower than expected. The MAG/ER had come in a half a watt lower; the spectrometers came in a little over a watt lower; the sun sensor came in over a half a watt lower; and the Earth/Moon limb-crossing sensor came in just a tad lower. We needed two watts less than expected. We were trying to find the transponder, which had been shipped to Lockheed, to get its final power numbers, but as usual, it was lost (everything that got shipped to Lockheed seemed to get lost. I didn't know why Lockheed has a Shipping and Receiving Department — they have more need for a Lost and Found Department). We hoped we would be lucky (if we ever found it) and it would be 2 or 3 watts lower, too (it was supposed to take 38 to 39 watts). If that were the case, we were going to be OK.

After having previously wrecked the borrowed firing squib mechanism, which was an embarrassment to all, and after considerable fussing around, the pyro-shock test, that was supposed to have occurred sometime after lunch, finally occurred about 7:00 PM. It was really neat. The spacecraft was attached to the TLI Stage casing with just enough tension to take the weight of the spacecraft off the Styrofoam, but not the weight of the TLI Stage.

As Woody had so brilliantly suggested, we were just going to fire the first three pyros instead of all six. It was really neat to watch the ordnance technicians put the ordnances in. They are little things, very much like a 22 bullet in size and charge, but the ordnance technicians were very careful with them, obviously they could do some real damage to hands and fingers or even more. They started wiring the things up and then the damned test connectors wouldn't fit. As soon as that error was found, we realized that the pull-apart connector between the TLI Stage and the spacecraft was in the wrong place! We found two screw-ups.

Finally the ordnance guys had put everything together very carefully and connectors were found that would work for the test. It was really a very long procedure — they had been getting ready to do the test for days. The spacecraft had sensors and wires all over it — it again looked like somebody in an intensive care unit.

Then the test procedures started; the high intensity lights were turned on; the various recorders were turned on; an ordnance technician armed the pyros; then there was a countdown — 3, 2, 1 and than there was a very loud BANG. The spacecraft and the TLI Stage casing separated about a millimeter. The whole thing was very exciting. It was filmed at high speed, since it went so fast you could not see any motion — there was just the loud bang and the test was over — and it was a successful test. We got good data. Everybody on the Lunar Prospector Team was over there to watch.

Friday, September 6, 1996: The First Pyro-Separation Test

We did the first pyro-separation test and it was really beautiful to watch. The TLI Stage casing dropped away from the suspended spacecraft structure as the pyros blew and the separation was clean and beautiful. It was really wonderful.

We had a long meeting over at Ames on the commanding of the pulse burns.

Scott, Bob McMurray, Bill Feldman, and I had a telecon about the GRS temperature set point. We decided to set the set point at –25° C and have the GRS fully blanketed to ensure thermal stability. We expected to get 9 to 9½% resolution.

The shake test of the booms was postponed until the following Tuesday, or later.

Monday, September 9, through Wednesday, September 11, 1996: The Boom Shake Tests

I flew down to Santa Barbara and then the Able engineers drove Warren Hoskins (our lead Structural Dynamics Engineer), Steve Honodel, and me down to Point Mugu Monday to watch the shake test of the booms. It was one of the most boring times I have spent in my life. The guys down there were so slow — everything took forever and the mosquitoes ate us alive.

The first day of the testing, Tuesday, we just stood around while the technicians finally got everything set up.

The next day, Wednesday, we finally shook the boom assembly (the booms were in their launch configuration in their canisters) along the Z-axis and it was very exciting to see it being shaken. We did a low energy (−20 dB) shake initially, just to check out all the connections and to see if everything was OK. We looked at the readout graphs, which took forever to get printed out, and everything was OK, so we began the real test and went up to −9 dB. We looked at some of the outputs again, which again took forever, and then we went up to −3 dB, looked at the graphs again and then went all the way up. The boom canisters and the booms were mounted in a test structure made of 1 cm thick aluminum that represented the side panels of the spacecraft, and man, that assembly was really hopping around. The whole assembly was vibrating with more than 1 cm amplitude! The mass simulators for the instruments were moving like crazy. Though the long waits between the tests were boring as hell, it was worth the waiting to see the tests.

After the tests were successfully completed, one of the Able engineers drove me back up to Santa Barbara where I was going to catch my plane back home. As we drove up the coastal highway, we passed the little town I had seen on TV where an enormous mudslide had come down a mountainside and had buried several houses during the previous rainy season. It was amazing to see the effects of such a devastating, but very interesting geological phenomena.

Thursday, September 12, 1996: Staff Meeting Day

Everything was going quite well with the spacecraft, with a few exceptions.

Increasing the height of the solar array would cause trouble with the antenna pattern, though the main interference was due to the A3&A4 engine mounts. We could solve the problems by either attaching the cabling to the antenna to the top of the raised antenna mount instead of the bottom, or we could drop the engine mounts by 7 cm. I had to figure out which solution was the simplest.

Southwest wasn't getting the spectrometer electronics unit (SES) done on time because the Southwest administration was giving Cassini's electronics priority over Lunar Prospector's, so the SES was not getting done.

We found that we only needed two doors, instead of four doors, built into the LLV2 shroud to allow access to the destruct system firing units. That would save us a quarter of a million dollars, since each extra door beyond the first two that are part of the rocket package cost $125,000.

It was a good day. I got a lot of work done. The spacecraft was being mounted on the shaker so we could start the shake testing. Dougherty was being extremely good, even Tom thought he was enjoyable to be around, so things were getting better.

Friday, September 13, 1996

I called Dave Curtis to see if we could delete the nitrogen purge for the MAG/ER that was meant to keep the MAG/ER clean while on the rocket waiting for launch and he thought that would probably be OK. I tried to reach Bill, without success, to ask the same question for the APS.

I called Ron Black about Southwest's delay in delivering the SES to Bill Feldman.

In my absence, Alex and Marcie had convinced Dougherty that we needed the Store-and-Forward mode, so Alex and Gerry were working on getting the C&DH capable of handling it, so I would have both direct and Store-and-Forward commanding options.

We were worried about the power as usual. Woody and I went over the shadowing effects again to make sure that we had done that correctly. Happily, the transponder came in 4 watts lower than predicted, so it looked like the spacecraft was going to need 8 or 9 watts less than we were using in our calculation! But there was a problem with the Sharp solar cells; they might be only 16%, rather than 17% efficient, and that would more than cancel out the positive effect on the power budget that the decrease in the power usages of 8 or 9 watts would have. Thus, we were just going to have to wait to see whether we were going to have enough power when the Sharp cells finally came in.

The spacecraft's shake tests in the X and Y directions were scheduled for Sunday.

Finally, Able had finished the booms, so that part of the schedule was no longer slipping.

Chapter 3-22
Shake Testing the Spacecraft Structure — A 57 Hz Resonance!

Sunday, September 15, 1996: Shake Testing

Rebecca and I went up to Lockheed for about 5 hours during the afternoon and watched the sign-vibe (sinusoidal vibration) test on the basic structure. Because the spacecraft was sitting on the shaker, it was a good 2½ to 3 m above the floor. I wanted to be as close as possible to the spacecraft as it was being shaken, to look and listen for problems, so I took the ladder the technicians used to get to the spacecraft and put it right next to the shaker. I climbed up there and waited for the test to begin. The shaker is really a gigantic loudspeaker whose upper surface vibrates and the test starts at 10 to 20 Hz and then the frequency sweeps up to the highest test frequency in about a minute. The shaker makes a lot of noise, and when one of the fundamental frequencies of the spacecraft, or one of its components, is reached, the spacecraft rattles very loudly. Our main concern was to find any resonances in the 50 to 60 Hz range where the Castor 120s have their pipe organ effects.

Finally, the sine-vibe test got started, and as the shaking frequency swept up to the 50 to 60 Hz range, the spacecraft really began to shake, rattle, and roll. It sounded like an old Model T Ford that was going down a bumpy gravel road and was about to fall apart. Something was definitely loose in there and it looked and sounded like it was the inverted tripod that was holding the backs of the tank mass simulators. Since the tripod had to be adjustable, it was not a solid unit and it was clear that something was wrong.

Monday, September 16, 1996: More Shaking

Bill and Dougherty were at Southwest Research getting the SES checked out and tested. Bill found that his GRS calibration curves were off because there was a 3.4-hour time lag in the cooling of the BGO crystal vs. what the temperature sensor showed. We decided to try to get the operational temperature of the GRS down to $-30°$ C; I hoped that was the final decision on that issue.

Able Engineering broke one of the longerons in one of the booms when they were re-stowing them after a deployment test! Happily, and to our great relief, the break was caused by a technician's error rather than a design error. It would take about a week to get it repaired.

We did a series of shake tests on the spacecraft. We had finished the Y-axis shake on Sunday and we finished the X-axis during the day. We were going to try and get the Z-axis shake done and thus have the shake testing all finished.

The spacecraft had held up well during the X and Y axes random-vibe and sign-vibe tests. The knocking we had heard on Sunday was due to the inverted tripod; two of the legs were loose. The legs were tightened and that seemed to fix the problem. We would still have to inspect the tripod once we dismantled the spacecraft after tests to make sure it was OK before final assembly.

Tuesday, September 17, through Friday, September 20, 1996:
A Trip to Denver and Los Alamos

Before I flew to Albuquerque Tuesday morning, we had a meeting with Jim Beffa and his antenna guys to discuss the degradation of the antenna pattern by the A3&A4 engine mounts. The medium gain antenna intrinsically had an 8 dB gain and the ripple caused by the engine mounts would drop that down to 6 dB. If we raised the antenna by 6 cm or lowered the engines by 6 cm, we would minimize the degradation due to the ripple and have a 7 dB gain system. The obvious thing to do was to lower the engines, because the antenna was finished and the engines were not yet mounted. Also, lowering the engines would help keep the critical moment of inertia ratio above 1.07, while raising the antenna would do the opposite. Further, raising the antenna would cost three times more money than lowering the engines and there would be a two-month delay caused by the changes to the antenna. It was obvious what we needed to do, but nothing was ever obvious to Dougherty, so we had to go through the usual rigamarole, wasting time, but ended up deciding to lower the engine mounts. I would have made that decision two weeks earlier when the issue came up if I really had the authority I was supposed to have.

As soon as that was resolved, I left for the San Jose Airport to fly to Albuquerque, stayed there overnight, and then drove up to Los Alamos the next morning to see Bill. The GRS and NS were finished and were beautiful. The APS had a minor problem with one of its five channels due to a bad component. They changed out the component and the APS was fine.

We discussed the need for the nitrogen purge for the APS and everything I found out indicated we could do without the purge.

The only concern Bill had was how to protect the APS light filter foils from rippling in the air-conditioning breeze in the shroud prior to launch. Bill was concerned that the constant rippling would eventually tear the very thin and very delicate foils. We were trying to design a little cover box that would cover the APS until just before launch, when it would be removed. But the two existing doors in the shroud were down by the TLI Stage where the launch preparation technicians had to get to the destruct system to arm it just prior to launch. If we added a door to have access to the APS, it would cost an extra $125,000 — we could not afford an APS door. The protection of those damned foils was still an open question.

After seeing Bill Wednesday morning, I drove back down Albuquerque and flew to Denver where I gave a talk on Lunar Prospector at an AIAA meeting.

As I was flying between the cities, I was thinking about — and getting more and more interested in — a suggestion Dave Lozier had made a few days earlier. Dave suggested that instead of doing our TLI burn at the first node (the point where the parking orbit crosses the translunar orbit) after only about a quarter of an orbit around the Earth, we should stay in the parking orbit for three quarters of a revolution and do the TLI burn at the second node. If we did, then our post-separation communication angles would be a lot better and we would get in range to communicate with the spacecraft via the Goldstone tracking station in California much quicker. Further, the ΔV required to put us into lunar orbit would be about 30 m/sec less if we used a second node burn rather than a first node burn. Clearly, that was the way to go; so, instead of doing the TLI burn over the Atlantic Ocean just south of West Africa, we would do it about 45 minutes later over Australia.

I flew back to San Jose Friday. Tom picked me up at the airport and we immediately went to the test facilities. They had done the Z-axis shake of the spacecraft while I was gone and had found that the spacecraft had resonance at about 57 Hz — right in the middle of the Castor 120 pipe organ effect and that was not good! Thang thought we could shift the 57 Hz resonance up to 70 or 80 Hz, i.e., out of harm's way, by putting stiffeners on the longerons of the main, load bearing structure.

Also, the tests showed that the inverted tripod tank holder was not going to work because of all its adjustable parts. We were going to have to redesign it with solid, nonadjustable legs (the spacecraft's cg had been fixed, so we no longer needed to be able to adjustable the tripod to accommodate any changes in the cg) to minimize the places it could move around and shake.

Dougherty was getting extremely cooperative and friendly. It was almost more than I could bear. He understood the results of the shake tests and made sure the problems were corrected. I was proud of him for that.

Stiffening the load bearing structure and rebuilding the inverted tripod would cost us about two weeks of schedule slip. We were not going to get the spacecraft finished until about the end of October. That was still OK. Money, not time, was our problem.

As a result of the testing of the spacecraft with the tank simulators at the subsystem level, we were getting the feeling that we didn't need to redo tests with water in the tanks.

Dan was working on his analysis of the performance losses of the TLI burn due to both nutation and the tilting of the Spacecraft/TLI Stage stack, or "tip-off," at separation from the LLV2. He thought we could lose up to a couple hundred m/sec in velocity! I thought that was excessive by a factor of 10, but he was going to finish doing his analysis, and if he were correct, errors of that magnitude would cause me to have to use a large amount of fuel to correct for such large launch errors. Based on the record of previous Star-37 burns, I was skeptical about Dan's results.

Bill had told me at Los Alamos that he would deliver the spectrometers to Lockheed on October 16 and then he and his Danish wife were going on a two-week vacation to Denmark. The MAG/ER was to be delivered a little later. I expected that the spacecraft and payload would be finished by the end of October.

Monday, September 23, 1996: Finally, A Launch Date

I stayed home with the flu.

Tom called to tell me that the Cape had given us September 24, 1997, as our prime launch date — launch was in one year and one day! Rebecca and I went to the local bakery and got a "one-year to launch cake" made that I would take to work the following day.

Tuesday, September 24, 1996: One Year to Launch!

One year to launch!! We sent a letter to Denver saying we were launching on the 24th at 11:012 GMT (Greenwich Mean Time).

Dougherty said he was finally getting Uselman replaced.

We had the "one-year to launch cake." Everybody liked it, but I was a little disappointed, because many of our guys were not there to enjoy it.

Both Tom and I were sick, so we went home very early.

Friday, September 27, 1996

I was getting more and more ticked off at Dougherty who was always trying to push aside the Outreach Program and shortchange Mission Ops. His concern was getting the spacecraft built and launched and he didn't care what happened after that. He did not want to spend money to get the tools we needed to fly the spacecraft; he acted as though he believed that once launched, Lunar Prospector would both somehow find its way to the Moon and do the mapping all by itself.

I was also getting a little tired of Scott, who, since his promotion, was pontificating more than I liked. He had become an arrogant, self-serving SOB and I did not like it one little bit.

Those two SOBs were trying very hard to turn Lunar Prospector into the Scott/NASA and Dougherty/Lockheed show in which the PI was nonexistent (shades of Tenerelli).

Technically, we still didn't know exactly what to do about the 57 Hz resonance of the spacecraft's main structure. Nevertheless, we were pushing ahead with strengthening the longerons of the main structure. However, everybody, including Dougherty, was a little uncomfortable about that because, if, after we got it all put back together, the resonance had not shifted to a high enough frequency, we would be in big trouble.

Irv had devised a high-pressure (3000 psi) nitrogen jet system for the TLI Stage that would pull the stage away from the spacecraft after separation fast enough so the chugging TLI Stage would not collide with the spacecraft.

Dan Swanson had continued to work on the effects of nutation on the separation of the TLI Stage and the spacecraft. Dan found that, if the stack were nutating wildly before separation, even if we got a clean separation with Irv's system, the nutation itself could cause the TLI Stage and spacecraft to spin around and hit each other. He wanted to get the TLI Stage moving away from the spacecraft a lot quicker than Irv was planning. Basically, Irv's system was going to let the 3000 psi nitrogen jet out at low thrust over several seconds, but Dan said we had to have high thrust jets that fired only a second or so. We discussed how to do that.

I raised the question about the possibility that such high-pressure jets might blow out the fragile APS foils. Remembering a similar problem on the Viking Landers where we did not want the landing engines to blow away the sand and dust of the Martian surface where we landed, the engineers had devised multi-nozzle engine bells that spread the exhaust over a big enough area to eliminate the problem. I thought we could use the same trick to fix the nitrogen jets to protect the APS filters.

Irv changed his story and found that the high-pressure jets would not be as bad as we had thought. The APS filter would be OK.

Some of us had a discussion about how to protect the science instruments while the spacecraft was in the shroud and on the rocket waiting for launch for at least a few weeks. My science guys, the engineers, and I all agreed that A) the instruments would be OK for as long as necessary, B) we would not need two extra ($250,000) doors in the shroud, and C) we would not need nitrogen purges for the APS and the ER — if 1) we had a little cover for the APS so its foils wouldn't be damaged by the airflow, 2) the humidity was less than 30%, 3) we had class 10,000 air going into the shroud, and 4) the temperature was always below 30° C.

Because Scott had continued to try to push George French out of the Outreach Program and did not want the data released to the public, George, with my blessing, had gotten Congressman Sensenbrenner involved. Sensenbrenner was not happy about Scott's little games and had started to make some political waves. Scott called Frank and

Frank called Dougherty and me into his office. As I arrived, Dougherty was telling Frank "we won't release the data and that is that!"

I said, "NASA is making fools of themselves. The data should be released."

Frank said "Hell yes, there is nothing wrong with getting the data out, this is silly." Frank put Dougherty in his place regarding the Outreach activities, but I did not know what Scott was up to.

By day's end, I was very tired, because I was still under the weather with the flu and because I was tired of Dougherty's stupidity and Scott's growing arrogance.

Saturday, September 28, 1996: Scott Gets Put in His Place

George French called me at home at 7:30 AM. He had talked to Scott late Friday and wanted to let me know what was up and it was good. Sensenbrenner's aide had called Scott and had told him that if the data were not released to the public and if George could not do Moonlink, some very bad things were going to happen to Scott in particular and Ames in general. Boy, that was that music to my ears. That was why Scott had called Frank and Frank had called Dougherty and me in on Friday. Scott had gotten his fingers burned and his wienie slammed in the door.

As a result, George said Scott had changed his position completely and thought what George was doing was wonderful. In fact, it did not take Scott very long to start pretending the Outreach Program had been his idea all along. What a stinking, fat little, two-faced bastard Scott turned out to be, just like Tenerelli.

Though I was happy that Scott had been forced to do a turnaround, it was just another example of the same old NASA crap. If you don't have the politicians behind you, NASA's arrogance and stupidity wreck everything.

Regardless, George did a good job and NASA could either like it or lump it.

Monday, September 30, 1996: Subsystem Review Day

We still had the problem with the 57 Hz resonance of the main structure. In addition to stiffening the longerons, we were remaking parts of inverted tripod (which we had to do anyway because it was shaking so much) in an effort to move the resonance frequency up to 70 or 80 Hz. I feared we were just fumbling around with the problem.

Dougherty and I went to Ames to meet Scott to discuss the schedule slips and the Outreach Program (I was very interested to see what Scott had to say after Sensenbrenner's aide had gotten done with him). I had called Scott before we went over to Ames and I told him I didn't want Dougherty and Lockheed involved in the Outreach activities anymore, they were just making it more difficult, and Scott agreed.

We discussed the schedule and Dougherty did a good job of that. He said we could make up a lot of the time because the tests we had already done showed we had no major problems.

Then Dougherty said, "We have one other topic to do and that's the French thing."

I said to Dougherty, "Well, Scott and I are going to discuss that after this meeting."

Dougherty was not happy about that, sputtered a bit, made some comment about "leaving that stuff to the bureaucrats," and sort of wandered out of Scott's office. I was pleased; I was tired of Dougherty sticking his nose into issues he had no business dealing with.

We talked about George and Moonlink. Scott told me his version of the story, which was very different from George's. Scott said that NASA (not him) was getting into trouble and that Sensenbrenner's aide was ready to raise holy hell about it.

I told him, "As far as I am concerned, French has every right as a citizen to complain (to Sensenbrenner) about this, and I am unhappy with the way it has been evolving anyway. I want the data out. I don't see any reason for not having it out."

Scott replied, "Well, we can release it after we get it validated."

I told him, "The validation for Level 0 data is nothing more than integrating the data streams, checking for bit errors, and separating the data according to instrument. There is no calibration. That is all we are promising for Level 0, so there is no reason to hold that for six months and not let the world get it."

Scott still wouldn't give in. I told him that, from my experience, people want to have the thrill of seeing the data in real-time and feeling as if they are part of it. Scott tried to counter with, "The PIs work for years on the science and they want to be able to announce the results they are working on."

I said, "Well I don't and I asked all my Co-Is and they don't either; they want to get the data out to the public, too. If you are worried about the data being interpreted by the public, so what? First of all, nobody can interpret it, certainly not the GRS and the ER data. Even if someone did interpret the NS data and said that there is water ice there before we did, so what?"

Scott said, "You might not care, but NASA might."

I said, "BS."

Whether Scott liked it or not, whether he agreed with me or not, he was going to have to yield, because if he didn't, Sensenbrenner was going to raise hell.

Tuesday, October 1, 1996

We had a Ground Segment telecon. Dougherty participated in it, which I wasn't pleased about, but he was very meek and quiet. I thought he was pouting after being thrown out of the meeting between Scott and me the day before. He tried to assert himself a couple of times, but I felt I was dealing with a little wet puppy.

I talked to George French and told him I was going to push to get the data released and I thought everything was going to be OK.

Wednesday, October 2, 1996

We had a 9:00 AM meeting with the solar array people. Dougherty wanted to get the people who were actually going to fabricate the array to come over so we could give them a pep talk and let them know what Lunar Prospector was all about. We did, and I had to admit, Dougherty did a good job. After a half hour, I had to leave to go to Ames for a Ground Segment meeting with some JPL engineers.

When I came in — a little late, Tom found me a place to sit next to a JPL guy who I didn't know, so Marcie introduced me to the new guys. She said, "This is Alan Binder, our chief troublemaker."

I had already begun to dislike Marcie, who is a typical NASA engineer — not particularly competent, but, because she is a NASA employee, she thinks she knows more than anyone else. Her troublemaker comment was a direct reference to the fact that I wanted things done my way, not the NASA way and hence, not her way. Anyone who dared to challenge NASA or a NASA employee is automatically a troublemaker. But, as far as I was concerned, Marcie could say whatever she wanted, I had no intention of paying heed to her nonsense.

When we got around to discussing the commanding, it was clear Marcie and the JPL guys believed Mission Ops were going to be carried out by normal NASA type mission controllers. I said, "I hope you guys understand that I am the Mission Director and that only Dan Swanson and I are going to do the commanding." Marcie and the JPL guys didn't like that one bit. There was a modest uproar and I said, "That is the way it is going to be done." At that point, I had to leave to go to another meeting.

Tom said that after I left, Marcie made a big stink about my telling them I was going to be the Mission Director, not her, and that Dan was my second in command. Typical of a NASA wienie, Marcie had decided that Lunar Prospector Mission Ops were her responsibility, not mine, and she was there to tell me what to do. I was giving serious thought to telling Scott to get rid of her. She was really beginning to tick me off with her aggressive and snotty attitudes about everything.

I got back to Lockheed at 11:00 AM for a meeting with the antenna guys. In the final analysis, the average gain of the medium gain antenna was over 6 dB (not the 8.7 dB that we had been told since March), but the ripple dropped the gain down to 5 dB. I said that would be OK, because we didn't even need the medium gain antenna as long as we were being tracked by the 26 meter antennas, and even a 5 dB gain would be OK when we were tracked by TOTS, assuming that TOTS was as good as we thought — but some serious questions had been raised about that. A communications engineer had made some new calculations and found that TOTS was down 19 dB from where they thought it was! If it was that bad, it would not be usable, but I doubted those calculations were correct.

Then Gerry Grismore made a very interesting suggestion. Jim Beffa pointed out that, if they rewrapped the helix, they could get another ¾ dB in gain out of it. However, the beautiful, elegant, and simple little helix antenna was lying right there, ready to be mounted on the spacecraft, so Gerry added, "But, we are going to find out in a few weeks what is going on with the TOTS antenna. If it's down 19 dB, nothing is going to help, and there is no sense in rewrapping the helix just to get ¾ of a dB." I could not have agreed more with Gerry, so we left it at that.

Dougherty and I met with Dan Lebel, the guy who had replaced Uselman. Dougherty gave him the history of Lunar Prospector, let him know we had not been happy with LLV, that I wanted to be on a Taurus, and the fact that every time we sneezed the SOBs at LLV charged us for it.

That was when I found out that because Uselman never remembered anything and claimed we didn't tell him the things that we had told him, Dougherty had been sending formal letters to LLV about all the things we had discussed with Uselman. The Denver SOBs, behind Dougherty's back, considered those letters formal modification requests and were trying to charge us extra for every single one of them! That was unbelievable, and I was more than a little ticked off at Dougherty for hiding that from me after he found out about it.

Dougherty said, "You know, we don't have money, we can't have all this crap, you have to help us, not hurt us." Then Dougherty said, in a Dougherty way, "We love you (LLV), we'll forget the past, but these are the problems we have had and they have to be fixed." I was surprised; Dougherty did a good job of laying it on the line with Dan and actually got most of his historical facts right!

I said a few things and left, because Tom and I had to go to Palo Alto to talk about the computer screen displays for Mission Ops. I had to understand what the possibilities were so I could design the displays the way I wanted them.

It was a long day, just one meeting after another all day long, but, I was really surprised at Dougherty; he really did well with Dan Lebel. I went home happy.

Thursday, October 3, 1996: Staff Meeting Day

We were still fussing about the 57 Hz resonance. Everything else was pretty much OK.

I talked to Marcie about the commanding and the controllers. She made a very good point and that was, "Every time you send a command with Store-and-Forward, you have to shake hands with JPL and do a number of things to send the command." Well, I did not want to fool around with all that; I just intended to do the commanding. What she suggested, and I tended to agree, was to have a controller actually type all that stuff into the computer, do all the handshaking and the verifications, etc., and that I just issued the commands. She had reluctantly accepted the fact that I would run Mission Ops, control the spacecraft, and issue the commands, but she was correct in saying I should not actually send the commands.

Despite my having made it clear that this was my spacecraft and that I was going to run it, she found it hard to believe that a scientist would be at Mission Ops all the time, but I said I would and, as the PI, it was my responsibility. Then we agreed that the command team would consist of three of us: Dan, a controller who would actually send the commands to the spacecraft upon my order, and me, and that we would have a backup command team. As a result of that conversation, I thought she and I would eventually come to an understanding.

Dave Troup, George's computer guy, was at Ames; so Scott, Sylvia, Lisa, Dave, a co-worker of his, and I talked about the educational program they had been working on. Scott still did not want the data released until it was at Level 0, so that was a battle he and I were going to continue.

Friday, October 4, 1996

The film crew for a program called *Discover Beyond 2000* was at Lockheed most of the day. It was a crew of four Australians, including a very attractive young lady who was the interviewer. Clearly, she was also there to provide some very good scenery.

It took them a long time to get set up and then they did some filming of me in front of the spacecraft-engineering model. It was kind of fun; she asked me some questions and I described the spacecraft. Then we did bits and pieces so they could get different camera angles, and so on, and so forth.

Then we went to the Lockheed display area and did the full interview. I enjoyed that more because one of the guys asked some really good questions that allowed me to say all of the things that I always tried to get across to the public, i.e., what the purpose of Lunar Prospector was, besides its scientific aspects — it was a good format.

Next they interviewed Dougherty and he did really well.

Finally, they interviewed Scott. Scott was nervous and stilted and was sweating so much they had to make him wipe his brow. I was sure Scott was worried he might say something NASA would not like (and I was quite right).

Marcie got dragged over there — Scott kept trying to sell her as being a big part of the mission (he was right, she was big — a big pain in the butt) and I really did not like her being interviewed. She did quite poorly. She didn't have enough experience to do well and she knew next to nothing about Lunar Prospector, so that was a bust.

In the short time I had been interfacing with Marcie, I had really gotten sick of her. First of all, she was just a young, female Tom Dougherty, and that was enough to drive anyone to drink. Second, before her interview, she and Scott were giving the interviewer some background; Scott explained there were two levels of interaction between Ames and us (Lockheed). One was at the administrative level with Scott and Sylvia and the second was that Ames provided services to me and one of them was Mission Ops that he said Marcie was heading up and Marcie said, "Yeah, I work for Tom Dougherty."

Well, BS. I saw I was going to have to have a little talk with her because she had no idea of what was going on or who she really worked for — I was also going to tell Scott to replace her with someone who knew something. It was bad enough that I had to put up with Dougherty until the launch that was still over eleven months away, but I was sure as hell not going to put up with that little bitch for 2½ years. She is just as bossy, self-centered, and arrogant as Dougherty is. The only difference between them is that she has a modicum of intelligence, while he is just a big stupid oaf, and because she is a female in "the man's world of engineering," she always has a chip on her shoulder, while Dougherty always makes fun of the females in the aerospace world — what a great pair!

Monday, October 7, 1996: Subsystem Review Day

Subsystem reviews were becoming happily boring; with the spacecraft construction well under way, there was not much to review.

Bill Jacobs was there, crabbing as usual that he and his crew couldn't do this and couldn't do that — was there anything they could do? He questioned our need to receive data from two stations when one was coming on line and the other was going off line to check out the new link. Dougherty said, "No, it's not baseline, not going to do it, end of story."

I said, "Wait a minute, I need to understand something, I thought we had this capability."

Dougherty kept trying to say, "Nope, that's not baseline, we aren't going to do it." I just kept asking and he finally shut his mouth. Dougherty was right in the sense that if it was going to cost us money (money we did not have), I would agree that we wouldn't do it. But I wanted to make sure of that before we decided not to have that capability.

It was very aggravating the way Dougherty just said no to anything that had anything to do with Mission Ops, even though he had no idea of what it was or what we needed to run the mission. As always, Dougherty was just a damned idiot.

Then there was the business of trying to determine the fuel load for the Star-37 of the TLI Stage. Dan had brought up what he thought was the problem of slag (unburned, molten aluminum). No one really knew how much slag would build up and we had to guess, based on just the 4 lousy data points, the amount of slag that could form. If we guessed wrong, we would have a bad under-burn or bad over-burn of the TLI Stage. Like all the questions Dan had about the Star-37's performance, I was skeptical about its validity, since the Star-37 had been used successfully on so many missions.

Finally, Woody went through the power and said that as things stood, we would have no contingencies during the lunar eclipse at end of the mission. I thought we would make it power-wise. I had thought so for a long time, but it would be touch and go.

Tuesday, October 8, 1996

We had the telecon about the tracking; unfortunately Frank Donovan and the guys who were supposed to have talked about the TOTS link were not on the telecon. We covered a few other issues, mainly the tracking of Lunar Prospector right after launch. I finally got the tracking people to understand that I wanted to get the velocity of the spacecraft from the Doppler measurements as soon after the TLI burn as we could, so I would know if I had to make an immediate, emergency corrective burn or not. They suggested that the NASA's Tracking and Data Relay Satellite, called TDRS, might be able to track us immediately after separation, i.e., 20 minutes before Goldstone could pick us up and they said they would look into that possibility. That would be great.

I talked to Marcie after that and explained to her that she was working for me not for Dougherty. Surprisingly, that went quite well. Scott had never explained the management structure of Lunar Prospector to her (I suspected on purpose), so she assumed that, as always in the past, the Project Manager, Dougherty, was in charge and that I was just window dressing. I told her that Dougherty, despite his always trying to run everything, worked for me, as did she and everyone else. I also told her that as a Discovery Mission PI, I was the one who was responsible for the success of the mission. I was surprised that, as a NASA employee, Marcie had no idea what Discovery was all about and, though she said she accepted what I had just told her, I did not believe she really did accept my authority any more than Scott, Dougherty, or NASA did — it was just not the NASA way.

Tom and I went to lunch and we had a long talk; I told Tom that, although he was doing a great job of helping me, I was very concerned about his lack of learning anything about the spacecraft and the mission, as witnessed by the fact that I had to ask Dan Swanson to be my second in command during Mission Ops instead of him. Tom and I know each other well enough for him to understand that I was just trying to help him do his job well, so that went very well.

I went home early and exhausted; I fell asleep right after I got home.

Chapter 3-23
The 57 Hz and
TLI Burn Issues Solved

Wednesday, October 9, 1996: My 57th Birthday

We were not going to have a regular weekly subsystem review anymore because they no longer served any purpose.

Unfortunately, we couldn't get the usage of the test area for a week to re-do the Z-axis shake test to see if our 57 Hz resonance fixes really did the job, so our schedule slipped another week. I was getting more and more concerned about that.

Irv, Dan, Ken Galal, and I discussed the Star-37 propellant load, and for some strange reason, Irv was very slow on the uptake. According to Ken, the ΔV requirements for all possible launch dates varied by only about 13 m/sec. Thus, if we had Thiokol load the Star-37 for the middle of that range, we would have a maximum launch velocity error of only ± 6.5 m/sec due to the differences in the launch dates. We talked about loading for the highest possible ΔV and then, once we knew the day of launch, we would add up to a couple of kilograms of ballast to bring down the velocity to the desired value for that day. However, considering the magnitude of the other possible launch errors, we thought that might not be worth fooling with and we thought we would just load for the mean ΔV.

We went through Dan's nutation analysis and he wanted us to increase the spin rate of the Spacecraft/TLI Stage stack from 60 to 75 rpm for the TLI burn. That would give the stack more stability and help reduce the nutation caused by the slag. According to Dan's calculations, based on just four data points, we could get as much as 1.5 to 3 kg of slag built up during the burn. The resulting nutation or wobbling of the stack would cause as much as a 70 to 140 m/sec under-burn if the stack was spinning at 60 rpm, but only (!) a 50 to 100 m/sec under-burn at 75 rpm. We were going in the direction of biasing the propellant load to compensate for the nutation losses and using the 75 rpm spin rate.

We started looking at some of the data and it turned out that the amount of slag actually increases with spin rate! The reason is that it is the centrifugal force that causes the heavy, molten aluminum droplets to separate out from the much lighter, hot exhaust gasses and collect on the sides of the rocket casing — in the same way that a spinning cream separator separates the light cream from the heavier milk — as every dairy farmer knows. Since centrifugal force goes up the square of the spin rate, increasing the spin rate as Dan had suggested in order to increase the stability, would only make the nutation worse! While going to a very lower spin rate would decrease the formation of slag, the stack would then lose stability and that would not be good either. We decided to stick with the 57 ± 3 rpm spin rate we had in the original specifications.

I was still bothered by Dan's slag analysis, since I found out that the four data points he had used were from ground tests on the much larger Star-48 rocket engine. The little bit of Thiokol information we had on the Star-37 rocket engine suggested that no more than a ½ kg of slag would form during a Star-37 burn. Thus, I thought

Dan's calculations were off by a factor of 3 to 6 and we were just chasing a ghost, i.e., it was problematical whether nutation would be a problem and I thought it would not. Unfortunately, Dan was going to be gone the rest of the week and Irv was going to be gone the following week. We were not going to get that issue resolved very quickly.

Regardless, it was going to be touch and go to get the right fuel load. However, as long as the launch velocity uncertainties were down to about 30 m/sec, I would be OK in terms of my ΔV budget for the mid-course maneuvers. If the actual errors were over 40 or 50 m/sec, then I would have to do an emergency burn right after launch, otherwise I would have to use too much fuel for the mid-course maneuvers.

Thursday, October 10, 1996

Early in the morning (I awoke at 2:00 AM, so I went to work very early), I looked over the slag information and decided that Thiokol had probably calculated the amount of slag based on the performance of the engines compared to what they were supposed to be, i.e., since the engines performances were lower than expected, Thiokol assumed they were carrying extra mass along in the form of slag. Dan then took the data and assumed that the lower performance was all due to nutation caused by slag. Thus I thought Dan had taken those data out of context. I called Thiokol and they agreed with me. Then I was even more convinced that Dan's slag/nutation issue was totally bogus and I would have to discuss it with him when he got back the following week.

Since I woke up at 2:00 AM, I was very tired, so I went home early.

Friday, October 11, 1996: Stuck with Marcie — Ugh!

Early in the morning, I talked to Scott for about a half-hour before Dougherty came to Ames for a meeting. I had gotten tired of other lunar scientists snipping at Lunar Prospector because we were not carrying a camera, a germanium gamma ray spectrometer, and everything else that Bill Boynton's Lunar Polar Orbiter Mission was supposed to carry. Most lunar scientists felt we had pushed Boynton's mission out of first place by being inexpensive. I asked Scott if he knew the ranking of the other five lunar missions that were proposed during the first Discovery selection process.

Since Wes Huntress had said at the Discovery News Conference (Part Two, February 28, 1995), that he had simply selected the top four ranked missions, with Lunar Prospector definitely being ranked number 1, I assumed the other lunar missions had to be ranked no higher than number 5 and below. My answer to our critics was, "Hey you've got a lunar mission, if you didn't have this one, you wouldn't have anything," but I wanted to be sure of that.

Scott answered my question about the ranking with, "They can't have been anything better than about 9th or 10th, because I know what the 5th, 6th, 7th, and 8th ones were." That confirmed what I had long believed — there would have been no lunar mission if it weren't for Lunar Prospector, period.

After that, I told Scott how the spacecraft was doing and about our continuing schedule slips.

Then I told him I wanted him to replace Marcie and why. He didn't like that one bit. The interesting part about the following discussion was that it became clear to me that way deep down in his heart, Scott really believed Dougherty was supposed to be running the show and not me.

I told Scott I had told Marcie that she worked for me, not for Dougherty and that Dougherty himself worked for me. Scott got up and drew what he considered to be our organizational chart with Dougherty and me up at the top and everyone below (he had left himself off the chart, but clearly, he thought he was over both Dougherty and me). Then, based on the way he drew it, Scott said, "See, she works for him."

I said, "No she doesn't. First of all, if you drew it correctly, Dougherty is only responsible for the rocket and the spacecraft and I am responsible for Ground Systems and Mission Ops. And as I said, I do most of the spacecraft anyway."

However, it was clear he wanted Marcie to run Mission Ops. He liked her and he wasn't very pleased that I wanted to get rid of her and said, "Well, you can't substitute poor people, who you do like, for good people, who you don't like."

First of all, Marcie is not a good engineer, she is a lousy engineer, and second, I did not need someone to run Mission Ops — I was going to do that (and I did). Since Marcie was clearly Scott's little darling female NASA engineer and since I really could not control whoever NASA (Scott) gave me (any more than I could control who Lockheed gave me), I was stuck with one more useless and aggravating person I would have to put up with for the rest of the program. I was more than a little disappointed about that and Scott was disappointing me more and more — he was not the guy I had selected to be my NASA partner over two years earlier. Had I known how he was going to turn out, Scott would have been my last choice.

Finally Dougherty came in and we had a good meeting. We talked about the upcoming test readiness review.

As we left Scott's office, Dougherty asked, "What were you talking to Scott about?"

I said, "Oh, I always see Scott once in while."

He asked, "Were you talking about the Outreach stuff?"

I just said, "No." Dougherty laughed, but I thought he got the message.

Later a guy from Palo Alto came by who was doing a proposal for JPL and said, "Since Lunar Prospector is the star example of a mission that is keeping on schedule and on budget, I want to find out how Dougherty is doing it."

I said, "Dougherty has gone for the rest of the afternoon."

The guy asked, "How can he do that?"

Woody answered, "He's the boss."

To which I replied, "No, I am the boss." Then I introduced myself to the guy.

He said, "Oh yeah, you're the PI — you are the boss!"

Woody said, "It's great having the PI here," in a joking way.

And the guy said, "I am sure it is; it keeps the program going as long as you have a good Project Manager to keep it going right." How little did he know! But I told the guy he could talk to Dougherty about the scheduling and budget, since that was what he was good at.

Monday, October 14, 1996

Dan and I talked with Thiokol about the fuel load for the Star-37. Dan agreed that the amount of slag we could expect was less than he had calculated, but we continued our discussions with Thiokol — we could not afford to make a mistake about the Star-37 fuel load or we might not get to the Moon. I was hoping the launch errors would be no more than 30 m/sec and I had a feeling they would be no more than 20 m/sec.

The spacecraft's mass had crept up about 4 kg, in part because of the changes we had had to make to stiffen the spacecraft's structure and partly because of ballast — unfortunately.

Tuesday, October 15, 1996: The Mass, the Mass

Al Tilley posted the new mass properties list and the critical moment of inertia ratio was 1.07 — which was great, but the dry mass was posted at 157 kg, which was 10 kg higher than from the previous calculations. That had to be BS. We had added 2 to 2½ kg of mass to stiffen the structure and, as Al had said "and some ballast."

I said to Al, "You're not telling me you've had to add 7 or 8 kg of ballast, because if you did, I'm going to kill somebody!"

Wednesday, October 16, 1996

It was a quiet day — Dougherty wasn't around. I worked on the propellant model that was, by then, in excellent shape — it really worked.

I thought about Tilley's mass calculations and I talked to Bob Goldin because I was sure they had double booked some items. I was sure we were really only at about 290 kg fully fuelled. Tilley was going to look into it, but I was going to be really ticked off if the mass was well over 290 kg.

Thursday, October 17, 1996:
Outreach and the Data Release Issue, Again!

We had a subsystem review and my science guys were there too. Dougherty was an ass as usual, huffing and puffing, trying to belittle Bill Feldman, me, and everyone else.

Later, George French gave his Outreach pitch to Scott and me and Scott liked everything, which I found annoying as hell, since Scott had done everything he could to kill it before he got his ass chewed out by Sensenbrenner's aide. Scott had become (or maybe he had always been) a typical NASA kiss ass.

Then we discussed the release of the data, i.e., if it was going to be released immediately or not. I reminded Scott, "We specifically state in the archiving management plan that the engineering and science data are to be put out in the raw form in real time. Scott, you signed it; Joe Boyce at Headquarters signed it; the two guys from the Planetary Data System signed it; and, of course, I signed it."

To prove that, I showed Scott the archiving document, which was really a contract between NASA and the Project. Scott read it and said, "Well, this wouldn't hold up in court, the lawyers would change this." The two-faced, lying bastard. I was amazed and disgusted; to him that document we had all signed was meaningless when NASA and he wanted to change their minds. Like everything about NASA, it was just a façade!

We discussed it a little bit and I told him again that holding back the data from the public was a great mistake, "Day-old data is of no interest to the public, they want to be part of the live thing and there is nothing in this data that the public can misuse. If they are going to misuse it, they will do it anyway, whenever it appears. Also, we have a one bit/million error rate and since only about 35% of our data is downlinked a second time, we can't even bit check the majority of the data and that is the data that is going into the archives as Level 0. What would you gain by waiting for us to archive Level 0 before letting the public see the data?"

Scott, in his typical NASA way, tried to find a way around that, but in the end, he had to admit that everyone had signed the document and it was probably valid. Then he added, "Boy, I'm sure glad you had Joe Boyce sign this at Headquarters," i.e., he was glad that he was not the only NASA official with his head on the chopping block. What a coward; I was really disgusted with him.

Friday, October 18, 1996: The Mission Director Issue

Scott, Sylvia, Dougherty, and I met in the morning to discuss Mission Ops personnel. I said, "We have 6 people plus Tom."

Scott asked, "Who is going to be the Mission Director?" expecting Marcie would do that critical job.

Dougherty answered, "Alan wants to be Mission Director."

Scott said, "Oh no, he can't be that, he can't do it."

I said, "Yes I can, this is my spacecraft and nobody knows it like I do. I've written the Mission Operation Documents, and I'm running the spacecraft."

When we got back to Lockheed, I explained to Dougherty that "by running my own spacecraft, I don't mean that I'm going to send up the commands, rather I'm going to lay out the commands in the Mission Profile and I will issue them. I'm going to be the Mission Director and that is the end of it."

Dougherty said, "Well, you know, you really ought to let Marcie do it."

I said, "It isn't going to happen that way. Nobody knows the science, the spacecraft, and the mission but me. You know damned well the problem is that they (Scott and NASA in general) can't conceive of a PI doing this."

Dougherty agreed and said, "Yeah, this is not the way PIs act. They usually go off in the corner, wait for the results and want to be left alone."

Monday, October 21, 1996

There were no meetings all day, so I got a lot of work done on the velocity errors and fuel load for the TLI burn. In order to keep the velocity errors small, we were going to have to have a zero tip-off rate (tipping or tilting of the Spacecraft/TLI Stage) at its separation from the Orbit Adjustment Module of the LLV2. That required doing the spin-up of the stack right at separation. The biggest uncertainty, of course, was still the nutation.

The spacecraft was finally over in the test area again and hopefully would be prepared for the Z-axis shake by Wednesday or Thursday, and hopefully the test would be conducted on Thursday or Friday. Then we would know if our fixes for the 57 Hz resonance had worked or not.

Good news, we were informed that LRI was officially incorporated in the State of Arizona. I was going to call George French and have him get Sensenbrenner's staff to push our tax-exempt status through the IRS as quickly as possible. Maybe we would be ready to start getting into LRI in a month or so; I hoped so. If we did, then I could hire all the Mission Ops personnel through LRI and cut the Mission Ops costs considerably.

Tuesday, October 22, 1996

We had the telecon at Ames about the tracking and Tom and I went over an hour early to discuss Mission Ops staffing with Marcie, since that was an Ames — and hence, her responsibility. I was surprised that Dougherty showed up since I had not wanted him at the meeting and had not told him about it. I suspected Marcie had told him, and that, despite my telling her that she worked for me, she still considered Dougherty in charge. My suspicions were heightened because she was embarrassed when he came in. Further, she was uncharacteristically very nervous and very cautious about what she was saying. I suspected that Scott and/or Dougherty had told her that she had to stop me from being the Mission Director and commanding the spacecraft. Dougherty was also visibly upset and it was clear he did not like the situation.

Knowing that these guys were going to try their best to stop me from doing what I intended to do, I decided the best way to handle it was to take total control of the meeting immediately. Before Dougherty or Marcie could say anything, I went to the blackboard and said, "OK, let's figure out our manpower requirements. Let's talk first about the manning of the operations control center during the non-commanding parts of the operations. We have three eight hour shifts," and I drew three boxes on the blackboard. Dougherty and Marcie said they wanted to start at the top, i.e., with the Mission Director's position and I said, "No, I want to start at the bottom and work up to the top to see what we really need," and continued discussing the positions that would fill those three boxes, saying, "These are monitoring controllers with little training, since they only have to monitor the spacecraft and call me if anything goes wrong."

Marcie said, "We need a supervisor who could also fill in as one of these people. That person could be a controller and do all the staffing and scheduling of shifts and making sure the DSN is on, and all that sort of stuff." She also felt there was a need for two more people in a box above those controllers, people who could also fill in as monitor controllers, but who had more training and those two guys would be the actual Command Uplink Controllers, i.e., the guys who would actually uplink the commands. They would have command uplink capability, but not command authority. Then we decided there should be one more shift at the monitoring level. I drew a fourth box in the row of monitoring controllers and we all seemed to agree about that level of effort.

I said, "The only thing left then is Dan and me, who have command authority." I drew a box at the top and put Dan and me in it and said, "That's it, we're finished!"

Marcie said, "Well, we need a backup for that (for the top level)."

I answered, "That might be you (Marcie) and Dave Lozier, or some other pair of people. Also, the backup team can run the simulations to train Dan and me for emergencies," and that was the end of it. I had it exactly the way I wanted it and Dougherty was livid because he hadn't been able to stop me. And I had forced Marcie to do her job the way I wanted. Clearly that was not what they had planned.

I told Marcie what her role and the roles of the various controllers were going to be in detail. Basically, she and these other guys were not going to have much to do except passively watch the spacecraft, and she would do the shift scheduling. That way, she would be out of my hair, which was exactly the way I wanted Mission Ops.

Finally, we refined the personnel list, with the uplink controllers serving as monitoring controllers when I was not commanding the spacecraft, and concluded that we needed six people plus Tom, Dan, and me.

I was pleased with all that; I had cornered Dougherty and his little henchwoman very nicely.

After that, the telecon started and I brought up the first issue — TOTS. We went around and around about TOTS because the communications engineers did not understand that we would command the spacecraft through the 0 dB gain Omni antenna. They thought the medium gain antenna (which was for downlink only and which they thought had a 9 dB gain) was to be used for command uplink! Finally, they realized that and when they did, it looked like TOTS was marginal for uplink.

Regarding using TOTS for receiving the downlink, it would have only a 6 dB gain when the spacecraft was transmitting on the medium gain antenna, so that was marginal, too. It did not look good for the TOTS.

I brought up us using TDRS for the short period between the spacecraft's separation and turn-on and its being picked up by the Goldstone tracking station in California. I explained that given the range of possible launch velocity errors, we had to know immediately what our launch velocity errors were, so I could decide if I had to do an immediate emergency corrective burn, or we could be in deep trouble. I said I had to know several things about TDRS.

First, could we get one-way Doppler data and get it after 3 data points, which would either be after 3 or 30 seconds, depending on whether our sampling rate was once per second or one every ten seconds? If that answer was yes, then I would have at least 12 minutes more time to find out what I needed to do and get ready to do it. Everybody agreed we could get the Doppler data without any trouble. Great!

Second, could we also get downlink data so I could also see if the spacecraft was OK or not? And the answer was, "Maybe, but we'll have to see about that."

I said, "I hope that TDRS doesn't cost us any money, but if it does, I need it badly, so we will have to find a way of paying for it." Dougherty was forced to acknowledge that.

After the telecon was over, we went through the other items Dougherty had on his ever-present list and Tom got into trouble when we were talking about Mission Ops staffing. Dougherty asked, "Well, OK, who is going to do what? We need to hire these people. We have six people plus Tom, but what is Tom going to do?"

Well, Tom, of course, had done nothing to turn himself into a mission controller of any type, let alone my deputy or anything and I said, "I am going to have Tom do the Outreach and the data archiving."

Marcie said, "The archiving can be done by the controllers, because they have nothing else to do and it is just a matter of running these programs."

All of a sudden, there was no job for Tom. The question that everybody had on their minds was, "What use would Tom be in Mission Ops?" and unfortunately, the answer was, "None."

After that, we got into a discussion about TDRS, in part because Dougherty had no idea of why I really needed it, especially if it was going to cost any money. I tried to explain it to him and succeeded by saying I wanted TDRS with downlink so I would know if the spacecraft was OK or not, so I could be prepared to do something about it as quickly as I could send up commands via Goldstone and/or do an emergency burn if the velocity vector was all screwed up. He couldn't understand the fact that a 20-minute heads-up in knowing what our velocity vector was or knowing if the spacecraft was in trouble was a good thing! He then rattled on and on, trying to negate what I had said.

It was very interesting to watch Marcie as Dougherty made a fool of himself, she just sank down in here chair with a shocked look on her face as she listened to Dougherty being stupid. It was a good lesson for her. She had picked the wrong side; she was kissing his butt and working against me to try to help him meet his goals, but right then and there she was finding out that he is an idiot. Regardless, I was sick of both of them.

After the meeting, Tom and I went to lunch and Tom was obviously thinking, *I'm going to be out of a job.* I tried to soften the blow for him and said, "I'll try to figure out something for you to do, Tom — but, clearly, you have no real role in this (Mission Ops). The only thing that I can tell you is that you are going to have to do the things you came out here to do. You are going to have to learn everything about the spacecraft, the mission, and everything else, and then you can at least be the head of the backup command team."

Despite my words, I didn't think he could do it. He had been working very hard since the last time I had kicked his butt, but he had lost two to three years by not learning anything about Lunar Prospector when I had asked him to start doing so and I didn't think he could make up for that in the few months remaining before launch.

He acknowledged he had no real role in Mission Ops and I said, "Tom, I can't simply give you a job because you are my friend. If you can't do this stuff (Mission Ops), then we will have to find something else for you to do." We talked about the possibility of him managing the data analysis contract in LRI I hoped we would soon get from NASA, while I was busy running the mission. Still, that was a pipe dream, partly because we were still not in LRI, but mainly because I had not even talked to NASA about the data analysis contract. Tom was finally realizing he was in big trouble.

I was also quite disappointed because Tom's main motive seemed to be trying to find ways to get back at Dougherty rather than learning what he had to know. Further, I thought I was probably going to have to tell Tom that because he was not doing the job he was brought to Sunnyvale to do and because the job he was doing was really at the systems level rather than at the level of my deputy, I didn't see how I could possibly justify paying him $80,000 when we got into LRI. I decided I would have to let the Tom chips fall where they may.

Wednesday, October 23, 1996: Launch Errors and Recovery Strategies

Dan and I called Thiokol early in the morning and asked their opinion about the slag build up and the resulting nutation. Like me, Thiokol didn't think that either was a problem. I was convinced Dan had gone completely overboard.

I finished working on the spreadsheet that gave the various sources of the launch errors, from which it was very clear that we had to minimize every source of error we could in terms of loading ballast for the different days of launch, making sure we had an on-time launch, and having the spin-up occur immediately at separation.

I also worked on a spreadsheet showing the resulting lunar transfer orbits for every 5 m/sec deviation from the nominal velocity. From that, I thought we could handle a 25 to 30 m/sec launch error, without having to do an emergency burn, if we could get a mid-course maneuver done within 4 hours after separation.

However, if our launch velocity errors got as high as plus 80 m/sec, then our transfer orbit would be hyperbolic and we would go zipping by the Moon and I sure in hell didn't want to get into that situation.

The spreadsheet modeling showed that for overburns between 30 and 80 m/sec, I could put the spacecraft into a highly elliptical orbit around the Earth and it would be back near the Moon a month or two after launch. At that time, I could get it into lunar orbit. However, such highly elliptical orbits are not stable because of the gravitational effects of the Sun and the Moon, so making it into lunar orbit a month or two after launch would be possible, but difficult, and, of course, it would use a lot of fuel. Nevertheless, I had a recovery strategy for launch overburns in that range.

Similarly, in the case of a launch underburn, I would just stay in the resulting orbit, do a burn correction to get the timing right and then, one month after launch, I would do a second spacecraft burn and then get to the Moon.

We had good backups for both over- and under-burns and I was satisfied we had good mission-saving recovery strategies.

Thursday, October 24, 1996:
Eleven Months to Launch and the Z-Axis Shake Test

We did the Z-axis shake test on the spacecraft structure shortly after 11:00 AM. Tim Maloney and I went to the test area at about 11:00 and, as usual, I got up on the big ladder next to the spacecraft. Then the ¼ g input test started at the lowest frequency and the sweep up to the higher frequencies began. There wasn't much noise until we reached 45 Hz and then it started getting loud. However, we got an output vibration of 1 g on the structure only after we had reached 60 Hz and the maximum of the resonance peak was at 69 to 70 Hz! We had succeeded in moving the spacecraft's fundamental resonance frequency out of the range of the Castor 120's pipe organ effect and hence out of harm's way. Boy, were we relieved!

That resonance frequency would drop a little bit after we added the rest of the parts to the spacecraft, but not enough to hurt us.

After lunch, we redid the test at ½ g, ¾ g and 1 g inputs. They were all perfect. The inverted tripod structure holding the tanks was really firm and I was right up on the ladder all the time watching it and it was beautiful.

Friday, October 25, 1996: The End Of the Nutation Issue

I had called Preston Carter a couple of days earlier and asked him to help me find out what happened on Clementine since they had used exactly the same Star-37 engine for their TLI burn as we were going to use. Preston later emailed me the names of about four people to call. I gave them to Dan and he called them and their information was beautiful. They had an active nutation damping system on the TLI Stage, but they found from their pre-launch data that they probably didn't need the system, so they turned it off during launch and their TLI was perfect! They only had 1.6° of nutation, i.e., it was trivial. We could totally forget that issue, which I had always thought was bogus anyway, and get everything ready to define the propellant load for our Star-37. I was then certain we would end up with just a few meters per second velocity error, maybe 10 m/sec, which would be great. I was very happy we had that critical task done, and that Dan's stinking red herring was finally dead and buried.

Other than that, it was a quiet day, mainly because Dougherty stayed at home to care for his wife who was having an operation on her elbow.

Chapter 3-24
Starting Plumbing the Spacecraft

Monday, October 28, 1996:
Getting the Fuel Tanks Ready for Installation

Tom, Lee Larson-Bergman (a rather stiff and formal, Test and Integration Engineer that Dougherty had just hired), Irv, and I went to the facilities where the thermisters, thermostats, and heaters had been put on the 3 fuel tanks and they were in the final stage of being wrapped in their thermal blankets in preparation for their being mounted in the spacecraft. When we got there, the last tank was being wrapped and the other 2 tanks were beautiful in their silvery blankets.

Within two weeks, we expected that the 3 tanks, the 6 engines, the PIV, the 2 filters, the pressure transducer (to measure the tank pressure), the fill and drain valve, and all the propellant lines of the Propulsion Subsystem would be mounted in the spacecraft and the welding of the joints would be finished, or, as we said, the spacecraft's "plumbing" would be "plumbed." We were finally beginning to really move on integrating the various components into the spacecraft structure.

Tuesday, October 29, 1996

Mario had sent us the equipment we needed to demagnetize both the spacecraft components and the tools we were using to assemble the spacecraft (once a spacecraft component is demagnetized, if it comes in contact with a tool that is still magnetic, the component becomes magnetized again — we could not even wear our wristwatches near the spacecraft), as well as a set of three Helmholtz coils, some 2 meters in diameter, in which we would set the entire spacecraft so we could map its magnetic fields and get rid of them. Tom had taken on the responsibility of managing and doing a lot of the magnetic cleanliness work and he was doing a good job of getting the spacecraft and everything else demagnetized.

Buddy Nelson called and said a Channel 2 reporter had read something about Lunar Prospector and me and wanted to do a personal interview with me the week before Thanksgiving. Buddy thought we wouldn't have enough to show him (spacecraft-wise) and was going to put the reporter off until we had our press conference. I said, "No, we're going to have the spacecraft presentable in a couple of weeks and if the guy wants to have a personal interview with me, that's fine. If he wants a technical interview, then we should just put him off until we have the technical news conference."

He said, "Yeah, that's a good idea."

Wednesday, October 30, 1996

Thiokol had come to Lockheed to talk about the Critical Design Review of the TLI Stage and we discussed what we had found out about the Star-37's nutation. Thiokol agreed that was a dead issue.

Dan Lebel, our new contact for LLV2, reported on the results of a Minute Man Missile test launch of the new LLV avionics they had conducted a month earlier. They had checked the avionics' position calculations against the measurements from the global positioning satellites and found the avionics had gotten the position of the rocket correct within 3 m!

Based on that result, I thought if the damned rocket worked, it would probably give us a good ride to the injection point and then the Star-37 shouldn't contribute anymore than a few m/sec to the TLI velocity error. If that happened, we would have a good launch and for the first time in a very long time, I was optimistic about the launch.

Everything had been going very well during the previous few days and I was very optimistic about the mission.

Thursday, October 31, 1996: Halloween

We had a staff meeting and the spacecraft was in Building 158, where the technicians were getting ready to put the tanks in it on Friday and Saturday. Other than that, not much was going on.

Friday, November 1, 1996: An Ominous Rumor

Kim Foster, the engineer who was the head of the Test and Integration Team, wanted to talk with me. He said his wife worked with a guy who had been part of the LLV team in Denver and he had quit. He told Kim's wife there was no way in hell LLV was going to have the rocket ready by fall, that at best, it would be six months late!

That was not the kind of rumor I wanted to hear so I went over to Ames and talked to Sylvia. She said she had heard the rumor, too. That was ominous. I was convinced if we didn't get launched in the fall, or shortly thereafter, the mission was dead. I was very concerned.

Monday, November 4, 1996

The spacecraft was sitting in Building 158 where the technicians were going to plumb it, i.e., put the propulsion system in it. They were supposed to have gotten the tanks put into the structure on Friday or Saturday, but the tanks were still sitting next to the structure — all bright and shiny in their aluminized thermal blankets. The alignment technicians were over there aligning the spacecraft! We were slipping as usual and I didn't know when they were going to get the plumbing done.

The way I saw it, the spacecraft wouldn't be completely assembled until early December, at best. It was supposed to have been done in mid-September, which meant we had a three-month slip. Since we had moved the original launch date from June to September 1997, a three-month slip meant we had to eat up the three-month schedule reserve, and any further delays would mean we were not going to make our September launch date.

Sylvia and I talked to the damned LLV people and I grumped about the LLV2 not being ready. Dan Lebel also had the same concern, so Sylvia and I were going to start raising some real hell about the damned launch vehicle.

Tuesday, November 5, 1996: Election Day

I went in late because I voted.

Dougherty was not around much, which was great.

We had a Ground Segment telecon and the issue of the TOTS antenna gain was still unresolved.

The damned spacecraft was still just sitting over in building 158 — the alignment guys were taking forever. We continued to slip and I was getting very concerned.

Bill was back from Denmark. He was rested and ready to roll. The GRS, NS, and APS were all in good shape.

Wednesday, November 6, 1996: One Hell of a Day

What a day. When I got in, Frank came over and asked, "What is going on with the (launch) pad?"

I answered, "I don't know, what is going on with the pad?"

He said, "I just got this email from Dougherty," and he gave it to me. Spaceport Florida had been promised a $381,000 grant from NASA to work on the launch complex, but they hadn't gotten the money. They said if they didn't get it sent pretty soon, it would delay Lunar Prospector.

I perked up for two reasons. First, I didn't think that the problem was in itself that serious. I thought the Spaceport Florida staff was saying to NASA, "Come on, quit screwing around and get us the money."

But second, the thing that worried me was since LLV was behind in the development of the LLV2, they were looking for any excuse to blame somebody else for delaying the launch, and Dougherty's email indicated that Larry Price had said, "If this (the launch pad delay) is going to delay Lunar Prospector, we will have to know the impact." As expected, LLV had been just waiting for something like that to happen.

Karen Ramos, who was coming to visit Lockheed to see the spacecraft and to tell us how she was coming along getting the launch pad built, had left a message for me, asking where she could stay that was inexpensive, close to Lockheed, and safe. I called her and I gave her that information and then I said, "I also have a question." I read her the email and asked, "Is this serious?"

She said, "Yes, it is."

We talked a little about it and then I said, "Karen, when things like this come up, just call me, because Lockheed is Lockheed and I can get things done quicker." She said she would do so the next time. That was a hell of a way to start the day.

I called Sylvia and we discussed the launch pad issue and I told her the spacecraft was still not assembled and would not be assembled until mid-December. We fussed about the fact that we had slipped three months and hence we had lost our three-month of schedule reserve, and any more slippage in the schedule would impact our launch date.

Belatedly, Dougherty sent Scott, Sylvia, and me the email he had sent to Frank. As always, he was trying to hide Lockheed's problems from us and thus had sent it to Frank first, so Lockheed could cover its butt before we were told.

To make matters worse, Pegasus, Taurus's little brother rocket that is launched from an airplane, had just failed in its last launch attempt. Pegasus had worked perfectly, but the final stage's power failed after it was in orbit, so the payload didn't separate and the satellite was lost. That, of course, made everybody at NASA even more nervous about our launch.

The next thing that made my day was I was informed that the only software guy up at Palo Alto who had done a lick of work on the software said he would be leaving the program and going back to work on Gravity Probe B. He was a young guy who stood up to his bosses, tried to get things done right for us, stuck his neck out for us, and exposed all the problems.

I went to Dougherty as soon as he got in and said, "I'm very disturbed about this. He's the only one who has done a damned thing and now he is leaving us." Dougherty called Palo Alto right away and got the usual BS from Bill Jacobsen — the guys that were still there could do the job; there was nothing to worry about and blah, blah, blah. That was such a load of BS — just the same old crap.

Scott called about the seminar I was to give at Ames later that day, so I told him about the software engineer's leaving, the delays in getting the spacecraft assembled, the launch pad mess, and the LLV crap. We decided we had better have a talk with Larry Price's boss.

Sylvia and I commiserated about all that. The real problem was that Dougherty was never proactive. He never saw the problems coming, even though they were like the bright headlights of a truck speeding right at us. Instead of fending off the problems while there was ample time to do something about them before they hit us like a truck, he always tried to sweep them under the rug, because he didn't like to have Lockheed looking bad. Only when the problems had gotten so big that, having been swept under the rug, there was a big hump in the rug that everybody could see, then he would say, "Oh, we have a problem!"

I told Sylvia, "You know, when we got rid of Tenerelli, Frank said I couldn't have another one (Project Manager) after Dougherty, but if we don't have this spacecraft put together by January, I think we have to get rid of Dougherty. Instead of going over to shop people and raising hell if they aren't getting the work done, as Tenerelli would have done, Dougherty just tells Mary (Mary Piasecki, the young girl who did our procurement work) or Tim, neither of whom have any authority or clout in Lockheed, to put pressure on the shops to get the work done. He is afraid to go over to the shops himself and raise hell. He doesn't want to rock the Lockheed boat. We have to seriously start thinking about getting rid of him, if we still are not moving ahead by January."

Sylvia asked, "Who would we replace him with?"

I answered, "That is the real problem. I don't think there is anybody in Lockheed who will do the job right. I just don't think there is anybody in this company that's worth anything."

Within two hours of getting to work, all that crap had hit the fan and I was worn out before the day had hardly gotten started.

Despite all that, I got a lot of work done on the Mission Operations Document.

After lunch, I gave a seminar at Ames about Lunar Prospector. It went over very well. Scott was happy with it. Even Dougherty was there, but why he was, I would never know.

Since we knew absolutely that nutation was not a problem, Dan, Irv, and I sat down and did the sequencing for the TLI burn and the Spacecraft/TLI Stage separation. The sequence would start out by having the Orbit Adjustment Module of the LLV2 spin us up to 3 rpm (the maximum it could handle) and simultaneously starting the TLI Stage timer. Then the Spacecraft/TLI Stage stack would separate from the Orbit Adjustment Module. Less than a second later, the TLI Stage spin-up rockets would fire and spin the stack up to 57 ± 3 rpm and then the Star-37 would ignite. Some 10 to 15 seconds after Star-37 burnout, i.e., long enough so we didn't have a collision problem and long enough so we didn't have to worry about separating before the Star-37 quit burning if, for some unlikely reason, the burn was extra long, the timer would essentially simultaneously fire the explosive bolts, open the nitrogen jets, turn on the spacecraft, and we would have separation and be on our way to the Moon!

Thursday, November 7, 1996: Subsystem Review Day

The subsystem review was a waste of time; the real problem was that the schedule slip was getting bigger all the time.

After the subsystem review, I went over to see what was going on with the tanks and found that the tanks didn't fit into the structure properly because the thermal blankets and the wires for the heater and thermisters were getting in the way. There was only about 5 mm of space between the tanks and the longerons and the tank bosses were not even touching their mounting plates on the longerons!

Several things had to be changed. The electric wires had to be moved so they were not near the longerons, the longerons probably had to be trimmed to accommodate the tank, i.e., so the tank bosses were in contact with their mounting plates, and enough space had to be created to allow the tanks to expand and contract as the pressure changed.

Then I found out that the spacers that were in there were not even flight hardware, so new spacers had to be made, and the engineers hadn't even drilled the holes for the fill and drain lines to the tanks!

Needless to say, I was not happy; we were going to lose more time and slip further behind.

It was a tiring day. It was just one problem after another.

Friday, November 8, 1996

Once the technicians took the thermal blankets off the tanks, they confirmed that the wires were interfering with the fitting of the tank bosses to their mounting plates. We had to re-route those wires, which was no big deal. Then there would be plenty of clearance.

We had ordered new slip bearings to replace the old ones on the inverted tripod that supported the tanks at their back-sides (the bosses supported them on their frontsides). When they were delivered, we found that the new bearings were bigger than the old ones. The bearings had to be moved back further on the central mounting plate at the apex of the inverted tripod. We decided to slot the central plate bolt holes, slide the bearings back, and bolt them in place. All that would cause us another two or three days of slippage.

I had lunch with Scott and I told him we had not only slipped, but we continued to do so and I was very concerned. I said the problem with Dougherty was that he was not proactive, rather he just reacted to problems, and worse, it took him forever to realize there was a problem when a new one came up.

Other than that, I worked on the Mission Operations Document.

We were also getting ready for the Test Readiness Review, which I thought was going to be fun.

Monday, November 11, 1996

I was annoyed to find out that the bolt holes in the central plate of the inverted tripod had not been slotted Friday as I had expected, rather they would be finished after lunch! Crap, I could have done that on my own lathe and mill at home in ten minutes.

Anyway, Tim Maloney and I picked up the freshly slotted plate and took it over to Building 158 in our hands. When we got over there, the tanks were neither rewired, nor were the thermal blankets put back on them. The technicians had just shot another day. I said to Tim, "I'll be surprised if tomorrow morning we are any further along. We are just wasting time."

Another day shot — that ticked me off.

Tuesday, November 12, through Thursday, November 14, 1996: A Denver Trip

Just before I left to fly to Denver for an LLV2 review meeting on Wednesday, I went to see what was happening with the spacecraft. They still hadn't gotten the tanks put in the structure, because Lee and Tim couldn't find any tape to re-tape the thermal blankets onto the tanks and then they couldn't find any epoxy glue!

It was times like that I wished Tom had some authority, because he could really get things done. Tom would have found some tape and some glue in five minutes and the job would have been done in a jiffy.

If they had found the damned tape and epoxy, then they could have gotten the tanks finished, installed, and aligned, the Spider installed and aligned and even gotten started putting the sides panels on. I hoped they would get all that done by the next day, but I doubted that they would. I was getting disgusted.

I left Lockheed, went to the San Jose Airport and flew to Denver.

The LLV2 review started Wednesday morning and went fairly well. Dougherty got on Denver's case, as did I. It was the same old story — they said they had been working on the Destruct Firing Units for the TLI Stage and Dougherty crabbed that they had not really done anything. He got them riled up and I then got mad and made my usual statement, "This is not supposed to be us vs. you. I'm damned tired of not having a team that works together."

Larry Price got peeved and bitched at Dougherty after he jumped on Larry's LLV guys for not doing their work on the TLI Stage. Larry said, "We offered to do this (the TLI Stage) for $13 million, so don't crab at us now."

I said, "That's crap, I had a quote from you guys for a rocket with a TLI Stage for $25 million and then you wanted an outrageous extra $13 million for the TLI Stage alone. Don't give me that same old line of BS."

Dougherty pointedly asked Larry when the rocket was going to be ready and asked, "We've been hearing you guys are talking about an April launch, so what is going on?"

Larry said, "That's not true, we will be ready by the fall," but we didn't believe him. We just continued battling with LLV the way we had always been doing.

The next day we talked about — and looked at — hardware. It sounded like Thiokol was making plenty of Castor 120s right then. The fuel had been poured into our Castor 120 first stage and was being cut and trimmed (when the solid fuel is first made, it is a thick liquid that is poured into the rocket casing where it hardens and cures, then it is cut and trimmed to yield the exact fuel load required) and our second stage Castor 120 casing was being fabricated.

Then we went to see our Orbital Adjustment Module; there were four of them in the highbay we visited. They told me which one was mine and then I was told it might be a different one! I wondered if they were playing a shell game with me.

Nevertheless, as we discovered, they had hardware all over the place. I didn't think we were going to have any trouble getting our hardware, but I was worried about the software, even though Larry swore it was in good shape. Nevertheless, when I flew home Thursday, I still felt that LLV was playing games with us.

Friday, November 15, 1996: Karen Ramos's Visit

Karen Ramos was at Lockheed all day. I showed her the spacecraft and she gave our team a talk on the progress she was making building the launch pad. Rebecca and I had dinner with her in the evening.

The fuel tanks were finally in the spacecraft and the side panels were on. The engineers and technicians were still fooling around with the Spider and I hoped they would have it mounted in the spacecraft by Monday. Then they could start putting in the rest of the Propulsion Subsystem components and start welding everything together. Nevertheless, we were still behind in the assembly work and it was driving me nuts.

Bill called and said there was an oscillation in the low voltage supply of the spectrometers at temperatures below zero. He didn't know what was causing it, but said they were changing some of the circuitry so the phasing would be different, and he hoped that would minimize or stop the oscillations.

Chapter 3-25
The Official Beginning of Testing

Monday, November 18, 1996: The Test Readiness Review

Though we had been testing the various components of the spacecraft as they were being assembled, we had to have our second formal NASA review — the Test Readiness Review — before we could start preparing to test the completely assembled spacecraft, even though we were nowhere near finished with its assembly. Like our first formal review — the Technical Design Review — that had been held fourteen months earlier (Part Two, September 6 and 7, 1995), Jim Martin and his review committee were there for the review, along with my science guys and the Lockheed engineers.

The first day of the review went pretty well, with a few exceptions. Steve Honodel totally screwed up his discussion of the booms because he can't give a decent talk. He went into far too much detail and dragged everything out to the point where no one could understand anything.

Bill discussed the problem he was having with the low voltage supply of the spectrometers. He had found that cosmic rays were causing the oscillations, so it was a design problem rather than being a problem with some component. He said they could easily design an electronic filter that would take care of the problem, so the spectrometers were in great shape.

Dave Curtis discussed the MAG/ER and they were also in great shape and ready to go.

The one thing that disturbed me was that the review committee kept complaining about our having a single string (no backup subsystems) spacecraft. They had agreed to our building a single string spacecraft during the Technical Design Review fourteen months earlier, so they shouldn't have been saying, "Well gee, you're going single string and you have all these potential single point failures, you had better do something about that."

Unfortunately, the review committee's concerns about our being single string were heightened because the launch of the Russian Mars 96 spacecraft had failed two days earlier (Saturday, November 16, 1996), leaving it stranded in its low Earth parking orbit, until it burned up some twelve hours after launch. That had, of course, also set NASA Headquarters off like a 4th of July rocket.

Tuesday, November 19, 1996: Passing The Test Readiness Review

The second day of the test readiness review went quite well. We ended up getting a lot of Bs; they won't give us any As on principle, which was fine, but they did gives us a few Cs. They thought our Mission Ops plan was good. They loved the science and thought it was great. I found all that very amusing, because Dougherty was always trying to belittle the science instrument development efforts of my science guys, and our highest marks were on science and our lowest were on the test procedures — the very thing that he was supposed to be so good at, ha!

Al Schallenmuller complained to Jim Martin because Jim didn't want to put enough in their report to Headquarters about how well we had done. Al said, "When we were here a year ago, nobody thought you would have any (money) reserves left or you would be as far as you are by this time. You've kept all your promises and we are quite impressed."

The committee made several suggestions about things that they wanted us to look at, most of which we wouldn't do, because we didn't have the time and money, e.g., they wanted us to buy a second boom system and to look for potential single string failure points (they were all over the place).

I was really surprised and pleased that Gentry Lee, who had been a major player on Jim's staff during Viking, and who had been uncharacteristically quiet during the Technical Design Review, was the main contributor to the Test Readiness Review from the committee's side.

When we were done, we all felt it was a good review and we were ready to proceed with the rest of the assembly and move into the test phase of the fully assembled spacecraft.

After the meeting was over, I went to see the spacecraft and it was finally being plumbed. The tanks and the Spider were in. Some of the plumbing had already been done and they were going to put in and align the engines the following week. I didn't know if we were going to be finished by December 15 or not. But I thought if they could get the alignment finished fairly quickly, we could get busy on the plumbing and then we could start the wiring of the spacecraft's electronics — if so, we might just be able to make it by the 15th. However, we just kept slipping and Dougherty, of course, did nothing about it. As far as I was concerned, he was totally useless.

Wednesday, November 20, 1996: The International Lunar and Planetary Exploration Meeting at San Diego

Tuesday night, after the review had ended, I flew to San Diego and gave my talk at the San Diego meeting on Wednesday.

I talked to Karen, who was at the meeting after visiting us in Sunnyvale, and told her that Dougherty had written a letter to Larry Price based on her talk. Dougherty told Larry and his LLV team to get their butts in gear, because they were holding her up from finishing the launch pad. Then Larry sent a stern email to the LLV staff down at the Cape, telling them to get their butts in gear. That email prompted Bob Mellor, the head of the LLV team at the Cape, to go see Ed O'Connor, Karen's boss at Space Port Florida, and complain about Karen's having talked to us in Sunnyvale and tried to put the blame on her for their delays — typical. There was a big stink going on for a little while. I told Karen to find out what was going on and I said I would call Ed and set the record straight for her.

She got the details and told me that Ed was not worried about it. He knew the whole thing was just a lot of finger pointing, blame shifting, and general BS. However, Karen was very disappointed because she hadn't expected that type of backstabbing. I told her if she needed my support anytime in the future, just to let me know and I would take care of it.

Pat and Julius, who were at the meeting, flew back with me to see the spacecraft and to spend a long weekend with Rebecca and me. Unfortunately, because they were not Lockheed personnel, I couldn't get permission for them to see the spacecraft.

Thursday, November 21, 1996: Staff Meeting Day

While working on the Spider, Steve Honodel had broken a screw and we decided we were just going to leave it in the Spider since it wouldn't hurt anything. Nevertheless, Kim Foster was just livid that Steve had messed up the screw by doing something he was not supposed to do. Kim said, "This is flight equipment and you have procedures you have to follow. If you find a problem, you just don't go in there and change things on your own. You note the discrepancy; then it is reviewed and then we get the right people to fix it, and that is not you!"

Friday, November 22, through Sunday, November 24, 1996: A Long Weekend with Pat and Julius

I took Friday off and Pat, Julius, Rebecca, and I spent a nice long weekend seeing the sights around Gilroy. Julius was his usual goofy self.

Monday, November 25, 1996

Monday was a bad day. First of all, I talked to Sylvia and she said the rumors were getting thick and fast that NASA was going to take us off the LLV2, put us on a Delta as a piggy-back payload, and we would be launching in May, 1998. If that were the case, then all I would really have was the primary mission, since the extended mission would be no more than two months long. And, it would cost several million dollars more to do the mission, money NASA would have to cough up.

Tom said that Tim Maloney had asked him about the program Mario had given us to reduce the magnetic measurements we were making on the spacecraft. Tim was worried about one of the constants in the program, since he had modified the program by putting in a constant to convert the measurements into nanotesla (nT, the unit of magnetic field strength we were using), and he thought the coefficient was too small by a factor of ten. If so, the spacecraft magnetic fields were ten times bigger than he had been calculating. I would have to check that out to see if the spacecraft was magnetically clean or dirty. If the latter were the case, and I thought it was, we would have to demagnetize the whole spacecraft again.

I took a look at the spacecraft with Lee and we found that the technician was still screwing around. He couldn't figure out how to put the engines in correctly and he had the spacers in backwards! All he had to do was to flip them 180° and everything would have been OK. I didn't know why they couldn't figure those things out themselves!

After finding that error, I looked under the spacecraft and found that the fill and drain fuel line to the manifold at the bottom of the spacecraft was facing in the wrong direction by 110°! That would have to be cut off, remounted, and re-welded!

Finally, the engines didn't fit properly because the fuel inlet lines or nipples that came as part of the engine were longer than the drawings showed, so the nipples would have to be shortened by about 3 cm.

What a mess — couldn't the technicians and engineers do anything right?

When I got back to Building 107, Dan Everett and another technician had brought the spectrometers from Los Alamos. Tom and I took them to the highbay, where we were going to assemble the spacecraft, and we found the area where the spacecraft was to be put together was a catastrophe! We were using a corner of the highbay where the Iridium communications satellites were being assembled and there was Iridium stuff all over our little corner. There was a huge battery cover lying in our area and their battery charger was on our table. There were boxes all over our area and it was not cordoned off.

Tom and I had to clean off the tables to be able to put the GRS and the APS/NS assembly shipping boxes on them. Tom had been trying for weeks to get Kim Foster to get the nitrogen purge ready to protect the APS and to get a storage cabinet for the radioactive calibration sources, but none of that was ready! Here we had flight instruments in and no place to put them or to work on them. I got really ticked off.

I called Kim and said, "This place is a mess. I want it cordoned off and I want the Iridium stuff out of here. Get over here and get this mess straightened out."

We waited and waited, but he didn't come over. I went to Building 107 and he was just sitting there. When I asked him why he was not over in the highbay, he said, "I had to make a call."

I said, "I want you over there now." Kim was useless. He just sat around making his little calls. In stark contrast, Tom got stuff done; he hounded the people until they got it done.

I found Dougherty and I told him that things were catastrophic in the highbay. I told him about Kim, the mess over in the highbay, that there was no nitrogen for the purge, that Tim had screwed up the magnetic cleanliness stuff, and that I had the spectrometers in with no place to put them.

Since I was in rare form, I continued. I reminded Dougherty about Jim Schirle's having screwed up all the thermal calculations because he had not checked the thermal modeling program before he used it, and that Tim had done the same thing — he had modified the magnetics program without understanding it and had screwed it up. As a result, we had a magnetically dirty spacecraft. I said, "We have no discipline. The guys are just doing things helter-skelter. This is exactly what Kim was crabbing about when Steve broke the screw; he wasn't supposed to change flight hardware without going through a review to see how it was to be done and without getting the appropriate people to do it. It is just one thing after another." Dougherty agreed, but so what?

After lunch I had to go and waste my time listening to some Lockheed administrative stuff and then I went over to the highbay and found Tom again. He and the Los Alamos technicians had checked out the spectrometers; the APS and NS had checked out OK, but the GRS had some electronic noise. Also, they still didn't have the nitrogen purge on the APS!

Dougherty and I had to go over to see Scott and Sylvia. First of all I told Scott about the signature page I was making for everyone to sign and that it would be put on the spacecraft; he was happy with that.

Scott had had some little models of the spacecraft made in the Ames model shop. Apparently, Dougherty had been given two on Friday; one was for Henshaw and then Dougherty said in his snotty way, "Well, the second one was for me or Alan or Frank or I would put it in the display area. I decided not to give it to Alan, so I gave it to Frank and he put it in the display area." That was really nice. Dougherty used every opportunity to treat me like a piece of crap, just to show me who he really thought was in charge and Scott was apparently OK with that. What a pair of asses.

Finally, we got around to Marcie and Mission Ops. Marcie had been whining to Scott about how Mission Ops was going to be run and she was obviously mad because I was going to run it and she wasn't. Scott was dancing around about my running the mission, but accepted that I was the only person who was going to have the authority to send commands. Then Dougherty said, "Well, I am not going to allow Alan to send up the commands. That's the end of it, period."

I said, "Look, the person that is going to issue the commands that are going to be sent to the spacecraft is me, but I'm not going to type in the commands and hit the send button and I'm not going to worry about the tracking network, that's what the controllers are for." We went back and forth. Dougherty and Scott were pushing for Marcie to do it and to keep me out of it. I said, "This is my responsibility. I am the PI. This is my mission and nobody else knows it like I do, and nobody else knows this spacecraft like I do." With that, Dougherty grumpily backed off, as did Scott.

The really dumb part of the conversation was that Dougherty didn't even understand what was really going to happen in Mission Ops. I was really getting sick of his crap and his saying what he would or would not allow me to do. He is too stupid to even know what was being done, let alone know enough to decide who could do it.

I decided to hammer home my point a little bit more, so I brought up the point that during the Test Readiness Review we were discussing that issue, and Jim Martin had said I was taking on too much responsibility. Immediately, both Al Schallenmuller and Gentry Lee jumped on Jim and reminded him, "You took on the absolute responsibility of the four Viking spacecraft and the whole Viking Mission and what you said was law. Since you did that, Alan has every right to do so on Lunar Prospector since he is the PI and it is his mission."

I said, "This is the way Discovery was set up; the PI has the responsibility and nobody else. I took on that responsibility and I am not giving it to anyone else."

Then Scott said, "Well Viking was a different thing. Jim Martin was Project Manager."

I said, "Yeah, well, having a Project Manager run the show was OK in those days, but in Discovery, the PI has that responsibility, not the Project Manager and that is that."

They backed off a little, but Dougherty tried to cajole me into having Marcie be the Mission Director. I felt like saying, "Screw Marcie! I don't really give a damn what she does. I am sick of her sniveling and if she doesn't like it, tough! She doesn't know anything and she is of no importance to the mission and that is the end of it," but I refrained from doing so, but just said, "Hell no," to Dougherty.

I had spent two wasted hours with that BS and with those idiots. When I went back to Lockheed, I was annoyed as hell.

Kim still had not gotten Tom the nitrogen, so I asked Kim, "What in hell is going on?" It turned out that he had gotten a nitrogen bottle, but the regulator was broken. Tom and I jury-rigged up a hose between the nitrogen bottle and a plastic bag and put the APS in the bag as temporary purge. Kim was just useless. He didn't try to find anything. Tom had asked Kim to go look for a new regulator, so he finally did.

Kim found one and said, "This one doesn't go to low enough pressures, so it's no good."

Tom said, "We'll use it for now, at least it will keep the nitrogen flow rate down and the APS will be OK in the bag." I was disgusted, Kim didn't think about solving the problem and he didn't do anything about it on his own.

Tuesday, November 26, 1996

Tuesday was another bad day. When Tom and I got in, we immediately went over to see if nitrogen was flowing into the bag holding the APS — and there was none flowing! We quickly found out Kim didn't even know how to turn on the valve. He assumed you turned it on one way, but he had actually shut it off! All we had seen the previous day was the little bit of flow caused by the nitrogen that had been trapped in the line when we started. Shortly after we had left, that little bit of flow stopped. Kim was just totally useless.

When I went over to the spacecraft, the engineers were talking about the fuel input nipples on the A1 and A2 engines that were 6 cm long instead of being 3 cm long, so they impinged on the spacecraft's structure.

We discussed what we had to do about that. Obviously, one of the things to do was to cut them off, but that is very dangerous, because the cutting and trimming process could lead to little metal chips getting into the valves and that could cause them to stick open. If that happened, we would lose the engines and the mission. Irv was very concerned about that.

We found out that the A3 and A4 engines had a similar problem, but since the upper brackets were taller than the lower brackets, we could just trim the brackets and that would solve the problem for the A3 and A4 engines.

The long nipples on the tangential engines did not pose as big a problem since there was plenty of clearance for the longer nipples. All we had to do there was to bend the fuel lines to accommodate the longer nipples on the T1 and T2 engines.

However, in all the cases, the drawings had to be redone and the process of trimming the A3 and A4 brackets and bending the fuel lines would cost us a half a day each. Irv was going to check with Olin to see what we could do about cutting the nipples off the A1 and A2 engine. We would probably lose another week.

I worked on the magnetic problem and answered some other questions Tim had come up with. I didn't understand exactly what Mario had in his program — I am not an expert in magnetism — but I straightened out what Tim had screwed up.

Then there was the question of whether we were getting the right measurements from the magnetometers Tim and Tom were using to measure the spacecraft fields, because none of the magnetometers gave consistent results. Since the magnetic cleanliness work was a mess, too, I called Scott and told him I wanted to talk to him over lunch.

I met Scott at the Ames cafeteria and told him about all the screw-ups: the magnetic cleanliness screw-up; the plumbing screw-ups; the engine screw-ups; the broken screw screw-up; and the fact that we were just continuing to slip.

I said, "There are so many screw-ups, I can't even keep them straight. Basically, there is no discipline. Nothing is happening. These guys are just sloppy; they don't know what they are doing, and we are in serious trouble. As far as I am concerned, there is no hope of us getting the spacecraft put together until after Christmas — if then — at the rate we are going. Everyday is a slip. Everyday is something else. We've lost at least a week because of the engine problems. If we have to take the graphite epoxy brackets (for the A3 and A4 engines) off and mill them that will take two, three, or four days the way they do things at Lockheed. I am tired of this crap and Dougherty does nothing about it, he has to go. He is not doing his job and he is stopping Tom and me from doing our jobs. Kim is no damned good. I just can't believe he didn't have a work area prepared where we could put the scientific instruments — flight hardware — when they were delivered. There is no place for them, no purges, no nothing. People are tromping all over our area. I'm appalled."

When I was finally finished with my tirade, Scott said he would come to Lockheed at 9:00 AM the next day to discuss the problems. I said I wanted to get Dougherty thrown out. If that didn't happen, I was afraid Lunar Prospector was going to go down the tube. I warned Scott that I had reached my limits with Dougherty shooting off his big mouth and screwing everything up — I really wanted him out.

After the lunch meeting with Scott, I found Tom, and since Kim had not gotten our area in the highbay cleaned up, Tom had cleaned it up himself. After he was through, the Iridium bastards came over and took the chains down, walked all over the place and put some of their junk in our area again. That was just stupid and intolerable; we couldn't even have a clean work area — I hated Lockheed.

Wednesday, November 27, 1996

I talked to Mario about the magnetic cleanliness measurement issue and then I talked with Lockheed's magnetic expert about it. As a result, I thought we had everything straightened out — at least we knew what we were doing for a change.

Scott came over at 9:00 AM and we met with Frank, who had gotten excited when he knew I had bitched to Scott about Lockheed and Dougherty. Dougherty was very defensive at first, but when he saw I wasn't going to put up with that, he calmed down. He tried to do his usual song and dance and said we're doing this and we are doing that, and blah, blah, blah. He said he couldn't do anything about the manufacturing delays, because he didn't believe you could! In reality, he wouldn't do anything about them because he did not have the guts to go over personally and raise hell with the manufacturing people. If Domenick were still the Project Manager (which thankfully he wasn't), the work would have been done in a few hours rather than in several days. Despite Dougherty's rhetoric, both he and Frank knew for certain they couldn't fool around any more. They knew I was ticked off and that Scott was also concerned. Clearly, Dougherty didn't like the fact that I was raising hell, but screw him, that was the only way I could get the spacecraft done right.

Despite Dougherty and Frank's assurances to the contrary, I didn't believe we were going to get the spacecraft put together until the middle of January — at best. I thought we were going to be six months behind. It would be at least a week before the plumbing was finished, and then Woody had to get the spacecraft wiring started and that would take two weeks, if not longer. Even if everything went smoothly from then on, it meant we would not be done before Christmas, and that meant the spacecraft would not be finished before January. I suspected that, at best, it would be finished around January 15.

I told Dougherty and Frank I was really unhappy with Kim and that I wanted Tom to watch over Test and Integration. I wanted Tom to represent me when I didn't have time or when I was on travel and I wanted Kim to understand that was Tom's job. I was curious to see if they would do as I asked — I doubted it.

We finally located a pressure regulator for the nitrogen bottles, but when it finally came in at about noon, the hoses were wrong and we didn't have any sealant, so Tom still could not get the proper nitrogen purge for the APS set up!

I got a call from Headquarters in the afternoon because Stu Nozette had a paper in *Science* saying they had discovered water with their Clementine bi-static radar experiment. NASA wanted to have us put something together because they figured the press would be asking questions about the Lunar Prospector NS mapping experiment.

Finally, a very frustrating day ended and I was looking very much forward to resting up over Thanksgiving.

Thursday, November 28, through Sunday, December 1, 1996: Thanksgiving and Universal Studios

Rebecca and I had reserved a room at a hotel next to Universal Studios down in LA, where we were going to spend Thanksgiving. We got up early Thanksgiving morning and drove down to LA, checked in, and had a delicious Thanksgiving dinner at the hotel — like the turkey, we were stuffed.

We spent the rest of the day and the next three days relaxing and enjoying Universal Studios. I especially liked the attractions from the movies *Back Draft* and *Jurassic Park*. The only thing we did not like was that it was quite cold and we had not brought warm clothes with us.

Finally, late Sunday afternoon, we drove back to Gilroy and I got prepared to face the mess I knew was waiting for me Monday morning.

Monday, December 2, 1996

Tom and I went over to the highbay and the Iridium people had gotten in our area again. Kim had not bothered to tell us, or maybe he didn't know, that the posts and the chains we used to cordon off our area belonged to Iridium. We thought they were general highbay equipment and nobody told us differently. Also, we were set up in an area that was part of their integration area. Why Kim had not gotten that straightened out much earlier, I would never know.

We had a 1:00 PM review meeting about Assembly, Integration, and Test. Dougherty behaved himself — pretty much. He snipped at Sylvia, which surprised me, but that was typical. The man is a total idiot. Apparently my chewing out everybody before Thanksgiving had some effect, because Dougherty told everyone to get their butts in gear. I was still skeptical. We were at least four months behind schedule.

There was to be a celebration dinner because we had gotten another 100% award fee, but I was not going to go. I wasn't going to show any approval of Dougherty when we were so far behind schedule.

A technician had trimmed 3 cm off the nipples of the A1 and A2 engines and we decided to send them back to Olin for some tests to make sure that they were OK.

Tuesday, December 3, 1996

Stu Nozette and Paul Spudis held a Clementine news conference about their supposed discovery of lunar polar water ice. Since then I had been called four times for interviews about Lunar Prospector. Even though Stu and Paul tried to pretend that Lunar Prospector didn't exist, everybody understood that what they presented was very questionable and that Lunar Prospector was going to deliver the real data. It was very funny, even though they were trying to steal our thunder, they were actually giving us more thunder. I called Preston, since he had worked on Clementine, and he said, "They held a news conference and you got all the good press," and then he laughed.

All in all, *USA Today*, *Gilroy Dispatch*, Channel 5 in San Francisco, and a Cincinnati late night radio talk show host called for interviews!

The best part of the day was when Tom told Dougherty I wasn't going to the dinner, because I didn't feel it was appropriate since we were so far behind schedule. Dougherty was upset by that and didn't know what to say (for the first time in a long time).

Wednesday, December 4, and Thursday, December 5, 1996: The Clementine News Conference Fallout

Thanks to Clementine, we got a lot of publicity. There was an excellent article in *USA Today* and its headline was *97 Space Probe to Settle the Water Question*. Bill Feldman had had eight or nine interviews. Scott and I went up to KQED in San Francisco for an interview.

My good old friend and supporter from LMSC, Bill Beatty, was in Sunnyvale because LESC was trying to get a new contract to do tracking and mission operations. He asked me about Lunar Prospector's requirements as an example of a typical mission they might support. I showed him the spacecraft and Mission Ops and he was really thrilled. I was very pleased about that, because Bill had always supported my effort (see Part Two) and I was happy to be able to show him the results of his support.

We were still having problems getting the nitrogen purge set up, so I grumped at Dougherty, and because he knew I was boycotting his dinner, he was as meek as a little kitten. He also told me how he planned to recover from the schedule slips and he was just as sweet as honey and cream. Tom and my bitching at — and about — Kim had put both Kim and Dougherty in the doghouse and they were being really cooperative and nice. All of a sudden, we were all hugs and kisses.

Dan Everett, who was still in Sunnyvale, Tom, and Jim Schirle put the heaters on the GRS and they were trying to get it ready to go. Some technician was supposed to do the wiring of the GRS, but Woody was sick and had not told the technician to do it, so someone else finally got a technician to start wiring the heaters and thermisters — I just hoped he was doing it right. Tom was doing an excellent job keeping the spectrometer preparation activities going and I was very pleased.

The plumbing was finally underway. Hopefully, it would be finished by the following week.

Nevertheless, I was very concerned that we were still slipping. Jim Schirle thought it would take two months to do the wiring. If that were the case, then we were in big trouble. Dougherty said it would be done in two to three weeks, but I believed that Jim was right.

It had been a good and exciting two days, but I had worked twelve hours or more each day, so I was very tired.

Friday, December 6, 1996

Things were still all screwed up with the nitrogen bottles. The bottles we had leaked and their threads were so beaten up you couldn't even put the regulator on them. What a mess. Tom was doing an excellent job of trying to keep everything going, but he sure wasn't getting any cooperation from anyone.

Because Woody had been out ill the day before, the wiring of the GRS heater and the thermisters was not finished, so we had to fuss with that. We needed Woody over in the highbay to help, so Tom called Mary and asked her to get Woody. When she found him, Woody told Mary, "I haven't got time for this." I couldn't believe it, here we had Dan Everett from Los Alamos standing around, and Woody would not come over to do his job! I had to personally drag Woody out of his office and get him over to the highbay to do his work! Finally, thanks to Tom, who pushed everybody, we got the GRS wired up. Jim Schirle was going to put the thermal shields on the spectrometers on Monday and then they would be pretty much done.

Tom was doing a very good job; he was getting to do the things he is good at and he had the authority to force the guys to do their work; I thought that was very good for Tom. Nevertheless, he was frustrated with the engineers the same way I was; he had seen me deal with that before, but finally he was getting a firsthand feeling for what I had been dealing with.

Dougherty and I went over to see Scott and Sylvia. We talked about various things that needed to be done. Sylvia asked about the dinner and Tom said it was good. She turned to me and said, "How did you like it?"

I said, "I didn't go." Dougherty ducked a little bit and that was the end of that.

We talked about getting more people from Ames working on Lunar Prospector, because we had written in the proposal that young engineers from Ames were to get some experience on the project. It had finally dawned on Scott that he needed to do something about that.

I had brought along the signature sheet we were going to put in the spacecraft. Scott fussed about it because he didn't like that I had put my name on the upper left side as the primary person running the mission and his was on the upper right. He clearly thought he was the primary person of the mission and should have been on the upper left, but let it go after grumping a little bit. I was amused and thought, *well, piss on you.* He changed and added a couple of things and corrected the title I had given him. NASA had changed his title, but nobody had bothered to tell me that.

When Dougherty showed us the new schedule, I pointed out there was no place in the schedule for balancing the booms and we had to do that before they were integrated into the spacecraft. It took ten minutes to make Dougherty understand what was going on. Finally I said to him, "This has to be done; if the spacecraft isn't balanced, we can't fly it." Finally, it dawned on him that I was right. We talked some more about that later and decided we would have to meet the following Monday to determine how we were going to balance the booms.

I talked to Dan Swanson in preparation for that meeting. Dan agreed with me that the simplest thing to do was to balance the booms on a teeter-totter.

Dougherty and Steve recognized that we would have to take the boom canisters off the spacecraft if we balanced the booms later, but that we might have to do that to keep on schedule. I told Dougherty, "I don't care when we do it (balance the booms), but we have to do it with them off the spacecraft." We didn't like deploying the booms any more than we had to and if we did it the way that I thought we could, we would deploy the booms for one of the deployment tests, then take them off the spacecraft, and balance them. At least the issue was on the table, but Dougherty kept forgetting about it no matter how many times I reminded him about that critical issue.

The plumbing was still not finished — though Dougherty said it was. The technicians thought they would be done by the following Friday. The fuel inlets and the engines were welded together. The engines could still be adjusted a little and the final alignment work was set for early in the following week. Pressure testing of the completed propulsion system was scheduled for the latter part of the following week. Nevertheless, Lee thought it would be the following Friday before they could get the spacecraft out of the plumbing shop and over to the highbay where the rest of the assembly and wiring was going to be done. I didn't doubt she was right. We were still slipping and there was nothing I could do except to continue to bitch.

Tom and I were getting a lot done, but it was taking both of us to keep everything moving forward. I was just appalled that Tom and I had to do most of the work to keep Test and Integration going.

Monday, December 9, 1996

Irv, Dan, and I talked about the fuel load we needed in the Star-37 of the TLI Stage. We decided to set the mass of the TLI Stage's payload at 310 kg, the payload being the spacecraft plus ballast on the stage. Right then, the spacecraft's mass was 297 kg, so we would have to add 13 kg of ballast to the TLI Stage to match the Star-37's TLI burn capability. If the spacecraft's mass grew, we would just have less ballast on the TLI Stage; if it dropped, we would add more ballast — up to 25 k. That way, the Star-37 of the TLI Stage would always have a 310 kg payload to accelerate to TLI. Given where we were, there was no way the spacecraft's mass would even get close to 310 kg, so we had plenty of margin.

We were going to tell Thiokol that their Star-37 propellant load had to be for a 310 kg payload so they could start loading it. We were going to use the same philosophy with LLV2. Its payload would be some value that included the 310 kg payload of the TLI Stage, plus the still-to-be-determined mass of the TLI Stage, plus some extra ballast.

We had an Assembly, Integration, and Test meeting in the afternoon. Kim was so bad. I began to see why he never got anything done. He was always making a whole bunch of viewgraphs instead of getting any real work done.

Scott was also at the meeting and I was a disturbed because he just did not get as annoyed about all the problems as I thought he should have. He just accepted everything Dougherty said, even though we were still slipping. We were four months behind. I wouldn't have been concerned if we would have stopped slipping, but everybody except Dougherty thought the wiring was going to take two months. If that were the case, we were going to be six months behind schedule.

Al Tilley, Dan, and I had a meeting on balancing the booms and it turned out we could do it by calculation — the balance was not as sensitive as I thought it would be. If we got really good data on the masses and cg's of each instrument, then we could calculate the amount of ballast needed to balance the booms and they would not have to be removed from the spacecraft — to everyone's relief.

Tom was doing really well keeping things moving forward. I was very pleased at how well he was working.

The plumbing still wasn't done! The engineers couldn't get the PIV to open and it had to be open before they could finish. I asked them, "If you knew you had to open the PIV, why didn't you have the equipment over there to get it open?" They had wasted a whole day again just because those guys couldn't plan ahead and didn't know what they were doing. I was getting more and more disgusted. They were supposed to be good, experienced engineers who knew what to do. Nevertheless, they were always getting caught with their pants down; it was really disgusting.

Dougherty got after Woody for not having things ready for the wiring, and Woody said, "Oh, well, I had to help with the wiring of the GRS." He had spent a whole 20 to 30 minutes doing that! Tom didn't let him get away with that BS and called him on it. He was just looking for an excuse, because he hadn't gotten his other tasks done.

I was disgusted with the whole bunch of them.

Tuesday, December 10, 1996

I wasn't feeling too well when I went to work, but when I got there, I got a lot done on the Mission Operations Document.

We had the telecon about the Ground Segment and that was coming along OK. All the bits and pieces of the tracking, communication, and Mission Ops systems were discussed and the main job was getting them all put together to form the Ground Segment. Happily, Dougherty was finally keeping his big mouth shut regarding that issue.

Dave Curtis called and said he was going to bring the MAG/ER down to Lockheed on Thursday and Bill was also coming to Sunnyvale soon. The instruments were in good shape.

With the boom-balancing question answered, the next questions we addressed were the spin balancing of Lunar Prospector by itself and the spin balancing of the Lunar Prospector/TLI Stage stack.

I called Todd Greenwalt and got the information needed so Tom and I could get the paperwork done for our application for LRI's tax-exempt status. Todd also said he would continue helping with LRI, *pro bono*, which was great. As soon was we were finished, we were going to send the paperwork off to George French, who was going to get one of his politician friends to help get it processed before the New Year. Then we could go ahead and get LRI recognized as a foreign corporation in California with the help of a local politician. Hopefully, we would be done with all the formalities by the end of January and be in LRI by February.

Since I was not feeling well and since it had been a slow day, I went home early.

Chapter 3-26
Finally Moving Beyond
the Plumbing

Wednesday, December 11, 1996

The plumbing was finally done at about noon. Then the spacecraft was moved into another room so the technicians could start aligning the thrusters. Because we were so far behind schedule, the alignment guys were going to work over the weekend. Nevertheless, we had lost at least another week. After the alignment was done, we had to do the pressure and leak tests on the Propulsion Subsystem and then get the spacecraft over to our area in Building 150 for the beginning of what I expected was going to be a long and time consuming wiring effort.

I worked on the Mission Requirements Document and Tom got our LRI paperwork done so we could send it off to get our tax-exempt status.

Other than that, not much happened, except we were still slipping!

Thursday, December 12, 1996

As Dave Curtis promised, he delivered the MAG/ER and, of course, we didn't have the right stuff for purging the ER with nitrogen!

Bill arrived with his people to start the thermal-vacuum (or thermal-vac, as we say) testing of the spectrometers, so there was mass confusion. Nevertheless, all five instruments were there in the highbay!

I had to go to the dentist and was in the dentist's chair all afternoon.

Friday, December 13, 1996

I worked on the Mission Operations Document and it was almost finished.

Tom was herding the GRS through the system and it was ready to be put into the chamber for the thermal-vac test by afternoon, so we could see how it was going to perform, temperature-wise.

The spacecraft engines had been aligned. Unfortunately the tangential engines were misaligned, one was $3/4°$ off and the other was almost $1/2°$ off. Those alignment errors couldn't be fixed. There would be bigger burn errors than I wanted. However, except for the first mid-course maneuver and perhaps the second mid-course maneuver, the alignment errors wouldn't make too much of a difference. However, those alignment errors meant that the spacecraft's cg was not exactly in the plane containing the tangential engines and that was not the way I wanted it, but that was the way it was. Despite all that, the errors were small and would not cause any serious problems in flying the spacecraft, but they would cause me to make additional, corrective reorientation maneuvers.

Monday, December 16, 1996

We started the thermal-vac testing of the GRS and it wasn't working! There was electronic interference in the chamber, or a short in the GRS, or the GRS was temperature sensitive, or whatever. Bill and his instrument engineers were busy trying to get the GRS working.

Dougherty had finally gotten worried about our being so far behind schedule and was hollering, ranting, and raving at the engineers at our 1:00 PM meeting. Of course, he pushed everything off on poor Mary saying, "Mary, you've got to go tell your boss to call that guy and tell him he has to answer your calls." Well, why didn't Dougherty call the guy? Why should Mary have to tell her boss to do Dougherty's dirty work? I was disgusted with big, loud-mouthed Dougherty hiding behind the skirt of a nice young woman who weighed considerably less than half as much as he did! I was going to have a talk with Dougherty about him doing his real job — interfacing with the other managers in his own damned company.

Dougherty was bitching at Tom, because Kim had taken the nylon tubing we had gotten for purging the APS and ER and washed it with soap and water! As a result of that stupidity, we had 30 m of small diameter tubing that was all wet inside. Tom had cut a 2 m piece off the tubing, dried it and put the APS and ER right next to the nitrogen bottles to get them purged continuously, as was necessary. However, since in general we did not want the instruments around big, heavy pieces of equipment, like the bottles, that could fall over and damage them, Dougherty barked at Tom and Tom barked right back and stood his ground. I was proud of Tom.

Everything was a mess; we were behind schedule and getting more and more behind every day!

Tuesday, December 17, 1996: One Lockheed Mess Up After Another

I talked to Dougherty; it was a very amiable conversation that began about our being so far behind schedule — he was meek and agreed with most of what I said. We talked about the mess regarding Tom's trying to get the instruments purged. I said we were not in a position to keep the instruments secure and we should consider sending them back to Los Alamos and Berkeley, where they could be properly stored until we had everything properly setup in the highbay to keep them safe. If there was ever a clearer indication of how badly things were being done at Lockheed than the fact that we could not keep the instruments at Lockheed after they had been delivered, I do not know what it could be.

I told Dougherty that Tom was doing a good job and Dougherty agreed that Tom is a good expediter and gets things done. Dougherty said, and he is correct, "If you have people who are good at getting things done, let them do it." In saying that, however, Dougherty admitted that he is not an expediter and I thought, *how in hell could Lockheed make you a Project Manager if you don't have that capability.* We discussed the need for him to start expediting things to stop the schedule slippages.

I brought up each issue I was concerned about, one of which was that Kim was simply not doing his job and that Tom had been trying his best to make up for Kim's messes. Dougherty tried to defend Kim, but I stopped him.

Then I talked about the poor alignment of the engines and Dan Swanson heard us talking and came in Dougherty's office to back me up. I said, "This (the poor alignment) isn't a catastrophe, it's just an extreme annoyance after all the effort everybody made to have the cg located exactly in the plane of the engines. They're (the tangential engines) supposed to be in that plane and now they are off by a significant amount. We can get around it (while flying the spacecraft), but I don't want to have errors build up like this. We can make up for it (the alignment errors) every once in a while by reorienting the spacecraft, but this is not the way you build a spacecraft, this is just sloppy engineering."

We also talked about the mess with Woody getting the wiring done. Dougherty was hoping it would be done by the end of January and I said the word on the street was it would take until the end of February!

I went to Ames and bitched with Sylvia. Like me, she had been worried about the slips for a long time. I told her that Dougherty was not doing the job. I said, "I don't care why, but he is not pushing, he's not getting things done. We cannot continue this way or we are going to lose the mission."

Sylvia called me later and said she had talked to Scott. Scott said that Friday, when Scott and I had our usual Friday meeting, he would ask me, "How are you going to get back on schedule?"

I said that my answer would be, "One of my jobs, as PI, is to tell NASA if, and when, I feel that the Mission is no longer doable on time and on budget. We're getting to that point and if this doesn't change — if we don't see some light at the end of the tunnel by January — I'm going to have to write you a formal letter saying I have serious doubts about the ability of Lockheed to get this spacecraft done on time and on budget. You know damned well I do not want Lunar Prospector canceled, but we are in trouble. It's about time somebody did something about it."

Sylvia then asked, "If we want to get rid of Dougherty, who do we have to replace him?"

I said, "Sylvia, that's not the question. You don't stay on a dead horse just because you can't find another one; you get off the damned dead horse and do something. You just don't sit there looking at the dead horse."

The GRS just wasn't working right. It would turn on and work for a while and then shut off. Something was screwy, so Bill and his guys thought they might have to take it back to Los Alamos and get it fixed.

Dave Curtis was getting ready to come down to Sunnyvale to pick up the MAG/ER since we couldn't protect them. That was great. It was wonderful that we had to send our instruments back to Los Alamos and Berkeley because they were not safe at Lockheed!

Wednesday, December 18, 1996

Because we were so far behind schedule, I talked to Dougherty about having our people work over the holidays. He said he couldn't force people to work then. I told him, "It's simple Tom, all you have to do is put a gun to their heads and tell them to do it, just like they did in (the movie) *Get Shorty*," and he laughed.

Bill was still having trouble with the GRS. It worked at room temperature, but there was apparently a lot of electronic noise they didn't understand when it was in the thermal-vac chamber and in its conducting casing.

The technicians had finished the alignment on the 4 axial engines and they were, happily, within specifications. I hoped that, when they aligned the sun sensor and the limb crossing sensor, the technicians could spend some more time adjusting the tangential engines.

Thursday, December 19, 1996: The Slip and My PI-ship

The GRS had a problem when it was colder than $-35°$ C and it had several grounding problems caused by the test setup and the thermal shield. It was also possible that part, or all, of the problem was the fact that the test cables were longer than the cables Bill had been previously using and hence, there might not really have been a problem with the GRS. Regardless, we had to understand and fix whatever was wrong with it. Bill wanted to take it back to Los Alamos to work on it. I agreed and I also told him I wanted him to take the APS and NS back, because we couldn't keep them safe at Lockheed. Bill said he would send someone out to get them after Christmas. I said that was too late, I wanted them out of Lockheed right then, as did Dougherty, since we could not protect them.

I found Tom and said we had to talk to the Los Alamos technicians to see if they would drive the spectrometers back to Los Alamos rather than fly back. When we got over to the highbay, the only Los Alamos person who had not already flown home was Karen. Bill and some other Los Alamos scientists were up in San Francisco, attending the American Geophysical Union Meeting, and they were going to fly directly home later in the afternoon, so that left Karen, who said she was not willing to drive back to Los Alamos by herself. She asked, "Can Tom drive with me?"

Tom was off trying to call somebody at that time and I when I found him, I asked, "How would you and Shelley like a nice free vacation?" and I explained the situation and said that he and Karen would have to leave for Los Alamos the next day, Friday.

Tom did not like the idea, in part, because he and Shelley were going to finish moving into their new apartment over the weekend. He complained that if he went to Los Alamos, they wouldn't be able to get completely moved out of their old apartment and would have to pay another month's rent. That was BS, all they had to do was to clean the apartment and take their clothes out. He had the rest of the Christmas holiday to do that. Nevertheless, he made a big to-do about my request, but as far as I was concerned, that was tough luck! He always wanted more responsibility and that was his big chance. I was quite disappointed that, instead of rising to the occasion, all he did was grump, but I said, "You are going and that's that."

We went over to the test facilities to get the spectrometers and all their support equipment out of the test area and put it back in Building 150, so we could be ready to pack all of it the next day. Then we had a hell of a time trying to find a van to rent. We ended up having to rent a U-haul truck that was far bigger than we needed. But finally, we got everything arranged and Tom complained the whole time.

Tom, Karen, and I were talking about getting everything ready to go and Tom said, "You always said I could go to Los Alamos sometime, but I sure don't like having to do it this way."

I said, "That is too bad, I have to go on trips all the time that I don't want to go on, but that is just the way it is."

He said, "Well, I would rather do it when it would be fun and blah, blah, blah."

As I had told him in the beginning, I said again, "Why don't you just call Shelley and you two can drive out there, rent a car, and drive back. You can see the Grand Canyon and do all kinds of stuff."

He said, "Well, why don't you do it."

I answered, "Frankly, I would, if we (Rebecca and me) didn't have airline and hotel reservations for our trip (to La Paz in Baja California over Christmas)."

I was more than a little ticked off at Tom. He was always bitching that he never got to do anything and never got to travel. He should have simply shut up and done his job. If Rebecca and I had not had airline reservations, I would have called her and said, "Honey, we're going to drive to Los Alamos and have a paid vacation," and she would have been ready to go. So what if we would have had to drive in a truck for a couple of days. How many times had I been gone on a long trip, flown someplace for something, and spent my weekend on travel? I was really ticked that Tom had made such a big fuss about his having to drive to Los Alamos.

Dougherty's father had gotten very ill, so he was trying to fly to New York as soon as he could. As a result, Dougherty didn't think he was going to be at the 2:00 PM meeting with Scott, when Scott was going to raise hell about the schedule slips. But it turned out he couldn't get an early flight, so he was at the meeting.

Scott said, "I'm going to have to beat up on you guys." He was mad because of three things.

First Scott jumped all over Dougherty because Buddy Nelson, who is the Lockheed PR guy, was setting up media things and answering calls from the newspapers and TV and not coordinating with Scott and his people. From my standpoint, Buddy was doing a good job and Scott was bitching about penny-ante crap, because I don't think NASA ever does a good job at PR. Nevertheless, Scott read the riot act to Dougherty and Dougherty said, "OK, the simple solution is that we will just tell our people not to do anything, which is fine with me."

Then Scott jumped all over me about an article in the December 9, 1996 (pp. 64–67) issue of *Aviation Week*. The article had many quotes from me about the mission and because I had said "The Discovery program is being run as a data buy — the only thing I deliver to NASA is data," and, "The spacecraft and instruments are not part of the contract. How I fly the mission and get the data is my business."

Scott was all bent out of shape and, "You are being confrontational and this is a NASA mission." He handed me part of the contract and said, "I want you to read this. We have joint responsibility. This is a NASA mission."

I retorted, "It also says in there that the PI has the sole responsibility for the success of the mission, not NASA and not Lockheed, but me!" I said further, "First of all, I don't care what one says to the press, it's going to come out differently anyway and they write what they want to write. If you look at the article, you'll see it has every possible combination of NASA, Lockheed, and me, concerning who is running this show. There's nothing that we can do to stop this sort of stuff, other than just not talk to the press and that would be stupid."

Dougherty said he agreed with Scott and he thought that when there was going to be an interview, all three of us should be there so that nothing would be said that was sensitive. I said, "No way, I will not do that. I am not going to sit there and weigh every single word (as Scott always does) to decide whether somebody might or might not like it, because no matter what I say, somebody is not going to like it. That's just tough — I'm not going to do that. I refuse to do that."

Scott then said accusingly, "You twist things the way you present them to the press and make them think what you want."

I shot back, "You know I'm not doing that. This is supposed to be a data buy program and this is supposed to be a PI run mission — go read what was said about Discovery in the original information and what Wes said at the initial press conference." That ended that part of our meeting and Scott just sort of left that.

With that stalemate behind us, we got on the business of the schedule and Scott read the riot act to Dougherty again. We discussed all the things each one of us thought were going wrong. Dougherty admitted that the engineers and technicians weren't following through and I said that Kim, who they portrayed as such a great Test and Integration guy, was, as far I had seen, a total failure. Dougherty said, "Well, he does a great job on the other stuff."

I said, "That may be, but what I have seen is not good. He fumbled the ball on the purge stuff and put our instruments in jeopardy. It may very well be that he is tremendous and what I have seen may not be representative, but I am not impressed."

Dougherty said, "Well, that's a fair observation. You've only seen him in this capacity and this is your frame of reference. I agree with you that he has done a bad job, but it's not representative."

We went around and around in an amiable way about the schedule slips. Dougherty felt strongly that the spacecraft was going to finally get out of Building 158 and go to our highbay in Building 150 the next day, since the propellant system had been completed and pressure tested and was found to be OK. Dougherty felt that once we got control of the spacecraft, everything would be OK. He said that slips had occurred every time the spacecraft had been in somebody else's shop where he couldn't (in reality, wouldn't) control it. However, that was his fault, because he didn't have the guts to push those guys and he had to admit that he could have done things differently, and blah, blah, blah. He again said he was sure that once we got the spacecraft over in Building 150, we could control our own destiny. I was not convinced.

The thing that made me distrustful was that, every time we had a problem that should have taken an hour to correct, it took days to correct — like when we needed to slot the six holes in the central plate of the tank support. If Kim had taken the plate over to a machinist and said, "Look, we need this done immediately. Can you slip it in? Can you get it done?" it would have been done in an hour. But no one would do that (except Tenerelli), so every problem caused us to lose four, five, or even seven days. Kim and the rest of them just let the system chug along and Dougherty had to admit that was probably true.

I said, "Look, you guys remember that when we had our Technical Design Review a year ago, Jim Martin said to you and me, Tom, that our problem was to make a big company act like a little company. Well, we haven't been successful at that. This company is still simply doing things in the old way."

Scott asked, "Do we have a team of good people who are really enthusiastic?"

I answered, "Yes, the guys we are working with are motivated; they are proud of Lunar Prospector and pleased to be working on it. They are having fun, but they still interact with the rest of the company in the same old way. The minute they get outside our group and interface with anybody else — purchasing or whoever — then it is the same old mess. It just doesn't work."

I said, "I wanted to get back to what you said earlier, Scott. I don't agree with your assessment of whose mission this is and who is running it. When Wes announced that Lunar Prospector had won, he clearly stated that this was a PI-run show, that the mission was my responsibility, and that it was not a NASA show. If you look at the AO, it says the same thing. This (what I had said in the *Aviation Week* article) is exactly the way this mission is described. I just don't agree with you."

Scott said, "Well, you have to remember that it's a NASA program, it's NASA's responsibility, and if you don't like it, that's just tough luck."

I said, "I don't agree with that, this is a people's mission. The taxpayers paid for this mission."

He said, "No, this is NASA money."

I said, "No, it's not NASA money, it's the American taxpayers' money, not yours." As usual, we left it at that.

After we left the meeting, Dougherty wished me happy holidays and all that. Then he said, "What you're doing is good; it's good you're pushing me, because I need to be pushed every once in a while."

I said, "Well, I'm glad you like my pushing." Then he started saying something about the PR issue and I said, "Scott is dead wrong on that. He's hurting the program as NASA always does," and he had to agree with me.

Friday, December 20, 1996

Tom and Karen left for Los Alamos right after we picked up the truck early in the morning and got everything loaded. Because Tom was mad that I was making him drive the instruments to Los Alamos, he was a wee bit rough on the instruments as we loaded them — I was going to have a little chat with him about that when he got back.

A little later, Dave Curtis came and got the MAG/ER to take them back to Berkeley.

I talked to Scott and he apologized for being so grumpy the day before. I still wanted to talk with him more about our different opinions as to how Lunar Prospector was to be run and I wanted to write a letter to Wes Huntress to get Wes's opinion.

The guy who was modeling the adiabatic cooling of the fuel tanks during the long Lunar Orbit Insertion burns for me found out there would be enough convection in the fuel, because of the acceleration of the burn and the centrifugal force, that the fuel would be isothermal, and that was good.

The spacecraft had been brought over from Building 158 to our highbay in Building 150 in a big box. Tim Maloney wanted to uncrate the spacecraft and mount the electronic units on it while it was still in the Building 158 receiving area, where it wouldn't make any difference if they made a mess. Ralph Fullerton, our Quality Assurance Engineer said, "No, either leave it in the box or put it on the stand (a specially built dolly on which the spacecraft was to sit and which we could roll around as we worked on the spacecraft) where it's protected." They were discussing those options and I said, "I want to get it on the stand now!" If I had not been there, it would have ended up staying in the box and we would have lost another day.

We got the spacecraft out of the box — a very delicate process. We opened the box and then carefully lifted it off the spacecraft. Then we hoisted the spacecraft up and weighed it. It had a mass of only about 70 kilograms, so had less mass at that stage than I thought it would have. Then we very delicately put it on its stand, bolted it down, and rolled it over to our work area, where we put the chains and signs around it to protect it. It took four hours to complete that very slow, very delicate process.

The day before Christmas was a good day. The instruments were back where they belonged and the spacecraft was finally where it belonged. I hoped we were finally going to begin to get back on schedule and I was looking forward to Rebecca's and my vacation in La Paz.

Saturday, December 21, 1996, through Wednesday, January 1, 1997: Christmas and New Year's

Rebecca and I flew down to La Paz in Baja Sur Monday, the 23rd, picked up our rented car and drove to Los Arcos Hotel on the bay. Since I had been there to see the great solar eclipse of July 11, 1991, and found the Baja as enchanting as Arizona, I had wanted to show Rebecca the area. We had decided to spend Christmas there.

We enjoyed the vacation very much, though I was a little disappointed by two related things. In 1991, La Paz was a relatively untouched Mexican city where few people could speak English. By 1996, La Paz had discovered that tourism brought in a lot of money and the place had been somewhat Americanized and all the shopkeepers spoke English — there went my chance to practice my Spanish. Nevertheless, we enjoyed La Paz and its beaches very much, drove down to Cabo San Lucas, which is just an extension of LA and which I did not like any better in 1996 than I did in 1991, and visited Todos Santos, which had also begun to lose its quaint fishing village atmosphere as it was developing into a tourist oriented village.

We flew back home on the Friday the 27th, after having an enjoyable and relaxing time in Baja Sur.

Then we just rested and relaxed at home, where we spent New Year's Eve and New Year's Day.

Finally, 1997 had arrived, the year I expected to launch Lunar Prospector to the Moon. I was looking forward to the coming events, still worried that we were way behind schedule, but still believing in the ultimate success of my mission, despite Dougherty, despite Lockheed, despite Scott, and despite NASA.

Thursday, January 2, 1997: Back to Work

Not a whole hell of a lot had been done on the spacecraft in my absence. They had the heaters on the fuel lines, but the thermostats had not been installed. Jim Schirle wasn't around to finish it, so we were stalled again.

I talked to Woody about the wiring and he thought we could get it done by the end of January, but that was not a firm estimate. I told him I was getting very concerned.

Then I was horrified. I found out we didn't have any technicians who were working fulltime on Lunar Prospector! We just had whomever we could grab from Iridium. That was absurd. We were supposed to be launching in eight months and three weeks and we didn't have a spacecraft. We were five months behind schedule and my concerns were growing.

Friday, January 3, 1997

No one was doing a damned thing on the spacecraft. I was going to start raising hell with Dougherty about it on Monday, when he got back from NY.

I had asked Kim and Tim, "Why aren't people working?"

They answered, "Well, we can't do anything because Jim (Schirle) isn't here. We can't finish up the (propellant) lines and we can't do anything with the wiring until we get the fuel lines done."

It was always the same thing, "We can't do this; we can't do that."

I said, "We have to quit this crap of doing everything in series. We have to start doing things in parallel. Even if things are inefficient, it's better to be working inefficiently than not doing anything at all — which is what we are doing."

I decided I was going to have to give them a talk at the Monday meeting and say, "Look, the rules are that if we don't get ready on time, we are canceled. One of my responsibilities as the PI is to recommend its cancellation. If I feel that we are not going to make it, believe me, I will do so."

Monday, January 6, 1997: Building to a Schedule Crisis

I talked to Dougherty, whose Dad had died over Christmas, and told him we weren't moving ahead. There was nothing he could do but agree with me, since any idiot could see that nothing was getting done and we were five months behind schedule. I told him I was very disturbed to come back after the New Year and find that very little had been done over the holidays. Though Jim had started putting the heaters on the fuel lines, he had been called down to the Western Test Range and everything had come to a stop. I said, "This is killing us." No one knew how to get in touch with Jim and we didn't have anybody here who could continue the work without Jim. I said, "You know, Tom, we're getting to the point where we are going to lose this." He agreed with no argument.

I also told him I was concerned because the troops seemed to have the attitude that, *so what if we are two weeks late or a month late, no big deal.* He said that he too had noticed their attitude was, *things have slipped, but it's OK, it's just a slip.*

We talked about the problems and Dougherty said, "What we are going to do is, that every day, you and I, Tim and Lee, will meet at 8:30 AM to see what is going on. Everyday we will find out what is to be done and what has been done and watch over it much more closely." I could tell it was a strain for him to say, "You and I have to watch this and you and I will have these meetings," but that was they way it had to be. That was the first time he had included me in that way, but he had no choice.

He said, "Don't worry about the money, we still have a half million dollars left in reserve." As usual, he was doing an excellent job of holding on to the money. I complimented him on that and said he had done a fantastic job controlling our spending. He said, "Also, we have two to four million dollars of the profit we can use if necessary." He must have had a talk with somebody about that, because he would not have said that on his own.

He admitted that we had lost so much time that if things went badly during the rest of the testing, we couldn't recover — we had pissed away the four months of schedule security we had. He did not make any excuses about his screw-ups and he said he would have to get rid of Woody and that he had waited too long to do so. But, it was the same old story; he always waited far too long to do everything. That was always his excuse and that is not what a good Project Manager does.

We found Lee and Tim and we went over everything. For me, the meeting was a mixture of stupidity and amusement — Dougherty knew nothing about what was going on with the spacecraft; everything had to be explained to him. He knew nothing about the work area in the highbay — he had never even been over there! As Project Manager, he should have been over there with me every damned day checking everything out.

Later, the Ames Quality Assurance guy was over in the highbay area, looking over our shoulder. He said to me, "I was very disappointed to come in this morning (at 9:00) and find that no one was working."

I said, "I was just as disappointed last Thursday when I came in. I raised hell about it. This has to change. We are not getting anywhere. Lockheed has to do something."

We had our 1:00 PM staff meeting. Dougherty made a little speech about our being so far behind schedule and started to push the guys. Then he asked me, "Do you want to say something, Alan?"

I answered, "Yes," and I started my little tirade. "You know guys we are supposedly 8 months, 2 weeks, and 5 days from launch and we are 4 months behind schedule — this is not going to work. In talking to some of you guys, I find that you seem to have the attitude that it doesn't make any difference if we are a few weeks late. Apparently some of you weren't in on the beginning of this or have forgotten what Discovery and this mission are all about. We were chosen as the first competitively selected, peer-reviewed mission, and when I was told I had been selected for flight, Wes Huntress told me flatly that as the first one, I had to prove the concept. I had to be on time and I had to be on budget and my budget was $63 million and that was it — not a penny more. Tom has done a great job of keeping us solvent, so I'm not worried about the money, but we are running out of time. For those of you who don't think we can get canceled, let me tell you that we can get canceled — in fact I have the responsibility of canceling the program myself if I don't think we can do it on time and on budget, and I will do so if necessary. Also, because Lunar Prospector is small and inexpensive, the scientific community thinks we have a lousy mission, which is not true. But if anything distracts from our mission — if we are not on time or are over budget — the community is going to jump up and down and say what a lousy mission Lunar Prospector is. That will not only hurt us and possibly get the mission canceled, it will also hurt Discovery, so this is serious. Also, if we don't launch on September 24, it will cost us a half a million dollars and that will come right out of Lockheed's profit and this company is not going to like it if we throw away the profit." I only hoped my little talk would do some good.

I thought I was done, but Sylvia brought up another point. She said, "Up until the schedule slips began to get serious, most everybody at Headquarters had been on our side. But we may have a very tough time from now on. Headquarters is now really giving Scott and me a hard time, because they no longer believe we can do it."

I said, "That reminds me, up until the Test Readiness Review, we were the shining example. We were on time. We were building the spacecraft and everybody had the greatest confidence in us. There were questions about the launch vehicle, but the spacecraft was fine. Now, they are losing confidence in us, and if this continues, what is going to happen is that we are going to have a damned review every damned month. NASA will be sitting right on us."

Sylvia added, "That has already started, from this point on, we (Scott and Sylvia) have to send Headquarters a monthly report." Sylvia was visibly upset during the whole meeting and she was quite worried.

After our meeting, I went over to the highbay to see what was going on and when Jim Schirle came in he kind of ducked. I asked, "Why are you hiding?"

He said, "Kim sent me an email saying you were on the warpath."

I said, "Yes, that is true, but I am always on a nice warpath."

He said, "Yes, you are."

Jim and the technicians were supposed to start putting clips on the thermostats in preparation for mounting them on the lines. It seemed to take forever for them to get started, even though they knew it had to be done by the end of the day. They got one main heater on the spacecraft, but had not started with the clips by the time I finally left because it was dragging on so long.

Part of the problem was that the clips were very tight, so the technician had to pry them open. Then it turned out that the thermostats were popping off the damned clips. That meant they would have to pry them all off and re-glue them onto the clips and that was going to take a while. Another day was lost, not that it was anybody's fault, but we slipped a little further.

We had a screw break on a small L bracket that secured one of the engine mounts and that bracket was still over in Pat McCormick's graphite epoxy shop being fixed. I told Tim, "Get the damned thing out of there. Don't let it stay there for a week." Tim said, "Well, Pat has to have drawings before they can start." Again, the same old story; they had to have drawings for a little L shaped bracket that they could already carve out of an existing piece of graphite epoxy left over from our other parts. Lockheed just can't do anything rapidly. Everything took three, four, or five days, even the simplest thing that I could have done at home in five minutes.

Tuesday, January 7, 1997

I got into work and again nobody was doing anything, but that was because they had gotten all the thermostats on and were getting ready for the next step. Everybody was just beginning to work.

We had a small review meeting at Ames. Larry Price had heard from the guy who was in charge of launch vehicles at NASA that we were going to have to wait for CRSS and not launch until March. As far as we were concerned, that was just the same old rumor we had heard before. Until somebody gave us a different directive, we were just going to continue on towards the September 24 launch date and I was going to build the case that if they made us wait, we would lose science.

While at Ames, I was shown a NASA PR brochure that indicated that NASA and Scott Hubbard were running the program and that the PI was responsible only for the scientific success of the Mission. I had had enough, I was going to write Wes and find out what they were up to as soon as I had some time during the following week or two.

Happily, perhaps because of my tirade, people were beginning to work hard. The electronic units were going to be mounted the next day and if we picked up the pace, we would be OK.

Headquarters had just told Lockheed if they screwed up Lunar Prospector, they were going to be in deep do-do! I was sure that Lockheed got the message. There was no more concern about whether Lockheed made a profit. We had the money to have two or three shifts. I hoped things would begin to get better. I would know in a couple of weeks — by that time, we would know if the guys were really busting their butts or if they were just responding to their last kick in the butt.

When I went to lunch, essentially no one was around and Kim Foster ran right over and said, "Everybody was here just a few minutes ago. We had a meeting about the next steps and they are aware they had better bust their butts." I enjoyed that.

Kim said further that after I had raised hell, Tim Maloney said, "If we don't get this done, Alan is going to come and crab at us and ten minutes later, Tom Polette is going to come over and crab at us, and then Alan will be back crabbing at us, and then Tom will come back." Between Tom and me, they knew I was not going to put up with that crap any longer. Dougherty was also finally doing what he should have been doing all along, i.e., riding the guys hard. I was happy about all that, but I was still worried, because we were so far behind schedule, so I not only had my fingers crossed, but also my toes and my eyes.

Chapter 3-27
Wiring the Spacecraft

Wednesday, January 8, 1997

We hadn't gotten up to a full head of steam, but we were moving ahead, albeit slowly. We didn't get the electronic units mounted on the spacecraft, at least not before I left the highbay at 3:00 PM. I hoped the slow start was just because of the time it took to get everything ready to get started on the wiring. The engineers and technicians were getting the wiring for the heaters finished, but we hadn't been able to maintain the schedule we had set up. But at least we were moving forward.

Thursday, January 9, 1997: A Slow Start

I was in the highbay with the spacecraft all day. It took the guys forever to do anything because "this was missing and that was missing." Crap, weren't they ever prepared to work? Frank Costa, who was the head of the wiring effort, just stood around while Tim taught the two wiring technicians, Shawn and Jesse, the magnetic cleanliness procedures.

We finally got all of the electronic units mounted on the spacecraft that were ready to be mounted, i.e., the IR Earth/Moon limb crossing sensor, the transponder, the radio frequency switch, the temporary (it was not flight hardware) GRS thermostat circuit box, and the engineering model of the C&DH (again not flight hardware). All we had left to mount were the spectrometer electronics or SES box, the battery (which is put on much later in all programs), and the flight model of the C&DH.

Lee was going to start putting the thermostat clips back on the fuel lines.

Everything was done very slowly and inefficiently; there was far too much standing around, with only about two hours worth of real work being done every day.

I was over there to see how everything was going and I caught several errors. One was, when they were going to mount the GRS thermostat circuit unit, the technician was going to bolt the bracket down first and then bolt the unit on the bracket, but there was no way to put the unit on the bracket after the latter was bolted to the spacecraft — because the bolts came in from underneath the bracket! He had to bolt the thermostat unit on the bracket first and then bolt the bracket onto the spacecraft!

The two wiring technicians were going to work from 5:00 AM until 1:00 PM — and they really did work very hard. I decided I would see how they were doing at 5:00 or 6:00 every morning. That way they would know that someone else was working as hard as they were and that I appreciated their hard work.

Friday, January 10, 1997: The Antennas

The main event of the day was that we put the antennas on the spacecraft, but not permanently, because we had to get the wiring under them finished before we could permanently mount them. In reality, we shouldn't have put them on at that point in time, but Dougherty wanted them on so it looked like we were farther along when Piotrowski and Ledbetter came from Headquarters the following Monday for their informal site visit.

Tom got his revenge for my making him drive the instruments back to Los Alamos; he gave me a bad case of the flu.

Monday, January 13, 1997: The NASA Site Visit

I was sick with Tom's flu over the weekend, but I went to work Monday to be there for Piotrowski and Ledbetter's site visit. Bill Feldman was also there. We discussed the science and the spacecraft. Marcie did a really good job on the Ground Segment and I went through the science and explained what we were going to get during the extended mission and what we were going to lose if our launch was delayed.

I wanted to get it across to Ledbetter and Piotrowski that if they put us behind CRSS, then I would have no idea when I would get launched. I had talked to one of the CRSS engineers and I had asked him point blank when they were going to launch. He said, "Officially, in December."

I asked, "Well, what's the truth."

He answered, "We hope sometime in the first quarter of 1998," but CRSS was nowhere near as far along as Lunar Prospector was and it was many times more complex. I knew if NASA wanted us to wait for CRSS, we would not get launched until the spring of 1998, at the earliest.

I showed Ledbetter and Piotrowski how the 18-month mapping mission would easily fit in the eclipse window between September 1997 and July 1999, if we launched between September 1997 and January 1998. But, if we launched after January 1998, then we would cut into the extended mission and if we didn't launch until after July 1998, then we would start cutting into the nominal mission. I said, "I have no confidence that if we get behind CRSS, we will get launched before the summer of 1998."

Dougherty, of course, wouldn't back me up. He said, "That's just Alan's opinion," and then gave the Lockheed party line (remember, CRSS's first launch attempt did not occur until *April 27, 1999 — a 16-month slip*, so whose opinion was correct?).

The meeting went well; Ledbetter and Piotrowski liked the spacecraft, but they were indifferent to what we were doing. They just listened and said, "That's nice, you're doing a good job," their reaction was just plain vanilla.

When I asked Dougherty for his opinion of the meeting he said, "Clearly, they're taking a hands off approach. They're just letting us do it."

During the afternoon, Tom, Bill, and I went through all the commands needed to test the GRS, NS, and APS.

Tuesday, January 14, 1997: A Science Team Meeting

I had a Science Team Meeting on Tuesday and all the guys were there, except Mario. We went through all the science issues, the proposal for the data reduction, and the electric grounding of the instruments. Unfortunately, Bill's engineer was stuck in the snow in Los Alamos and couldn't be there, but we got almost everything done anyway.

Bill and I decided that Tom should go to Los Alamos Wednesday, Thursday and Friday of the following week to learn how to do the testing of the spectrometers. That was going to be good for him. Then he was going to bring the spectrometer electronics unit (the SES) back in his lap in the airplane, unless, of course, the tests didn't go well — which was possible, since Bill had found some things wrong with it. There was one connection that hadn't been made, but the SES worked anyway, because that part of the circuit was grounded to the unit and the electrically conducting casing closed the circuit! He had to have that fixed and properly connected.

Wednesday Morning, January 15, 1997

Despite my flu, I went in to Lockheed for a meeting and because very little was being done on the wiring. Thus, I wanted to crab at Dougherty again, as I had done every day, because Frank and his wiring technicians were not working on the spacecraft.

Wednesday Afternoon, January 15, through Sunday, January 19, 1997: Home With the Flu

I was feeling so bad that I left work at about noon Wednesday and went home. I spent the next few days in bed, including the weekend!

Monday, January 20, 1997

When I came in at 5:00 AM, I immediately went over to the highbay to see the spacecraft. Some of the heater wiring was done, but not all of it. Some of the straps that held the wire bundles securely to the spacecraft's structure were on, but not all of them.

Later, at the Test and Integration Meeting, we found out that Woody hadn't ordered the connectors for the C&DH unit and the science instruments and that was causing a delay! Woody tried to explain why he had not ordered the connectors and said that he was not holding us up — which was pure BS. Dougherty was fed up with him — Woody just didn't perform.

Regardless of why, the wiring was going slower than expected and some other things had gotten only partly finished. The stand-offs (little 2 to 3 cm high plastic mounts that firmly attached the propellant lines to the structure and stopped the lines from banging into the structure during launch) on the propellant lines were still not installed because they couldn't get enough shop people to come in over the weekend to finish the little stand-off pieces. That was not really holding us up, but it was just one more thing that still had to be done. My attitude is, *get it done today, not tomorrow*, and one of my mottos is, *if I wanted it tomorrow, I would ask for it tomorrow*, and the engineers adhered to neither of those concepts. I was sure we were not going to get the wiring done by the end of the month; at best, it was going to be the middle of February before we were done wiring. We were still slipping and slipping.

Tuesday, January 21, 1997: Still Sick — Both the Spacecraft and Me

I went home before noon because I had a hacking cough and Dougherty was afraid I had walking pneumonia.

It was clear it would be the middle of February before the damned wiring was finished — and, of course, we still didn't have the connectors. Woody had screwed up; Frank was working on it and blah, blah, blah. I had heard all that before.

On top of all that, a good old, reliable Delta launch vehicle blew up shortly after launch, and who knew what kind of conniption fit NASA would have about our launch as a result.

It was the same old song, just a different verse every damned day.

Wednesday, January 22, 1997: Too Sick to Work

Because I had a weeklong trip starting the next day and because I was half dead from the flu, I stayed home and rested, so I would be able to endure the trip.

Thursday, January 23, through Thursday, January 30, 1997: A Trip to JSC, BJ Link, and the Cape

I flew to Houston on Thursday to talk to Bret Drake and the other guys in the Exploration Office at JSC about Lunar Prospector on Friday and I spent Saturday in Houston.

Sunday, I flew to Greenville, NC, where Dick Seeley picked me up and took me to the Hotel on the Bob Jones University campus. I spent the next day doing B.J. Link TV classes with Dick. The kids were very interested and asked a lot of questions about Lunar Prospector, the Moon, the universe, and everything in between. Regardless of their strict, religious beliefs, the kids had a thirst for knowledge, even if some of my answers flew in the face of those beliefs.

To say the least, it was an interesting experience being an atheist at a fundamentalist Christian University. When I arrived, I asked Dick if there were any objections to my being there since, even though I had no intension of deliberately stepping on anyone's religious toes, I intended to speak my mind and answer the questions as I saw fit. Dick said there had been considerable discussion about my coming there, but he had told the faculty that, despite my beliefs — or lack thereof — I was an upstanding, honest, moral person who was dedicated to expanding human knowledge and would only have a positive effect on the students, as I had already done via the video interviews and the telephone Q&A sessions we had had. He also argued that it would do the students good to find out that not all people believed as they did! I was welcome at Bob Jones University!

When we were not in the TV studio, Dick showed me around the campus and I was impressed at how well equipped and up to date all the facilities were. I was particularly amused when he showed me through the Geology Department and I found numerous models of dinosaurs — for people that reject evolution, they still could not deny the existence of the fossil record, even though they believe the Earth is only 6000 years old and the fossils were put in the rocks by their God to make a complete picture!

Dick also introduced me to the Physics Department faculty, with whom we had dinner Monday evening. As I always do, even though I may hold very different views than the people I am with, I enjoyed the evening with Dick's colleagues and found their interest in the space program and Lunar Prospector very refreshing.

Tuesday morning, Dick drove me back to the airport and I flew on to Florida for the meeting at the Cape.

When Dougherty arrived at the Cape, he told me that there was a meeting at Headquarters the following Monday about the launch vehicle. It was just for Sylvia and Scott. I said, "Like hell it is." I said I would just stay on the East Coast and go straight up to DC for the Monday meeting. I was not going to let them pull that crap on me and run the program behind my back.

I called Sylvia and she said Scott was going to be at Headquarters Friday, not Monday. I thought Scott would be going directly to DC from Kentucky where he was burying his father who had just died. She said, "No, Scott is coming back to Ames first."

I said, "Well, then I'll go up there Friday."

I made the plans to go to Headquarters, but then Scott got the same flu I had and canceled his trip. I couldn't help wondering if my insisting that I be at the meeting caused Headquarters and Scott to cancel the meeting. Regardless, I didn't have to go to DC and, sick as I was, I was very glad about that.

We had our meeting with the LLV people at the Cape and had a walk-through of the facilities. It really wasn't a walk-through, because they weren't prepared to show us the things that some of our guys came to see, so they got bawled out about that. Basically the meeting and the so-called walk-through were a waste of time and travel money (and since I was still sick with the flu, I was not very happy about that).

I had dinner with Karen Ramos. She had gotten in trouble again because she had told me about the long lead items they could have gotten on time if the LLV staff would have let her order the equipment from a different vendor. Lockheed wouldn't let her do that because they (Lockheed) didn't want to change their drawings. Naturally, I got into the fray and bitched at LLV for crabbing at Karen because she had tried to help me out.

Friday, January 31, 1997: Back at Lockheed

I went to work even though I was still not completely over the flu. When I got there at 5:00 AM, I found that some, but not enough, work had been done on the wiring. I asked Frank Costa, "What the hell is going on?"

He answered, "My target is the 15th (of February)."

I said, "Yes, but when are you really going to get it done?"

He said, "Well, by the end of the month (February)." We were still slipping and it was getting more and more serious.

At the 8:30 meeting, Dougherty asked if all the parts were there to finish the wiring and I started asking some very pointed questions of Costa and explained to him that we needed more people working and said, "There are 24 hours in a day."

He said, "Oh, I can't do that. Besides, we don't have all the parts!"

Unfortunately, Costa was correct. They still didn't have the damned connectors; they still didn't have the cable mounting parts and they still didn't have all the brackets! Why wasn't all that stuff thought of and ready for assembly when Costa, Shawn, and Jesse needed it? Lockheed just doesn't know how to build a spacecraft, period. The engineers just seem to think it up as they go along. I was appalled.

Chapter 3-28
Another Launch Vehicle Crisis

Monday, February 3, 1997: The No-First-Launch Rule Hits Us

I was still sick as a dog, but I went to work anyway. When I got in at 5:00 AM, some progress had been made on the wiring and two connectors were done on the C&DH unit, but it was agonizingly slow. Frank still expected it would take until the end of the month to finish. If so, then we would be 5½ months behind schedule!

At 8:30 AM, I pointed out to Dougherty that we couldn't take forever to get the wiring done. Those guys just don't know how to build anything, at least, Dougherty doesn't.

Later, I went over to the spacecraft, because the spectrometers had came back to Lockheed and we were also getting the solar panels in to fit check them and to see where their connectors needed to be mounted.

Mary came over and said Dougherty had sent her over to get me because Sylvia and Scott were coming. I knew something was up. What had happened, of course, was that Goldin and Karen Poniatowski had levied the "no-first-launch rule." We were going to get the official letter in a week to ten days. They were trying to get a Delta for us for a shared launch in April of 1998. They even suggested we use the shuttle (which we could not do, since Lunar Prospector was not a man-rated spacecraft, i.e., safe enough to be launched along with humans)! If those things wouldn't work, then we would have to wait for CRSS, retrofit the spacecraft with a bigger battery so we could survive the eclipses and blah, blah, blah. I was beside myself.

Dougherty and I discussed that and I was blunt about his sticking to the Lockheed party line about CRSS. I said, "Look Tom, we have to get this company to fess up to what is going on. It is a lie for Lockheed to say that CRSS is going to launch in December, when everybody tells me they won't be ready until the first quarter of 1998. We can't continue pretending." Dougherty agreed, but he said he was going to find out from the top people when CRSS would be ready. Well, that was BS! All he had to do was to go on the other side of the partition that separated Lunar Prospector from CRSS and see for himself that CRSS was just a shell with no guts, no wiring, no camera, no nothing, and he would see that CRSS was at least a year from launch, if not much longer.

I went to Ames and told Scott that it was futile to have Dougherty try to find out when CRSS would be ready to fly and Scott agreed. He was going to have Wes or somebody at Headquarters get Lockheed to tell the truth about CRSS. I said to Scott, "If this mission gets delayed so much that we get pushed into the eclipse period, then we will have, at most, five months of mapping and the scientific community is going to have a fit. They're already griping about us being no good. If, all the sudden, we cost another $20 million and we only get 30 or 40% of the science, then their crabbing will be justified." Scott agreed.

I had already worked during the previous weekend to figure out how to get around the no-first-launch rule because we knew it was coming. I had already worked out the science value versus duration of the primary and extended mission. But much more was needed. I called Pat Dasch and asked her to see if she could get the National Space Society to talk to Sensenbrenner's Committee and get me invited to testify. She said there was a news conference about launch issues later in the day, in which she was already involved. She had already sent an email saying she would like to coordinate with George French about the news conference. I said I would get George after them, too. She was also going to have the Society suggest that they have a meeting between Goldin, Jim Martin, Wes, and me to find out what in hell was going on. I didn't know if that would happen, but at least Headquarters was going to know the Society was ticked off.

Tuesday, February 4, 1997: The Bigger Battery BS

I got up at 2:00 AM and worked some more on trying to define the loss of science value of the mission if we were forced to launch after CRSS and had a shortened mission. Later in the morning, I went to Ames and showed it to Scott. He knew it was all smoke and mirrors, because it is hard to define what value scientific data has and the relative value of one experiment versus the other. Nevertheless, it was something that we could at least hang our hat on.

I went through what it would do to the program if Headquarters forced us to add a bigger battery to the spacecraft. We had been through all that before and I said again, "Look, the ripple effect will kill us. If we have to add more mass, we are going to end up having to build a new spacecraft." After we talked a few minutes, Scott realized it was true.

When I got back to Lockheed, I sat down and made four viewgraphs that showed what would happen if we had to add a bigger battery. First we would have to add 7 to 15 kg of extra battery mass. That increase would have to be balanced out by adding another 7 to 15 kg of lead ballast on the other side of the equipment shelf. Then we would have to add 14 to 30 kg of lead ballast at the bottom of the spacecraft to balance out the extra mass at the top. All of the sudden, we would have 30 to 60 kg of extra mass. Since I would lose a month of orbital lifetime for every kilogram of extra mass and my nominal lifetime was 36 months, I would have no mission left, even if I could get launched. If Lunar Prospector's mass were 30 to 60 kg more than we were planning, then neither the LLV2, nor the TLI Stage could even launch it! We were almost up to the limit of what they could launch as it was.

Even if all that were not true, then there would be the question of where to put such a big battery in the spacecraft and there was no place for it. The spacecraft was plumbed and partially wired. If we found a place for the bigger battery, we would have to redo the wiring and redo the plumbing. Then we would have to stiffen the structure because the spacecraft would be a lot more massive. That all meant we would have to rebuild the whole spacecraft.

On top of all that, the solar array would have to be taller because we would need more power to charge the bigger battery. That would push the antenna complex up and then the moment of inertia ratio would go to hell and the spacecraft would be an unstable spinner. It was very easy to write four viewgraphs about why we could not, "just add a bigger battery," and hence show it was absolutely absurd for Headquarters to say, "Oh, just add some more batteries." It just amazed me how little they know about spacecraft.

I talked to George French and he was ranting and raving because a long launch delay would hurt his Moonlink program, so he was going to call Pat so they could coordinate their activities in supporting me.

If all else failed, I hoped I could force Headquarters to leave us alone, because they had no money to pay for the costs of rebuilding the spacecraft. Dougherty went through the costs of doing just what I had on my viewgraphs and it was $15 million!

What Goldin and Poniatowski had told us to do was absurd. NASA just doesn't think about what it is doing. One would think that after all those years, NASA would know that one just couldn't do such things.

Sylvia found out there was a Delta launch in November. She asked, "Why don't we try to get that."

I said, "I would be happy to, if NASA paid for it." I thought, *if NASA is going to screw us, then let them get us a Delta. A Delta might not even need a TLI Stage and that would be a beautiful launch.*

The launch vehicle saga just went on and on and NASA just never thought before it leapt. I was disgusted and annoyed and I was very tired after a very, very long and frustrating day. I went home exhausted and still sick with the flu, so I took a nap when I got home. What a mess.

Wednesday, February 5, 1997: Headquarters Begins to Wake Up

I was worn out after the events of the previous day and since I had never really gotten over the flu, I had a relapse. I stayed home — feeling and sounding like hell.

Nevertheless, I called Pat and George and they had talked with Congressmen Sensenbrenner and Rohrabacher (one of the original Congressmen who signed the letter asking NASA to give the project the Apollo 17 GRS eight years earlier). While they were concerned, they didn't want to give NASA a directive telling Goldin what to do about our launch, but they said they would carefully watch the issue.

Scott and Sylvia called me and said Headquarters was beginning to realize they had given us no viable options. They didn't have the money for a Delta rocket; they finally understood that if we had to wait for CRSS and CRSS blew up or if CRSS slipped a lot — then we were dead and they also realized we couldn't rebuild Lunar Prospector.

It was a mess and I thought it would take Headquarters at least a week or two to sort it all out. I also thought we stood a good chance of losing Lunar Prospector if Headquarters kept jerking us around like that. I had to do everything possible to get Lunar Prospector launched in the fall.

Thursday, February 6, 1997

I was still too sick to go to work, so I talked to Scott and Sylvia on the phone and then I called Dougherty. We were trying to tell the idiots at Headquarters to leave us alone and let us get on with the mission and the LLV2 launch. We couldn't afford to do anything else. Dougherty came up with a $5 million price tag if they delayed us until after CRSS, $15 million if they insisted that we refit the spacecraft (which we really couldn't do — I would veto that) and $80 million if we went on a Delta. NASA was finally waking up to the fact that what they had required of us just wasn't going to work. The real choices were: give us a wavier to launch on the first LLV2 and let us go in the fall or we try to go after CRSS in March. The latter was fraught with danger, because if CRSS slipped, then we slipped.

I was very sick and very annoyed!

Friday, February 7, 1997: Two Launch Options

I was still sick and still at home.

I called Scott and Sylvia, who had talked with Headquarters about our launch options and they were: First, we might possibly get a waiver right then and proceed towards a fall launch; though that was doubtful, I thought we could push it through. Second, we launched after CRSS, but if CRSS started to slip, we would then get the wavier. Headquarters finally understood that the costs of redoing the spacecraft and or buying a Delta excluded those two options.

Tom called and told me that Steve Honodel was worried about cavitation (formation of bubbles in the viscous fluid in the viscous damper due to a decrease in the dynamic pressure as the devices went into action) in the viscous damper of the boom release mechanism and he wanted to put new ones in the spacecraft! That was nonsense; the damper was inside the spacecraft and we were already plumbed and partially wired. There was no way we could get in there to put in new viscous damper! I didn't know what the answer was going to be, but they were going to have a meeting about the issue in the afternoon.

Monday, February 10, 1997

I was well enough to go to work.

Tom and I were trying to get all the LRI paperwork done, so we could get out of Lockheed. We knew that the IRS was doing something, because it had cashed our check and we had George French's Congressional friend to thank for getting the IRS going.

I talked to Steve Honodel about the viscous damper issue and tried to diffuse that BS. As far as I was concerned, it was just another red herring. Steve found out that the vendor had properly tested our damper. There wasn't any reason to think there was anything wrong with it and I wanted Steve to forget it.

Eagle Picher had screwed up its last batch of battery plates, so they were having trouble getting the battery done. Woody came up with the bright idea of using a 9 amp-hr battery he could quickly get, but it would add an extra 5.5 kg of mass. I couldn't get it across to him that that would not just be an additional 5.5 kg, but an additional 20 kg of battery and balancing ballast. Happily, Dougherty told Woody to forget it and then Dougherty told me he had done so. I said, "That's fine. That was the right thing to do."

The wiring had come a long way. Frank kept saying, "the end of the month," but he told Tom privately he thought it might be done in about two weeks. He wouldn't say anything to Dougherty or the engineers about the wiring being done early because they kept bugging him and he was getting ticked off at them.

I talked to Karen and things were OK down in Florida. I told her what was going on with our launch and she asked if there was anything Spaceport Florida could do. I said, "Yes, if you guys are going to lose business and money because of the no-first-launch-rule, you need talk to your Congressman and your Senators and have them go crab at NASA."

We were still 5½ months behind schedule, but Dougherty was pushing for getting all the testing done by June. If he were successful, that would save our butts and we would have nearly three months to spare before launch.

Tuesday, February 11, 1997: Still Sick

I stayed home to, hopefully, get over the flu.

Wednesday, February 12, 1997: Spacecraft Tours

I went to the spacecraft early in the morning to look at it. They had made a lot of progress while I was out sick.

I had the two technicians, Shawn and Jesse, who were doing the wiring, sign the Lunar Prospector signature sheet and they were just thrilled. Dougherty told me before I went home that afternoon that the technicians talked all day about my having asked them to sign the sheet. I was very pleased they were so excited.

At 10:00 AM, George Collins from BJ Link came to make a second video, which we did with the spacecraft.

Steve Durst, the publisher of *Space Fax Daily*, and his associate, Kay Woods, came by. I showed them the spacecraft and then we went to lunch. We talked about three hours. Steve was promoting a commercial lunar orbiter that would sell live video pictures from the Moon. I was, to say the least, skeptical about the commercial viability of such a satellite (anyone could get all the pictures of the Moon they wanted from NASA for free — to be sure, not live pictures, but since the Moon is unchanging for all practical purposes, dead pictures are just as good as live ones). Nevertheless, they had done a good job of marketing and I gave them credit for having gotten a deal with the Russians for an $18 million spacecraft.

When I got back from lunch with Steve and Kay, Scott came over to the highbay with some guests. I showed them the spacecraft and by then it was 4:00 PM.

Dougherty was starting to get snotty again, since the spacecraft was getting nearly done and hence he was not in so much hot water with Scott and me. He said, "You're not supposed to touch the spacecraft when you're over there showing it to people." First of all, I knew that — we always had gloves on and were grounded to the spacecraft when we worked on it (so it would not get a static electricity shock from us) — so I didn't need the idiot to tell me that or anything else. Then the fool wrote a memo about that and I was beginning to think he had crossed the line.

Scott called and told me NASA was backing down on the no-first-launch-rule. Headquarters said, "Stay on the path that you're on, but be prepared for a possible launch delay." That NASA merry-go-round had lasted just 10 days.

Chapter 3-29
Finally Finishing the Spacecraft

Thursday, February 13, 1997: Lee Over Does It

Thursday was a slow day. The main technical issue that arose was that the pressure in the tanks, which had been under pressure since the pressure test in the middle of December to detect slow leaks, had dropped to 10 psi. I told Lee we were going to have to do something about it. However, she was about as useless as handles on a handkerchief, so nothing happened!

Like Marcie and Dougherty, Lee has an attitude and is stuck in the pre-Discovery (in her case pre-historic) way of doing things and believed that only exalted engineers had any business being around a spacecraft. She wrote a BS memo telling me, and everyone else that she felt did not belong near the spacecraft, that the spacecraft work-stand was only for workers. Well, Lee could kiss my ass — if I was not a "worker," then nobody was.

She even went so far as to bawl out Tom, Tom Chinn, and the Ames QA guy who were on the work-stand and Tom got miffed about it. I felt I was dealing with children who had the mentality of dead rats!

Friday, February 14, 1997: Valentines Day!

Shawn and Jesse were doing an excellent job, but the spacecraft was getting wired very slowly.

I went over to Ames in the afternoon and met Ric Campo, an experienced Pioneer Mission controller, who was going to be one of my two senior controllers, and who would uplink the commands for me.

The work on the spacecraft was going slowly. Happily, Dougherty was seldom around. Lee was a pain in the butt. Tom was fighting with Lee. What a circus!

Monday, February 17, 1997

The engines were wired over the weekend, so the wiring was almost finished. However, we were waiting on some damned little Winchester connectors that weren't going to be delivered for a couple of weeks. Regardless, we were going to go ahead and, hopefully, start turning Lunar Prospector on the following week.

I went home early; it was President's Day and most everybody else was off, so there was no one to bug and little I could do.

Tuesday, February 18, 1997

Dave Curtis brought the MAG/ER down to be integrated into the spacecraft.

I went through the Mission Operation Document (MOD) with the Ground Segment staff. Marcie, of course, didn't like the MOD, because it was not the way an engineer would do it. As far as I was concerned, she could stand in line behind Lee to kiss my ass.

Surprise, the Winchester connectors came in early, so the wiring of the spacecraft was almost finished. We were planning to get everything done by Friday or Saturday and turn the spacecraft on Monday. We were finally getting there. The spacecraft looked really good. The technicians were getting it all tidied up.

Tom was doing a good job, but he was having more and more trouble handling the engineers and the stress.

Wednesday, February 19, 1997: A Missing High Voltage Cable

Tom and I drove in together at 5:00 AM. Frank Costa was going to connect the science instruments to the boom cables and we both needed to be there to get the instruments mounted on the booms. Tom and I partially deployed the GRS boom and started bolting the GRS to the boom tip plate. Frank noticed the wire leads from the GRS were kind of short and said, "I'll have to splice these damned things." Then we noticed there were no tags on the various wires, so he couldn't tell which was which. Sloppy work again.

Frank said, "Maybe we should check the rest of them to see if their leads are too short also." We went over to the NS/APS and started looking at their leads.

Some were short and then I said, "Wait a minute, there's only one high voltage line here! Where is the second one?" We looked, but there was only one high voltage line among the boom cables. We dug out the drawings to check and see if I was correct or not and, sure enough, there were supposed to be two high voltage lines going to the NS! One high voltage line was missing from the completely wired boom, whose cable bundles had been very carefully laced to the boom longerons by the engineers at Able Engineering and were ready for flight! "Oh crap (actually I said something much, much stronger)!"

I called Bill immediately and said, "Look Bill, I know the answer to this, but tell me anyway — there are two high voltage lines going to the NS, correct?"

He said, "Yes," which was the answer I knew was correct, but I did not like.

I went to Building 107 and waited for Dougherty to get to work. When he arrived, I told him of the major screw-up and I could have killed him when he said, "Why do you need two, can't you just take the one high voltage and put a T in it?"

I was appalled at his total ignorance and said, "No, we can't. There are two different sides to the spectrometer and each one has its own high voltage supply and they require different voltages."

He said, "Well, I don't see why it has to be that way." I was really ticked off; the man knew nothing about the instruments (or anything else) and yet he stood there and said, "Well, I don't see why it has to be that way."

Thinking, *you dumb SOB, because that's not the way it works*, but saying instead, "I am sure that these are independent high voltage supplies, one for each of the detectors, and it can't be done any other way, but I will check with Bill."

He asked, "What about test, can we test if we don't have the second one?"

I answered, "No, but I'll check with Bill."

I went back to the highbay and tried to call Bill. Frank and the technicians were fussing with the boom cables and putting on all these damned splices. The fact that the cables weren't long enough meant that at least a day and a half or two days of work had to be done just to get ready to do the work that they were supposed to be doing, i.e., connecting the boom cables to the instruments.

I called Bill and said, "Look, Bill, I know the answer to this, but I still have to ask it. Dougherty wants to know if we could just use the one line."

He answered, "Well gee, we would have to put a T junction in there and then we would have feedback problems like we had with the GRS, remember? Also we would have to go in and change the electronics unit and we would have to do —."

I interrupted, "Bill, I don't want to discuss all the details, I just want the basics."

He said, "OK, the first reason for having two supplies is in case one of the detectors fails, if we had just one high voltage supply, we would lose the whole experiment. If we have two supplies, then we would still get data from the good detector."

I said, "I don't want to hear that, because that sounds like the second one is just a backup and that's not true, is it? Isn't the real reason that each detector requires different voltages? Ideally, they should be the same, but they are different, right?"

He answered, "Yes, they are really different, so we have to tune each one separately."

I said, "That's all I want to hear. You have to understand Bill, if we give Dougherty and Lockheed even an inch, they will take a mile and take the easy way out and leave us with one high voltage line and a compromised instrument — so don't even think about it. If I need you to discuss this with Dougherty, don't mention the back up mode; the real answer is that we have two supplies because we have two spectrometers in there and each has to have its own supply because they require different voltages."

Bill said, "OK, I understand."

By that time, Dougherty had talked to Lee to see if we could finish the work and have a high voltage cable temporarily strung on the boom so we could start testing and then later, when we had the time, properly string and lace the second high voltage cable into the cable bundle on the boom. Dougherty correctly wanted to get into testing — we had lost enough time as it was already.

My biggest concern was that Able Engineering had those bundles of cables tied and laced to the booms that were all coiled up in their canisters and they had been fully tested that way. They had been shaken, they had been verified, and they had gone through all the testing done by that time. If Able went in there and unlaced those cable bundles in order to add the missing high voltage line, we might have to start all over again with the testing.

I asked Dougherty, "If Able has to redo the entire boom, isn't that going to cost us weeks?"

Dougherty answered, "Able is going to be here for the meeting about the booms today anyway, so we can talk to them then and maybe they can tell us what we can do," a particularly good thought.

It appeared that the problem was a stupid mistake that I thought Woody had made, but Dougherty seemed to think it was Able's fault — as I expected him to think. He thought that, after the cable bundles had been sent down to Able to be laced onto the booms, that Able had left off one of the high voltage cables during the lacing. I said, "But Tom, I thought those things were already bundled up when Woody sent them down to Able."

He said, "Well, they might have had to take them out of the bundles or something," which was very unlikely — why would Able un-bundle the cables and then re-bundle them when they laced them onto the booms? That defied logic.

I didn't know who screwed it up and it was irrelevant. But I was a little ticked off that Woody didn't show any concern about the screw-up; regardless of who caused the problem, the wiring was his responsibility and he should have said something about it. When Jim Schirle screwed up the thermal stuff, Jim hung his head and said, "I screwed up. It's my fault and here is what we need to do to correct it and I am sorry," but I got nothing like that from Woody.

As soon as the Able engineers arrived, as we were standing around eating donuts and the like, I told them about the missing cable. I said, "Please tell me there is an easy way to get around this and that we don't have to tear the cabling apart to fix it."

They thought a minute and said, "We can probably fix it without too much trouble."

I said, "Good, when we get done with this meeting, we can to go over and look at it and see what can be done." Dougherty then told Lee she was responsible for the fix and she was going to be the interface with Able on that issue.

We had a good meeting with Able, except Steve Honodel talked so slowly and in so much detail it took him forever to discuss the status of the booms. We finally got through listening to Steve and the meeting ended at about 2:00 PM!

The meeting was very interesting in one aspect, as soon as the meeting got technical and down to the nitty-gritty, Dougherty, as always, disappeared.

We went over to the spacecraft and I showed the Able guys what was going on. Of course, Lee had her marching orders from Dougherty, so she tried to tell everybody what to do. Ignoring her (brilliant engineer that she is, why didn't she notice the second high voltage cable was missing, even though she was overseeing the wiring work? She could go to hell as far as I was concerned), I told the Able engineers what I wanted to know and what I wanted done. Lee just sputtered away as I talked to Able, and good old Tom put her in her place.

The Able engineers and I talked about adding the second high voltage line to the NS/APS boom cabling and one of them asked, "Do you want us to take it back (to Able) to do it?"

I answered, "Take it back right now," and they said they would have it back by Friday or, by early the following week.

While Able was fixing the NS/APS boom cabling, we were going to finish up all the remaining wiring, put the other booms on and get everything else done so when the NS/APS boom was back, we could finish up very quickly. If Able was able to get the cabling fixed fast, we would not lose too much time. Though we might not be able to start the turn-on Monday, we would be able to do so no later than Wednesday or Thursday. Man, that screw-up was a bad one — we did not need it. However, it looked like we were OK.

A new guy named Paul Gillett came over to the highbay to look at the spacecraft. Paul had been at the morning meeting with Able and was new to Lockheed in Sunnyvale, but had worked with Dan Swanson back on the East Coast. Paul is a nice guy who is really quite sharp and had made a lot of good suggestions and comments at the morning boom meeting. When I was getting ready to leave at the end of the meeting, I introduced myself to him, thanked him for all his good comments and questions and said he should come over to the highbay later to see the spacecraft.

Paul came over and I showed him the spacecraft. He was really interested in it, thought the mission was a great concept, and Lunar Prospector was great spacecraft. He asked all kinds of good technical questions and then asked, "Who is doing your mission planning?"

I answered, "I am. I've done mission planning all my life. I was a PI on Viking and did all the camera sequencing."

He said, "Is this the Lunar Prospector that was started a long time ago by LPI or whatever it was?"

I answered, "Yes, but it was SSI and LEI that started it." He had heard about Lunar Prospector; I found that interesting.

He then said he would love to see my Mission Profile and my Mission Ops stuff and I said, "Sure, anytime."

Paul explained that his job is "mission success," which I found strange, but he was one of the people in a new engineering group called "Mission Success" which sounded kind of stupid to me. Their task was to try to learn how to make sure every mission worked. I feel like asking, *what was Lockheed's policy before — Mission Failure?*

Thursday, February 20, 1997:
The MAG/ER Cable and Grounding Problems

I met Frank Costa at 5:00 AM at the spacecraft and I jokingly asked, "Well, I wonder what we will find today?" so I started mounting the MAG/ER on the boom tip plate. Then Frank found the wires weren't what he expected and there were some problems with the grounding. There was a 22-gauge wire where he thought there should have been a 26-gauge wire and visa-versa. I immediately thought, *damn, another screw-up.*

I went over to Building 107 and talked to Dougherty and Woody. It turned out that when Woody bundled the cables, he was trying to keep the diameters of the three bundles of wires (one for each of the three longerons) equal. He put like wires in the different bundle even though the wires went to the same connector and that was what was confusing Frank. We got that straightened out, but then there was still the issue of how to properly ground the MAG/ER, since the last meter of the boom cabling was shielded to prevent static charge build up that would foul up the ER measurements.

I got Dave Curtis on the phone and we went through that issue. Dave pointed out that the last couple of inches of the shielded leads were all underneath the thermal blanket, so they wouldn't be exposed to the solar wind and hence, they wouldn't charge up. There was no grounding problem. That got the problem straightened out, but it was well into the afternoon before Costa and his technicians got back to splicing the MAG/ER leads!

I worked on straightening out some of the MAG/ER command procedures. When Dave brought the MAG/ER down to Lockheed the previous Tuesday, he and I went through some of the MAG/ER commanding sequences that I didn't completely understand. There were differences between the procedures for testing and the procedures I knew we had to have for flight. We straightened all that out and I put it into the Mission Ops Document and the Mission Profile.

Friday, February 21, 1997:
Spudis and Nozette Try to Get Lunar Prospector Canceled

I woke up at three o'clock and got into work at 5:00 AM.

Tom and I went over to the spacecraft at about 5:30 AM and we were getting ready to bolt the MAG/ER onto its boom, so Shawn and Jesse could finish connecting the boom cables, when I found there was a problem with the routing of the cables of the MAG/ER, as well as the NS/APS.

We were going to use the spacers that went between the MAG/ER and its tip plate and the NA/APS and its tip plate, as part of the ballast on those two booms, but couldn't make the ballast spacers until we knew exactly how much ballast we needed. Tim had had some temporary spacers made for us to use to bolt the instruments onto their tip plates, so Frank, Shawn, and Jesse could finishing the wiring. Not knowing that, Frank was about to connect the instrument lead wires to the boom cables in the space between the tip plates and the instruments, i.e., where the ballast plates were going to go! When I noticed that, I said to Frank, "You can't route the wires under there (between the tip plates and the instruments), that's where the ballast plates go, you have to route them around the tip plates." Unfortunately, Frank had already cut the cables and they were almost too short to reach the instrument leads when properly routed, but Frank said he could still do it.

I told Tom to go look for the ballast plates for the MAG/ER and NS/APS, because I couldn't find them anywhere. Later Tom found that Steve Honodel had taken them.

I had to leave because Dougherty and I had a meeting at 9:00 AM with Scott and Sylvia. Scott had been at Headquarters and had some bad news. Paul Spudis and Stu Nozette had been at Headquarters trying to get Lunar Prospector canceled so they could get our money for their Clementine 2! They had told Wes that Lunar Prospector was no good and that we were not going to get any good science data! Wes was stupid enough to believe those backstabbing, self-serving SOBs and then he also wanted to know why we needed an extended mission, when we were supposed to get all the data during the nominal mission and blah, blah, blah.

I was angry at Paul and Stu, but I knew those two well enough to know they were capable of any dirty trick to further their cause, and I was disgusted and appalled at Wes for knowing so little about science that he would even consider what Paul and Stu had said about our science data. His doing so simply strengthened my belief that if you are no damned good, you go to NASA and become a NASA official (just like Scott). Scott had tried to straighten Wes and Headquarters out the best he could, but Scott and I were summoned to go to Headquarters for a meeting with Wes and his crew on March 4, which was two weeks away. It was up to me to make Wes understand what in hell our mission was all about. The whole affair sickened me.

Similarly, Scott had given a talk at UCLA and had gotten a lot of static about Lunar Prospector. The UCLA scientists, I assume Chris Russell and others, had said that little missions in general were no good, that Lunar Prospector, in particular, was no good and that NASA should only fly big missions. It was clear to me from the comments Scott had brought back that part of the criticisms of Lunar Prospector was just sour grapes; I won; they didn't; they hated my guts and they hated the mission, period.

The other part of the criticisms went back to the fact that most of the scientists, led by Chris Russell, insisted that NASA really wanted missions for $250 million, which was not what the RFP said. Discovery missions were supposed to cost just half or a third of that, but the science community just would not accept that (see June 14, 1995, Part Two). Thus the criticisms were not just an attack on Lunar Prospector, they were an attack on the whole Discovery concept of inexpensive missions.

Scott and I also had to go to Headquarters because the issue of the launch vehicle was tied in with the science. If they didn't think our science was any good, then why should they care if we launched after CRSS and got even less "poor science"? If I could make Wes and the rest of them understand that Lunar Prospector was a good mission (after all, the review committee of 100 scientists and engineers had concluded that Lunar Prospector was the best mission out of the 28 that had been submitted to the Discovery program — so why was Wes stupid enough to question their judgment over two years later, just because two backstabbers were trying to advance their own personal agenda?), then I would be able to make them understand that we needed to get launched on time and have the extended mission. I was certain I could do that, but the entire mission hung in the balance because of NASA's stupidity and Paul and Stu's dirty tricks.

We went through the other issues that were troubling us, i.e., the schedule slips and the battery. Dougherty did a pretty good job of discussing how we were going to get back on schedule — though everything had to go well from then on; if we had any big problems during test, we were toast. Regarding the battery, Dougherty reported that although Eagle Picher had had a bad batch of plates, all of a sudden, our battery was nearly done! They were going to deliver it almost on its original schedule!

We discussed the news conference we were beginning to plan for March 5. We were going to show the world Lunar Prospector, which by that time was supposed to be finished and functioning. David Morse, Ames's PR person, had sent each of us a straw-man schedule and it started out with David introducing the principals, Scott, Dougherty, and me, and describing what we did. Then Dougherty or some other Lockheed official would give a welcome speech, Scott would then discuss the concept of Discovery, and finally I would talk about the science and the spacecraft. I had objected to that when I read it a few days earlier. I had called Sylvia and she immediately said, "I knew you weren't going to like this. I told David that immediately."

I said, "I'm not bitching at David, he just made a suggestion as a starting point, but I don't like this at all."

When Dougherty brought up this business of the news conference, I said, "I'm not happy with this at all. This is my mission and I am the Principal Investigator. This looks like a Lockheed program and I am tucked down at the bottom like an after- thought."

Since I had bitched to Sylvia, Scott already knew my feelings and he knew that I was fed up with Lockheed, so Scott said he understood and we began discussing it. I said, "I have no objection to a welcome speech being given by MacDonald (the head of Ames) and one being given by Henshaw, but then, as the PI, I should also give one. I'm getting more and more concerned about the decay of the role of the PI in Discovery missions — Discovery can't work if NASA doesn't let the PI do his job, and by pushing me into the background at the news conference, you're just making that worse." Scott said that he understood, but I noted he didn't say he agreed with me!

Though I get annoyed more easily than I can be insulted (it is nearly impossible to insult me, I don't give a damn about what most people think of me), I was beginning to be both annoyed and insulted by the treatment I was getting from Scott, Headquarters, Dougherty, and Lockheed. But right then, we had a major launch vehicle issue and the problem caused by Spudis and Nozette's attack on the science and the mission. I was not willing to destroy the mission by letting my personal feelings get in the way — but my personal feelings were beginning to get very close to "getting in the way."

I left Ames about noon and went right to the spacecraft to see what had happened with the wiring of the MAG/ER. When I got there, Frank was really concerned because there was very little room for the wires where they came out through the tip plates; in fact, the uncut ballast plate sat on the wires! He said, "I can't wire these things unless that ballast plate is in there and properly mounted. We can't have these little (temporary) spacers in there. I need to have the real ballast plate in there."

I was about to find out what was needed to be done to get the ballast plates finished when I found out that Tom had done something he shouldn't have done. The plates had sharp edges that could chafe the cables and Tom had filed them off — that was a no, no.

I pulled Tom aside and said privately, "Tom you really can't do that. If we were doing this in LRI, I would take those things down to my shop and fix them. That would be the end of it; they would be fixed. But we can't do that here. If Lockheed finds out that you did that, then they are going to blame us for everything that goes wrong. You just can't do that, even though it is the right thing to do. As long as we are in this environment, we can only go so far. You've pushed Lee to the point where she has backed off. I've got Dougherty backing off. They leave us alone now because we are getting the job done even though we are bending the rules — but we can't bend them so far that we break them. If we weren't bending the rules, the mistakes you and I have found in the last three days would have set us back three weeks. But we've never touched the hardware before and we can't start doing it now or we will lose all that we've gained." Tom understood, but was miffed about having to work that way, as was I.

I found Ramon Zaragoza, who had designed the ballast plates. He didn't know exactly where the wires were supposed to be located and he had left what looked like enough space for them. I said, "OK Ramon, we need this (the plates trimmed) done right now, not in three or four or five days. Can you get them milled right now? Here is what we have to whack off so we can get the plate in there without crushing the wires. Ramon, we can't wait for all kinds of new drawings. This can't take forever." He said he would redline the drawings and take them over to the shop and see what could be done. I asked, "Can we get them in a couple of hours?"

He answered, "No, I don't think so. But maybe by the end of the afternoon."

Ramon got his butt into high gear and came back and said, "They will be ready at 10 tomorrow morning," not as fast as I wanted, but days faster than would normally have been the case.

Tom and I got everything ready to put the GRS boom canister on the spacecraft, so Frank could measure how long he had to make the wires so they would reach the connectors. Tom was ready to screw the canister on and I said, "No, Tom, you and I can work with the instruments because that has always been our responsibility, but we don't across the line and start working on the spacecraft."

I had Tom go ask Tim Maloney to find us a technician to screw the canister onto the spacecraft. Tom came back and said Tim said it was OK for us to do it and I said, "No way!" I found Tim and I said, "Tim, you can't really mean OK." He said, "Well, no, a technician should do it." We grabbed a technician and got the canister screwed on so Frank and his guys could work on the GRS cabling.

Frank, Shawn, and Jesse were going to work Saturday to get things done and they were going to start at 5:00 AM. They were going to be finishing up the Winchester connectors for the heaters and then I was going to be at Lockheed at 10:00 AM to help them with the MAG/ER. If we were successful Saturday, then, except for the NS/APS, the spacecraft would be completely wired by Monday.

Thus ended an interesting, but long and hard workweek.

Saturday, February 22, 1997

Rebecca and I went up to Lockheed at 10:00 AM and I put the MAG/ER on the boom. Frank, Shawn, and Jesse wired it and checked a couple of things out. Then the GRS and the MAG/ER booms were both done! We only had one boom left to do. They finished the Winchesters connectors for the heaters and, when Rebecca and I left, they were working on the connectors for the engine. When they were done, we only had the NS/APS boom left to do and it was still at Able getting the second high voltage cable installed. Finally, Lunar Prospector was getting close to being finished!

Then Rebecca and I drove to Rebecca and Francisco Andolz's and spent a nice evening with them.

It was a good day.

Monday, February 24, 1997: Seven Months to Launch

The wiring of the spacecraft was just about finished. When I went over early in the morning, they just had a couple more engines to do and, of course, the NS/APS boom that Steve Honodel was picking up from Able the next day, Tuesday. Frank, Shawn, and Jesse would finish wiring that boom the next morning. We were planning — unless a catastrophe or an earthquake hit us — to start turning on Lunar Prospector on Thursday.

To my great surprise, Al Tilley came by in the afternoon and said that the MAG/ER's mass was more than 7 kg — it was supposed to be about 5½! I went over and weighed it myself and there was something screwy there. The MAG/ER was so light that we had Dave Curtis put tantalum ballast plates on it and I still expected to add ¾ kg more ballast. If we took the tantalum plates off, the MAG/ER would weigh just a tad less than the GRS, which had always been the heaviest instrument by a kilogram. I didn't know what in hell was going on with the MAG/ER.

I called Curtis and he didn't know what was going on either; when they weighed it, it had a mass of 5½ kilograms; so there was a 2 kg discrepancy!

Tuesday, February 25, 1997

I gave a talk at the Paradise School in Morgan Hill.

Afterwards I went to Ames and we had our telecon with Headquarters. The disturbing thing was it looked like the Lewis Mission, the first launch of LLV1 after its failed first flight more that 18 months earlier, and a launch that had to work for us to have a chance of launching on the LLV2 before CRSS, was going to be postponed from April to June! That would give us just three months between the Lewis launch and our launch! Headquarters didn't know for sure, but they were talking about it at Goddard. That would make things really tight and tough for us because, if Lewis kept being delayed, then we were not going to be able to launch. At least one damned LLV had to successfully get off the ground and leave enough time for us to launch, if we were going to make it before CRSS.

After the telecon, I went over the Mission Operations Document (MOD) with my Mission Ops crew and I got sick of Marcie and Ken Galal. Both were negative about everything and did nothing but complain that nothing was right. Marcie said she didn't understand how we were going to use the engines (no surprise there — she knew nothing about the spacecraft) and that I ought to have engine diagrams in the document. I answered, "You know, everyone who is going to work on this spacecraft is going to have to know it from head to tail or I won't have them on the Ops Team, so there is no reason to add diagrams to the MOD." After the meeting, I said to Tim Bridges something about getting rid of those two.

He said, "Yes, they sure are a pain in the ass."

Dave Curtis called about the MAG/ER mass and he said he thought Paul Turin had put *all* the available tantalum plates on the instrument, so it would be OK for us to take part of them off.

I went over to the spacecraft and it was almost completely wired. We were waiting for Steve to get in with the NS/APS boom. Dougherty had told Lee to find out when Steve was arriving so we would be prepared to get it wired. Of course, she didn't do a damned thing; she never made the call and Tom said she was upset because, for some strange reason, she thought Tom or I was supposed to do it! All I did was to walk over to Delores (Delores Arenas, the very nice and very competent secretary of our group) and ask her what Steve's travel schedule was. Such crap, Lee and some of the other engineers are so damned incompetent — they can't figure out how to do something as simple as asking a secretary about a travel schedule — it is unbelievable. I found out that Steve was not going to arrive until much later in the afternoon.

Given Steve's late arrival, there was nothing more I could do and I decided to go home early (at 1:30 PM), so I could work on the presentation for Wes. The trip to Headquarters to counter Spudis and Nozette's stab-in-the-back had been postponed to the 6th and we had postponed the press conference for a week.

Wednesday, February 26, 1997: Finally Finishing the Wiring

I got to work at 5:00 AM. Frank, Shawn, and Jesse had already started working on the NS/APS boom that Steve had brought back from Able. There were just a few things left to do on the spacecraft and they had all of it done by the afternoon. The wiring was finally finished, except maybe a ground wire or two. They were starting to do connector pin checks and continuity checks to look for any wiring errors they might have made and they would be through with their checks very soon.

Bill and his crew from Los Alamos and Dave Curtis and his crew from Berkeley were there to do the final checks of the instruments. We found out that, as David had thought, the extra 2 kg on the MAG/ER was just due to the extra tantalum plates, so we took all of them off. It was then back down to 5.8 kg where it was supposed to be. That was a minor screw-up, but not something that hurt us.

We had a meeting at Ames and went over the presentation for Wes. Scott, Dougherty, and everybody made good suggestions. Scott was going to give a brief introduction and say how great everything had been going, and I would explain the science and would be doing most of the talking.

Pat called and said that Congressman Rohrabacher's aide, Jim Muncy, wanted to talk to me, so I was going to arrange that. If I couldn't see him on the 6th, I would just stay over until the 7th. One way or another, I was going to get Lunar Prospector done and launched on time.

We heard that Lewis was not going to get delayed until June as we had heard, rather just to the end of April. If it didn't get delayed any more, we would be OK.

We had a team Test Readiness Review and we were going to have another one on Monday. Frank and his crew were going to finish the continuity checks by the next day, Thursday. Able was going to be at Lockheed Friday to make the final installation of the booms. We were going to put the instruments on permanently Friday night and we were going to start turning Lunar Prospector on Saturday. We were going to carefully and very slowly check that all the voltages were correct on all the lines and slowly turn on one system after the other as we checked them out, one by one. We expected to be at the point where we could power up everything on Monday.

We were getting there and it was getting very exciting. All of us, the whole team, were just trying to make sure that nothing went wrong with the turn-on. If we were lucky and if there were no real problems, we could have the turn-on testing done in two weeks. We actually had six weeks to do the turn-on, because we couldn't get into the thermal-vacuum chamber (or just thermal-vac) until the middle of April. If it all worked, we could use the last four weeks to let the electronics burn in and to practice Mission Ops. I was very optimistic that everything was going to be OK.

Thursday, February 27, 1997: Minor Problems

When I got into work, Frank and his crew were doing the continuity checks and they did so all day. They found that one of the high voltage lines on the NS/APS boom was shorting. That was too bad, we would have to replace it. We didn't know if that was the one we had just replaced or not; it didn't make any difference — it had to be replaced.

There was another slight problem, for reasons unbeknownst to us, Frank had decided not to shield the low voltage power lines from the Spectrometer Electronics Unit (SES) to the booms, even though Bill had planned it that way. It was not clear if that line required shielding or not. If the line did need shielding, then Frank would have to put shielded wire in there and I assumed that would also have been the case for the MAG/ER low voltage lines.

Then several other issues came up. For example, Ron Black was appalled that the connectors did not have back shells on them and that they were not potted. Frank said, "We (Lockheed) never pot them or put back shells on them because that has a tendency to break them." Those two issues were a matter of differences of opinions as to how best to do something. Similarly, Frank said (regarding the unshielded low voltage lines), "We never use shielded lines for low power and low voltage on a spacecraft." I wondered if it was OK for science instruments, but we would find out. Those are the type of things one tests for and corrects if necessary.

We were getting ready to have Able come up the next day, Friday, to put the booms on permanently. Come hell or high water, Frank, Shawn, and Jesse were going to be done with the continuity tests by that evening. Then the next day, Friday, we would put the booms on the spacecraft and then put the instruments on the booms permanently. Saturday, we were putting power on the C&DH to see if we had the right ground support power, and then Monday we were going to start the actual turn-on.

I went over to Ames at 3:00 PM and the Ops Team and I worked for two hours on the MOD, which was actually fun for a change. Marcie was not on her high horse and the rest of them were well behaved.

It was a long and exciting day, hopefully we would soon have the spacecraft turned on and maybe, if we were lucky, it wouldn't have any problems. If so, that would again give us credibility in the eyes of Headquarters.

Friday, February 28, 1997: A Completed Spacecraft

It was a long day. I got up at 3:30 AM and went to work. When the day ended, the booms were on, the instruments were on, and the spacecraft was basically done. All that remained was a little clean up wiring work and the installation of the battery and the solar panels, both of which would go on the spacecraft much later in the program.

Though the spacecraft was ready to be turned on, Kim didn't have the cables and connectors ready so we could hook the spacecraft up to the ground support equipment! We couldn't start the C&DH turn-on test the next day. We probably wouldn't be able to do that until Monday — if we were lucky — and then the turn-on would probably be Tuesday. Such incompetence!

I talked to Jim Muncy. He asked about Lunar Prospector and the launch issue. I explained the whole thing to him and my feelings about the launch. They (Rohrabacher and Jim) didn't see any reason to delay Lunar Prospector. They understood the risks. I hoped that Congress was going to kick some NASA butt.

I also called James Paul and we were going to get together, too. He asked me if it was true that the Clementine people had been stabbing us in the back and I said, "Yes." I hoped there would be some repercussions because of that. He also said Stu Nozette was no longer the head of Clementine.

The main thing was that the spacecraft was basically done. We were still losing time, because of the incompetence of Dougherty and his people, but we had made a big step forward.

Monday, March 3, 1997

Frank, Shawn, and Jesse did the final bits and pieces of wiring on the spacecraft. That consisted simply of plugging in the science instruments and connecting the plug for the boom Spider. Unless we found some wiring errors during the turn-on, they were done.

We had the final turn-on meeting at 8:00 AM to go over every single detail before we started the turn-on — that was not the point to make any mistakes. Of course, we didn't get turned on, but Dougherty was trying to at least get the first C&DH test done, but even that didn't happen until the next day.

I got a call from Julianne Potter of the House Science Committee. She asked me about Lunar Prospector and the launch risk. I told her the value of the mission would be wasted if we didn't launch as soon as possible. If the LLV2 was going to fail because of a design defect, there was nothing we could do about it and waiting after CRSS would not help because that design defect would cause CRSS to fail. Since it had taken Lockheed more than 18 months to recover from the first LLV1 failure, if the CRSS LLV2 failed, it would be a year or so before Lockheed would be ready to try Lunar Prospector's launch and by then, we would be completely outside the eclipse window, so I would have no mission. Waiting for CRSS would serve no purpose, except to put Lunar Prospector in great jeopardy.

I called Jim Muncy and James Paul and set up meeting times with them.

Then I got a call from the lady who ran the NEAR Mission Control Center and who wanted to find out about George French's educational program. I told her about George's Moonlink and recommended that she do a NEARlink with George. Then she asked me to come and visit the NEAR crew and give them a talk on Lunar Prospector.

By the end of the day, the spacecraft was looking good. I brought Scott over and he was happy when he saw it. Ralph Fullerton was doing a walk around — a final Quality Assurance inspection — of the spacecraft when Scott and I were there and we were getting it all set to turn on.

Chapter 3-30
Turning on Lunar Prospector

Tuesday, March 4, 1997: Starting the Turn-On

Until that point in time, Lunar Prospector had first been a concept, then a bunch of drawings, schematics, and requirements documents — i.e., a paper spacecraft — and then it had become something real, something you could touch, something made of graphite epoxy, plastic, metal, tanks, fuel lines, valves, engines, electronics, wires, and the like, but it was dead, just a pile of carefully crafted materials with no life of its own. But finally, like the mad scientists in the *Frankenstein* movies, we were about to put the electrodes to Lunar Prospector's brain (the C&DH) and hopefully, we too would cry, "It's alive. It's alive." However, unlike Frankenstein, I did not want Lunar Prospector to slowly get up and start terrorizing the village peasants (well, maybe it could terrorize Lockheed and NASA just a little), rather I wanted it to purr along like the good little spacecraft it was meant to be.

We were getting ready for the electrode-to-the-brain event at about 4:00 PM. Getting ready to do that was like surgeons getting ready for brain surgery — so we took our time and then we found out the test battery was dead! Though we could power the spacecraft in two ways (we could use the test battery connected to the solar array simulator or we could use the ground test equipment power supply), we were supposed to use the battery. The problem started because Kim thought you couldn't put a fully charged battery on the spacecraft, which was a bunch of hooey, and thus did not charge it! The battery was dead and I said, "Damn it, let's put the power on from the console (the ground test equipment). We can't put it on from the solar simulator without the battery and you can't have the solar simulator on when you are charging the battery." Kim finally agreed to start the turn-on using console power.

We started by sending power from the console, through the umbilical, up to the point where the power wires would connect to the C&DH. Of course, everything was unplugged. We then tested the voltages on all 40 pins in the umbilical connector. One pin had 22 v on it that should have been 0 v and three pins that should have had 30 v had no voltage at all — so, as expected, there were some screw-ups. We worked only until 5:00 PM, since Lee had to leave by then and Kim had to go pick his wife up. Nevertheless, the turn-on process had begun.

When I left the highbay, Woody was trying to figure out what to do about the battery and how to get it charged, since there was a problem with the hookup. It was possible that the problem was just an incorrect connector pin assignment, but who knew — I sure didn't.

The Denver LLV guys and the LLV crew from the Cape, who would prepare the vehicle for launch, were at Sunnyvale for a meeting. As TC Noble and I were standing in front of our respective urinals, he was crabbing that all he could get out of those asses was, "We can't do this and we can't do that. We wouldn't sign anything and we are not responsible for anything," i.e., the same old LLV story.

When I finally left Lockheed, Dougherty was still there and he said, "They (LLV) won't do anything, I am going to talk to Henshaw."

That really ticked me off; I had said a year earlier that we were getting nowhere with those guys and I wanted off that damned vehicle. Nobody would back me then and all I got was the BS about how the company wouldn't let us down. I said to Dougherty, "The difficulties we're having with LLV are the same ones CRSS is having. When I talked to the CRSS guys about LLV, they just throw up their hands."

Wednesday, March 5, and Thursday, March 6, 1997: The DC Trip

I flew to Washington Wednesday and stayed with Pat and Julius. Thursday morning I met with James Paul and told him about the launch vehicle mess and about how my PI position had very quickly degenerated.

Then I went to Wes's meeting and did a good job of convincing him and his staff that Paul Spudis and Stu Nozette were full of crap, that we had an excellent science mission and that we needed the extended mission. I did my job and everyone was impressed, nevertheless, I was not pleased about the interactions we had just had with the Headquarter wienies.

As I was leaving NASA to go see Jim Muncy, Joe Boyce stopped me in the hall and apologized for us having been dragged to Headquarters to defend our mission from Paul and Stu's backstabbing and explained, "Once they made their allegations, Wes had no choice but to ask you to respond." That was nice of Joe, but I did not agree with him; if Wes knew anything or had any guts, he would have thrown Paul and Stu out of his office instead of making Scott and me defend the mission.

I went up to the Hill and talked to Julianne Potter and Jim Muncy. Jim was very aggressive and he wanted me to come back to testify to the House Committee and to raise hell. The issue was, who was running the show, NASA or me? That went very well.

Friday, March 7, 1997: Back at Lockheed

Ed O'Connor from Spaceport Florida called and said he was going to Headquarters the following week and he would be talking to Goldin about the launch vehicle issue.

I told Dougherty what I had been up to with the congressional aides and let him know that Congress expected me to run the mission, not Lockheed and not NASA. I told him I might be asked to testify to the House Committee on Science on the role of the PI and on the launch issue.

Dougherty said that Sam Venneri, who was responsible for Lewis & Clark, said there was no way that I was going to launch until after CRSS launched. He said further that Sam was screwing with the LLV1 guys, making them do all kind of things to get ready for the Lewis launch. I thought Sylvia was right, Headquarters was just trying to jerk Lockheed around and Lockheed was getting to the point where it was going to raise hell with NASA and tell them to get Lewis ready for launch or else.

I talked to Scott about our meeting with Wes and his staff. He thought everything went extremely well. Scott felt we had won and Headquarters had no choice but to allow us to launch in September.

However, Scott was miffed that I had rubbed Wes's nose in the fact that Headquarters had agreed to my changing the spacecraft so it would not survive eclipses. I objected and said, "I wasn't trying to rub his nose in it. I was just reminding him that Headquarters had agreed with what I wanted to do." Scott was getting a little too sensitive. He was trying to protect his butt and didn't want his superiors getting upset with him for not controlling me (screw you, Scott).

I decided the best thing to do was just to let the question of the role of the PI play itself out and only go to Congress to testify if NASA started to pull the rug out from under me. If Headquarters decided to allow me to proceed, there was no reason "to rub their nose in it" regarding my being in charge. Testifying right then would only tick NASA off and tick Scott off, because I would be insulting his precious NASA bosses.

We worked on turning on the spacecraft most of the day and got a lot of testing done. We were getting power into the C&DH and power was coming out of it and going to units that were to be turned on during the automatic turn-on sequence, i.e., the Sun sensor, the Earth/Moon limb crossing sensor, the transponder, the pressure transducer, i.e., all the engineering units.

We had not turned on the SES unit, the engine heaters, or the instruments since we couldn't determine if their voltages were correct until we could command those units on. That's where we got stuck — we couldn't get commands into the C&DH from OASIS, (the program we were going to use to run Mission Ops and command the spacecraft).

However, we were finding all the little bugs in the system and making good progress with the turn-on. Most of us thought that most of the bugs were in the ground support equipment, rather that in the spacecraft.

Saturday, March 8, 1997: A Big Step Forward

I went to Lockheed in the morning and Kim, Tim, Gary Schlueter (one of our new Test and Integration Engineers who was going to be responsible for running the spacecraft throughout all the testing), and the computer guys were working on the turn-on, but they were having some trouble.

Bill showed me how to run the spectrometers, so I could run them during the turn-on and testing and then, when I finished learning that, I went home late in the afternoon, because Kim and the crew still had not gotten the C&DH to work properly and because I needed to finish doing the viewgraphs I would need to justify having the extended mission as long as possible, so we could get the best GRS data set possible.

I got a call from Kim and Tim at about 9:00 PM. They had finally found out what was wrong — there was a ground that was very ticklish about the way it was connected and they fixed it. After correcting it, they were able to command the spacecraft and get data back! There were still some things that weren't quite right, but they could communicate with the SES unit and they were getting the right voltages on the right connector pins for all three spectrometers. Kim was going to stay and finish checking the spectrometers pins and then checked all the MAG/ER pins.

We had made a big step, but, unfortunately, I was at home. I would like to have been there, but since it seemed like they were not getting anywhere and since I had work to do, I had missed that part of the turn-on. Oh well, I couldn't be there every minute of every day, even though I wanted to. I was hopeful and optimistic that we would get the baby completely turned on and have a complete functional test during the coming week.

Monday, March 10, 1997

The turn-on was going slowly. I thought we were going to get turned on in the afternoon, but there were still little things going wrong, so we made little progress.

I checked and found out that progress was being made in getting LRI's tax-exempt status done, but we were still not there.

Tuesday, March 11, 1997

We had hoped to get completely through the turn-on, including turning on the science instruments, but we did not get that far.

I was very concerned because we found if the connectors weren't plugged in absolutely perfectly and weren't screwed down really tight, they weren't connecting properly. I thought, *if they are that sensitive, what will happen when they get the hell shaken out of them during launch? Will they partially disconnect?* I was told that was not a problem, but I was not convinced.

Then there was something screwy with the commanding; when we sent one command, something else would happen, i.e., we would send the command to turn on the Sun sensor and the Earth/Moon limb crossing sensor would turn on instead! We thought maybe we had the wrong command table in the C&DH or in the console. The engineers were trying to figure that out. As a result, we could not get the science instruments turned on.

We received word that Code S was finally convinced we had to get Lunar Prospector launched in September; so I had succeeded in getting that point across to Wes and his staff. However, Goldin and Karen Poniatowski were still resisting that conclusion.

Wednesday, March 12, 1997:
Lunar Prospector's Coming Out Press Conference

We had the big press conference. There were about 60 TV and newspaper reporters there, both national and international. It was really good and a lot of fun. Numerous reporters interviewed Scott and me; everyone seemed to be awed by our little, inexpensive spacecraft. There were a number of reports on Lunar Prospector during the evening TV newscasts.

After the press conference, we went back to working on the turn-on. The commanding was still all screwed up, either the engineering model of the C&DH did not have the updated program in it or the console didn't. Anyway, that had to be straightened out before we could proceed. Nevertheless, I thought we were doing well.

Thursday, March 13, 1997

The morning newspapers carried good stories about Lunar Prospector and there was a really big article in the San Jose *Mercury.* The press conference was a big success.

I worked on the spacecraft with the guys. Kim, Gary, and I were finally able to command the spacecraft from the console, so we worked through the various sequences and we used OASIS to read the temperatures and other engineering data. I was getting used to running the spacecraft — that was the beginning of my practicing how to fly the spacecraft. It was really fun and easy and the latter was why I wanted a simple spacecraft with simple commanding — that philosophy was paying off handsomely. I was just having a ball working with my little spacecraft.

Unfortunately, everything was getting way over Tom's head and I thought that had to come to an end.

We got a lot done during the day, but we couldn't get the spectrometers completely turned on. We got the SES on, but the 28 volt current readings were just at the level expected for the SES alone. When I commanded the NS/APS and GRS on, the 28 volt current did not increase. Either the 28 volt current drawn by the spectrometers was too small to register, or there was no current getting to the spectrometers and I could not tell which was the case. We went through an exercise of watching the bus current increase as we turned everything else on, one at a time, i.e., the pressure transducer, the primary and secondary heaters, the Sun sensor, and Earth/Moon limb crossing sensor — all of which also drew only a small amount of current but that did register — and watching the temperatures of the units rise to make sure they were drawing current. That had all worked, but I still couldn't tell what was going on with the spectrometers' 28 volt current.

However, we did notice there were still a lot of calibration errors of all kinds. For example, the spacecraft's temperatures were reading 15° C and it had to be at least 20° C or 22° C in the highbay. We also saw a big structure current, which would indicate there was a short, but we thought it was just another calibration error (and it was). Nevertheless, all that was part of the turn-on process and we would get it all worked out. We were getting a little closer each day.

Friday, March 14, 1997: Tom

I showed the spacecraft to the students of the University of San Jose Aerospace Engineering Department; I had given them a seminar on Lunar Prospector several weeks earlier and had promised them they could see the spacecraft after the press conference.

After the tour, I went back to help with the turn-on. Lee had tightened down the connectors that weren't connecting very well, so I was not the only one concerned about that. In fact, Kim had been given the task to find out why the connectors were not connecting properly, but no one ever figured it out. We just made sure they were screwed down very, very tightly.

While the engineers were fooling around with the connectors, I was working on the spectrometers. I finally got a reading on the 28 volt current of 270 milliamps and that was OK. But, I didn't dare turn on the high voltage to the spectrometers, because we couldn't get the spectrometers to synchronize (or get in sync, as we say) with the C&DH. Spectrum Astro had found they had to change a capacitor in the C&DH to get it to sync up properly with the spectrometers, but while they had changed that capacitor on the flight model they were still working on in Arizona, we suspected they had not changed the capacitor in the engineering model we had on the spacecraft! Anyway, we needed Alex Kochergin to look over the problem, but he wasn't around; so Kim went to find him. Alex came over, but wasn't too happy about doing so, and started doing some tests to see why the C&DH wasn't syncing up with the spectrometers.

We also needed to talk to Ron Black to get his input from the SES electronic side of the problem, since the C&DH might have been OK and if that were the case, then the problem had to be in the SES unit. But do you think the engineers would call Ron? No, I had to call him. That was one of the things that was also frustrating Tom to the point of going bonkers. The damned engineers wouldn't pick up a phone; they wouldn't do anything. Time and time again, they would say, "Well, somebody needs to do that."

I would say, "It's your damned sub-system, so go do it yourself!" I was amazed.

I checked the calibrations on all the temperatures and they were still all screwed up, they all read 5 to 6° C low. All of those things had to be understood and corrected.

I got a lot of compliments about my performance during the news conference. Jim Schirle said I had done a much better job than Scott and I looked very sophisticated — me sophisticated; I had to laugh at that. He said he was very proud to be associated with me, or something like that. I thought that was very nice. I got an email from Lisa Chu-Thielbar, Ames's new Lunar Prospector PR person, who said I was the centerpiece of the whole press conference. Delores, Tom Chinn, and several other people also said some nice things and were all very pleased about being associated with the mission that was so well received by the press. I thought they were pleased because the mission was probably the first one they had ever worked on that was not a secret military satellite, so it was the first time their work had ever been acknowledged. Whatever the reason, everybody was happy.

Jim Muncy had left a message for me. I tried to call him to let him know what was going on, but I could not reach him. He had heard a rumor that LLV was trying to pull out. I thought if that rumor had any basis at all, it was an attempt on Lockheed's part to scare NASA into leaving LLV alone, so they could proceed with the Lewis & Clark mission launches on the LLV1s and proceed with the LLV2 launch of Lunar Prospector. On the other hand, it might very well have been true, because they still had not launched an LLV1 (except for the abortive first flight) and maybe they were finding that their damned rocket wasn't any good. If that were true, and if LLV held out long enough and defaulted, then Lunar Prospector would be in a heap of trouble.

George French had been in Washington at the Aerospace States Association meeting, and Senator Stevens had bought one of George's Moonlink packages for his daughter's school. The Senator had then told Goldin, or somebody, that they better not delay Lunar Prospector past September, because his daughter wanted to fly her Moonlink mission. George was doing his job.

As the day was ending and as Tom and I were leaving the highbay, getting ready to go home, Tom was very upset because the engineers were working so slowly and he blew up at me because he didn't think I was aware of how poorly things were going. I was not too surprised at Tom's outburst, since he had not been handling the stress of working on the mission, working with the engineers, NASA, and Lockheed very well. His health, especially his post-polio problems, was suffering noticeably and the fact that he did not understand the spacecraft and mission well enough to follow what was going on during the turn-on and testing was weighing heavily on him. I had been contemplating telling him he simply wasn't doing his job well anymore, because he had never learned what he had to know about the mission, the spacecraft, or the instruments, and he was just so far behind the curve, there was no way I could justify keeping him on after we launched. When he blew up, I knew he had reached his limit and if I did not tell him right then, his health was going to rapidly go to hell. I said, "Tom, call Shelley and tell her you're driving home with me tonight — we have to talk."

Tom, of course, knew something serious was up and did as I asked. Shortly thereafter, as we were driving home together, I had to tell my best friend, someone who I like, admire, and respect very much, and who had played a vital role in helping me fight NASA, Lockheed, and the engineers during the previous eighteen months, that I was letting him go. I told Tom I would keep him on through launch, because he deserved it and because there were still things he could do to help me (though those things were getting to be fewer and fewer in number). Also, that would give him six months to find a new job. I told Tom he had done an excellent job and, though I truly wished he had been able to learn enough about the mission and spacecraft to help me fly it, I had no regrets about the role he had played in the mission. Nevertheless, my letting him go was very hard on Tom, but that's life.

I got home late, after a very long day that had ended on a sad and frustrating note. The frustration was not just because I had to let Tom go, but also because it always took the damned engineers until 4:00 PM to finally get their butts in gear — I had already worked an 11-hour day before they decided they could go over to the spacecraft and do something! It was frustrating.

Saturday, March 15, 1997

Dave Curtis brought the MAG/ER down to Lockheed and we got it going. We couldn't get the engineering data to come out correctly; there was some interface problem between the MAG/ER electronics and the C&DH, but the science data came banging right through. Thus we still had the sync problem between the science instruments and the C&DH and we hoped it would be fixed on Monday.

Monday, March 17, 1997

There were a lot of little things wrong with the spacecraft, e.g., one wire was wrong and that was one of the reasons why we weren't getting some of the MAG/ER engineering data.

Professor Bob Twiggs came from Stanford University and we had a really good time discussing the spacecraft and preparing for the seminars he had asked me to give to his aerospace engineering class.

Tuesday, March 18, 1997:
Almost Getting the Spectrometers Turned On

I did a lot of work on the computer model of the spacecraft, so we could soon get started training to fly Lunar Prospector.

Then I went over to Ames to work with my Mission Ops crew and immediately got annoyed with Marcie, who is Ms. Negativity personified. In her arrogant, NASA opinion, no one can do anything right except her, even though she did not understand one thing about the spacecraft or the mission. People like her are the reason why NASA is as bad as it is. Nevertheless, Scott would block any attempt I made to get rid of his little darling, but if there was a way of getting rid of her, I was going to find it.

The C&DH flight unit was supposed to have been finished and Dougherty wanted to have it flown in from Phoenix the next day, Wednesday, and get it put on the spacecraft. However, Spectrum Astro hadn't made some of the fixes they were supposed to make, so it was going to be at least another week before we got the damned thing. As a result, we jury-rigged the engineering model so we could go ahead and work with the spectrometers and the MAG/ER and hence, get into systems testing at the baseline functional level.

We were all over at the spacecraft and, of course, nothing got started until 2:00 or 3:00 PM — Kim just couldn't get his butt in gear. He was good when he got going, but it was hard to get him going.

We replaced the capacitor in the C&DH several times and finally got the right one, so we could finally get the ground system to sync up with the spectrometers — at last, we were ready to go! For the first time, I could see the voltages and the line currents on both the spectrometer monitor and the spacecraft monitor, hurray! Then I started to turn on the high voltage to the GRS. I commanded the first step of 500 volts and it actually worked! The voltage jumped from 0 to 500 volts on the spacecraft monitor, but I saw nothing on the spectrometer monitors, so I didn't go any further. I wanted to talk to Bill to find out what he thought was going on with the spectrometer monitor. Despite that, we had made progress, but there was still a lot left to do in the turn-on.

I was tired at the end of the long day; I was tired of Marcie; I was tired of having one thing after another not work, and I was tired of waiting to see the spacecraft get completely turned on. Since Rebecca and I were going out to dinner, I went home at Lockheed's regular quitting time rather than later — as I usually did.

Wednesday, March 19, 1997: All the Instruments Turned On

Kim was in early and we started working on the spectrometers. I talked to Bill early in the morning and I told him what we had done the day before. He said I could go ahead and increase the high voltages on the spectrometers and just use the spacecraft monitor to check if everything was OK. I stepped the voltages up to their operational values and we got all three spectrometers on and working perfectly! Then I checked them out completely.

I called Bill and told him the good news and he said he would fly over on the coming weekend to give the spectrometers their final, complete checkout. The only thing we still did not have right was that we were not getting the engineering data on the spectrometer monitor, even though I was getting it perfectly through OASIS (the spacecraft monitoring system), and even though we were getting all the science data on the spectrometer monitor. We suspected the problem was just that Alex was not aware that the engineering data were also going to be displayed on the spectrometer monitors, along with the science data, so he never gave Ron Black any of that information. If so, we thought we could easily take care of that the next day.

Dave Curtis was also there and he worked on getting the MAG/ER running. He got through all his tests of the science data, but he too was not getting his engineering data on his MAG/ER monitor, although I was getting it on my OASIS monitor. They were trying to figure that out and Dave was very close to getting his problem solved when I left.

Thus, we were just about at the point where the whole spacecraft, instruments and all, was working. One or two more days, that was all we probably needed to clean up all the remaining turn-on issues. Then, on the weekend Bill, Dave, and I would give the spectrometers and the MAG/ER a good shakedown. If that all worked out, we would be very, very close to having the spacecraft fully checked out. It was a great day. Bill, Dave, and I were just ecstatic over the science instrument turn-ons.

Thursday, March 20, 1997:
Lockheed Starts Pushing Lunar Prospector Around

I had to go to the dentist before I went to work. When I got there, the engineers were monkeying around with the C&DH. It turns out that Gerry Grismore had forgotten to tell Spectrum Astro about the changes we needed in the flight unit! It was going to be another ten days before we got it — a nice big screw-up! Also, Gerry hadn't even bothered to tell Spectrum Astro what they needed to change in the flight unit based on our turn-on tests with the engineering model! Tom overheard the conversation and Gerry said, "Oh, I forgot to tell them various things." Those wonderful engineers; what would I do without them? Stay sane?

I was only at work a few minutes when Dougherty came in and said, "We have to look at the launch dates!" Since Lockheed management thought CRSS was going be ready for launch in December or January, CRSS was taking precedence over Lunar Prospector (that tells you how much Lockheed management knows about building spacecraft, CRSS was not ready for its first launch attempt in 9 months, rather it took 25 more months before CRSS was finished).

That ticked me off. I had my September launch dates and Dougherty was trying to get October 24 and 25 for our backup dates and Lockheed was saying that if I didn't get launched before November, I would have to sit on the launch pad and wait for CRSS for two months — the dirty SOBs. The damned company did what it had done all along — screw Lunar Prospector. We were just the dog's hind leg, or worse, what the dog left behind! I was so ticked off I did not say anything when Dougherty asked about launch dates in January, February, and March. My hatred of Lockheed had reached new heights.

I left building 107 and went over to the spacecraft where Alex was checking out the interface problem between the C&DH and instruments, since we still couldn't get the engineering data on the MAG/ER monitor and we still were not getting the spectrometer engineering data on the spectrometer monitor. I hoped we would get both of those problems straightened out during the course of the day. There were still a lot of little things we were trying to clean up.

Friday, March 21, 1997

I called the person in California that was handling our LRI paperwork for the state and the IRS person in Cincinnati, OH, who was handling our tax-exempt request and they both had some questions. As soon as those questions were answered, they could finish everything up and I could get into LRI. I asked them to fax me the questions and I would answer them and fax them back the next day. I was getting very close to having LRI all set up and getting out of the hated Lockheed.

There were still a lot of little things wrong with the spacecraft and especially with the C&DH and that worried me. Irv was trying to get the thermisters on the engines to read correctly, the data were being sent properly to the C&DH, but something was wrong. Also, the C&DH was still not talking to the MAG/ER properly.

I went to Ames to talk to Scott and what he said was unbelievable. First of all and the greatest thing was that he had the fifth draft of the letter from NASA about the launch vehicle issue. When the letter officially came, they would be telling us officially to go ahead and launch on September 24! But that decision was contingent upon three things. First, Lewis had to be successfully launched and that was finally set for May 10. Second, any anomalies on the Lewis launch had to be understood and corrected. Third, there had to be a review of the launch vehicles. Headquarters was going to accept just one successful flight of the LLV1 before giving us the green light — they had given up on trying to launch both Lewis and Clark before Lunar Prospector. If the Lewis launch failed, we would have to wait until after CRSS, but we would not have to wait any longer than March, because they recognized we would lose significant amounts of science if we launched after March. We had won the battle! I was happy; Scott was happy. Everybody was off our backs; even Karen Poniatowski seemed to be satisfied with the directive.

I went back to Lockheed and told Dougherty the good news and Larry Price called and said he had some contrary marching orders from Lockheed Corporation regarding CRSS's priority over Lunar Prospector. Dougherty said, "To hell with that, we're going to do it this way (Lunar Prospector launching in September before CRSS) and that's the end of it. We don't have any money and we are not going to change our launch date." Dougherty was getting ticked off about CRSS too. Regardless, all of the sudden, everything was moving in the right direction for the first time.

I talked to Dougherty about the January, February, and March launch dates that he had asked about the day before and I said, "We had two pairs of launch dates before and now we're talking about five sets of launch dates. We can't afford that, that's two and a half million dollars for launch trajectory calculations alone and we can't have that spacecraft sitting around for three months on the pad like that. We would have to de-stack the spacecraft and take proper care of the instruments." Even Dougherty woke up to that and agreed.

Then it dawned on me that, because we had the September 24 and 25 launch dates and we were trying to get October 24 and 25 as backup dates, that gave us only four tries before CRSS would get in our hair. However, we could also try to get the original October 9 and 10 launch dates, too, even though the latter dates were less favorable than the others, and then we would have six tries before CRSS got in our way.

If worse came to worse and we lost all six launch dates due to weather or mechanical problems, then LLV would have two extra months to start calculating the February and March launch trajectories since each trajectory calculation takes three months. If we got in trouble, that wouldn't be too bad, except for the money.

However, there was still one very big fly in the ointment — Cassini. Remember that the $3.5 billion Cassini had taken our early October launch dates? Well, Cassini was in trouble. One of the two big solid fuel rockets on the sides of Cassini's Titan C-4 launch vehicle had a big gouge, 10 to 12 cm long and 2 to 3 cm deep, in the Teflon lining of its engine bell. Headquarters said that the change-out of that segment would delay Cassini's launch until sometime between October 15 and 18. That opened the door for us to try and get October 9 and 10 for Lunar Prospector. I was going to shoot for September 24 and 25 as our prime dates, with backup dates on October 9 and 10 and then on October 24 and 25.

Bill was at the Lunar and Planetary Science Conference in Houston and called to tell me that everything was going well. Mike Drake had asked him how things were going. Mike said that most everyone was sorry they had bitched so much about us winning in the beginning, but they were all peeved at not having won themselves. He said further, "You guys really have a good mission," and wanted to see if he could get on our analysis team. Everybody was trying to do that, of course.

Even Paul Spudis asked how things were going and Bill answered, "Quite well." Paul said, "Good."

I guessed the community had finally given up trying to stab us in the back; it was about time.

Chapter 3-31
Functional Testing

Saturday, March 22, 1997: The Instruments' Functional Testing

Bill Feldman, Dave Curtis, Gary, Tom, and I got started a little after 1:00 PM turning on the spectrometers and the MAG/ER for the full Functional Test. Everything worked perfectly. The only things that were still wrong were we still could not read the engineering data on the spectrometer monitor and Dave Curtis still couldn't get the MAG/ER data engineering on his monitor. However, those were problems with the ground support equipment and not with the spacecraft and instruments, so they were not of great concern, but they still had to be fixed.

I got most of the questions answered for the IRS, so I was hopeful that LRI would be a reality in the very near future and I could get the hell out of Lockheed.

Monday, March 24, 1997: Getting Ready for the Burp Tests

We had wanted to do a functional test (burp test) on the engines, which meant sending firing commands to each of them and, in the absence any hydrazine propellant in the tanks (one does NOT do live firings of the engines on a spacecraft to test them — that would be very dangerous), a little of the helium pressurant we had in the tanks, at about 50 psi, would squirt out. We would detect those burps of helium using a sophisticated helium sniffer and thus see if the engine valves were properly opening on command. However, as usual, though Kim had requested the Lockheed sniffer, he never brought it over to the highbay! The guy just can't do things in parallel; everything is serial with him! We would have to do the burp tests the next day!

Since Tom was officially out of the Mission Ops picture, I asked Dan Swanson to be my second in command in Mission Ops, i.e., to be my backup, and for him to be the other half of the Primary Uplink Command Team. He loved the idea. Then I asked him if he would like to eventually be in LRI and he said yes, very much so. Dan was really excited about LRI and asked me a lot of questions about its goals and history. I thought everything was going to be great. I was really pleased.

Tuesday, March 25, 1997: Testing the Engines

Of course, Kim hadn't gotten the damned sniffer, so we had to go find it and when we did, the thing was outfitted for testing little bitty one-Newton thrusters, so the sniffer bells didn't fit over our engine bells that were about five times bigger. I had had it and said, "I'm not waiting around to get that fixed, because it will cost two or three days. Let's get some toy balloons and put one on each engine. When we fire the engines, the helium will blow up the balloons and we will see if they are working — to hell with the sniffer."

I found Irv and asked him if we could go ahead and do the test with balloons or even with the surgical rubber gloves we wore when we worked on the spacecraft. He said, "Well OK, let's do it with the gloves." We waltzed over there and did it. We put rubber gloves on each engine and watched them inflate as we tested each engine — they looked like fat cow udders when they were fully inflated and made our beautiful little spacecraft look very silly — but who cared, it worked and we had a blast (pardon the pun) doing the engine tests.

First we were going to fire all six engines with zero time delay in all the firing modes. I fired engine A1 for one second and it worked perfectly — there was a bang as the engine valve slammed open for one second and the glove inflated. Then I fired A2 for just half of a second, but the A2 engine glove hardly blew up at all, so I gave it a second blast that hardly had any effect, except for the bang! I thought, *well, OK, that's strange*, and I decided to try engine A3 and nothing happened at all, except the bang! I thought, *oh no,* and tried again and nothing happened. Then Irv asked Gary, "Did you open the PIV?" Gary had not opened the PIV (the Propellant Isolation Valve), so the helium that blew up the A1 engine glove was just the little bit that was in the fuel lines between the PIV and the engines and it ran out after the first couple of burps. I sent the command to open the PIV and then everything went just beautifully. Every firing mode worked perfectly.

Ecstatic, we broke for lunch, after which we wanted to test the engines when they were fired by a pulse from the Sun sensor. In order to simulate the Sun as it flashed through the slit of the Sun sensor once every 5 seconds as the spacecraft rotated in space, Dan had brought his flash camera from home, rather than having a $25,000 solar simulator purchased (similarly, when testing the IR Earth/Moon limb crossing sensor, Dan brought his wife's steam iron from home to provide an inexpensive infrared source)! That was great, but we first had to learn how to use the "home made" Sun simulator. The Sun sensor didn't like the broad source of light and would only work after Dan put a narrow slit over the camera flasher. It took Dan quite some time to figure that out and to get it so it would really work.

When Dan finally got to the point where he could trigger the Sun sensor every time, we ran the pulse mode on each engine — just one main pulse plus the half revolution (rev) pulse and it worked perfectly.

We took the rubber gloves off the engines, cleaned them with alcohol and then we wanted to blow them out, so I sent each one a 3-second pulse. Man, you could hear the engines hissing like crazy. The sniffer and even my rubber glove trick were wastes of time. We could have done the functional test just by having someone sit next to each engine and just listen to it burp — it would have been that easy. As usual, the engineers had made a mountain out of a molehill and we could have done the whole engine functional test the day before! Dummies!

Wednesday, March 26, 1997

I met with Steve Durst and Dan Green; Dan was one of the people pushing for generating solar power in space and microwaving it down to Earth. Dan was a real sharp guy and I had an interesting discussion with him and then I showed him the spacecraft.

Frank Martin came by with a guy from SIRTF (the Space Infra-Red Telescope Facility) that Lockheed was working on and Frank wanted me to show him Lunar Prospector, so I did. Frank bragged about everything!

Thursday, March 27, 1997

I spent part of the morning, between 10:00 to 11:30, with Scott, David Morrison, and some people from Astrobiology talking about the somewhat stretched connection between Astrobiology and Lunar Prospector. Basically, it boiled down to the Cosmochemistry at the very beginning of the formation of the solar system and resources for human habitation at the other end of the spectrum. It was a very interesting and delightful session.

Woody and I went over to the spacecraft at 1:00 PM to measure the structure current. We were getting one or two milliamps of current when everything was turned on. That corresponded pretty closely to what I was reading on my OASIS monitor, so that was OK.

We were still fussing with the C&DH engineering unit. We had to keep using that unit until the flight unit finally came, but the time we spent correcting it was just wasted time. However, Alex and Gerry didn't want to plug in the flight C&DH until they did some testing and comparisons of the both units, because they were afraid the flight unit might blow up! Other than that, we had a functioning spacecraft and we were getting ready for the first of two boom deployment tests that was scheduled for the following Monday.

Because the booms were very flimsy, they could not be deployed in Earth's gravity unless properly supported. The engineers had built a large test rig with essentially frictionless bearings that would allow the booms to uncoil and deploy. Given that the three booms were each 2.5 m long, the whole rig was quite large.

Our first task was to get the spacecraft moved over to the test rig, but the crane operator wasn't there, so we couldn't get that done! The guys were going to try to get everything set up the next day.

Henshaw, Dougherty, and I went over to Scott's office for a meeting. As I expected, Henshaw talked about Scott being Lockheed's customer and totally ignored my being the real customer. The topic was that Henshaw and Dougherty were going up to Denver the following Monday to talk about the launch vehicle. Of course, I was excluded — that was Lockheed business and none of mine!

Henshaw was going to go tell the LLV guys they had better get their damned rocket ready because he (Henshaw) was getting his butt chewed out by his customer (Scott, not me, Lockheed and Henshaw paid no heed to what I said anymore) — though that was not really true, Henshaw wanted LLV to think it was. He asked Scott if it was OK and Scott said, "Sure, tell them that."

I was really getting sick and tired of Lockheed ignoring my presence. Dougherty, of course, used every viewgraph I made (as well as those everyone else made) and ran up to Henshaw pretending he understood what was going on. Dougherty understood just enough to make Henshaw think he knew something, which made me wonder about Henshaw's brainpower — or lack thereof. Similarly, Scott was acting more and more like he was the big cheese. I was really getting fed up with those self-important SOBs, who were always looking out for themselves and not the mission's best interests.

Finally, the ground support equipment computer for the spectrometers blew its drives and they had to be replaced. I expected to have it back from Southwest the next day.

Friday, March 28, 1997

We spent the whole day getting Lunar Prospector in its boom deployment test rig, so we could do the test Monday — it was going to be fun!

Monday, March 31, 1997: Boom Deployment Day

I got to work really early, as did the Able engineers. Dave Curtis got there about 9:00 AM, since the MAG/ER was to play an important role in the test. First, because we had to pop the little MAG extension boom and second because Dave would monitor the deployment of the boom (from our consoles, in a glass walled, test operation room that looked down into the highbay, from which we could see the booms deploy) as the Earth's magnetic field appeared to rotate four times as the boom rotated four times during the deployment.

Dave and I did a test opening of the ER dust cover and it popped beautifully, just like it was as supposed to and then Dave reset it.

We waited and waited for Paul Turin, who had to be there for the MAG extension boom deployment. We waited an hour after he should have been there, while Dave kept saying, "I told his wife and I told him eight times to be here on time." Dave started trying to call him on his pager.

Finally, it was almost 11:00 AM and I decided I would call Paul's office. Paul answered with, "Hi, what are you doing?"

I said, "You are supposed to be down here for the boom test."

He said, " Oh, my God, I forgot, with the new baby and everything, I just forgot."

I said, "Get down here as soon as you can," which would be in about an hour.

Sylvia had called and left a message, so I called her before I went back to the highbay. Remember, we had just gotten the draft of the letter from Headquarters given us the green light for the September 24 launch. Well, Sam Venneri had decided that since, once in a while during testing, the LLV1 was having a slight problem with a slight leak of the hydraulic fluid from the engine bell of the Castor 120, the Lewis launch was going to be delayed — up to six months — until the leak was fixed! The dumb part of that was the leak only occurred when the engine bell was under tension, i.e., after the engine had stopped firing and hence, during the coast phase before the separation and firing of the Orbus second stage of the LLV1 — i.e., when there was no danger to the launch from the slight leak! It was stupid for Sam to delay the launch and that, of course, threw Lunar Prospector into turmoil, because we could not launch until they had a successful Lewis launch!

Thus, though the ink was not even dry on the letter saying we could launch in September, NASA was getting ready to reverse itself again! And one wonders why NASA is a failing agency! Well, that was not yet official, so we were just going to charge ahead.

After that, I went over to the highbay and told the guys I had found Paul.

While we were waiting for Paul, the twenty or so of us who were involved with the boom deployment test went to lunch.

When we were finished with lunch, Kim just stood around, getting into conversations with various people. I said to him, "We're ready, let's go." Instead of moving his butt, Kim just stood there and talked to somebody else about some other program for twenty minutes, while everybody else was just standing around wasting time and money. I finally dragged him out of the cafeteria and then, as we went into Building 150, someone else said something to him and he again stopped, stood there and talked for ten minutes, while the rest of us went to the highbay and got ready for the test. Kim just has no comprehension of what the priorities are and is totally unable to focus on the job at hand. If I had had the authority, I would have fired him on the spot. While Kim is very good at what he does when he finally gets going, he is useless most of the time and is totally inconsiderate of all the people around him. He really ticked me off.

Finally, we got everybody, including Paul who had arrived and was very embarrassed, assembled at about 12:30 PM and got ready for the test. I was downstairs on the highbay floor when we started. We sent the command to release the MAG extension boom and there was a soft little "pop" as the little pyros blew. As expected, since the MAG extension boom leaned back on the spacecraft when the latter was setting on its base on Earth, the MAG extension boom was just pushed outwards a few centimeters by a little spring when the pyros blew, but it did not flop down into its extended configuration. In space, it would have 2½ g's of centrifugal force that would whip it outwards into its fully deployed configuration. The first part, the MAG extension boom deployment, of the boom release test went exactly as expected. Also, when we popped the MAG extension boom, Dave could see from the magnetic data that the magnetic field shifted its apparent orientation as the little boom changed its orientation by about 10°. We could detect even the slightest bit of movement of the booms via the magnetic data, and though we had expected it, it was great to see it really happening. Paul gently extended the MAG extension boom into its fully deployed configuration and then we got ready to start the test of the main booms.

The first thing we had to do was to deploy the boom about 10 cm using the reset motor (that motor was generally used to re-stow the booms after they had been deployed) so we could get some temporary electric insulation off the MAG/ER boom that would not be there during flight.

After we got that done, they re-stowed the booms and tried to reset the paraffin actuator. The resetting procedure was done by turning on the actuator heater for two to three minutes to re-melt the paraffin and then by pulling out the plunger and resetting it. Well, they couldn't get it properly reset. We had to try it again. By then, I was up in the control room watching the monitors and I saw a very slight temperature increase in the viscous damper temperature that was due to the heat generated by the heater of the paraffin actuator and there was a clear increase in the load current and the bus voltage dropped a little when the paraffin actuator heater was on. All that meant I would have three ways of knowing if the paraffin actuator was heating up properly after I sent the command to start the boom release sequence when we were in space — and that made me feel really happy.

Nevertheless, when we tried to reset the paraffin actuator again, it still didn't work and by that time it was about 4:00 PM and we had been at it for quite some time. Finally the engineers figured out what was wrong. When they attached the re-stow motor to the boom release mechanism, the motor shaft had to be exactly in the correct position or it would not work. However, during the time it took to command the heater on and for the paraffin to heat up, the motor shaft would move a little bit and hence be off center, so they could not reset the paraffin actuator. By the time they got the paraffin actuator properly reset, it was about 7:00 PM!

Finally we were ready to go. By that time, even though it was well after normal working hours, Frank Martin and a number of other Lockheed people were over there to watch the test. However, the only people on the floor were the Able engineers and Steve; everyone else was up in the control room with me.

At about 8:00 PM, I sent the command to start heating the paraffin actuator. Steve had calculated, based on the viscous damper's temperature and the bus voltage, that the actuator should pop in about 80 seconds. I immediately saw the increase in the load current and the drop in the bus voltage and slowly the viscous damper's temperature began to rise. At 87 seconds the actuator popped and the booms started to deploy — it was absolutely beautiful. The booms moved out quite smoothly, though the little bit of friction in the support rig did cause them to jerk once in a while, especially the MAG/ER boom, since the MAG extension boom stuck out another 1.2 m and put an extra load on that arm of the support rig. The booms were fully deployed after about 15 minutes. The deployment was very slow, but absolutely synchronized and all three booms locked into their fully deployed configuration at exactly the same time. It was a picture perfect deployment.

Steve and the Able engineers began to inspect the booms and found that one of the longerons on the NS/APS boom had broken about 3 centimeters back from the tip plate! That hadn't hindered the deployment and wouldn't have endangered the mission had that been a post-launch deployment, but we did not like it and the question was, "Why did it break?" It was an annoying thing to have happened during such a perfect deployment test. Also, I was concerned because that was the second time a longeron had broken and I did not want any more such breaks.

The silver lining to the breaking of the NS/APS longeron was that the NS/APS boom had to be taken off anyway, because we had to replace the high voltage cable that had failed. If a longeron had to break, at least it did so on the right boom. However, it was too bad the longeron (one of three on each boom) that broke wasn't on the same one with the failed high voltage cable, because the Able engineers had to unlace and re-lace both bundles on both longerons.

As we were down on the floor inspecting the booms, Lee was being her usual Gestapo self, trying to keep everyone away from the spacecraft. She tried to chase me away and I told her, "I'm not leaving. This is my spacecraft and I have things I have to tend to and things I have to see to make sure I understand how to fly this spacecraft." She backed off, but the woman is really bizarre and like Marcie, I could have easily lived without having her on the project.

I didn't get out of work until 9:00 PM, so it was a very long day, but a very good day. Then I picked up Rebecca, who had been in St. Louis visiting her daughter and grandkids, at the San Jose airport and that made it an even longer day.

Tuesday, April 1, 1997: A Wrench into the Monkey Works

While I was busy with the boom test, Dougherty and Henshaw had gone to Denver (without me, of course) to meet with LLV. Dougherty told me that as a result of the meeting, we would take precedence over CRSS! If necessary, CRSS would even be delayed to allow us to launch in November or December.

Lockheed was getting ticked at NASA about all the delays in the Lewis launch and Larry Price was just moving ahead towards a May launch of the LLV1 with Lewis. Dougherty thought that if NASA didn't want Lewis to be the payload, then Lockheed was just going to launch the thing with a brick on it. Everybody in Denver thought all the delays were just NASA's way of blackmailing Lockheed into flying a demonstration flight before they flew a NASA mission on an LLV1. I thought that was probably true.

Regardless, Lockheed's position was finally that we were going to launch Lunar Prospector in September, October, or November; CRSS was not going to interfere with us and Headquarters could go to hell — a sentiment I agreed with fully. That was basically what Brashears and others at his level were going to tell NASA. If it didn't work, then they were going to send Tellep to Headquarters to get the message across. Lockheed was finally getting ticked off because NASA had a strangle hold on them about the LLVs — it was about time.

I told Dougherty about the successful boom deployment (from the standpoint of the development of the spacecraft, I served the project much better by being involved with the boom deployment test rather than my being up in Denver arguing with the LLV crew). I said I was totally satisfied with the boom deployment test and it had shown me I could get my booms deployed after launch even if one of them had a broken longeron. I was just not worried about the booms anymore — they would be OK. Besides the technical details, I told Dougherty just how beautiful the test was — it was just gorgeous.

We had a Ground Segment meeting. I told everybody what was going on with the spacecraft, the launch vehicle, the September 24 primary launch date, and the backup dates and that I had decided how I wanted Mission Ops done in case something happened to me. Because we just didn't have the personnel for two complete primary and secondary Command Teams and because I didn't have enough people who knew the spacecraft and mission (meaning Marcie), I was not going to have two parallel Uplink Command Teams, rather I was going to use a waterfall scheme. Dan would be my replacement if I was not there and we would get a replacement to back him up. That was all we really needed. Dan knew the spacecraft and since Lunar Prospector was a spin-stabilized spacecraft, flying it was mainly a question of dynamics and Dan is one of the best dynamists in the business. Marcie didn't react to my decision and I didn't care whether she liked it or not. I had the structure of the Operations Teams I knew would work — without Marcie.

Despite my general dislike for Marcie and her dumb, NASA ways of doing everything, she had been working on various questions that were raised during the Test Readiness Review and had come up with some good ideas. One of the questions was, "What are you going to do if a big earthquake strikes California and wipes you out?" Her series of solutions were: If Ames were wiped out, we would go to JPL and run the mission from there. If Ames and JPL were both wiped out, we would go down to the Goldstone tracking station and command the spacecraft from there. In both cases, if the earthquake occurred days or at least many hours before launch, we would fly down to JPL or Goldstone. If it occurred a few minutes before launch, then I would call the personnel down at JPL or at Goldstone and tell them which commands to send to the spacecraft and when to send them. Thanks to Marcie, we had ways of handling all emergency situations.

I spoke to Scott briefly about the Sam Venneri mess and Scott was saying something about our having had everything straightened out about our launch policy, when he said, "and then Sam *threw a wrench into the monkey works*," rather than, "a monkey wrench into the works." Having realized his error, he thought about what he had said for a few seconds and added emphatically, "Boy, that is really accurate," and I could not have agreed with Scott more — *NASA really is a monkey works*!

Wednesday, April 2, 1997

I had a telecon with Able about the NS/APS boom; they were going to fix it and try to figure out why it had broken.

The flight C&DH arrived, I hoped we would install it on the spacecraft during the next couple of days.

Thursday, April 3, 1997

Wayne Stevens visited and I showed him the spacecraft and Mission Ops and we talked about LRI and the future. Since I had fired Tom, I asked Wayne to join our little

LRI staff as the Chief Financial Officer (in addition to being an engineer, Wayne has an MBA from the University of Chicago) and to become a member — and the Vice President — of the Board. Wayne was very happy to do so.

Al Tilley, Dan, and I very accurately measured the cgs and masses of the instruments so we could calculate the ballasting and balancing of the booms.

We all took a look at the flight C&DH, but all in all, Thursday was a quiet day.

Friday, April 4, 1997

The big shootout about the launch vehicles between Lockheed upper management and Headquarters occurred and, of course, we won — as I thought we would. Lockheed had finally gotten on its high horse and said, "Damn it, get out of our way and let us do our job," so Lewis was going to launch on May 10.

Dan and I talked to Bill Jacobsen about getting the computer simulation model of the spacecraft running and getting somebody to help with that.

Dan, Al Tilley, Steve, and I worked on the calculations for balancing the booms; we were going to do the boom ballasting early the following week.

Alex, Gerry, Kim, and Tim tested the C&DH engineering unit in preparation for putting the flight unit on the spacecraft.

The spectrometer ground computer was still half dead, so Tom was going to again send it back to Southwest.

Though there were a lot of little things we all had to do, it was clear we were over the hump with the spacecraft — it was just a matter of time before it was ready to be launched. We still had the critical functional, thermal-vac, and acoustic tests to do, but one could feel that the spacecraft was ready to go and do its job.

Monday, April 7, 1997

Everyone was getting ready for the final functional test we had hoped to start in the afternoon, but, as usual, it didn't.

Dan, Al, Steve, and I were almost finished with the boom balancing work. All we needed was a little bit of information on the masses of the thermal blankets of the instruments and we would be done and ready to do the ballasting.

Dan and I had been working on the computer model of the spacecraft, so we could start Mission Ops training.

Paul Turin and a lady from Mario's group at GSFC put all the thermal blankets on the MAG/ER, weighed it, and found its cg, the same way that we had done — by hanging it by a string.

I gave the first of four seminars at Stanford.

Tuesday, April 8, 1997

Since Paul Turin had finished the blanketing of the MAG/ER and since we had finally gotten the mass and cg data for the GRS and NS/APS thermal blankets from Jim Schirle, we calculated the ballasting of the booms. I had checked all the data several times and compared my results with Dan Swanson's. We were getting the same answers, but Al Tilley had his calculations all screwed up. I was a little bit concerned because he had really fouled them up, so I wondered what else he had fouled up in the mass property calculations of the spacecraft. In any case, the ballasting calculations were finalized.

I had an "Ask the Scientist" computer video Q&A session with Rice University at 10:00 AM. It was a bust because the students asked virtually no questions. When they did, it was about how to be an astronaut or what education I had had. There was really nothing of any substance. I was quite disappointed.

The flight C&DH was finally mounted on the spacecraft and we were going to get started on the baseline functional. But when I arrived at the highbay at 3:00 PM, they still had not gotten started. Poor Gary was getting frustrated. It was the first functional and it took 3½ hours to check everything out, so I decided not to waste my time and left.

Rather than sending the hardware for the ground support computer for the spectrometers back to Southwest, an engineer came from there and fixed it. It was all screwed up, because it had gotten badly knocked around during shipment!

We had a meeting about the launch, because the TLI point and its velocity data were all screwed up. Ken Galal did not understand that a memo concerning those issues Denver had sent to Range Safety at the Cape was just an attempt to get Range Safety off our back — Ken had taken the memo seriously. Ken just had no understanding of what was relevant and irrelevant. Nevertheless, we got everything straightened out.

One error Denver was squawking about concerned the launch azimuth, but they had input the wrong numbers into their calculation. Dave had given them the correct information and when they finally put the right numbers in, the answer came out right.

Then there was a discrepancy because LLV thought we wanted the injection point to be at an altitude of 90 nautical miles and we wanted it at 100 nautical miles (pardon the non-metric units, but the Cape still uses nautical miles). That misunderstanding came about because the calculated orbit altitude right after separation from the LLV2's third stage would be 90 nautical miles altitude, but by the time the injection point was reached, the spacecraft's altitude would have risen to 100 nautical miles.

Thursday, April 10, 1997: The NS/APS Boom

Rebecca and I went to the State University at Sacramento, where I was to give a talk to the Physics Honor Society. The audience of about thirty people was very interested in the mission. Then we had dinner with the Physics Honor Society. Rebecca and I enjoyed the entire event.

While I was gone, Able delivered the repaired and rewired NS/APS boom. They had shake-tested it and it was OK. Then it was put on the spacecraft.

Also, the Able engineers thought they knew why the longeron on the NS/APS boom had broken. Frank and the wiring technicians had heat shrunk the covering of some of the wiring that was right above a hole in the tip plate, exactly where the longeron broke. In order to see if the heating was the cause, the Able engineers took a hot gun and heated a longeron for about 20 seconds — it became brittle and just snapped! The boom material just cannot take heat. We understood the probable cause of the longeron break.

Friday, April 11, 1997: Beginning the Functional Testing

When I went over to the spacecraft in the morning, Dave Curtis and Paul Turin were there getting ready to put the MAG/ER on its boom permanently. Unfortunately, the tip plate ballast plates for the MAG/ER and the NS/APS booms weren't there because Ramon had asked one of the technicians to pick them up from the shop and the technician forgot to do so (sound familiar?). When I found that out, we went to the shop and got them ourselves. Then Dave, Paul, and I mounted the MAG/ER on its boom, a procedure that took a while.

Finally, we were ready to start the functional testing and Lunar Prospector just turned on beautifully, but for some strange reason, we couldn't get the spacecraft data to the MAG/ER ground support equipment. Alex Kochergin poked around and poked around until, all of the sudden, Dave started getting data. There must have been a loose connector in the ground support equipment, a loose plug or a loose something. But then Dave found that the MAG/ER wasn't syncing up with the C&DH — they were out of sync by one bit. When we had had the engineering C&DH on the spacecraft and the MAG/ER was not syncing up, it was because they were off by one bit. Dave had adjusted the MAG/ER software to take care of the one-bit shift in the engineering unit. However, we soon found that the flight C&DH had a two-bit shift and that was why the MAG/ER would not sync up. Dave did a quick software fix and then the MAG/ER synced up perfectly.

However, because of the two-bit shift, I couldn't get OASIS to sync up and that required a software fix to OASIS that Pete Carley, our Palo Alto software engineer, would have to do.

Also, the flight C&DH could not sync up with SES. It seemed they were off by two whole bytes — the last two bytes in the frame. Ron Black thought he could solve the problem with a software patch for the SES that shifted the entire frame by two bytes. They were writing the patch and we hoped we would get it Monday. Then maybe the SES and the spectrometers would work; we were hopeful about that.

Since the MAG/ER data were coming in on Dave's ground support equipment, we ran through all the test procedures for the MAG/ER and they checked out perfectly. We were finally well into the final functional test.

I called Bill because I needed Danny Everett to come to Sunnyvale to do the final mounting of the NS/APS. Unfortunately, Bill was really sick. He had been hit by a car while riding his bicycle to work and had a number of stitches. The doctors decided he needed to have shots for tetanus, Hepatitis B, and pneumonia. He gave Bill all that and it made him sicker than a dog, poor guy. But Bill said he would send Danny out to mount the NS/APS and to put the software patch in the SES. Hopefully, the SES would then sync up with the C&DH and we could then run the functional test of the spectrometers on Monday. I was sure I could run through a functional test of the spectrometers without any difficulty. If so, then we would have all the instruments done.

We then tested the Sun sensor and the battery and they both worked fine. We determined that the battery was charging and discharging properly. After that, we fully charged the battery and I ran the spacecraft from the battery to map out the battery discharge curve. The discharge followed the form Woody told me to expect, so I was beginning to understand how my spacecraft would behave in space.

Jim Schirle told me his boss said, "Since Iridium is done and since Lockheed doesn't care about Lunar Prospector, you are supposed to work on something else."

Jim said, "Well that's silly, we are going into thermal-vac in just a week."

His boss said, "I don't care," and Jim argued with him about it. The guy then said, "OK, if you're that close to thermal-vac, you can do it, but you should really try to find somebody else to do it for you." I immediately bitched to Dougherty about that, even though I knew it didn't do any good. Lockheed sucks!

Slowly but surely we were beginning to build up momentum. Everything was coming together beautifully. It was getting to be a lot of fun and very exciting.

Monday, April 14, 1997: First Look at the Solar Panels

Dougherty and I went over to the Solar Array Fabrication Facilities and saw the solar panels. One was done, one was almost done, and one was partly done and they were beautiful.

Danny had arrived from Los Alamos and Tom and he mounted the NS/APS on their boom. However, Tom didn't check to see if the spacecraft was powered up when he started. It was powered on and that ticked off Gary Schlueter and me mightily.

We were still waiting for the computer patch that none of my engineers thought was going to solve the C&DH/SES problem. According to Ron Black, every time we turn the SES on and off, the patch would have to be patched in. I was not going to fool around with that sort of BS during the mission, so we would just build a command file that did that automatically along with the SES turn-on command.

I gave my second seminar at Stanford late in the afternoon.

Tuesday, April 15, 1997

I talked to Scott about my finally getting into LRI. He had some reservations, but he knew he couldn't stop me, so he was going to make sure Headquarters was happy about my doing so.

We did the thruster engine functional test and they all worked perfectly. We used the sniffer as Kim wanted, but that was a waste of time. We could have done it better without the sniffer.

We still didn't have the patch for the SES and we still had quite a lot of testing to do. There were still some problems, besides those with the SES, e.g., the C&DH was not talking to the Earth/Moon limb-crossing sensor properly. But we were coming along with the functional testing.

Pete Carley again didn't come down when we needed him. Dougherty had to call Palo Alto because Pete had been told he couldn't work on Lunar Prospector except during overtime. What a bunch of BS — where was all the help the crappy company promised me at the very beginning of the effort. Lockheed management consists of nothing but a bunch of backstabbing liars.

Wednesday, April 16, 1997: The Spectrometers are OK

Though we still did not have the software patch, we wanted to check something in the SES unit and when we did, the damned thing turned on properly! We tested the spectrometers and they were fine.

There were still some problems with the ground support equipment. We had some erroneous data written over the real data and we didn't know why, but the guys would figure that out.

Thursday, April 17, 1997: Starting the Full Functional Test

When I got in early in the morning, we tested the spectrometers and found a way of getting them to come on and sync up every time — so to hell with the patch. We tested all three spectrometers. Everything was perfect. We still had some problems with some of the displays, because the computer was pulling up old data and displaying it when it shouldn't have, but that was no big problem. And we still didn't have the engineering data on the spectrometer monitors, but that would be easily taken care of.

Up to that point, we had been doing functional testing on each of the subsystems and the instruments, one at a time. We were done with that and we were ready to do the full functional test, turning on each system in sequence and leaving them on until everything was working, as it would be in space. At about 3:00 PM, we started doing the full functional testing and everything worked perfectly! *We had a fully functional spacecraft — what a milestone!*

Woody came over and we did a test of the battery for a full day/night — charge/discharge cycle. Except for the solar panels that would be installed after thermal-vac testing, we had a spacecraft that was ready to fly!

Dougherty said Lockheed had legal or moral reservations about my leaving the company and going to LRI (they did not want me there, but they also did not want me to leave), so I would have to talk to the Lockheed lawyers. I was sure Lockheed was going to try to screw everything up.

Friday, April 18, 1997: Finishing Up the Functional Testing

We tested the SES a couple of times to see if it would sync up every time and it did. It was clear that the sync problem between the SES and the C&DH did not exist in the spacecraft; it was a ground software problem! We finished up the baseline functional tests. There was still one problem with the communications in that we could not command using the antenna, but that was fairly well understood and was certainly another ground support problem. There was also one problem with the Earth/Moon limb-crossing sensor, but that was also understood.

Anyway, we would be able to go into thermal-vac with what we had. We were going to make two quick tests on some of the subsystems just before we close the door of the thermal-vac chamber to be sure we could proceed. We were done with the functional tests and getting ready to move the spacecraft over to the thermal-vac test facilities.

Gary Schlueter was mad, annoyed, and overworked — he was at the spacecraft test console all the time — and he hated working with Kim (who could blame him). He was just totally grumpy and you couldn't even talk to him anymore. I like and respect Gary very much, he is reliable and takes his responsibilities very seriously and, like everyone else at Lockheed, he is treated like dirt. Lockheed has to be one of the worst companies in the world to work for — I feel sorry for every good engineer who works there.

I called up John Palochak, the Lockheed lawyer I had dealt with before, and made an appointment to see him.

We had our first annual meeting of the LRI Board with George French, Wayne Stevens, Rebecca, and me. It was a good meeting. The biggest problems were getting into LRI and getting a contract from Lockheed to do my work from LRI. Both Lockheed and Ames were fussing about my leaving Lockheed, but I was going to force it through one way or another. I was sick of both NASA and Lockheed and the way they were trying to stop me from going to LRI and hence, trying to keep me chained to Lockheed where they thought that they could control me for their benefit — screw them.

Chapter 3-32
Thermal-Vac Testing —
The Big One

Saturday, April 19, 1997: The Move to the Thermal-Vac Chamber

Thermal-vac — the big one, the one where we put the spacecraft into the simulated space environment to see if it would work in a vacuum and under the intense heat of the Sun and in the equally intense cold of the Moon's shadow during the night time passes. Though the static and shake tests showed the spacecraft and the instruments could survive the violence of the launch, the thermal-vac test would show if they would work in the extreme environments where they would spend all of their operational lives after launch.

If we got through thermal-vac, we essentially had it made and I would know if my concept that a simple, inexpensive spacecraft could do the job or if NASA and the aerospace companies were right — you need big, expensive spacecraft managed by a huge bureaucracy to explore space.

Also, since we were not testing an engineering model, but the flight hardware, if we had major problems during thermal-vac or worse, if we broke Lunar Prospector, we would be out of business. However, I had the greatest confidence that my little spacecraft would come through thermal-vac with flying colors as I drove up to Lockheed Saturday morning to help Tim, Kim, Gary, and some of the other engineers and technicians move it to the thermal-vac building.

When I got to the highbay, it was neat to see the spacecraft. It was all wrapped in its thermal blankets and it looked kind of ugly without its solar panels. But it was a hell of a little spacecraft and, like the father of the ugly duckling, I loved my little ugly duckling.

Shortly after I got there, we started wrapping Lunar Prospector with big sheets of plastic to protect it while it was being transported the several blocks to the thermal-vac building. That took some time, because we had to make sure it was well protected, but finally we started to roll it, on its work stand, out of the highbay where it had spent its entire, but short existence as a live spacecraft.

As we rolled it out onto the loading dock, a huge flatbed truck pulled up. The driver got out, looked at Lunar Prospector and said jokingly to me, "You call that thing a satellite? You mean we have to put that little thing on my truck to haul it over to thermal-vac? This is a joke, right?"

I answered, "It may be little, but it's going to the Moon." He laughed and asked me if I wanted to ride with him in his truck and I said, "Sure," and hopped in as soon as Lunar Prospector was loaded and secured.

We drove the short distance to the thermal-vac building, unloaded the spacecraft, and rolled it into the facility, which is awe inspiring. The chamber is 20 m in diameter and 26 m long — it was build for really big military satellites, not for little Lunar Prospector and that drew some more good-hearted comments from the thermal-vac crew when they saw my little spacecraft. They expressed their great concern that it was so small we would lose it in the chamber and never find it again! Well, we would see who had the last laugh.

With Lunar Prospector safely in front of the chamber, the engineers and technicians began to unwrap it in preparation for the final tests we would perform before putting it in the chamber on Tuesday.

Finally, the engineers had laid out a series of thermal-vac tests, two hot runs and two cold runs that would take 10 days. Since spacecraft never, ever get through thermal-vac testing without problems and have to be removed from the chamber and fixed once, and frequently twice, we had reserved the chamber for three weeks in the hopes that would be enough time to find and fix all the expected problems.

With that in mind, I left the engineers to do their job of getting Lunar Prospector ready to go into the chamber and drove back down to Gilroy to spend what was left of the weekend with Rebecca.

Monday, April 21, 1997

Bill came to Lockheed, but we never got to turn the spacecraft on in order to test the instruments. However, Bill looked at the data we had taken during the functional tests and said everything was absolutely perfect.

The engineers were busy getting everything ready, so we could command the spacecraft through the antenna, as well as through the umbilical cable as we had been doing. But, as usual, there were some problems with the ground support equipment, so getting ready to transmit via the antennas took most of the day. We didn't get to do the pre-door closure testing and we, of course, didn't get into the chamber.

I talked to John Palochak, about my leaving Lockheed and got that straightened out. We were going to get Dougherty and Maryann Williams over there for a meeting with John and me to discuss how to write the contract between Lockheed and LRI. I suspected I had a good shot at getting into LRI in three or four weeks. I was sure going to try.

I gave my third seminar at Stanford.

Tuesday, April 22, 1997

We got Lunar Prospector in the chamber, but we didn't get the thermal-vac chamber door closed. There was still a lot of work to be done. The engineers were very busy getting everything ready, putting on the dummy solar panels, setting up the solar heat simulators, and on and on.

I had the meeting at Ames with Marcie and the Mission Ops staff, but everyone was focused on the thermal-vac testing, so the meeting was kind of blah.

Wednesday, April 23, 1997: Important Lessons

We had had what appeared to be a serious problem late the previous night. The chamber was very cold, so was the spacecraft. When Gary turned the spacecraft on for the first time, he got a large load current spike that meant that there was a serious overload — possibly a short — and the ground equipment automatically shut the spacecraft down as the current spike immediately reached the 5.2 amp protection limit.

Gary told me that as soon as I got to work in the morning. Of course, Kim was not around for quite some time, instead of getting his butt in there. It turned out the reason for the current spike was that, because the spacecraft was so cold, every heater immediately went on and hence the total current was way above what we ever expected to see and hence, we had set the overload current trigger at a relatively low value of 5.2 amps. There was no short and no problem with the spacecraft at all — it did just what it was supposed to do, i.e., it tried to get warm. We changed the overload trigger and turned Lunar Prospector back on and the load current jumped up to 10 amps. To be certain that we were just seeing a lot of heater power usage, we turned off the secondary heaters and we saw the current drop 0.6 amps and then we turned off the primary heaters and the current dropped all the way down to where it was supposed to be. That confirmed our analysis, so we turned everything back on and let the heaters warm everything up and start to cycle.

I watched the pressure in the tanks rise as the tanks and the helium in them began to warm up. It was beautiful to see that in the data, even though I knew it had to be that way. I was really pleased because I was getting a better and better feeling about the engineering information I would have when I was flying my spacecraft.

I viewed the entire event as a good learning experience because if the spacecraft ever got very cold during the mission and all of the heaters went on, I would know exactly what to expect, i.e., a very high load current, and not be tricked into thinking I had an electric short in the spacecraft.

Despite being pleased that I had learned something that would help me fly Lunar Prospector, I was really frustrated with Kim because he was so damned slow — it takes him forever to understand anything; then it takes him forever to start doing anything about it; and then it takes him forever to do it. Any idiot could see from the data that when Gary turned the spacecraft on, the primary heaters turned on and the current went up and then it jumped up again when the secondary heater clicked on, but not Kim. As we were looking at the data, he was trying to calculate the current differences out to the third decimal place, when the data were only accurate to the first decimal place! The guy is an idiot!

After resolving that little event, it took the rest of the day before we were ready to run the final instruments checks. Dave came late in the afternoon. Then someone was there to take pictures of us in the chamber with the spacecraft. Finally, at about 5:00 PM, we got ready to test the instruments that we were supposed to have started testing at 7:00 AM or 10 hours earlier in the day!

We did a quick health check on the MAG/ER. It worked perfectly and then we popped the MAG extension boom. Then we started on the APS, but the electronic test pulser we used to test the APS wasn't working properly, so we couldn't test the APS properly. We checked the NS and the GRS and they were both OK. Finally, we tried putting a source of alpha particles next to the APS, which was very hard to do, and the APS seemed to be detecting alphas, so I thought it was also OK. However, I wanted to talk to Bill about the test pulser and the APS to be sure that everything was OK with it before we closed the big chamber door — then it would be too late if something were wrong with the APS.

It was a very good day. It was exciting when we were trying to figure out why we had the apparent current overload. Then it was fun running the spacecraft remotely while testing the instruments. Both activities were good training exercises for flying the spacecraft, because we were running it remotely, just like I would be doing when it was in space.

Thursday, April 24, 1997: Lockheed Starts its Dance Regarding LRI

Damned Kim, he did what he always does. First of all, it was kid's day at Lockheed and it seemed like there were 50 million kids around. Everybody said, "No work will get done today."

Well, Kim had worked most of the night with the spacecraft because, though we could command the spacecraft through the antenna, we could not command it through the umbilical, and I give him credit for that. Dave Curtis came down early, since we were going to finish the instrument checks starting at 9:00 AM and Kim said, "Yes, I'll be there," and then he just disappeared. After waiting until about 10:00 or 10:30, I got Gary and we got started turning the spacecraft on just as Kim got back. He had gone to get his kids and just left us standing there. Kim is just totally rude and doesn't take anybody or the work into consideration.

Despite Kim's asinine behavior, we finished the last tests of the instruments and the engineers thought they would be able to close the door during the afternoon. But knowing Kim and the rest of them, I could guarantee it was not going to be closed until the next day and I was right!

I had an interesting talk with Maryann Williamson, our nice contracts lady. She asked me if I had any objection to Dougherty, Bob Garner, and her meeting with Palochak about my leaving Lockheed and I answered, "No, that would be fine with me." She said the meeting was set for Monday and there was a big conflict of interest about my being in LRI. I asked, "What are you talking about?" The conflict, which I thought was smoke and mirrors, stemmed from the fact that all the work done at Lockheed was done under my direction according to the NASA/Lockheed contract. Thus, some people (and who that might be was a mystery to me) might say I directed Lockheed to set up my company. I said, "Don't make me laugh. Lockheed won't do anything I tell it anyway and it sure wouldn't help me set up my company — that's a joke."

She said, "No, this is going to have to go up to Henshaw."

I was surprised at that and said, "Look, you say this is a conflict. Well, the real conflict has been that ever since I've been in this company, the company has worked for me, yet it pays my wages, so I have been forced to do a lot of things because the company says what I wanted to do is against Lockheed's interest."

She said, "That's your perception."

I said, "No, Maryann, let me give you an example. I wanted to get off the LLV2 and I was told I could not get off it because it was against company policy." She had to concede that wasn't just my perception — that was reality.

The thing that was nice about our conversation was that Maryann was really on my side and was trying to help me by forewarning me about what Lockheed was up to. She said, "You better have lawyers to protect yourself against this company." Then she added, "They might try to force you to make concessions, like making you give up your control of the project."

I said, "I'm the Principal Investigator and that is the end of it. If this company doesn't want this, then I can always try to have NASA rewrite the contract. There are other ways of doing it."

It was clear that the whole thing was just smoke and mirrors. The company just didn't want to yield anything. They wanted me to be their puppet and they wanted to get all the credit for the mission.

I talked to Dougherty about some of those issues and, I'll say one thing for him, he thought Lockheed was being foolish. He said, "Just do it." He was on my side too and he was not going to make waves with Palochak.

Monday was going to be an interesting day.

Friday, April 25, 1997: We Close the Door and Get Started

First of all and to my great surprise after the previous day's conversation with Maryann, I got the OK from Lockheed and the lawyers to get into LRI! I just had to submit a budget and negotiate a fixed price contract. I thought Dougherty probably played the major role in getting Lockheed to back off and get everybody to calm down. If that were the case, then I owed him one (or maybe that made up for him being such an ass most of the time).

After that good news, the next good thing was we finally closed the thermal-vac chamber door and started pumping it down at 11:00 AM. There had been a problem with the connectors for the solar simulator, but that was quickly corrected, so Lunar Prospector was in the chamber and the vacuum pumps were pumping like crazy.

Given the size of the chamber, I was surprised that we would have a hard vacuum in less than eight hours and that we were going to start the tests at 7:00 PM. We would do an "aliveness test" to make sure that everything was OK and then start the chill-down of the entire chamber with liquid nitrogen the following day. We would be testing 24 hours a day, every day, and my 10-hour shift was from 6:00 AM to 4:00 PM. At last, we were beginning and it was very exciting.

I went home, got Rebecca and we went back to Lockheed at 7:00 PM and got back home at 12:30 AM. We did the spacecraft aliveness test and then Dave Curtis, Paul Travis (the second experienced Pioneer mission controller, who was going to be a senior controller along with Ric Campo), Ric, Gary, and I ran through the aliveness check of the science instruments. When we were finished, we were ready to go into the full thermal-vac test program, just as soon as it was cooled down and that process had already started. I could hardly wait to get back the next morning.

Saturday, April 26, 1997: Starting the Thermal-Vac Testing

I got up at 5:00 AM, after less than four hours of sleep, and went into work, excited as hell. The spacecraft had gotten down to –30° C and when Gary turned it on, just like the first time he turned it on when it was cold, the load current jumped up to 10 amps because every heater, primary and secondary, was on. As the spacecraft quickly warmed up, the heaters turned off and the load current quickly dropped down to its expected value. Each one of those events taught me what to look for and what to do when we had a problem in space.

The main thing I did was just to watch things very carefully all day as the spacecraft cooled down.

Jim and the other thermal engineers were doing the thermal balance checks. Everything was going very well, so well in fact that we decided to move up the second part of the first deep chill test and let Jim and his guys finish that part of the thermal balance testing — then we would do all the functional tests. I also wanted to do some training with my Mission Ops Team while the spacecraft was on its several hour cold-soak plateau.

When I went home, I was really tired. I had dinner and went to bed at 6:00 PM.

Sunday, April 27, 1997: The First Cold Soak Test

I went to work at 5:00 AM. We started doing the cold soak science functional tests. I did the spectrometers. Dave came in and we did the MAG/ER. All the science instruments worked perfectly at the cold temperature, although the APS was giving us some weird stuff. Bill would have to come to Sunnyvale to figure out what was wrong with the APS. Everything else was fine.

We started doing all the rest of the spacecraft functional tests. We did the engine heater tests and we found an error. I had asked Gerry and Alex to program the C&DH so that, after I turned on the engine heaters to pre-heat the engines I was going to use in a burn sequence (the pre-heating is necessary to prolong the life of the engines), the heater for each individual engine would turn off automatically when I fired that particular engine, but the rest of the heaters would stay on until I fired each of those engines.

Because it took Gary a long time to get everything set up after we had turned the engine heaters on, the engines got quite hot. Then I fired the first engine and the helium that was released flooded the chamber and it took quite a while to pump it out. As the pumping was underway, I noticed that all my engines were cooling, not just the one that I had fired! All the heaters had turned off when I fired the first engine in the sequence! Gerry and/or Alex had misunderstood my instructions when they designed that part of the C&DH command capability.

Had we not had the problem of letting out too much helium during the first "burn," I might not have noticed that all the engines heaters had turned off! Then I looked at the load current and saw that when I fired the engine, the load current dropped 1½ amps and that also told me all of the engine heaters had shut off, not just the one whose engine I had fired.

Jim Schirle found during his testing that some of the primary heaters were wired into the secondary heaters circuits and visa verse.

None of those things were serious or would hurt anything, but we would have to fix them.

After checking out the heater circuits, we continued testing the cold soaked engines by "firing" the helium and they worked perfectly.

Then we tested the communications subsystem.

After that, Dan came over and we tested the Sun sensor and Earth/Moon limb-crossing sensor.

Woody came over because we were having problems with the power, and we worked through some of that. It was kind of fun and, again, very instructive for learning how to fly the spacecraft — which we were doing in a certain sense.

We did all the testing; we checked every single thing and ran everything we possibly could run.

When we got done with the cold soak tests, we told the technicians to heat up the spacecraft, i.e., turn on the Sun simulator. Boy it was neat to see what happened as soon as they turned on those heaters. The APS, which was way down to −23° C, just 2° C above its lowest allowable temperature, immediately started heating up. The solar array went from −10 to +50° C in about ten minutes, just the way it was supposed to. It was really interesting to watch and I knew everything was going to be OK.

We had worked from 5:00 AM until 1:00 AM the next morning. It was a 20-hour day! I went home and slept about 3 hours and went back to work again.

Monday, April 28, 1997: The First Hot Soak Test

When I got in at 5:00 in the morning, the spacecraft was pretty hot. Dave Curtis came in fairly early. I went to Building 107 and found Kim and said, "Dave is here and

I would like to run his tests on the MAG/ER, so he can get out of here and not have to wait until 12:00 PM when the spacecraft has reached thermal equilibrium."

Kim said, "OK, fine."

Of course, he didn't come to the highbay and that ticked me off. About a half hour later, I went back and I said, "Kim, I'm going to run the MAG/ER test and I assume you're not coming over."

He said, "No, we're not running it because we have to wait until it's all in thermal equilibrium."

I said, "That's foolish. We can run the test without it being in full equilibrium," and he just blabbed his same statement. I said, "I'll call Jim Schirle and see if Jim has any objections to my running the test now."

I called Jim and he said, "It doesn't make any difference if the instruments are in equilibrium or not, go right ahead." After testing the MAG/ER with Dave, I tested the spectrometers and then I went to lunch.

After lunch, I saw Dougherty talking to Kim about the testing procedures, or procs as they are called. The procs are cookbook instructions that are written out step by step so the engineers can do the testing properly. While I agree that procs are necessary for complex spacecraft, following them religiously while testing a simple spacecraft like Lunar Prospector is a waste of time. Gary, who had to do all of the procs, felt the same way as I did. While, of course, Kim, who is incapable of an original thought, has to have his stupid procs, because that is the only way he can work.

I wanted to thank Dougherty for helping get Lockheed and Palochak off my back about LRI, so I stuck my head in his office and I said, "I assumed you were the one who calmed Palochak down. Thanks, I appreciate it."

He gave me a nice wave and said, "Well, we still have to get through the signatures. But as long as Palochak is happy, nobody is really going to object."

Finally, Kim came over to the thermal-vac facility and started testing using his damned procs. Being very tired of Kim's behavior and attitudes, I said, "I don't want to do the testing that way, it's a waste of time."

Kim said, "Oh, we have to do it this way because we have to follow procedures."

I said, "It takes you three times as long to do the tests if you follow the procs and I refuse to do it that way." We had a blow up and then we ran the tests my way — without the damned procs. I concluded again that Kim is a damned idiot.

We continued with the thruster tests, the same tests we had done under cold conditions, but under hot conditions.

During the entire time, since we had started testing on Saturday, I had been watching the temperature regulation on the GRS and the dead-band was $1\frac{1}{2}°$ C, which was great, but unfortunately, the GRS temperature was a little higher than we wanted — it was $-28°$ C and we had wanted $-30°$ C, but that was OK.

Also, there was some noise on one of the NS detectors at very low temperatures, but was not significant, and it went away when the NS temperature was in its normal operational range, so that was no big deal.

When I got home, I found out the State of California wouldn't accept our being a foreign corporation because of a formality, so Rebecca and I had to fool around with that.

Tuesday, April 29, 1997

Jim Schirle finished thermal balance testing for the hot soak, which took all day and most of the night.

Wednesday, April 30, 1997:
The First Training Session with the Spacecraft

Bill Feldman, Dave Curtis, and I had a training session on the spacecraft. We went through the entire initial, Day 0 instrument turn-on sequence in real-time and that took several hours. Then we did the Day 1 high voltage turn-on sequence for the GRS, NS, and ER and that took a few more hours. The training went quite well. However, it was hard to get Bill to settle down and pay attention, partly because Bill is Bill, and partly because he had trouble sitting around since his body still got stiff from his bicycle accident.

Dave found that the ER had a lot of noise on the sweep current at step voltages of 500 v and higher and he didn't know why. He assumed it was caused by a piece of dust in the ER. He had not seen the noise during the cold soak testing, so we thought maybe it occurred only when the ER was hot, but we couldn't be sure about that until we did the next cold soak runs.

Neither of my senior controllers, Ric and Paul, showed up for the training session and that ticked me off. Ric came late, thinking the session was scheduled at 1:00 PM. Since that was the time I had originally told him, I guessed I was at fault, since I had apparently not told him of the schedule change. But he brought Marcie along, so she could get her Lockheed badge picture taken, which he spent most of his time doing. I asked myself, if he didn't come to train, why did he bother to come at all?

We had gone completely through the Day 0 and Day 1 sequences and I wanted to do just the high voltage turn-on sequence of Day 1 again for two reasons. First, we didn't have the time to do both the Day 0 and Day 1 sequences again since Bill wanted to get home to Los Alamos and Dave Curtis couldn't stay there forever either. Second, we could do the Day 0 sequence anytime, because no high voltages were turned on during Day 0, and we couldn't turn on the ER high voltage to do the Day 1 sequence except in vacuum (however, we could turn on the GRS and NS high voltages without having them in a vacuum, as we did many times). Thus the only chance I had to do the complete high voltage turn-on sequence was right then, while the spacecraft was in the thermal-vac chamber. That went very well and Bill did a better job than he did during the first practice run. I learned a lot from the exercise, and afterwards I began to modify the Mission Profile based on what I had learned. When we got done, the technicians started the cool-down for the second cold soak test.

When I got home, Rebecca had figured out that we had sent the wrong form to California and that was why they rejected our request for LRI to become a foreign corporation. She had got everything ready and had sent it in. I was really proud of her for doing such a good job. I thought we would soon be in our company and I worked on the LRI budget for Lockheed whenever I had a chance.

Thursday, May 1, 1997: The Second Cold Soak Test

I got in at 5:00 AM to start the testing during the second cold soak, and I wanted to run a test on the engine heaters to determine how long it took them to heat up and how hot they got. They heated up to about 100° C and it took about 50 minutes, so then I knew what to expect in space and I could adjust the Mission Profile for the time it took the heaters to heat up the engines.

Dave Curtis came to test the ER and to find out what was causing the noise, but when we turned it on, there was no noise! However, the test was not only a low temperature test, it was also an under-voltage test with the bus voltage at 22 v, rather than the standard 31 v. The MAG/ER worked fine during the under-voltage test. However, we had changed three things since Dave saw the ER noise. First, we were not using the solar simulator, so the power supply was very constant. Second, we had dropped the temperature. And third, we had the low voltage. Dave said, "We have three variables, any one of which could have affected the noise." We raised the voltage back up to 31 v and the noise didn't come back, thus it had something to do with the higher temperature or the solar simulator.

In addition to Dave's noise problem, I noticed there were large over-current and under-current spikes on the SES 28 v line of the spectrometers. I thought the current spikes were correlated with the variations in the bus voltage, because the SES required a constant 10 watts. Since the wattage is equal to the voltage times the current, when the voltage changes, the current has to change in the opposite sense to compensate for the change in line voltage. When we did the under voltage test and the voltage was down to 22 v, the SES 28 v current went from 0.31 to 0.44 amps. Thus, I concluded that the SES 28 v spikes were caused as the power regulator rapidly switched the battery between charge (higher voltage) and discharge (lower voltage), as was the case when the spacecraft was on the solar simulator. I was just seeing the changes in the 28 v current that corresponded to the voltage changes and that was exactly what was happening — another mystery solved.

There was also some noise on the GRS, but the one pre-amp, i.e., the one that was closest to the very cold floor of the chamber, was at –55° C, which was well below its operational temperature of about –30° C. That probably caused the noise and hence, was of no concern. Everything we saw that was not quite right with the instruments was because we had been pushing them to extreme temperatures, well outside their normal operational temperature ranges.

We were going to run the ER at 500 v to see if the noise came back when we heated the spacecraft back up for the final hot soak test. Then we would also go on the solar simulator to see if the noise came back then.

Everything was really going well, so I went home early to rest a little.

Rebecca and I were getting everything ready for us to get into LRI — the sooner the better.

Friday, May 2, 1997: Complete Success

We did the final hot soak functional. The noise on the ER was there, but it was weird!

We were done — we were done with the thermal-vac testing! The spacecraft was going to come out of the chamber Saturday. We would then do a final functional test and then we would be completely done in the thermal-vac facility. Saturday was going to be a long day, but so what — we were done!

What had happened during the previous week *had never happened in the history of Lockheed* (or so I was told) and maybe not even in the entire history of the entire aerospace industry, for all I know. *A spacecraft had gone into a thermal-vac chamber, had passed all of the tests and was ready to come out of the chamber without having to go back in for a second set of tests after fixes had been made to it.* Remember, we had reserved the chamber for three weeks to allow time for two full 10-day test sequences. Well, we had not only needed to do *just one test sequence*, but we did it in just 7 days, not the planned 10 days! *Not only was Lunar Prospector the first Lockheed spacecraft that had to do only one thermal-vac run, it was also the first one to finish the testing AHEAD OF SCHEDULE!*

Everyone at Lockheed was amazed; first, we had been getting 100% fee awards every quarter (that had never happened before) and second, little Lunar Prospector had passed the thermal-vac testing on the first run and was coming out of the chamber ahead of schedule!

I was not only happy, but more importantly, *I had already proven my point to Lockheed, NASA, and the world that one could build a small, simple, inexpensive spacecraft using flight proven hardware with a small team of engineers led by someone who knew what he or she was doing and it would work. True, I had to fly the mission successfully to drive that point home, but we had just "flown" the spacecraft in the space environment — actually in the extremes of the space environment — and it had worked perfectly on the first try. No one had ever accomplished that before and I knew right then that if Lunar Prospector was successfully launched, I would be able to fly a completely successful mission and achieve all my programmatic and scientific goals. As far as I was concerned, we had just proven that "Faster, Better, Cheaper" and KISS really worked.*

Chapter 3-33
The Interlude between Thermal-Vac and Acoustic Testing

Saturday, May 3, 1997

We opened the chamber door and the spacecraft was in great shape. We covered it and got it out of the chamber. We were going to do the functional test on Monday.

Monday, May 5, 1997

I didn't feel too well (I was mainly exhausted from the intense work of the previous week or so) and went home early. While I was at work, we did a really brief functional test on the science instruments, but basically, everybody was just trying to recuperate from the thermal-vac testing. I wanted to stay home the next day, but I would have to go in to do one more functional test on the APS using the test pulser.

Tuesday, May 6, 1997

We tested the APS, but the pulser was still not working right. There seemed to be some noise on the APS. Bill was going to come out Saturday and we were going to try to figure out what was going on with it.

Wednesday, May 7, 1997

We had our post-thermal-vac test review of the spacecraft. Jim said the only heaters that were miswired, i.e., where the primary and secondary heaters were switched, were those on the engines. That made no real difference, so we were not going to do anything about it. The A2 engine backup heater was not working and that had to be fixed. As I had discovered, all the engine heaters shut off when I fired any engine, but we were not going to change the C&DH to fix that — that would require a hardware change, and since I could work around the problem during operations, we were just going to let it be. Strangely, the tank temperatures were somewhat different from each other, but Irv thought that was OK. Nevertheless, I was going to go through the calculations myself, since I didn't trust him. We had a concern about the power subsystem and there was a problem with the battery heater not cycling. Nevertheless, those things were very minor and easy to fix (or just leave some of them as they were). Other than those things, the spacecraft was fine. We still had the problems with the APS and ER noise that had to be taken care of.

Things were going well, but were slowing down a little bit after the thermal-vac effort and triumph.

Thursday, May 8, 1997

I met with my Mission Ops Team and Marcie did a sloppy job as usual. She thought she was going to run everything, e.g., she was going to watch the battery and set up commands. I had news for her, she wasn't!

Dougherty and I had a meeting with Scott and Sylvia in the afternoon and discussed various issues. Both of them were getting relaxed about my going to LRI.

I got some great suggestions from Wayne about the LRI budget after he had reviewed it. I was real pleased about that. He is a good guy and knows his business and was going to be a valuable asset to LRI.

We checked the APS test pulser and found it was OK, so something was wrong with the APS itself. Bill was coming to Sunnyvale the following Wednesday or Thursday to work on the APS.

The MAG/ER system we used for Lunar Prospector was a rebuild of the MAG/ER systems that flew on the ill-fated Mars Observer and then on Mars Global Surveyor. However, the original systems had two magnetometers, hence the MAG/ER electronics unit (DPU) had two sets of magnetometer electronics, which we called Side A and Side B. Since Lunar Prospector had just one magnetometer, we needed to use only one side, Side A, so we were going to use Side B as the backup to A. The thermal-vac testing showed that Side A had a drift in all of its engineering data, apparently because there was a drift in its reference voltage. Also, the noise Dave had found on the ER had to be filtered out better than it was. Dave was going to take care of both of those issues when he refurbished the MAG/ER for flight.

When I got home, Rebecca was ticked off because she had gotten the letter from California telling us the State had rejected our application again, because we didn't have the right information from Arizona where LRI was incorporated. She had called up the Arizona Secretary of State's people and they said they would get us the correct material by the following week. When we received it, we were just going to drive over to Sacramento and get everything done. I wanted to get into LRI on June 1, 1997.

Friday, May 9, 1997: Launch Vehicle Disconnects — As Usual

There was an issue about the damned launch trajectory because LLV didn't want to do anything but launch the Spacecraft/TLI Stage stack into our low Earth parking orbit. I had always said, "There is going to be a disconnect between the TLI and the LLV2 if we don't have one single organization responsible for the launch." Of course, what my Ames Nav guys had given the LLV guys was the velocity vector at the end of TLI burn and LLV assumed (and I didn't know why) that the TLI burn was instantaneous! Such nonsense, the TLI burn would last 51 seconds, so there was a serious difference between the real launch trajectory and what LLV had calculated — LLV had screwed it all up.

In addition, the range didn't want us going over Africa, so we had to change the launch azimuth by about 0.3° to miss Africa. All that meant we had to readjust everything, including the TLI Stage fuel load and Thiokol was just about to start trimming the fuel of the Star-37 motor, so they had to put that off for a couple of days. If we had found all that out just three days later, it would have been too late, because the Star-37 would have been trimmed!

There we were, flopping around trying to get the TLI Stage and the trajectory right. It was the same old crap, so I gave LLV's Roger McNamara my usual lecture —

"Damn it, I wanted one rocket, not two. I told you guys over and over that the launch had to be done as one single rocket with one point of responsibility. This interfacing isn't working and now we are paying the price, as usual."

I went home early because I wanted to work quietly on the things I hadn't been able to get done during the thermal-vac testing and to change the Mission Profile. One such change was, because all the engine heaters turned off when any engine was fired, the strategy I had prepared for the engine burns was no longer valid. But, since it only took the heaters about 20 minutes to get hot, I only had to change the timings of the engine firing a little bit and add some additional heater turn-on commands to make it all work OK.

Monday, May 12, 1997: Piotrowski and Ledbetter Pathetic Site Visit

Piotrowski and Ledbetter came for their usual site visit. Though it didn't make any difference, I showed them the spacecraft, which was working just perfectly.

We got started with the little review and as usual, Dougherty proved to be a bozo. I cannot believe how dumb the guy is. He was the only one who talked because it was a very short visit, and what are you going to say to Headquarters that means anything anyway? Nevertheless, I was amazed at how Dougherty could screw everything up. He couldn't even present the prepared viewgraphs correctly, because he understood so little about the engineering, the spacecraft, and the mission.

Dougherty tried to explain the issue about the engine heaters shutting off when any engine was fired and he got it all screwed up. I had to say something to try to clarify what was really going on. By then, of course, Ledbetter was totally confused and asked, "You mean all the engines shut off?" and I finally got him to understand the issue — I could have killed Dougherty.

I had made him a viewgraph about the science instruments so he could discuss them. About half way through, he decided he didn't know what in hell he was talking about, so he asked me to explain what was going on.

He totally screwed up two unrelated problems. One was with the Sun sensor and the other was with the solar simulator for the solar arrays and he thought those two things were the same damned thing! He had a viewgraph that said something about the Sun sensor. As he showed the viewgraph, he explained the solution to the solar simulator problem as the solution for the Sun sensor problem! It was a good thing Ledbetter and Piotrowski knew nothing about the spacecraft and engineering and hence, knew nothing about what Dougherty was futilely trying to explain. It was painful to listen to him just babble incoherently on and on. Dougherty is totally incompetent and ignorant.

Ledbetter was wetting his pants about the launch vehicle. Headquarters people are useless. I knew they were worried and I understood that, but what were they going to do about it? Nothing. Of course, Dougherty lied when Ledbetter asked about the launch vehicle status and our waiting for Lewis to get launched on the 23rd (Lewis had been postponed again). Then, when Ledbetter asked, "What is the situation with CRSS? Is it still on time for a December launch?"

Dougherty answered, "Oh yes, it's going forward just fine." That was another big fat lie. Dougherty would never say anything that would be anywhere near to the truth when it came to protecting Lockheed from its own incompetence.

The meeting lasted only an hour and Dougherty's botching the entire thing didn't make any difference because Piotrowski and Ledbetter just trusted Dougherty and what we were doing, but that was pathetic, just absolutely pathetic. Piotrowski and Ledbetter were too stupid and ignorant to even notice that Dougherty knew absolutely nothing about what he was trying to explain to them — it was truly the blind leading the blind. There was just no way for them to be able to judge if we were in trouble or sitting on top of the world — their oversight of the mission was absolutely pathetic.

I was also beginning to wonder more about Scott. I had accepted a lot of his bad behavior and poor performance as being due to the fact that he is a NASA official. I accepted that he is part of the bureaucracy and he has to fit in. Nevertheless, I was really beginning to wonder about him. Scott didn't seem to see through Dougherty either. He bought "hook, line, and sinker" what Dougherty told him, like, " Oh, CRSS is OK," — "Yeah, well, OK." When I told Scott the troops told me that CRSS was not going to be ready until well after March, Scott just sort of sloughed that off and believed Dougherty. I was beginning to think that Scott is no better than the rest of them (and he proved to be much worse than the rest of them). As I always say, *"There are no good people in NASA, because the good people always leave NASA very quickly."* Well, Scott wasn't leaving; he was making his career there.

Tuesday, May 13, 1997: Ground Segment Review

We had a semi-formal Ground Segment Review all day. There were five members on the review team. My good friend from Viking and from Jim Martin's formal review committee, Al Schallenmuller, was the head of it, and Charley Hall, who was there from the Ames Pioneer days, was also on the review team. I really didn't know any of the other reviewers.

The review went very well. I gave the introduction. I was supposed to have talked about 20 minutes and I ended up talking about 40 minutes because there were so many questions. Then Marcie got up and did a surprisingly good job. She too talked a lot longer than she was supposed to. Between us, we did the bulk of the review. The guys that followed, like Dan Swanson and everybody else, just filled in details. By the time we were done, we had really broken the back of all the questions and gotten the Lunar Prospector Ground Segment work off to a good start.

The review team was extremely impressed, extremely complimentary, and had some good suggestions. To a man, they said they had come with a lot of questions and concerns, but every question and every concern had been answered. They thought they finally understood that Lunar Prospector was a very simple spacecraft, that it would be easy to fly, and that the mission would be easy to do. They were very pleased and felt that we had a great mission. They also thought I had done a marvelous job on every aspect of the program.

I was pleased because, in the end, they were just talking to me. Marcie was sitting next to me, but they were talking to me, which they should have been doing all along. It was my mission, I was the PI, and they finally understood that. I wished that Lockheed and NASA had realized that, too, and hence, had realized that letting a PI do his job is the best way to do missions.

The best part was when Al Schallenmuller said that when he was reading through the various documents, he initially thought there were probably a lot of important things we would have missed. But he said, *"The more I read, the more I realized this is a perfect example of a very simple spacecraft and a very simple mission. I realized there is nearly nothing for you guys to do. This thing gets launched, it gets into orbit, it takes data, and transmits data, and that is the end of it."* Finally, someone had recognized the simplicity of my mission — I was ecstatic!

Al, who was on the review committee that selected Lunar Prospector, said to me during a break, that there was just no comparison between my proposal and the other 27 — "There was your mission, way on top, and there was this bunch of other (27) missions, way down at the bottom." That was very nice to hear.

Al and I rode to lunch together and then I showed him the spacecraft. Al then gave me the greatest compliment. He said, "You know, there are very few PIs who I would think could possibly run a mission and whom I would trust to run a mission. You're doing it and you're just doing a fantastic job."

I said, "Well, coming from you, that is quite a compliment."

He added, "The combination of you and Tom Dougherty, that's just perfect." Unfortunately, Al and the other old-time managers just did not realize that Dougherty did not understand anything. They saw that the job was getting done and they assumed that Dougherty was doing his job as Project Manager and that I was doing my job as the PI and the Project Scientist. But they didn't understand I was also doing the Project Manager's job — except for managing the money and the Lockheed personnel.

It was funny, the reviewers always ended up having to ask me the questions. They knew I knew what I was talking about, but *they just couldn't get over the old idea that engineers build spacecraft and fly them and that scientists don't. Even though they recognized what I was doing, they just couldn't accept it deep down in their hearts. Unfortunately, until they do and until NASA as a whole does, scientists are never going to get to run their missions. As a result, NASA missions will just keep on being "Slow, Unreliable, and Costly" instead of "Faster, Better, Cheaper".*

I got a call from Roger McNamara at 3:00 PM and I had to leave the review meeting for a while. Roger called about the launch trajectory. Everybody was ticked off at LLV because they had screwed up again. LLV had done the new calculations, but we still had to correct it before we could have Thiokol trim the Star-37 fuel load and that was supposed to have been done the next day. As a result, we had to postpone the trimming until Thursday or Friday and that was a crappy thing to have to do at that stage of the game. Nobody was happy with LLV, except stupid Dougherty, who tried to blame Ames for the mess — he is such a bozo.

I wrote the one page budget proposal to Lockheed for LRI's work on Lunar Prospector and gave it to Ilda Grimm, our finance and program controller, who was going to review it and show me what I needed to change.

I talked to Sylvia because I wanted to find out what Ledbetter and Piotrowski said about my leaving Lockheed. She said that Scott had presented it and the reasons why to Ledbetter and Piotrowski in a very good way. I was sure Scott did, because Scott knew I was not happy with the situation at Lockheed. Although I was losing respect for Scott because he is a gutless wimp, I knew he was caught between his bosses and me.

Ledbetter had told Scott they would think about it. Sylvia said that they told Dougherty the same thing. Dougherty told them, "Well, I am not going to do anything about his leaving until I get the word from you." The fact that Ledbetter and Piotrowski talked to everybody but me about my private and professional life ticked me off.

I said to Sylvia, "This is none of their damned business. There is no way in the world that my going to LRI will have a negative effect on the mission. If there were, you know I wouldn't do it. I'm not crabbing at you, I am just saying I'm getting damned sick and tired of this. This is none of NASA's damned business."

Wednesday, May 14, 1997

I talked with Scott about Discovery, the MAG/ER, the APS, and the spacecraft.

After I finished, Scott said he had told Piotrowski and Ledbetter about my going into LRI. Basically, Scott told them it was going to happen and if they had any concerns, they better say something right then. Piotrowski thought what I was doing was a great idea and he said I was doing it the right way, i.e., starting my institute with a mission already underway, as compared to LunaCorp, which "is a business without any business, just an idea of future programs." Piotrowski was quite positive about LRI.

As a result, Scott was OK with LRI, but he said he would rather have me wait until after launch, but since I had my reasons for leaving Lockheed right then, he would accept it. He said, "I'll let you do it." I thought, *you can't stop me anyway*.

Other than that, we fooled around with the launch trajectory. LLV had finally gotten it ready to go and had given the information to Ken and Dave and they were starting to work on it to see if it was going to work.

Thursday, May 15, 1997

Bill Jacobsen brought the computer model of the spacecraft we had been working on for some time and he and Dan worked on getting it set up temporarily on a computer in the highbay control room in Building 150. I had been over to Ames and had missed all that, but Dan said the program was really neat.

I talked to Maryann about the LRI budget proposal and then I called Wayne about it. Wayne suggested we get some up front money, so we would have some money in our account and I said I would ask Maryann about that the next day.

We had another meeting on the spacecraft to review all that had happened during thermal-vac testing. Things were just going very well.

I had the feeling that everybody had accepted my going to LRI and it was finally beginning to happen.

Friday, May 16, 1997

A slow day, so I was able to work on revising the Mission Profile and the Mission Operations Document based on what I learned from the thermal-vac tests.

Monday, May 19, 1997

Dave Curtis and Paul Turin came down from Berkeley. Dave ran some noise tests on the ER and found the filter was not filtering out the noise. Paul put on the new wire cutter pyros on the MAG extension boom in preparation for the second and final boom deployment test.

Bill and some of his crew came from Los Alamos and looked at some of the data we had taken on the APS.

Marcie, Bill Jacobsen, and I had a meeting at 1:00 PM to discuss how we were going to get the data to the home institutions of my Co-Is and how we were going to do the bit error checking of the data. It was a good meeting; we got a lot done. I also pointed out that I wanted the ground support equipment for the science instruments in the Command and Control Center, which Marcie didn't want. Of course, they were going to be in there.

Then, 25 to 30 students from a class I was lecturing to at Stanford came to see the spacecraft. It was fun showing it to such enthusiastic students.

Tuesday, May 20, 1997

Bill, his crew, and I went through the APS and it really looked like it was OK and that the noise we had seen was due to the fact that there is a lot of electronic noise in the thermal-vac room. We got some good alpha particle sources, put them on the APS and it easily detected the alphas, so it really looked like we were just picking up noise from the environment. That made me think that the ER noise problem might also just be due to electronic noise in the thermal-vac room — though Dave did have the reference voltage problem on Side A, and that was a real problem.

Wednesday, May 21, 1997:
Getting LRI's Paperwork Finished at Sacramento

Rebecca and I got up very early and drove the 200 or so km to Sacramento in order to be there when the state offices opened up and we arrived with plenty of time to spare. Interestingly, though we had spent many weeks dealing with the State, trying to get LRI accepted as a foreign corporation operating in California, we spent less than an hour getting it done in person! At last, the last governmental roadblock was swept aside and I could proceed with getting a contract from Lockheed and I could resign from that detested company.

We had expected to spend most of the day monkeying around with the California bureaucracy, so when we were done so early in the morning, Rebecca and I said to each other, "What should we do with the rest of the day?" Since I had no intention of driving back to Lockheed to work, we decided to drive up to Lake Tahoe. We drove up I-80, through the beautiful Sierra Nevada Mountains, passed through the infamous Donner Pass where many members of the Donner party of pioneers died and others survived through cannibalism, and arrived at beautiful Lake Tahoe. We drove around looking at the scenery, had a nice lunch, and started back to Gilroy in the late afternoon. We had a grand time.

Thursday, May 22, 1997: The Spacecraft Computer Model

Dan and I worked on the computer model of the spacecraft. There were a lot of errors in it, but it was really neat. It was going to be a really fantastic tool to work with and to train on.

In preparation for my leaving Lockheed, I went to the administration building and found out about my Lockheed retirement benefits — little as they were.

We had a staff meeting to review where we were and where we were going, specifically we discussed starting the acoustic testing the following Wednesday. Also, we discussed the Lewis launch delays since, during a ground test, there was an unexplained problem with the avionics in that the first stage engine bell was commanded hard over to one side for no reason. If they didn't get Lewis off the ground soon, we were going to be in trouble with our September launch.

Friday, May 23, 1997

I worked on the spacecraft computer model, checking commands and everything else I could.

We had a telecon about the science data and how we were going to electronically transfer it and the spacecraft ephemeris data to Los Alamos and Berkeley.

I had a talk with Marcie to let her know how I was going to run Mission Ops, i.e., that I was going to run the effort and that she was going to have very little to do with it. As usual, it was really hard to deal with her because she gets quasi-hysterical. Every time she feels she has to do something she doesn't want to do, or doesn't like, or doesn't understand, she gets very worked up and tends to lose it. I hated having to deal with her, but I had to. Though she hated it, I was forcing her to accept that I was running the mission and she was going to sit on the sidelines all the time.

We took the spacecraft over to the acoustic chamber in preparation for its acoustic test. I took a look around the acoustic chamber — a fantastic facility with its big horns that create the noise for the tests. The horns are really just very big trumpets that are "played" by blowing high pressure nitrogen through them and which can be tuned to any frequency or "note," just like a trumpet.

Saturday, May 24, through Monday, May 26, 1997: Memorial Day Weekend

Rebecca and I just enjoyed the long weekend and saw the movie, *Lost World*.

Tuesday, May 27, 1997

I talked to Maryann to make sure that she was working on the contract stuff so I could get the hell out of that damned company.

I filled out my Lockheed retirement forms. Then I worked on the computer displays I wanted in OASIS and started making the list of the red, yellow, and green operational limits for all the engineering data we would be getting from the spacecraft and that would be displayed by OASIS.

Wednesday, May 28, 1997

We checked the APS and it was noisy as hell in Building 146, where the acoustic chamber was located. There was so much electronic noise in there that the NS was saturated with noise and we weren't seeing any signal at all! We had a lot of time to check all that out, because our acoustic tests had been delayed a few days.

I wanted to get Henshaw to sign off on my retiring from Lockheed, but, of course, he was not around!

The rocket business was the same old crap. Happily, the rocket crew was processing our LLV2 in parallel with the LLV1 for Lewis, so we could keep on track for our September launch, but Lewis was still slipping!

Sylvia said NASA was going to have to face up to the fact that Lockheed was not going to launch CRSS until Lunar Prospector was launched, because the launch insurance for CRSS would be sky high if it was a first launch. Because of the insurance costs,

Lockheed simply would not launch CRSS before Lunar Prospector — so Lockheed had been lying to NASA all the time — something I had known all along, though the insurance twist was new to me. The other point about CRSS was that, even though Dougherty kept fibbing to NASA, it wasn't going to launch in the fall anyway. CRSS would launch in the spring at the earliest. NASA was going to have to face up to that and Lockheed was going to have to take the heat. It was a stupid mess of lies as usual.

Marcie was a big pain in the butt as always. The BBC wanted to have access to Mission Control and she was trying to dictate what they could and could not do. One way or another, I was going to try to get rid her.

Thursday, May 29, 1997

Lockheed decided I couldn't retire because there was some stupid rule about hiring somebody on a subcontract who is retired, although they had done it a hundred times before, e.g., Tim Bridges and Bob Goldin, who were working on Lunar Prospector with me! Lockheed was dragging out my leaving the company in every way it could. Nobody had enough guts just to let me get the hell out of that crappy company. I was extremely annoyed.

Other than that, I finished the OASIS display plots and the red, yellow, and green limits list. I was getting all kinds of little things done that had to be done and documented, so I would be ready to fly my spacecraft in less than five months.

Friday, May 30, 1997: More Trouble Trying to Leave Lockheed

Bill Gibbons, from the Palo Alto computer group, came to work on the spacecraft computer model or the simulator as we were beginning to call it. The simulator was beginning to work and the data coming on the computer monitors really looked realistic. It still had errors in it, but it was getting there and we would soon be able to start training to fly the spacecraft using it.

We had a meeting with Scott, who said Headquarters was convinced we wouldn't be able to launch on September 24 because of the Lewis launch delays. We still thought we could make it, but Headquarters was pessimistic. We knew we might be pushed back a month or even two, but as far as Dougherty, Scott, Sylvia, and I were concerned, we were just continuing to go for the September launch. Lockheed was trying hard to keep our LLV2 launch on schedule and I gave them credit for that.

We also talked about the Statement at Work for my contract between LRI and Lockheed. I had given Lockheed a Statement of Work and they had rewritten it, which I didn't mind, because they knew how to write one better than I did. But I didn't even get a copy for my approval before Lockheed sent it off to Scott. Lockheed and NASA were always doing things behind my back. I was sick of them.

Scott had some suggestions, so I went back to Lockheed and rewrote the Statement of Work, explaining more fully what my responsibilities were and what expertise I was bringing to the program. Such crap, it was my program — if that didn't show what expertise I brought to the program, I didn't know what did. All of that was just bureaucratic gobbledygook.

I gave it to Maryann and asked her if there was much more to do and her answer was no. She said she could get everything done in a week. I asked, "Is Henshaw around to sign it?"

She said, "He is supposed to be back next week, but he may not sign it." Henshaw's henchman thought Henshaw didn't want to sign it and he would send it to my old buddy Mel Brashears at Corporate Headquarters on the East Coast for signature.

That ticked me off. That would only delay my getting out of there. I said to Maryann, "Just because some little henchman said Henshaw won't sign it or they might not let me go, doesn't mean they won't." What a bunch of cowards. Nobody in Lockheed has any guts. My leaving that stinking company was no big deal, I was not that important to Lockheed and they didn't want me there anyway, so they should have been happy to get rid of me. Such BS!

Saturday, May 31, through Tuesday, June 3, 1997: The COMPLEX Meeting in Flagstaff

I had been invited to give a talk at the COMPLEX meeting that was being held in Flagstaff, AZ. COMPLEX is an advisory COMmittee on PLanetary EXploration and the members wanted to hear how Lunar Prospector was coming along.

Since Rebecca and I love Arizona and since her sister, Shirley, lives in Scottsdale, AZ, we decided to fly to Phoenix (that is how you get to Flagstaff anyway), spend the weekend with Shirley and drive up to Flagstaff for the meeting. We had a great weekend with Shirley and then drove up to Flagstaff Sunday night.

We went to the meeting Monday; both Gene Shoemaker, the legendary lunar and planetary scientist from Cal Tech and the US Geological Survey Branch of Astrogeology, and Ron Greeley, also a well-known planetary scientist from the Arizona State University in Tempe, were there. Rebecca was very pleased to meet Gene, whom she had seen on TV many times because of his work searching for near-earth asteroids that can, and have, collided with the Earth with catastrophic results, e.g., the one that killed off the dinosaurs.

I gave my talk in the morning and everyone was impressed with what we had accomplished in two years and for $63 million. After my talk, I told Gene to come over to Sunnyvale and see my spacecraft, but Gene said he couldn't, because he was heading off to Australia to look for more impact craters.

After lunch, Rebecca and I drove back down to Scottsdale and spent the evening with Shirley.

Tuesday I went to Spectrum Astro in Mesa, AZ, to the south of Scottsdale, where Woody and Gerry Grismore were discussing the battery Charge Control Board (CCB) in the C&DH and it was clear we did not exactly understand how it functioned, although it was probably OK. Also, Spectrum Astro was going to come over to Lockheed to do some tests with the spacecraft to make sure the CCB worked as Spectrum Astro expected it to work (only much later did I fully understand how it functioned). I was pleased that Spectrum Astro responded to the fact that we didn't exactly understand how the CCB worked and to the questions we had as to whether it was working properly.

I had a good talk with Martha, the President of the company, and her husband about my future activities once I got into LRI.

Then I gave the Spectrum Astro staff a talk about the mission.

Chapter 3-34
Acoustic and Pyro-Shock Testing and Mission Training

Wednesday, June 4, 1997: The Beginning of Acoustic Testing

The engineers began the acoustic testing while I was on travel. The acoustic tests consist of blasting the spacecraft with very high levels of noise. The noise levels simulate first, those present during rocket ignition and the first couple of seconds as it lifts off the pad, when the roar of the rocket is reflected off the launch pad right back up to the rocket and the payload, and second, those when the rocket goes through Max Q, i.e., the maximum dynamic pressure when the rocket breaks the sound barrier. During both of those periods, both of which last only a few seconds, the noise levels are so high they can damage the rocket and/or the spacecraft. As Dougherty said, "The first thing you do when you open the acoustic chamber door after a test is to look on the floor for shattered solar cells and other debris from the spacecraft." Also, it is worth noting that the acoustic levels during a Titan missile launch from one of their silos would rip the skin off the rocket if it weren't properly protected. Acoustic testing is a vital part of the test program.

Since each test lasts just a couple of seconds and since the spacecraft is inside a noise-abating chamber with no windows (the noise levels are lethal to humans), there was nothing for me to see or hear, so I was not present for most of the acoustic test, nor were most of our engineers — there was simply nothing for us to do except let the acoustic test engineers do their job.

When I got back on Wednesday, we had a meeting on the problems the engineers had found during the low level acoustic tests. Most of the spacecraft's sub-structures had resonance frequencies in the range of 200 to 400 Hz, which was OK. However, the brackets for the PIV (Propellant Isolation Valve) and the attitude sensors (the Sun sensor and Earth/Moon limb-crossing sensor) on the spacecraft and the bracket for the timer, the nitrogen tanks, and one other thing on the TLI Stage had resonance frequencies around 900 Hz and those were too high. We spent a lot of time discussing how to fix those problems.

We tested the spectrometers and Dan tested the attitude sensors to see if they had survived the first acoustic test. The GRS had some noise at the 1,000 v step, so I called Bill. He told me to go up to the operational voltage of 1600 v and when I did, it was fine; I got a beautiful spectrum. The neutron spectrometer worked beautifully and I turned the APS on and there was *no* noise! The problems we had earlier were gone and all the spectrometers were OK, as was the attitude sensors.

Maryann said my contract was ready to go over to Ames for signature. I was going to be allowed to retire and there didn't seem to be any more fussing about getting Henshaw's signature. That was not to say he was going to do it, but there was a somewhat different mood about my leaving. I hoped to be out of Lockheed by the following week.

We were getting the spacecraft computer model done, so things were moving rapidly ahead towards our being able to start training to fly the spacecraft.

Thursday, June 5, 1997

Tad Theno and Greg Dickman, from George's Moonlink group in Green Bay, were at Lockheed and I showed them the spacecraft.

Dan and I worked on the computer model of the spacecraft. It was getting very good. There were still a few more errors in it, so we had some more debugging to do, but it was getting better and better.

I gave a talk to the AIAA steering committee, a committee of just twelve people. At first I thought the talk was going to be a waste of time, but it turned out those twelve guys were really interested and asked a lot of good questions

We had a staff meeting in the afternoon. One of the five problems we had during the low level acoustic test wasn't a real problem, the gain on the test device was set a decade too high, so that problem didn't exist. Then, another problem was found to be OK — the engineers found that the components were tested ten times longer than they would be required to function during launch. And we were looking at ways to fix the PIV bracket and the attitude sensor bracket, like backing them with a rubber-like material that would increase the damping. Basically, we thought we would get around those issues without too much difficulty.

It was a good day. We were getting there. The launch was just a little more than three months and two weeks away.

Friday, June 6, 1997

Dan and I worked on the computer model all day and it was getting better and better. The simulations were getting more accurate.

We had a meeting with Scott and Sylvia about the usual stuff. Dougherty just blabbed on and on and it was a waste of time, because he didn't know what in hell he was talking about.

Nevertheless, we were charging ahead towards our September launch.

Monday, June 9, 1997

Lockheed was still screwing around with my paperwork. John Palochak hadn't gotten it, so I politely kept after Maryann to push the paperwork along.

Dan Swanson and I worked most of the day on the computer model. Unfortunately, Bill Gibbons was not around to make all the corrections we needed to have done, but we were getting more and more used to using the model and it was fun — just like a super computer game.

Tuesday, June 10, 1997: Beginning Training

Dan and I again worked on the computer model most of the day. It was working well enough so we could start training in the afternoon. We did a boom deployment exercise, but the model didn't show the spin down of the spacecraft as the booms deployed. Dan was going to fix that the following morning.

There were just a few more things we needed to correct in the model, which was getting very realistic. The main thing that was wrong was that the computer was using the initialization profile for lunar orbit, rather than for the post-launch trajectory. When we practiced the first few hours of the mission, we had the wrong orbital ephemeris in the system. However, that would be easy to change as soon as we had a little time. Anyway the computer model was working and we were learning to fly Lunar Prospector!

I pried out of Maryann that Scott was still concerned about my getting out of Lockheed. I asked Maryann, for the second or third time, for a copy of my contract that Lockheed and Ames were debating, but she still wouldn't give me a copy — I was not even allowed to see my own damned contract! That ticked me off because everything was again being done behind my back. I was going to find out from Sylvia what was going on.

In addition to that crap, Kim was really doing a number on us. We were supposed to do the pyro-shock test to make sure the firing of the three explosive bolts to separate the spacecraft from the spent TLI Stage would not damage the spacecraft and that was supposed to have happened two days earlier. However, the cables Kim was supposed to have gotten made for the test weren't done. Since Kim had not gotten the cables ready for the baseline functional or for the thermal-vac tests, why should one expect that he would have them ready for the pyro-shock test?

When Tim was ready to start setting up the test and found there were no cables, he tried to find Kim, but Kim wasn't to be found. He would not acknowledge a page and he would not answer his telephone. Tim finally cornered Kim after two days had been wasted. Kim refused to say where the cables were being made — he was protecting the people who were making the cables, but who hadn't gotten them done.

Of course, Dougherty did nothing about it. All he did was to grump that we didn't have the cables, instead of grabbing Kim by the neck and making him do something. The coward reacted as he always did; if he couldn't make poor Mary do his dirty work, then it didn't get done. He is absolutely useless — and that's what Lockheed calls a Project Manager!

Wednesday, June 11, 1997:
The Beginning of Trouble Getting Out of Lockheed

Dan and I brought Ric and Paul in during the afternoon and did a SIM (mission simulation, i.e., a training session) of the first six hours of the mission in fast-time, but we were still using the initialization file for lunar orbit rather than that for the post-TLI trajectory.

I had set the Mission Profile up with a ten-minute wait period between each command and commanded event, in order to leave plenty of time to check out the spacecraft and to watch the results of a burn, etc., before issuing the next command. Thus, the spacecraft operations were to be done very slowly and deliberately, so we would have plenty of time to catch any developing problem before we did the next step, which might turn a developing problem into a catastrophe. In the beginning, we were doing our SIMs in fast-time, instead of waiting ten minutes between commands, to quickly test the system and to get used to working together to fly the spacecraft. The simulator worked just beautifully. There were a few glitches, but nothing serious. It was just a marvelous training tool.

I talked to Sylvia and she said Scott was not concerned about my getting out of Lockheed; rather she thought Lockheed really didn't want me to leave and hence they were not cooperating. What was going on was just finger pointing. It was always "the other side" that was causing the trouble. She said I should talk to Cathcart, the Ames contract guy, and it turned out he had several (contrived) concerns.

First, Cathcart asked, "What would happen if you get killed? Who would run the program?"

Well, OK, that was the same BS I had been given five years ago when Mike Griffin and Jay Green pulled the rug out from under me after they were going to give me the money to have Lunar Prospector be the first mission in the Space Exploration Initiative (See Part Two). Nevertheless, I answered that dumb question with, "What would happen if I get killed on the highway (run over by a NASA van, I assumed) is that somebody else would take over, regardless of whether I am in LRI or in Lockheed!"

Second, "Well, OK, but who would take over? If you're in LRI, then Lockheed has no responsibility to find anybody else."

Such contrived BS; I answered, "Lockheed would still be responsible, because I will have a subcontract with them!"

Third, "Then there's the question of what Lockheed would do with poor widow Binder?"

I could not believe he would stoop that low (well, Lockheed or NASA could just shoot her), "If I get killed, then obviously the sub-contract is null and void and you have to fend for yourselves."

If I was so damned indispensable, then NASA and Lockheed should have been treating me a hell of a lot better than they were or they should have closed the damned mission down at the very beginning.

Finally, Cathcart said, "We have to check over your budget to see if it's legal." Crap, because of LRI's low overhead, I was costing the project a lot less money than before.

After the Cathcart BS, I talked to Sylvia again and she finally admitted I would have to talk to Scott, because it was really Scott's call. It just boiled down to whether Scott wanted to tell those guys to cut the BS and get it done.

Behind my back, Dougherty said, "If Alan gets killed, then we (Lockheed) would want Scott to be the PI," such a brown-nosing bastard — Scott couldn't PI his way out of a wet paper bag, let alone run a mission. What a joke!

Then I found out Scott wanted more detail in the Statement of Work because Lockheed had cut out all the BS in it. What was the big deal? The Statement of Work in the original NASA Ames/Lockheed contract for the entire project was just two pages long. In contrast, just because I wanted to leave Lockheed, Scott wanted a Statement of Work for me alone, and that was just for the flight phase of the project, that was four or five pages long!

Then there was some talk about Lockheed wanting clauses defining specific data sets and other things I would have to deliver in order to get paid. Such BS! I couldn't be trusted to run my own mission — a mission I had defined and fought for years to get accepted and for which I had done everything possible to get its spacecraft built and launched properly — unless there were deliverables! I was being treated like crap and I was getting more and more angry with both Lockheed and NASA. All they were doing was throwing up one smoke screen after another in order to stop me from leaving Lockheed. They were just delaying and delaying; neither side wanted it and they were trying to make the other side look bad. I was not going to put up with that disgusting BS any more, but I didn't know what I could do about it.

Adding insult to injury, NASA was starting to holler about having big reviews of the LLV2. The reviews were going to take six weeks for the first part and two weeks for the second part — three damned months before launch! The stupidity swirling around the mission was reaching a hysterical crescendo.

Regarding the problems we found during the low level acoustic test, the engineers determined that all we had to do was to stiffen the bracket for the attitude sensors and it would be OK. But they still hadn't quite figured out what to do with the PIV, though that wasn't a really big problem.

We needed to get the damned pyro-shock test and the low level acoustic tests done the following week, if we were going to move a step forward. Added to that, there was the whole rocket business that was just getting insane. NASA and Lockheed were driving me nuts.

Thursday, June 12, 1997

I didn't get to see Scott about my getting out of Lockheed because he went home sick. I was still very annoyed about the situation.

The acoustic issues with the rest of the brackets were getting resolved.

We did a test of the TLI Stage timer and it worked perfectly. It fired all the explosive-bolt squibs and the nitrogen gas jets and sent the signal to turn on the spacecraft. However, the spacecraft did not turn on and it would not turn on with the ground support equipment either, so something was seriously wrong!

After that, Dan, Ric, Paul, John Breakwell — Dan's new backup guy, and I ran a SIM. It was really neat and we had a lot of fun doing it. We still didn't have the initialization file for the post-TLI trajectory, so we were still using the lunar orbit file, even though we were practicing the first six hours of the mission and doing it in fast-time. But SIM went very well.

Despite the good SIM, I was ticked off about the difficulties Lockheed and NASA were creating to stop me from leaving Lockheed.

Friday, June 13, 1997: LRI Problems and a Great SIM

Scott was still sick. Nevertheless, he was going to fly to DC Sunday for meetings at Headquarters on Monday and Tuesday to try to get Headquarters to leave us alone. I couldn't see him about LRI until he got back.

Dougherty said the engineers found the reason why the spacecraft didn't turn on during the timer test. Two 28 v wires that were used by the timer to turn on the spacecraft were reversed, so an arc suppresser blew. As a result, the 28 v current didn't get to the spacecraft to turn it on. That was being fixed.

Then Dougherty and I talked about the launch vehicle mess that was getting worse and worse. NASA was seriously talking about taking the Lewis spacecraft off the LLV1 and not letting it fly. We didn't know what in hell they would do with Lewis then, but NASA was fussing again and the whole issue about our launch vehicle was up in the air. Dougherty said, "I don't worry about it any more," which was ironic because I thought the same thing. All we could do was just get the spacecraft ready and bitch, since we couldn't really do anything about the damned launch vehicle.

After that, I told Dougherty I wanted to find out what was going on with Lockheed regarding my leaving. He said, "Well, I've gotten everybody in the company to agree, so there should be no problem at NASA. All we're trying to do is to get you in the situation you should have been in from the beginning. You should never have been in this company as the PI."

I was floored at that statement, but Dougherty had been getting nicer and nicer as we had gotten the spacecraft done and I thought maybe, after a year and a half, during which he had believed a scientist should not be in there mucking everything up and doing everything so differently, he finally saw it had worked — and had worked better than anything he had been involved with before.

I then told him about my stupid conversation with Cathcart regarding my getting killed on the freeway and the similar story about Jay Green and the Space Exploration Initiative effort. I said jokingly "Tom, I am getting a little bit concerned. Every time NASA has concerns about me, they end up talking about me getting killed on the highway. I always turn up as a corpse." He laughed, but he too thought it was very peculiar.

More seriously I said, "What bothers me is all this is just smoke and mirrors." He said, "I agree with you. This is trivial stuff, none of the things (how we would run the program if I left Lockheed) change."

We had a very good conversation and I felt relieved that he seemed to be honest about everything.

I talked to Sylvia about the LRI issue and she said the same thing, i.e., that Dougherty had voiced similar things to Scott and her, so maybe Dougherty was actually being civil about the whole issue and was really trying to help me get out of Lockheed. She said, "Tom was quite surprised and annoyed that it is dragging on and on. He thought it should have been taken care of much earlier." We all agreed Scott was going to have to sit down with Cathcart and the Lockheed contracts guys and just get it done.

Nevertheless, Sylvia said she thought there might be some trouble a little further up the line in NASA. While that probably was true, I felt relieved that Dougherty was on my side, but concerned that Cathcart was the main problem at that time.

My Mission Ops Team and I ran another SIM. Dan had changed several things we wanted changed, based on the previous days' SIMs, that would make the computer model even more realistic, e.g., he changed the time constant for the heating and cooling of the fuel tanks. I had originally put in a very long time constant that I thought was realistic when the tanks were full. But we wanted to see some changes in the tank temperatures during the SIMs, so Dan shortened the time constant and as a result, we could see the tanks starting to heat up when we did the SIM.

We started the SIM, did the initial commanding and then we started firing the engines in order to do the first reorientation maneuver. To our surprise, the spacecraft started moving the wrong direction! The minute we saw that, I issued an emergency stop engine command to shut them off. We had just had our first spacecraft problem and it was very realistic. I said, "OK, let's figure out what in hell is going on with the spacecraft." Dan realized he had changed the reorientation software in the computer program and had made a simple mistake while doing so. He quickly corrected the error and we restarted the SIM just before the reorientation event. When I issued the reorientation commands, the spacecraft moved in the right direction — the home team hit a homerun!

We were getting ready to start the boom deployment sequence, but by that time the ephemeris said the spacecraft was soon going to go into the shadow of the Moon (we were still using the lunar orbit initialization files because we still did not have the post-TLI files) and we then would not be able to proceed until the computer said the spacecraft was again in sunlight. I said, "OK, let's finish the boom deployment before the nighttime pass starts, then we will take a lunch break and by then it (the spacecraft) will be in the sunlight and we can go ahead and do the mid-course maneuver."

The first thing we had to do in the boom deployment sequence was to decrease the spin rate from 60 rpm to 30 rpm; if we didn't, the booms could be damaged as they were deploying. When I had the T1 Engine fired to do the de-spin maneuver, I noticed that the tank pressure didn't drop as it was supposed to (there are two pressure levels — the dynamic pressure, when fuel is flowing to the engines and the static pressure, when the fuel is not flowing to the engines. The dynamic pressure is slightly lower than the static pressure, because there is a drop in the pressure because of the friction between the flowing fuel and the fuel line walls. When an engine is fired, the pressure immediately drops from its static level to its dynamic level and that gave me the first indication that the engines were actually starting to fire — the second indication was the engines rapidly began to heat up.) I said, "What the hell is going on, I'm not seeing the dynamic pressure drop and I'm not seeing any drop in the pressure because of the fuel usage (the latter part of my comment was wrong, because the amount of fuel that would be used during a very short de-spin maneuver, wouldn't be enough to cause a measurable pressure drop, but those were the things that we were beginning to learn from the SIMs). Something is wrong here. We have an anomaly in the spacecraft." Boy, that was exciting, it was just like flying the real thing and everything we did, taught us something new, it was really exciting.

We noted I had not seen the dynamic pressure drop (we would find out why after the SIM) and proceeded with the SIM. After the short despin maneuver, I deployed the booms, which went well, except we were in the nighttime pass by then, so we couldn't see the spin down of the spacecraft via the Sun sensor data as the booms deployed.

I couldn't get the spin rate graph to come up on my monitor (Dan monitored that graph all the time, but I just wanted to check it myself) and we realized if we didn't have a graph on the monitor before we started, it wouldn't start displaying data immediately, because the computer didn't have any memory of the earlier data. That was another anomaly we had figured out in the OASIS software. However, we found out that could not be changed in the software; so if we wanted to see data on some parameter infrequently, all we had to do was have that particular graphic activated, but stored as an icon on the computer screen. When we needed to see it, we would click on the icon, the graphic would appear with all the data, we could then find out what we wanted to know and then click on it again to return it to an icon — simple and efficient.

Then I noticed the tank temperatures and said, "Look, the tank temperatures are getting to their red limits." The computer program still wasn't correct — it didn't shut the tank heaters off when the upper dead-band temperature was reached, i.e., the heaters didn't cycle — they just stayed on. I said, "OK, I am declaring a spacecraft emergency. Our tank heaters are not shutting off. The tank pressure is increasing and increasing" (as it should do as the temperatures continued to rise — so that part of the program was correct). Then both Dan and I realized, at the same time, that the rise in the tank temperatures and the corresponding increase in tank pressure were the reasons I had not seen the dynamic pressure drop when I had fired the T1 engine — the raising pressure had saturated the pressure sensor! We couldn't read the true pressure any more and the actual value was way above the upper limit set for the tanks. Then I said, "OK, we are having an emergency; it is clear we don't know what the pressure is in those tanks and those tanks could explode."

We quickly devised ways of burning off fuel to reduce the tank pressure. We worked out two procedures and tried one. We despun the spacecraft to five rpm and then did a standard reorientation maneuver, but with very long burns so that nothing really happened. We were just burning fuel. It was like putting your car in neutral and revving up the engine — you just burn up gas. It probably would have worked, except the computer program had increased the tank temperatures to 600° C or 700° C, so the tank pressure was sky-high by that time. As a result, because the engines have higher thrust as the tank pressure goes up, the spacecraft was wobbling all over the place when we fired the engines. It didn't work. Nevertheless, it was really fun because we very quickly came up with a procedure to burn off fuel if we ever had to, without changing the spacecraft's trajectory or orbit.

The gist of the SIM was that we had a series of anomalies, even though they were anomalies in the computer program and not in the real spacecraft, they were anomalies that could occur during the mission and we got around them. After all, a heater could stick on and cause the fuel tanks to overheat. Since all that could really happen, it was a great SIM. It was fantastic. We sat there, saw the three or four anomalies, discussed them, fixed them, and had a really great time doing the SIM. I was extremely pleased — we were learning how to fly the spacecraft and it was exciting!

Monday, June 16, 1997: The Pyro-Shock Test

We did the pyro-shock test late in the afternoon. Steve Honodel and I were standing behind a plastic shield about six feet from the spacecraft; not that it could have hurt us, but according to Lockheed rules, we had to be protected. There was a big bang as the three explosive bolts blew and the spacecraft just sat there on the TLI Stage casing as it was supposed to. We got the required data and found the shock levels were OK — one more step finished.

We had a good talk on the thermal subsystem by Jim Schirle at our seminar series on the spacecraft for the Mission Ops Team.

Headquarters was trying to make us wait to launch in the spring, since Goldin had said we couldn't launch until after CRSS launched. Of course, CRSS was getting further behind schedule, as even Dougherty was beginning to admit, so CRSS was not going to launch anytime soon. In addition, Lockheed was saying more and more loudly it would not launch CRSS before Lunar Prospector, because the launch insurance would cost several millions of dollars extra if CRSS went first. The merry-go-round kept going around and around and it would continue to do so until somebody started admitting to the realities of the situation. The launch mess was just a total catastrophe, as is NASA.

Dan and I made several changes to the spacecraft simulator and we were going to check it the next day to see if it all worked.

Tuesday, June 17, 1997: A Useless Headquarters Telecon

Dan and I worked on the spacecraft computer program during the morning. We found some more bugs, but we were getting the program really cleaned up. We started it and left it running for about three hours and we saw it was mimicking the spacecraft's expected activities quite well, e.g., the temperatures of the various subsystems were varied the way they were supposed to as their heaters cycled on and off, but when some of them turned on, there was not a corresponding increase in the load current, so we fixed that. There were just a few more things we needed to correct in the computer model, but as far as we could tell, it faithfully mimicked the spacecraft as well as we wanted it to right then. The next thing we had to do was to put in the "gui interface" that would allow us to mimic various system failures. Our all-important training tool was getting finished and I was very pleased about that.

Dougherty, Sylvia, Scott, Headquarters, Larry Price, and I had a telecon about the launch vehicle issue that was getting to be a total mess. The telecon started and Karen Poniatowski summarized Headquarters' position as follows, "We want to delay Lewis until we can have a complete review of the Mission Success Study to make sure it (the launch vehicle) is going to work. If that delays Lewis until September, then Lewis has to be taken off the launch vehicle and refurbished and won't be available for launch until spring. We know Lunar Prospector wants to be launched by February, but you also want to wait until everything is absolutely certain."

We all looked at each other and said, "Where in hell is she getting that crap? We don't want any of that BS."

Scott had previously said he wanted to do all the talking for Lunar Prospector, so the rest of us were supposed to be quiet, which was OK with Dougherty and me. We didn't want to say anything anyway, because the telecon was so stupid we couldn't believe it. Scott said, "We're not planning to launch by February, we're planning to launch in September and we don't want to lose science."

Huckins jumped on Scott, saying, "You mean you want to launch without being sure you're going to get launched, you're going to take that risk?"

Scott replied, "We want the thing to be as certain as possible, but we do not want to delay it forever." Scott made his point, but got his hand slapped, which was BS to me.

It was clear the Headquarters' people were all worried about their jobs. They didn't want Goldin bawling them out if there were failures, so *by making no decisions, nothing happens, there are no failures, and they don't get into trouble*. They were all just trying to protect their butts. Also, Karen was trying to keep both her position as the great launch vehicle authority and her little kingdom. They disgusted me.

Karen said, "We don't want you launching until we have all of the reviews." All in all, they were talking about reviews that would last about 6 months!

Larry said, "You must understand we are under contract to launch Lewis in July and until I get new contractual directives and the money to back it up, we are moving towards a July launch. That is our contractual obligation." With that, Karen backed off a little, because NASA didn't have the money. In reality, Headquarters was trying to bluff Lockheed into backing off on the Lewis and Lunar Prospector launches and to make Lockheed absorb all the associated cost impacts. Every time Karen tried another way of accomplishing that, Larry would stop her and we all applauded Larry. He did a good job of stopping Headquarters in its tracks.

It was becoming clear that nothing was going to come out of the telecon. It was just going to be two hours of haggling and then we would be back to where we were in the beginning.

The only thing that came out of the telecon was we found out that Lewis had slipped enough so that it was going to be damned hard for us to launch in September. If Lewis didn't get off by mid-July, there was just no way that LLV could physically get our rocket ready in time. However, that didn't mean we had to jump from September to February as Headquarters maintained. They did so, because they still believed Lockheed's lie that CRSS would be launched in December, so NASA would have its demonstration of the LLV2 via the CRSS launch. Scott said, "What you're trying to do is to put Lunar Prospector behind a mission that is not controlled by NASA. There is absolutely no pressure on Lockheed to launch CRSS until it is good and ready. If they decide they want to wait two or three more months before they are ready to launch, then we will just be pushed back into June." Though the NASA wienies at Headquarters make up all their little rules to save their butts and ignore the true consequences of their decisions, Headquarters could not ignore Scott's point, because NASA does not want to lose control of anything.

Then Headquarters started on "Guaranteeing Success" and Dougherty pointed out, "When a Titan IV is launched, we go through all these reviews. But a Titan IV costs $400 million for the rocket alone! We have a $25 million rocket and you expect to have the same level of reviews!" I was about to add my 2¢ worth when Dougherty said quietly to me, "Keep quiet, this is just BS." I kept my mouth shut as we listened to a lot more BS.

Headquarters said they were going to send somebody out to Denver for a review and it would take a couple weeks to set up the review. However, they were just stalling.

We listened to absolutely inane stuff for a long time. Then Larry said, "Look, our corporation stands behind this (the launch vehicles). We have done everything we can."

Somebody at Headquarters said, "If we have more reviews, we can guarantee success." Such BS. NASA reviews everything to death and rockets and spacecraft still fail. That is why programs cost two or three times more than they are supposed to — NASA has a review every five minutes. That person continued with, "You know, you had some problems with your rocket's first launch. If we have a review, maybe we can find some more problems."

Larry answered, "You could have spent a million dollars on reviews and never found the problems we had."

That is the truth. You have to test rockets; you can't paper-study them, you have to launch them. Headquarters people have no idea about how to do anything and they are too cowardly to do anything anyway.

Finally, the nonsense ended without accomplishing anything, other than making it clear that we were not going to make our September launch because of the Lewis delays, and that NASA was about to require an endless series of useless launch vehicle reviews.

After the telecon ended, Scott, Sylvia, Dougherty, and I discussed the mess. Scott was doing his best to stop the nonsense, but he was powerless to do so.

We called Larry Price again and Larry said, "What the hell can I do."

I answered, "Two things; first of all, those (NASA) guys are running scared, they are in a panic mode and you can't calm them down with any rational arguments. They're scared and getting more so every minute. The only thing that will satisfy them is if you launch LLV1 with no payload. That's what they want. The second thing is the question about how they could be reassured. Well, they can only be reassured if we get Lockheed's top management to go straight to Goldin and say that we (Lockheed) stand behind this and we are going to do the job, so get off our back."

Larry then said that, when Brashears was at the last review for the Lewis LLV1, Goldin walked up to him, stuck his finger in Brashears face and said, "You're going to guarantee that the rocket is going to work."

The telecon had lasted until about 2:00 PM and by the time we were done talking to Larry, it was nearly 3:00.

After that, I went back to Lockheed and I saw Maryann. She asked me how things were going. I told her I needed to meet with Scott and Cathcart, but that Scott had been sick and then was gone and I was going to the Cape, so I would not see them until the following week. She said she would like to be there too, which was fine by me.

I hoped to get our contracts person and the Ames's contracts person together and get everything done regarding my leaving Lockheed. I had a very slight hope that we could get everything done by the end of June and that I could start working in LRI on July 1, but realistically, the way it was going, I thought it would be the first or second week of July before I would be in LRI and that ticked me off.

Wednesday, June 18, through Sunday, June 22, 1997:
A Trip to the Cape

I was on a trip to the Cape during the latter part of the week for a meeting that was mainly about the TLI Stage interface with the LLV2. Someone had found that the bottom of the TLI Stage, where it fit onto the LLV2 adapter, was not quite round, so it did not fit properly. We would have to put a stiffening ring in the TLI Stage casing to get it back to being round.

On the way back to California, I passed through Chicago and spent the weekend with my Mother, who was going to be 90 on her July 7 birthday.

While I was gone, the engineers did the final acoustic test and the spacecraft fared well. They found that the PIV was rattling, not only because it needed some stiffening, but also because it was not properly screwed down. They fixed that. The bracket for the Earth/Moon limb-crossing sensor was a lot better, not 100%, but good enough. Basically, the spacecraft was OK.

However, four of the damned light filters on the APS were totally ripped apart, so they weren't going to work.

Chapter 3-35
Going Through Hell to Get Out of Lockheed

Monday, June 23, 1997: The APS Problem

Lockheed was actually expecting me to leave, because I got all the information from the administration about retiring! I didn't think Lockheed was the problem; rather I thought Ames was the problem.

I called the LANL guys about the APS light filters being destroyed during the acoustic test. Bill was on vacation in Greece, which did not help, since we had to fix that problem, pronto. Also, I was getting very concerned, because the calculations of the free molecular heating showed it was higher than we had thought. I thought the heating could wreck the upper two filters on the APS. Similarly, I was worried that the exhaust of one of the TLI Stage spin-up rockets might impinge on the bottom and one side of the APS and destroy four more of those delicate filters. Bill simply had to get those filters right or the APS wasn't going to work.

Then the damned computer crashed that we had the spacecraft simulator on, so we couldn't do any training or improve the model. It was going to be out for a week!

Tuesday, June 24, 1997: More Launch Vehicle Issues

The first thing I did was to call Bill in Greece (where it was afternoon) to discuss what we were going to do about the APS light filters. I convinced him we should have the aluminum films deposited on the detectors and do away with the delicate plastic films. He said he would have to rematch the gains on each of the pre-amps of the five detector pairs, because the gains were set for the existing configuration and that would require a fairly big effort. Bill was also worried that some of the detectors might have been broken during the acoustic test, but I doubted that was the case.

Dan, Irv, and I had begun to believe we had too much fuel in the TLI Stage. Denver's new LLV2 calculations came out with 10 m/sec more velocity than we had expected and they had forgotten that 1.09 kilograms of fuel would be burned during the spin-up of Spacecraft/TLI Stage stack, so the velocity error would be more like 16 m/sec. Also, Denver didn't account for the inert mass ejected during the Star-37 burn and that oversight would also lead to an even bigger TLI velocity error. When we calculated it, we got a 30 to 40 m/sec TLI over-burn error and we were trying to verify all that via a series of telecons. We spent a lot of time on that critical topic. We knew, of course, that the solution was to add ballast to the TLI Stage to make it heavier and hence, to get the correct velocity from its burn, but we needed to know exactly what the over-burn was before we could do the ballasting.

I was more than a little ticked about the over-burn problem, because when Irv, Dan, and I were doing the calculations back in the fall, I assumed Irv was keeping track of all of those things and I was beginning to find out that Irv didn't keep track of much of anything. He couldn't find any of those calculations and he couldn't find any of the data we had used. Before we could make the corrections, we had to understand how we had gotten to where we were and why there was too much fuel in the Star-37. I said we needed to call Thiokol because we had faxed them the information back in the fall, so we could get the data from them.

Instead of Irv or even Dan calling Thiokol, which was Irv's job as the Propulsion Engineer, they just sat there. I picked up the phone and called Thiokol. Why the engineers would never call a vendor to get the required information was a mystery to me. Tom complained about that, too. Tom and I would pick up the phone and get it done, right then and there.

I was really disturbed by their unwillingness to make a simple call and even more so by their slovenliness; there we were, we had an error in the propellant load, and if we had not caught it, we would have had a bad over-burn that would have cost an enormous amount of spacecraft fuel to correct.

However, there was one nice thing about that whole mess, since we had to put the stiffening ring in the TLI Stage to make it round, we could put a lot of the extra ballasting mass on that stiffening ring.

Scott, Sylvia, Dougherty, and I had a meeting — the six-months worth of launch vehicle reviews NASA had wanted during the big flap of the previous week had disappeared! I thought NASA was trying to slip one over on us with all that baloney. Also, all of a sudden, Headquarters had no objections to Lewis being launched as soon as the LLV1 was ready! LLV hoped they could get Lewis off on July 23. If they did and if it were a good launch and if they understood any anomalies, then we could still launch on September 24!

However, we all agreed among ourselves that with Lewis getting launched that late, a September launch of Lunar Prospector was pushing it. We all suspected we would slip to the end of October. Also, the Cape had to know by July 2 when in hell we were launching and that was just eight days away! It really looked like we might end up being forced to move into October. Then, if Cassini slipped, we would be in trouble.

I found it highly annoying that the big flap centered on Karen Poniatowski; she was always stirring the pot, making statements that were incorrect and seeing what she could get away with — it was frequently all a bluff to put the screws to Lockheed. In that particular flap, I thought she was hoping, when she made her grand pronouncement about the LLV1/Lewis and LLV2/Lunar Prospector launches and their new policy, everybody would just roll over dead and she would sneak in a policy that was not official. Regardless of how or why, that big flap had passed (as had so many others just like it) and we were again moving towards a September or October launch, if everything went well with Lewis.

Finally the meeting was over and Dougherty and Sylvia left so Scott and I could have our meeting about my leaving Lockheed. I said to Scott, "I'm really concerned that this (meeting) was supposed to have happened two or three weeks ago. I know you were ill and then I was on a trip, so I'm not complaining about that. But the point is that nothing has happened about my leaving Lockheed and I'm quite annoyed that I'm being kept in the dark. I had to press Sylvia and Maryann to find out what had been going on and as a result, I found out there are discussions going on about my career, my future, my Institute, and my program that I am excluded from. I'm not happy about that. This is not the way things should be done. The other thing, Scott, if what I have been told is correct, Lockheed keeps saying — oh, we are ready to go, but Ames isn't — then Ames says — oh, we are ready to go, but Lockheed isn't. The bureaucrats are just pointing fingers at each other and none of them are doing anything — it's just a snow job. I just want to get this thing done."

Then I told Scott about my asinine conversation with Cathcart and said, "If those are real issues, then we need to discuss them and get it done. I want to get out (of Lockheed) and get busy (in LRI). I have a lot of things to do. I don't have time for this."

I said, regarding my getting killed on the freeway, "The solution is simple, Dan Swanson knows how to fly the spacecraft and could easily do so, and Bill could run the science. Also, I understand Dougherty suggested you be the PI and you declined."

Scott said, "I know nothing about that."

I said, "You see, there are all kinds of things being said, but nobody knows what is really going on."

Scott said, "OK, let's cut this short. We agreed to this. I agreed with what you want to do. I wanted it to be later, but you have your reasons. I passed it through NASA and nobody could figure out any reason why this wouldn't be OK. I agree with you that this has dragged on long enough, so let's get the thing done."

I said, "Good, I wanted to have a meeting tomorrow with you, Cathcart, and Maryann, so we can sit down with the issues and get them on the table and get them resolved."

Scott said, "OK, let's do that."

Scott surprised me; he said, "I don't want anything interfering with our relationship. As far as I'm concerned, we are working well together on this mission, it's a joint effort and I don't want anything to come between us."

I was pleased with what Scott had just said and I chuckled a little to myself, because I was wondering how much of what he said was just, "Uh-oh, Alan is getting mad and the last thing we want is for Alan to get mad."

However, Scott seemed quite sincere about making sure that nothing was hurting our working relationship, so I said, "Yes, Scott, I have always considered that you and I are partners in this. I've always believed that and I don't want anything getting between us."

Wednesday, June 25, 1997:
Finally Getting Agreement About My Leaving Lockheed

I had my meeting with Scott, Maryann, and Cathcart. It was interesting because, as I suspected, each side told me only what the other side was doing wrong. Cathcart had his trumped-up concerns and Maryann was forced to say what Lockheed wanted her to say. She apologized for that and said Lockheed wasn't going to do anything that was not in its best interests and wouldn't do anything that might make it look bad. I knew Maryann was basically on my side, and I felt sorry for her because she had to present Lockheed's side, even though she did not agree with it.

Cathcart then voiced more and more concerns and wanted to insert more and more things into the contract. Scott saw the direction Cathcart was going in and said, "Well, let me explain the background of this," and proceeded to explain that my leaving Lockheed and going to LRI was something he and I had been discussing for some time.

Scott said, "We all agreed that nobody wanted to do anything that would upset the program. We are trying to set precedents here and we are obviously doing a good job. But Alan wants to do this for a number of reasons and it is a reasonable time to do it. I've checked this out with Lockheed and I've taken it up to Headquarters. Headquarters sees nothing wrong with it and, in fact, thinks it is a good idea. This is all positive. This is what NASA is promoting. Also, there are other cases like this, correct?"

Cathcart answered, "Yes, there was a guy in the Pioneer Program. But he was trying to get more money — as much money as he could."

Since Cathcart was trying to put a negative spin on it, Scott cut him off short and said, "The point is that NASA thinks this is a good deal and they have no objection. I waited another week and asked them again if they had thought it over and they said they had no objections. Thus this has to be done." That was a strong message to both Lockheed and Cathcart.

Nevertheless, Cathcart kept yapping about various pseudo-issues. Everything he brought up was pro forma issue, bureaucratic gobbledygook that he was trying to use to cloud the real issue. Finally we got done and, despite Cathcart, I was going to get out of Lockheed in a few days, I hoped by July 1.

Thursday, June 26, 1997

I talked to Maryann in the morning about the contract to make sure I had everything correct. I hoped I understood everything. I also called Wayne and he was going to read the new version of the contract.

Because of the APS light filter problem, we ordered ten new APS detectors with the light filters deposited right on the detectors. Bicron said they had four that could be shipped right way and they would be light tight. The rest would follow shortly. That was what Bill should have done in the first place, instead of fooling around with those damned delicate plastic light filters.

Woody talked about the Power Subsystem at our Mission Ops seminar in the afternoon.

The engineers were doing proof testing of the spacecraft to see that the engines and tanks and plumbing were OK.

Friday, June 27, 1997

Friday was a quiet day. We still could not do any training, so I got a lot of little things done. Also, Dan and I gave a seminar on the Attitude Control Subsystem to the Mission Ops Team.

Monday, June 30, 1997: No Contract

I went to see if Maryann had the contract done. Of course, she didn't. She was supposed to be on vacation, but she was too busy and too overworked to take a vacation or to get to my contract, which had no priority at all. Then she said, "After I get done with it, it has to go back to the Lockheed lawyers and then to Cathcart. It will probably be next week, towards the end of the week, before we can get it done." That was it, I went to Ames and moaned at Scott about the foot dragging and he said there wasn't much he could do about it unless it really looked like they were doing it on purpose.

Tuesday, July 1, 1997

It was again a slow day, so I went home at noon because there was not much going on and I was tired. Before I did, I talked to Maryann and, of course, nothing was happening on my contract. She said one of the reasons she was having so much trouble was that Lockheed had fired all of the people who did contracts, so the people, like her, who work on the projects directly, had to fill in for the fired contract staffers! I felt sorry for her, but what difference did it make? There was always an excuse for everything at Lockheed.

Wednesday, July 2, 1997: No September Launch

We got the official word — we could not launch in September because of the delays of Lewis, so we were going for October 24 and 25, if the Cape gave its approval and if Lewis got launched, and blah, blah, blah. Nothing was certain until Lewis launched, but we were pretty sure we were going on October 24.

I would rather have launched in September, but given the circumstances, I thought that the delay was a good. The October launch windows were slightly better windows than the September windows and I did not want to rush the launch — one more month would not hurt anything.

Scott was handling NASA pretty well about the slip. Karen Poniatowski was going to try to raise all kinds of hell, but Scott stopped her. I don't understand NASA. The woman is totally counter-productive. She is disruptive. She is negative. She is always causing problems. Why do they put up with a person like her? Why don't they just fire her or give her to another job where she can do no harm?

Irv gave the Propulsion Subsystem seminar to the Ops Team and it was pretty good; he made some interesting points.

LLV called and said they thought they could only launch 1520 kg to the parking orbit, so they wanted us to take 3 kg out of our ballast. Al Tilley was concerned about that because we were going to need at least 12 kg of ballast on the spacecraft to get the cg and the spin balancing right, because the wiring was all asymmetrically placed on the spacecraft. He was not willing to give up that 3 kg and we had to fight with LLV and tell them, "No way!" They would have to find another way of getting around the problem, which was just a matter of changing the parking orbit parameters a little. Simply put, LLV didn't want to have to deal with the Cape on that issue and hence have to resubmit their launch trajectory for approval, so they just wanted us to take a 3 kg hit. As usual, LLV expected us to make all the adjustments so they could take the easy way out.

Thursday, July 3, through Sunday, July 6, 1997: Steve Durst's Meeting, Mars Pathfinder, and a Little Vacation

Rebecca and I drove down to Pasadena, CA, on the 3rd so I could give a talk on Lunar Prospector at Steve Durst's meeting on commercial space activities on July 4. July 4 was also the date for the Mars Pathfinder landing and Scott was going to give a talk on Lunar Prospector at the *Planet Fest* being put on by the Planetary Society, just across the street from Steve's meeting, to celebrate Pathfinder's landing.

Steve's meeting was quite interesting and I met John Spencer, who is promoting space tourism, who has a lot of good contacts, and who knows what in hell he is doing.

Dan Greenwood, who is promoting commercial power from space, was there, and as always, Dan and I had some good discussions. Mike Simon from International Space Enterprises was there and did a good job. There was a lawyer who discussed space law and whom everyone found aggravating. The other speakers weren't very good, but the whole trip was worth it just to meet John Spencer.

I had asked Wayne Stevens to be there so he could begin to be an active member of the LRI staff; as a result, he and Rebecca finally got to meet. However, since the LRI contract was not finished, there was not much that we could talk about.

Because of Wayne's considerable persuasive powers, Wayne, Rebecca, and I were able to crash the JPL Pathfinder friends and family party and got to watch the Pathfinder pictures coming down from Mars. It was beautiful; the pictures from Pathfinder were great and the mission was fantastic, especially the little Sojourn rover. Of course, the Pathfinder landing brought back all my old memories of the Viking 1 and 2 landings twenty-one years earlier.

Rebecca and I had a short vacation over the weekend. We drove up the coast and re-met Wayne at his Mexican fast food restaurant in Thousand Oaks (to the west of LA) where we had lunch (Rebecca and I did not like the food). Then we continued up the coast and enjoyed the beautiful scenery.

Monday, July 7, 1997

The team from JPL came up with their big trailer full of electronic gear to test the communication link between Lunar Prospector and NASA's Deep Space Tracking Network, i.e., the so-called RF (Radio Frequency) Test. Lunar Prospector had been taken to another building while I was in Pasadena and the JPL team was getting everything hooked up between the spacecraft and the trailer that was parked just outside of the test building.

Tuesday, July 8, 1997: RF Testing

The RF testing was going quite well. Maryann, of course, didn't get my damned paperwork done. I was getting really sick of that crap. The spacecraft was in good shape. The launch vehicle was the same old mess. Nothing had changed. I was just getting annoyed.

Wednesday, July 9, 1997

Everything was continuing to go well with the RF testing, the 3600 bps (bits per second) science and engineering data downlink mode worked perfectly.

Maryann had, of course, done nothing.

Dan and I compared our models of the propulsive maneuvers and his had a lot of mistakes in his model. That really surprised me, because Dan is a really sharp engineer — but that is why we crosschecked everything several times.

Channel 2 TV interviewed me all morning about the commercial aspects of Lunar Prospector.

Thursday, July 10, 1997: More Launch Delays

I talked to Dougherty; he said he had told Maryann that my contract had the highest priority, so he thought it was done and he was going to take it to upper management later in the day. I said, "Well, it's not done." Unfortunately, Dougherty was going to be gone the following day, Friday, because his son was visiting. It would not be done until the following week! I was stuck in Lockheed for another week.

Dougherty said he talked to LLV and gave them holy hell. He said, "We didn't part as friends, but we made up today." Basically, he said Larry Price thought they could get us launched in October.

Nevertheless, Dougherty was getting very skeptical about that and said, "I didn't have a good feeling about this because there is only six days of margin."

Unfortunately, about ten minutes later, we found out that LLV had another problem with the LLV1 avionics. When we heard that, I was pretty sure we would end up launching in November rather than October.

As a result, Dougherty sent LLV a bill for half a million dollars to cover the costs we were incurring because of the delays. Who was going to end up paying the money was a company problem. Either way, corporate would have to pay for the delays.

In addition, CRSS had finally come clean. The guy who headed CRSS said to Dougherty, "Don't get Lunar Prospector stuck behind CRSS. We are scheduled for launch on December 1, but I don't have a spacecraft. We have to go through thermal-vac. We have to go through acoustic and we have no flight software."

Lockheed was going to have to admit pretty soon that CRSS wouldn't be ready for launch until, at least, spring, just like I had been told by the CRSS engineers. That ticked me off, because every time I told Dougherty that was what the engineers had told me, he would say, "No, no, they're are going to make it." Lockheed had lied to the very end because they would not tell the stockholders that CRSS was going to be at least six months late.

What bothered me about that was if Lockheed had told NASA the truth when they started all the fussing about us launching after CRSS, we wouldn't have wasted all the time and money on the useless discussions about the LLV2.

I asked Dougherty, "How are we were going to pay for all the launch delays? Are we just going to delay one month at a time?"

He answered, "Yes, because the only cost is the cost of the trajectories and the company is going to have to pick that up." We were going to get into the mode of having one-month delays, one delay at a time! Now that was something to look forward to!

I thought, *well, with any luck, we'll get off in October or November, probably November.* Anyway, the cards were finally getting on the table.

Scott got promoted from his division's Associate Deputy to its Deputy and got a nice pay increase. Also, after seeing how much good PR Pathfinder got by showing its data to the public in real-time, Scott was excited about getting good PR for Lunar Prospector and showing our data in real-time. Gee whiz, let me think, who had wanted good PR and to have the data shown to the public in real-time long before Pathfinder, and who was against all that? Damn both Scott and NASA to hell.

Because we were definitely delayed until October, I had to redo the Mission Profile, so I finished the October 24 version, which I feared was probably not going to be used.

The RF testing was going well. The only problem was that they were having trouble syncing up with the 300 bps, engineering-data-only, downlink mode; but they said they would get that fixed because it was just a software problem.

When I heard they had had trouble syncing up with the 300 bps engineering-data-only data rate, I only planned to use from spacecraft turn-on to the point in time when I switched to the 3600 bps science and engineering data rate less than a hour after turn-on, I began to think about skipping the 300 bps data rate and just have the C&DH turn on the 3600 bps data rate as part of the initialization sequence. That would save me one step in the initial commanding of the spacecraft, during the critical first hour or two of the flight; so even though it would be just one less step, I decided it was worth doing. Nevertheless, when I found Tim Bridges, told him what I was thinking and asked for his opinion from the communications standpoint, Tim said it would be OK, but asked, "Do you really want to start at 3.6 kbps? If we are having communications problems right after launch, you might want to have that little bit of extra signal strength that the 300 bps gives you."

I answered, "Yeah, but we'll be so close to Earth that the 300 bps can't make too much of a difference, and I like not having to switch from 300 bps to 3.6 kbps; it's just one less thing that can go wrong."

Tim said, "Well, if you really want to change the initialization sequence, that will require a hardware change in the C&DH — are you sure that you want to do that now, after everything is tested?"

My answer was a reluctant, "No, but —."

Tim added the final blow, "Also, TDRS can't lock up on us if we're at transmitting at 3.6 kbps, but it can at 300 bps. Do you want to lose TDRS coverage?"

My answer was, "No," and I dropped the issue.

Dan and I again worked on comparing our two models for the burn maneuvers and, interestingly enough, my model was much more accurate than his, even though his model was much more complex than mine. We had slowly, but surely worked through the two programs one step at a time. When the numbers we got differed, we checked out why and, in every case, Dan had either made an error in his programming or had made an approximation that he shouldn't have. Dan is extremely good and I thought that the fact that my modeling was essentially error free while his was not, was due to the fact that my model was very simple and his was very complicated — another example of why I believe in the KISS principle so much. However, by the end of the day, our numbers were getting very close and I was very pleased about that.

Friday, July 11, 1997

Dan and I finished working through our burn programs and got all the little errors out of them.

I got a call from a *Business Week* reporter who was helping a colleague do an article on cheap rockets, so he called me about that. I said I was not a rocket expert, but I could tell him about inexpensive spacecraft. I told him all about Lunar Prospector and he got excited and said that was the kind of stuff they wanted.

Maryann said we had gotten the 3rd 100% award fee, so there was going to be another pizza lunch party on Thursday. More importantly, she had finished typing my contract and she got Mike Coats, the new Vice President, moving on my contract. She was sending it over to him and had talked to Palochak and Cathcart. I hoped they would get my contract done next Monday, because the contract was supposed to be signed the next Friday.

RF compatibility testing was nearly finished, but there was still a problem sending commands to the spacecraft and that had to be fixed.

Chapter 3-36
Another Lockheed Stab in the Back

Monday, July 14, 1997: The Stab in the Back

Maryann had my contract finished and it was ready for Dougherty to take it to Coats and Henshaw for signature, so I got to see it in its completed form for the first time — *and I was outraged!* Lockheed was going to hold back 30% of the money until the end of the mission and pay LRI only $10,000 a month during the mission — that was less than my wages and benefits and left nothing for travel expenses and other expenses (remember, as a Lockheed employee, I cost Lockheed at least $30,000 per month, given Lockheed's enormous overhead). The fact that they were going to withhold 30% of the contract value clearly said I could not be trusted to run my own mission unless Lockheed had a stranglehold on me and Lockheed was going to make me pay for leaving their damned company. I was outraged at both the insult and the stab in the back. My hatred of that disgusting company grew exponentially with every second.

I said to Maryann, "This doesn't even cover my wages and why on Earth are you holding money back?"

She answered, "Well, the 30% is standard."

I said, "This won't work. Just flat out, I won't be paid less than I am getting now and do all my travel on less money."

She said, "We can adjust it (the 30%)."

I asked, "How much can you adjust it? Is this all negotiable?"

She said, "Yes."

I asked, "Can it be zero?"

She said, "Yes."

We began to negotiate, she cut the withholding percent enough to cover LRI's monthly expenses, but there was no upfront money so I could get computers and the other office equipment that I needed. I asked her, "How am I supposed to work?" As a result, she put in $20,000 for the upfront costs plus $20,000 every month — which was everything I had originally asked for, leaving only $7,000 for the final payment.

I said, "I want to check the numbers again, but I think that it's acceptable; but my whole point is why? Why is this necessary? This is my program. I am not going to run off. If I don't deliver data, the only reason will be because the spacecraft failed, not because I am going to run off. This is an insult. Lockheed is accusing me of trying to renege on something I've worked eight years on. I'm the driving force behind this mission and it's my mission. It's not a Lockheed mission. It is my mission."

Despite my anger at Lockheed (I never was angry at Maryann, she had to do Lockheed's dirty work and I knew she did not like doing it), I was ready to settle for the minimum we had just negotiated, so we could get the contract signed, sealed, and delivered and I could get back to spending all my time on the mission. However, I was absolutely disgusted with Lockheed for the low down way in which they were treating me and had treated Lunar Prospector from the beginning. As far as I am concerned, Lockheed should be banned from the Earth.

On top of all that crap, Scott got all bent out of shape because he didn't like what I had said in interviews on CNN and FOX, fearing I would get him in trouble with Headquarters. He didn't say anything to me, rather he had Sylvia call me and I said, as always, "This is a bunch of BS. If Scott has a problem with me, he ought to talk to me. I'm getting a little tired of this."

Sylvia said, "The real problem is that everyone (Scott and his higher-ups) here is sensitive because Ames is always on the verge of being closed down and they're trying to use Lunar Prospector as a way of keeping the doors open. They get very upset about anything that makes it look like they are not totally in charge. Also, there is the ego part of it too" (Scott did not like me getting good PR coverage instead of him).

Well, clearly Scott and I were going to get into it again. But first things first, and the first thing was getting my contract done and getting out of Lockheed. Then, if we were going to do battle, Scott couldn't stop me from getting into LRI. Since Scott and I were both very busy the whole week, I was just going to try to keep the PR issue off the table until I got a signed, sealed, and delivered contract. If we signed the contract the next day, then Friday would be my last day at Lockheed, and that was the only thing that really counted — Scott could wait.

We were finishing up the RF testing — the engineers finally found out why we couldn't send commands to the spacecraft. There was one damned bit that was wrong in the first two bits in the sync word, so the spacecraft wouldn't accept the commands. Finally, we could command and get downlink from the spacecraft through the entire system. Thus, we were ready to start the "End-to-End Test" that would last several days. Up until then, all the RF testing was conducted between the spacecraft and the electronics trailer parked just outside the building. The End-to-End Test consisted of data being transmitted from the spacecraft, via temporary ground lines, to the Goldstone tracking station via JLP, just as if the spacecraft were in space. Goldstone would "pick up" the spacecraft downlink signals and route them through JPL, via the normal ground lines, to our Mission Control Center at Ames, where we would see the data on our monitors. Then we would send commands to the spacecraft in the reverse direction. Thus we would test every link in our communications network between Mission Ops and the spacecraft as if the latter were in space.

Bill and his technicians arrived at Lockheed at noon and started working on the APS and they were getting nowhere. We got the old test cables out and plugged them in between the APS and the SES and then the APS worked perfectly! We knew the electronics and the spectrometer were OK, but when we went back to using the flight cables that were on the boom, the APS was saturated with electronic noise — so we knew that the problem was somewhere in the cabling. I had my fingers crossed that the problem was in those parts of the cables between the boom canister and the SES, since it was not too hard to get to those parts of the cables or that the problem was in the connectors outside of the canister, because in either case, it would not be too hard to fix. But if there was something wrong on the damned cables on the boom itself, then that boom would have to be taken off the spacecraft again and rewired and that would cost us a lot of time and money. Worse, we had the final boom deployment test coming up, so we had to have the booms in their final configurations — so the situation was very serious.

Bill was concerned about the light tightness of the filters deposited on the APS detectors and he still wanted to use the foils. Going back to the thin foil filters was to be avoided if at all possible because I didn't know how high the free molecular heating was going to be since the launch vehicle issue was still all screwed up. We had two big problems with the APS that had to be fixed — and soon.

Regarding our launch, Lewis was not going to be launched on August 6 (in the meantime, Lewis had been delayed from later July to August 6), so that almost certainly meant we weren't going to be able to launch in October and we would know that for sure in a couple more days. Thus, it was really looking like we would have a November launch, if then! Also, every time LLV did something, they found more problems with the Lewis LLV1. The Lunar Prospector Mission was in jeopardy because the question was, "Are the LLV rockets pieces of crap?"

Tuesday, July 15, 1997:
End-to-End Testing and More Contract Aggravation

I worked a large part of the day on the End-to-End Testing, which was really fun because we were communicating with the spacecraft through the DSN. But the MGDS, the JPL system we had to use for uplink was really cumbersome. It took a lot of time for the uplink controller to prepare each uplink file. The MGDS was not well suited for Lunar Prospector. It was too bad we had decided to use it. I was told we could have used another system that was not quite as bad, but the files would have to be made up by a technician at the transmitting DSN station at the same time we were making them up at Mission Control, and that was a sure setup for making commanding errors — big time.

Given the poor alternative, we were going to have to change our simple commanding scheme of sending just one command per file — that just took too much time and effort. It took five minutes or more for the controller to setup one file and there was a lot of room for error in setting it up. To cut down on the file preparation time and to insure that we had no command errors, I was sure we would have to have several related commands in each file, rather than having just one command per file. I did not want to do that, but I didn't think I had much of a choice. To be sure, we were going to practice sending commands both ways, i.e., one per file and a series in a file, the next day. All in all, the testing showed us there were a lot of things we didn't know about commanding through the DSN, e.g., we couldn't get commands into the spacecraft because we didn't know the exact format. But, it was a very good learning day and we were very interested to see how well we would do the next day.

I talked to Maryann; she said that she had taken our agreement of the day before to her boss, Ray Edinger, and he hit the ceiling. She said, "It just won't work. Ray insists on doing it Lockheed's way and wants to pay the $100,000 at the end."

I replied, "That's fine, but I can't do the work. Either I pay my wages and don't travel or have any equipment, or I travel and have the other things I need and I don't pay my wages. You simply are taking the guts out of this thing. This is ridiculous."

I showed her the spending data I worked on the previous night. I said, "Look, I have all this travel in the early part of the contract, the next few months until launch, and the costs of buying all the support equipment I need. I can't pay for all that at the end of the mission. What Lockheed wants is just unreasonable, I can't do it." I said, "Besides, it's an insult that Lockheed says it has to hold back money so I have an incentive to finish my own program I've worked on for nine years. Does Lockheed think I'm going to run away? Who makes these decisions?"

She said, "Ray does."

I said, "Well then, I'll go talk to Ray. Ray knows what Lunar Prospector is all about. This is absurd. But I guess I'll talk to Tom first, because this isn't going to work."

She said, "Tom doesn't have the authority either."

I replied, "I understand that, but he is my interface with Lockheed, so I'll talk to him before I go to see Ray."

When Dougherty came back from lunch, I talked to him. He knew a little bit about the mess and said, "One of the things they are fussing about is the upfront money (which was only about $18,000)," and he suggested, "Why don't we just loan you the computers and stuff you're already using here?"

I said, "That's fine with me. I would prefer to just keep what I'm using and not have to buy all that stuff and set it up. That would be just a pain in the butt anyway. I could work exactly the same way I am working now; that's fine with me."

We discussed the incentive payment at the end of the mission and Dougherty was somewhat appalled and said, "That's ridiculous."

As I did with Maryann a little earlier, I showed Dougherty my spending curve for the mission, with all the early travel, etc. and I said, "The money does me no good at the end — I need it in the beginning of the mission. Also, it's damn ridiculous to talk about me needing an incentive to do my own mission," and Dougherty certainly agreed with that.

After that, we talked about Henshaw; Dougherty said he had told Henshaw what I wanted and Henshaw had asked, "Why does he want to quit?"

Dougherty answered, "Because he wants to."

Henshaw said, "Well, OK, I'll sign it."

Dougherty said to me, "Henshaw is not the problem, but unfortunately, there are other people involved besides just him. What it really boils down to is that Henshaw can make it or break it, but everybody else wants to get his 2¢ in. I'll go see what I can do. Since it's actually between him and Coats, I'll go see Coats and Coats will go see Henshaw." Then Dougherty said, "I'm very sorry about this, but it's obviously not going to happen this week. It will have to be next week," and that was a fact I had to accept. I was grateful to Dougherty for sticking up for me — there were times like that when he was a very good guy and I appreciated it very much.

Wednesday, July 16, 1997: A Good End-to-End Test SIM, the End of FR Testing, and a Bad Contract Day

We had a beautiful, all day, End-to-End Test SIM and that ended the FR testing. It started off at about 8:30 AM and we went through all of the Day 0 events and all the Day 1 events, including turning on the GRS and NS high voltages, but not the ER high voltage, since I could not do that without damaging it. We were able to keep on the timeline of the Mission Profile. There were a few screw-ups, in that we were late by five to ten minutes sending a couple of commands, but the rest of the time, we sent the commands within a minute of the designated time or were right on time. We learned a lot. It was an excellent exercise. Also, I was finally getting my command team to be quiet and not talk except when required. Marcie, of course, complained about everything — too bad I couldn't send her to Siberia.

Maryann showed me what Lockheed was willing to do and that was to pay me my current salary plus 5%, which, of course, was what I would have anyway because it was soon time for the FY yearly raises! The travel budget was cut down to what it was in the original Lockheed contract, so I was concerned about that because we were traveling a lot more than we thought we would and there was still the issue about the incentive money.

Maryann, who was on my side, told me that I could ask for a 10% fee, so I was going to add that in and I was going to fight with them about my wages, since I was still, after two years of raises, not getting anywhere close to the $120,000 that had been written in the original proposal to NASA! I was sure I was not going to get everything I wanted, but I was going to get as much as I could. I hated Lockheed for screwing me so much, just because they knew I would do whatever I had to do to get my mission done and I hated NASA for the same reason.

Thursday, July 17, 1997: More SIMs and More Contract BS

We ran three SIMs and they all went absolutely perfect. We were getting very good. It was great.

I talked to Dougherty, who said Lockheed couldn't pay me anymore than I was costing the company already. I said, "That's fine, but given the big difference between LRI's overhead and Lockheed's, that is at least $40,000 more (per year) that I could get at LRI and still cost less than I do at Lockheed. Besides, according to the Discovery proposal, I was supposed to get $30,000 more than Lockheed ended up paying me when I was hired out here."

We discussed that particular screw job some more and Dougherty thought it was Gus's doing, because Gus was famous for that sort of crap. Dougherty added, "As far as I'm concerned, it's fine as long as it isn't anymore than you cost here. I'll do what I can."

We talked to Garner and he, of course, said "You can't do that!" Dougherty said Cathcart had said I couldn't make a lot of money out of the situation. Well BS, all I was trying to do was to get the wages that had been written into the Discovery proposal and no more. Dougherty agreed with me and said he was going to try to do that, but Garner kept saying, "You can't do that, but it does depend on what Cathcart says." Apparently Cathcart thought I was after a 30 to 50% raise, while in reality it was about 20%.

I said, "OK, if you can't get me the raise, what about the 10% fee?" Dougherty agreed he would try to get one or the other.

I was still concerned about the incentive crap and I said, "If Lockheed is going to have the incentive clause, then give me $30,000 as fee and hold it back until the end. I can't use the fee until later anyway."

Dougherty was quite sympathetic, which was surprising, and wanted to get it done. The thing that really floored me though, was when he said, "You are extremely valuable," which came a little late in the game if you asked me.

After we got done, Tom grabbed me because the new test cables we needed to checkout the APS cable problem were finally done. We first connected the cables between the SES and the spectrometer and there was no noise. Then we put the cables between the SES and the boom canister and there was no noise. Unfortunately, that seemed to mean that the cable problem was in the boom cables. Then we checked that out and found the problem was in one of the two connectors on either end of the boom cables — boy what a relief it was that the problem was not in the cables, since we would have had to remove the boom and have it rewired again. Since the problem was in one of the two connectors, we could isolate it, fix it, and then we would be OK.

Just before I left work, Maryann told me what Dougherty and I had agreed on about the contract was OK and we could get the contract done — finally!

Friday, July 18, 1997: More Frustrations

We had a good SIM, but that was the only thing that went well all day.

Maryann told me in the morning, before we started the SIM, that what she had told me the night before was incorrect. She had misunderstood what she had been told; instead of her bosses accepting what Dougherty and I had agreed on, they said I would just get my current wages plus 5% and no fee. Everything else in the budget was untouched, they didn't squawk about anything except my wages and my travel. She said she didn't know what the numbers really were, because she didn't have them on paper. She said I should come back at noon and she would have the real information.

When I went back to see Maryann, she said they were scrutinizing the budget because they wanted to make sure my wages were consistent with their regulation, so they had to know what my degree was in and other crap like that. That told me they were just looking for some regulation to knock my wages down. I said, "They aren't going to bring it up any are they?"

She answered, "No, you are probably going to get about what you're now making."

Then she dropped the real bomb, "They refused to have the payments tied to the monthly reports; they are going to be tied to deliverables."

I said, "Maryann, the first of the Level 1 data deliveries aren't due until six months after the mission starts. I can't wait six months to get paid! Lockheed is doing everything possible to make it impossible for me to leave this damned company!"

Since Maryann was really on my side, she said, "Well, the deliveries can be other things besides the data, like your Outreach activities," so we discussed other things I had to do to run the mission and that could serve as "deliverables," so I could get paid something every month. As we talked, we came up with enough "deliverables" that were spread throughout the some two years of the contract to keep some money flowing into LRI each month. The deliverables were small things like the training sessions we did, the new Mission Profiles that were required because the launch had slipped, my Outreach activities, and the big mission events like the launch and spacecraft turn-on, reaching lunar orbit, the data deliveries, etc., each of which was allocated a contract dollar value depending on its criticality to the success of the mission.

The deal was that, in order to get LRI paid each month, I would have to submit a monthly report and an invoice to Lockheed stating which of the deliverables I had "delivered to Lockheed," i.e., completed, since there was really nothing to deliver to Lockheed — even the data went straight to NASA, and then LRI would receive the amount of money that month that corresponded to the total value of those deliverables. Thus LRI would get widely differing amounts of money each month, depending on what phase of the mission we were in and, of course, by the nature of the mission, LRI would earn little money early on and, assuming the mission went well, more money as the mission progressed. Thus, Lockheed was going to be able to keep more of the money for itself in case the mission failed and keep LRI (and hence Rebecca and me) on a short financial leash for many months. That was just another way for Lockheed to stab me in the back. I was being treated like an untrustworthy subcontractor who had to be kept in line by the possibility of non-payment of funds on a program I had brought to that damnable company. As such, my contempt for Lockheed and those in it who were stabbing me in the back, over and over again, reached new heights. Every time they stabbed me in the back, I thought I could not despise them any more, but each time my contempt grew, and if Dante were correct, Lockheed belonged down in the eternal ice in the Central Pit of Malebolge with Satan.

Besides hating Lockheed and the disgusting people I had to deal with, I was really getting sick of Scott and his Little Lord Fauntleroy attitude of *I'm now the big shot*. The higher Scott got up in the Ames hierarchy, the more of a pompous little ass he became.

I was sick and tired of Scott. I was sick and tired of NASA. I was sick and tired of Lockheed. I was sick and tired of the whole mess. The only way anyone can do anything right is just to get away from the big companies and big organizations, period.

Monday, July 21, 1997:
Day One of the High School Teachers Seminars and Much More

As part of the Outreach and Education Program, I had asked each of my Co-Is to invite a high school teacher to participate in the mission. However, because of the lack of funds, their participation was basically limited to them attending a two-day seminar we held at Ames on July 21 and 22. In addition to the teachers, Bob Lin brought along several high school students, who were attending a special summer educational program at UC Berkeley. As my high school teacher, I had invited Dick Sealy, who came with his wife, from BJ Link at Bob Jones University, and I was very interested to see how a fundamentalist Christian University physics teacher would react to our world.

The seminars went extremely well. I talked about the Moon in the morning and Scott talked about Discovery. Then we went over to see the spacecraft and everybody enjoyed that very much. After lunch Bill, Bob, Alex, Lon, and Mario discussed the mapping instruments and their objectives. All the guests were interested and had a good time.

After the seminar, I talked to Maryann. She said the contract was for $181,000 and they were not going to allow me the 10% fee. I said, "That is just not acceptable."

She said, "Then you're going to have to talk to Ray."

I said, "That's the way it should have been in the beginning." She said she would set up a meeting for Thursday at 8:00 AM.

Maryann admitted that Lockheed was trying to make it as hard as possible for me to leave and go into LRI. She also said there was a rule that you cannot leave and get a subcontract from Lockheed until six months after you have left, but they had allowed that to happen once before. Well, I already knew Lockheed has a bunch of arbitrary rules they use when it is in their best interests. She then said if they won't sign, then it was up to Henshaw. I said, "I've known that from the beginning. That's the way it's going to end up anyhow."

We had gotten the sad news that Gene Shoemaker had been killed in car accident in Australia several days earlier and Scott emailed me that, at the request of Carolyn Porco, a planetary scientist from the University of Arizona who had a sappy, high school girl-like admiration of (crush on?) Gene, had asked NASA to fly Gene's ashes on Lunar Prospector. Thus, when I crashed it on the Moon at the end of the mission, Gene would have finally gotten to the Moon, at least symbolically, as he had always wanted to do in life.

As much as I admired and liked Gene, I wrote Scott an email that said, "This is a very bad idea. This sets a precedent for having every NASA mission carry somebody's ashes and NASA missions will become flying graveyards. The scientific community will appropriately honor Gene and he will get a crater named after him."

In addition to my personal view on the matter, there were the technical issues, since we had a completely finished and tested spacecraft that was basically flight ready and only an idiot would add un-tested, non-flight hardware to a spacecraft that had gone through thermal-vac and acoustic testing! I hoped that the issue would go away, but I was afraid that it wouldn't.

Tuesday, July 22, 1997:
Day Two of the High School Teachers Seminars and More

Dan and I ran a SIM for the teachers and students in the morning. The students were late because there was a wreck on the freeway from Berkeley. We had a good SIM; the teachers were all very interested, as were some of the students, but some of the students were just bored stiff, which surprised me. Well, you can't win them all.

In the afternoon, one of the teachers and one of the students ran a mid-course maneuver SIM. They did fairly well and got a real kick out of it, but they were very nervous about trying to run the spacecraft — even one in a computer.

I talked to Maryann about the negotiations and she said she was out of the picture. I was to negotiate with Maryann's boss on the following Monday. I was getting tired of the mess.

As a result of the fact that Lockheed was putting the screws to me about the contract, I didn't think Rebecca and I would be able to go on the vacation to Crater Lake we had planned in early August. I needed to get the contract done by August 1 if we were to be able to go on the vacation and I did not see that happening. I was annoyed.

Wednesday, July 23, 1997: The Pre-Ship Review

Except for fixing the APS and doing the last boom deployment test, Lunar Prospector was ready for launch, so we had our Pre-Ship Review to discuss all the details about shipping the spacecraft to the Cape. The review went very well. The major concern, of course, was the launch vehicle and there was some concern about the TLI Stage timer. Other than that, the review went smoothly.

However, Marcie got grilled because she hadn't gotten a lot of her Ground Segment tasks done, but basically, everybody was happy with everything, so we were almost ready to go — though we still did not have a firm launch date and were still waiting on the Lewis launch!

Thursday, July 24, 1997: An Important SIM

We tested commanding the real spacecraft from Mission Ops at Ames most of the day. We found an interesting logic error in the commanding that we would have to be careful about during the mission. We *accidentally* fired the engines by loading the engine fire command sequence, but, because we did not really want to fire them on the real spacecraft, I did not issue the Execute Command, rather I went to the next step in the Mission Profile, which was to turn on the MAG. When I issued the Execute Command for the MAG Turn-on Command, the engines fired instead! We realized then that the MAG Turn-on Command did not write over the engine commands, as we thought, rather, the Execute Command acted on the first command, not the second! We quickly decided our operational procedure would be — *without exception* — that I would send the "Clear Engine Parameter Command" after each engine firing. The Clear Engine Parameter Command put zeros into all the engine parameter registers, e.g., zero seconds for the burn duration, zero seconds for the time delay after the sun pulse, etc., and that would absolutely ensure there would be no inadvertent engine firings. That was a most valuable lesson to have learned and would protect us from an event that could have cost us the mission had we not discovered it during the testing SIM!

The only bad thing about the SIM was that Dan wasn't there, so Marcie sat in on the SIM and she just kept yapping. She is just not capable of shutting her mouth.

Friday, July 25, 1997

I found out from Maryann that the negotiations of my contract were not going to be done with her boss, Jim Pappas, his boss, Ray Edinger, and Coats, as I wanted. It would be done just between Jim and me, which was BS. I tried, without success, to find Edinger all day to get that changed.

Dougherty and I had a meeting with Scott. I tried to get Dougherty to understand that we needed to merge the spacecraft simulator and MGDS commanding, so we could do the SIMs exactly the way we were going to fly the spacecraft, but, of course, he couldn't understand that. As usual, he refused to do anything I told him we needed to do. He was trying to spend as little money as possible for anything except getting the spacecraft done.

I was ticked at Scott, because he didn't back me up, even though he understood the critical need for us to train exactly the way we were going to fly the spacecraft.

All Scott did was to complain about the TV interview I had done with CNN and Fox and the mistake that the interviewer made when he said that I was Project Manager. I was sick of Scott's childish crap. Scott had become an insufferable pompous ass and was becoming worse every day. He thought he was running the entire show with his arrogant "I'm a big NASA official" crap. I was just sick of it. That was when I had my first thoughts about kicking Scott off the program. I thought there was probably no way I could do it, but if there were, I was going to do it.

At the end of our meeting, Dougherty announced he had been promoted again and was Lockheed's new Chief Spacecraft Engineer — what a joke, he didn't know one end of a spacecraft from the other and he had become Lockheed's Chief Spacecraft Engineer! Even he found it amusing. He was moving to the same building that Henshaw was in, so he had been climbing the ladder on Lunar Prospector's back. Both he and Scott had been moving their way up their ladders because of Lunar Prospector, which I thought was, in a perverted sense, a good reflection on the mission. Ironically, while they were getting big promotions, Lockheed was doing its best to screw me to the wall — well, if you kiss enough ass, you get ahead in organizations where ass kissing is more valuable than competence!

Monday, July 28, 1997: A Useless Negotiation Meeting

I finally met with both Ray Edinger and Jim Pappas at 1:00 PM and we talked about the contract until 5:00 PM. I made them listen to the background of Lunar Prospector and what I was attempting to accomplish programmatically, but they didn't care. Ray had known about Lunar Prospector since the Discovery proposal effort and I hoped he would be reasonable regarding my contract, given what I had brought to Lockheed, e.g., a million dollar spacecraft design for free, a $63 million contract, etc. and that was why I wanted Ray there, but all that made no difference.

Jim seemed to be a nice guy and I had always liked Ray, but they were still contract people who were solely looking out for Lockheed at my expense. Their bottom line was they had a standard way of dealing with subcontracts and blah, blah, blah. They were offering far less than $200,000, while I was asking for $300,000. I said,

"Somehow we have to get this done," and they agreed, because the contract was supposed to start at the end of the week. I told them, "If we can't come to an agreement, I'll just talk to Henshaw, because you guys don't really have rules, what you have are guidelines. Guidelines that can be changed depending on the circumstances, so change them and get this done." But we did not get it done. About all that I could say was we were converging. It was frustrating, because Lockheed was really just making the circumstances impossible for me to leave, but somehow I would get the hell out of that corrupt company.

A week earlier, Dougherty had said at the staff meeting that Teats, who I think was one of Lockheed's Vice-Presidents, was coming to Sunnyvale and Dougherty wanted to have a display near Lunar Prospector so Teats and Coats could understand the mission. Since Dougherty was skirting around the issue of who was going to show them the spacecraft and explain the mission, somebody piped up and said, "That's Alan's job, he has to show the spacecraft to Teats." Dougherty was embarrassed and fumbled around and it was clear he did not want the PI showing Teats and Coats anything and I just laughed to myself at how transparent he and Lockheed were about not wanting me around (but not wanting me to go, either). Well, Dougherty had gotten the display made and he had asked Tim to help him take it over to the spacecraft and set it up. I didn't know when Teats and Coats were coming, and Dougherty had not said a word about me presenting the spacecraft to them, so I knew I was not going to be asked to do so. Again, it was the same old crap, they wanted Lockheed to get all the credit for Lunar Prospector and have me disappear.

Tuesday, July 29, 1997: Tentative Agreement

I had a meeting in the morning with the ground crew to discuss the future training schedule.

After that, I prepared everything and went to talk with Jim Pappas. He wanted to keep the contract down to $225,000 and I started at $275,000. I talked him into letting me have money for Wayne, because NASA wanted me to have somebody in LRI with some business knowledge and Wayne has an MBA from the University of Chicago. Also, Maryann had told me I could expect to get the standard 9% for G&A and 30% for overhead, but Jim wouldn't agree to that. He said, "Why should we set you up. You expect us to pay all the costs of setting yourself up."

I said, "Because I worked for seven years on this program, brought it to Lockheed, and won it for Lockheed. What you are getting is $4 million from the mission and you already have a second mission based on Lunar Prospector (the IMAGE program) and a whole new line of business as we discussed the other day," and that shut him up. I said, "I can't do the job for $225,000 and that's that. You know that I want $275,000 (with a 10% fee) and you are offering $225,000, so we have to meet somewhere in the middle."

He asked, "What can you live with?"

I crossed the fee off the budget sheet and answered, "$253,000." That number had my full wages in it with a 5% increase right then and the standard 5% increase at the beginning of the FY, i.e., October 1.

Surprisingly, he tentatively agreed and said he would look it over to see if he could justify everything and that we should get back together at 8:00 the next morning. He said "However, even if it is OK, I don't think we can get through with the paperwork by Friday, but I'll try."

Wednesday, July 30, 1997: Finally, An Acceptable Offer

I went to see Jim at the appointed 8:00 AM and he had dropped the contract back down to $229,000. I said, "No way. You're wasting my time. Good-bye," and I then made an appointment to see Henshaw the following Monday! Enough was enough; I had had it with Lockheed's backstabbing.

Later in the day, I talked to Dougherty about the solar panels. Their wires were supposed to be in twisted pairs to cancel out the magnetic fields the individual wires generate. Even though the technicians were told to do that a hundred times, they did not do it near the cutouts for the tangential engines. Instead of having twisted pairs going around one side of each engine, they had split the pair and had a wire go around each side of the engine and thus, created a perfect ground loop with a big magnetic field! There were two magnetic hot spots in the solar array drum with field strengths of 20 nT, while they were supposed to have fields strength of less than 0.05 nT, i.e., they were 400 times worse than they were supposed to be! The cutouts had to be rewired.

Ray came into Dougherty's office and he asked me how things were going. I said, "I had been at $275,000 and you guys were at $225,000 and we sort of compromised yesterday at $253,000. But when I came in this morning it was back down to $229,000. That is just not acceptable."

He said, "We'll find a way of getting this done. I'll go talk to Jim."

I said, "Good, I want to get this done."

I said nothing about my appointment with Henshaw; I was going to keep that in my hip pocket until it would do the most good. Ray added, "We're so close, we can get this done."

I said, "I hope so." Then as I left Dougherty's office I said, "I'll see you later this afternoon. If you don't come to me, I'll come to you. I need to get this thing done, because it's interfering with my work. I have too much to do to be worrying about this." I was sure after I left, Dougherty said something to Ray about getting it done.

About 2:30, Jim came to my office — clearly Ray had talked to him. Jim said that Ray was under the impression I was leaving, come hell or high water and they were getting worried I would quit before the contract was all done. I said, "No, that's not the case. I don't want to lose any leverage, but no, I do not intend to quit" (maybe that was what they were hoping?).

I asked, "OK, what do you want to do?" They only wanted to give me 30% overhead instead of 30% overhead plus 9% G&A, i.e., instead of a total of nearly 40%, they wanted to lump all such administrative costs into one lower category, but they would give me all the travel. I said that I needed the 40% administrative costs or it wasn't going to work.

Jim added, "We have to find a way of doing this. Let me take what you got and see what I can come up with," and left again.

To my surprise, he came back in about five minutes. I said, "Well, it's either good news or very, very bad news if you are that quick."

He said, "That's the magic of computers, just a few key strokes and you're done. I think you will find this is acceptable."

It was $245,300, which was close enough. I said, "OK, that's close enough."

We initialed the changes and signed and dated the offer. Though I had a firm offer, it still had to be reviewed and he had to get a whole mess of signatures. We were still far from being done and some SOB might not sign it. Nevertheless, I thought we had gotten over the hump. I had a budget I could live with — barely.

Thursday, July 31, 1997:
Getting Ready for the Final Boom Deployment Test

First things first, I got the negotiated agreement for the payment and everything else from Jim and gave it to Maryann to type up. Before I could officially sign it, it had to go to legal and everywhere else. She was worried, because Jim thought there was some sort of a problem, even though Ray Edinger thought there would be no problem. Would it never end?

We got started preparing for the final boom deployment test late in the afternoon, but the guys had lost the damned device needed to re-stow the booms, so we didn't get started with the actual preparations until very late in the afternoon. It was so late I actually went home for supper and a few hours of rest, rather than just standing around like an idiot.

When I got back, we ran a baseline functional test on the instruments; the NS, GRS, and MAG/ER were fine, though the APS was still noisy and it had to be fixed. But we were ready for the boom deployment test that was set for the next day.

Friday, August 1, 1997: The Final Boom Deployment Test

I saw Dan when he came in the morning. He had on a suit and tie. I asked, "What are you all dressed up for?"

He answered, "Tom asked me to show Teats and Coats the spacecraft." I chuckled to myself; clearly, if somebody was going to show those guys the spacecraft, it should be the PI, not an engineer. I knew Dougherty was trying to hide the visit from me, because he didn't want me being there — he wanted to take as much credit for the mission as he could and make Lockheed look good, without having the pesky PI around. The last thing he wanted Teats and Coats to know was that I was the only one who really knew what was going on with the spacecraft and the mission. Anyway, the situation was building up to a very amusing end.

Regarding Dan's willingness to be part of Dougherty's "hide the PI" game, I was a little disappointed that Dan had so little integrity that he would go along with Dougherty's sham. I had a much higher opinion of Dan than that and I would not have guessed he would do so — but, if you are going to get ahead in an ass-kissing, back-stabbing organization like Lockheed, then you have to kiss ass and stab backs.

The most amusing aspect of Dougherty and Dan showing Teats and Coats the spacecraft was that I would almost certainly be there when they saw the spacecraft, because we were going to be working on the booms deployment test all day! I was looking forward to seeing Dougherty's and Dan's faces if I were there when they came in.

We finally found out why the APS was noisy. One of the Los Alamos technicians found out very quickly what was wrong with the APS. First he found that one of the shielding wires was not properly connected. He said it was a design error and they could just bridge it. Second, he believed that most of the noise in the APS was due to the SES power supply for the ± 5 v and the $+12$ v lines, which I was really unhappy to hear. I was concerned that the noise was due to a component that was beginning to fail and they would have to go into the SES to look for it. Monday they were going to pick up the spectrometer and the SES unit and take them to Los Alamos to fix the problem.

Scott sent me an email saying NASA was going to put Gene Shoemaker's ashes on the spacecraft. The family was all for it and Wes said NASA would take care of whatever issues there were about getting the ashes on the spacecraft. Scott had mentioned my objection that if NASA put Gene's ashes on Lunar Prospector, then every NASA space-craft might become a flying graveyard. Wes's comment was, "We'll handle that issue one case at a time."

During the afternoon, we got ready for the final boom deployment test. Every-body was there. We did a functional test on the instruments and then we were ready to go. I commanded the deployment sequence as I had done on the first deployment test and we had a perfect deployment — the booms were fine. However, some of the boom cable wires were slightly dinged and the insulation on one wire was cut, but none of that was serious.

After the test, and after normal working hours, we were inspecting the boom cables when Dougherty, Dan, Teats, and Coats came in. They milled around over by Dougherty's display, while a couple of us were working on my spacecraft. Coats and Dougherty came over and looked at the spacecraft and they never batted an eye. It was as though I was invisible. I wondered if Dougherty or Coats was even the slightest bit embarrassed to find the PI there, working on his spacecraft, while they were kissing Teats's butt, but I doubted it. Anyway, I found the entire situation was very funny — I didn't expect anything better from Dougherty or Lockheed.

Monday, August 4, 1997: Trying to Get the APS Problem Resolved

I talked to Maryann in the morning. She was busy trying to get my paperwork done, though my paperwork was always last on her list. When I saw her in the after-noon, she had already gotten the OK from the lawyers and two other signatures, so I thought the thing was moving along.

I worked on the Mission Profile, since Dan wanted me to put in the times when he wanted to command the ground (not spacecraft) recorder to be turned on and off to record the attitude data he needed to determine the spacecraft's attitude.

Bill and I had a long telephone conversation about the APS. We had decided Fri-day that Dan Everett was going to pick up the APS and SES unit and take them back to Los Alamos because we believed there was a problem with the power supply in the SES. But over the weekend, Bill and Dan talked themselves out of that and decided the prob-lem was not in the SES, rather it was in the cabling. Bill wanted everything brought back to Los Alamos. I said, "To hell with that. That's nonsense. We don't know what in hell is going on, so you guys fly out here and figure it out."

Bill said that he didn't want to fly out; rather he wanted to have everything brought to Los Alamos. Then he agreed to come, but then changed his mind again. Finally he agreed to come, but later he called Tom and said that he wouldn't come. Dougherty told Tom to call Bill and tell him to, "Get out here and get the damned thing fixed."

With that, I got back into the mix and I called Bill again. By then he again want-ed us to send everything out to Los Alamos, even all the ground support equipment! That was nonsense; we were not going to send the ground support equipment back and forth because every time we did, it had gotten broken. But Bill would not listen and I had had enough. I said, "Look, I have a spacecraft sitting here with the booms deployed, so it's vulnerable and the only way we are going to get the APS checked out properly is with it on the deployed booms. Get out here and fix it."

Bill still did not want to come to Sunnyvale. The trouble was that Bill had been coming to Lockheed for just a half day at a time. He always ran back to Los Alamos because he had other work to do. As a result, Bill always ran off before the problems were really fixed. He said, "We should have had this discussion last Friday and then we could have come out and worked all weekend."

I said, "Well, Bill, quite frankly, we did have this conversation last Friday."

I was more than a little bit ticked at Bill, instead of coming out and getting the damned APS fixed once and for all, he had been dicking around with half measures. I again said, "Look Bill, the spacecraft is sitting there with the booms out. They can't be out forever because it's dangerous. Somebody could hit those booms and if they get broken, we are out of luck. The other point is that we are running out of time. We are shipping the spacecraft off (to the Cape) in seven weeks. Either you get the APS fixed, or it doesn't fly."

Well, Bill didn't want that, but he still argued against coming out and fixing it. Finally I said, "Just come out and do it because if you don't, you're putting the APS, and worse, the mission in jeopardy. We have a spacecraft that is in flight configuration and you expect us to break flight configuration, take off the SES, take all those cables off, and do all that. This damned spacecraft is ready to fly, so get out here and fix the APS." With that, Bill finally gave in and said that he would be at Lockheed the next day.

Tuesday, August 5, 1997: Gene's Ashes

We had a meeting with Scott and I knew one of the topics was going to be Gene Shoemaker's ashes. Apparently Scott was not very pleased about having Gene's ashes on the spacecraft either. Scott said the container was supposed to be the size of a tube of lipstick. NASA was trying to find out about the container from Orbital Sciences because they had put the ashes of four people into orbit a few months earlier for Celestis, the company that does it as a commercial venture.

I said, "Let me tell you a story about that. Richard (Richard Lynch who had left the project months earlier and was working for Orbital Sciences) told me the families were told by Celestis that they had a method of compacting the ashes of a human being, which normally fill a pretty good size vase, so they all fit into the little tube, but what they really do is fill the little tube and then throw away most of the ashes!"

Scott said the issue was taken out of our hands because Carolyn Porco had gone straight to Wes and Wes had said yes, though it was really up to Goldin who had yet to make the final decision.

I restated my objections and Dougherty chimed in and said he had the same objections and added, "If we have to put the ashes on the spacecraft, we have to do so before we spin-balance and ballast it, because once that was done, I'm not going to have the added expense of balancing it again just for some ashes."

I said, "There are several aspects to this. One is that I knew Gene since I was a grad-student, though I was not a close friend of his. However, I have the greatest respect for Gene, so my objections have nothing to do with Gene, I just think this is a bad idea. First, I am concerned because, if Lunar Prospector goes into the drink, that's not a great place to have his ashes. Second, and worse, if we never launch and Lunar Prospector ends in the Smithsonian, that would be a mess."

Scott said, "Then they would take his ashes off the spacecraft. Besides, no one would know (that Gene's ashes were on the spacecraft), because NASA will not let it be known until we are actually in orbit."

Then we talked about a CD he wanted to put on the spacecraft just before launch with the names of people who could write to NASA and ask that their names be carried to the Moon. I said, "You know, I'm getting very concerned about this. We know how sensitive the spin balance is — just taking the spacecraft off the TLI Stage and putting it back on disturbs the balance even though you would think it would go right back on the same way. We can't do anything that screws up the spin balance."

Scott agreed and said, "We will just veto anything that is going to be a risk, but maybe we could have the signatures on a microdot instead of a CD, that should not cause any problem."

I was not thrilled about any of that. Then I reminded them of a movie made back in the sixties at the beginning of the space program called *Dearly Beloved*. It was a satire on the cemetery business, where a guy had a cemetery in Los Angeles and the value of the land had gotten so high he wanted to sell it for high-rises and condos. He got an Air Force general to start launching the corpses into space. I said, "That is what this reminds me of." Scott remembered the movie, too, and agreed.

The news from Headquarters about the launch vehicle was good. NASA had finally agreed that if the Lewis launch was good, then they would only have a very short review and it had to be done by September 1. Then we could proceed with our launch. According to Denver, the list of objectives for the review was the same as those reviewed before any launch. Apparently NASA was calming down about the LLVs.

Dan and I rounded up Paul and Ric and we went through the first few hours of the mission at our Mission Control Center at Ames, just to check out the spacecraft simulator, since it was finally working on the computer over there, and we found a number of errors.

At the end of the day, I caught Maryann. She said everything was done and when Jim got back from his vacation Thursday, he would take care of everything.

Wednesday, August 6, 1997

Bill and his technicians were over in the highbay trying to find the source of the noise in the APS. As the one technician had thought the previous week, the problem was in the shielding and all they had to do was to bridge across the shielding and that took care of it. Then the APS spectra were beautiful. Thus, there was nothing wrong with the SES power supply, so Bill's wanting to break the spacecraft's flight configuration and have everything shipped back and forth between Sunnyvale and Los Alamos would have been a colossal mistake that would have endangered the mission.

To be on the safe side, Bill wanted to bridge the shielding on the NS and GRS, but correctly, Dougherty wouldn't let him do that, since there was nothing wrong with either of them, i.e., "If it ain't broke, don't fix it." We had flight configuration hardware, all tested and ready to go — so leave it alone.

Thursday, August 7, 1997: Almost Out of Lockheed

Bill and his technicians took the APS off the spacecraft and took it to Los Alamos to fix the light filters.

The LRI contract was still not completed, because some guy in Human Resources wouldn't sign it! I had talked to Jim at 8:00 AM about the status of my contract and he said we had to go see Maryann. Maryann said everything was ready except for a little bit of this and a little bit of that. Jim said, "Come back at 2:00 and we should have the signatures."

I went back at 2:00 and asked, "Well, what's going on?" and I was told the Human Resources guy wouldn't sign it! He had called Legal, he had called Dougherty and he wanted to call some other people, because he had a number of questions he wanted answered. That really ticked me off. At that point, everybody else had signed. He saw their damned signatures. There was no reason for him to call all those people, since they had already signed, what a stupid SOB.

I said to Jim, "Come hell or high water, I'm out of here tomorrow."

He said, "It will be tomorrow, because we can't seem to get it done today. But it's on the front burner." But it never really was, they were just screwing around, making it as hard as possible.

Chapter 3-37
LRI Becomes a Reality

Friday, August 8, 1997: "Free at Last, Free at Last, ..."

Finally, I was free from Lockheed! Everything was signed; I retired from Lockheed and the LRI contract officially started. The Lunar Research Institute was a financial reality. It had been a long and annoying haul, but we were on our way. Both Rebecca and I were relieved and happy to be free of Lockheed.

The bad news was that Lewis had slipped again! Something in the LLV1's avionics was running twice as fast as it was supposed to. The new launch date was the following Wednesday.

The launch vehicle saga went on and on, but at least I was out of Lockheed.

Monday, August 11, 1997: The Quarterly Review

Guenter Riegler, an Austrian who was in charge of the flight phases of missions, and a couple of other Headquarters officials were at Ames for the Quarterly Review. Since, except for the APS, Lunar Prospector was ready for flight and our Mission Ops training was well advanced — the review went smoothly.

Bill reported on the APS and said the light filters ripped during the acoustic tests because the epoxy resin they had used to glue the filters to their frames had wicked out and formed very sharp edges that effectively cut the thin filters and caused them to rip apart. Since Bill did not like the idea of having the filters deposited right on the detectors and preferred the thin film filters, and since we knew the cause of the latter's destruction during the acoustic tests, we decided to stick with the thin films, though I still had some heartburn about it. Bill was going to replace the torn filters and then the APS would be flight ready and the spacecraft would be in its final flight configuration.

I showed Guenter the spacecraft after the review and he had a lot of questions, since he had essentially no knowledge about it.

Rebecca, who is LRI's Executive Administrator, made great progress in setting up LRI in our kitchen in Gilroy, e.g., started getting LRI's books and records set up and getting our "office" organized — and she was having fun doing it. It was great being free from Lockheed and on our own!

Tuesday, August 12, 1997

I went to Stanford and gave a seminar to the aerospace students.

Wednesday, August 13, 1997: Delayed Until November?

Lewis didn't go. It was postponed another week to ten days! I didn't think the thing was ever going to fly. We were almost certainly going to be delayed until November.

I stayed home and got my part of the LRI office set up in my library and talked with Dorothy Van Fosson, a Gilroy tax accountant, who was going to be our accountant and do the LRI payroll.

Thursday, August 14, 1997: Outwitting Lockheed, $264 at a Time

I started to move out of my office at Lockheed and into my new office in Mission Ops at Ames; so I was not only not a Lockheed employee any longer, but also I no longer had an office at Lockheed — what a relief that was!

Because our launch was almost certainly going to be delayed from October to November, I had a month's extra work ahead of me that was not covered by my freshly finished contract with Lockheed, so I talked to Maryann about what we needed to do to extend the contract the extra month. She said, "We will just add a month's cost to the contract." Then she said they had to rewrite the contract anyway, because Scott objected to some of the wording about the data products, the description of which was taken right out of the Archiving Document between NASA and me, but Lockheed had inserted itself into the mix and Scott didn't like that. Specifically, when I wrote the Archiving Document, I retained the right to check all the data that went out — as was my job as PI. The way Lockheed wrote my contract, Lockheed had that right (remember, I had a subcontract with Lockheed, so they were legally responsible to NASA for the data, not me). Since it was simply a formality with no real meaning, I didn't care — but Scott did and that was fine with me. My attitude was, *let Scott argue with Lockheed about it.*

I wanted to make sure I understood exactly how I was going to get paid for each of my Outreach events (showing visitors the spacecraft, giving public talks, visiting schools, etc.), there were supposed to be 5 to 6 such events every month according to the contract, i.e., the average number of them per month that I had been doing as a Lockheed employee. I said, "Each one of these is worth $264 (according to the contract). What happens if I do more than the five or six in a month?"

Maryann answered, "You get paid for all of them."

I said, "I've been doing a lot of them; I already have done ten this month."

She said, "That's fine, then you will get paid for all of them this month." That was great, by doing a lot of Outreach work early in the contract, and before I got really busy flying the spacecraft after launch, I could get most of the money due LRI in the entire contract for the Outreach activities right away and, in that way, partially foil Lockheed's attempt to pay LRI as little as possible early in the contract! That was also good for LRI (and hence Rebecca and me), because if the damned rocket failed, we would at least have a little money to keep us going for a couple of months.

Despite my contempt for the way Jim Pappas (a nice guy, but a willing tool of Lockheed) had helped Lockheed screw me with the contract, I told him I would show him the spacecraft sometime. He and about ten contract and budget people came over to the highbay at 9:00 AM and I gave them a nice tour of the spacecraft. They were ecstatic. They said, "Nobody has ever shown us a spacecraft before. They ought to do this more often. It's so nice to see something like this, we're all enthralled." I found that interesting — another example of how little Lockheed thinks of its workers. They are just supposed to sit in their little cubicles and do Lockheed's dirty work, while getting as little benefit as possible from Lockheed — they don't even get a chance to see the spacecraft Lockheed builds with their help! They all thanked me and said I was really knowledgeable and, "If Oprah ever comes (to Lockheed), this (Lunar Prospector) is the one that Oprah should do." That was all very nice and I had just earned $264 for LRI for the month of September (see my plan was working)!

As I was about to walk out of the highbay, Sylvia came in with some people from Ames, so I showed them the spacecraft. That was another $264!

I got a call from the San Jose Tech Museum, because they wanted to start getting a Lunar Prospector display set up I had said I would help them with it — and that would be another Outreach $264.

I called Scott and told him I was in the process of moving to Ames and I wanted to see him sometime in the next few days, probably Monday after hours, so we could have a chance to really chat. He didn't know what a blast in the ass he was going to get. Then I went to lunch.

I saw Buddy Nelson at lunch. Like me, Buddy had been called on the carpet many times because he had set up interviews for me without Scott being able to run the show. Buddy knows NASA in general and Scott in particular (Buddy hates Scott with a passion that exceeds my hatred of Lockheed) and thinks they all are a bunch of arrogant asses. He said, "You know, you have done such a good job. Every night, when I go out and see the Moon, I think — I'm helping Lunar Prospector get there. You make people feel like they are helping." He wanted to know all about LRI, so I told him how it was going. He said, "I'll do anything I can for you, I'll help you do your PR for free. I don't care about the money, I'll help you everyway I can. You've done such a marvelous job." I thanked Buddy; he is a great guy and was being treated by both Lockheed and Scott in a very shabby way.

Steve Durst called after lunch and we talked about the mission, the launch delay and an upcoming meeting. I said, "You know, because of this delay, I won't be able to go to the meeting on the 7th of November and that's too bad, because I wanted to meet Jim Benson." I asked Steve if he had Jim's number. He said he didn't know it, but he would find it, which he later did.

I then called Jim Benson, a millionaire in Steamboat Springs, CO, who wanted to do a commercial near-Earth asteroid mission patterned after Lunar Prospector. He seemed to know me well and said, "Everybody keeps saying — you've got to go talk to Alan. Everybody says that you're great and that you are the guy to talk to."

I said, "Jim, the reason I called you is I wanted to get acquainted with you. We're obviously trying to do the same types of commercial missions and I wanted to invite you to come to see my spacecraft."

He said, "Oh gee, I probably wouldn't have the time, but I would sure like to." I explained that we were delayed a month and he said, "In that case, if I can, I sure will."

I said, "Even if you don't, come and see Mission Ops after we get launched."

He said, "I will surely do that."

Then we talked about his near-Earth asteroid mission and my future plans for commercial lunar missions. It was clear from our conversation that Jim was thinking about hiring me, but he also realized that, as he said, "Well, you have your own ideas and you want to do the Moon, but we can still cooperate."

I agreed and said, "Sure, we're not competing with each other. What we're doing is trying to plow new ground and if you get it (the first true commercial mission), that's great and if I get it, that's great, because that would mean the other one will get a mission later. I think some of the other guys who have commercial programs don't have much of a chance, but I champion all of them, because they might get it done and then that would help me. The whole purpose of Lunar Prospector is to open this door. Because I'm doing it with government money rather than private money, I haven't completely broken the ice, but I sure as hell cracked it." Jim and I got acquainted a little and I had found a new ally. I was pleased.

Leonard David from *Aviation Week* called and wanted to know what was going on with the spacecraft. He said, "I'm sure you're just spitting on it and polishing it up."

I said, "Yes, that's about right. The problem is the damned rocket." I told him about LRI and he asked all kinds of questions about it, so I hoped we would get some good PR from that.

He asked me about the future and what I wanted to do. I answered, "Do commercial lunar missions, and eventually, I want to have my office on the Moon."

Friday, August 15, 1997: LLV1/Lewis Ready to Go?

Not much went on during the day, so I actually went home early. The only real event was I talked to Larry Price about the LLV1/Lewis delay and he said they knew exactly what was wrong, which chip was bad on which board and they had sent it to the vendor to be fixed. Everything was ready to go and they were confident it would really go this time. He also said that everybody had stopped working on the Lewis LLV1 and was working on Lunar Prospector's LLV2. Thus, they were not losing time and they even thought they still had a chance to get us off on October 24. I hoped so, but I doubted it.

Monday, August 18, 1997: A Conversation with Scott

First of all, the stupid LLV1 launch was postponed again — from Thursday to Friday. It was getting sickening.

I had a good Day 0 training session with Dan, Paul, and Ric and I got my Ames keys and did some other things to get ready to work out of Ames.

But the main event of the day was my two-hour meeting with Scott that started at 4:00 PM. The purpose of my seeing him was to again voice my concerns about the Discovery program sliding back to the old way of doing business. I started the conversation by saying, "Scott, you have to understand that I worked for six years before the Discovery Program started, trying to prove that missions can be done in the 'Faster, Better, Cheaper' way, even though we didn't use those exact words (but very, very close, see Appendix 1-3, also see www.lunar-research-institute.org). I'm not pleased that Discovery is moving away from its own goals. As I said earlier, when we had a brief conversation about this, I never expected NASA would change all the way to having the PI completely run the mission the first time — we would be lucky to get 90% or 95% of the way towards that goal. However, as you said, things have not gone in the direction Discovery had originally wanted. Headquarters has added this extra layer of administration through JPL or Goddard (for the newly selected Discovery missions) and the role of the PI is being squelched, PIs are now just Project Scientists. If I don't make a stand now, Discovery is never going to happen the way it was originally defined and the PI role is going to become nothing."

Scott was defensive and not happy about what I was saying. He asked, "What are your specific gripes?"

I answered, "Well, the (Lunar Prospector) NASA fact sheet says I'm responsible for the science and nothing else. That's not true. Discovery was sold to the science community, the American people, Congress and me as being science community missions run by the PIs. As Wes so eloquently said at the news conference (see Part Two), Discovery missions are not NASA missions with community support, but community missions with NASA support, and the PI is solely responsible for the success of his mission. I want NASA to admit that and go back to having the PI in charge. You know very well Lockheed absolutely refuses to accept my position as the PI and their customer. That fact compromises my authority over the mission and resulted in your taking on a lot of the responsibility of the mission. That's not your fault (boy was I wrong there), it's Lockheed's fault. By the same token, NASA has never given you full authority for the things you need to do for the mission. Both of those things have worked against the original Discovery concept."

Scott said, "Well this sounds like an attack on me."

I said, "No it's not, Scott. I have always considered you are my partner in this."

He said, "Yes, well, you know, these things were set up (by the Discovery Program) as a team consisting of the PI, the Industry Partner, and a NASA Center Partner."

I said, "No Scott, that's not true. The NASA Center Partner is optional. The NASA announcements clearly state that the PI has to have an Industry Partner, but it is not a requirement that the PI have a NASA Center Partner — if he wants one, he can choose one, but that's his choice." That statement stopped Scott dead in his tracks. I added, "I'll tell you right now Scott, I absolutely did not want a NASA Center Partner. It was bad enough to have to get in bed with Lockheed. I figured Lockheed would squash me — which they haven't been able to do (but not because they weren't trying). I didn't want to add to my problems by having to deal with a NASA Center. But Gus would only agree to have Lockheed become my Industry Partner if I agreed to have Ames be my NASA Center partner — he was trying to brown-nose Ames. Remember when you and I first talked about adding Ames to my team and you told me the list of people I could select from for the head of the Ames team, I told you, because you and I had the same vision as to how Discovery Missions were to be run, I said I wanted you to be my NASA partner."

He smiled a little and answered, "Yes, I do remember that."

I said, "Good, that is the point, Scott. You and I had exactly the same idea of how Discovery was supposed to be done and we have done it that way."

Having to concede all that, Scott then argued, "Hey, we've succeeded and you have 95% of what you wanted. You're getting all kinds of good PR and you're going to get a lot more. What do you want?"

I said, "Well Scott, it's a matter of the philosophy behind the mission. This is very important; NASA is at a crossroads and it has been going down hill ever since the end of Apollo. Discovery and Lunar Prospector represent a way to change things for the better. I'm not going to settle for 95%, because Discovery is already sliding back to the old ways. We may have 95%, but the next PI is going to have only 50% and the next one 30%. It's up to you and me to go all the way if we want Discovery to work the way Goldin originally wanted it to work."

Scott then changed to an attack, "All you are doing is pissing everybody off, including me."

I said, "Well Scott, that's just too bad — I'm pissed off too."

He said, "If you keep on, you're just going to anger a lot of people."

I replied, "Good, the only way you get change is to get people angry."

We continued discussing the issues, but he couldn't (or wouldn't?) understand what was the matter. I kept saying, "Scott, I'm interested in doing this right — to set the precedent. The thing that really ticked me off a year ago was when you and I were getting the job done on time and on budget, Headquarters came and told us that despite our success, NASA was never going to do a mission our way again — that they were going to put in this extra layer of management (JPL or Goddard — but not Ames) between the projects and Headquarters. That's just stupid, Scott. They're taking a perfect model of what they said they wanted and just throwing it away — because they don't directly control every little thing we do. If this (Discovery) is going to work, NASA is going to have to really give the PIs the total responsibility of their missions and then they are going to have to make the PIs do their jobs. NASA can't have PIs who are just figureheads and that is where Discovery is now going. If the PI is given full responsibility, then he has to take it and he has to do it. In my opinion, if a PI is not willing to go fulltime on his mission, then he cannot be a PI."

Scott said, "That will exclude a lot of people."

I replied, "So what. You're never going to get scientists to run missions if you don't do it this way. You remember the time when James Paul was here and he turned to me and asked — where is NASA going to get people like me to run missions — and I answered that NASA has to give them the chance to do it and make them do it and then they will learn to do it."

Well, we just kept going around and around on the issues and Scott kept asking, "What do you want, what do you want? It sounds like you believe that Ames has done a bad job."

I answered, "No, that has nothing to do with it. You've done a good job. Look at the way it really is. You have had to spend tons and tons of your time fending off Headquarters. How many times have you had to go to Headquarters to stop them from messing up our launch?"

That made him smile and he said answered, "Yes, I've had to fight Headquarters all the time. Other than that, things have been quite nice. But, do you know how much time I spend making sure that Alan is happy?"

I laughed and answered, "That's time well spent," and I added, "You've done your job of fending off Headquarters and I've fended off Lockheed and I got the spacecraft built the way it had to be build. We've both done our jobs and, as such, I've always felt you and I stood back to back — I've protected us from Lockheed and you've protected us from Headquarters."

With that, Scott appeared to begin to catch on to what I was saying, but he said, "I still don't understand what you are after. You want 100%. I don't get it."

I answered, "Look Scott, in every other field of science, the programs are run by scientists. In nuclear physics, the big atom-smashers, like in Texas, are run by a scientist, not a bureaucrat, not an engineer. Look, all the things that are done in Astronomy — the big observatories are built by astronomers, not by an engineer or a bureaucrat. Same thing in geology, geophysics, biology, you name it — in every single field of science you have a capable, experienced scientist running the big programs, not an engineer or a bureaucrat. There are two problems with our business. First of all, in the beginning, building a rocket and a spacecraft and making them work were engineering tasks, not science tasks. The little bit of science that you could add on was just an afterthought. Scientists got used to the idea of just coming along for the ride and not taking responsibility for their own science and the engineers at NASA got used to bossing everybody around. The whole purpose of Discovery is to finally get the scientists back doing their real jobs, taking on the responsibility of their missions; they have to and NASA has to give them the responsibility to do so."

That finally clicked with Scott and he mentioned that Lawrence Livermore and all the other great physicists of the past ran their own programs. He said, "You know, that's right. That's what we have to get across." All of the sudden he started to flip sides. Then he said, "The thing is, you don't know how hard this has been. I've tried to protect your interests and to make sure NASA lets you do what you want to do. I spent half my time doing that. You don't know how much time I spend making sure that Alan is happy. Do you know remember Guenter Riegler, who was here last week and who is now leading the flight phases of missions for Code S? He could not believe we were going to let you — now don't take this the wrong way — let you run your spacecraft, command it, and everything. You're six times better than anybody in the business — you're unheard of in this business. Nobody can believe that you (a scientist) can run a mission — they just don't accept it. I've had to fight many battles for you. I do it partly on faith and partly because of all you've accomplished."

I said, "Yes, I know and that is the whole point. They don't expect this from a scientist. They don't expect scientists to know what I know and be as capable as I am. But they have to understand that many scientist can do this, if they're given the chance!"

Slowly but surely, I began to get Scott to understand, but he was afraid he was going to be made the villain in the battle I was conducting. He said, "You have to promise me two things: First, that you won't do anything that harms me and second, that you won't do anything that harms Ames."

I answered, "Scott, you are my partner in this. I'm trying to win this battle for us — and NASA. Lockheed could have been our third partner, but they didn't want that."

He didn't argue that point at all. Then he repeated his earlier statement, "The problem is that people just can't believe that you can do this all this, because scientists just don't do it. I've fought a lot of battles for what you want to do, but I am going on faith."

I said, "Well Scott, I know and I appreciate that, but we have to win the whole damn thing if Discovery is going to work."

I said, "Scott, let's go back to the business about my being ticked off that we are doing the right thing and NASA won't use the Lunar Prospector model anymore and about your being ticked off because Headquarters doesn't want Ames to run any more missions. Scott, they're the same damned thing. You and I have succeeded, so Ames has succeeded. Why is this working? Because you guys (Ames) did all the Pioneers (missions) and Lunar Prospector is essentially a Pioneer — a simple, straightforward spinner. That's why this has clicked. You're concerned because you and Ames are getting screwed, pushed out, and that's what I'm trying to stop. Look, you can say to Headquarters that Ames and you and I have done it and then ask them why are they excluding Ames from using the Lunar Prospector model to do more missions?"

That finally got him. He began to appreciate the fact that I was going to go for the gold. There was nothing he could do to stop me anyway. I wasn't going to hurt him. I wasn't going to hurt his precious Ames. I said, "Look Scott, you have to understand I'm not out to hurt you guys, but to make sure that what we accomplish gets the appropriate recognition and that the PIs get the real responsibility for their missions. And I have to be given the full responsibility, because if I don't get it, I can't do this."

Scott said, "We've (Ames) got all these things that we can do and we can do more missions. We have to keep Ames in there."

I said, "I understand that and also that as a NASA official, you have certain restrictions and can't do certain things. I don't have any restrictions. I can fight these battles and nobody can hurt me. I can go out and do anything I want and talk to any politician I want. I can make it plain to politicians that it is stupid to exclude Ames from running missions when Ames is the only NASA Center that did it right. Look at our costs. We have the only mission with a budget down where Goldin wanted it. Everybody else costs $200 to 250 million. Look Scott, I don't know about all the intrigue between Ames and JPL and Headquarters, but I am willing to help you fight that battle in any way I can. But you have to tell me what the hell is going on because I don't know what's going on. I know my end and I know the public side, but I don't know what is really going on inside NASA." That perked Scott up considerably.

Then we talked about the PR flaps. I asked, "Why are you and David (Mores) mad when the reporter wrote that I was the manager. I am the manager, that's what it says in your own damned propaganda. Secondly, this is my mission and my spacecraft. I spent eight years on it."

He said, "Yes, I know."

I continued, "Another thing you have to understand and accept is that I don't worry about being taken out of context. It's going to happen all the time and you're just going to have to desensitize yourself to it. So don't crab at me about the newspapers. I do a better job of PR than your NASA guys do by far. I'm much more effective in dealing with the public and with the media than you guys are. You're just going to have to get used to it. If Headquarters complains about what I do, just say — Well that's just Alan. We can't do anything about him — instead of coming and crabbing at me. Also, you annoy me when you accuse me of not being a team player and not doing things for the American public. That is what Lunar Prospector has been all about. I have gone out of my way to include the American public and make it their mission." He sort of agreed and apologized, somewhat, for his earlier remarks and said he didn't quite understand what I had been saying to the public.

We left it that way and when I left, Scott was smiling and seemed happy with our discussion. He said, "We should have lunch together more often. We have to have more talks like this."

As I left his office, I thought, *he's not as smart as he thinks he is. He only sees this from his personal perspective and only from NASA's perspective, but he doesn't catch on to what the public wants.* But, I accomplished what I wanted to accomplish, that was the main thing and I left feeling good about the meeting.

Tuesday, August 19, 1997: Mission Success BS

During the morning, we did a good training session on the 3rd mid-course maneuver leading up to the reor (reorienting the spacecraft) for the 1st LOI burn. I wanted to do a SIM of the 1st LOI burn in the afternoon, but I had to go to the Kick-Off-Meeting for a Mission Success Review Lockheed was doing internally for Lunar Prospector, which was run by Paul Gillett. The review was somewhat interesting, probably because Dougherty was not there, he was in Denver, and Lee was standing in for him. She did pretty well. Lee and the other people, especially Paul, treated me like a human being. I had only interfaced with Paul a couple times, but he respected me and my position as PI, and I respected Paul.

Lee and I introduced Lunar Prospector to the review committee. I described what Lunar Prospector and the Discovery programs were all about and the committee members were clearly not used to such programs! I said, "Lunar Prospector is a very inexpensive mission and it is only supposed to be 95% reliable. We have very little money, $63 million for everything — the spacecraft cost just $20 million — and the emphasis is on simplicity and reliability. We have a good spacecraft and we are doing well, as I think you will find out, but this is not what you are used to seeing done." They seemed to be interested in what I was saying.

The review went on until about 2:30 PM and then I said, "You guys should see the spacecraft."

They said, "We would love to." I took them over to the highbay and I gave them the full-blown tour of the spacecraft. They had a lot of questions — that is their job! They were supposed to look at everything, find out if we had made any mistakes and determine for Lockheed if Lunar Prospector was ready to fly. They were impressed with my little spacecraft.

I had told them that Dan and I had to get back to the Mission Control Center for more Mission Ops training and that they should go over to Ames with us and see it. They agreed, because that was also part of what they were to find out, i.e., were we ready for operations and did we have Mission Ops setup correctly?

As it turned out, the SIM we had run in the morning was supposed to be still running, leading up to the 1st LOI burn, but the computer had crashed. I said, "Well, we will show you what is on the screens." We discussed Mission Ops in great and glorious detail until 6:00 PM! They were going to review Mission Ops anyway, but it was much more effective to do so at the Mission Operation Center where they could see exactly what we were doing instead of in the meeting room at Lockheed. Their only concern was that we had not hired all the rest of the guys on the team. We were supposed to have six junior controllers to do monitoring and one more senior controller and then somebody who was Dan's backup — but we didn't have them at that time.

It was a very long day. I had gotten to work at 5:00 AM and left at 6:00 PM. The Mission Success review was to go on for two more days, though I did not have to be there all the time, so we were going to run more SIMs the next couple of days. The Committee was going to talk to each subsystem engineer and discuss all the subsystems. It wore me out.

Denver was still trying to get us launched on October 24 — I had my fingers crossed.

Wednesday, August 20, 1997: More SIMs and More Review

We ran the 3rd mid-course maneuver and 1st LOI burn SIM and then went over to the Mission Success Review because the Committee had some more questions and that shot the rest of the day. They were very interested in Lunar Prospector and very complimentary. They were beginning to understand what I could do and they treated me like a human being — unlike the rest of Lockheed. That was very nice. One young engineer on the committee wanted to know how many spacecraft I had built before and he couldn't believe I didn't build spacecraft all the time! That comment was especially nice.

I went home early so Rebecca and I could get our Gilroy business license for LRI. That was a 20-minute affair and cost us nothing, since LRI is non-profit, so we were all set up.

Thursday, August 21, 1997: More Training

During the morning we ran good SIMs for the 2nd LOI burn, the follow-on aposelene, orbital correction burn, and a reor burn. The training was going very well and was a lot of fun.

A British guy from the BBC came and saw Mission Ops and talked to us about what he wanted to film.

Then we had a staff meeting and that finished off the day.

Denver was really trying to get us launched on the 24th. There were a lot of scheduling conflicts at Astro Tech (at the Cape, where we were going to prepare Lunar Prospector for launch) that were screwing up our November launch dates, so LLV was trying really hard to make the October 24 launch.

Friday, August 22, 1997

Brian Cox and his family came to visit. We did a 3rd LOI burn SIM for Brian.

Chapter 3-38
Finally — Cleared to Launch and Ready to Launch

Saturday, August 23, 1997: At Last

At 3:00 AM I called the hot line and found out that Lewis had been successfully launched at 11:52 PM on the LLV1. At last, we had a clean bill of health on the damned LLV1 — "October 24, here we come."

I called Bill to tell him that the LLV1 was successfully launched and he said they had had a problem. When they did the shake test on the APS, one of the capacitors broke and then they found there were fatigue cracks in the welds on the rest of the 20 capacitors! They pulled all the capacitors and replaced them. He was not sure, but he thought it might put him behind schedule a couple days, but since he had planned to bring the APS three days early anyway, that would be OK. As long as he got it to Lockheed on the 29th, that would be fine.

There was a beautiful little article in the September 1997 issue of *Scientific American* called "Buck Rogers, CEO" about those of us who are the vanguard commercial space people. It was a very nice article.

Monday, August 25, 1997: The First Lockout Incident

With the successful launch of Lewis behind us, I figured Headquarters would calm down a bit, but I didn't think it would calm down as much as it did. Sylvia said that, instead of a two-week or ten-day review of the LLV1, NASA just wanted a two or three day review! She had also heard that Goldin had told Sam Venneri that Lunar Prospector was ready to go. Headquarters was backing down and getting brave!

We ran a SIM of the 3rd and final LOI burn.

Mike Chobotov called and wanted to see the spacecraft on Thursday. Gene Beley, publisher of the local *Country News* was going to interview me the following evening. Dave Strack from Houston called and told me the he and Jana were coming to the Bay Area and wanted to see Rebecca and me and the spacecraft on the weekend. And a nice Japanese guy, Yoshitake Yamaguchi, who worked for Toshiba and was at Loral for several months, wanted to see the spacecraft. All in all, I would have at least 14 Outreach events during the month and "earn" at least $3700 for LRI instead of just $1300 as Lockheed expected. Though the contract was only two weeks old, I had already done over a quarter of the total number of such Outreach events the contract called for during the entire first year. I would be able to get quite a bit of money for LRI during the first month of the contract — revenge is sweet!

However, the weirdest thing happened. Dougherty had hired a guy named Wendell Welter, who was supposed to help Kim Foster with the launch preparation activities and who is rather weird. Instead of working, he was always whining about his miserable life, his divorce, his kids, his never having a woman and asking about how he could find a girl friend and whine, whine, whine. He pestered everybody who would listen to him and even those who wouldn't — he just never shut up. He was worried because, though he had never been fired, Lockheed was always saying to him, "We can't use you on this project anymore, go find yourself a job within Lockheed in the next couple of weeks or you will be fired." Well, he was getting more and more upset and blaming everybody for all his personal troubles and he especially began to hate Kim Foster (gee, I can't imagine why).

Finally Wendell cracked — he said, in deadly seriousness, to either Mary Piasecki or Maryann that he was going to bring in an AK 47 and shoot Kim Foster and a few other people. Then he said the same thing to several other people, including Tim Maloney, but in a more or less joking fashion, but Tim told him, "You had better quit this crap or you're going to get locked out." Correctly, Tim and Mary or Maryann reported it. Tim thought it was serious, because Wendell had said it so many times to so many people. Dougherty took it very seriously and had him locked out (have his magnetic key-card deactivated, so he could not get into Lockheed buildings) and Lockheed was probably going to fire him. There was a security guard standing around all day at Building 107. I was, of course, not there, since I had moved in at Ames.

Tuesday, August 26, 1997: More Training

We had a good SIM — it was the first time we tried an orbital maintenance maneuver (OMM), which lasted a long time, but it went very well. We were getting well trained to run Lunar Prospector.

The rocket launch preparations were moving forward, but, as Sylvia said, it was getting tough to get off in October. We were still planning to do so, but it was getting very, very tight.

Then we got the word that the Lewis satellite had failed within a day after launch! At first, that did not concern us, because the LLV1 launch had been completely successful and that was what counted in terms of NASA allowing us to proceed with our LLV2 launch. However, there were repercussions for Lunar Prospector because of the Lewis satellite failure a few weeks later.

I went home early to set up our LRI business account at a local bank.

Wednesday, August 27, 1997: Emergency Training

We ran a 1st LOI burn SIM, in which Dan (whose job it was to set up the failure modes for the SIMs, since he and I were the only ones who knew how the SIM program worked and since, as Mission Director, I was the one who was primarily responsible for detecting an emergency situation and acting on it in a very rapid manner) had set up a failure that the rest of us didn't know about, i.e., we began to train for emergencies. I had uplinked the engine firing parameters for the A1 and A2 engines that were to be used for the long LOI burns and when I issued the Execute Command, the A1 engine began to heat up, indicating that it was firing, but the A2 remained cold — it had failed.

The 1st LOI burn was the crucial "capture burn" and would normally last 32 minutes with both the A1 and A2 firing continuously. The first half of the burn was required just to burn off Lunar Prospector's excess, hyperbolic velocity, so the Moon could capture it and it would not go sailing by into oblivion. Though Lunar Prospector would be "captured" by the time of the midpoint of the burn, its orbit would be very unstable, so the second half of that burn was needed to bring the initial capture orbit down to a relatively stable orbit with a 12 hour period. A single engine, 32 minute LOI burn would achieve capture — barely, but would result in a completely unstable orbit. According to the emergency procedures I had written in the Mission Operations Document (MOD), in the case of an engine failure during the 1st LOI burn, we would restart the functioning engine after the burn was over and do a long enough burn so that Lunar Prospector would be in a stable capture orbit. As long as the spacecraft was in such a capture orbit, we would have a few days to workout the new burns required to get the spacecraft down into its mapping orbit.

As soon as I saw the A2 engine was out, I asked Dan to prepare a burn parameter file for an emergency 15 minute burn on A1 that would start as soon as we could load and verify the file after the end of the initial A1 burn. It took us only 2 minutes to get the new load uplinked, verified, and executed at the end of first burn. We were pleased with ourselves.

After the SIM ended, we discussed it. Ken Galal argued that we could have done the emergency burn a few hours later, after we had had some tracking data and did a reor, and then we could burn down directly to the 12 hour orbit — a procedure that he said, "would only cost you 70 m/sec of ΔV." Unfortunately, Ken, who is a very sharp guy, was just too academic at that point in the training; he didn't get the practicalities of the mission and he just didn't get the real point of the emergency procedure. I said, "Ken, that (the 70 m/sec of ΔV) is a whole year's worth of orbital correction fuel. You can't just throw that away; you have to minimize the loss."

He asked, "Even in an emergency?"

I answered, "We are certainly going to waste some fuel in an emergency situation, but you just don't throw fuel away. You have to find the best and quickest way to minimize the ΔV losses." I had to pound that into his head, but that was also the purpose of the training — teaching my Mission Ops team how to best run the mission — when it was going smoothly and especially if it got into trouble.

I finally got all the last of the pre-launch science papers together that described the mission, its science goals and the instruments, that my Co-Is and I had written for publication in *Science* and got them ready to Fed-Ex to the publisher. I asked an Ames secretary to take the package to the Ames Fed-Ex drop-off point and, like a typical government secretary, she thought she was going to die because I had asked her to do a lick of work!

After that, I talked to Maryann and she told me what I needed to do to get paid for August. I asked her what I had to do about the Outreach events I had done. I thought Lockheed would want a list of names, phone numbers, and addresses of the people I had done Outreach activities with, so Lockheed could check to make sure I was doing what I reported. She said, "No, a list of the events is good enough."

Though I trusted Maryann, I didn't trust Lockheed — and I was right. Then I found out Lockheed told Dan Swanson and Lee Bergman to watch what I was doing and Dan said, "I can't believe this." He thought it was dumb that Lockheed was making me report milestones to get paid in the first place, and worse, that he had been asked to check up on me. Nevertheless, he had to do it — he was a Lockheed employee.

We did a SIM in the afternoon that started at TLI, but in which the TLI burn was an underburn, so we had to quickly do an emergency burn to make up for the low injection velocity. John Breakwell, Dan's backup was finally there, so we started to train him — he started his training by setting up the initialization files for the SIM.

When the SIM started and we began to get data on our screens, there was something very screwy about the spin period. We couldn't figure it out and Dan and I said, "We can't proceed with the emergency burn until we get the spin period corrected."

We did a de-spin burn that had no effect whatsoever, so we just gave up and stopped the SIM. That was when we found that John had erroneously put in a spin rate in the initialization files that was about 10 times higher than was correct. That high spin rate caused the computer program that calculated the spin rate to completely saturate, so we got false spin rate data. Because of John's error, it was a good exercise! That mistake taught us something about the limitations of our software. If, for example, a tangential engine stuck on during a spin burn and the spacecraft spun up to a very high spin rate and hence, the computer program saturated again, we would know what that indicated — there is always a silver lining.

Later, I talked to Tim Maloney about Gene Shoemaker's ashes. I wanted to know how much mass they and their container had, where and how we would put them on the spacecraft, and a number of other things. I was really ticked off about having to put Gene's ashes on the spacecraft. Everyone on the project hated the idea. No one wanted to add non-flight hardware like that to the spacecraft after it was completely tested. That was just plain crazy (only NASA would do such a dumb thing). After I had asked my questions, Tim said, "I have it right here," and he showed me a little capsule, like a lipstick tube, made out of very thin aluminum. He opened it up and there was a little bottle of Gene's ashes in it.

When I looked at it, I was concerned — he had correctly punched a hole in the aluminum canister so the air inside could get out — and I said, "You know we have to get the air out of that little bottle too and that opens up the possibility that the ashes could get out and perhaps get into the sun sensor or on the optics of the Earth/Moon limb sensor." I was really ticked off and I was going to lodge a formal protest to Scott. I wanted it on record that I was against having Gene's ashes on the spacecraft — it was the wrong thing to do and I was totally against it. As far as I was and am concerned, Carolyn Porco is a silly twit who should never have started that mess — she has no idea about what you can and cannot do with spacecraft or she would not have started the nonsense about Gene's ashes.

When I got home, Rebecca and I did LRI's first invoice for Lockheed — it was for some $17,000 — and we got everything ready to go to Dorothy Van Fosson, so we could get paid for our office costs and our wages. I got the business bank account set up and a $15,000 credit line for LRI, which we needed so we could pay our wages since Lockheed would take several days to process the invoice I had turned in and to cut LRI's check. LRI was beginning to function; we would soon have money starting to come in — and go out — of our accounts, and everything was set up.

Thursday, August 28, 1997:
Finishing the Construction of Lunar Prospector

Bill and his crew brought the APS to Lockheed and installed it on the spacecraft and it was working fine. While installing it, they found that all the other spectrometer connectors had gotten loose, so they tightened them. I told Tim to check all the other connectors and tighten them if necessary.

With that event, *we had completed the construction of Lunar Prospector* — it was ready to fly. We had done it in just 22 months after receiving the official word to start Phase C/D in the last week of October 1995. We had built the spacecraft in the 22 months that we had scheduled (actually, in well less than 22 months, because we did not actually get started on construction until well after the official start date, because we had to finish with the Phase B design work that Tenerelli had so badly screwed up before we could really start Phase C/D). We had proven the "Faster" part of "Faster, Better, Cheaper." Also, since we had done it on budget and since the thermal-vac test had shown that Lunar Prospector really worked, I felt we had proven all three parts of "Faster, Better, Cheaper." All we had to do was to get launched and fly a perfect mission to put the frosting on the cake! Needless to say, I was pleased

Since the spacecraft was finished well before launch, we were going to start burning it in, i.e., turn it on and just let it run to see if any of the subsystems or components failed, and continue burning it in until we shipped it to the Cape for launch. The reason for the burn-in is simple; statistically, spacecraft fail within three days of launch — infant mortality — because of a design problem or a component failure. If a spacecraft makes it through its first three days, it will almost certainly stay alive for a lot longer than its designed lifetime. The way to insure that a spacecraft does not suffer infant mortality is to burn it in for as long as possible. That way, any failure is very likely to occur before launch and hence before it's too late to fix the problem.

We did a Day 0 SIM that started at turn-on and went through the 1st mid-course maneuver (MCM) with our Goddard Navigation Team feeding us trajectory information for the first time.

Unfortunately, Ken Galal, who, along with Dave Lozier, formed the Ames part of our Nav Team, still just didn't get it. When he gave Dan and me the velocity vector for the 1st MCM burn, he told us that it was only a tangential engine burn. We did the burn that way and then we found out there was also supposed to have been a 1.5 m/sec axial burn on the A3 and A4 engines! When I asked him why he had not told us that, he said, "It was so small, I didn't think it was worth it." He just did not understand what we had to do to run a successful mission — but after we talked about it, believe me — he understood what he was supposed to do!

On top of Ken's mistake, Goddard had given us their velocity vector file in a form we couldn't read, even though we had agreed on the form. However, the purpose of the SIMs was to uncover problems like that, so we could fix them.

Mike Chobotov and his guys came and I gave them tours of the spacecraft and Mission Ops.

I turned in the first LRI report and the first LRI invoice to Lockheed.

Friday, August 29, 1997

We did a retest of the APS and found it was still OK and then we did a SIM with a major TLI underburn.

Saturday, August 30, through Monday, September 1, 1997: A Long Labor Day Weekend

Rebecca and I just spent the entire three days resting up for the big push that would lead up to the launch that was still possible on October 24.

Tuesday, September 2, 1997: Training, Training, and More Training

We did four SIMs during the day. They were really good. John Breakwell was doing the training with me, while Dan was setting up emergencies that popped up during the various SIMS.

Our first SIM started at turn-on on Day 0, with a TLI velocity that was so low (–37 m/sec) that we had to go into phasing orbit around the Earth in order to save the mission, so we could get to the Moon a month later. That SIM went well and we learned a lot.

Our second SIM again started at turn-on, but Dan had programmed in an engine leak. When I opened the PIV, I saw immediately that an engine was heating up and immediately ordered that the Close-PIV Command be sent to the spacecraft and that took care of that. Then, as I had written in the MOD, I sent a series of Engine–On and Engine-Off Commands in rapid succession to the leaky engine, in the hopes that the series of commands would (in the real case) get the leaky engine valve to seat properly and stop leaking.

In SIM number three, Dan set it up so the transmitter did not turn on during the turn-on sequence! We listened for eight minutes, while TDRS was supposed to be tracking the spacecraft and we didn't get any signal. But, since our using TDRS to track Lunar Prospector between turn-on and Goldstone Tracking Station's acquisition of the spacecraft was an experiment that might not work, we assumed TDRS was at fault. But then, when the spacecraft came up over Goldstone and Goldstone did not hear from Lunar Prospector, I knew we had a serious problem. Dan had been unsuccessfully looking in the MOD for the correct emergency procedure, so I grabbed it and looked up what I was supposed to do — which was, logically enough, to try to turn on the transmitter. I issued the command and it was sent to the spacecraft — and it worked. The transmitter came on, but Dan's changing the unitization sequence had screwed up the computer program, so it could not generate any downlink data. We tried to play with the simulator to see if we could find a way to continue the SIM, but we finally had to give up. Nevertheless, we had done everything correctly and in the real world, we would have saved the mission.

In the fourth and last SIM, which also started at turn-on on Day 0, the spacecraft turned on correctly, but the pressure in the tanks was zero! Either the pressure transducer had failed (annoying, but not serious) or the tanks or the fuel lines had ruptured (very serious). I asked John, "Is the spacecraft still in the dark (in the Earth's shadow)?"

He said, "Yes."

I said, "Tell me, as soon as we come into the sun light, if there is any excessive nutation or if the spin rate is changing, because, if the spacecraft is venting fuel, that would cause it to wobble and to spin-up or spin-down."

Soon John said, "We are in sunlight and there is no large nutation or spin rate changes."

Since there were no indications the spacecraft was venting fuel, I went ahead and had the command to open the PIV uplinked to the spacecraft. That went OK, so I said, "Good, let's do the reor and see what happens," and John prepared the file for the reor and I had it uplinked to the spacecraft. After I had verified the burn parameters, I issued the Execute Command and the engines fired perfectly. It appeared that we had a defective pressure transducer, a problem that would not really affect our ability to fly the real mission, but would have made us rely on our fuel usage model calculations to determine the tank pressure that we needed to calculate the burn parameter.

We had some really good emergency SIMs that were very realistic and we had gotten through the emergencies each time. We were all very pleased with ourselves and we were gaining confidence that we could really fly Lunar Prospector — no matter what.

After the SIMs were over, I talked to Tim and Kim about preparing the spacecraft for shipping and launch. I wanted to be part of the final pre-ship testing that was scheduled for the 17th, 18th, and 19th. We were still going for October 24, but we all were asking, "How in hell can LLV do it if they're not going to ship the Orbit Adjustment Module of the LLV2 as soon as they need to for an October 24 launch?" Everything we heard told us that they were slipping and we doubted that they could make it. But, the LLV guys were busting their butts, trying to make the October launch and we were wrapping things up with the spacecraft. Everyone had the feeling you get a few days before Christmas when the packages are being wrapped and the bows are being put on them. That was just the way we felt about Lunar Prospector.

We were considering shipping Lunar Prospector to Astro Tech on the 29th, but there was still the question of the availability of Astro Tech for doing the processing in November, if we missed our October 24/25 launch windows. We thought we might just ship the spacecraft down to the Cape in September anyway, get it processed, and if we couldn't launch until late November or December, at least we would be all ready to go.

Dougherty had left me a message; he wanted to know the alternative launch dates in late November and December, so I knew we were seriously talking about those launch dates!

I went home — Rebecca and I had to see Dorothy. Dorothy had done our paychecks right, but I thought I had already paid the maximum yearly amount to FICA, if so, she should not have taken out money out of my wages for FICA — she was going to check.

Wednesday, September 3, 1997: A November Launch

We got the word that launch was not going to occur until November, no big surprise there. It was not going to be officially announced for another week. I thought there was some small possibility that we might be able to keep October in play until the official announcement came out — but that was really wishful thinking.

Regardless, we were almost certainly going to take the spacecraft down to the Cape towards the end of the month and get it prepared for launch, because of the Astro Tech scheduling problem in November. I was happy about that. Dougherty said we could still burn in the spacecraft while it was at the Cape. As he said, "We can have the best of both worlds." I really liked the idea of getting Lunar Prospector down there, getting it prepared for launch, and getting it encapsulated in its shroud where it would be safe and ready to go. As long as it was at Lockheed, we would have all of that before us and I am a firm believer that the more steps you have behind you, the better things are.

Dan and I ran two SIMs. We tried a battery conditioning procedure, which we would use if, as the battery aged, it started to have difficulty getting fully charged. The procedure consisted of very carefully causing the battery to nearly completely discharge and then letting it charge back up to full charge. It was a very interesting SIM. Then we did a power saving exercise, which consisted of shutting off all the non-essential units, i.e., the science instruments, the pressure transducer, all the heaters, the Sun sensor and Earth/Moon limb-crossing sensor. That was also very interesting. We were learning and having fun. As Dan and I both said, "This is so much fun and we get paid for it."

Gene's ashes were on the spacecraft. The little tube was glued onto one of the solar array panel brackets as tightly as possible and the fact that the only thing we could do at that late stage of the game was to glue it onto a carefully crafted spacecraft with big gobs of glue is a clear statement that doing something like that is just not the thing to do with a spacecraft that is flight ready — such utter nonsense. If I got the chance, I was going to raise as much hell as possible about it.

Well, besides that nonsense, there was the nonsense of Scott wanting a little microdot with the signatures of all the people who were visiting the Ames Open House and others all over the USA. I had no objection to a microdot, but that microdot had turned into 5 or 6 plastic cards. Dougherty told me that and he said, "I give up. You'll have to handle it with Scott." I was just going to go tell Scott they were not going be put on the spacecraft, period.

Scott had first suggested that, like Gene's ashes, the plastic cards just be glued to the spacecraft. Well, the only place they could be glued to the spacecraft was on its bottom. To do so, we would have to peel back the thermal blanket, then glue the cards on, then replace the thermal blanket and then spin balance and ballast the spacecraft again (we were going to spin balance and ballast the spacecraft in a week — long before Scott would have his damned microfiche)! Such stupidity. Alternatively, Scott suggested we just tape the cards to one of the solar array brackets, which would also require spin balancing the spacecraft again and if the damned cards fell off during the mission — well what does one have to say? It was all just stupid BS. Scott is an idiot for even suggesting such crap.

Most of Thursday, September 4, 1997: More SIMs

Rebecca came with me to work and we did a SIM with Goddard online. Unfortunately, they screwed it up. The SIM started with Goddard setting it up with a 37 m/sec underburn. By my calculations and mission rules, any under-burn of more than 35 m/sec required that we use the phasing orbit mode to get us back to the Moon a month after launch. Instead of telling us that we had a 37 m/sec under-burn in the beginning, they told us it was a 33 m/sec underburn, because they wanted us to practice an immediate emergency burn to correct for the under-burn. If they were going to do that, they should have changed the damned initial velocity vector to one with a 33 m/sec under-burn, but they didn't, they just reported a 33 m/sec under-burn. Dan and I went ahead and did the emergency burn and it was a very long burn. When we got done, they gave us the data for the first MCM and it was a 55 m/sec burn! That put us in the hole, fuel-usage-wise.

We then discussed the SIM. I said, "The point is that we have to be careful we don't end up wasting so damned much fuel. By not giving us the correct velocity information for the under-burn, we did the wrong procedure and I used three quarters of a year's worth of orbital fuel." They got my point, and other than that, it was a good SIM.

My old Lockheed supervisor and friend, Mick Culp, was at Ames for a Space Station meeting, so Mick got to see Mission Ops. Unfortunately, he didn't have time to see the spacecraft. But I was glad to see Mick and have him at least see Mission Ops — after all, he had helped in many ways to get Lunar Prospector where it was.

Scott brought some Ames officials and John McNamara, from JPL, to the highbay to see the spacecraft. We both showed them the spacecraft and Scott wanted to show off as much as he could. He did most of the talking, which was fine by me. But in my opinion, if he wanted to show off, then what was the use of having me there? It was kind of strange if you ask me.

I went over to Scott's office for part of a telecon between Scott and Headquarters about the launch vehicle review and Scott won. The Headquarters people agreed they would just be part of the normal LLV1 post-launch review and it would last just a couple of days. That was great. Scott did a good job on that. He said it was the ultimate victory, because he had made that same suggestion much earlier and, of course, Karen

Poniatowski wanted to make a big deal out of it, as she always does. Finally it ended up with her suggesting exactly what Scott had suggested, but since she suggested it, Headquarters adopted it. Dealing with Headquarters is idiotic. All you have got to do is to make them think they came up with your idea and then they are happy. What a bunch of two-year-olds!

It was absolutely certain we were going to slip into November. It still was not official, but we began to make the plans for a November launch. We were to get the official word by the end of the week. We were still planning on taking the spacecraft to Astro Tech in a couple of weeks, process it, and then store it until the launch, hopefully on November 23 or 24.

I was getting very optimistic that things were going to go ahead nicely. The spacecraft was in good shape. The solar panels were on. The flight battery was on. The spacecraft was in flight condition. We were going to do the final functional test the following week. Basically, we were ready to rock and roll.

Thursday Afternoon, September 4, through Sunday, September 7, 1997: A Long Weekend at San Simeon

Rebecca and I took off at about 4:00 PM and drove down to San Simeon and had a great, long weekend. We went to the Hearst Castle and did the 4th tour and the nighttime tour. We really enjoyed ourselves and relaxed and had a great time.

When we got home Sunday night, we got ready for the next week. LRI was getting in really good shape. We had gotten our first invoice into Lockheed and we had gotten LRI's money and our paychecks. LRI was really beginning to roll, as we better understood how the Lockheed system worked. Rebecca and I were quite happy and content.

Monday, September 8, 1997: The November Launch is Official

It was official; the launch was postponed until November 23/24.

We did a SIM in the morning that was a repeat of the maximum TLI under-burn (−35 m/sec) we could correct for without going into a phasing orbit. I had written a special Mission Profile for the SIM. We got through the emergency corrective burn part of the SIM very nicely.

Then Dan put in an electrical short in the spacecraft. I quickly saw the load current spike and, since we did not yet have a power shedding command (an emergency command that shut everything off, except the transmitter and the C&DH, to stop the power drain caused by a short), I started commanding the science instruments off as the first in a series of steps designed to cut the power drain. When I sent the MAG/ER Off Command, the power drain stopped, so I had found the source of the problem. I then turned the spectrometers back on and we continued with the mission. It was a good SIM.

Later, I went to Lockheed and then I went home to apply for an LRI corporate credit card and to straighten out a problem with our business account at the bank. The bank had called because the LRI account was overdrawn, which was very strange. I called Dorothy and she called the bank. The bank then called me and it turned out the bank had put LRI's money into some other account! When Rebecca and I cashed our paychecks, there was no money in our LRI account to cover them. The bank was very embarrassed by its mistake, especially because they had made a very big to-do about our new account being overdrawn the very first month!

Tuesday, September 9, 1997: Learning from Mistakes

We did a SIM in morning, in which we had to go into a phasing orbit because of a very big TLI under-burn. We went into the phasing orbit, and then the MAG/ER was turned on and it shorted out (again — Dan liked that problem). That was easily taken care of, but I had not actually commanded the MAG/ER to turn on! I had issued the MAG/ER Turn-On command, the uplink controller, Paul Travis, had uplinked it and I had verified it, but I had not issued the Execute Command! What had happened was that, as soon as I had verified the MAG/ER Turn-On command, Paul just sent the Execute Command without waiting for my command to execute. As soon as I saw the jump in the spacecraft's load current, I realized what had happened and I immediately issued the MAG/ER Turn-Off Command and told Paul he was never to uplink any command, especially the Execute Command, until I gave the order to do so. Again, that was something the uplink controllers had to learn, because in the real mission, if a command was sent without my knowing it, it could cause real problems.

We started a SIM of the 3rd MCM and the reor that would put the spacecraft in the correct attitude to do the 1st LOI burn, and John Breakwell was substituting for Dan. The first part of the MCM was an axial engine burn of just 1 m/sec and when I executed the command to fire the A1 and A2 engines, only A1 engine fired — A2 was dead! As soon as the burn ended, I ordered an immediate second burn of A1 to make up for the loss of the A2 engine.

We proceeded with the pulsed burn part of the MCM on the two tangential engines. However, Dan had programmed the SIM so that, instead of pulsing, the T1 engine would stick on and begin to fire continuously. When I started the tangential burn, the spacecraft quickly spun down to a zero spin rate and then started to spin up backwards! John, who, as the Dynamics Controller, was supposed to monitor the spacecraft's spin rate, did not notice that the spacecraft had spun down to zero and did not tell me that the spacecraft was spinning up (backwards) rapidly! I just saw that something was wrong with the engines — T1 was getting hot rapidly and T2 was heating up very slowly. At first I thought it was that the T2 engine wasn't burning properly (in reality, the engines heat up slowly during a pulsed burn and rapidly during a continuous burn, but I was not then well trained enough to recognize that difference). I should have immediately shut both of the engines off right then, but I was trying to figure out what in hell was going on with the engines, rather than reacting properly — that was another valuable lesson learned. Finally, I saw for myself that the spin rate was getting out of hand and immediately issued the emergency Stop Fire Command. That did nothing (remember the T1 engine was stuck on), so I immediately issued the emergency Close PIV Command, which finally stopped the T1 engine from firing. By that time, the spacecraft had a spin rate of minus 90 rpm!

Despite the errors, it was a very good SIM. First, because it was clear that John did not understand what he was doing. He was learning, but he was nowhere near as good as Dan. Second, we decided we had to have well defined abort criteria and we learned a whole lot of other things we had to change to make sure that if something like that did happen during the mission, we wouldn't get in as big a mess as we got into during the SIM. The mess we had gotten into was solvable — we just had to learn to react correctly and more quickly.

However, the way Dan had set the SIM up, i.e., so T1 couldn't be shut off, meant the end of the mission, because, if that happened during the flight, I could not have reopened the PIV without T1 firing! Well — you can't win 'em all.

Wednesday, September 10, 1997: A January Launch?

I started a SIM in the morning with our Nav Team at Goddard online. Goddard reported a TLI under-burn of 37 m/sec. But just as we got started, Dougherty called. LLV didn't want us to have launch dates in December because they couldn't get the launch trajectory calculations done for the December 7/8 backup launch dates and they did not want to be at the Cape just before Christmas (because of all the Lewis delays, we had decided to have two sets of launch dates every month, two with short-coasts in the Earth parking orbit early in the month and two with long-coasts two weeks later), so they wanted us to move our backup dates into January. I had to leave Mission Ops and go to Lockheed to talk to Dougherty. Thus, Dan took over, for the first time, my position as Mission Director and John took his place as the Dynamics Controller (as was planned if I was ever absent).

When I got to Lockheed, Dougherty had LLV on the phone and was trying to explain to them that we had to have at least one pair of windows in December and that we did not like losing the December 7/8 dates. But, it came down to the fact that they couldn't get all the trajectories done, period. They could only give us two trajectories per month, and that was it. Given that, I preferred to stay with the long coast trajectories. I said I wanted to use the November 23/24 and December 22/23 windows. I initially said the same thing for January, but, since the late January windows required high inclination lunar transfer orbits that would cost us extra fuel, and I thought I would use the short coast options early in January, if I had to wait that long.

When I got back to Mission Ops, Dan was still commanding the SIM. Interestingly enough, when setting up the SIM, he had accidentally left the computer program with the T1 engine stuck on as it was in the previous day's SIM. When he opened the PIV, T1 immediately started to fire. Dan did not notice that at first and the spacecraft spun up backward to about 200 rpm by the time he finally noticed it (again John was asleep in the Dynamics Controller's chair). Thus, when I walked in, they had a real mess on their hands and I watched them as they tried to recover. As a result, Dan learned a lot about being Mission Director (not so easy — huh?).

As a result of the last two SIMs with the stuck T1 engine, I began to think about what to do if a tangential engine (or any engine) did have a valve stuck open as a result of the launch vibrations. Since it took up to two frames (64 seconds) before we would get the downlinked data on our screens, if a tangential engine began to fire when I opened the PIV, the spacecraft would spin up or down in that critical minute to the point where there would be 60 g's of centrifugal force on it and it would fly apart — and I would not know it until it was too late. I started thinking about having a safe-engine-verification-sequence I would use before opening the PIV for good.

The sequence would consist of uplinking a PIV Open Command and, after that command was verified, uplinking a file with an Execute, a 5 second wait (just long enough to see if an engine was getting hot, i.e., if it was firing, but short enough so the spacecraft could not spin up or down much at all), a PIV Close Command and an immediate Execute. I told Dan about my idea and he thought it might be a good one. The downside was there was a very small chance that the PIV would not reopen after I opened and closed it for the test and that would spell the end of the mission. Howev-

er remote that possibility was, nobody liked closing a PIV once it had been opened during flight. We said we would have to discuss the idea with Irv and others to get their
opinions as to which was safer — opening the PIV once and taking the remote chance
that an engine would fire or doing the safety check and take the remote chance of not
being able to reopen the PIV after the test.

After the SIM, I had a telecon about the archiving documentation and the software
interface specifications.

Finally, I went home to work on the Mission Profile and the MOD; there were lots
of changes that I needed to make as a result of what I was learning from the SIMs.

Chapter 3-39
SIMs, SIMs, and More SIMs

Thursday, September 11, 1997: An Important All Day SIM

We had a really interesting, all day, Day 0 SIM. Goddard was online and I had Steve Honodel come over because I wanted him to learn what he had to do when I deployed the booms. We started the SIM at about 8:00 AM and Goddard reported a TLI burn error of −15m/sec, so I could follow the nominal Mission Profile. I was about to start the normal commanding sequence, when Dan noticed on his console there were no signals coming from the Earth/Moon limb-crossing sensor. Since that was not a critical problem, we waited until I got the PIV opened, the spacecraft reoriented and despun, and then we turned up the detection threshold of the Earth/Moon limb-crossing sensor, since Dan thought maybe it had become insensitive due to the absorption of water, i.e., the problem we had encountered during testing, but that didn't work. I turned it off and back on and that did the trick — it came on! Apparently, the Earth/Moon limb-crossing sensor didn't get turned on during the initialization sequence, although the downlink data indicated it was on. With that corrected, we were ready to proceed.

I commanded the MAG on (via the MAG/ER On Command that turned on both the MAG and the ER on, but since the high-voltage of the ER was not turned on by that command, only the MAG started to deliver data) in preparation for the deployment of the booms and I asked Steve to come into Mission Ops (no one was allowed in the Glass Room where we actually did Missions Ops until I needed them and I had asked them to come in). I asked Steve to calculate how long I should command the paraffin actuator heater on to ensure the actuator would start the deployment of the booms. The turn-on time depended both on the temperature of the actuator and the bus voltage of the spacecraft. Steve calculated the time and then I proceeded with the boom deployment, which went very well, and I then asked Steve to leave Mission Ops.

Next we did the post-boom-deployment spin-up burn to get the spin rate back up to 12 rpm and then I did the initial turn-on sequence for the rest of the science instruments. By that time, we were at the point in the Mission Profile where we were ready for the 1st MCM.

The 15 m/sec TLI error Goddard had reported at the beginning of the SIM should have converted to a 63 m/sec MCM burn 4 hours after TLI, i.e., at the time when we planned to do the MCM burn. But when Goddard gave us the MCM burn parameters, it was an 83 m/sec burn, using just the tangential engines! I said, "Wait a minute, something is wrong here."

The Goddard Nav guys said, "Oh no, it's correct," and then we discussed the burn parameters in detail.

I asked, "Is there really no axial component to the burn?"

They answered, "You don't need to do the axial component, because it's so small, only 0.6 m/sec."

I asked, "OK, fine, but are you sure of that?"

They answered, "Yes."

I replied, "OK, fine. But why do we have an 83 m/sec burn? The TLI error should translate to about 60 m/sec."

They answered, "No, that's not correct."

I said again, "I don't believe it. We should have a 63 m/sec burn 4 hours after launch based on a 15 m/sec TLI error."

We went back and forth about that and then Dan noticed that the velocity vector they had given us was not the same as the thrust vector! He asked, "What angle are you guys using between the thrust and velocity vectors? I need to have that angle."

Goddard answered, "We don't have that angle."

That blew my mind and I said, "I'm not making this burn, because I calculate you are 20 m/sec too high. This is simply not acceptable."

They said, "Well OK, we'll look at it."

Dan got the angle data and made his calculations and said, "I'm getting a 7 m/sec axial component." Obviously, there was something all screwed up.

Finally, we found out what Goddard had done — they had constrained the MCM velocity vector so it did not have an axial component, and so the transfer orbit had a constant time of flight! I thought, *why the hell did they do that? I've told them a hundred times not to do that and not to keep a constant time of flight!* The way they did the trajectory analysis, we would have gotten to the Moon, but we would have eaten up an extra 20 m/sec worth of fuel doing so!

Dan and I talked about that after the SIM. We agreed the Nav guys just didn't get the fact that we had to save fuel and if they didn't catch on to that fact fast, we would make them come out to Ames, make them sit down with us and we would tell them how to do the damned maneuvers without wasting fuel. As I had said about Ken, the Nav guys were just too damned academic; they just didn't seem to understand the practicalities of what we were doing with the mission. I didn't see why in hell they were having so much trouble with the concept and why they always wanted to get away without having an axial component to the burns. I just didn't get it.

Regardless, they finally gave us the correct burn vector — it was 64 m/sec. We loaded it into the spacecraft and we started the MCM burn. Dan had set up the input files so there was a big alignment error on one of the thrusters. Since he didn't want to know how much the alignment error was (because he wanted to be surprised at the results — don't forget, Dan was also trying to train for emergencies, but since he created them, he was never surprised like I was), he just threw some number in the file.

As the burn progressed, we began to see that each pulse burn caused the spacecraft to reorients itself a little bit. Though we could see that effect as a slow change in the Solar Equatorial Angle (SEA), as determined from the Sun sensor data, we didn't know where the spacecraft was pointing. The reason for that was, we did not know what the second angle was that we needed to completely define the spacecraft's attitude. Dan would get that angle only after a lengthy analysis of the data from the Earth/Moon limb-crossing sensor.

We started discussing that problem and Dan said, "If the SEA gets more than 17°, we'll have to stop the burn."

I said formally, "Is it your recommendation that we do not do the second part of the burn?"

Dan said formally, "Yes."

I said formally, "I concur. We have to figure out where the spacecraft is pointing, before we do the second part of the burn," (Because of bit limitations in the C&DH, the maximum number of pulses we could upload in one file was 255. Because the ΔV of that pulsed MCM burn was so large, we needed well over 500 pulses to achieve the required ΔV, so the burn was broken into two parts. We would do the first 255 pulses via the first file we uplinked and then start the burn again, uplinking a second file to do the remaining number of pulses).

The engine alignment error that Dan had programmed into the SIM was causing a bad (but not critical) situation and would end up costing us quite a bit of fuel to make the burns needed to correct the trajectory and the spacecraft's orientation. As we watched the first part (255 pulses) of the burn come to an end, we knew that the attitude error had gotten significant, but we were trying to get as much out of the burn as possible, because, at that stage of the mission (SIM), a poor burn was better than no burn at all.

When the burn ended, it was lunchtime and the Ames lunch truck had just arrived. We quickly sent someone down to got some sandwiches and then we just kept at it. Dan was trying to figure out what the spacecraft's attitude was and I was trying to get a better estimate of what had happened during the burn in terms of the ΔV we had achieved.

Also, I had been saying all day, and had just said again as we were working and eating, "I sure hope we have some spacecraft anomalies."

Paul Travis, who was the uplink controller for the SIM, asked with a sly smile, "You haven't noticed one?"

I answered, "No, I just looked at all my screens and the spacecraft is fine."

He said, "Well there might be one."

I looked at all the engineering data from the spacecraft and I couldn't find a damned thing wrong. I said, "Whatever it is, I don't see it. Whatever you've got going isn't showing on any of my screens, everything is green."

Dan looked at his screens and asked, "Why do we have an eclipse flag?" An eclipse flag meant the spacecraft was in the shadow of the Earth or the Moon or the Sun sensor was turned off. Since in the SIM, the spacecraft was in full sunlight on its translunar trajectory, and since the Sun sensor was on, Dan should not have had an eclipse flag! He said, "This is strange, I had a flag for a couple of seconds; I'll try to figure this out. I don't see how we could have an eclipse flag." Then he got a couple more flags.

Dan and I had just begun discussing the flags when I saw the solar array current go max, the battery current go max, and the load current go max! I said, "We have a short. Load and uplink the Power Saving Command immediately!" and boy, Paul got it uplinked in just 7 seconds!

I said, "OK, we have a short, let me see if all our systems come back on." The Power Saving Command shut everything off except the C&DH and the transponder (the C&DH and the receiver of the transponder could not be shut off; if they were, the spacecraft would be irrevocably dead). I watched the voltages and currents of the bus, the battery, the solar array, the C&DH, and the transponder and they were all OK, so the short was in something that had been turned off. The battery had discharged just a little bit due to the short, so I waited until it was fully charged up and saw that everything was safe and sound. I said, "OK, I'll start turning things on to see where the problem is."

Dan said, "Given the problems we were having with the sun sensor and the Earth/Moon sensor, I think we ought to start there, rather than go through the standard turn-on sequence."

I said, "I wholeheartedly agree."

I told Paul, "Have the emergency Power Saving Command ready to go and make test files for the Sun sensor with a Turn-On, an Execute, a Turn-Off, and an Execute. If the Sun sensor is shorted, we will see a power spike while it's on and we'll be able to turn it off without wasting time." He did and then I had him uplink the files. There was no power spike while the Sun sensor was on, so it was OK. I said, "Well then, let's put the Sun sensor back on," and we did.

I then said, "Make the same type of test file for the Earth/Moon limb-crossing sensor." He did and I said, "OK, send it."

I saw the echo of the Turn-On Command on my screen, and was about to say "Execute," when Paul said, "We have a power surge," just as I saw it too. Before I could even say a word, Paul (correctly) uplinked the emergency Power Saving Command, which was very, very good on his part. He did a perfect job.

I immediately thought what we were seeing was the Earth/Moon sensor coming on with a short, and I said so, because I thought Paul had sent the Execute Command without waiting for me to say, "Execute."

But Paul had not sent the Execute Command. He said, "No, it's the Sun sensor and that's why I sent the Power Saving Command up."

I said, "Well that's strange, we must have an intermittent short in the Sun sensor. I'll keep it off," and then I turned on the Earth/Moon sensor and it was fine. We turned the Sun sensor back on and I said, "I don't really trust it very much, since we're having problems with it. I'll wait and watch it a little bit." After a little while, during which the Sun sensor behaved itself, I began to slowly turn on the rest of the spacecraft, one thing at a time. Finally we were back to the condition that the spacecraft was in before the short and everything seemed to be OK.

Dan and I discussed the problem with the Sun sensor and as I pointed out, "The ER experiment is pretty well shot without the Sun sensor" (the ER used the Sun sensor pulse to synchronize its data collection with the spin period of the spacecraft). We decided, "What we will have to do if there ever is an intermittent short in the Sun sensor is to use it only when we have to — for pulsed burns and periodic determinations of the spacecraft's attitude — and always be ready with the Sun sensor Turn-Off command." We also decided we would use the medium gain antenna pattern to give us additional information on the attitude, so I sent the command to switch from the omni antenna to the medium gain antenna.

By that time, we had spent 8 hours doing the SIM and I said, "Enough is enough." It was one hell of a good SIM. We had uncovered a lot of problems with the NAV guys, problems that had to be fixed.

Dan was unhappy with himself, because he had really bad solutions for the attitude, but we had the problems with the attitude sensors and he was not getting good data. He had lost track of the Earth (it was not showing up in the Earth/Moon detector) and that puzzled him. He decided, "I have to take more time and collect more data to get the attitude right."

I was really pleased with Dan and I was pleased with myself; we were getting really trained and catching the problems before they became catastrophes. Paul did an excellent job, too. Ric also did well, he was very good, but Paul was actually the better of the two. If nothing else, Paul spoke louder and clearer than Ric did, which was very important, so there were no miscommunications when Paul was the uplink controller. I had often said, "Everybody has to speak very distinctly and very clearly. Ric, you have to speak louder, I have trouble hearing you." It wasn't a matter of personalities, Mission Ops had to be done right. If people couldn't do their jobs, we couldn't use them, period. We couldn't lose the spacecraft and that required clear communications.

At the end of a very long SIM, I was sure that between Dan, Ric, Paul, and me, we had one hell of a team to run the spacecraft and we were going to impress a hell of a lot of people.

Friday, September 12, 1997: Where is the Lockheed Check?

We didn't do any SIMs! Everybody had a lot of other things to do. I went over to see Maryann to ask why Lockheed had not paid LRI. She checked her computer and said that Lockheed hadn't cut our check. Of course, I had to get my work done on time but those SOBs didn't have to pay me until they get around to it. Those bastards!

I talked to Al Tilley and he said the spacecraft would only need about 7 kg of ballast. I thought the mass was going end up at 297 or 298 kg, i.e., the spacecraft was coming in really nice and light. The cg was right where it was supposed to be on the Z axis, but it was off 3 cm in X and Y and that was where the ballasting came in. I was pleased. Anyway, Tilley had made some wrong calculations, so they were not going to be able to finish spin balancing and ballasting the spacecraft until Monday.

I had lunch with Buddy Nelson. He took me out to an Italian restaurant that was very nice. He said again he wanted to help me by doing LRI's PR for free and anything else he could do. We had a real nice chat — Buddy is a true friend and I appreciate his sincere interest in what I am doing very much.

Jim Benson called; he wanted to visit Mission Ops and see the spacecraft. I told him that I was going to be gone between the 23rd and the 29th, but he could come anytime before or after those dates. He said that his wife, Susan, arranged their schedule and she would be coming with him.

I gave Maryann the budget, the deliverables, and my proposal for the extra month of time that had to be added to my contract because of the launch slipping from October to November.

Monday, September 15, 1997: Spin Balancing the Spacecraft

We ran a SIM for the Day 3 MCM and the reor to the LOI burn attitude in the morning. John was the Dynamics Controller and he didn't do very well. If he didn't get better, he was going to be useless.

I went to the spin balance facility to watch for the last spinning of the spacecraft. It was neat to see it spinning away, as it would in space, and it was very interesting to see the equipment that the technicians used to determine the spacecraft's spin-balance. The final amount of ballast required to balance was only 7 kilograms — just as Al Tilley had calculated. Lunar Prospector was completely ready for flight (except for the fuel, of course) and its launch mass would be between 297 and 298 kg — I was pleased.

However, I wasn't feeling too well, so I went home after watching the spin balancing.

Tuesday, September 16, 1997: Lockheed at its Best

We again did the Day 3 SIM with John Breakwell in Dan's place. The SIM went fairly well. I learned a lot, but John just was not catching on. If I had to rely on him, the mission would be a failure.

Maryann said the Lockheed invoice payment check for August was "in the mail," but, of course, LRI had not received it!

I had given Maryann the Statement of Work covering the extra time I would have to spend working on the mission due to the fact that the launch had slipped and Maryann sent me a copy of a letter she had sent to her boss, saying I would be working full time during the extra month *at no cost*! I thought, *this had better be a joke. They had better not be serious about this, because if they are, I'm going to start raising some serious hell about this damned company.* I could not believe how self-serving and absolutely disgusting Lockheed is.

Wednesday, September 17, 1997

We did a SIM for the perigee burn during the first orbit of a phasing orbit in order to train for the case where we had a large TLI under-burn and had to go into a phasing orbit so we could reach the Moon a month after launch. The SIM took a long time to do, in part because John just didn't know what in hell he was doing. He was really not very good. He certainly hadn't learned much. That took quite a bit of the day!

I went over to Lockheed to talk to Maryann and she said the reason they wrote the letter with the "no cost" clause was there was confusion in the contract because the first month of the mission after launch was defined by Discovery as being part of Phase C/D and hence, Phase E was only 11 months long. Since my contract was written for a 12 month Phase E, Lockheed claimed the extra month caused by the delay was already covered by my current contract! What a bunch of SOBs. That little sleight-of-hand trick still meant I was not going to get paid for the extra month of work.

I talked to Bob Garner, who said, regarding the extra month's work, "You've already done all the work, so why should you get paid for it."

I answered, "I don't do Mission Profiles for missions we are not going to fly. I only do the ones we are going to fly and hence, if we are delayed, I have to do new ones." What a bunch of crooks.

LLV was whining, saying they didn't think they could get us launched until January, or even spring! Every time I turned around, they were whining they couldn't do anything.

After all that stupidity, I just went home early and worked on the new Mission Profile.

Thursday, September 18, 1997: Getting Ready to go to the Cape

We did a 1st LOI burn SIM in the morning. John was again the Dynamics Controller and did poorly. When we started the burn, the A1 engine was out. I finished the one engine burn and then started doing the additional burn to make sure the spacecraft was in a stable, two day capture orbit. Paul very cleverly let A1 come back on, which was a neat twist in our emergency training. I let the two-engine burn go to completion, since that would get us closer to our planned 12-hour capture orbit. Anyway the SIM was fun, but I was disappointed in John.

After that, we had a staff meeting and Dougherty wanted to ship the spacecraft to the Cape on October 9, which I did not like. The reason was that Lockheed was planning a big PR to-do on the 8th, so the spacecraft had to be at Lockheed for that event. The PR event should have been done a month earlier, but Dougherty kept procrastinating. He didn't want to do it too early before the launch. Of course, what happened was that all of a sudden, everything had to be done all at once and we didn't have time to do everything properly.

That also meant I would have to fly to Florida for the Fourth International Lunar and Mars Exploration Conference I had promised to attend on October 5, 6, and 7, and fly back on the 7th for the PR event on the 8th; well, at least I would be home for my birthday. The plan was to get the spacecraft processed and put it on the launch vehicle shortly after the 28th, where it would sit for a month. Then, if the whiny butt LLV guys got the LLV2 ready in time, Lunar Prospector would be launched in November. All the LLV guys could do was whine and snivel, "We can't do it, we can't make it."

Friday, September 19, 1997: Delayed Until December

We ran a SIM in the morning with John as the Dynamics Controller and he finally did a half way acceptable job. However, the most interesting thing for me was that he said he had heard about Lunar Prospector from Dougherty. All Dougherty had talked about was his spacecraft and his mission and it was only later somebody told John it was my mission. I found that amusing.

LLV dropped the ball again; all the cabling in our LLV2's Orbit Adjustment Module was screwed up. That would cause a two-week delay, which meant we could not launch until December! LLV hadn't officially said that, but it didn't take a rocket scientist to figure out! They also canceled the review, so I didn't have to go to Denver. I feared LLV was going to screw around until they totally screwed up the mission.

Four people from Gilroy came to see the spacecraft at 4:00 PM, followed by another group of seven people. Then a TV guy came and did a nice interview — so I did three different Outreach events and earned $792 for LRI.

The TV interview was fun. Rebecca and I watched it on TV that evening; it was short and sweet. I was sure if Scott saw it, he would get ticked off, and if he did, I was going to tell him to go to hell.

Saturday, September 20, 1997

I showed the spacecraft to another group of Gilroy people. It was really a good group of very interested people.

Monday, September 22, 1997:
PR Issues and the Formal End of Training

We started a SIM in the morning. It took us a while to get it set up and then the simulator bombed on us, so we quit. We all decided we had enough training. We were getting to the point where we were getting over-trained. That was nice, because I could and did claim that my training "deliverable" was done. That, plus the fact that the spacecraft was finished, i.e., it was ready for shipment, and the fact that I was going to have at least 16 Outreach events during the month, meant that LRI would get over $30,000 for the month of September!

I talked to Sylvia and she said we were going to have a telecon the next day at 9:00 AM with the dummies at Denver about the launch vehicle. They were fussing again. There were stirrings at Ames to tell LLV, "Stop stringing us along, month by month; give us a real launch date you can meet."

I was against that, because I believed they would say January or February or, even worse, March. If we did not keep pressing LLV, I was never going to get launched.

I saw Lisa, the Ames Lunar Prospector PR person, who was doing a great job, in the hall and she said, "You didn't tell me you were going to have an interview."

I said, "No."

She said politely, "You're supposed to do that. I turned on the TV news at 11:00 and there you were."

I said, "I have no objections to telling you, but it just came up, so I did it."

She said, "OK, but in the future, tell me if you can."

I replied, "Sure."

I thought that was interesting and I assumed Scott and David Morse had seen the interview and had bitched at her. I was really sick of those two anyway. They had written a press release about the launch delay and Buddy Nelson had given me a copy for editing. There was not one word in there about LRI or me, just Lockheed and NASA Ames, so I changed it. Of course, the press release was released before Buddy had a chance to get it back to David. Also, there was an article in the September issue of the Ames newsletter about Lunar Prospector and it only talked about Lockheed and Ames. I was just waiting for Scott to say one damned word to me about the TV interview.

As Lisa and I were talking, she mentioned there were only three more packages of the Lunar Prospector posters left and they would have to have more printed up. Since the poster was developed and printed before I had left Lockheed, the posters only had Lockheed and NASA written across the bottom. Since I was in LRI, I wanted to have LRI added to the poster, so I said, "Good, now we can get LRI added on there."

She started fussing and said, "Well gee, we have it laid out so well, I don't know if we want to change it."

I said, "Hey look, it doesn't have LRI on there. That is the Principal Investigator's Institute and it is going on there."

She said, "Well, there is this little thing right under the NASA logo that says copyright stuff. Maybe we can put something there."

I said, "No, LRI is going to be just as big as the NASA and Lockheed. What we can do is put the LRI logo and Lunar Research Institute next to the NASA logo right up here."

She said, "Well, I guess we will have to talk about this."

I thought, *it better end up my way, because Scott is not going to get away with pulling this kind of crap on me anymore. If he keeps this up, I'm going to throw him off the program. I'm going to write to Wes and tell him that I want Scott off the program — I mistakenly brought him on and now I want him off.*

Chapter 3-40
The Second Lockout

Tuesday, September 23, 1997:
"Honey, You Won't Believe What Happened Today!"

Buddy called to tell me Scott was on a rampage about Friday's TV interview and I was preparing to do battle with Scott anyway, so, "Let the games begin."

I went to the 9:00 AM meeting and Scott was just as sweet as could be, joking and laughing, ho, ho, ho. Nevertheless, Scott was very concerned that we had lost three launch opportunities and he didn't want to have another launch date come up, have us take it, and then have it canceled — he was getting worried about being criticized by Headquarters. He said, "I don't want any criticism and blah, blah, blah. I want us to wait until January and not go in December."

Denver thought they could be ready for a launch in the December 22/23, long coast windows and, if we were delayed, they would be able to be ready to go during the short coast, January 5/6 windows. They had five different scenarios and we discussed them. Scott was clearly running scared. He didn't want a failure. He didn't want delays. He wanted launch windows far enough in the future, so there were no questions about LLV being able to be ready, so he wouldn't have to explain anything to his beloved Headquarters that terrified him so.

I kept pushing the other scenario and said, "We are running out of launch opportunities. If we don't take the ones we have, we'll end up losing the mission."

Scott kept worrying about mission success. I said, "Of course I want mission success. What I don't want is for us to delay ourselves out of the mission eclipse window and end up having Lunar Prospector sitting in the Smithsonian." The meeting ended with no resolution (and with no mention of the TV interview).

I went looking for Lisa. She was to bring some people, who were doing some of the Outreach work for Ames, to see the spacecraft. It turned out she was ill and I hadn't noticed the note on her door, until it was well after 11:00 AM, saying she was home sick. I went to lunch.

When I got back from lunch, I checked my phone messages and there was one from Maryann saying Ames was very upset about the TV news interview, they wanted my contract changed and I had to come over to see her immediately.

Thinking little about Maryann's message, in part, because, as far as I was concerned, I was not changing my contract for Ames or Lockheed or anyone, but I went over to Lockheed to do some other things I needed to do there and to see what the toot was all about.

When I got to Building 107, I couldn't get in the door — my keycard would not work. My first thought was, remembering that Lockheed had locked Wendell out just a month earlier, when he threatened to shoot Kim Foster and some other people with an AK 47, "The SOBs have locked me out. I'm put in the same class as the guy who threatened to kill everybody!" but I dismissed the thought as being ridiculous and figured my keycard had become demagnetized or something.

Just then Francisco entered the building and I went in with him to find Maryann, but she was not around. I saw Tim Maloney, whose cubicle was near Maryann's, and Tim said, with a twinkle in his eye, "I guess you upset NASA again, huh?" We were bantering around and finally Maryann got back to her cubicle.

I asked, "What in hell is going on, Maryann?"

She said, "Oh, nothing; it's all taken care of."

I said, "Don't give me that, something is going on."

She said, "Well, yes." Then she gave me a copy of an email (Appendix 3-1, also see www.lunar-research-institute.org) Scott had written to Cathcart on Saturday, stating I had given an unauthorized TV interview and demanding all kinds of things: I should not be allowed near the spacecraft unless accompanied by someone, Buddy Nelson was to be banned from the program, the contract had to be modified, and on and on.

I couldn't believe what I was reading and asked, "What kind of crap is this?"

She replied, "Well, it has all been retracted. Tom took care of it."

I said, "Then I'll go ask Tom what in hell is going on."

I went to Dougherty's office and, without showing him my copy of Scott's email, I asked, "Tom, what in hell is going on?"

He answered, "Oh, nothing."

I asked him, as I showed him my copy of Scott's email, "Then what is this?"

He asked, alarmed, "Where did you get that? Just throw that away, just ignore it."

I said, "No Tom, what's this all about?" Clearly he did not want me to know about the email and he certainly did not want a copy of it in my hands, but it was too late for that!

Dougherty had to spill the beans and he said Scott had shot off the email in a fit of rage without checking on anything. None of his allegations against Buddy and me were true: Scott charged I had not gotten authorization from Ames to do the interview, Buddy had illegally set up the interview and passes for the TV people that were in the Lockheed Building doing photography, and Buddy was not coordinating anything with David Morse. Well, Buddy *had* informed David and David had dropped the ball (Appendix 3-2, also see www.lunar-research-institute.org) and further, regarding the Lockheed passes and photography permits — that was Lockheed's business, not Scott's. Scott, the arrogant, fat little bastard that he is, had gone off the deep end because I was on TV and he wasn't. Dougherty (who also had it with the pompous little bastard) said he said to Scott, "What in hell do you want? Everything was done according to the way things are supposed to be done. Now that you've made a fool of yourself, what are you going to do about this thing (the email)?"

Dougherty said Scott calmed down then and said, "Oh nothing, we're just going to forget about it (meaning, don't let Alan find out about it)." Well, unfortunately for Scott, the cat was out of the bag.

I said to Dougherty that something was wrong with my keycard and I had not been able to get in the building, so I needed to get my card fixed. Dougherty said, "Maryann had you locked out (Appendix 3-3, also see www.lunar-research-institute.org). She was just supposed to lock you out of Building 150 so you couldn't get to the spacecraft."

I said, "Well, I'm not only locked out of 150, I'm locked of everything!"

He said, "That was a mistake on her part," then he said he had reamed her out for overreacting to the email, period. Then he said again, "Just throw that email away, forget the whole thing."

I was really ticked off and I said, "BS. No, I'm not going to forget it, I've been locked out of my spacecraft I work on every day and I've been locked out of Lockheed like a common criminal. But, first things first, how do I get this fixed (getting my lockout reversed)?"

He said, "Maryann is taking care of it. It shouldn't take but a little bit."

I went to Maryann and I showed her my keycard and I said, "What's going on with this Maryann?"

I felt sorry for Maryann; she was caught in the middle, but she had reacted hysterically when Cathcart had called her, just as Cathcart reacted hysterically when "The High Lord Almighty" Scott Hubbard had screamed at him. I said, "Maryann, this is absurd. I'm not hollering at you, but I am the Principal Investigator of this Program, this is my spacecraft, and I have hired this company to build it and locking me out is absolutely unacceptable. I am just telling you flat out, don't ever do this again. You know I will handle this my way. I'm taking this to Congress."

She said, "Don't get Lockheed in trouble; please don't get Lockheed in trouble."

I said, "I don't intend to get Lockheed in trouble, I intend to get Scott and Ames in trouble. Lockheed is in the middle of it. You should not have reacted like that, but Scott, not Lockheed is the problem." I left at that point saying, "I'll be back tomorrow to see if I can get into Lockheed with my keycard."

By the time I left for home, I had already decided I was going to do everything I could possibly do to get Scott removed from the mission — I had had it with the pompous, arrogant, fat little SOB (though I hoped I could get the SOB removed from Lunar Prospector, I knew that I could never get him fired from NASA itself, NASA would never fire the little bastard. Besides, it is almost impossible for NASA to fire one of its government employees, except for real criminal acts, if then).

However, I knew that right then was not the time for me to try to get rid of the SOB. Headquarters was so nervous about the launch vehicle and the mission, it would most certainly cancel the mission if I raised hell about their little darling at that critical time. I would have to keep my mouth shut until after launch and after Lunar Prospector was safely in its lunar mapping orbit. Then I would write Wes, layout the evidence of what Scott had done and demand he be removed from the mission. Much as I hated to and much as I hated the fat little, self-serving SOB, I had to wait a couple of months before I could try to do him in.

When I got home, I called Buddy, who was as outraged as I was about Scott's treatment of both of us. Buddy hates Scott even more than I do — if that is possible. I told Buddy that after launch I was going to write Wes and demand that Scott be removed from the mission. Buddy was ecstatic about that and said he would help me in every way he could and he would immediately get me all the emails he had that showed he had properly informed NASA of my PR activities, etc.

Wednesday, September 24, 1997: The Day After

We did a SIM in the morning. We were getting burned out on SIMs, but though we were officially done with the training, we had to do a SIM every couple of days to keep sharp, but not do too many and lose our fine edge.

I went over to Lockheed. I still couldn't get in, so I told Dougherty and he called up the security guy and left a message saying they better get it fixed because it was getting very embarrassing to Lockheed that the PI couldn't get into the place.

It was kind of amusing because I had to get Irv to let me in. Everybody knew what had happened and they were riding me about it, but they all knew the shit was going to hit the fan. As Tim Maloney said, "I know somebody is going to pay for this." It was interesting, because they all knew exactly what had happened and why — Scott's ego.

Thursday, September 25, through Saturday, September 27, 1997: A Trip to Los Alamos

Thursday, I flew to Albuquerque and then drove up to Los Alamos. That trip always took the better part of a day.

Friday morning I gave a seminar on Lunar Prospector to the Los Alamos staff in the morning and then we discussed lunar petrology and other mission related topics in the afternoon.

After that, Bill and I went on a nice hike down at some Indian ruins.

I flew back home on Saturday and, again, that took a good part of the day.

Sunday, September 28, 1997

I gave two tours of the spacecraft to Dorothy Van Fosson and her family and friends.

Monday, September 29, 1997

It sounded like LLV was still trying for a November 23 launch. Dougherty was skeptical, as was I.

I had a telecon Q&A session with Dick Sealy and the BJ Link students. That was fun and I showed the guys who were setting up the NASA Ames Lunar Prospector web site the spacecraft and Mission Ops. Two more Outreach events and $528 in LRI's pocket.

NASA and Lockheed were going nuts about the rocket and pre-ship meetings. They are all lunatics (woops, sorry, I did not meant to insult the Moon) if you ask me.

Tuesday, September 30, 1997: Another Set of Lockheed Lies

Lockheed Denver was pushing like hell to get us launched in November, which I was pleased about. But we couldn't process the spacecraft at Astro Tech, so LLV was going to try to get us processed at the Air Force facilities at the Cape. It was going to cost LLV quite a bit of money, but as Sylvia said, "Who gives a damn?"

My good, old friend, Don Davis, and a couple of his staff from the Planetary Science Institute in Tucson were at Ames doing breakup studies of ice projectiles and ice targets, trying to understand how Kuiper bodies at the solar system's outer edge react when they collide. I showed Don and his co-workers the spacecraft and then Don and I had lunch.

I turned in LRI's September invoice; it was for $30,000. When I gave it to Maryann, she said, "Oh, Lockheed made a mistake in paying you so fast last month, you won't get paid for this for 30 days — it's a Lockheed rule."

I said, "Well, I'm going to get paid now, not in 30 days. If it's not one thing with Lockheed, it's another — they have an excuse or a rule for everything so they can screw me."

She said, "Well, they say that they won't pay the invoice so fast — about the only thing you can do is laugh about it."

I said, "I don't think it's very funny, this may be a big joke to Lockheed, but it's not a big joke to me. Somehow, I'm going to make sure LRI gets its money in a reasonable amount of time. It was bad enough it took two weeks to get it last month."

She said, "Why don't you get Garner to sign it, then I'll sign it, and you can take it right over to Accounts Payable yourself."

I got the signatures and took it over to Accounts Payable (like I had nothing better to do, than be an errand boy). When I got there, the guy asked, "Are you 10-day or 30-day."

I asked, "What do you mean?"

He asked, "Is you account payable in 10 days or 30 days?"

I answered, "I was told it was 10 days."

He said, "Well, I'll look it up." He did and the dirty SOBs had written in the contract that LRI was payable in 30 days, rather than in 10 days.

I said, "Give me the invoice back."

I took it back to Maryann and asked her to get it changed and she said, "Well, I'll just change it." She did, but I was outraged at Lockheed. That was just another attempt to make my being in LRI as difficult as possible — it was the same old BS. Lockheed wanted to delay payment as long as possible, so they could keep the contract money in their pocket and keep it out of LRI's. I had to do their damned milestones exactly on time, but they would pay LRI at their convenience. Lockheed continued to treat me as badly as possible, even after I was out of the damnable company. As far as I am concerned, Lockheed and the people who run it have no morals or standards. They are just scum.

Buddy sent me a preview of the press release for the up and coming Lockheed PR to-do and wanted my comments. Buddy had told me I was one of the main speakers and that didn't seem to be the case according to the press release. When I called him, I asked him about that. He answered, "Oh, it's OK. Henshaw changed everything and none of the speakers are to be mentioned in the press release." He also changed the title so it said that Lockheed had put together a "Lockheed Led Lunar Prospector Team." I was astounded; these guys are the biggest bunch of liars and backstabbers. I was amazed — how could Henshaw say Lockheed had put together the Lunar Prospector Team — I didn't remember seeing him leading Lunar Prospector any time between late 1988 and 1994, before Lockheed agreed to become *my Industry Partner and support my Discovery proposal* effort, but I must have dreamt all that!

Despite my disgust, there was no use getting Buddy in trouble, since Henshaw wouldn't change it anyway. I was disgusted: disgusted with Lockheed, disgusted with the launch vehicle, disgusted with Scott, and disgusted with NASA. All that each of them wanted to do was to try to screw everybody else and take all the credit for everything. It doesn't make any difference what you do or don't do, they just stab you in the back. Funny enough, though I was in the middle and getting stomped on by both sides, Lockheed complained to me, "NASA is trying to take all the credit for Lunar Prospector," and NASA complained to me, "Lockheed is trying to take all the credit for Lunar Prospector." Too bad they didn't get into a big battle over whose mission Lunar Prospector was and annihilate each other — the world would be a better place if they did.

On top of all that BS, Headquarters stuck its head even further up its ass. Because the Lewis satellite had failed right after launch, NASA was in a panic about Lunar Prospector and, in its infinite wisdom, NASA told Sam Venneri, the guy who was responsible for Lewis and hence, who was responsible for its failure, to lead a team to review Lunar Prospector! Henshaw was going to have a final pre-ship Lockheed review of Lunar Prospector, but since NASA didn't trust Lockheed, Henshaw's review was going to become a NASA review. Instead of Discovery, it was business as usual. NASA cannot be reformed — it can only be shut down. Lockheed cannot be reformed — it can only go out of business. They are scum.

I digress here a bit, but understanding the Lewis failure is important for the Lunar Prospector story: Lewis failed because of the bad management that is typical of NASA programs and hence of Sam Venneri. When Lewis was being built by TRW, NASA decided to use commercially available software developed to automatically stabilize helicopters — a good idea to save money. However, as the software was being adapted for use in controlling Lewis's attitude control system (Lewis was a three-axis stabilized spacecraft, totally unlike the simple, spin stabilized satellite Lunar Prospector was), a junior TRW engineer discovered that under unlikely, but possible, circumstances, Lewis could get into an unstable mode and could start spinning. If left uncorrected for a few hours by mission controllers, that spin would become so bad that Lewis would be lost. Typical of a NASA run program, the junior engineer wrote a memo (no one reads memos) about the possible failure mode and sent it up the (weak) chain of management, where, I am sure, someone promptly filed it away. After Lewis's successful launch on the LLV1, the Lewis Mission Ops Team was so happy and tired they went home for some 12 hours to sleep. Meanwhile, Lewis promptly got into the unlikely unstable mode and began spinning. By the time the Mission Ops Team came back to Mission Ops, Lewis was irrevocably out of control and nearly out of attitude control fuel. Thus a satellite that cost $65 million was lost because NASA management had failed — again. Unlike Lunar Prospector, no one person had total responsibility of the mission, no one person understood the entire spacecraft and mission, and no one was smart enough to know you do not leave a newly launched spacecraft unattended for a half a day right after launch! Given that chain of bad management, NASA was sending the very guy who was at the top of that chain, Sam Venneri, to review Lunar Prospector and to tell us what we were doing wrong — now that made a lot of sense, correct?

Wednesday, October 1, 1997:
Launch Date Indecision and an Attempted Lockheed Screw Job

I went over to the Ames facilities where Don Davis and his crew were conducting their ice ball impact studies and then we went to lunch. Then I showed them Mission Ops.

At 2:00 PM, I went to Scott's office for a telecon with Denver. LLV said they could still make the November 23/24 windows! The issue was, how to tie the November windows with the December 23/24 windows, since there were problems at the Range with the latter dates because of Christmas. If LLV could resolve those problems, then we would go with November as our primary windows and December as our secondary windows. Then there was the issue of whether we would skip November and December, which I did not want to do, and go to January and February as the primary and secondary windows. I hoped we were going to end up using November and December — I was pushing hard for that and everybody seemed to want to do that, too. Of course, Denver and NASA couldn't make a decision, but I was hoping we would get a decision from them the next day.

I thought we had resolved the question of the timing of the payment of the LRI invoices, but when I talked to Maryann, she said Lockheed claimed I had signed an agreement that said LRI would get paid 30 days after an invoice was turned in. What I thought I had agreed to was LRI would get paid every 30 days, i.e., once a month, but they had it written so it really meant the payment would be made 30 days later, not every 30 days. I had not understood their gobbledygook, in part, because of their clever wording, but mainly because every one of the lying SOBs I had asked, told me the payments were due within 10 days. I said, "Maryann, this is BS, everyone told me 10 days. I asked them a dozen times to be absolutely sure. If they deny it, they are lying." After I had raised hell with her, I raised hell with Bob Garner, and then I raised hell with Dougherty. I was going to make those SOBs pay LRI in 10 days come hell or high water. Lockheed is just disgusting, they screwed me (and the rest of their employees) every chance they got. They just did not care or understand that they had made such an enemy out of me and I was going to try to make them pay, big time.

Chapter 3-41
Delayed until January

Thursday, October 2, 1997: Delayed and Screwed

We had another launch date telecon in the morning. I was trying to preserve the November and December windows. Denver was still having some problems with the Orbit Adjustment Module, so we had to have another telecon at 4:00 PM.

Coats came to the 4:00 telecon; Dougherty was going to use him to put pressure on Denver to launch us in the November windows. But, to make a long story short, LLV couldn't make the November windows and we could not launch in December because the Cape wouldn't support a December 24 launch and we did not want a 1-day window. We were going to launch during the January 6/7 windows, with the February 4/5 windows as the backup — crap, I was ticked off!

Maryann called and said they were going to change the contract to say LRI would get paid for the extra month's work caused by the launch delay from October to November (well, that change was already out of date). But she added Lockheed was charging LRI 1% of the increase in the value of the contract to make the change! She said, "The change in the value is $30,000, so the charge is just $30." Well 1% of $30,000 is $300, not $30, so her arithmetic was a little off, but I was not about to let Lockheed steal $300 or even $30 from LRI for just a few key strokes on their computer. I went over, I grabbed Dougherty, dragged him to Maryann's cubicle and said to him, "I want you to hear this."

He listened to Maryann and he said, "Well, that is typical when you change a contract." Lockheed had found another way of screwing me and it was BS. The whole thing was just BS.

Friday, October 3, 1997

I went in late and came home early. I was very annoyed about our launch slipping until January and the latest Lockheed screw job. But there was nothing I could do about either one of those things.

**Sunday, October 5, through Tuesday, October 7, 1997:
A Trip to Florida**

I flew to the Cape Sunday and attended the first day of the Fourth International Lunar and Planetary Exploration Conference on Monday.

I met and talked with Jim Benson. Jim was doing a very good job of trying to do a commercial mission to a near-earth asteroid. Jim is really quite a sharp guy and he has his own money to back him up. He wanted me to join him; I was not interested in doing that, but I said we could talk about it. He wanted me to give a talk to his staff to make sure they understood how I did Lunar Prospector. He said he was planning to visit Sunnyvale and see the spacecraft in a couple weeks.

While we were talking, Jim asked me a very interesting question. He said he had been asked by a space reporter, "Why is Lockheed trying to pretend that Lunar Prospector is their program and that Alan Binder doesn't exist?"

Jim said he answered, "I think because Alan won't be there (at Lockheed) very much longer and they don't want the father of the baby to leave and they wanted to take all the credit for the baby."

Jim asked me, "Is it OK that I said that?"

I answered, "Hell yes, that's about as accurate as you can get."

My talk went over very well, as did Jim's.

Ed O'Connor, the head of the Spaceport Florida, from whose launch pad I was to launch, gave a really good talk about Spaceport Florida.

Mike Lawson, who had tried to get Coke and Pepsi to support Lunar Prospector back in the "Early Years" (Part One), was there and we had a nice chat. He congratulated me on my success and we talked about doing things together in the future.

Karen Ramos, who was hobbling around on a cane, had arranged for me to go with her, her son, and her boyfriend to a very nice banquet in the Saturn V Pavilion that had just opened at the Kennedy Space Center. The banquet was nice and the pavilion was phenomenal. They have a beautiful Saturn V, all painted and nicely restored, lifted off the ground, inside the pavilion — it was really great.

It was a good trip, although it was very tiring. I got to San Jose about noon on Tuesday. Rebecca picked me up at the airport and we went home to rest.

Wednesday, October 8, 1997: Lockheed's PR Event

Lockheed held its big PR event to honor all the subcontractors, especially those in Silicon Valley, who helped to build Lunar Prospector. The press was well represented and, all in all, it was a success — though Lockheed made it look like Lunar Prospector was their program. Henshaw spoke first, welcoming everyone and thanking the subcontractors. Then a bigwig from Hewlett-Packard spoke. Both he and Henshaw waxed eloquent about Lunar Prospector. David Morrison from Ames spoke next and was very complimentary about the program and about me. Then Dougherty spoke; he didn't do too well — he never does. But the thing that floored me was Henshaw's introduction of me — he made a point of talking about LRI and the PI. To be sure, Buddy had written everything out for him and made sure he knew what he was supposed to say, but he did say it. After he was done introducing me, I talked about the mission and the spacecraft and then I led everyone into the highbay and I showed them the spacecraft — that was a lot of fun.

After it was over, Rebecca and I went home.

Thursday, October 9, 1997: My 58th Birthday

We ran a SIM in the morning using the new Mission Profile that I was working on for the January 6 launch date.

It looked like we were going to ship on November 21.

I went home. Rebecca and I went to a movie and had an Italian dinner to celebrate my birthday.

Friday, October 10, 1997

Yoshitake Yamaguchi came to Ames and watched us do a SIM. He had invited Rebecca and me to dinner at his house in the evening. At first, Yoshitake and his lovely wife were going to serve sushi, but knowing that Rebecca would certainly die at the sight of a raw fish, I politely requested something cooked — so I saved her life! We had a very nice evening with Yoshitake, his wife, and their cute little daughter.

The so-called Black-Hat Review (the one that started as Henshaw's review, but became a NASA/Sam Venneri Review after the Lewis failure) of Lunar Prospector was going to be in Sunnyvale on the 20th and 21st.

There was also going to be a review of the LLV2 and Dougherty said it would be a waste of my time and it really would. For once, I agreed with him regarding my not going to an LLV meeting.

Monday, October 13, 1997

I worked at my LRI office at home and got a lot done.

Tuesday, October 14, 1997

We still didn't know for sure if we were going to ship Lunar Prospector to the Cape on November 21 or not, there was a possibility we would not ship until the 28th.

Denver still claimed we were going to launch in November, which was a big load of BS.

Wednesday, October 15, 1997

I went in late, because Rebecca and I went to our first Gilroy Chamber of Commerce Breakfast and were introduced as new members of the organization.

Bill called; Lockheed wouldn't give him his Phase E money because the mission was delayed. He wouldn't get any more money until Phase E started (see, Lockheed also screwed my Co-Is every time they could, using any excuse they could). Of course, he still had plenty of work to do to prepare for the mission, so he needed the money. Thus, I was going to go raise hell about that as soon as Dougherty was back.

Thursday, October 16, 1997: The General Dailey Visit

Jim Burke came to Lockheed; he watched us do a SIM and I showed him the spacecraft. I was pleased to be able to have Jim see what had become of our joint efforts during the "Early Years" of Lunar Prospector (Part One).

The best thing of the day though, was that General John (Jack) Dailey, Goldin's Deputy, and Alison McNally from Headquarters were at Ames. I was asked to show them, as well as Coats (Lockheed) and David Morrison (Ames), the spacecraft and, of course, Marcie tagged along to make it look like she had some important role in the mission for the benefit of David and the General.

Given that I had Goldin's Deputy in my grasp (despite the fact that Goldin was at Ames three or four times during the entire project, he never once came to see the spacecraft or Mission Ops), I gave them the entire Lunar Prospector spiel. General Dailey was utterly fascinated by Lunar Prospector and how I had defined it, got it built, held its mass down, and everything else. I told him how we had gotten through thermal-vac in just seven days, how Dougherty had held down the costs and all of our other triumphs.

General Dailey was amazed and thought Lunar Prospector was the greatest thing. He said, "Boy, Goldin has got to hear this. He would love this. He has to come out here. I am going to have him come out and hear you tell about Lunar Prospector. Not only do you know all this, but you present it in a way that everybody can understand it. You're extremely good at presenting this stuff. I've got to get Goldin out here." Then General Dailey, David Morrison, and Alison tried to figure out how to get Goldin out to Ames to see the spacecraft. They said he had been invited to the Extraterrestrial Biology Conference in November, so I could show him everything then. The nice thing about it was if Goldin came, then Henshaw would be along and I would have a golden opportunity to show both of them who really knew everything about the spacecraft and the mission and who was really running the show. I was extremely pleased about that possibility, because it would make all the things I wanted to do, in terms of getting back in total control total of Lunar Prospector, proving that "Faster, Better, Cheaper," really worked and showing that scientists should be running the programs, not engineers and bureaucrats, a lot easier (unfortunately, Goldin never came to see the spacecraft or me).

Friday, October 17, 1997

A reporter for the *Palo Alto Weekly* came for an interview, the *Discovery Channel* people in Toronto wanted an interview on the following Monday, and a local newspaper wanted an interview the next Tuesday. Lunar Prospector was becoming hot news!

Monday, October 20, 1997

The Black Hat Review of Lunar Prospector was moved to Tuesday and Wednesday and it had gotten bigger and bigger (as usual).

Sylvia was skeptical about the LLV2 evaluation that the NASA launch vehicle guys at Huntsville were going to have. She thought Huntsville would judge our LLV2 launch as a "high-risk launch" and expected they would recommend delaying us until after CRSS, which, of course, wasn't going to work. I didn't know what to think, except that the launch vehicle mess just never seemed to end. And, of course, the incompetent bastards in Denver were whining about trying to get us launched in January. It was the same LLV crap — just verse four hundred!

Sylvia had finally recognized what I knew from the very beginning, i.e., the famous, "Lockheed is a big company and will get behind the launch vehicle," was a fraud from day one. Dougherty had been touting the company line all along.

I went home disgusted and worked all day on the January Mission Profiles and other things.

Tuesday, October 21, 1997: Day One of the Black Hat Review

The review started today. It was kind of fun. Dougherty did amazingly well! He actually knew what in hell he was talking about — at least, while he was doing his summary review in the beginning. In the afternoon, he fell apart — as usual.

LLV looked like it had a good shot at January. They were even shipping the Orbit Adjustment Module to the Cape a day early! They thought they had a 90% chance of getting us launched in January, whereas just a week earlier, they thought they just had a 50% chance of getting us off. Everything looked fairly decent with the LLV2.

Scott was concerned about Huntsville's evaluation of the LLV2, but he wasn't as skeptical as Sylvia was. He said if Huntsville said it was a high-risk launch, we could probably get Huckins, Piotrowski, and the other guys at Headquarters, who were sympathetic to us, to support our January launch. I thought Scott was correct and hence, that we were probably OK.

As a result, I had a sneaking suspicion we were going to get a good shot at January. But it appeared we would have do the launch processing at Astro Tech after all and that we would not ship until November 28 — those two things were putting a slight kink in our schedule again.

David Morrison was there and he came over to me and said, "Boy, you really impressed Dailey."

I said, "Well, that's good."

Actually, the review was fun, i.e., we had as much fun as you can have in a NASA review.

Wednesday, October 22, 1997: Day Two of the Black Hat Review

First of all, Earle Huckins came over to me before the review got started and said, "You really know everything about your spacecraft and mission and, as a PI, you are quite exceptional."

I was, of course, pleased that someone at Headquarters was finally recognizing that, but much more importantly, his compliments gave me the opening I was looking for. I thanked him for saying that, but added, "I don't agree that I'm exceptional, I know a lot of guys who could run missions just as well as I'm doing, if you guys gave them the chance. They need to be given the full responsibility for their mission and you guys have to make them become fulltime PIs, in residence where their spacecraft are being built, as I have done."

However, Earle disagreed totally and said, "No other scientist can do what you did. We had such trouble with the scientists on Galileo (the spacecraft that was orbiting Jupiter). The spacecraft was fine and ready to go and none of the damned science instruments were done on time or done particularly well."

I said, "Well, the problem is that you have to have someone in charge who is going to lay down the law and make them stick to it." I explained that I had told my Co-Is at the beginning of Lunar Prospector seven years earlier, "You have your allocations for the mass, power, and data rates for your instruments and that is it. Don't come back asking for more." I added, "And the payload I defined in 1990 is the payload we have on the spacecraft today, with the same data rates, slightly less power, and because we changed the spacecraft around some, just a little more mass." Then I told him how I had controlled the spacecraft's mass, that the OMNI design had a mass of 299 kg and that we were at 297 or 298 kg (we actually flew at 296 kg).

While he thought that was all phenomenal, he just did not agree that any other space scientist could do what I did. I felt like I was hitting my head against a brick wall! The NASA managers were just too steeped in the old way of doing missions. They think that some incompetent jerk engineer like Tom Dougherty knows how to manage missions, because they themselves are too incompetent to recognize how little engineers like Dougherty know. I didn't know what in hell I could do to make NASA see it — NASA simply could not accept what I was saying and just blew it off by saying that I was so exceptional — well, BS. I was getting nowhere with Huckins, so I just dropped it and waited in disgust for the review to start.

Nevertheless, I realized after talking to Huckins and after thinking about the long conversation Scott and I had had on August 18, that whole bit about the PI being totally responsible for his or her mission and that NASA was turning the missions upside down as Wes had said in the 1995 Discovery Press Conference, was just a bunch of NASA BS. NASA never meant for Discovery missions to be run that way — it was all just a big fat NASA lie. What NASA intended was, as Scott liked to say about my role, the PI was the "central figure" of the mission. All I could hope to do was to make Lunar Prospector a total success, i.e., fly a perfect mission, so I would then have some leverage with Congress and the public. Then, maybe I could get my points across and get NASA to accept what they themselves had said about how Discovery missions were to be conducted and how to get the US space program back doing what it was supposed to be doing!

I had the most interesting conversation with Sam Venneri, who was sitting across the table from me during lunch and who started lunch by bitching — big time — about Goldin and the space station. Sam said, "The space station is such a mess, nobody wants the damned thing. It's going to cost another billion dollars and the money just isn't there. It's going to take forever, it's a waste of time, and scientists hate it." Though none of Sam's statements were news to most of us, I was surprised at how open he was about it.

Sam said further that everybody else at Headquarters agreed with him, but the problem was that Goldin identified with the space station. Goldin had led the effort to redefine it and since his scent was on it, Goldin was determined it was going to work — no matter what. Finally, Sam said, when they were talking about the budget a while back and everyone in the room said to Goldin, "Hey, you're going to need another billion dollars for this damned thing."

Goldin just got up, stormed out of the meeting, and said, "Fuck all you guys." Clearly, Sam was not impressed with Goldin's leadership.

Sam said another thing I thought was very interesting, but I didn't quite get because I tended to think Discovery was the forerunner of "Faster, Better, Cheaper" and all the other NASA programs were similar, but were not being done exactly in the "Faster, Better, Cheaper" mode. Sam said that Goldin was really getting concerned, because he had only one complete success with "Faster, Better, Cheaper" and that was Mars Pathfinder; he had a total failure with Lewis and he was having a partial success with Mars Observer, which was in big trouble because its solar panel didn't deploy properly and hence, it could not do a proper job of aerobraking to get down into its mapping orbit, without using most of the fuel that had on board. Sam said, "We have one complete success, one total failure, and a sick satellite, and what everybody is telling Goldin is that, *you can't have all three, Faster, Better, Cheaper just does not work."*

I thought, *BS, Lunar Prospector has done all three and now I have to prove it by flying the mission successfully. I'm going to remember Sam's words and I'm going to quote him later. I'm going to say that Sam said you can have any two, but you can't have all three. I'm going to pull this off and then I'm going to say this is how you do it — you do it with a simple satellite, you do it with limited payloads, you do it with simple missions.*

While the review itself was just another useless NASA meeting, the conversations I had had with Huckins, Venneri, and others were very illuminating and were very good for me in terms of my fully understanding what I was up against. Similarly, though some of the people, i.e., Huckins, Piotrowski, and Ledbetter, had seen what I had done, they were so enmeshed in the old NASA way, they just did not pay any attention to my saying that scientists could and should run their programs, as Huckins clearly indicated during our conversation. Well, the road to reform is a bumpy road, and it usually leads to hell instead of to change.

After the review ended, I talked to Bob Garner about the six-week contract extension I needed because of the new launch delay and he said, "We can't change your contract and make it longer until we get permission from NASA to change Lockheed's no-cost contract and make it longer," which was probably true.

I said, "Well OK, what I need to do is to have you guys add the new milestones in my contract so I can get paid. I have to do the work and I'll be damned if I am going to do it without you guys paying for it." I said to Bob, "I'll be back tomorrow to finish this," but I thought I had already won.

Thursday, October 23, 1997

I gave a talk to a group of teachers at Ames.

Dougherty, Scott, Sylvia, and I had a meeting in the afternoon, during which Scott was to try to figure out the schedule. I couldn't believe it. NASA was asking for 12 new reviews — mainly of the LLV2, but also of the spacecraft and Mission Ops — during the two remaining months before launch! They were out of their minds! I said I would not go to any of them, except the ones that were about what I was actively working on. Dougherty agreed it would be a waste of my time to go to all the LLV2 reviews. Having 12 reviews in two months on a program that had produced a flawless spacecraft (remember how Lunar Prospector skipped through thermal-vac testing?), that had no developmental problems and a Mission Ops program that had already been reviewed and was found to be ready to go, was idiotic. Though one could argue about the LLV2's readiness to launch Lunar Prospector, it had already been reviewed to death and more reviews would not change anything. Unfortunately, the NASA Headquarters mentality (if you can call it that) is, "We will have so many reviews, that if something goes wrong, we can say we carefully looked at everything, so the failure is not our fault." The whole thing was totally absurd.

In addition, Huntsville had trashed the LLV2. They grumped about the LLV2 so much that their complaints didn't even sound believable, so we didn't think there was a real problem there. Huntsville's comments were only recommendations anyway and LLV didn't have to respond to them.

I went home and I had an interview with the *Gilroy Dispatch* that went very well.

Friday, October 24, through Monday, October 27, 1997: A Long Working Weekend

Except for a tour of the spacecraft that I gave to a group at 9:00 AM on Saturday, I stayed at home and worked in my LRI office on all the things I needed to get done in preparation for the processing of the spacecraft at the Cape, launch, and Mission Operations, e.g., I finished the January 6/7 launch windows Mission Profiles and the new version of the Mission Operations Document (MOD). I also used the time just to stay away from Lockheed and NASA and get rested up.

Tuesday, October 28, through Thursday, October 30, 1997: A Good Trip to Washington

I left for a National Space Society Conference — Space Summit: Building The Bridge To The 21st Century — in DC on Tuesday, October 28. The conference on Wednesday was pretty good. The thing that I was very disappointed about was that Lou Friedman, head of the Planetary Society, and Bob Zubrin, Head of the Mars Society, are both on evangelical missions to get us to Mars and they are both nuts. Lou just dismisses the Moon as a religious statement of fact, "There are no resources there, there is no water there, there is nothing there of any interest, nobody is ever going to live there and blah, blah, blah." Zubrin is just about as bad. He is smarter than Lou, but I just couldn't believe the crap I was hearing from him. Anyway, it was just amazing how uninformed or intentionally ignorant those two guys are about what the Moon offers us in terms of science, resources, experience in exploring other planets, and it being the jumping off place for the human exploration and colonization of Mars and the rest of the solar system. It was just unbelievable and I could not understand why anyone pays any attention to those nuts — but then, snake oil salesmen have always been able to sell snake oil.

Thursday, I went to the Hill and talked with James Paul, had lunch with Jim Muncy, and then had a meeting with two people from the Commerce Department.

Everybody was very pleased with Lunar Prospector. I told Jim and Paul that I was very concerned about the way Discovery was evolving, and said, "After talking with Huckins, it's clear to me that Discovery was a façade from the beginning. NASA will not relinquish control of the missions to the PIs, so I'm not going to waste my time doing battle with them to make them do Discovery right, until I get my mission successfully behind me. It's also clear that *the only way we will explore the Moon and planets right, is to do it commercially,*" and they both agreed.

We talked about how a data buy program could be setup so one could do commercial missions without NASA being able to interfere and that was to have a Nation Data Archive that NASA had nothing to do with.

I discussed the commercialization of lunar and planetary exploration with the people from Commerce and they were very enthusiastic about the idea and also tried to figure out ways of accomplishing it.

The lady I was talking with said, "You know, there is another company that was here talking about commercializing space exploration," and she described what had been discussed.

I said, "That must have been Jim Benson from SpaceDev."

She said "Yes, that's right."

They were putting two and two together and came to the same conclusion that Paul, Jim, and I had come to, i.e., the way to accomplish getting a commercial data buy program started was not to have NASA involved, rather there should be a National Data Archive and people who wanted to sell data commercially would be paid directly by the government. I said, "That's the way to do it." I also hit a very good chord with Commerce when I said, "Look, I'm being asked by the Japanese, the Chinese, and the Europeans to be a consultant on all their missions, which I won't do, but they're interested in doing this. You certainly know what is going to happen if the United States doesn't get a commercial data buy program going — these other countries will be doing the missions commercially and America is going to lose out on the technology and the commerce." They agreed. When I left Commerce, I was very pleased about my meetings, but I was glad to be on my way home.

Friday, October 31, 1997

I went in to Ames and got the Mission Profiles and the MOD copied and took those deliverables over to Lockheed. As a result, I managed to get LRI's October invoice for $26,000 by Garner and Maryann. I thought they were getting used to the idea that they were not going to win the battle to financially screw LRI.

Scott was again sticking his nose in where it didn't belong and I was getting more and more tired of that pompous little SOB. He wanted a giant review of our Mission Ops procedures because of the Lewis failure. He wanted to make sure we didn't make the same mistakes that led to Lewis failing — did he think I was an idiot? Had he never read the MOD (no)? Did he not attend the Mission Ops review that we had back in May (yes)? Was he not there when we discussed the staffing requirements and the need to have controllers in Mission Ops 24 hours a day during every day of the mission (yes)? Had he become just as arrogant and self-serving as any other NASA ass (yes)? Was I sick of him (yes)? He didn't know how to do anything except bitch about things that he knew nothing about — typical of NASA managers.

Saturday, November 1, 1997: Jim and Susan Benson's Visit

Jim and Susan Benson came to see the spacecraft. Rebecca and I met them at the good old Maple Tree Inn (where I had told them to stay) and had a nice breakfast. We talked about the issues he and I were facing. He was confident that we could get NASA to do what we wanted, while I was not. I told him about my meetings on the Hill and that there was growing interest there for commercial space exploration. I told Jim about the idea that Paul, Jim, the people from Commerce, and I had discussed, i.e., about having a National Data Archive and keeping NASA out of the loop; he agreed that would be absolutely perfect. Jim and I had a good time discussing all those issues over breakfast and Rebecca and Susan also got along very nicely.

After breakfast, we went to Lockheed and I showed them, and a freelance reporter Jim had invited, the spacecraft. Lunar Prospector awed Jim and Susan. Then Rebecca and I took Jim and Susan to the Mission Operations Center and showed them how it worked. Jim and Susan thought everything was great; they had, of course, never seen a spacecraft or an operations center before.

The impression I had was that Jim had a lot to learn and what he wanted to do was not going to be as easy as he thought. But, I was really pleased with Jim and I was getting very optimistic about our commercial space activities.

Monday, November 3, 1997

I worked on the list of the people I wanted to have NASA invite to the launch and therefore called a lot of old friends to see if they could go to the launch. Of course, they were all happy to be invited to see Lunar Prospector take off for the Moon.

Scott called and said, "I heard a bunch of Congressmen tracked you down," which worried him and NASA greatly.

I said, "No, I was on the Hill talking to various aides and at Commerce."

He said, "I hope you didn't do anything Goldin wouldn't like, he doesn't like people doing anything behind his back and blah, blah, blah."

I said, "I wasn't talking about Lunar Prospector, I was talking about future programs."

He said, "Well, enough said." The pompous little prick, I would have liked to have kicked his fat ass.

Tuesday, November 4, 1997: Scott vs. the Public's Right to Know

Scott was fussing because he had to go to Headquarters the next two days to talk about the Outreach activities and what we were going to show the public.

But first, he said Headquarters was basically going to ignore what Huntsville had said about the LLV2 and we were going to proceed to launch. Scott did a good job of keeping the launch vehicle issue moving in the right direction. No matter how much of a NASA wienie I think he is, he did a lot of good things for the program.

However, his big concern was, once again, "We can't let the public see the data until it's edited," — it was amazing how quickly he always reverted back to that theme. He was so worried, "Someone will get hold of the data, misinterpret it, and make NASA look bad."

I asked, "First of all Scott, how are they going to misinterpret it? They can't interpret it without the calibration data."

He asked, "Well, where's the calibration data?"

I answered, "The calibration data is in the archives and sure, somebody could get it, but what good is it going to do them? First of all, all they are going to see on the display screen is the 32 second frame data as it comes down from the spacecraft and the only way you make sense out of it, is when you integrate it over a long period of time, and finally, after weeks or months of data collecting, you get something that is intelligible."

I didn't know why he always forgot all that. He is just such a wienie and a coward — he is so afraid Headquarters will get mad at him that he just about wets himself every time some Headquarters wienie looks his way. He said, "We just can't do anything that might make NASA look bad or give somebody who hates NASA the chance to use the data against us." Scott was beginning to sound like he lived in paranoidsville!

I said, "Scott, there is no way they can do that. They will only see the individual 32 second spectra, you have to sum them up and that takes weeks!"

He said, "What about the school kids in George French's Moonlink program?" He was even afraid of little school children — I bet they were all just waiting for the chance to do NASA and Scott in!

I said "Scott, it's the same thing, it would take them forever. They're not going to get anything of value out of this. It's an educational experience."

He finally conceded (again) that maybe it would be OK to let the public see the real-time science data, but then he (again) started on the engineering data. He said, "We just can't show them the engineering data. If something goes wrong with the spacecraft, we can't have people seeing us in an emergency situation. If we do show the engineering data, *anytime you get into trouble, we'll just block the data out.*"

I said, "Scott, that is exactly what makes it interesting for them. If you block the data out during an emergency, you will only make the public suspicious that we have some big secret to hide. The whole idea is to get them to watch and enjoy the mission, to let them participate in the actual mission operations. Let them see how it is done and have them follow the Mission Profile."

Scott agreed that was all good and wonderful, but insisted, *"If something goes wrong, we'll just have to block it."*

I said, "Well that's just great, Scott. What's going to happen when the public starts hollering and screaming that you're hiding stuff from them?"

Scott and the NASA wienies are all nuts! They did the same thing during the Challenger disaster. First thing NASA said, without even knowing the truth, was that the astronauts died instantly — they never felt a thing. Later on, it came out that the astronauts were alive all the many, many minutes they were falling through the sky — until the cabin they were in hit the water. NASA always lies about such things and they always get themselves in a jam. They always think the American public is too ignorant and too stupid to understand what they are doing. I made those views clear to Scott, but with little impact on his fearful thinking. He and NASA are so frightened of the public, because they don't really know what they are doing and they are afraid somebody will expose them. Well no wonder. Most of them, Scott included, are incompetent.

Wednesday, November 5, 1997

We did a SIM of Day 0. We went from the beginning to the end of the Day 0 activities for the first time. It took over 5 hours and it went very well. It was also the first time we used the MGDS commanding system and it worked quite well.

Dougherty called me at home at 9:00 PM to tell me that Sam Araki wanted to have a review of Lunar Prospector in the morning and he needed Dan and me there!

Thursday Morning, November 6, 1997: The Sam Araki Review

If we stayed on schedule, we were less than two months from launch and it was looking pretty good.

Dan and I showed up at Lockheed for the Sam Araki review. Dougherty got up and tried to give Sam the basic information about the mission. The man is so pathetic. He just didn't understand or know anything about the spacecraft or the mission. It was such an embarrassment to have him blab on and on. The dumb part was that the engineers are so used to his stupidity, most of them hardly noticed it, although the younger guys just rolled their eyes when Dougherty screwed up trying to explain something to Sam. Dan, or the other engineers, or I were always correcting him.

Finally he turned the review over to me. I got up and discussed the mission. Sam was concerned that we forgot or missed something, because Lunar Prospector was a very low cost and very fast program. As Dougherty had mentioned and as I explained in more detail, the spacecraft design and the mission had a 9 year heritage, so it was not done in as much of a hurry as Sam believed and I got that critical point across to him. I also got Sam to understand that Lunar Prospector was a very simple spacecraft. Then Dan, a couple of the other engineers, and I hammered it home to Sam that the spacecraft and mission were both so straightforward there was no way we could screw them up and the spacecraft was very fault tolerant and robust and the mission was very well understood. When it was over, it was clear that Sam was satisfied. We had answered all his questions.

Later, Dougherty said something about Scott saying he was the Mission Manager. If Scott had decided he was going to run the mission, then I would not wait until after Lunar Prospector was safely in lunar orbit to try to have him thrown off the program. He knew nothing about the mission and the spacecraft, so there was no way he could be the Mission Manager of the flight phase of Lunar Prospector, even if I did not object. I guarantee I would not have put up with anyone, especially a pompous, arrogant ass like Scott, telling me how to run my mission. If, on the other hand, he wanted to run the launch to inflate his ego, I could not have cared less — let LLV deal with the pompous fat-ass.

However, Marcie had written me an email in which she wrote, "This a decision for the Mission Manager to make."

Maybe there was some fire where there was smoke, so I wrote back, "The Mission Manager is the Mission Director, who is the PI, who is me. End of story."

Thursday Afternoon, November 6, through Monday, November 10, 1997: The Space Frontier Foundation Meeting and a Little R&R

Rebecca and I drove to Los Angeles on Thursday to attend the Space Frontier Foundation Meeting and to visit a small aerospace company called Microcosm that was interested in what I was doing commercially. The visit to Microcosm on Friday was interesting, but nothing special.

However, I enjoyed the Space Frontier Foundation Meeting and gave them a Lunar Prospector update talk on Saturday. Some of the other talks were interesting. I met a lot of good people and we discussed numerous things. I had a good time talking with Jim Benson again.

After the meeting was over at about noon Sunday, Rebecca and I did some sightseeing in the LA area during Sunday afternoon and most of Monday. We drove back to Gilroy later Monday night.

Tuesday, November 11, 1997: Headquarters Finally Lets the Data Go Public

While I was in LA, Scott had come back from Headquarters with a report, "Gee whiz, Headquarters sees nothing wrong with letting our data get out to the public in real-time," now who would have guessed that? Everything I wanted and everything I said should be done with the data was going to get done in exactly the way I wanted it done. Headquarters even agreed that it would be a mistake to have a panic button to shut the TV off so the public couldn't see what was going on if something went wrong. All of Scott's ranting and raving about not letting the public see the data was nonsense. However, I wasn't going to get to have a national TV pool camera looking into the Glass Room at Mission Ops; instead, all NASA would allow was a slow scan camera looking at the backs of our heads (how interesting) for the internet. That was a serious PR mistake that I was going to fight (but lost).

Scott also said Headquarters insisted that he sign off on the launch, i.e., be the Launch Mission Manager. Since that did not make any difference to me, I said, "Fine, if that's what Headquarters told you." As long as Scott didn't try to be the Flight Mission Manager, I did not care what he did.

Scott said NASA was planning a pre-launch science news conference with him, me, and maybe some Outreach guy. The news conference would be for science reporters, not for general news reporters. It was set for 1:00 PM on December 4 and they wanted a dry run the day before. I said, "Look, I'll be busy at the Cape. I don't mind coming, but why can't we have the dry run in the morning? Then I could fly in from the Cape late the night before and get back late the next night." He did not know, but I was going to try to insist on that.

Then we found out we couldn't put the DFUs (Destruct Firing Units) on the TLI Stage at Astro Tech because they didn't have a license to handle radioactive materials and there is a very small amount of radioactive material in DFUs. Thus, the DFUs would have to be mounted on the TLI Stage when it was on the launch pad! That meant we couldn't spin balance the Spacecraft/TLI Stage stack in its final configuration and that was a bunch of crap! There was always some new aggravation, but we would get Lunar Prospector done, one way or another.

Wednesday, November 12, 1997

We had a great full-up Day 0 SIM in morning with the all engineers — Woody, Jim Schirle, Jerry, Irv, Steven, and a few others — who were going to support the Day 0 activities.

A reporter came during the day, but he came too late to see the spacecraft.

Chapter 3-42
Steven's Boom Canister Crisis

Thursday, November 13, 1997: Steve Has a Problem

We had the final Mission Ops Review in the morning. You can always tell how a review is going by the amount of joking and laughing that goes on, especially towards the end. Well, the last few reviews, especially the Araki review, all ended with a lot of joking and laughing. In the case of the Ops Review, the joking and laughing started at the very beginning. It was not even a real review in my mind. Marcie had set it up. I gave the introduction and went through the mission philosophy and the way we were going to do Mission Ops. I laid it on thick to shut up the review committee members in the very beginning and then Marcie bored them to death by giving them more detail than anyone in the world wanted to hear. Nevertheless, we breezed right through the review and that took care of that.

After the review, I gave a talk to a group of about 15 teachers. They loved it and got very excited about the mission.

I went over to talk to Dougherty, Irv, and some of the engineers. When we did the Day 0 SIM the day before, Irv didn't like our safe-engine-verification sequence. He did not like me opening and closing the PIV and then opening it again. Dougherty wanted to discuss that, which was fine with me, because I had the same concerns Irv had. I told them my reasoning behind the safe-engine-verification-sequence and Dougherty agreed it was a good idea! Also, Ralph Fullerton, our QA guy, thought it was the safest thing to do. Then we all agreed that PIV's were made to be opened and closed many times, so there was little danger the PIV would not reopen after the test. Thus, it was unanimous; everybody agreed I should keep the safe-engine-verification sequence in the Mission Profile.

When we were done with that discussion, Steve Honodel dropped his bomb! He was concerned that the boom canisters could get so cold after launch and hence thermally contract enough so the locking pins would bind and not release the booms when I started the boom deployment sequence 2 hours after launch! As usual, he had done 50 million calculations and he wanted to measure how loose the latching pins were. He said, "If the pins have more than 3/1000 of an inch (0.0075 mm) clearance, then there is no problem."

We went around and around about that. I said, "One of the things I can do to minimize their cooling off too much, is to deploy the booms 40 minutes earlier than I am planning to do it." We all agreed it was a good thing to do. Then, there was the possibility of tilting the spacecraft so the sun was shining on the bottom of the spacecraft and that would keep the canisters warm. I didn't like that idea, because I needed to get the spacecraft in the appropriate attitude, so we had good communications right after launch.

Steve then said, in response to a question about how loose the pins were, "When we put the boom canisters on the spacecraft, you could feel the pins wiggle with your fingers."

I asked, "Well, if that's the case, if just finger pressure wiggles the pins, are they OK?"

Steve answered, "Yes."

I said, "OK, why don't we just go over there right now and poke at them."

He said, "No, no, you can't do that, you have to do it right."

I said, "OK, fine. But that's the difference between a scientist and an engineer. You guys make up a big long procedure to test something that a scientist would find out just by sticking his finger in it."

Dougherty said, "No, we wouldn't dare do that."

Nevertheless, I was concerned about the science instruments, because Steve wanted to hang weights on them and to push on them to put torque on the pins. Ralph was also not at all happy about that idea. We all agreed that the first test we would do before Steve got started putting his measuring devices on the canisters the next day, was the finger-poke-test. If the damned pins wobbled, then we were OK.

After nearly everyone left, I said to Tim Maloney, "Let's go over and look at the spacecraft right now."

He said, "Yeah, let's go over."

Tim and I went over to the spacecraft, got our rubber gloves on and started looking at the canisters and the science instruments. We looked at the MAG/ER first and I didn't see where one could hang weights on it or push on it. We went around to the GRS. We could see the high-voltage wires were coming out of the top and the bottom of the GRS and I said, "We can't touch the high-voltage wires, we have to be very careful about this." I started carefully pushing on the upper rim of GRS.

Tim said, "Oh my God, I can see the tip plate wobbling."

I asked, "Are you sure?"

And he said, "Yes."

I pushed a little more and I said, "I think I can see it too." Then Tim pushed on it — he pushed a lot harder than I did, because I had been gentle — and the damned thing wobbled all over the place.

He said, "OK, let's go look at the APS." We did, and when pushed, the APS wobbled like an old lady in a rocking chair!

I said, "Well, we just did the test," and added, "Tim, you know, you should really be a scientist, not an engineer, because we just did what a scientist would do and that's to go poke at it, rather than make up an elaborate test like Steve wants to do with weights and balances and measuring devices. However, Steve will still want to do that, otherwise he and Dougherty won't be happy. But you make sure things go OK and they do the finger test first, because I have a meeting at 8:00 AM and then one at 10:00 AM and I'm not sure that I'll be here. I'll try to get over here so I can sign off on everything." Dougherty was insisting I sign off on everything — was he finally realizing I was the PI?

Tim answered, "Don't worry, I'll watch them and protect your instruments."

Friday, November 14, 1997: Testing the Canisters

At 8:00 AM, Marcie, Dan and I went over the final SIMs that we wanted to do in preparation for the first few days of the mission. There really wasn't much time for SIMs, but we needed to do what we could to keep at peak performance.

After that, the three of us had a meeting with Ken, Dave Lozier, and Dave Folta (Dave was on the telephone at Goddard). We talked about the Mission Profile. I was always struck by Dave and Ken's lack of any understanding of how you setup a Mission Profile. Though they are both very good Nav guys, they really didn't understand how to do a mission like Lunar Prospector and they just didn't get why I did things as I did. The only way I could proceed was just to say, as politely as possible, since I like and respect both Dave and Ken, "This is the way I want it done, period."

I went over to the spacecraft to see what in hell Steve was doing to the damned boom canisters. Steve and his crew were going to start at 10:00 AM and Dougherty and Henshaw were supposed to be there. I got there about 10:45 and, of course, Dougherty wasn't there, so everyone was just standing around waiting. They had already done the finger test and it was clear that there wasn't a problem, but Steve wanted to have his measurements. I didn't like the idea of him poking and pushing the instruments, so I said, "As far as I am concerned, as long as we see motion that is easily detectable, the issue is resolved. But Dougherty has to get over here and we have to agree on this."

Somebody asked, "Where is Dougherty?" and nobody knew. I called Delores and told her to tell him to get over there. She thought he had gone to a staff meeting — but he was over there ten minutes after I called. It was funny nobody would call him and tell him we were waiting on him, except me.

Well, anyway, he came over after I called, which surprised me a little. But the closer we got to the end, the easier Dougherty was to get along with — he had become very accommodating and gracious. He had even fended off Scott more than once during the previous few weeks by saying, "Hey, Alan knows what he is doing, just let him alone."

After Dougherty arrived, we talked about the tests and Dougherty said, "Let's let Steve make some measurements, because if we don't, then I'll have a hell of a time explaining to the failure review board why we didn't get some measurements, if this thing fails. If I just say it looked OK and I don't have some data, they would crucify me." We all agreed it was worthwhile saving Dougherty's skin if the booms failed, but I stayed, worked with them and helped make the measurements, because I wanted to protect the instruments from Steve's fervor to get his measurements.

However, one of the Able engineers was also there and he said, "This is exactly what I expect, it wobbles. That's all we need to know, it's OK."

But, Steve, of course, wanted his subsystem to work and he wanted all the measurements he could get. He pushed the instruments around, poked them harder than I thought was necessary or prudent. But, he felt compelled to get his data and he unfortunately didn't have the balance to say, "OK, we have a flight ready spacecraft here and we should not even be touching it. But since we have to touch it, we will touch it as little as possible," but that was just not Steve.

I made sure that he only did the absolute minimum number of tests; I stopped him from poking and pulling too much and told him where he could poke and pull on the instruments to insure he did not harm them. I guarantee, if I hadn't been there, he would have made a long series of intrusive measurements that could have resulted in damage to the instruments or the booms. I'm not saying that he is sloppy or anything else, it was just that he wanted to be absolutely certain and hence, he just could not say, "OK, that's enough."

I did appreciate Dougherty's concerns, in the sense that Lockheed did not want the mission to fail and hence, they wanted all the information necessary to insure it did not fail (and to cover their butts in case of a failure). But what Steve was doing was not necessary and was even dangerous. If I were doing the mission in LRI alone, I would have given Steve the choice, "Stop this nonsense or get fired," and that would have been the end of it.

By the time Steve was finished, it was after 3:00 PM. Everybody left feeling the canisters were fine. I called Scott and told him that the booms were OK.

Scott also told me about the up-and-coming Lunar Prospector Pre-launch Science News Conference at Headquarters. Wes, Scott, and I were to be there and they wanted somebody from the lunar science community to comment on the mission. I said, "Jeff Taylor (U Hawaii) should the one." Jeff is a great guy and one of the best scientists in our community. I also told Scott, "Remember, I said I have a lot to do down at the Cape getting Lunar Prospector ready? I don't want to spend any more time in DC than I absolutely have to. See if we could have the dry run in the morning and the conference in the afternoon."

Scott agreed and said, "I'll take care of both things" (Jeff and minimizing the time I would have to spend in DC).

Monday, November 17, 1997: Seven Weeks to Launch

I reviewed the PR material for the news conference with a nice young lady from Ames PR.

Then I went over to the spacecraft, where Dan was doing the pre-ship functional test of the attitude sensors. They were fine.

After that, I had lunch with my old friend, Dale Cruikshank, to discuss the data reduction program and how it was going to be structured, since Ames had assigned Dale to be a member of the NASA evaluation team.

After lunch, I went back to the spacecraft where Dave Curtis was doing the functional test on the MAG/ER. It was perfect.

Bill Feldman arrived from Los Alamos and we did videos for the NASA PR people — who did a crummy job.

After that, Bill did the functional tests on the spectrometers. The GRS and NS were perfect, but the APS had a little noise on it. However, when he put the APS detection threshold up very high, it was fine. Also there were no light leaks in the filters. The noise problem was due to the fact that the APS was just so damned sensitive to acoustic and electronic noise in the highbay environment, but basically, it was OK. I was not going to worry about the APS, until we got it turned on in space, where we expected it would be fine.

NASA called Scott about the damned news conference on the 4th. We had to be there on the afternoon of the 3rd for a dry run and then the next morning was a dress rehearsal and then the damned thing was in the afternoon. Scott insisted he talk about the Mission Profile. The trouble was Wes Huntress was going to talk about the Discovery Program and I was going to talk about the spacecraft and the science and if I talked about the Mission Profile too, Scott would have nothing to say (a very good idea if you asked me), so Scott was insisting he talk about the Mission Profile, even though he knew nothing about it. I was really getting sick of Scott. I would be glad when the launch was over and I could, hopefully, get rid of the arrogant, self-serving SOB.

After work, Bill, Danny Everett, and Gary Schlueter, who was still running all the spacecraft tests and hating every minute of it, and I went to the Hoffbrau House for dinner.

Tuesday, November 18, 1997: More LLV2 Launch Problems

We were going to do a SIM with all the engineers and the science guys — the first absolutely fullup SIM! We finally got everybody — Bill, Dave Curtis, and the engineers — over to Mission Ops. Then we couldn't get the damned simulator started via the MGDS. There was some incompatibility. We screwed around for a while and then decided we would start and just assume we had gotten a communication link with the space-craft. That dragged on and then we couldn't get the commands uplinked and then noth-ing would work. After two hours, I just said, "To hell with it." Obviously, it wasn't going to work and there was no use trying to continue, so everybody left.

We were going to have a discussion about the Mission Profile; I had changed things around in the profile and I wanted to get agreement on the changes. We were going to do that after lunch, but I then got a note from Dougherty saying to call him in Denver — he went up there for the final Top-Hat review of the damnable rocket — there was a problem!

When I called, Dougherty said there was a three second error in the launch time! I assumed that LLV would have written the LLV2 guidance program to take care of any time variations in the launch and in the coast phase, so the TLI burn would occur exact-ly when and where it was supposed to, but they hadn't. They were trying to cover that up by saying we hadn't told them we wanted to have a constant argument of perigee for the parking orbit. I said, "That's BS."

First of all, we always talked about a circular parking orbit, so it was impossible to talk about the argument of perigee being constant and since we had always told them we had to hit the node between the lunar transfer orbit and the parking orbit at a well defined time and place, it shouldn't have taken any brains to figure it out. Then LLV said, "Well, it wasn't in the ICD." They always had an excuse!

Well, the point was, the lift off errors result in a 19 m/sec TLI error for every sec-ond the launch was delayed! LLV was telling me that the sum of all the different launch time delays could be up to 9 seconds, which would result in a 170 m/sec TLI error, or over a factor of two times the maximum error I had planned for! When I gently expressed my great concern about that, LLV whined, "If we change the software so it can account for the delay, then you will be delayed until February."

I was deflated; it was just one thing after another with that damned rocket. It was the same old story with LLV, delayed to February or March, then what? I said I would get with my Nav Team and call back.

I got Dave, Ken, Marcie, Dan, Scott, and Sylvia (that is how important a 9 second launch delay was) and called Denver back. Someone at Denver said, "Well, you have all that extra fuel on board, so you can take care of the error."

I responded, "Nobody plans for a launch error like that. That fuel is there in case we have a bad launch, but you don't start out knowing you have bad launch and use your damned fuel for that."

Denver said, "But you only have to be there (in orbit) a year." It was the same old BS. I was supposed to make up for their lousy rocket by using the fuel I needed to con-duct the extended mission.

I got annoyed at that point, because they were, as always, trying to wheedle their way out of fixing their damned problem and said, "Your lousy rocket is causing me to lose my mission."

Denver shot back, "We don't have a lousy rocket."

Then they tried to push the blame off on Ken and Dave, by saying again, "It wasn't in the ICD."

I said, "This is just basic celestial mechanics and it shouldn't have to be in the ICD." By then they had made me mad enough I said, "Look, you guys cost me Septem-ber, October, November, December, and January, and now you are talking about March or April. When is this going to stop? This goes back to the beginning, when you guys said you were only going to launch us to LEO (the Low Earth Parking Orbit) and we had to get out of LEO ourselves. I told you then that I wanted a launch to TLI and that breaking it up into two segments — you doing the LLV and us doing the TLI Stage — was only going to lead to trouble, which is exactly where we are right now." I was totally ticked off; as far as I was concerned, Denver was just totally incompetent. They might know how to get you into LEO, but they sure as hell didn't know how to do anything else and they were just floundering around, trying to get another launch delay.

I told Scott, "Look Scott, when you get back (from an up-coming trip), let's sit down together, because we're going to have to make a decision here. Are we going to risk losing the extended mission, because that's what we are talking about? If they cause a delay until March or April or later, then we will start losing more and more of the extended mission, time-wise. If we had the maximum 9 second launch delay, then the 170 m/sec TLI error would cost me all the fuel I had planned to have for the extended mission — either way, we lose it. This is your (NASA's) and my decision, we have to decide what we want to risk. This is a decision that goes to the very heart of the program NASA is paying for, so we have to decide which risk to take."

My inclination was just to say, "You (LLV) fix it the best you can and we'll take our chances in January," because I doubted very much we would end up with a 9 second delay — most of those 9 seconds were just due to the usual ultra-conservative engineering assessments of the real errors (remember Dan's big toot about the huge TLI burn/nutation errors?), while if we slipped into March, April, May, or beyond, we definitely were going to lose part, or all of the extended mission. I thought we just had to go ahead and launch in January, because, no matter what we did, there was always going to be something wrong with that piece of junk called LLV2.

I was, as usual, disgusted with the whole damned thing.

Wednesday, November 19, 1997

We tried to do a SIM, but JPL screwed up again and we couldn't do it.

We all thought the launch vehicle error BS was bogus and we all wanted to keep on track for the January launch. Dave and Ken were looking at some launch error models with Goddard, but I thought that was a waste of time.

Thursday, November 20, 1997: Getting Ready to Ship

We had the final pre-ship review, which was a waste of time. Nevertheless, several things of interest came out of it. Headquarters insisted that Scott be the Mission Director for the launch — or so he said. Goldin, Wes, and a host of other NASA wienies were going to be at the launch and they were fussing about it. The point was, as I was slowly learning, NASA was never going to let go of the missions. They were always going to demand to be in control.

I found out Dougherty was going to Headquarters to give a briefing to Goldin, which I found to be hilarious. It told me just how stupid all the Headquarter people are and what a lie the whole Discovery Program is. Headquarters really thought Dougherty knew all about the spacecraft and the mission and, despite the fabrication that "the PI is responsible for the success of the mission," he, the Project Manager, was still in charge in their eyes — a fact that was clearly demonstrated when, during the Mission Ops Review, one of the NASA/Ames guys said, regarding the need to deal with press questions right after launch, "Well Tom, you know all about this stuff, you can answer all the questions from the media. Alan will be too busy in Mission Ops to answer the questions.

And Scott can answer them down at the Cape." What a joke! NASA just didn't have any comprehension of what really was going on. They simply do not believe that a scientist can know more than a bunch of engineers and NASA managers. They're just too stupid to get it.

Then, in an interesting intentional admission of just how dumb Lockheed upper management is, Dougherty leaned over to me and said, laughing at the stupidity of what he had to say to me, "Oh, upper management says I've got to give you a full briefing on the status of the spacecraft." Then he said, "Here it is — it's OK and you know it." I was highly amused at that; even Dougherty knew how absurd that directive from Lockheed management was.

Then there were the issues about the boom canisters and the dispersions in the TLI velocity due to the launch time delays. Regarding the former, Jim Schirle calculated the temperatures of the canisters would never be higher than 5° C. Dougherty said, "You shouldn't deploy the booms at temperatures lower than we tested at, because if they get colder than that, we won't know if they will work."

I said, "I agree, Tom, so I have two or three ways of doing it. If we are on a nominal trajectory with no problems, I'll put the spacecraft at an SEA (Solar Equatorial Angle) of –30° right away and pop the booms as quickly as I can — while they are still warm from the pre-launch environment (the temperature at launch would be about 20° C, or about 15° C higher than the lowest temperature the booms were tested at. Once launched, the boom canisters would slowly cool off and, after a few hours, get down to just above 0° C. Tilting the spacecraft so the sun would shine on the canisters, would slow the cooling and the sooner after launch that I could deploy the booms, the warmer they would be). If we have an emergency burn situation, I'll go into the normal attitude to get that burn done, then I'll reorient the spacecraft to a –30° SEA to get its bottom warmed up again. If we go into phasing orbit, we can go to a –30° SEA immediately, get the booms popped and then make the orbital adjustments later." Those were the only options.

Dan, who was on a Thanksgiving vacation, called and I explained the situation to him. We both agreed there was really no reason for all that — the booms were fine. But, we were dealing with two big organizations and they were not going to let anything go they did not understand, and it was impossible to make them understand there was no boom problem, especially when Steve kept hollering there was a big problem in the background.

Friday, November 21, 1997: Steve is at It Again

We did a SIM with John Breakwell and some of the engineers. After a couple of false starts, we got it going. It was a pretty good SIM, but John just didn't get it — Dan had better always be there. Just before the SIM started, I got a call from Dougherty. He said Steve was finding more problems with the boom deployment and we were going to have a meeting at 1:00 PM. Since I had that meeting at 2:00 PM with Scott and Sylvia, I called Sylvia and told her that I would be late. We finished the SIM and then I went to Lockheed.

When the meeting started, Steve's conservatism was so bad Dougherty had gotten scared, not only about the booms, but also about the entire spacecraft. He said to the engineers, "Everybody check your subsystems and see if they're OK."

Steve got up and said he had forgotten a temperature expansion term in his equation and he had found his error. He didn't like the fact that we didn't get all the data he wanted when we tested the boom canisters a week earlier. He wasn't 100% sure they were OK! BS, he and everyone else agreed, even the Able engineers agreed, if the booms wiggled, they were OK. But that didn't satisfy Steve. Even after he had gotten some of the data, he said, "I don't have enough data. I need some more data before we can go."

Exasperated, I said, "Look, what is the differential coefficient of thermal expansion between the booms and the canisters?" He told me what it was and I made the calculation on a piece of paper. Given that we had deployed the booms at 5° C and that the lowest temperature they could cool down to was just above 0° C, there was less than a 5° C change difference between those temperatures, and the parts of the canisters in question were only 10 cm long. My calculations showed that the differential contraction between them was just a little bit more than 10% of the maximum allowable amount of contraction he had said a week earlier would be OK. I said, "This comes out to one tenth of what you are worried about. This is just bogus; there is just no problem here."

He said, "You don't know that. You're not using the right equation." He put his equation on the blackboard and it was exactly the same equation I had (it had to be, it was just straight physics), except he had used the thermal expansion terms for each component individually, while I had used the differential form of the equation, hence I had asked him for the differential coefficient of thermal expansion for the components, which I quickly pointed out. Not believing me, he plugged in the numbers in his equation and, of course, got the same answer that I had gotten.

I said, "See, there is no damned problem."

Steve, not one to give up so easily, went through some more calculations and brought up another factor, i.e., that the booms would cool off quicker than the canisters, to which I said, "Fine, that offsets the whole effect you are concerned about. Every single thing makes it better! There just is no problem!"

Nevertheless, Dougherty started talking about delaying the launch for two or three months, so we could test the spacecraft again in thermal-vac and he was getting ready to call Henshaw to say, "We can't launch this thing and blah, blah, blah."

I said, "Look, I'm not going to let this launch be delayed for some ultra-conservative calculations that have no basis and are simply wrong."

Dougherty said, "You scientists, you don't know anything." It was the same old crap. Dougherty is one of the most ignorant people I have ever met. He doesn't understand any of the engineering and physics involved and when all else fails, he belittles you and insults you. What a dumb ass!

Interestingly, Lee understood what I was saying and she tried to back me up. It was the very first time she and I had been on the same side of the fence! She said, "What Alan is saying is absolutely right."

Steve still wasn't happy, but Dougherty calmed down a little bit and he just said, "Well you know, we can't pay attention to scientists. Steve go on and finish your calculations."

Steve said, "OK, but I want to go get more data."

I said, "No, you're not poking around on those instruments again. It was bad enough what you did last week. There is absolutely no basis for this. Every number up on that board shows we have more than enough margin. There is no problem. This is a non-issue."

By that time, I was more than annoyed and frustrated with Steve, Dougherty, and the engineers in general and I said, "Look, I don't want to insult anybody, but this is the same thing that happened with the big nutation issue, which was also totally fictitious. There was no nutation problem and I told you guys that. This is exactly the same thing."

Dougherty asked, "Well, aren't you glad that we went through the exercise (about the nutation)?"

I answered, "No, because now we have a whole mess of junk (e.g., the bumpers next to the A1 and A2 engines) on that spacecraft because of nutation that didn't exist."

I was sure he did not even understand what in hell I was talking about, but then Lee finished it off when Dougherty again said to Steve, "Go make your calculations, don't let a scientist worry you."

Lee said, regarding Steve's calculations, "Well, I am sure he'll find a way of having no margin!"

Dougherty didn't like that and neither did Steve, but it was absolutely true and even Dougherty had to recognize it (after all, one of his engineers had said it, not a dumb scientist). All of a sudden, Dougherty became very jovial, laughed his stupid sounding, "ho, ho, ho," and said in jest to Lee, "You're not supposed to say stuff like that."

I went over then to see Scott, who was in a Lunar Prospector PR meeting with Lisa and some other PR people. He asked me how the boom meeting went and I told him and added, "Look Scott, Dougherty and Steve are getting petrified over there. I will not allow the launch to be stopped by baseless fear and conservatism, but they aren't going to listen to me. It will take both of us stop this nonsense."

Scott is smart enough compared to Dougherty that he could figure out himself there was no problem with the canisters. But instead of helping me take the bull by the horns, Scott backed off and said, "Well you know, cooler heads will prevail. I'm sure Tom will come to the right conclusion." Such BS, Scott is just a wimp. He is just as bad as Dougherty and he was getting worse and worse the closer we got to launch. I could see I was going to have to go through hell until we got Lunar Prospector launched.

Also, when I had walked into Scott's office, it was obvious Scott thought the Lunar Prospector PR issues they were discussing were none of my business, just like Dougherty thought the launch issues were none of my business. Scott had his little court of serfs in there, most of whom I knew thought he is a pompous ass. I knew that Sylvia was sick of Scott, because she had said, "Scott got a new pager and a new pocket phone. Since then, I can never find him, he is always out, playing around with his new toys." He is such an ass!

Monday, November 24, 1997: Steve and the Boom Again

We had another boom meeting. Actually, it went extremely well. Steve hadn't really changed his story, but Dougherty had gotten much more reasonable and the whole conversation was quite civilized. Instead of trying to shut me up the way he usually did and/or just ignoring me, Dougherty and the rest of us discussed the whole issue. Jim Schirle came in with some reasonably good temperatures. It turned out that he hadn't computed the canister temperatures at SEAs of $0°$, $-10°$, $-20°$, and $-30°$ earlier, he had just done it for $+20°$, which is the SEA the spacecraft would have right after launch and even at that SEA, the canisters were fairly warm. He found from his new calculation that the Sun would get the canisters extremely warm at negative SEAs.

Nevertheless, we made some more measurements on the spacecraft because Steve was just so unsure. As usual, the measurements weren't as good as Steve wanted, but they never would be. But Jim's calculation showed to everyone but Steve and to a much lesser extent, Dougherty, that there really wasn't a problem.

While we were working on the spacecraft, Dougherty brought Mel Brashears over to see the spacecraft. I chatted with Mel a bit and it was nice to see him again (I had not seen him since the Tenerelli days), since he was the only VP who had really backed my

request for Lockheed to become my Industry Partner and to support my Discovery proposal effort.

Finally, by day's end, the boom canister crisis had about run its course, though
Steve was still very nervous and Dougherty was cautious. All of what had happened during the previous 10 days was just a tempest in a teapot and we were again moving
towards the launch.

The spacecraft was to be boxed up the next day, put on the truck Wednesday, and
then driven to the Cape. We were finally going to launch the damn thing. I was very tired
and very aggravated. I hoped that as soon as we got launched, there would be a lot less
aggravation because I was getting worn-out from fighting both NASA and Lockheed.

Tuesday, November 25, 1997:
Launch Dispersions, Boom Solutions, and Getting Ready to Ship

We had a meeting about the launch dispersions at 8:30 AM and basically they were
tolerable. Ken and Dave had done their calculations and even in the worst cases, the TLI
1-σ errors (68% probability) were only 40 m/sec, so we were going to be OK. If you took
the worst case, 3-σ errors (99.7% probability), they were fairly bad, but there was less
than a 0.3% chance of them being that bad. Also, the results of the LLV1 launch of Lewis
showed that the dispersions were a factor of 10 less than the pre-launch calculations.
We were fine.

Nevertheless, Scott was huffing and puffing around. He wanted to make sure
everything was OK. He didn't have a good understanding of any of those issues, but he
was playing the role of the great and glorious NASA official and protecting his fat ass.

Sylvia and I were talking before the meeting and I said something about all the
damned reviews that had come up because everybody had gotten in a panic. I said
something like, "Well, better Scott and Dougherty doing them than me."

Sylvia said, "Yeah, Dougherty hates it, but Scott really likes it. He likes to be in the
thick of it." That really surprised me — no sane person likes reviews. But, apparently,
Scott got to play the role of the "important NASA official" in the reviews and got to boss
everyone around.

During our meeting, Scott indicated the thing he didn't like about the situation
was that most of the information about the mission was in my head. He was worried
that little was written down, so the mission would be in big trouble without me
(remember the NASA van that was always going to run over me on the freeway?). Well,
that is the price NASA has to pay if they want missions to be "Faster, Better, Cheaper."
Putting everything down on paper costs a lot of time and money (remember, half of the
cost of a typical NASA mission is spent on paperwork and documentation). Anyway, I
didn't really give a damn what worried Scott; as long as I got the mission successfully
done, he and NASA could go to hell.

After putting the worries about the launch errors to bed, we had our weekly Mission Ops telecon with JPL and Goddard and, as usual, it dragged on and on. JPL was
fussing about the emergency commanding in case there was an earthquake at Ames and
we couldn't send the commands to put Lunar Prospector into its lunar capture orbit.
We were going to store the commands at the Goldstone DSN station and they would
uplink them to the spacecraft if we fell into the ocean.

We had another meeting about the booms at Lockheed and, of course, Steve was
still fussing. Dougherty, to give him credit, was even more reasonable in terms of his listening to what I had to say. But, it boiled down to the fact that Steve's continued harp-

ing had made even Able worried, and Able wouldn't say if the booms would deploy below 5° C or not, even though they had said earlier that they would deploy down to minus 20° C. Apparently, if Chicken Little says the sky is falling long enough and loud enough, he can make even people who know better nervous.

Jim Schirle made some more thermal models and said if we put titanium tape around the canisters to absorb the Sun's heat, rather than having thermal blankets on them to keep them from cooling off very fast, and if I tilted the spacecraft to –30°, we could keep the canister quite warm and that was the solution. Steve also wanted to put some oil on the pins to make sure they would slip out of their restraints, though it was questionable that oil would do anything. Finally, everyone agreed that the tape and tilting of the spacecraft would do the trick (if there was a trick to do) and those two solutions to the (non-existent) problem were non-intrusive. We did not have to make a lot of changes to the spacecraft and delay the launch by two or three months, we would just put the tape on the canisters, and that was finally that.

However, even putting the tape on at that stage of the project — a day before shipping the fully tested spacecraft to the Cape — was a big deal. The engineers would have to put the tape around the lips of the canisters, behind the instruments and right next to the solar panels. The potential for damaging something was very real. We decided that to avoid any delays in shipping the spacecraft, we would put the tape on at the Cape. Finally Steve was quasi-satisfied and that artificial crisis was behind us.

I was quite pleased that, in the end, everything was done fairly rationally and Dougherty was not his usual stupid self. The last two meetings had been quite reasonable and even respectful — after all of his "don't listen to the dumb scientist" insults during the earlier part of Steve's near nervous breakdown.

The spacecraft did not get put into its shipping box, but everything else was packed up. Tim said they would cover the spacecraft with plastic sheeting and put it on its shipping pallet that evening. Then they would put it into its shipping box the next day and load it on the truck. Dougherty suggested it should go down to the Cape a day or two early, if the drivers agreed, and I wholeheartedly agreed with that.

We were getting there. One more day of Lockheed nonsense and then I would be free of Lockheed, except for getting LRI's money every month.

Wednesday, November 26, 1997:
The Day Before Thanksgiving, Boxed and Ready to Ship

As soon as I got in, I went over to Building 150 and my spacecraft was still on its shipping pallet. I just stood there, all alone with my spacecraft, and looked at it. It was a great feeling knowing it was ready to go after nine years of working on the mission. As I stood there, admiring the beautiful little creation that would (hopefully) soon be orbiting the Moon, I thought back nine years to that fateful day — for all I remembered, maybe it was exactly nine years to the day, since it was also just before Thanksgiving — in later November of 1988, when Larry Friesen asked me if I wanted to help the Houston Chapter of the National Space Society build and fly a lunar orbiter mission to look for the polar ice deposits (Part One). It had been a long, often difficult and disappointing nine years, but there I was, standing next to my completed spacecraft — it was a wonderful, magical, and nostalgic moment.

We did a SIM of the 1st LOI burn with the full communications network and discovered some differences in the way the Nav guys calculated the burn and the way that Dan and I did, which was a good thing to discover!

I went over to Lockheed at noon to see the spacecraft. When I got there, Lunar Prospector was in its wooden box (we could not afford a fancy shipping container, so the engineers had a suitable wooden box built over in the Lockheed wood-working shop) and there was a hole in the box, about half a meter square, where the air filter was to go. I looked in and saw my spacecraft. That was another great feeling, seeing it in its shipping box, all ready to go to the Cape.

I had lunch, after which I found Tim, and we went over at about 1:00 PM to help put the spacecraft on the truck. I helped him put the air filter and some steel straps on the box and then Tim said it was going to be a couple hours before the box was put on the truck, because they were going to load the test equipment first. I decided not to wait, because I had to get a flu shot to be sure I was not sick during the mission.

I talked to Jim Schirle and he showed me the new temperature curves he had calculated for the cooling and heating of the canisters and they were OK. We could even stay at the nominal SEA attitude of $-11°$ to $-12°$ and the canisters would be warm enough. Dougherty also wanted the thermal blankets put on the canisters, but all we needed was the tape and the correct SEA. Neither Jim nor anyone else wanted the blankets on them. Since it was not worth arguing about it right then, I would stop that from happening down at the Cape.

I got my flu shot.

The spacecraft was loaded and it was going to start its trip to the Cape Monday morning at 6:00 AM. I would miss that, because I would be at the Cape by then. It was getting very, very exciting.

It was a very nice feeling to have the spacecraft boxed up and to look across the Building 150 highbay, where we had assembled Lunar Prospector over the previous 8 or 9 months, and see it empty. It was another great moment — a little poignant, but wonderful.

Dougherty called about 8:00 PM because he was trying to finish up his viewgraphs for the presentation to Wes. It was a joke that he was giving Headquarters the briefing. He said he couldn't remember what had been wrong with the APS and why we didn't have much burn-in time on it after it was fixed. Well the APS wasn't fixed, it was the cabling that was fixed — we had to change the shielding! The man knew nothing about the spacecraft. He knows nothing about engineering. He knows nothing about anything and yet he was going to Headquarters to tell them about my mission. It was a joke, a bad one, but still a joke.

Thursday, November 27, 1997 — Thanksgiving Day

Rebecca and I had a simple Thanksgiving with some turkey from the Nob Hill Deli. I finished the final version of the Mission Profile and the MOD and checked all the commands. They were ready and I was ready.

Friday, November 28, 1997

Rebecca and I went up to Ames and printed out the flight versions of the MOD and the January 6 (GMT, the launch was on the 5th Local Time) Mission Profile and then bought a beeper and a cell phone. At that stage of the mission, everyone had to have a beeper and a cell phone — we were all on duty 24 hours a day, seven days a week through launch and LOI. Everything was ready. In two days, I would be at the Cape.

Chapter 3-43
Preparing Lunar Prospector for Launch

Sunday, November 30, 1997: My Eventful Trip to the Cape

When I left for the Cape Sunday, I was elated but worn-out from all the battles and the intense work of the past many, many months. I flew uneventfully from San Jose to Houston, where I changed planes. On the second leg of the trip, from Houston to Orlando, I was sitting in the left window seat of the last row in the back of the plane and an India couple, with their very young child, was sitting next to me. As the flight was nearing its end, I started getting a headache and I got really sick — I realized later it was from a combination of exhaustion and the *flu shot* that I had gotten four days earlier!

I started to feel like I would vomit and grabbed an airsickness bag just in case, hoping we would make it to the Orlando Airport before disaster struck. No such luck. A few minutes before landing, I threw up, but it was only the dry heaves, which, of course, made me feel even worse — my head was about to split in two.

After we landed, I waited until every one else had left the plane before I did, just in case I had to make a dash for the airplane's restroom. Though I had my doubts, I made it through the secondary terminal and to the automated trains that run between the secondary terminals and the main terminal of the Orlando Airport. Since there is no place to throw up on the train, I waited until I was sure that I could make the few minute ride to the main terminal without incident, before I took the chance and boarded the train.

My head was splitting and immediately after I left the train, I was clearly going to vomit again, so I ran to the nearest men's restroom and started throwing up and then retched with the dry heaves. Someone, either an attendant or a passenger, heard my plight and asked if I was OK.

Despite my wretched condition, but since I was not dying, I answered, "Yeah, I'll be OK. Thanks." When I stopped retching, I left the restroom, only to stop at the next one for a repeat performance.

I knew I would never be able to drive from Orlando to Cocoa Beach, where Rebecca had rented a small apartment in the Ocean Dunes Apartments for me. It was already quite late in the evening and since there is a beautiful Hyatt Hotel right in the Orlando Airport, I decided to see if I could get a room there for the night, so I could recuperate before driving to the Cape in the morning. I wobbled up to the reception desk and asked if they had any rooms left and to my dismay, the answer was, "NO."

Well, with that possibility shot, and with my head still pounding and my stomach still churning, I braved taking the Hertz van to pick up my car, with the hopes of finding a hotel with at least one available room. I drove to a nearby hotel, asked for a room and received a, "Sorry, we are full." After a couple of more futile attempts, I decided that, rather than futilely driving around Orlando any more, I might just as well to drive to Cocoa Beach — or die trying.

The nearly one hour drive along the Bee Line Expressway from Orlando to Cape Canaveral was excruciating. I left the window open so I would get some cold air and so, if I started to vomit, I could pull off the expressway and throw up out the window. My head kept pounding and I had trouble breathing because of the pain. I was really not in any condition to drive, so I drove rather slowly — though safer, it just prolonged the agony.

When I finally got off the Beeline Expressway at Cape Canaveral, I had to vomit again, so I pulled into a very large gas station with a big, empty parking lot, jumped out of the car and started retching with the dry heaves. That lasted for several minutes and when the dry heaves subsided, I began to feel a little better (I no longer wanted someone to come along and shoot me), so I started to drive the few miles to Cocoa Beach and to my Ocean Dunes apartment.

I was not sure of the streets, so I stopped at a fast food joint and asked some teenagers where the street was I was looking for. They gave me directions and I proceeded to find the apartment complex. I went to the owner's apartment to get my key. She and her husband were very nice and she showed me to my apartment. I immediately went in, quickly got undressed, flopped on the bed and thankfully fell asleep. The nightmare of the past few hours was finally over.

Monday, December 1, 1997: Five Weeks to Launch — A Missed Chance

When I woke up after a long night's sleep, I felt much better, but was still wobbly. Since our work preparing the spacecraft at Astro Tech would not start until the next day, I decided to go to the Epcot Center in Orlando for a little R&R. However, I still didn't really feel too well, so I was not enjoying Epcot very much. I drove back to the apartment and took a nap.

Rebecca called to tell me I had to call Lockheed. I did and it turned out that Mel Brashears was concerned I was not going to be at a briefing the next day! I said, "Nobody told me about a briefing tomorrow!" It was the final briefing on the mission and Mel thought I should be there. Finally it had dawned on at least good old Mel that I should be there.

Unfortunately when the guy said, "You really should be at the briefing," I was still feeling quite badly and the first thing that crossed my mind was that I simply couldn't get on another airplane feeling the way I did. That ticked me off — I was too sick to take the opportunity to show Lockheed upper management who really knew the spacecraft and mission. I told the person I was at the Cape and just could not make it back to Sunnyvale the next day and he asked, "Well, can you at least call in during the meeting?"

I answered, "Of course," and I gave him my cell phone number and told him I would be at Astro Tech all day. I was told that Mel would call me shortly to talk about the meeting. But Mel never did call and I never heard another word about the briefing!

Tuesday, December 2, 1997: Safety and the TLI Stage Hardware

My Lockheed crew and I had our safety training at Astro Tech in the morning. Astro Tech has very strict safety regulations that we had to know and follow — without exception! They wanted no accidents and the resulting deaths in their processing facilities. We were told about the warning system of lights and sirens and how to get out of the processing facility, fast, in case of an emergency. Also, there was a strict protocol to even get near the processing building itself, where we would soon have a fully fueled Star-37 rocket motor, Lunar Prospector with 137 kg of highly toxic hydrazine monopropellant, two small solid fuel TLI Stage spin-up rocket motors, 12 explosive devices, two tanks filled with nitrogen at 3000 psi, and a partridge in a pear tree (after all, it was nearly Christmas) — and where there was another spacecraft being processed for launch in the adjacent highbay!

The protocol started with a visit to a safety shack that had green, yellow, and red lights on it. If the green light was on, one could go to the facility, yellow was for safety personnel only, and red meant — get the hell out of there very fast. When you got to the shack, you had to exchange your personal picture Astro Tech badge for a numbered badge, putting your picture badge in the slot where the numbered badge had been. The reason for that is simple, if there were an explosion or fire or leak of toxic fuel, they would know quickly from the picture badges in the shack whose bodies they needed to look for in the rubble and which number badge each body would have. Once inside the processing building, you had to put on a clean-room bunny suit, booties, and hat before you went through the airlock that opened into the big clean-room itself. Clearly, when you reversed the process and left the processing facility, you returned the number badge, to its slot in the shack, and took your picture badge so they would know you were not in the facility. It is a neat system.

After going through the impressive and thought provoking safety training, we sat around for a while waiting for the TLI Star-37 and the TLI casing to arrive. Finally they got there and we went over and pushed the big container that held the Star-37 into the highbay. Then the Thiokol guys chased us away because they had to get started getting everything ready to get the Star-37 out of its container and the casing out of its box.

At about 2:00 PM, we went over again and we helped Thiokol take the TLI casing out of its box, which was fun. Even though I had seen the casing many times before, it was still really neat to see it there because we were processing it for launch.

We had the most fun when we opened the container — actually it looked like a big tin can — of the Star-37. That motor was just beautiful; it was sitting upside down with its nozzle pointing upwards. It was simply beautiful, with its titanium casing and its black phenolic carbon fiber nozzle. It was so beautiful it took your breath away. I just looked at it and was amazed at the chemical energy that was stored in there. That rocket motor was going to propel Lunar Prospector out of its Earth parking orbit into a transfer orbit to the Moon! That all took until about 4:00 PM. We helped get everything ready because Thiokol had a lot of work to do to get the TLI Stage processed. They were going to put the TLI Stage together the next day, while I was flying to Headquarters for the pre-launch news conference.

I went out to dinner with Karen Ramos and had a good time chatting about everything in the world. Thus ended an exciting day.

Wednesday, December 3, and Thursday, December 4, 1997: The News Conference Side Trip

First of all, when I woke up at a little before 4:00 AM Wednesday morning to drive to Orlando to catch my early morning flight to DC, there was no damned electricity! I had to shower, shave, and pack in the dark. As a result I forgot my damned coat and it was going to be cold in DC (remember, I had just got over being sick from the flu shot and exhaustion)!

Anyway, I got to DC and went to Pat and Julius's apartment to put my bag in my room, and then I went over to NASA for the news conference dry run, which had been postponed until the next morning!

I met Scott and Dougherty on the way and we talked about the boom deployment issue, which was still not completely dead in Dougherty's small mind, but at least he was getting more reasonable about it. He didn't understand the deployment non-issue, but it was getting easier to make him do things right. We were going to wait until we had the final thermal data from Jim Schirle before discussing it further.

Dougherty also wanted to discuss the Mission Profile, which he did not understand at all. In the absence of knowledge, Dougherty just made up a big story about how the mission should be done, without knowing how it had to be done.

Then Dougherty, Scott, and a couple other NASA officials had a telecon about the launch. It was so funny; they were fussing about who got to sit where in the observer's section of the launch control room at the Cape! It was pathetic. They were debating, "If Goldin comes, then he should sit here and if he doesn't, then Wes should sit there and who gets to sit over here. Well, we can't have this guy here and blah, blah, blah." What a bunch of idiots!

I went to have lunch and they were still arguing about the seating when I came back. When they finished, we reviewed the viewgraphs for the news conference. That went quite well and we had put together a good presentation.

I went to Pat and Julius's. Julius was on travel, so Pat and I went out for a nice dinner together. Julius came home later in the evening.

I got up really quite late Thursday morning because I hadn't gotten a really good night's sleep since leaving California.

Julius and I went to Headquarters and then it was time for the dry run. Then we had the news conference in the afternoon (NASA had decided not to have a dress rehearsal after all) and it went really well.

After that, Pat and I went to see Jim Muncy (Congressman Rohrabacher's aide); he had been talking to George French about the web site and he wanted to talk to me. He was concerned because George French had told him I had been locked out of Lockheed and Scott was taking over the mission and was going to be the Mission Director. I explained to him what the real situation was, which was not as bad as George had said, but was bad enough so I wanted to get rid of Scott. The general consensus of opinion was, "OK, this is not the right time; so we will let it go until after launch and then we will get rid of the bastard." Muncy was going to try to set up a meeting between Wes and George, so George didn't get screwed.

After that, I flew back to the Cape, but I didn't get to my apartment until after midnight and didn't get to sleep until nearly 1:00 AM.

Friday, December 5, 1997: The Baseline Functional Testing

Because I had gotten in so late, I again didn't get a really good night's rest, and just as I was waking up, there were some interesting sonic booms — yes, I was at the Cape!

Dougherty and Dan were at Astro Tech when I got there, so we went over the thermal issues with the boom canisters. We all concluded we needed the titanium tape and we did not want the canister blankets, though we probably did want the little tip plate blankets. Dougherty finally understood and agreed.

Then he wanted to review the Mission Profile, but I said we could look at it the next day. Regardless of what he said, I was not going to change it.

Later, at mid-morning, we all went out to the launch pad and saw the rocket. Of course, I climbed all around it, i.e., on the gantry that enclosed it, and looked at it from every angle. It was really neat seeing that big sucker.

Later in the day, Dougherty was talking to Sylvia about Scott and I heard him say, "Scott may be the Launch Director, but he has nothing to say. The people who have something to say are the ones who are going to make the decision. All Scott is going to get to do is to concur. If he thinks he is going to stop the launch he is mistaken." Clearly, Dougherty and Lockheed were not interested in Scott's attempt to become the Little Tin Dictator of the launch.

I thought that was very funny and I later said, "Gee Tom, I enjoyed your conversation with Sylvia," and he smiled and we had a good laugh about it. He too was getting tired of Scott's arrogant, self-centered crap.

Thiokol still didn't have the Star-37 in the TLI casing. That was going slowly, but we had plenty of time.

Though Gary Schlueter had done quite a bit of the functional testing, when Dave Curtis, Bill Feldman, and Danny Everett arrived, we did a full baseline functional test of the spacecraft, the spectrometers, and the MAG/ER. I wanted to wait around for the engine test, but Irv and Dan had left for dinner. They hadn't had any food all day and it was going to be another 45 minutes to an hour before they got back. It was already 6:00 PM, so I decided to hell with it. I wanted to go to my apartment and get some things ready for the next day. We had done most of the baseline functional and since it had gone just as smooth as silk, I was sure they would be finished with it within an hour or two.

We were scheduled to do the communications End-to-End Tests with JPL and Mission Ops at Ames from 8:00 AM to 5:00 PM the next day and then Sunday we were scheduled to do TDRS End-to-End Tests from 12:00 PM until 3:00 PM. That would pretty much finish up the spacecraft. After the TLI Stage was finished, we would fuel the spacecraft and have the dress rehearsal. Things were going extremely smoothly, better than we had a right to expect — but remember, Lunar Prospector was designed to be simple and to work — which it did.

As I went to bed, I looked at the clock — it was 9:20 PM — and I thought, *one month from today, I will be launched. I'll be just about getting ready for the TLI burn.* And I said to my sweet Rebecca in far off California, "It's getting there, baby, it's getting there."

Saturday, December 6, 1997: The End-to-End Testing

We did the End-to-End communications test, but we had a lot of trouble getting the ground link set up between Astro Tech and the Cape. It took us about 4 hours before that was straightened out, but once we got going, we just whizzed right through the End-to-End test, though we had some problems locking up when we were in the 300 bps downlink mode. Marcie was on the other end, i.e., at Mission Ops in Ames, with the controllers. I issued the commands over the telephone to Marcie and the uplink controller uplinked them via JPL to the spacecraft sitting right in front of me! I then verified the commands on the ground support equipment there at Astro Tech, while Marcie verified them at Mission Ops. We went through everything — the spacecraft and the science instruments — just everything and everything worked perfectly. The spacecraft was working beautifully.

While we were doing the End-to-End, the shroud arrived. It was all wrapped up in plastic. It was a lot smaller than I thought it would be, but it was quite beautiful. The shroud had the NASA logo on its side, below which was the mission logo. Since Scott had not allowed LRI to be added to the mission logo decal during its second printing, which occurred after I was in LRI (his paper thin excuse — it would have cost too much money to change the art work), only NASA and Lockheed appeared on the shroud. I called Sylvia and asked to have the LRI logo added to the shroud and she said she would ask Scott if that was still possible. She called back a little later and said it was far too late to add any decals to the shroud or the rocket. I assumed that was correct and forgot about it, since I had more important things to do than fight with Scott about the exclusion of the LRI logo from the launch vehicle.

Slowly but surely, all the pieces were getting there. We were beginning to really move.

When I left the Astro Tech control center at about 4:00 PM, the first quarter moon was up in the sky. It was beautiful and I realized that was the last first quarter Moon I would see before we launched. In just one more lunation, I would be on my way. It was thrilling. It was a thrill to have seen the rocket and to know it was there because of all my years of hard work and it was a thrill to see Lunar Prospector working perfectly and knowing it was ready to go to that quarter Moon up in the sky. It was just a joy to be there at that moment — all the annoyances with Scott and NASA and Dougherty and Lockheed were gone (at least for that moment).

Sunday, December 7, 1997: TDRS Testing

I got up late because we weren't going to start the TDRS test until noon and I was tired, or more correctly, exhausted.

It took most of the three hours of the scheduled test time just to get the link established, because TDRS didn't have a wide enough frequency sweep to linkup. Finally, they got that straightened out and the test was successful — Lunar Prospector was ready to go, test-wise.

Karen and her boyfriend came to Astro Tech and I showed them the spacecraft. Then I watched a football game at the apartment, and after that, I met Karen and her boyfriend and we went out to a good German restaurant for a good German dinner.

Monday, December 8, 1997:
Four Weeks to Launch — Loading the Propellant

I got up early and arrived at Astro Tech a little before 6:00 AM, all set for the loading of Lunar Prospector's propellant. All of our people, as well as several others, were there and the Propellant Loading Conductor said, "Everybody that is not essential has to leave" (no need for too many dead bodies). He added, "I need 95% of you people out of here."

He looked at me and I said firmly, "It's my spacecraft."

He said, "OK, you're essential." Irv, Kim, and Dan were allowed to stay, but Tim Maloney and the rest had to leave.

We were beginning to bring life to the monster — we were putting the lifeblood of the spacecraft into it.

Since we had to monitor the pressure and temperatures of the three tanks, we powered Lunar Prospector up so we could get telemetry from it through the umbilical. We also had 9 remote temperature sensors on the tanks. The tanks already contained the correct amount of helium pressurant, at about 120 psi. As we added the fuel, the helium would compress adiabatically and heat up. We could not let it get too hot, so our loading procedure was to put some fuel in, watch the tank temperatures and pressure rise, wait until the helium (and hence the tanks and fuel) cooled off, and then repeat the process, until all 137 kg of fuel were loaded and the tank pressure was at about 450 psi. It was going to take all day.

Also, we had the spacecraft sitting on three accurate electronic scales, or load cells, so we could monitor the amount of fuel in each of the three tanks as the fuelling proceeded. We were ready to go from our end and the fuelling crew was ready, too.

The spacecraft was in the middle of the fuelling area, the two fuelling technicians were behind a very heavy blast barrier with a thick glass window and we were in a room with thick glass windows just back of — and to the side of — the blast barrier. The technicians wore full body, toxic material protection suits with their own oxygen supplies. They started going through the strict fuelling procedures and one guy had a computer graphic showing all the plumbing of the loading equipment and the spacecraft. As they went through the checklist, he noted on the graphic, which valves were open and which were closed — a mistake could be disastrous. They very, very carefully checked everything and they moved very carefully, in part, because they were very clumsy in their bulky protective suits.

They finally opened the first fuel valve and the canister on the graphic that represented the hydrazine storage canister slowly filled with blue and then the blue moved along a line (that represented a fuel line) that led to the next valve. They did some more checking and then they opened that valve and the blue graphic line crept along further towards the spacecraft graphic and it finally reached the last valve just before the spacecraft's propellant fill and drain valve. The blue line stopped moving at that valve and they switched a couple more valves and checked for leaks.

By then, it was about 8:00 AM and they were finally ready to load the hydrazine into Lunar Prospector's three tanks, and I would soon know if the simple loading method I had proposed would work, or if Irv had been right.

Finally, they opened their last valve with a wrench and the blue line moved to our fill and drain valve. They did some more checking and then — our fill and drain valve was opened and the hydrazine began to flow into the spacecraft. They put the first 9.1 kg (exactly 20 lbs — they still used the English system) of fuel in at a very slow rate, about 1 kg per minute, and as they did, the tank pressure and temperatures crept up very slowly as Kim and I watched them on the monitors. Dan, Al Tilley, and Irv were watching the data from the other room. Then they stopped the filling so the tanks could cool down, and we looked at the scales; Tank 2 had about 3.2 kg of fuel, while Tanks 1 and 3 each had about 2.7 kg. That difference was more than I had hoped for, but we thought that as the fuelling continued, the loading would level out.

We got ready and started loading the next 9.1 kg and the pressure went up corresponding and the temperature rose slightly. Surprisingly, the tanks cooled down rather quickly, so we were able to proceed at a faster pace than we had planned.

Since the fuelling was going so well, the technicians started adding 18.2 kg of fuel per step. The pressure continued climbing, the temperatures rose and dropped and Tank 2 always had more fuel in it than the other two. But the fuelling was going well and the spacecraft's cg was not shifting.

I began to get worried because Tank 2 was always getting a little bit more fuel in it than 1 and 3. Finally, we got to the point where the tanks were 60% full and that was when the fuel lines to the three tanks would finally be covered by fuel and that would cut off the exchange of helium between the tanks. By that point, Tank 2 had nearly a kilogram more fuel in it than did the other two! That difference still hadn't shifted the cg significantly, but I really didn't like it. However, we thought at that point, the tanks would stop filling differentially.

Then I remembered that Tank 2 was under the transponder. I asked Tim to confirm that and he said, "Yes it is."

I said, "Great, that means it (Tank 2) will be hotter than 1 and 3 (because the transponder puts out a lot of heat), so that is going to force some of the fuel out of it into Tanks 1 and 3!" I was relieved.

We proceeded and the fuelling process was going remarkably fast. It looked like we were going to be done in a total of about 3 hours.

However, even after the fuel had covered the fuel lines in the three tanks, the amount of fuel in Tank 2 kept increasing with respect to that in Tanks 1 and 3 with each loading step and that did not make any sense. I was beginning to be really concerned about that because the measured difference was up to 1.5 kg! Then the reason dawned on Dan; he said, "You know what, this is impossible, unless Tank 2 is just a little bit farther from the cg than the other two." That made sense (if Tank 2 were a little bit farther from the cg, i.e., had a longer lever-arm than the other two tanks, Tank 2's measured weight would appear greater than that of the other two tanks, since their weights are equal to their lever-arm times the mass of fuel in them) and everybody agreed with it. If Dan were correct, and no one doubted that, since physically that was the only possible explanation, it looked like we were really getting equal amounts of fuel in each tank. Dan's explanation was supported by the fact that the amounts of fuel in Tanks 1 and 3 were almost identical, i.e., they were within 100 g of each other!

By then, we had loaded 118 kg of hydrazine (19 kg to go). The tank pressure was rising rapidly as expected and the temperatures were getting higher, but each time we stopped for a little while, the temperatures came right back down, not all the way, but always much quicker than I thought they would.

The next step took us to 128 kg; the pressure was at 400 psi and the temperatures were at about 30° C. Irv wanted to do the last 9 kg in two increments; he wanted to have them put in 8 kg and then wait, and then add the last kilogram to make sure that we had it just right — at 137 kg.

By that time, we were all absolutely convinced that the measured differences between Tank 2 and Tanks 1 and 3 were due to an offset of Tank 2 and not really to differential propellant loading. The technicians pumped the last little bit of fuel in; they stopped and measured the total amount and then added another tiny amount. They said they had put in 137 kg and we said the same thing. The pressure was a little over 450 psi and the temperatures were about 30° C. As soon as we stopped, the temperatures started coming down. I was still floored at how fast they came down, but the reason was that we were reading the temperature of the helium, which was getting hot because of compression, while the hydrazine that was flowing into the tanks was relatively cold and hence the cool fuel cooled the hot helium very quickly.

We finished at about 11:00 AM. Instead of taking more than 8 hours as we had planned, we had loaded the fuel in just 3 hours and my simple, unorthodox method of fuelling the three tanks had worked perfectly. If the measured difference between the amounts of fuel in Tanks 1 and 3 was real (that difference could also have been due to tank off-sets), then the filling was accurate to 0.2%. — not bad for government (supported) work!

We watched the data a while and as the tanks cooled, the pressure dropped to about 444 psi. Using that pressure, I calculated that the ullage (the volume in the tanks filled with helium) was 27%. The fuel fill volume was 73%, while I had always calculated that the fill volume would be 74%. It was just about perfect and we had done it in just 3 hours. It had been easy and it was wonderful. It was just thrilling to see the fuelling go so well.

Though the tank pressure was then at 444 psi, some of the helium would dissolve in the hydrazine over the following few days and the pressure would drop a few psi. Irv didn't think that was important, but one calculation he gave me indicated the pressure drop could be as much as 7 psi, so I would be watching the pressure very closely over the next several days.

I was extremely pleased; the spacecraft was fully fuelled and we had just a few more steps to do and Lunar Prospector would be ready to go to the Moon. My simple concept of having just one fill and drain valve for filling had been verified and my over-all concept of having a very simple spacecraft with a minimum of everything was really holding up — it simply worked and did so beautifully!

Because we had expected to be fuelling all day long, Kim had ordered lunch for everybody. Francisco and some of the other guys got the sandwiches from the local Hero Sandwich shop. We ate lunch and then I went to my apartment and took a nap.

With the major step of fuelling complete, we were getting close to having the spacecraft ready for launch — ahead of schedule. Similarly, the LLV crew was ahead of schedule in their preparing the LLV for launch. Things were going so well over at Pad 46 that Tony Soto, who led the LLV launch team, kept saying, "We're getting worried, because it's going so well!"

Also, Kim had told me earlier in the day that Dougherty had really clipped Scott's wings. As he had told Sylvia a few days earlier, Dougherty told Scott that his big role as Launch Director had been cut down to being just a ceremonial role — he really had nothing to say, he had no authority. I had a good laugh about that.

That evening there was an Atlas Centaur launch and I watched it go. It was absolutely beautiful. The Atlas stage had two ground-lit, strap-on solid fuel boosters that were lit at Atlas ignition and two air-lit strap-ons that lit about 60 seconds into the flight. The strap-ons burned brightly and when they dropped off, you could see them slowly falling back down to Earth. It was gorgeous. In a month, my LLV2 would be doing the same thing at about the same time of night, but I would not be there to watch it — I would have the best seat in the world, my Mission Director's chair in Mission Ops where I would be ready to take command control of my newly launched spacecraft as it raced towards the Moon and its destiny.

Tuesday, December 9, through Thursday, December 11, 1997: The Launch Dress Rehearsal

Tuesday I flew back to the West Coast for the launch dress rehearsal and home for a couple of days.

Wednesday morning, I went to Ames and we did a SIM starting with the 3rd LOI burn and ending with the final turn-on of the high gain antenna, i.e., the last command of the LOI sequence that would officially begin the mapping mission from the 100 km altitude, polar orbit. It was a good SIM. Troy Jessop, one of our new uplink controllers, did a really good job and was becoming a very good uplink controller.

Also, the dress rehearsal got started when the LLV launch Crew began its 34-hour countdown at the Cape, where it was raining and storming like hell.

I made some corrections to the Mission Profile, based on the changes to the boom deployment sequence caused by Steve's nonsense. Dougherty had said he thought he should also sign off on the Mission Profile(s), so no one could say I had acted alone if something went wrong. Since I had fought for my right as the PI to have the full respon-sibility for the success of the mission, I also expected to take full responsibility for the failure of the mission. Despite my saying that, Dougherty insisted, as Project Manager, he had to sign off on the Mission Profile, too, if for no other reason, because Lockheed had the main contract for the mission and therefore Lockheed expected him to co-sign the Mission Profile. While that was true, it was really just BS; Dougherty really wanted to help protect my butt in case of failure. I appreciated that and saw no way I could refuse to let him co-sign the Mission Profile without my looking like a real dumb ass. I let him co-sign.

Dougherty had been getting more and more cooperative and more and more relaxed as we got closer and closer to launch and as he saw everything was going perfectly. His wanting to sign the Mission Profile was just one more sign that he knew both the mission was going to succeed and I knew how to make it succeed. That was evident when he said, a few days earlier, "After we get into (lunar) orbit, you can do what you want with it (the spacecraft)." Just one day later, he had changed that statement to, "After the first *six hours* (after boom deployment), you can do what you want with it."

I had a nice interview with Gerd Meißner from Germany for *Das Deutsche Rundfunk*. That was fun — I love speaking German.

Thursday morning, the LLV2 countdown was progressing smoothly and I worked on getting the January 6 (GMT, Greenwich Mean Time) Mission Profile completely ready and did a number of other small things I had been trying to get done. I also got everything ready to take with me to the Cape, so I could finish up the January 7 (GMT) backup launch date Mission Profile, and to make sure the MOD was OK, while I was at the Cape.

Finally we got to –000/03:42 MET (–0 Days, 3 Hours, 42 Minutes Mission Elapsed Time, MET was the time before or after spacecraft turn-on and turn-on was to occur 56 minutes and 38 seconds after launch) point in the Mission Profile, which corresponded to minus 2 hours and 45 minutes in the LLV2 countdown. At that point, I, as Mission Director, had to poll my Mission Ops Team, the DSN at JPL and my Goddard Nav Team about our launch readiness. I had been bitching about having to fly all the way from the Cape to be in the Mission Control Center (MCC) at Ames for that dress rehearsal; I thought it could be done without me. How wrong I was!

The rehearsal was very useful because the polling is done in a very formal way. Everybody had a specific polling title. Further, the exact wording of the polling is very precise to avoid any confusion. Ten minutes (–000/03:42 MET) before Kim polled me (–000/03:32 MET), I had to poll JPL and Goddard and the polling had to be done at exactly the right time. Five minutes (–000/03:27 MET) after Kim polled me, he would be polled by the launch Director at the Cape, regarding both my teams' readiness to support the launch and the spacecraft status as monitored by Kim at the Cape (I had no way at Mission Ops to monitor the spacecraft, but Kim could monitor the battery charge level and the pressure and temperatures of the tanks via the ground support equipment at the Cape) — confusing huh? Thus, though it had seemed simple enough on paper (hence my reluctance to fly back and forth between the Cape and California), Marcie had to coach me through the first polling — that was when I realized that my being in Mission Ops for that dress rehearsal was well worth the time and money my trip was costing. I did much better during the second and final set of three pollings — the critical GO/NO-GO Polls — that started 25 minutes before launch and occurred at –000/01:22, –000/01:19 and –000/01:16 MET.

It was really neat because Launch Control at the Cape went right through 1st Stage ignition, 1st Stage burn, 2nd Stage burn, shroud separation, 3rd Stage burn, and the start of the Orbit Adjust Module burn. Then we at Mission Ops followed through with the TLI burn sequence and the spacecraft turn-on. Since TDRS was not on line, we pretended TDRS could not lock-up on the spacecraft, which made the rehearsal boring at that point and I sure in hell hoped TDRS would not fail us during the real mission.

After the dress rehearsal was over, I wrote out a script for the polling, so I would not screw up during the actual launch. In the end, I was very glad I was in Mission Ops for the dress rehearsal, but anxious to get back to the Cape to finish preparing Lunar Prospector for launch.

It was very late by the time we finished the dress rehearsal, so I hardly had any time at home to see my sweet wife before I flew back to the Cape the next morning.

Friday, December 12, 1997: Back to the Cape

Rebecca and I got up very early and she drove me to the San Jose Airport to catch my 6:50 AM flight.

When I got to Astro Tech and checked the spacecraft, the tank pressure was down to 441 psi, so more helium had dissolved in the hydrazine. I hoped that was the end of that, because I wanted the pressure as high as possible at launch, so my engines would have the highest thrust possible. The tank temperatures were down to 21° C. Everything was OK.

Al Tilley had the final, pre-launch mass numbers for the spacecraft. The mass of the spacecraft was 296.4 kg and we had exactly 137.7 kg of fuel on board. We had the mass information we needed to do the final ballasting of the TLI Stage, so we could stack the spacecraft on the TLI Stage and spin balance the stack. Tim said the TLI Stage was quite light, so we were going to have to add quite a bit of ballast.

Also, we were told that our launch vehicle — which had received its new name, the rockets were no longer called LLV1s and LLV2s, they were Athena Is and Athena IIs — would have a 10 m/sec under-burn! We could take care of that by decreasing our ballast by 2 or 3 kg. We had to get the ballasting of the TLI Stage right or we would have a large TLI velocity error and I was bothered because we could never get an exact answer from the LLV crew about the Athena II's real lift capability. It was always a stupid game with those guys.

Other than that problem, the Athena II countdown was going very well.

I called Lisa, because she had sent me a number of the newly printed NASA Fact Sheets on the Lunar Prospector Mission to give to people at the Cape. Since I was already in LRI before the new batch was printed, I had asked that my affiliation be changed from Lockheed to LRI. That had been done, but they had put my affiliation and me with LRI at the very bottom; NASA, Scott, and Sylvia were at the top, Lockheed and Dougherty were next, and last — *and least* LRI and I were at the bottom!

I crabbed to Lisa about that and she said, "Well Scott, wanted it that way, because Lockheed has the main contract and you're (just) a subcontractor." Such BS, the self-serving SOB always had some pseudo-bureaucratic crap to justify his making the PI disappear, so he could make it look like he was running Lunar Prospector as a normal NASA program.

I already knew the answer to my next question, but I asked, "Have you changed lunar geology to selenology in the PR materials as I told you was the correct thing to do?" (see Preface).

She answered, "No, it was thought that lunar geology was common usage and it would be better not to confuse people with selenology."

I said, "Who thought that — what you mean is that Scott wants it that way."

She said, "Well yes."

As I well knew, the pompous, self-serving little bastard was undermining everything I had been working towards for years. Scott consistently and systematically

pushed my interests aside and had maneuvered himself into the position of being the
leader of Lunar Prospector. The last two or three NASA press releases referred only to
NASA and Scott Hubbard and how he was managing the NASA mission. My role, when
it was even mentioned, had been as the Chief Scientist. I was pissed.

Scott and NASA were systematically obliterating the role of the PI in Discovery
Missions. I was furious; I was going to have him thrown off the mission, the only question was, "Should I wait until after launch or should I ask to have him removed right
then, before he could do any more damage to the role of PI in Discovery missions, to
LRI, and to me?" Unfortunately, the risk to the mission and hence to all my goals, was
just too great if I asked NASA to remove the fat SOB from a mission that was less than
four weeks from launch. I was going to have to wait just a few more weeks, and then I
would try to fix the fat little bastard.

Saturday, December 13, 1997:
Ballasting and Spin Balancing the Stack

I got up early and was at Astro Tech before 7:00 AM. Al Tilley and I carefully compared our mass and ballasting calculations — we had exactly the same numbers.

When all the guys got there, we went in to the spin-table room, where the TLI
Stage, complete with its Star-37 motor, was sitting on the spin-table and had, itself, been
spun balanced. We very carefully mounted the spacecraft on the TLI Stage.

When we were finished, I noticed with concern that, though it was fairly far from
the APS, one of the two nitrogen jets of the collision avoidance system was located just
off to one side and below the APS. It was close enough to the APS that I thought some
of the 3000 psi nitrogen that would come jetting out of that jet at Spacecraft/TLI Stage
separation might impinge on the bottom (–Z side) of the APS and blow out the thin
solar filters on that face. I mentioned that to Tim and Kim, but they thought it would
be OK and there was little we could do about it at that point anyway. However, I wondered if we could not put a thin sheet aluminum collar on top of the TLI Stage to protect the APS, but I decided that we would probably endanger the entire launch by
adding a piece of non-flight hardware to the TLI Stage and I reluctantly ignored my
concern.

We did the first spin and got the required data. The balance of the stack was very
close to that of the TLI Stage alone as we had expected — after all, we had balanced the
spacecraft very carefully back at Lockheed, but before it was fuelled. But we then knew
for sure that the spacecraft was in balance for flight and that the fuelling had worked as
well as we thought it had. That was a very good feeling!

We sat down and made the calculations for the final balancing of the stack and for
the final ballasting.

By that time, it was lunchtime, so we had some sandwiches brought in and then
we proceeded.

We arrived at the final answers for ballasting and for the spin balancing of the
stack based on the spacecraft's launch mass of 296.4 kg we had measured after fuelling.
We needed to add 15.2 kg of ballast to the TLI Stage to bring the stack's mass up to that
which our Athena II was designed to put into the parking orbit. Thus, my efforts to keep
Lunar Prospector's mass from growing and our concept of ballasting the stack "up to"
the lift capability of the Athena II had worked exceedingly well — we had 15.2 kg of
margin left that we had to ballast out. That was great. In contrast, the spacecraft in the
next highbay was 2 kg over weight and the engineers in there were going at their space-

craft with hacksaws to cut nonessential parts off of it! They were green with envy when they heard we had to "ballast-up" 15.2 kg.

We calculated that we needed 11.4 kg to fine tune the spin balance of the stack, with 1.7 kg on the bottom of the TLI Stage and 9.7 kg on its top. The remaining 3.8 kg was just dead weight that was to be added to the TLI Stage.

It took a really long time for the Thiokol guys to get the curve shaped lead and aluminum weights cut and measured. When they were finished, I said, "OK guys, I want everyone to sign the ballast plates, so your names will get launched along with Lunar Prospector towards the Moon."

The guys were surprised and someone asked, "Are you kidding?"

I answered, "No, I'm not kidding. Somebody get a felt-tipped pen and let's start signing." While my Lockheed engineers had all signed the mission signup sheet that was inside the spacecraft, the Thiokol and Astro Tech guys had, of course, not had that opportunity to have their names go to the Moon, so they were especially thrilled with my request. Someone wanted to know if the TLI Stage, with his name on it, would reach the Moon and I said that was unlikely, but I would know where it went after launch. We all signed the ballast plates and then got ready to mount the ballasting plates on the TLI Stage.

It was about 4:30 PM before we got the ballast in place on the TLI Stage. Mounting the bottom ballast plates was a torturous procedure because the guys, mainly Dan, had to reach in under the TLI Stage, through some holes in the spin-table stand to get the plates in the correct positions on the bottom ring of the TLI Stage. I admired Dan's ability to do that. Then we got the upper ballast plates in place with relative ease. Then we put the rest of the ballast on, got all of it screwed down very tightly and spun it. The stack's balance was well within the tolerances. Just like that, we were done!

It was well after 5:00 PM, so we decided just to leave the stack on the spin-table and everybody would go home after we put the protective red covers on the APS, the ER, and the attitude detectors and put the nitrogen purges back on the APS and the ER. All we had left to do was to put the explosive devices on the stack, fill the collision avoidance system bottles with nitrogen at 3000 psi, and do an aliveness test Monday, and that would be it — we would be done preparing the spacecraft for flight!

The Athena crew had to finish their work on the rocket adapter and the shroud, both of which were in the same highbay. Then we could put our stack on the adapter and put the shroud on the whole thing. The sooner that was all done, the better I would like it.

Saturday was a great day — one more giant step towards launch completed.

Sunday, December 14, 1997: One Day of R&R

I tried to show Karen and her son, Chris, the spacecraft. But I couldn't get them in the highbay because Chris was too young to be allowed in a hazardous area, so they saw it through one of the observer windows. Then we had dinner and a nice chat about the mission, NASA, and Lockheed. I told her I was going to try to have Scott removed from the mission and all my reasons for doing so. To my surprise, she then told me they, Spaceport Florida, just had their decal made and that it was soon going to be put on the Athena II. She added there was plenty of time for me to add LRI's logo to the rocket too! Scott had again lied when he told Sylvia it was too late for me to have the LRI logo added to the rocket — the dirty SOB. I asked Karen where I could get the LRI logo quickly made into a decal and she told me where to go. I was going to try to get it made, get it put on the launch vehicle and fix the fat, lying bastard!

Monday, December 15, 1997:
Three Weeks to Launch — Getting the LRI Decal Done

The technicians loaded the nitrogen into our collision avoidance system tanks and we took the spacecraft off the TLI Stage.

I talked to Dan Lebel about getting the LRI logo put on the shroud and he said, "Yeah, we can do that," and he got out the engineering drawing showing the shroud with the two existing decals.

I said, "Great, I want the logo put between the meatball (as everyone called the NASA logo) and the oval (the Lunar Prospector Mission logo)." Given that the space between the two logos was not too big, if I had the full LRI logo in there, the LRI letters would be very small; but if I just had the letters in there, they would be nice and big. Dan said he would check it out and he would call me to let me know if it would work. He did not call, so I called him a couple of times and he was always busy with something else, but said he would get to it soon.

After that, I had lunch and then I called Karen, because some Admirals were supposed to come to see the spacecraft. It turned out they could not come until Wednesday, which was very inconvenient, because we were going to do the final stacking of the adapter, the TLI Stage, and Lunar Prospector then.

I decided not to wait on Dan's call any longer, so I went to Hangar K and found him. I first asked him about my going to Pad 46 to see the roll back of the gantry from the Athena II the next day and he started fussing about my not having a white badge for the pad, so we talked to Dan's boss, who, of course, said, "Sure, go ahead and take him out there."

I asked Dan, "How big can I make the LRI letters?"

He answered, "I haven't figured that out yet."

I asked, "How about a foot?"

He answered, "OK."

I found the place where Karen said I could get the decal made and asked the guy if he could do it and he said yes, and he asked, "How quick do you need it?"

I answered, "In a day or so."

He said, "We can do it right now if you want."

I said, "Great, let's do it now!" We went into their shop, he put the instructions into the computer and in less than 5 minutes the LRI letters had been cut out automatically for a whole $18! I was going to take it to Dan in the morning and I assumed Scott would have a fit.

I also changed my airplane reservations, because we were almost certainly going to be done with the launch preparations a day or two early and I didn't want to sit around Florida over Christmas. I was going to try to get home the 23rd and I hoped I would not have to change the reservations back again.

Tuesday, December 16, 1997: The Rollback and No LRI Decal

I got up early and drove out to Pad 46 to see the rollback of the gantry. It was cold as hell and it took quite a while. They didn't even get started with the rollback preparations until about 9:30 AM. When they finally got going, it took a while because they had trouble getting the gantry doors open, but finally they got the gantry rolled back. The rocket was really impressive — of course, the shroud and payload were missing, but it was impressive seeing it standing there.

After the roll out, Roger McNamara called from Denver because the launch dispersion analyses were all finished and they had found we could tolerate a launch window of a few minutes duration, rather than requiring an exactly-on-time-launch. That was a relief, because, for example, a few days earlier an Atlas launch was delayed 10 or 20 minutes because some airplane was flying around the Cape! We had, of course, been concerned we could lose every launch opportunity if we needed an exactly on-time-launch, because the range frequently had small problems, like the errant airplane, that could be corrected in a few minutes.

I called Dougherty and Sylvia to tell them about our being able to tolerate a launch window a few minutes long and Sylvia said she didn't want to bother Scott with that news, because Huntsville had again said the launch vehicle was a "probable catastrophic failure," so she and Scott had that battle to fight — would the NASA indecision about the launch vehicle never end?

Then I saw Dan Lebel and he said sheepishly, "I'm not allowed to put your decal on the rocket."

Not surprised, and knowing the answer, I asked, "Who said so?" He admitted it was Ames. He would not say any more, but I know it was Scott's doing. I would find out later from someone else, probably Sylvia, if Scott had refused to have the LRI decal on the rocket. Clearly Scott's activities against me had gotten to the point where they were not funny any more.

Given Scott's latest crap, I had had it, so I talked to Karen, Pat, and some other people about getting Scott thrown off the mission. Karen was going to try to get a meeting with her family friend and local Congressman, Weldon, who is on the Space Science Committee. But I was just going to keep my mouth shut for the moment and save the decal crap along with all the other crap Scott had pulled until after launch — then I was going to drop the bomb. Somehow, perhaps with congressional help, I was going to get rid of Scott.

Rebecca called, because our formal invitation to the launch had arrived from NASA. Of course, there was no mention of the PI or LRI and that was intolerable.

Wednesday, December 17, 1997

I got in early and was in the highbay while Tony Soto and his guys were doing their part of the work on the TLI Stage, i.e., they were preparing the lower ring of the TLI Stage so it could be lowered onto — and explosively bolted to — the top of the Athena II rocket adapter. Unfortunately, it took all day, so we really didn't get anything done and we were going to have to wait to stack the next day.

That put me in a quandary, because I wanted to be there when we stacked, but Karen had gotten me invited to go on a Navy ship out in the Atlantic to watch the last battle readiness firing of a Trident ICBM from a submarine that her English Navy boyfriend was on — a once in a lifetime opportunity vs. another once in a lifetime opportunity!

Karen brought the two Navy guys to Astro Tech and I showed them the spacecraft. Other than that, I was tired and I was annoyed with Scott.

Thursday, December 18, 1997: A Submarine and a Trident

Well, the sub and the Trident won out over stacking. I met Karen at the pier early in the morning and we went on board the Navy vessel with a number of VIPs — Congressmen, Navy Brass, and the wives of the Navy personnel on the sub. It was an all day affair and quite interesting.

The best part was, of course, when the sub surfaced just before the Trident launch and then went under again. Suddenly, the Trident popped out of the water, ignited, did a quick turn to a nearly horizontal position for a second and returned to a vertical flight path — that surprising turn was clearly a safety maneuver to stop the Trident from falling back onto the sub if the Trident failed right after ignition.

Once it was vertical again, the Trident tore off at a very high rate of acceleration and with an exhaust flame that was so bright it hurt your eyes. After what was to me a short 1st stage burn, the 2nd stage ignited and the thing tore along its arched flight path faster and faster. Then there was a repeat performance by the 3rd stage. Compared to the very fast burns of the Trident, the Atlas Centaur I had watched and my Athena II moved at a snail's pace.

The cruise back to the port was anticlimactic and I was tired after being on the ship all day — but it was a fun day.

Friday, December 19, 1997:
The Encapsulation — Saying Goodbye to Lunar Prospector

When I got into Astro Tech in the morning, I was told they had trouble the day before with one of the TLI Stage circuits. The circuit was really OK; the problem was in the ground support equipment. But by the time they had figured it out, they were behind schedule. We still had to put all the ordnance on the TLI Stage, as well as the spin-up rockets. Finally all of that was finished and everything was secured. Then there was a big flap about the ordnances, because there was some discrepancy in the paperwork and that slowed everything down. By the time we got everything done, it was about 5:00 PM and of course, Tony Soto and his crew, who were there to put the shroud on the Spacecraft/TLI Stage stack, had been standing around complaining all day. However, when we had to wait on them all day, because they took forever to mount the TLI Stage onto their adapter TLI — that was a horse of a different color!

Finally we were ready; we took all the red covers off the sensors. Dave Curtis put the high voltage enable plug in the MAG/ER and we checked it out. With that, everything had its final check — the next time Lunar Prospector was turned on, it would be on its way to the Moon! Then we took the red covers off the APS — they were the last red covers to come off.

At that magical point in time, Lunar Prospector was totally finished — it was flight ready — and we turned the spacecraft and the TLI Stage over to Tony and his Athena crew. Our job at the Cape was done; from that point on, my crew and I were spectators. Lunar Prospector and the TLI Stage were ready to be encapsulated in the Athena shroud and Tony and his crew started their work. However, due to the late hour, my crew and I went to supper.

By the time we got back from supper at about 7:00 PM, they had connected the spacecraft umbilical to the umbilical extension going through the Athena II adapter, they had removed all the catwalks that surrounded the stand that the payload stack (the spacecraft, the TLI Stage, and the adapter) was mounted on; and they had rolled the payload stack into the air lock. When we got there, they were going through the long checkout procedure. Then they put guide rails on the stand on which the payload stack was sitting. Finally, everything was ready and they slowly hoisted the shroud up and moved it directly over the payload. That was an impressive sight!

Finally, they started the very slow and tedious process of lowering the shroud down over the payload and we were all there watching. It was magical — that was the first of the last three final steps in getting Lunar Prospector into its final launch configuration. That was the encapsulation — the last time I would ever see Lunar Prospector in its entirety. While I would be able to look in through the small door in the shroud, down by the TLI Stage, and see a little bit of Lunar Prospector after it was encapsulated, I would never be able to see all of it again — I would never again be able to walk around it and see it from all sides.

They got the shroud on the guide rails and, slowly but surely, the shroud started going down and then they checked it. Tim, Francisco, and I watched very carefully to see that the shroud did not hit the science instruments that were, of course, sticking out from the spacecraft very close to the shroud. Slowly but surely, Lunar Prospector disappeared under the shroud — never to be seen again. That was a very poignant moment for all of us who were there and who had worked so hard to design, build, test, and prepare Lunar Prospector for its trip to the Moon.

Finally, at about 12:30 AM, the shroud was completely down on the base of the adapter and all of my crew and I left. The Denver guys still had to bolt the shroud to the adapter and to connect the lines to the pyros that would blow the shroud so it could be ejected. In the morning, they would prepare the shrouded payload for transportation to the launch pad. We were to start taking it to Pad 46 in 24 hours, at midnight.

Thus one great series of events had come almost to an end. For me, watching the shroud being put on Lunar Prospector was the climax of all the years of hard work I had done on the mission. It was absolutely wonderful to sit there, as I watched the spacecraft being encapsulated, and think that my spacecraft was going to the Moon. It was the perfect ending to a great day.

Saturday, December 20, 1997: A Major Athena Crew Screw Up

I was out shopping for some minerals and fossils when I got a call from Kim on my emergency cell phone. The connectors on the shroud, i.e., those for the power lines to the pyros that were used to split the shroud in two pieces, so it could be ejected, did not fit the connectors on the adapter! The two sets of connectors were offset, left to right, from each other by about 15 cm!

Thus, there was no way we were going to take the payload to the rocket that night and put it on the rocket the next day. The Athena crew had to fix the mess and we were back to taking the payload out to the pad on the 23rd — there went my chance of getting home for Christmas!

I was annoyed. I went to Astro Tech, found Tony, and asked him what in hell was wrong and he repeated what Kim had already told me about the two sets of connectors not being in the right places. I asked, "Haven't you guys ever heard of fit-checking your equipment before you ship it to the Cape?"

Tony did not have a good answer for that simple question and just said, "I guess we should have." Then to make matters worse for them, Tony said, "But don't worry, we had the same problem with the Lewis shroud and adapter, so Denver already has a fix-it-kit that they are flying down here right now."

That did it; I said, "You're telling me, you knew about this problem, but did not fix it before you shipped the shroud down here! And worse, after not fixing it in Denver, you did not even bring the kit to fix it down here? What is the matter with you guys?" There was nothing Tony could say to excuse that kind of blundering and there was nothing more I could say, except, "You had better get it fixed fast and fixed right," and then I left.

Sunday, December 21, 1997: The Fix

Tony Soto and his crew were working on the connectors during the morning, and were finished by the afternoon. We expected to take the payload out to the rocket starting at midnight the next evening.

I postponed my flight home until Christmas Day. We were so close; I couldn't leave and let something get screwed up at that point.

Monday, December 22, 1997:
Two Weeks to Launch — Preparing for the Trip to the Pad

I went out to Astro Tech in the morning. The payload was all encased in plastic.

I went to the Spaceport Florida offices and talked to Ed O'Connor and Karen about future exploration activities, tracking networks, Mars, and the Moon.

When I got back to Astro Tech, the payload was on the truck, ready for its trip to the launch pad.

I went to bed early to get a couple of hours sleep and got up at about 11:00 PM. I left the apartment a little after 11:00 PM and stopped to get some donuts and candy to eat on the long trip to the pad. Then I stopped at McDonald's for a bit of breakfast. I left McDonald's somewhat after 11:30 PM and drove to Astro Tech, arriving just before midnight.

Tuesday, December 23, 1997:
A Midnight Ride to Pad 46 and Stacking the Payload on the Athena II

Shortly after I arrived at Astro Tech, the other guys arrived. There was a lot that had to be done to get ready to roll — we had to get the air flowing into the shroud, the nitrogen purges had to be hooked up to the APS and we had to check everything, so it was about 1:30 AM by the time we got ready to roll.

Transporting a spacecraft to a launch pad is a very interesting event. The distance from Astro Tech to Pad 46 is some 35 km and the trip takes at least 3½ hours — you drive at the pace of a slow trot! Remember, we had a fully fuelled spacecraft, a TLI Stage, a shroud, and an adapter on a big flatbed truck, all worth at least $30 million alone and if they were wrecked — that would prematurely end a $63 million mission! We drove very slowly and very carefully, but that is not even half of the story.

First, we were in a convoy and the lead car was a Florida State Police Car that was driven by a couple of police officers and whose red and yellow warning lights were doing their things. Immediately behind the lead police car was the flatbed truck with the payload. Next was an emergency truck, with spare tires and every spare part imaginable for the flatbed truck. Then came the car with Tim, Kim, Ralph (if I remember correctly), and me. Behind us another car followed with more of my Lockheed crew and finally a second Florida State Police Car, with its warning lights flashing, guarded the back of the convoy.

Second, part of our trip was along Florida highways and part was, of course, on roads within the military complex that make up Cape Canaveral. Well, when you are in a convoy with a spacecraft in tow, you are the master of the road and you drive right down the middle of that road — not on the right-hand side. All on-coming traffic has to pull completely off the road and no one can pass the convoy. If an on-coming driver does not get completely off the road or if some one tries to pass the convoy — they are arrested on the spot! Taking a spacecraft to its launch pad is serious business at the Cape.

Third, because of the slow pace and the need for caution, we stopped 4 times to give the drivers (and the rest of us) a rest break, to make sure everybody was awake and to check the payload to see if everything was OK.

That nighttime, slow motion trip from Astro Tech to Pad 46 was for me, one of the most memorable parts of the entire launch preparation activities. I will never forget the feelings I had, as we slowly drove along those dark Florida highways, with lights flashing, carrying my spacecraft to its launch vehicle. It was just grand.

We got to Pad 46 when it was still dark, so we had to wait until daylight before the pad technicians could get ready to lift the payload off the truck and put it on top of the rocket. While we were waiting, we tried to get some breakfast, but no place was open.

Around 8:00 AM, the Athena technicians started getting the crane hooked up to the payload and then they chased all of us out of the launch pad area! Everybody in our group was royally ticked off about that. We had to go behind the fence that surrounds the entire complex, so we were a couple of hundred meters from the Athena II and our payload. Ralph Fullerton was especially ticked off and said, "Who do they think they are, it's our God damned hardware!" — one more strike against the Athena organization!

Understandably, Karen had to come out to see and film the stacking of the first payload that was using the launch pad she had built. Bob Mellor was the head of Lockheed's Athena office at the Cape, and he had bitterly fought with Karen many times about the pad she was trying to build and that Lockheed wanted to take advantage of at Spaceport Florida's expense. When Bob saw she was there, he about had a conniption fit. You could see his face turn about six colors of red. He was going to try to make her leave and I said, "Bob, I invited her to be here, so she is going to stay," and that ended that.

Well, we were too far away to see much and too far away for Karen to film the event, so we entertained ourselves by periodically looking at a big alligator that was lying a few meters from where we were standing. Since we were all tired and very hungry (my donuts and candy had disappeared much earlier) and since it took the Athena crew a long time to get ready to stack the payload, we soon got bored, watching the tedious stacking and the alligator got bored since he could not eat one of us.

Nevertheless, we had to wait, because, as soon as they were done stacking, Danny Everett and I had to go up the gantry and put the protective red covers and purge back on the APS (we had removed them when we had arrived at the pad, so the crane could lift the payload off the truck), and Kim had to check out the electrical connections to the umbilical, so we could start monitoring the temperature and voltage of the battery and the pressure and temperatures of the tanks.

The stacking dragged on and on and as 9:00 AM approached, they were still fooling around. By that time, Francisco had left to catch his airplane home and a few others of our crew decided that enough was enough, so they had also left because they too were trying to get home for Christmas and good old, unreliable Kim had also left for parts unknown.

Finally, at about 9:00 AM, the payload was stacked, but before we could go up the gantry, they had to bring down all kinds of stuff from the gantry, using the crane. Before that got started, there was another delay, because one of the doors to the electronics in the Orbit Adjustment Module didn't fit. They had to modify the bolts to make them fit! I wonder if the Denver fools ever fit-checked any damn piece of equipment!

When the door was fixed, we learned that the damned crane crew had gone off for lunch! We waited around for an hour and then we were told it would be another hour before they would be back! They still hadn't come back by 11:00 AM, so Danny, one of our technicians, Chris Boyle, and I, who were the only ones left from our crew, decided we would go get some lunch (remember, we had had no breakfast). We assumed that the crane crew would have gotten back and would have finished their work by the time we got back from lunch. Well, we got back at 12:15 PM and the damned crane crew still was not there!

Finally, they got back; they had been gone at least 3 hours for lunch! Just when the crane crew was finished and they were starting to get their damn crane out of the way, a cherry picker came in and started puffing black smoke all over the place, especially into the air intake for the air-conditioning unit that was supposed to be pumping clean, dehumidified, cool air into the shroud to protect the spacecraft and the instruments!! I shouted, "STOP!" and I immediately called Bob Mellor, crabbed about the cherry picker's black smoke vehemently and said, "You know, I cannot start the APS purge and finish the APS until that thing is out of here."

Bob said, "Well, we have to do some repair work on the umbilical tower with the cherry picker," so we had to wait again! Happily, they got started quickly and finished quickly.

Nevertheless, it was 2:00 PM before they got the hell out of our way. Danny, Chris, and I went up the gantry, hooked up the APS purge, and then opened the door to the spacecraft and Danny and I looked in.

That was the last time I would ever see any part of my spacecraft. We took some pictures of it and Danny put the protective red covers on the APS detectors.

We began to worry a little, because there was a pretty strong air-conditioning wind in the shroud that could damage the thin APS light foils once the red covers were taken off before launch. Well, there was nothing we could do about it then.

Also, we had to insure that none of the 10 red covers, if dropped, could fall down onto the rocket, where you could never get to it. If that happened, they would have to de-stack the rocket, find the offending red cover and then re-stack the rocket. Each cover had a lanyard to secure it to something solid. We looped the lanyards over the destruct unit, which was still a dummy unit, since the real destruct units would be installed just before launch.

Finally, we were finished and we buttoned up the door and got the hell out of there — it was a little after 3:00 PM!

As we came down the gantry, there was that damned crane again and it was puffing out all kinds of exhaust smoke. I told someone, "We can't have that (exhaust) sucked into the air conditioning and into the shroud. It will wreck the ER and probably not do anything else any good. Shut the air-conditioning off until that damn crane is out of here." In addition to the crane, there was a big emergency truck, a fire truck, and a paramedic van and they were all puffing out smoke. The place was a pigsty! I said, "This stuff has all got to get out of here before you can have the air-conditioning turned on again." That critical issue clarified, I left. To say the least, I was dead tired and disgusted at the lack of care or concern the Athena crew was giving to protecting the spacecraft and the instruments from exhaust contamination.

I called Kim and he said he was going to go out later to do the electrical check out and Chris Boyle would then do the monitoring. I said I would check everything out the next day.

I was tired, hot, sweaty, and dirty — so I headed to my apartment to clean up and rest before I took Karen to dinner to repay her for taking me on the Trident missile launch cruise.

Wednesday, December 24, 1997: Christmas Eve

I went out to Pad 46 to see the launch vehicle for the last time. No one else was there. I climbed up the gantry and looked at the shroud, visualizing my spacecraft in there, waiting patiently to be launched to the Moon. I walked all around the shroud and then, as I descended the gantry, I stopped at each level and walked around that section of the Athena II. When I reached the bottom of the gantry, I walked to the base of the Athena and looked up into the engine bell that was sealed with thick aluminum (?) foil to protect the solid fuel inside the Castor 120 from anything that might ignite it (a particularly good idea, since I was standing right under the engine bell). In my mind's eye, I imagined what it would be like to be there (of course with superhuman powers to protect me) in less than two weeks, when ignition occurred and the exhaust would come screaming out of that engine bell and lift the Athena II off the pad, starting Lunar Prospector on its long journey to the Moon. Clearly, that was another very poignant moment for me and it was my last goodbye to Lunar Prospector before launch. The next time I had any connection with it, it would be electronic, not physical.

After my saying goodbye to Lunar Prospector, Kim was supposed to have met me so we could get the equipment set up to monitor the battery and the tanks. Of course, he had not done that the day before, because, as usual, the cables he had made were wrong! Also, as usual, the SOB kept Chris Boyle and me waiting for a good hour and a half while he dallied around before deciding to come to the trailer where we were waiting for him. Finally he came and we got everything hooked up. If I had my way, I would (again) have fired Kim on the spot.

I went back to the trailer that afternoon and Chris was taking data. The tank pressure had dropped to 438.8 psi, because the temperature was down to 18° C — a cold front had moved into the Cape.

I went to the apartment and got everything ready to leave the Cape the next morning to go home to my sweet Rebecca. I would be very glad to get home.

Thursday, December 25, 1997: Christmas Day, Flying Home

Once before in my career, many years earlier, I had flown home Christmas Day and the airplane was essentially empty. When I drove to the Orlando Airport, I expected the same. Boy was I wrong. Sometime in the intervening years, the airlines must have gotten tired of flying empty planes on Christmas Day and cut the airfares so that non-Christians would fill the seats. The airplane was chock-full of Chinese, Indians, and others of different religions and, of course, one happy atheist who had a spacecraft poised to go to the Moon.

Finally, I arrived at the San Jose Airport where Rebecca was waiting to pick me up. We drove down to Gilroy and enjoyed what was left of Christmas day and each other.

Chapter 3-44
Waiting to Launch

Friday, December 26, 1997: The Rocket Again

I got a call from Dave Lozier, who said the Denver idiots (my term, not Dave's) reported the Athena had a 7 m/sec over-burn instead of the 10 m/sec under-burn they had told us just before we did the final ballasting! Thus we had to deal with a total over-burn of 17 m/sec! The stupid asses didn't know what in hell they were doing.

Despite my great annoyance, by design, we could ballast out the grand total of 17 m/sec of over-burn relatively easily. Since we had planned to be able to ballast out the differences in the TLI ΔV required as a function of launch date, we had a place on the TLI Stage where we could add the date-of-launch ballast at any time. It would be a pain in the neck, but it could be done without too much difficulty. However, while we could correct for an over-burn that way, if Denver had come up with an under-burn of that magnitude, we would have been screwed. At least they fouled up in the right direction!

Saturday, December 27, 1997

I got a call from Ralph Fullerton; there was another discrepancy report I had to sign off on. The report was necessary because Lockheed had changed their rules on "metal heritage" and it turned out we didn't know the heritage of the little bit of metal we had in Lunar Prospector and in the struts between the TLI and the spacecraft. I had to sign off on that — what a waste of time.

Sunday, December 28, 1997: A Critical TLI Timer Problem

Kim called and I told him what to do about ballasting up to correct for the 17 m/sec burn error Denver had so nicely given us as a Christmas present. Also, Chris Boyle had talked to Irv and jokingly told him that the tank pressure was down to 300 psi — that was no time to be joking. Chris said that there was a problem with the "safe and arm" of the TLI timer. Because of Chris's bad joke about the tank pressure, Irv didn't know if he should believe Chris about the "safe and arm" problem or not. I asked Kim about that and unfortunately, it was no joke. It was quite serious and had to be taken care of.

The problem was that the damn TLI timer was not getting armed properly and Kim had been working on it all day. If the TLI timer could not be armed, then we couldn't launch — or worse, if we thought it was armed and it wasn't, then of course, the TLI Stage would never fire and we would lose the mission. Kim had Thiokol working on the problem and they were either going to get a new safe and arm device or else they would try to jack up the voltage on the ground support equipment to get the damned thing to arm. In any case, he said they were going to get it armed and, "Once we get it armed and verified, we are not going to disarm it again, since there are other safety features that take care of the danger of having the spin-up rockets fire on the pad."

Monday, December 29, 1997:
One Week to Launch — No Good TV Coverage

Karen sent me a NASA press release about the activities surrounding Lunar Prospector's launch, and what NASA was planning was absolutely absurd. NASA was planning a pre-launch press conference down at the Cape, which was fine. Then they were going to have the pre-launch coverage on NASA Select TV and an hour after launch, just after the TLI burn, NASA was going to shut off NASA Select! That was just when I would be taking control of the spacecraft and finding out if it was OK or not and starting the critical first few hours of commanding activities! The next news conference was planned only after we were in the lunar mapping orbit and there was nothing planned in between!

That was patently absurd. I saw Scott and asked him what in hell was going on with the NASA TV coverage and press conferences? Scott said we were going to have more coverage than I thought, but then he called later and said he had lost the PR battle. I thought he was lying, but I said, "Well, we have to discuss this."

As far as I was concerned, it was patently absurd not to have Lunar Prospector on the news and give people access to the mission activities. I wanted and expected to have NASA Select TV on whenever we were commanding the spacecraft, so the public could watch us and understand and enjoy the mission. I was absolutely appalled by NASA's lack of interest in the mission and its wanting to deny the public the chance to see it happening, live on TV!

However, much of that was explained by the fact that NASA is not interested in the Moon, rather it wants to spend its resources on getting man to Mars. Anything that might draw attention from Mars to the Moon, is to be suppressed — and suppress the Lunar Prospector PR they did!

We did a SIM of the critical 1st LOI burn.

Tuesday, December 30, 1997:
Six Days to Launch — PR Issues and Screwing LRI

We continued with the SIM that started the day before, i.e., we did the 2nd LOI burn.

We also checked everything in Mission Ops to be sure we were ready for launch that was only six days away.

I went to see Scott late in the afternoon about the PR fiasco. I said, "I'm just floored at the lack of decent TV coverage and decent PR. You and I talked about this in the past and we seemed to be in agreement; what happened?"

Scott answered, "Well you know, NASA has standard ways of doing this and it is out of my hands."

I said, "You know they are throwing away an opportunity to get the public excited and interested in the mission and Discovery!"

Scott asked, "What do you want to do about it?"

I answered, "I don't know, but I'm not going to give up on this."

Scott said, "OK, the best way to start is to have Wes and the Associate Administrator for PR sign off on what you want."

I asked, "How do I pursue that?"

He answered, "Start with Betsy."

I said, "OK, I'll go see Betsy right now," and I left to go see her.

As I was walking over there, Scott called and warned her by saying, "Alan is not happy with the PR plan. He is putting on his PI hat and he wants to change it."

When we started to discuss the PR issue, Betsy said, "Well, NASA is conservative."

I said, "I know that, but you have to understand that NASA does a very bad job at PR. It always has and it always will. We have a chance to change that, at least a little. Look, here is the way this should go PR-wise, starting with the first six hours of the mission. First of all, the launch is irrelevant; America has seen a million launches. We can have the best launch in world, but it's the first six hours after the launch that count. I want the whole first six hours — the spacecraft turn-on, boom deployment, initial turn-on of science instruments, and the 1st mid-course maneuver — that make or break the mission to be on NASA Select (the NASA TV Channel). We need a news conference the next day to report on how the mission is going. The next important thing is the turning on of the high voltages of the science instruments the following night and the 2nd mid-course maneuver, because once all that is done, I have a completely working spacecraft that is on it final course to the Moon — we need that on NASA Select. Then we should have a news conference the next day, because I have a mission ready spacecraft — all my instruments are on and they are working. The third mid-course maneuver, the next day, is not all that important. We may not even do it. If we can get it covered with NASA Select, that would be fine, but it's not necessary. The next critical thing is getting captured in the lunar capture orbit — that is the critical one, if we don't succeed with the capture burn, the mission is over. We need to have that on NASA Select and then we need to have a news conference about that. It would be nice to have the 2nd lunar orbit insertion burn covered by NASA Select, but that's not that critical. Finally, when we burn down into the lunar mapping orbit, we need to be on NASA Select and then have a final news conference. I want four press conferences and, at least, the 4 periods of time when we are on NASA Select. Now I know that NASA's attitude is that people won't watch all that, but they sure are not going to watch if it's not on TV! It's silly for NASA to simply assume that the public is not going to watch it. If we don't have it on NASA Select, how can the networks pick it up? NASA is just excluding this possibility. My experience over the last nine years is that people wanted to see how missions are really done, not just watch the launch. This is what I've been telling people we are going to do and this is what I expect to be able to do. Besides, there are only 26 hours of commanding during the whole seven days until we are in the mapping orbit and you're telling me that NASA can't afford to have NASA Select cover the mission for 14% of the time. That just doesn't make any sense. Most of the time, when I look at NASA TV, it's just showing old pictures of the Earth from orbit, which is a total waste of time."

Betsy agreed with me and I got the impression she had been trying to push for more, but not as much as I wanted. Anyway, I had gotten the ball rolling. Betsy was going to set up a telecon with Doug Isbell at Headquarters the next day. She was quite enthusiastic about my request, so I thought we could get it done.

I also talked to Lisa and she showed me the new Lunar Prospector coffee cup with great pride — the new cup with just Lockheed and Ames on! She said, "Isn't it nice?"

Knowing the answer, I asked, "Is LRI on it?"

She answered, "Well, no."

I said, "Then I'm not interested in it."

She handed me a big box of business cards. I asked, "What's this?"

She answered, "These are your web site business cards," and she handed them to me.

I said, "What am I supposed to do with them? This is not my web site; this is NASA's web site. I didn't approve of this web site. There is nothing on there about LRI or the PI, just NASA. I want to know why LRI is not on any of these things? Was there time to add LRI to the coffee cups, to the web site cards, and, more importantly, to the new posters?" She admitted that there was time to get LRI on the cups and cards, but not on the posters. However, I was sure there was time for that, too, if Scott had wanted it and I told her that. She then admitted that Scott was stopping LRI from being part of anything. In part, Scott was pandering to Lockheed since Lockheed didn't want LRI to be acknowledged. As long as I worked at Lockheed, they could say that Lunar Prospector was a Lockheed mission, but when I left, they didn't want to acknowledge it was an LRI mission, too. Having said that to Lisa, she then admitted that Scott was trying to promote the relationship between Lockheed and Ames, at my expense. What we did not discuss was that, at the same time, Scott was also promoting Scott and NASA at my expense.

Wednesday, December 31, 1997:
Five days to Launch — The End of 1997

I was worried because every time I called the Cape, Chris or Kim said the tank pressure was continuing to drop. I was quite certain the pressure drop was just due to the fact that the spacecraft was getting colder and colder, because of the very cold weather that Florida was having. However, there was also the possibility that we had a leak in the propulsion system and that would have been disastrous. However, the cold front had finally passed and the Cape was warming up. If the tank pressure began to rise as the spacecraft warmed up, I would know I was just seeing the temperature's effect on the pressure and that Lunar Prospector was ready to go — if the pressure *did not start to rise, well* —.

We did a Day 0 SIM and about everything went wrong that could go wrong. First off, we couldn't get the simulator started and when we did, Dan had accidentally left an old file in the computer that had an initial tank pressure of only 207 psi. As such, we had to assume we had a low tank pressure problem with the spacecraft. Goddard reported we had a –23 m/sec TLI velocity error, so we had to do an immediate corrective burn. The burn got delayed because we (really) lost command capability, because JPL broke down. The computer was overloaded and we kept dropping data. But somehow, we got through the SIM. What a way for a SIM to go with only five days left before launch!

A photographer from the *San Francisco Examiner* came and took pictures of the Mission Ops crew and me for an article in that paper. I also had two or three other interviews during the day; so, it was a busy day.

Betsy called and said she was making little progress with Doug Isbell about getting more NASA Select coverage of the mission. She said Doug was reluctant to do so, but I was going to try to talk to him Friday and make him do it.

I was told NASA didn't want people talking about PR issues with Lisa, because she is a contractor (and hence not worthy). Also, NASA did not want Spaceport Florida having any special events. The arrogant SOBs!

I had a number of good interviews with the *San Francisco Examiner*, ABC News, and Public Radio — so the interest in the mission was building up nicely.

Then I was told Lockheed wanted to have a news conference about the launch vehicle right in the middle of the critical boom deployment sequence! I had to put a stop to that nonsense. I was getting so sick of those self-serving bastards.

Thursday, January 1, 1998: Four Days to Launch — New Year's Day

Rebecca and I celebrated the New Year by just relaxing and enjoying the calm before the storm.

Friday, January 2, through Early Saturday Morning, January 3, 1998: Three Days to Launch — No PR and a Dress Rehearsal SIM

We got up at 4:00 AM and I took Rebecca to the San Jose Airport so she could fly to the Cape to see the launch along with her sister, Shirley. I dropped her off at the airport and then I went to Mission Ops.

I finished putting the Mission Profile in its final form, printed it, and distributed it to the Mission Ops Team and the engineers who were going to support the early part of the mission.

There was no one around Mission Ops, Ames or Lockheed at that early hour, so I drove back to Gilroy to take a nap. But then Ames PR called because Channel 5 TV wanted an interview. I drove back up to Ames and did it. Then I had calls from three different newspapers and I did those telephone interviews.

I called Doug Isbell to talk about the Lunar Prospector coverage on NASA Select. He was against any real coverage. I told him people wanted to see the mission activities and he snottily asked, "Who have you been talking to, space groupies?"

I answered, "No, I've been talking to a lot of people." Well, no matter what I said, he would not give me any more than the few hours of NASA Select after the launch, i.e., through boom deployment. According to him, the public had no interest in the mission! What an idiot and what a great PR person — instead of trying to get the most PR possible, he was seeing to it that there was no PR! I was amazed, but NASA just did not want the American public to participate in the mission. There was nothing I could do about it and I had no more time to try to do anything about it, so I washed my hands of it — I did not have the time to fight the idiots.

I checked into a motel right next to Ames — I had to be within minutes of Mission Ops during the pre-launch activities and, of course, after launch and for the first week of the mission, i.e., until we were safely in our mapping orbit.

We started a dress rehearsal SIM in the evening and it went extremely well. We were finished with the SIM at about 1:00 AM Saturday morning (we were shifting over to the night work schedule we would be on through LOI) and the SIM seemed to be almost the real thing, since we were less than three days to launch.

Things couldn't have been better if it weren't for Lockheed and NASA, but —.

Saturday, January 3, through Early Sunday Morning, January 4, 1997: Two Days to Launch — The Communications SIM

We did the final communications SIM, starting at launch time and running into Sunday morning. It went well. We were all set to go.

Sunday, January 4, 1997: One Day to Launch — A Little of Everything

There was a nice piece on CNN about Lunar Prospector. Of course, nothing was said about LRI or the PI, as was to be expected.

There was a good article on the mission in the *San Francisco Chronicle*.

The launch crew started their 34-hour countdown at 7:31 AM PST. Things were moving ahead. If the weather held, we would be on our way.

Bill Feldman and I went for a great lunch at the Hoffbrau House.

NASA held its Pre-launch Press Conference at the Cape with Wes, Scott, Joe Boyce, and other NASA bigwigs. Rebecca and Shirley were there and were outraged that, except for Wes, no one, especially Scott, mentioned the PI or LRI — Lunar Prospector was presented as a normal NASA mission with Lockheed playing the normal contractor role. Oh, how quickly they forgot what Discovery was all about; it was just three short years since the selection of Lunar Prospector as the 3rd Discovery Mission was announced. Only Wes said that, without the persistence of the PI, the mission would never have happened and they would not be holding the Pre-launch Press Conference. However, when asked if NASA had any follow-up plans for the Moon after Lunar Prospector, Wes gave the standard NASA answer to that question, "No, there are no follow-up plans."

There was a feeding frenzy by the local press when they found out via the press conference that I was at Ames and not at the Cape. I had about ten interviews with various TV, newspaper, and radio people. When I showed them Mission Control, the TV people were extremely impressed and interested and asked, "How can we get a live TV feed from Mission Ops?" So much for Doug Isbell's lying BS.

Since there was a Lockheed TV guy and an Ames PR guy there who were really excited and enthusiastic about the mission, I said to them, "The networks want a TV feed and NASA is not planning to give them one. Can you try to get a feed, so the public can watch us doing Mission Ops?" They said they would try, but they also failed!

We were in Mission Ops at 11:00 PM, 18½ hours from launch, finishing our final Day 1 SIM, i.e., when I turned on the high voltages of the GRS, NS, and ER; I wanted to do that, since Bill Feldman hadn't had much of a chance to practice that.

After finishing the SIM, just before midnight, we all went out for pizza and a cake that Ken Galal brought. We had a lot of fun.

I told Bill about the problems with Scott and that I was going to have him thrown off the project; he had talked to Rebecca earlier and he knew something was up. Bill said that he, too, was concerned about Scott, because Scott and Bob McMurray had published papers that Bill thought Scott had plagiarized from articles Bill and I had written. Bill had other serious concerns about Scott, so I was not the only one who wanted him out.

Chapter 3-45
Launch Day

Monday, January 5, 1998: Launch Day

I was up at 6:00 AM; there were less than 11½ hours to go.

Lots of TV coverage about the NASA/Ames and Lockheed's Lunar Prospector Mission to the Moon. No mention of LRI or the PI!

It was raining down at the Cape.

The Athena II countdown had progressed flawlessly and continued to do so as the day dragged on.

Right after lunch (lunch, not launch), we began assembling at Mission Ops to prepare for launch and Mission Ops. I made sure everyone who was needed at Mission Ops had a copy of the correct Mission Profile. Dan — my Dynamics controller, Paul Travis — my Uplink Controller, John Kohli — my Communications Controller, and I — the Mission Director — settled into our Mission Ops chairs, turned on our computers, and brought up our spacecraft monitoring screens.

My Ames Nav Team — Dave Lozier, and Ken Galal, my Lockheed Engineering Support Team — Woody, Jim Schirle, Irv, Gerry Grismore, and Steve Honodel, and my Science Instrument Support Team — Bill Feldman and Dave Curtis, all took up their positions in front of the auxiliary computers outside the glassed-in Mission Ops room, where they could watch us and I could call for their assistance if or when I needed them. Marcie, Dougherty, and the rest of my controllers, all of who wanted to be there for the launch and the first few hours of critical mission activities, were also there.

We checked out our headphones and mikes. Dave and Ken checked in with the Goddard Nav Team. Marcie and John Kohli checked with JPL on the status of DSN and the ground communication network that linked us to JPL and the DSN. I checked the phone line between Kim at the Cape and me.

There were a number of spectators — members of my Lockheed Engineering Team, who were not part of the Mission Ops Support Team, and Ames personnel — in the Mission Ops outer room, but they were not allowed in the half of the room that was cordoned off where my support teams were working. In addition, Ames had an open house at the main Ames auditorium, where other Lockheed and Ames personnel, plus the interested public could watch the launch and post-launch activities.

The MET (Mission Elapsed Time) clock above one of the computers, just outside the Mission Ops Glass Room, but right in front of me, was ticking down the time to spacecraft turn-on, i.e., at 000/00:00 (000 Days: 00 Hours: 00 Minutes).

We were ready to go and I had the Mission Profile opened to page 1, on which I had already checked off the first Mission Ops event — the establishment of the communication link with the Cape that had occurred the day before at –001:10:57 MET (7:31 AM PST) when the Athena II count down had begun and I was ready with my red pen to check off the rest of the events of the mission and to take command control of my spacecraft.

It was approaching 2:46 PM PST January 5 (22:46 GMT January 5 or –000/03:42 MET); we were almost 2 hours and 45 minutes from launch and ready for the first flight readiness poll.

–000/03:42 MET, I polled Mission Ops, Goddard, and JPL — red check.

–000/03:32 MET, Kim polled me — red check.

–000/03:27 MET, the Launch Director polled Kim — red check.

I asked Kim what the tank pressure and temperatures were and he told me the pressure was 438.3 psi and temperatures were 20° C; I wrote those data in red in my Mission Profile. We continued to sit, watching the launch preparations at the Cape on a TV that was sitting just outside the Glass Room, and waited and listened.

Then, an hour and a half later, one hour before launch, Kim called and said, "The launch has been scrubbed until tomorrow! A Range Safety Radar went down and they cannot get it fixed in time to support the launch." Just like that and totally unexpected, our first launch attempt had been scrubbed!

I told the people in Mission Ops the disappointing news and told my crews to throw away the Mission Profile for that day, because I did not want anyone to mix it up with the new one I would give them for the next day's launch attempt. I also asked most everyone to leave Mission Ops, so my Ops and Nav crews could get ready for the next day's launch effort. I then asked Paul to reset the MET clock for the next day's launch, which he did — the clock then indicated we were again about 26 hours from launch!

I, like everyone else, was very disappointed about the scrub, but that was why we had backup launch dates. However, if we didn't get launched the next day, we would have to wait until February, a prospect that I did not want to think about. Nevertheless, though I certainly wanted to have launched, I was not too disappointed about the one-day delay — there was a silver lining!

Though I had told no one, the next day's launch opportunity was better than the one we had just scrubbed. Had we launched right then, Lunar Prospector would have had nighttime passes of several minutes duration immediately upon having achieved its mapping orbits and those nighttime passes would have increased rapidly to a maximum of 47 minutes as the mission proceeded. While that posed no problem — after all, Lunar Prospector was designed to endure nighttime passes of more than 50 minutes duration as a regular part of the mission — the situation for the next day's launch was very different. When Lunar Prospector settled into its mapping orbit, it would be in sunlight for all of its 118-minute orbit and it would be several days before the nighttime passes would begin. By launching a day late, I would have several days in lunar orbit to see exactly how the spacecraft's power and thermal subsystems were working, before Lunar Prospector started to undergo the nighttime passes. Though not critical, that would be a nice, smooth way to start the mapping mission.

After leaving Mission Ops, I was asked by the Ames PR people to go to the auditorium where TV and press reporters wanted to interview me and to get my reaction to the launch delay. I talked to several reporters, but the one that stuck in my mind was Stacey Hendler from Channel 7 ABC TV, who asked me what I thought about the delay and I said, "I've been working on this for 9 years, one day doesn't make any difference," which really summed up my attitude. However, when I saw that interview on TV a few hours later, I was surprised at how I looked — there were huge dark circles under my eyes and I looked like I was exhausted — despite the slight smile on my face. In fact, I was exhausted, but, as I did during the exhaustive Discovery proposal effort over three years earlier, I was living on adrenalin and I had been doing so for weeks. I was simply not aware of the fatigue — at least, not until I saw myself on TV.

After the interviews were done, I decided to drive home to Gilroy and sleep in my own bed, instead of sleeping in my motel room. I wanted to get as good a night's sleep as possible in preparation for our next attempt to launch Lunar Prospector to the Moon.

PART FOUR

The
Lunar Prospector Mission

January 6, 1998
through July 31, 1999

Chapter 4-1
Launch and the
First Nine Hours of the Mission

Tuesday, January 6, through Early Morning,
Wednesday January 7, 1998

−000/15:30 MET through −000/00:57 MET: Getting Ready

I woke up at about 4:00 AM and, after a coke and donut at the local Gilroy donut shop, I drove up to Mission Ops. I checked the Mission Profile for that evening's launch attempt, made copies of it, and put it next to the various computer consoles in Mission Ops. I checked with the Cape — the Athena II countdown, that had been recycled to T–24 hours the night before, was again progressing smoothly, but the weather was poor — it was raining. The tank pressure was 438 psi and the tank temperatures were all at 20° C and holding. The only concern was the weather.

Later in the morning, I did some TV interviews and waited for the morning to pass. Launch was at 6:28:43 PM PST, an hour later than the day before and we were going to start getting assembled in Mission Ops by early afternoon.

As everyone came in, I made sure they all had a copy of the correct Mission Profile. Then Dan, John, Paul, and I again settled into our Mission Ops chairs in front of our computers and brought up our spacecraft monitoring screens.

My Ames Nav Team, my Lockheed Engineering Support Team, and my Science Instrument Support Team again all took up their positions in front of the auxiliary computers outside the glassed-in Mission Ops room. Marcie, Dougherty, the rest of my controllers, and the other spectators slowly arrived for our second launch attempt.

We again checked our headphones and mikes. Dave and Ken again checked in with the Goddard Nav Team. Marcie and John again checked with JPL on the status of DSN and the ground communication network that linked us to JPL and the DSN, and I again checked the phone line between Kim at the Cape and me.

Finally, I was once again ready, with my red pen, to check off the events of the mission and to take command control of my spacecraft.

At 3:43 PM PST January 6 (23:43 GMT January 6 or −000/03:42 MET, or 2 hours and 45 minutes before launch), we started the first flight readiness poll.

−000/03:42 MET, I polled Mission Ops, Goddard, and JPL — red check.

−000/03:32 MET, Kim polled me — red check.

−000/03:27 MET, the Launch Director polled Kim — red check.

I again asked Kim what the tank pressure and temperatures were and he told me the pressure was 438.8 psi and temperatures were 20° C; I wrote those data in red on my Mission Profile. We again continued to sit, watching the launch preparations at the Cape on TV, and waited and listened.

Two hours before launch, there were concerns about thunderstorms that were over Tampa and that were moving towards the Cape. Range Safety rules dictate that you cannot launch if there are thunderstorms within 16 km of the launch pad. As the count continued, one such storm was moving directly towards Pad 46 and we held our breaths. However, the Gods on Mount Olympus smiled on the little rocket that was try-ing to send its small payload to one of their own, their Moon Goddess Diana, because half an hour before launch, the weather people said the storms were not going to inter-fere with the launch!

At 6:23 PM PST January 6 (02:23 GMT January 7, or –000/01:22 MET, or 0 hours and 25 minutes before launch), we started the critical GO/NO-GO poll.

–000/01:22 MET, I polled Mission Ops, Goddard, and JPL — red check.

–000/01:19 MET, Kim polled me — red check.

–000/01:16 MET, the Launch Director polled Kim — red check.

I again asked Kim what the tank pressure and temperatures were and he told me the pressure was 438.8 psi and temperatures were 20° C; I again wrote those data in red on my Mission Profile.

By then, we were less than 20 minutes to launch and the feeling in Mission Ops was that we were going to launch — no one doubted that in a few minutes, the Athena II was going to lift off Pad 46 and begin its maiden voyage into space, carrying in its shroud Lunar Prospector.

–000/00:57 MET through –000/00:15 MET: The Athena II Launch

At –000/00:57 MET, there were just 22 seconds to lift off. I reminded everyone that I wanted it quiet in Mission Ops — all of it — both inside the Glass Room and outside of it. There was to be no shouting, jumping around, and celebrating the launch — we were there to do a serious job and we had to concentrate on it and not act like a bunch of high school kids, as did the Mars Pathfinder Mission Ops Team when Mars Pathfind-er successfully landed on Mars in July.

Then, as we watched the image of the Athena II on the TV screen, bathed in the glare of the launch-pad lights, the voice on the TV began calling out the final 10 sec-onds: 10-9-8-7-6-5-4-3-2-1-0.

Exactly on time, at T = 0, I saw a small bright light appear at the bottom of the Athena II — we had ignition; that was it — there was no more waiting, no more delays, we were irrevocably committed to launch. Once that 1st Stage Castor 120 started to burn, there was no going back and I was relieved. Good, bad, or indifferent, Lunar Prospector had started its journey to the Moon and there was nothing I could do to change the course of its fate for the next hour. Automatically, it would either get launched onto its proper translunar trajectory, or end up in the Atlantic, or burn up in the Earth's atmosphere after a failed TLI burn, or have such a bad launch that there was no way we could get it to the Moon — all that was out of my hands for a little more than an hour.

All that went through my mind at that instant of ignition. Then, in a fraction of a second, the small bright light grew to an ever increasingly brighter and larger exhaust plume as the Athena II lifted off Pad 46 and my thoughts turned to the acoustical waves that were assaulting my spacecraft. The noise that was being generated by the burning Castor 120, enhanced by its being reflected off the launch pad and back up the Athena II to the spacecraft, was so intense for the first few seconds of the launch that it could have damaged the science instruments and the delicate solar cells of the solar panels. Remembering that some of the delicate APS filters had been torn apart during our acoustic testing, I hoped — and expected — that they, and everything else on the space-craft, would withstand their first acoustical assault of the launch.

Simultaneous with the initial acoustical assault on Lunar Prospector, the infamous pipe organ effect had also started its work of violently shaking the Athena II and Lunar

Prospector — starting at 50 Hz. Though the amplitude of the pipe organ effect was large at the beginning of the burn, the amplitude decreased as the 1st Stage burn continued. Also, its effect was lessened because of the damping effects of the some 20 meters of rocket (the 2nd and 3rd Stages, the Orbit Adjustment Module or OAM, and the TLI Stage) between the top of the screaming 1st Stage Castor 120 and Lunar Prospector. I had little concern about the pipe organ vibrations during the 1st Stage burn, even though, as the burn continued, its frequency slowly increased towards its maximum of 60 Hz at the end of the 1st Stage burn, i.e., up towards the 65 to 70 Hz where the spacecraft did have some major resonances — but if we had done our work correctly, it would pose no problem.

In addition to the initial acoustical assault and the continuing pipe organ vibrations, the winds and the resistance of the Earth's atmosphere also buffeted the Athena II and Lunar Prospector as the rocket struggled to plow its way through the thick lower atmosphere. As the rocket's speed increased, the atmospheric buffeting increased until a crescendo was reached some 74 seconds after lift-off — when the Athena II passed through the sound barrier. As it did, the acoustical level, for the second time, reached an intensity that was great enough, for a few seconds, to damage the spacecraft. Finally, after passing through the sound barrier, the noise and atmospheric buffeting rapidly abated as the Athena II climbed out of the Earth's atmosphere, but the howling gasses inside the Castor 120 continued to shake the spacecraft. Finally, 89 seconds after lift-off, the 1st Stage burn came to its end and I hoped the spacecraft had survived the noise, the buffeting, and the howling of the 1st Stage burn. Also, during that 1½ minute, Athena Launch Control kept informing us, and the world, that the launch trajectory was near perfect!

As the 1st Stage burn trailed off, a sensor detected the end of the burn and sent a critical signal to ignite the Castor 120, 2nd Stage of the Athena II rocket. 2nd Stage ignition occurred while still attached to the 1st Stage. That "Fire in the Hole" ignition had never been done before and, while insuring that the Athena II was under positive attitude control during the transition between the 1st Stage and the 2nd Stage burns, it did pose some danger, since if the exhaust vents between the stages did not blast open at ignition, the back pressure of the igniting 2nd Stage could damage the engine bell and steering mechanism of the 2nd Stage.

Nevertheless, Athena Launch Control called out 1st Stage burnout and 2nd Stage ignition and we could plainly see on the TV screen that the bright exhaust plume (that was all one could see in the dark of the night) of the Athena II, suddenly and very briefly expanded as the exhaust of the burning 2nd Stage splashed off the top of the then dying and separated 1st Stage.

Unlike the 1st Stage burn, where the noise of lift-off, the breaking of the sound barrier, and the buffeting of the atmosphere presented dangers for the spacecraft, the only danger after 2nd Stage ignition was caused by the howling of the hot gasses inside the Castor 120, i.e., the pipe organ effect was at it again. However, unlike the 1st Stage burn, where there were 20 meters of rocket between the top of the burning stage and Lunar Prospector, Lunar Prospector was only 10 meters from the fiercely burning and howling Castor 120, 2nd Stage, so the howling was much more intense at the level of the spacecraft and certainly intense enough so that if there were an error in the design of Lunar Prospector, the consequences could have been serious. Regardless, the 2nd Stage burn began to die-out ninety-two seconds after 2nd Stage ignition or just three minutes and 1 second into the flight. As was the case for the 1st Stage burn, Launch Control kept reporting that we had a good launch trajectory — so far, so good.

After 2nd Stage burnout, the Athena II (minus the 1st Stage) coasted upwards for fifty-seven seconds, during which the shroud was to separate. Remembering that the shroud had failed to separate on the first LLV1 test launch and that the electrical connectors between the shroud and the adapter had had to be fixed by the launch preparation crew just two weeks before launch, I awaited shroud separation with some concern — for if it did not separate, the Lunar Prospector Mission would have, in effect, ended less than four minutes into its launch — the Athena II could not have even reached the parking orbit carrying along the heavy shroud, and even if it could have done so, the TLI Stage, and Lunar Prospector would have been destroyed as they tried to ram through the shroud at TLI Stage ignition. However, 52 seconds into the coast or 3 minutes and 53 seconds after launch, the shroud successfully separated and Launch Control announced the success of that critical event.

Five seconds later, at 3 minutes and 58 seconds into the flight, the two minute and 34 second burn of the Orbus solid fuel rocket 3rd Stage was to have begun. However, when that time came, no one at Athena Launch Control said a word about 3rd Stage ignition, so I thought it had failed to ignite! I immediately asked Kim what the status of the 3rd Stage burn was. It took two or three queries before Kim confirmed that the 3rd Stage was burning as planned — that was a relief! After the violent burns of the 1st and 2nd Stages, the 3rd Stage burn was relatively mild and posed no threat to the spacecraft. The worst of the launch was over. Finally, the Orbus burn came to its end and, throughout the 6½-minute launch, everyone had remained pretty quiet in the Mission Ops, as I had requested.

Immediately after the 3rd Stage burnout, the 7-minute burn of the OAM liquid fuel engines began. That very low thrust burn was made to correct all the errors in the trajectory caused by the relatively crude burns of the first three, solid fuel stages of the Athena II rocket and when the OAM burn was finished, the OAM, the TLI Stage, and Lunar Prospector would start their 42-minute coast in Earth parking orbit, a coast that would bring the stack over the NW coast of Australia to the exact point in time and space where the critical TLI burn was supposed to occur. About 45 seconds after the OAM began its corrective burn, it and the payload went over the horizon with respect to the tracking station and we had LOS (Loss Of Signal) at –000/00:49 MET, as planned. The next time we would hear from Lunar Prospector, it would be at turn-on, assuming it did turn on and assuming TDRS did pick it up.

Thus, we had a little over ¾ of an hour during which we would be in radio silence. I said to my Mission Ops Team and my Support Teams outside the Glass Room, that we had time to go to the bathroom, get a coke and a candy bar or whatever and get prepared for the post-TLI burn activities — our job was about to begin. I was at the head of the pack going downstairs to relieve and refresh ourselves and I went back to the Glass Room in a few short minutes — ready for the main event.

After sitting down at my console, I checked all my screens. The way the Oasis system worked, I could have as many graphs or data tables, each being about 8 cm or so in dimensions, active on my computer screen as I wanted and I could have any number of graphs or data tables activated and stored as little icons — to be called up at a moment's notice. Given the size of my computer screen, I could get 10 or so of the most important graphs on my screen and several others iconized all over the place.

The graphics I absolutely needed to be able to monitor the health of the spacecraft were the battery voltage and current, the load current, the solar array current and temperature, the tank pressure and the temperatures of the 3 tanks (all on one graphic), the temperature of the 6 engines on two different graphs (one from 0 to 150° C to monitor their normal temperatures and the second from 0 to 1300° C to measure their temperatures during the burns), one of two status tables that indicated which subsystems were turned on, and which were turned off, and a command table which told me the status of a command when I sent one.

The data on those graphics were also color coded: green meaning the data were within the normal operational range of the subsystem or it was turned on; yellow meaning the data were getting close to the upper or lower limits of the operational range; and red meaning the data were higher or lower than the operation limits of that subsystem or it was turned off.

The normal status table had the subsystem identified with dark letters, while the status words, On and Off, were in green or red, respectively. However, our SIM training had shown me that if the subsystem identifiers were also color coded, I would not waste precious time reading the table when the spacecraft was first turned on. In a special table — the "Acquisition Status Table" — all the engineering subsystems were written in green, since they were supposed to be turned on during the automatic spacecraft turn-on sequence initiated by the TLI timer and all the science instruments were written in red, since they were supposed to be off until I turned them on. Hence, all I had to do was to quickly glance at the Acquisition Status Table and see if every subsystem that was written in green had a green status word next to it and that each subsystem that was written in red had a red status word next to it — without actually reading any of the words. The Acquisition Status Table would be the first thing I would look at when we started getting data from the spacecraft.

Similarly, Dan was checking his numerous graphs, Paul had his uplink command screen up, and John had a little of everything on his computer screen. We were ready for turn–on.

–000/00:15 MET through +000/00:18 MET: TLI and Turn-On

Fifteen minutes before Turn-On, I polled my Command Team — Dan, Paul, and John; my Engineer Support Team; my Science Support Team; my Nav Team, TDRS, and the DSN to verify that they were all ready to support the mission at spacecraft acquisition and they all responded that they were GO.

At –000/00:10 MET, I issued my first command — though not a spacecraft command, it was the first command of the mission. I ordered the MAG/ER data line from Oasis to the MAG/ER console opened and had it verified 1 minute later.

At –000/00:05 MET, I ordered the Mission Ops recorder for the attitude data to be turned on and I had it verified 1 minute later.

Then, as we had practiced so many times during our Day 0 SIMs, I said to Dan, in a well-rehearsed way, "Dynamics, will you please take over the countdown to the TLI burn sequence?"

Dan answered, "Command, yes I will," and Dan started to count down to the TLI sequence of events that we expected would terminate with Lunar Prospector being inserted onto its Trans-Lunar Trajectory and being turned-on.

Though the Athena crew had wanted to have a tracking airplane flying over the NW coast of Australia and hence, under the TLI ignition point to monitor the final act of the OAM as it spun up our stack to 3.5 rpm, turned on our TLI timer, and separated itself from our stack, we had been told that was not going to happen. Also, when I asked them if the coast-time in the parking orbit was invariant, they had said, "Yes, it's constant." Hence, we expected the TLI events would occur exactly on time, since we had had an exactly on-time launch.

Dan began the count down to the initial spin-up (to 3.5 rpm), the separation of the stack from the OAM, the ignition of the spin-up rockets on the TLI Stage, and TLI Stage ignition, all of which would occur within 1 second of time! However, when Dan reached T minus 10 seconds, a voice came over the line from Athena Launch Control at the Cape saying, "Spin-up and OAM separation."

Dan stuttered and we looked at each other with surprised looks on our faces as we realized, a split second later, that the Athena team did have a tracking airplane under the TLI ignition point and that the coast-time was not invariant! The Athena crew had misinformed us about the launch right to the very last second of the their part of the launch — well, what could I say — well, how about, "Those bastards will never launch a spacecraft of mine again!"

Dan instantly recovered and counted down to the TLI burnout 1 minute later and the subsequent turn-on of Lunar Prospector. While he was doing so, the TLI Stage increased Lunar Prospector velocity by over 3 km/sec during its 1-minute burn!

As Dan was saying, "TLI burnout," the TLI Stage Timer was sending a signal to Lunar Prospector, thereby turning on the C&DH and the transponder's receiver — *after more than 9 years of work, the MET time was finally, 000/00:00!*

Six seconds later, the timer fired the explosive bolts that were holding the spacecraft and the TLI Stage together and essentially simultaneously opened the valves to the 3000 psi nitrogen tanks to blast the spent, but still chugging, TLI Stage safely away from Lunar Prospector. Lunar Prospector was finally free and on its way to the Moon.

One second after separation, the C&DH began its 23 second spacecraft turn-on sequence — safeing the engines and turning the rest of the engineering subsystems on, including the transponder's transmitter (at the 300 bps, engineering-data-only data rate) which immediately began sending Lunar Prospector's first signals — *Lunar Prospector's birth cry* — which were immediately picked up by TDRS!

TDRS immediately said, "We've picked up Lunar Prospector's signals, but we do not have a lock (TDRS could hear the spacecraft, but it could not receive data)."

Upon hearing TDRS's words, I, and everyone else in Mission Ops, knew Lunar Prospector had survived launch and was alive. I was relieved — I had a live spacecraft racing towards the Moon — at least I hoped so. Since Lunar Prospector had been turned on, none of us doubted that the entire TLI sequence had gone off like a charm. However, just hearing the spacecraft was no guarantee that the Star-37 had ignited and accelerated the spacecraft to TLI; we would know that for sure when and if TDRS got a good lock on the spacecraft or when we rose over the Goldstone tracking station 20 minutes later.

The fact that TDRS did not get a lock on the transponder and hence, that we could not get engineering data from the spacecraft, though disappointing, was not surprising, since it was an experiment. However, that minor disappointment was completely offset by my knowing Lunar Prospector was alive! We waited the twenty minutes for Goldstone rise, feeling very sure we had a good spacecraft on its way to the Moon.

As we waited for the spacecraft to rise over Goldstone, TDRS kept trying to get a two-way lock (a two-way lock is when the tracking station, in that case TDRS, sends a highly stable, reference signal to the spacecraft, which locks on the incoming signal and then, using that reference signal, transmits its data back to the tracking station, i.e., the signal goes both to and from the spacecraft) so we could get Doppler data to determine the spacecraft's velocity and to get downlinked data. Finally, I told them to just try to get a one-way lock (a one-way lock is when the tracking station just receives the signals being transmitted by the spacecraft without the use of a reference signal) and that didn't work either.

At 000/00:18 MET, as pre-planned as the spacecraft rose over Goldstone, I told TDRS to stop trying to lock-up on the spacecraft, because we were getting ready for Goldstone to pick us up.

000/00:18 MET through 000/01:10 MET: Goldstone and More Communications Problems

Very shortly after I told TDRS to cease operations, Goldstone, which was using both the 26-meter and the 34-meter antennas to track Lunar Prospector (to insure that we had coverage at the critical beginning of the mission), acquired Lunar Prospector. It was a little before 000/00:19 MET (the expected acquisition-time was 000/00:20 MET and was calculated on the assumption that the spacecraft had to rise a few degrees above the horizon to allow for the disturbing effects of the Earth's atmosphere, but they acquired Lunar Prospector very shortly after it had cleared the horizon). The fact that Goldstone had acquired Lunar Prospector just after it came over the horizon at the pre-calculated rise-time, said loud and clear that we had had a good TLI burn — if not, Lunar Prospector would not have been visible from Goldstone, period! The entire TLI sequence had worked as planned — what a relief!

At 000/00:21 MET, a couple of minutes after Goldstone had acquired Lunar Prospector, Goldstone got a two-way lock and the graphics on Dan's and my computer screens began to come live — Lunar Prospector was saying, *"Hello,"* to its masters!

However, there were data dropouts and data spikes — the data were as erratic as hell! We didn't know what was going on, but we clearly had low signal strength and a poor link. The data on my screen were coming from the 34-meter antenna and Dan was getting his data via the 26-meter dish. Dan started getting readable data first, so I looked over at his screen and it was apparent the spacecraft was in good shape. The spin rate was about 51 rpm, instead of the expected 57±3 rpm, but that was OK. More importantly, there was only a small amount of Dan's dreaded nutation — proving that whole fiasco had been a waste of time, as I had always believed.

Then we both got some more data, though it was still sketchy, with all kinds of dropouts and data spikes. I saw that the engine temperatures were spiking — normally a sign of an inadvertent engine firing, but not in that case, since the temperatures dropped to normal just as suddenly as they would spike. Then I saw that the pressure in the fuel tanks was exactly 438 psi and the tank temperatures were 20° C, just as they were before launch. Finally, the colorful "Acquisition Status Table" came to life and, at a glance, I saw that each green subsystem word had a green status word next to it and each red subsystem word had a red status word next to it — the turn-on had been perfect, so I immediately deleted that critical table; having served its purpose, it was never to be seen again!

Much slower than I liked, we began to piece more and more data together and, though the data were very erratic, we could see that all the subsystems were in perfect shape.

Goddard reported, based on very preliminary Doppler data, that our TLI velocity error was an amazingly low +1±2 m/sec, which meant we had essentially a perfect launch, and that took off some of the pressure of our communications problem — we did not need do an emergency corrective burn, we were right on target trajectory-wise.

After just a few minutes, we knew the spacecraft was in excellent shape and we had had a near perfect launch. Both of those things were very good to know, since I could not start sending commands until we were getting reliable engineering data, i.e., I was not in a position to try to do the safe-engine-verification and PIV open sequences until we had a good communications link (or com-link). We had to find out what was wrong with our communications!

We knew, of course, that the spacecraft was in its TLI burn attitude and hence Goldstone was looking nearly up the butt of the spacecraft, where the omni antenna pattern had a null point, i.e., right then, we had a very bad communication aspect angle. Nevertheless, we still thought there should be enough signal coming from the back of the spacecraft to gives us a good link. Since the aspect angle would get worse for a while and then start to get better as Lunar Prospector rose higher above the Earth, we expected the signal strength would start to improve within an hour, if that were the cause of the com-problem. Since the spacecraft and the trajectory were both in excellent condition, there was no rush to start commanding — time was on our side.

However, as soon as I had seen the erratic link, I asked John to find out what was wrong. Shortly after Goldstone had acquired the spacecraft, John had heard someone say on the com-network (or com-net), "We have a good lock," and he had immediately reported to me when I asked about the link's status. Since we had a good lock, I assumed the com-problem might be in the ground lines between Goldstone, JPL, and us and I asked John to check that out. I also asked Marcie, who had more experience than John with the com-net and the DSN, to come into the Glass Room and assist John — and Dougherty, who was greatly concerned, trouped in with Marcie, uninvited. The three of them were trying to find out what was going wrong with our com-link.

Unfortunately, the person who had said on the com-net, "We have a good lock," was not from the DSN, rather from TDRS! Even though I had told TDRS to cease operations at Goldstone rise, they kept trying to establish a lock on Lunar Prospector, which they finally did after they widened their frequency sweep. They had been using too narrow a frequency sweep to acquire Lunar Prospector during the 20 minutes they were supposed to be on line and achieved lock only after it was too late and that had caused confusion on John's and my parts. Since we thought the DSN had said they had "a good lock," (the only logical conclusion, since TDRS was supposed to be off line), I made the logical conclusion that we had a ground line problem, so I sent Marcie and John off on a wild goose chase. Had I known that the DSN *did not* have a stable lock on Lunar Prospector, I might have started looking in the right place for the source of our com-problem, instead of thinking about bad ground lines and poor aspect angles.

As a result, as Marcie and John found there were no ground line problems and as the improvement in the communication aspect angle did not reduce the data dropouts to an acceptable level an hour into the mission, it was clear I had to try to take command control of the spacecraft, before Lunar Prospector's increasing distance from Earth made the com-problem even worse.

I said to my Ops Team, "OK, let's get ready to send the safe-engine-verification-sequence," and John made a brilliant suggestion, for which I will forever be thankful to him.

John said, "Why don't you try sending a NOOP Command first" (we had two commands that I could send to the spacecraft that did absolutely nothing, hence the name NOOP, which is short for No-Operation, and hence I could see if commands were getting to the spacecraft without risking anything unfortunate).

I said, "John, that's a great idea; thanks a million!"

I quickly looked up the NOOP1 Command, its hexadecimal identification number and its VCID number, added the new command sequence to my Mission Profile with the red pen I used to check off the Mission Profile events and to modify the Mission Profile in real-time. I then asked Dan and Paul to verify that I had the correct command and identifier (we always did at least a triple check on every command that we sent to the spacecraft) and they did. *I was ready to take command control of Lunar Prospector and send it its first command.*

Then I turned to Paul and said, "Uplink, please prepare the NOOP1 Command for uplink."

Paul answered, "Yes Command." When he was ready, a few minutes before 000/01:08 MET, Paul said, "Command, I'm ready with NOOP1."

I said, "OK, send it on my mark in 20 seconds," and I began my well-practiced countdown, "20 seconds, 10, 5, 3, 1 and 0."

Paul immediately said, "Command away."

I watched the command table on my computer screen in anticipation of getting the echo of the command that the spacecraft would send back down to Earth after the C&DH had verified it was a valid command in its command table. The echo would appear in one or two data frames (32 or 64 seconds, depending on where the C&DH was in its 32 second frame cycle when it received the uplinked command). Then the hexadecimal numbers 640000 and 06 appeared on my screen and I said in my well-practiced way, "I have echo of 6-4-0-0-0-0, VCID of 0-6, both are correct for the NOOP1 Command. Paul, please execute the command on my mark at 000/01:08 MET."

Paul replied, "Affirmative."

At the appropriate time I began with, "20 seconds, 10, 5, 3, 1 and 0."

And Paul immediately said, "Command away."

A frame or two later I saw a CCA1F5 and 09 appear on my computer screen (the hexadecimal identifier and VCID of EXEC — the Execute Command) and I said, "I have Execute." Lunar Prospector had accepted, verified, and executed my first commands — I was ready to start taking control of the spacecraft, despite the numerous data dropouts. It was about 000/01:10 MET.

000/01:10 MET through 000/02:50 MET: The Initial Commanding and the Final Solution to the Communication Problem

Though we had the successful command test with the NOOP1 Command, I was in no rush to send the safe-engine-verification-sequence. We needed to be able to see if any of the engines heated up during the 5 seconds the PIV would be open during the tests, and the dropouts and data spikes were so numerous I could not be sure we could tell if we had a problem or not. We watched the data for another 10 minutes or so and then I told my Ops Team and the Engineering Support Team I was going to proceed with the engine test and I needed all eyes, especially Irv's eyes, on the engine temperature graphs to make sure we did not miss seeing an engine heat up amidst all the data spikes and data dropouts.

I then asked Paul to prepare to uplink the PIV Open Command and the file with EXEC, a 5 second wait, PIV Close, and an immediate EXEC. When Paul was ready, I had him uplink the PIV Open Command and I soon saw the command echoes, 5000AB and 06, on my screen, I read them off, verified them and then I said, "Send the file on my mark at 000/01:26 MET," and began my usual countdown.

Paul said, "Command away."

I watched for the echo of the EXEC and the moment I saw it, I said, "I have Execute — everybody watch the engine temperatures," and with one eye on the engine temperature graphic and the other on the command screen, I waited to see any rise in any engine temperature and for the echoes of the PIV Close Command and the EXEC. While those two echoes came very quickly, the engine temperatures remained constant, except for the dropouts and data spikes. We waited nearly twenty minutes to be sure we had not missed anything and/or for the com-link to get a little better (which it did not do) as the aspect angle continued to improve.

Finally, everyone agreed there were no engine leaks, so I prepared to open the PIV. I again asked everyone to watch the engine temperatures — even though the engine test had shown that none of the engines was fully on, one or more engines could have slow leaks that we would only notice after the PIV had been opened for several minutes, not just for 5 seconds. Then I had Paul uplink the PIV Open Command and, after having verified the echo, I had him uplink the EXEC at 000/1:46 MET. I saw and called out the Execute echo and watched the engine temperatures. Again the temperature remained normal. We were ready to reorient the spacecraft by 90°, to an SEA of –25°. Then the Earth would be in the best part of the omni antenna pattern — hopefully that would solve our com-problem — and the boom canisters could warm up in preparation for the critical boom deployment.

I told everyone we were going to do the 1st reor maneuver in the Mission Profile and I asked John to watch the downlink signal strength as we did the maneuver, expecting that our com-problem would cease once we got the spacecraft reoriented.

I asked Dan to select the appropriate pre-prepared reorientation maneuver file for the reor maneuver we had decided on. Given that there were not yet enough data for Dan to have determined the spacecraft's attitude accurately, that we had never fired the engines before, and that the file for this reor, by necessity, was pre-prepared, we did not expect, nor require, that the maneuver would be extremely accurate — all we needed was to get the spacecraft within a few degrees of the desired attitude.

After Dan selected the file, we started our formal burn parameter file verification routine we had developed during the SIMs. Dan re-checked the parameter file to be sure he had the correct one, then he called out its name and purpose and sent it to Paul's computer. Paul called the file up, read its name to Dan and me and asked if that was the correct file. Dan answered, "Yes." Then Paul opened the file, and with me watching over his shoulder and looking at my Mission Profile, Paul read the numbers in the four registers out loud to Dan and me and we checked the validity of each number (the four engine parameters were as follows: DELAYSUN, the time when the first engine [A1] fired after each Sun pulse was received by the C&DH from the Sun sensor [0.6817 sec]. SHORTDUR, the duration of the short burn pulses [0.167 sec]. HALFREV, the time after engine A1 fired, that engine A4 was to fire [0.4086 sec]. And DELAYNUM, this was two parameters in one; the first part [DELAY] was the time delay between the time the command was received by the C&DH and the execution of the burn [this could be up to 63.75 minutes, but was 0 seconds for all but 5 burns during the entire mission] and the second part [NUM] was the total number of pulses that were to be fired [230 pulses in the case of the 1st reor and 1 for long burns, i.e., 1 long pulse. It would take 9 minutes for all 230 pulses, 115 pulses on A1 and 115 pulses on A4, to fire and to reorient Lunar Prospector by the required 90°]).

When we were satisfied that the file and the parameters were correct, I asked Dan formally, "Are you ready to have the file loaded?"

Dan answered equally formally, "Yes, I am."

I told Paul to uplink the file, which he did on my usual time mark, "10, 5, 3, 1 and 0."

Paul said, "File away."

I watched my echo screen intently, waiting for the one or two 32-second data frames to pass and waiting to start our strict file uplink verification procedure with Dan — a procedure Dan and I had practiced over and over during the SIMs, so it was absolutely routine. Then, amidst the data dropouts and data spikes, I saw the first echo and I said, "I have echo of DELAYSUN of 3-1-0-2-9-D, VCID 0-6. Is that correct, Dan?"

Dan answered, "Yes it is."

The next frame appeared on my screen and I said, "I have echo of SHORTDUR of 3-1-0-1-2-C, VCID of 0-6. Is that correct, Dan?"

Dan answered, "Yes it is."

The next frame appeared and I said, "I have echo of HALFREV of 3-3-0-7-4-2, VCID of 0-6. Is that correct, Dan?"

Dan answered, "Yes it is."

The next frame appeared and I said, "I have echo of DELAYNUM of 3-0-0-1-4-0, VCID of 0-6. Is that correct, Dan?"

Dan answered, "Yes it is."

Having seen all four engine firing parameters correctly echoed back from the spacecraft, I then asked, "Dan, do you concur with the entire load?"

Dan answered, "Yes I do."

I asked Paul to send the Engine Selection Command for the A1 and A4 engine pair that I would use (and always did) for the reor maneuver. Then I told him to send it on my mark and then I waited for the echo. One or two frames passed and I said, "I have echo of 3-8-0-0-4-8, VCID 0-6, which is correct for the A1 and A4 engine selection." Then I again asked Dan, "Do you concur with the entire load (including the engine selection)?"

Dan answered, "Yes I do." We were ready, despite the data dropouts and data spikes that still plagued us.

I said to Paul, "Please send the Execute on my mark at 000/02:27 MET and have the Set Command Registers and Execute file (the SETCMDREG Command reset all the engine burn parameter registers to 0, so there could be no inadvertent engine firings when we were not looking) ready to send at the end of the burn."

Paul answered, "Affirmative."

And he waited until I said, "20 seconds, 10, 5, 3, 1 and 0."

Paul immediately said, "Command away."

We waited the one or two data frames for the verification that the silent fireworks had begun.

I saw the EXEC echo and started to say in my standard way, "I have Execute."

Dan said simultaneously, "NUMTIME, 229 (the spacecraft had fired the first [230th] pulse and was counting-down the number of pulses remaining, i.e., Dan was reading the second part of DELAYNUM which we called NUMTIME)." That was our first indication that our first burn was underway! A data frame later I saw that the A1 and A4 engine temperatures had jumped to several hundred degrees. Dan periodically read off the remaining number of pulses, the slight amount of nutation caused by the shaking of the spacecraft by the pulses, and the slowly decreasing SEA as Lunar Prospector was slowly reorienting itself towards the target SEA of −25°. Simultaneously, I read out the A1 and A4 engine temperatures, which had reached equilibrium at just under 1000° C after several frames, the periodic increases in the load current as the engines fired and the slight decrease in the tank pressure as we used the small amount of fuel required for the reor maneuver.

The burn was going well and it looked like we were going to end up with a SEA of about −20°, which would be OK. However, we still had numerous data dropouts and John saw only a modest improvement in the downlink signal strength! Slowly, the nine minutes passed and Dan finally said, "Burn time up." The burn was over.

Almost immediately I saw that the temperatures of the A1 and A4 engines begin to drop — the first positive sign that the engines had stopped pulse firing and I said, "A1 and A4 temperatures are dropping; the burn is over."

I had Paul uplink the SETCMDREG and EXEC file that was executed at 000/02:43 MET and we saw all the parameter registers go to 0. *Our first burn maneuver was completely finished!* However, we still had data dropouts and data spikes, not as bad as before, but still quite bad! We were sure that the reorientation of the spacecraft to the optimum aspect angle would have fixed our com problem, but it did not!

The next command in the Mission Profile was the command to change the downlink rate from the engineering-data-only, 300 bps to the science and engineering data rate of 3.6 kbps. Then it dawned on me — I remembered the trouble we had getting a good link at the 300 bps data rate during the RF Testing (July 10, 1997) and during the End-to-End Testing at the Cape (December 6, 1997) and I said to Dan, "Remember the trouble we had linking up at 300 bps during testing? I'll bet that what's causing the com-problem. I'm going to proceed with the changeover (from 300 to 3600 bps) and see what happens." Then I told John to tell the DSN that we were switching from 300 bps to 3600 bps at 6:14 GMT (000/02:49 MET) and I told Paul to prepare the T3600 Command for uplink. Paul did and I had him uplink it to the spacecraft. After receiving the echo and verifying it, I said, "Uplink, send the Execute at 000/02:49 (MET) on my mark. 20 seconds, 10, 5, 3, 1 and 0."

Paul said, "Command away."

A frame later, I saw the EXEC echo and a 3600 replace the 300 on the data rate indicator on my screen and I said, "I have Execute, the data rate has changed from 300 to 3600 bps." Immediately the data dropouts and data spikes ceased! Cautiously, I said, "Well, it looks like that did it," and we watched for a few more frames and the data were absolutely clean. The com-problem was gone and I again remembered that during the RF Testing (July 10, 1997), I had considered changing the initialization sequence so it turned on the 3.6 kbps data rate instead of the 300 bps data rate and, for all the right reasons, Tim Bridges had talked me out of it. I thought, *crap, I wish I hadn't listened to Tim* (he could not have anticipated that we would have trouble with the 300 bps link) *and I had changed the initialization sequence, or at least, I had recognized that the bad link was due to the 300 bps and switched immediately to 3.6 kbps. If I had done either of those things, I wouldn't have the com-mess I've had for the last two hours. Oh, well, hindsight is always better than foresight.*

Though slightly aggravating and though I had to completely change the Mission Profile around to makeup for the lost time, the com-mess had not really put us in danger. I redlined my Mission Profile to account for the many changes needed to get us back on track — the main change was shifting the 1st midcourse maneuver (MCM) from 000/04:30 MET to 000/08:30 MET to allow me to get the booms deployed as soon as possible, to do the initial science instrument turn-on sequence, and, just as important, to allow the Nav guys to get some good data, since their Doppler tracking data were also compromised by the poor com-link.

I told everyone how I was changing the Mission Profile and said, "I'll follow the redlined version starting with the despin maneuver that was originally scheduled for 1:09 (000/01:09 MET) and that will now be executed as soon as I can, but I want to get back to the original schedule, with the normal verification periods between events, as soon as I can."

000/2:50 MET through 000/04:30 MET: Boom Deployment and Back On Track

From about 000/02:50 MET on, everything was just like a SIM, so much so that sometime after boom deployment, I turned to Dan and said, "Man, this is just like a SIM."

Dan replied, "It sure is!"

Though we were nearly two hours behind the timeline of the Mission Profile, the spacecraft was still quite warm, about 10° C higher than expected, but Jim said the temperatures were slowly coming down to the levels he had expected, just more slowly than he expected. Apparently, the spacecraft was warmer at launch than it was supposed to have been and the cooling times were longer than Jim calculated. All that was very good, since the boom canisters were still warm. Dougherty, Steve Honodel, Jim, Dan, and I discussed the boom deployment and we all agreed that the canister temperatures were high enough for us to proceed.

The first step in the boom deployment sequence was the despin maneuver. The spacecraft was spinning at 51 rpm and we had to decrease it to 30 rpm for boom deployment. Taking into consideration the tank pressure and amount of fuel remaining, Dan and I each calculated the required burn time on the T1 engine. Dan did it using his program on his Mission Ops console computer, on which he automatically developed the burn parameter file, and I did it on my laptop computer, sitting next to my computer console. As was our practice, we compared our answers and had essentially the same result — a 6.09 second burn. Since there was no discrepancy (outside the very small differences due to the different ways we each had interpolated the test data on the engines Olin had provided), I said, "I accept your value (as I always did, if the results were essentially the same, since his values went directly into the burn parameter file in his computer and mine did not). Please prepare the burn file and send it to Uplink."

As soon as Dan did that, we went through our standard burn parameter file cross checks and read backs. When we were satisfied that the file was correct, I asked Paul to uplink the file on my mark. Then, as the echo of each of the four parameters plus the engine selection (T1), appeared on my screen, I read it, verified it, and asked Dan if it was correct. When all four parameters and the engine selection had been again verified, I asked Dan my standard question, "Dan, do you concur with the entire load?"

Dan answered, "Yes I do."

I said to Paul, "Please send the Execute and Engine Safeing File (burn Execute, wait 32 seconds, STOPFIRE [a backup Engine-Off Command just in case the engine did not shut off as planned in 6.09 seconds], SETCMDREG, and Execute) on my mark at 000/03:05 MET."

And Paul answered, "Affirmative."

And we waited until I said, "20 seconds, 10, 5, 3, 1 and 0."

Paul immediately said, "File away."

After the usual delay, I saw the EXEC echo and started to say my standard, "I have Execute."

Dan simultaneously said, "NUMTIME, 0."

A data frame later I saw that the T1 engine temperature jumped to several hundred degrees, the tank pressure dropped from its static value of 431 psi to its lower, dynamic value of 426 psi and the load current jumped by about 1 amp — all as expected. By the next frame (32 seconds), the 6.09 second burn was long over, the T1 temperature had started to drop, the load current had dropped back an amp, and the tank pressure had returned to its static value and I said, "T1 temperature is dropping, load current is again 5 amps, and the pressure is 431 psi — the burn is over," and I saw and called out the echoes of the STOPFIRE, SETCMDREG, and EXEC, and added, "The T1 engine is safed."

Dan had to wait a little while longer to call out the new spin rate, since at spin rates higher than about 20 rpm, the Sun pulses were coming so fast that the C&DH had to buffer the data and spit out the new spin rate when it had had time to get through its data overload. Finally Dan said, "The spin rate is 31 rpm." Which was 1 rpm high, but well within what was acceptable for boom deployment.

I called Dave Curtis into the Glass Room and he took his seat in front of the MAG/ER console. When Dave was ready, I had Paul uplink the command to turn on the MAG. After I verified the echo (2400D4, 06) and after Dave verified the command on his screen, I had Paul uplink the EXEC at 000/03:11 MET and a frame or two later, I saw and called the EXEC echo (CCA1F5, 09) and saw on my status table that the MAG/ER change from off (red) to on (green) and my MAG/ER plots come alive with the engineering data (voltages, currents, and temperatures).

Simultaneously, Dave said, "I'm getting data" (at that point in time, the spacecraft was still deep in the Earth's magnetic field, so we began to get the desired MAG calibration data in the well known geomagnetic field). *I had just turned on Lunar Prospector's first science instrument and we were getting the first science data of the mission!*

I asked Dave what the spin rate was according to the MAG data and he said, after a short pause, "31 rpm," which was correct (that was important since I would have to rely on Dave's determination of the spacecraft's spin rate, using the MAG data, during the first part of the boom deployment — when there was the delay in getting the spin rate from the Sun pulse data due to its being buffered as a result of the high spin rates).

I asked Dave if he was ready for me to pop the MAG extension boom and he answered, "Yes." I told Paul to uplink the MAGBOOM Command, which he did on my usual mark. Before issuing the EXEC, I reminded Dave to announce the apparent 100° rotation of the Earth's magnetic field and the decrease in the spacecraft's spin rate as the little boom deployed, and I reminded Dan to call out the increase in the spacecraft's nutation, the change in its attitude, and the decrease in its spin rate after deployment.

At 000/03:15 MET, I had Paul uplink the EXEC and out there, deep in space, the two little wire-cutter-pyros silently popped and the little boom swung out. Shortly thereafter, I saw the echo and I said, "I have Execute."

Dave said, "The magnetic field has rotated 100° and the spin rate has decreased by 0.6 rpm."

Shortly thereafter, Dan confirmed the decrease in the spin rate and added, "I have a degree or two of nutation and the SEA is now −19°." The deployment of the MAG extension boom went perfectly and we were ready for the critical deployment of the main booms.

I asked Steve to come into the Glass Room to prepare for boom deployment. Steve was nervous, as usual. I asked him if he was ready to support the deployment and he answered, "Yes." I told Steve what the bus voltage was and what the temperature of the viscous damper was and asked him to calculate how long I should command the paraffin actuator heater on. Steve calculated an on-time of 135 seconds, but said it should pop in about 70 seconds. Then I asked Paul to insert the on-time into the boom release command (RELBOOMS), which he did and then Dan, Steve, and I verified it.

Before I had Paul uplink the RELBOOMS Command, I reminded Dave to call out, "First motion," the instant when he saw from the MAG data that the booms had been released and then to call out each apparent quarter revolution of the Earth's magnetic field (as the booms uncoiled and rotated 4 times during the deployment), the decrease in the spacecraft's spin rate, and the final snap-over when the booms were fully deployed and locked into position. Then I reminded Dan to call out the decrease in the spin rate derived from the Sun pulse data, the nutation, and any change in the SEA (if the booms were not deploying evenly, the SEA would change and the nutation would increase dramatically). Finally, I asked Dan, Dave, and Steve if they were ready to support the deployment and each answered, "Yes," and then I asked Paul to call out the time every 10 seconds since heater turn-on.

Paul said, "Affirmative."

Finally, everything was ready and I told Paul to uplink RELBOOMS on my mark and I began my count down, "20 seconds, 10, 5, 3, 1 and 0."

Paul said, "Command away."

A frame later I had the echo and I called out, "I have echo of 2-7-0-5-4-6, VCID 0-6, which is correct for boom release." Then I said, "Send the Execute on my mark at 000/03:44 MET," and I again began my count down, "20 seconds, 10, 5, 3, 1 and 0."

Paul again said, "Command away."

Then I saw the EXEC echo and said, "I have Execute," and I saw the expected increase of 0.8 amps in the load current, indicating that the paraffin actuator heater had turned on.

Then we waited. Slowly, as Paul called out the time, the viscous damper's temperature began to increase a few degrees, indicating that the heater was heating the paraffin actuator, and we waited. Paul said, "10 seconds . . . 60 seconds, 70 seconds, 80 seconds."

At about 87 seconds, Dave said, "I have first motion!" — up in space, the paraffin had melted and forced the plunger of the actuator out; the plunger had tripped the release mechanism, which had caused the 3 latching pins on each of the three booms to disengage, releasing the three booms; instantly, the booms had jumped out about a centimeter and rotated a few degrees — *first motion* had occurred and it was faithfully detected in the MAG data by David. The critical boom deployment was underway.

Dave called out the first quarter revolution of the Earth's Magnetic field (and hence of the MAG/ER boom) and the corresponding decrease in the spin rate of the spacecraft. The buffered Sun pulse data started to yield spin rate data and Dan also called out the decreasing spin rate and the fact that, except for the small increase in the spacecraft's nutation caused by the jolt as the booms released, the nutation was not increasing. All were good signs we had had a simultaneous release of all three booms and they were deploying uniformly.

Dave kept calling out the quarter revolutions of the booms and the decreasing spin rate, followed 10 to 15 seconds later by Dan's confirmation of the decreasing spin rate and the steadiness of the nutation. After a few minutes, it was clear the spacecraft spin-down was following the expected curve as a function of the number of boom revolutions called out by Dave. The booms were deploying evenly and correctly. As the process continued, it got slower and slower as expected. Finally, after about 20 minutes, Dave called out, "Four revs and snap over!" Boom deployment had been successfully completed!

Dan and Dave both reported that the spin rate was 6.825 rpm and Dan said, "The snap-over caused a slight increase in the nutation, as expected, and the SEA has changed slightly to –20°!" We had had a perfect boom deployment! At that point, *Lunar Prospector was in its final flight configuration in terms of all of its engineering subsystems!*

We watched the spin rate and the MAG data for a few minutes to be sure everything was holding steady — and they were. Then I said formally, "We have successfully deployed the science booms and I will proceed on the redlined timeline of the Mission Profile." Then I said to Steve, "Thank you for giving me three good booms. Please say thanks to Able for the great booms and the great deployment. Now I would like you to leave Mission Ops."

Steve said, "Thanks and I'll thank Able for you, and boy, am I relived," and then he gratefully left the Glass Room.

Then, while Dave continued to monitor the MAG data (I still needed him in the Glass Room for the rest of the MAG/ER turn-on and the calibration test I would command in a little while), I got prepared for the final step in the boom release sequence — the spin-up to our operational spin rate of 12.0±0.7 rpm.

Dan and I made our respective calculations of the spin-up burn on engine T2 and came to the conclusion that we needed a 6.58 second burn. Dan prepared the burn parameter file; we verified it; he sent it to Paul; Paul, Dan, and I verified it; then we did the read-back check and when we were all satisfied everything was correct, I had Paul prepare the standard EXEC and Engine Safeing File. When Paul was finished, I had him uplink the burn parameter file on my mark. Then, as the echoes of the burn parameters and the engine selection came back, I read them off and had Dan confirm each one. Then I asked, "Dan, do you concur with the entire file."

Dan answered, "Yes, I do."

I told Paul I would execute the file at 000/04:21 MET and started my countdown. At "0," Paul uplinked the file and soon Dan and I were calling out our standard burn comments as we watched the echoes and data come in. Then the engines were safed and Dan called out that our spin rate as 11.2 rpm, 0.1 rpm less than the minimum we had shot for, but it was still OK. We would make the final correction to the spin rate after the 1st MCM in a little over 4 hours.

Then Woody, after having watched the battery's performance for the previous couple of hours, recommended I change the battery charge rate from VT2 to VT4 (VT meaning Voltage/Temperature curve). I redlined my Mission Profile and had Paul prepare a command file containing the VT4 Command. Then I had him uplink it and, after verifying its echo, I had him execute it and I watched my console for its echo and the change from VT2 to VT4. It was 000/04:30 MET when that was finished.

000/4:30 MET through 000/07:00 MET: Finishing the Initial Science Instrument Turn-On Sequence and the Reor to Cruise Attitude

After having changed the VT curve for Woody, I was ready to proceed with the rest of the science instrument turn-on sequence and the reor to cruise attitude. By that time it was clear the spacecraft and my Ops Team were both performing flawlessly — we knew we could run the spacecraft and it did what we asked it to do. *It truly was just like a SIM, though much better — it was the real thing!*

According to the Mission Profile, I was to do a two-step MAG calibration sequence and turn-on the ER. I told David to get ready to observe the test and to verify the commands at his console after I had verified them on my console. The MAG calibration sequence started at 000/04:32 MET and was finished, on time, at 000/04:36 MET. It showed the MAG was performing perfectly. Then I went through the normal command and verification sequence with Paul and Dave to turn on the ER's low-voltage, so it could start its degassing process that would allow me to turn on its high-voltage the next evening. The ER was turned on at 000/04:42 MET. Since there was more MAG/ER testing to be done in a little more than an hour, I allowed Dave to stay in the Glass Room to watch the MAG data until we would proceed with the MAG/ER tests.

I was ready to start the initial turn-on sequence for the spectrometers, so I called Bill Feldman into the Glass Room. Unlike Dave, who is always calm and collected, Bill was excited and slightly nervous — as Bill usually is at such times. As was Dave's job during the MAG/ER turn-on, Bill's job was to monitor the spectrometer commands and data as I commanded the spectrometers on and went through my command verification procedures. As always, every command was checked, at least twice, first by me at my command console and then by Bill at the spectrometer console, before I sent the EXEC for that command. Because Bill is somewhat excitable, and even though he had participated in turn-on SIMs, I carefully reviewed with him what I wanted him to do.

I had Paul uplink the command to turn on the Spectrometer Electronics System (SES). I executed that command at 000/04:45 MET and after seeing the SES had turned on according to my status screen and after seeing the expected changes in the load currents and voltages, I asked Paul to route the spectrometer data from Oasis to the spectrometer console and Bill began to see the engineering data on his screen and verified it for me. Then, on three minute intervals, between 000/04:58 MET and 000/05:04 MET, I commanded the low voltages on for the NS, GRS, and the APS. While I would have to wait for the NS and the GRS to degas before turning on their high-voltage supplies the following evening, the APS was fully operational, though I had to do an APS test sequence after turning on the A1 and A4 engine heater in preparation for our next reor burn. Nevertheless, at that point in time, I had *two of my five science instruments, the MAG and the APS, fully turned on* and they were providing data in a known environment so we could calibrate them before we reached the Moon.

According to the original Mission Profile, I would then have done a series of tests on the APS to fully check it out. However, because of the delays due to the initial com-problem and the resulting need to put the spacecraft in a negative attitude to warm the boom canisters in preparation for the critical boom deployment, I needed to get the spacecraft into its normal cruise attitude. Because time was of the essence until the booms were deployed (even under normal conditions and especially after the com-delays), I had not (nor had I planned to do so in the original Mission Profile) pre-heat-ed the A1 and A4 engines before firing them for the first reor, nor the T1 engine before the first spin-down burn, nor the T2 before the first spin-up burn. Though the engines can be fired cold a few times without problems, they need to be pre-heated to prolong their lifetimes. When I inserted a reor burn to get the spacecraft into its nominal cruise attitude in the redlined Mission Profile, Irv strongly recommended I pre-heat the A1 and A4 engines. Since time was no longer a problem, I followed Irv's recommendation and redlined a standard A1 and A4 heater turn-on sequence into the Mission Profile and asked Paul to prepare that file for uplink.

Paul got the file ready, we verified it and then, on my mark, he uplinked it. Shortly thereafter, I got and verified the echo for the A1 heater, which was executed at 000/05:10 MET, and then I got the echo for the A4 heater, which was executed at 000/05:11 MET. I saw the expected 0.2 amp increase in the load current when each heater turned on, and after a few data frames, the A1 engine temperature started to climb, followed shortly by the A4 engine temperature. Having successfully turned on the heaters for the first time, I returned my attention to finishing the APS and MAG/ER testing that was part of the initial science turn-on sequence — but I kept my eye on the increasing temperatures of the A1 and A4 engines.

Following the Mission Profile, I started the test of the APS with Bill and it ran from 000/05:13 MET to 000/05:35 MET, which just happened to be the time needed for the engines to heat up! During the test, I first shut off the detectors on all five faces of the APS and then turned on the detectors, one face at time, so Bill could check out each face's performance. Faces 1, 2, 3, and 4 were perfect, but Face 5 looked a little funny — Face 5 was the –Z facing Face I was concerned about when I saw where the APS was located with respect to one of the TLI Stage spin-up rockets back in June (June 27, 1997) and with respect to one of the nitrogen jets of the collision avoidance system when we were doing the spin balancing at Astro Tech (December 13, 1997). Bill said he would have to monitor the Face 5 data, with the APS fully on, for a while to see if anything was really wrong with it. We finished the APS test and I turned all five faces back on and asked Bill to leave the Glass Room, since I was about to do the reor-maneuver.

Also, by that time, over 5½ hours into the mission and just after 1:00 PM, Goddard Nav informed us that their original estimate of the TLI velocity error of +1±2 m/sec, which was based on the poor Doppler data yielded by our poor com-link, was off. The real ΔV error was about –10 m/sec, which would require about a 60 m/sec MCM burn at the new burn time of 000/08:30 MET. That was OK, since I had allocated 80 m/sec of ΔV for all three MCM burns, but the delay in the 1st burn was going to cost me an extra 20 m/sec of ΔV. Also, I remembered the Athena crew had told us the Athena was going to give us a 7 m/sec over-burn after we had stacked the payload on the rocket, so I had had Kim add ballasting to the TLI Stage to compensate for the over-burn (December 26 through 28, 1997). Had they not made that mistake, our TLI velocity error would have been just –3 m/sec, instead of –10 m/sec — one last blow from the Athena crowd!

While I was busy commanding the last of the initial science instruments turn-on sequence and testing, Dan was busy getting his first good solution for the spacecraft's attitude using the Sun sensor and Earth/Moon (EM) limb-crossing sensor data and preparing the file for our up-coming reor to the cruise attitude. With that file prepared and with the A1 and A4 engines hot, we began our standard and careful series of checks on the file and its burn parameters. Then I had Paul send up the file and I carefully read off the echoes, asking Dan if each parameter was correct and then asking him if he concurred with the entire file. When all the checks and rechecks were finished, I then had Paul uplink the EXEC Command at 000/05:58 MET. Shortly thereafter, I called out the Execute echo and Dan and I then called out the events of the reor burn. The reor maneuver took 8 minutes to complete, consisted of 45 pulses on the A1 and A4 engines, and changed the attitude by 21.2°. We then had the spacecraft in its nominal cruise attitude. At 000/06:07 MET, I had Paul uplink the Engine Safeing Command — our second reor-maneuver of the mission was finished.

Finally, I was at the place in my redlined Mission Profile where I would finish the initial turn-on and testing of the MAG/ER with Dave, who had been sitting at the MAG/ER console, watching the MAG data roll in and, when we did the 21.2° reor, he had noted the corresponding 21.2° rotation of the Earth's magnetic field. I told Dave I was ready to proceed and I first opened the ER cover (000/06:20 MET) and then we went through a 13 Step ER Pulser Test that started at 000/06:23 MET and ended at 000/06:45 MET. When we were finished, the ER was ready to go as soon as I turned on its high-voltage the following evening. With the end of that test, I was finished with the initial turn-on sequence of the science instruments and it was just after 3:00 in the morning.

Since the science instrument work was done for the night, Dave and Bill decided it was time to turn in, and, along with the few visitors who had not already left, they left Mission Ops. The only people who were left were my Mission Ops Team, the Ames Nav Team, Marcie, Dougherty, and the rest of the Lockheed support engineers and the Mission Controllers who would take over watching the spacecraft when my Command Team and I finished our first command session.

000/07:00 MET through 000/11:00 MET: The 1st MCM

The final event of our planned Day 0, post-launch, turn-on activities was our 1st MCM. By that time, Goddard Nav had the velocity vector data for the MCM. We had to do a 12.97 m/sec continuous burn on axial engines A1 and A2 and a 48.6 m/sec pulsed burn on tangential engines T1 and T2. Dan and I checked the Goddard data and we each calculated the burn durations. We independently calculated that the axial burn would last 55.5 seconds and the tangential pulsed burn would consist of 276 pulses and hence, had to be broken down into two burn files, the first with the maximum number of pulses we could put in a file, i.e., 255, and 21 pulses in the second file. The pulsed burns would last some 23 minutes, plus the few minutes we would need to uplink the second pulsed burn file. The whole 1st MCM would last about ½ hour.

Once Dan and I had made and compared our calculation for the burns, we had a conference with the Goddard Nav Team and our Ames Nav Team (Dave Lozier and Ken Galal), and with Marcie, who stuck her nose in. Though we had done two reor burns and two spin adjustment burns already, the 1st MCM maneuver was our first major ΔV maneuver and we could not afford to make a mistake. Finally we all agreed we had everything right and Dan prepared the three burn files and sent them to Paul. Then we began our careful checking and verification procedure. The files were correct and I was ready to begin the commanding sequence.

First, I had Paul prepare the standard A1, A2, T1, and T2 heater turn-on file, we checked it, Paul uplinked it on my mark, and then as I saw the first echo, I said, "I have echo of 2-E-0-0-2-A, VCID 0-6, that is correct for the A1 heater," then at 000/07:36 MET, the first EXEC went up and I soon said "I have Execute." Then in succession, the remaining three heater echoes and their Executes appeared on my screen and I methodically read each off and verified it. By the time the entire heater turn-on file had been uplinked, i.e., at 000/07:39 MET, the load current had increased the expected 0.8 amps and I saw the A1 temperature was already beginning to rise. Within a few minutes, all four engines were heating up towards their 120 to 140° C pre-burn temperatures.

As the engines were heating up, I asked Paul to call up the burn parameter file for the axial burn. He did and then Dan, Paul, and I checked and verified the file and when we were satisfied, I had Paul uplink it and I read and verified, with Dan, that each of the four burn parameters and the A1 and A2 engine selection were all correct as their echoes came back from the spacecraft. When we were finished, I asked, "Dan, do you concur with the entire load?"

Dan answered, "Yes I do."

I turned to Paul and said, "Please Execute the file on my mark at 000/08:30 MET."

Paul said, "Affirmative." Soon I was counting down in my standard way and when I hit "0," Paul said. "Execute away."

As I said, "I have echo of Execute."

Dan said, "NUMTIME 0."

I saw the A1 and then the A2 temperatures jump several hundred degrees, the load current jump an amp and the tank pressure drop by 17 psi from its static value (428 psi) to its dynamic value (411 psi). The axial burn was under way. The engine temperatures continued to rise for two frames and the pressure began to drop as fuel was being used. Then the 55 second burn was over, the load current dropped by nearly 2 amps as the engines shut off, the tank pressure jumped back up to its static value and the A1 and A2 engines began to cool off.

Then we verified, uplinked, verified via the echoes, and then executed the first burn file for the first 255 pulsed burns on the tangential engines. I watched the T1 and T2 engine temperatures, the tank pressure, and the load current for the usual signs of the burn's beginning and ending, while Dan called out the number of pulses remaining and the very slight spin-up and very slight reor of the spacecraft caused by the very slight misalignments and the slight differences in the thrust levels of the engines. We knew that both of those things would happen, but we did not know if the spacecraft would spin-up or spin-down during the burns and how much reor would occur. We were beginning to learn those things during that first really long set of burns (as it turned out, no matter which set of engines we used, the spacecraft always spun up a little during each burn — statistically we expected that some set of engines would have despun the spacecraft, but it just so happened that the slight misalignments and slightly different thrust levels of the engines all resulted in spin-ups).

As soon as I called out, "Engine stop," we quickly verified, uplinked, verified and executed the second file with the final 21 pulses of the tangential engines. When those 21 pulses were finished, I had Paul send up the Engine Safeing Command and suddenly we were completely done with the Day 0, post-launch commanding session — it was 000/09:05 MET or 4:30 AM Wednesday, January 7, 1998. We had been in Mission Ops for 14 or 15 hours and I had been up for some 24 hours, but my fuel tank was filled with adrenaline and though I could feel the fatigue in my body, I was not tired — *who could be with a perfect spacecraft racing towards the Moon!*

Speaking of which, Goddard Nav reported their preliminary evaluation of our 1st MCM burn was that we had over-burned by a whole 0.2 m/sec! That was an error of 0.3% on engines that were rated with a 1% uncertainty! What could one say about my simple little spacecraft after such an astounding 9 hours of operations, during which we had sent 130 commands without error — a dumb little spacecraft with no computer that was run by four people on the ground?

The only thing that I was concerned about was the temperature of the GRS, which had been dropping steadily from its launch temperature of about 20° C towards its operational temperature of –28 to –29° C, increased a few degrees during the pulsed burns of the tangential engines during the MCM. The reason was clear — because the two tangential engines pointed in the same direction as the GRS boom and the GRS was only about 3.3 m from those two engines, the GRS was enveloped in the hot gas plumes of the tangential engines during the pulsed burns. Jim Schirle was initially concerned that the plumes had degraded the thermal shield of the GRS and that the GRS would not cool completely down to its operational temperature. However, after the burn, we saw that the GRS temperature again began to decrease and it looked like it would probably be OK, but I would take a closer look at the GRS temperature as soon as I got back to Mission Ops after a few hours of sleep.

Even though we were finished with the first, critical commanding activities, we all stayed and monitored the spacecraft and the GRS temperature for more than an hour. While all the visitors had drifted away during the long night, my Engineering Support Team Members and Dougherty were still there, so I thanked them for their support and for helping me build such a perfect little spacecraft and then they drifted off.

Finally, I turned Mission Ops and my spacecraft over to the next shift of controllers that was led by Ric Campo and told them to call me at the motel across the street if anything at all looked funny. Then Dan, Paul, John, and I left to get some rest at about 6:00 AM or 000/10:30 MET.

As I walked the few blocks to my motel room, I was very pleased. Lunar Prospector had performed flawlessly — even when we had the damned com-difficulties because of the 300 bps data rate early in the flight — and my Ops Team and I had also performed flawlessly — all those SIMs paid off handsomely, as did my having a very simple spacecraft that was very easy to run. *My dream had come true.*

As I was about to go to bed for what I expected would be, at most, a couple of hours of sleep, I thought both about the question someone had asked me just before launch, if I was nervous and my answer, "No, there's nothing I can do about the launch, either the Athena works or it doesn't, and I completely trust my spacecraft and my Mission Ops crew. If we get launched, we will do our jobs. Also, if I were nervous, I would have no business being the Mission Director and the PI."

The Translunar Coast

Wednesday, January 7, through Early Morning,
Thursday, January 8, 1998

000/14:00 MET through 001/06:00 MET: High-Voltage Turn-on and the 2ⁿᵈ MCM

Technically, the translunar coast began at the end of the TLI burn (at 000/000:00 MET), since Lunar Prospector coasted most of the rest of the 105 hours it took to get to the Moon (except for the short periods of acceleration during the MCM burns). However, in practice, the coast began when we finished commanding the spacecraft at the end of the initial commanding session at 000/09:05 MET. By the time I had slept almost 3 hours and had returned to Mission Ops (at about 10:00 AM on the 7th), some four hours after having left it, the translunar coast was well under way. When I arrived at Mission Ops, I looked at my computer screen and Lunar Prospector was functioning perfectly.

I looked at the GRS cooling curve. The GRS had reached its operational range and was varying between -27.8 to $-29.5°$ C, as planned. The GRS, like everything else on the spacecraft, had come to thermal equilibrium and all the subsystem temperatures were well within their expected ranges.

The only problem we had was with Face 5 of the APS. Bill still did not know why, but its detectors had lost sensitivity. In an effort to try to understand what was wrong with it, Bill asked me to set the detection threshold to zero. I redlined the necessary commands into my Mission Profile, checked them with Bill and Ric Campo, who was the Uplink Controller for that shift, and then commanded the APS detection threshold to zero at 000/16:21 MET or at 11:46 AM. If Bill could not figure out how to correct the problem with Face 5, that would mean the APS field of view would be asymmetric, but that couldn't be helped and it would not pose a serious problem for the mapping.

After finishing the APS commanding and since I had not eaten after I got up, Bill and I went out for a Mexican lunch and then came back to Mission Ops to continue monitoring the spacecraft and to prepare for the evening's commanding session, i.e., turning on the high-voltages of the GRS, NS, and ER and doing the 2ⁿᵈ MCM.

Rebecca arrived at the San Jose Airport (from the Cape) early Wednesday evening, while I was busy preparing for the commanding session. Thus she took a cab to our motel room and called me at Mission Ops. I picked her up and brought her to Mission Ops so she could watch the evening's commanding activities.

Rebecca told me that right after launch, when we were just taking control of the spacecraft and everyone wanted to know its status, NASA and Lockheed held their post-launch news conference to congratulate themselves on the successful Athena II launch and to announce that Gene Shoemaker's ashes were on board Lunar Prospector! There was no mention of the spacecraft's condition, the quality of the trajectory or anything about the critical commanding activities that were going on in Mission Ops! The only indication that Mission Ops even existed was via a TV screen behind the seated NASA and Lockheed bigwigs that showed a view of the backs of our heads as we sat at our computer consoles in Mission Ops! Rebecca said she and others were trying to find out about the TLI burn and the spacecraft's condition, but no one seemed to know or care — they had had a pretty launch and Gene's ashes were going to the Moon, that was enough for them. NASA is just pathetic.

My Mission Ops Team (Dan, Paul, John, and me), my Ames Nav Team (Dave and Ken), my science guys (Dave Curtis and Bill Feldman), Marcie, and a few onlookers, including Rebecca, who was sitting just outside of the Glass Room right in front of me, plus the Goddard Nav Team (who where on the phone), were all set and ready to go for our second major commanding session by 9:30 PM or just a little after 001/02:00 MET.

First we discussed the 2nd MCM with Dave, Ken, and Goddard. The MCM we had to do consisted of a 1.16 m/sec continuous axial burn using engines A1 and A2 and a 7.27 m/sec pulsed burn on the tangential engines. That would bring the ΔV usage for the first two MCM burns up to 70 m/sec, still 10 m/sec lower than I had budgeted for the MCM's, with one possible, small 3rd MCM set for the next day. I was very happy with the low propellant usage at that point.

However, before we got to the 2nd MCM, which I had scheduled to start at 001/05:00 MET, my Mission Profile called for finishing the science instrument turn-on sequence. Dave and Bill were therefore also in the Glass Room, sitting in front of the MAG/ER and spectrometers consoles, respectively, as we got started with the second major commanding session of the young mission.

Unlike the previous night, when the early com-problems had forced me to completely change the sequence of events in the Mission Profile, I was able to follow my preplanned Mission Profile exactly. Like all commanding activities, we had first reviewed and verified all the commands before starting and then, when I began commanding the multi-step sequence, I verified each command echo as it appeared on my screen. Dave or Bill verified the echo when it appeared on his screen and then verified the validity of the changes in the voltages, currents, etc. and the instrument responses before I commanded the next step in the sequence.

I started the commanding, after having allowed the ER, GRS, and NS to degas for a day, by turning on the ER high-voltage at 001/02:44 MET. Then, on 3-minute intervals, I commanded the ER "sweep rate" to its "setup condition" and then, in 7 prescribed steps, I stepped up the ER sweep high-voltage to 3600 v and ended that part of the sequence by resetting the "sweep rate" to its "operational mode." As I went through those steps, Dave very carefully looked for any noise or anomalies and, having found none, we had completed the first part of the ER high-voltage turn-on by 001/03:20 MET.

I started the second part of ER high-voltage turn-on by stepping up the ER microprocessor voltage to 2400 v in 6 prescribed steps, again, on 3-minute intervals. When I finished, at 001/03:29 MET, the ER was completely operational and collecting translunar calibration data — *three instruments were then completely operational and collecting data — two to go.*

Ten minutes later, after waiting the standard 10 minutes to check the spacecraft and the turned on instruments to be sure they were all OK, I started turning on the NS Side 1 high-voltage at 001/03:39 MET and it was Bill's turn to verify each step in the sequence with me. I then stepped up the NS Side 1 high-voltage to 1200 v in 3 prescribed steps on the usual 3-minute intervals and Bill verified that Side 1 was functioning properly. Then we did the same for Side 2, which also functioned perfectly. When I finished, at 001/03:57 MET, the NS was completely operational and collecting translunar calibration data — *four instruments were completely operational and collecting data — only one to go.*

Again, after a 10-minute health check of the spacecraft and functioning instruments, I turned on the GRS high-voltage at 001/04:10 MET. I then stepped up the GRS high-voltage to 1600 v in 3 prescribed steps on the usual 3-minute intervals and Bill verified that GRS was also functioning properly. When I finished, *at 001/04:23 MET, the entire spacecraft and its science payload were fully operational, collecting science data and were on their way to the Moon!*

We had reached another major milestone in the mission — the science instruments would collect science data for the rest of the mission, without us doing any further preplanned interruptions or commanding, except for possible small changes in the voltage settings and the like. Having completely finished the science instrument turn-on sequence, I asked Dave to leave the Glass Room, since my Ops Team and I were about to start the 2nd MCM commanding sequence. However, I wanted Bill to watch the GRS during the pulsed burn of the tangential engines for two reasons: First, I wanted to know if the pulsed burns on the tangential engines again caused any temporary increase in the GRS's temperature, even though the burn would only have a small number of pulses compared to the 276 pluses of the 1st MCM. Second, since the GRS high-voltage was on, I wanted to know if there was any danger of high-voltage arcing caused by the gases in the exhaust plumes. Though we were quite sure that, since the GRS was well encased in its thermal shield, the gases in the engine plumes would not cause any arcing, I wanted to know that for sure. I asked Bill to very carefully watch the GRS voltages, currents, and temperature during the upcoming tangential burn.

I started the 2nd MCM sequence by having Paul uplink the engine heaters turn-on commands for the A1, A2, T1, and T2 engines we were going to use for the MCM burns, after the usual checks. The T1 heater was turned on at the preplanned time of 001/04:32 MET and all 4 heaters were on by 001/04:35 MET. Then I saw their temperatures begin to rise.

After that, Dan, Paul, and I went through our standard burn parameter file verification procedures for the 1.16 m/sec axial burn on the A1 and A2 engines, which Dan and I agreed would take just 5.6 seconds. We did the same for the 7.27 m/sec tangential component of the burn, which we agreed would require just 44-pulsed burns of 0.833 second durations on T1 and T2. The 44 pulses would take just 3.2 minutes.

After having had Paul uplink the axial burn parameter file and after having verified the echoes, I had Paul uplink the Execute at the preplanned time of 001/05:00 MET and we saw, shortly thereafter, the normal signatures of the axial burn on our computer screens.

I then immediately had Paul uplink the parameter file for the tangential component of the burn and after all the usual verification procedures, I had him execute the burn at the preplanned time of 001/05:11 MET. And we again watched the signatures of the pulsed burn sequence on our screens. When Dan called, "Burn time is up," and when I saw that the T1 and T2 engine temperatures had begun to drop, I called out the end of the MCM burns and I had Paul uplink the Safe Engine Commands. The 2nd MCM burn sequence was over at 001/05:16 MET and since the spin period of the spacecraft at the end of the two burns was 12.685 rpm, i.e., still within the 12.0±0.7 rpm range we wanted, and after getting Dan's concurrence, I canceled the preplanned spin correction tweak burn.

Also, since Dan wanted to get a better determination of the spacecraft's attitude before we put the spacecraft in its Lunar Orbit Insertion (LOI) burn attitude, I canceled the pre-planned LOI burn attitude reor maneuver and we rescheduled it for the next night. Thus, we were done with our second planned commanding session.

Finally, and to my relief, Bill did not see any evidence of high-voltage arcing in the GRS and we both saw no change in the GRS's temperature during the tangential engine pulsed burn. Thus, the thermal effect we had seen in the GRS data the night before was a single event affair, since I never again expected to do that many pulses during a tangential pulsed burn at any time during the rest of the mission. Also, after the three long LOI burns, ¾ of the fuel would be used and the tank pressure would just be about 150 psi. As a result, the thrust of the engines and hence the gas density in the engine plumes would be about ⅓ of that during the coast phase of the mission. Having seen no effects of the burn on the GRS during the 2nd MCM meant there would be no problems in the future. However, I did notice a slight increase in the temperature of the solar array during the tangential burn — an observation that caused no concern, it was just interesting.

It was then about 001/05:20 MET or about 12:45 AM on the 8th. Our second major commanding session had lasted just 2½ hours and we had increased the number of commands we had sent flawlessly to the spacecraft to 191. Since everything was fine with the spacecraft, except, of course, the behavior of Face 5 of the APS, I turned Mission Ops over to Ric and his monitoring team and, except Dan, who stayed behind to get the data he needed to accurately determine the spacecraft's attitude, my Command Team and Rebecca and I left a little after 1:00 AM to get some rest.

I got to bed about 1:30 AM and I got to sleep at about 2:00 AM.

Thursday, January 8, through Early Morning, Friday, January 9, 1998

001/10:30 MET through 002/06:30 MET: A Near Perfect Trajectory and the Reor to the LOI Burn Attitude

After getting just four hours of sleep, Dan called and woke me up at about 6:00 AM, because the MAG/ER +15 v line had reached its upper yellow limit and was staying there. I immediately went over to Mission Ops and looked at the data. I saw the bus voltage was 32.5 v, which was OK, but we had expected the maximum bus voltage to be 30.5 v. Since the bus voltage was higher than expected, that automatically meant the MAG/ER +15 v line was higher than expected, which was also OK. To be sure, I called Woody and he agreed with me. There was nothing wrong; I had just set the yellow limit for the MAG/ER +15 v line too low, based on the pre-launch data. All I had to do was to set its yellow and red limits a little higher and the yellow warning number turned green. There was nothing really wrong, but it got me up without my getting much sleep.

I went over to Lockheed to say, "Hi," to Frank Martin because he had called. Then Dom wanted to talk to me.

Against my better judgment, I went into Dom's office and, as he always did, he very quickly got into his mode of taking credit for the mission. He said he was following the mission carefully, he was very pleased that it was going so well, but he had kept his eye on the mission after he had gotten another assignment (i.e., after I had him thrown off the project) and he had told Dougherty what he needed to do to keep on track! I tried to be nice to him and said, "Well, you know, I really wish you and I were doing this together," and then he just got more worked up, so I left as soon as I could. I was very disturbed that the man couldn't even accept a gesture of kindness. His ego just forces him to go on and on and to say how he told Dougherty how to do the spacecraft and if it wasn't for him, it would not have worked, and blah, blah, blah. The man is just a nut case.

In addition to Dom's asininity, Scott was also being an incredible ass. I talked to Tim Bridges and he told me Scott had had the main Lockheed contract altered, against Dougherty's will, so that he, Scott, was the Mission Manager! Tim said that Dougherty had fought it every way he could. Unless I was completely nuts, since I, as the PI, had had to sign the main Lockheed contract, Scott's forcing Lockheed to change the contract without my knowledge and agreement was an illegal act. The whole thing was a terrible, incredible act of ego and self-centered behavior on Scott's part.

Scott came over to discuss the news conference that was going to be held Tuesday morning the 13th, shortly after I put Lunar Prospector into its 100 km altitude-mapping orbit. Scott, of course, wanted to have Dougherty and Marcie there and, since he could not avoid having me there, I was to be there too. He wanted Dougherty to talk about the spacecraft, Marcie to talk about Mission Operations, and me talk about science. He also said NASA had decided they wanted good coverage of the LOI burns, so they wanted to have a TV camera in Mission Ops. I said, "Hell no," to everything he wanted.

I first vented my anger about the poor TV coverage in general and then about the fact that, after having blown the post-launch Missions Ops coverage by having their stupid NASA/Lockheed launch vehicle press conference, NASA finally decided they wanted to have a TV camera in Mission Ops at a time when trying to set it up in the middle of our operations would be disruptive and endanger the mission. I said, "No, I'm not going to accept that. You wouldn't do it when I first asked and when we had plenty of time to have it properly setup without screwing up Mission Ops. Now it's too late — the important thing now is the mission, not the PR." Marcie jumped in and agreed with me that it was too late and too dangerous to let outside technicians into Mission Ops to set up a TV camera and that ended that.

I said, "I'm going to talk about the spacecraft and not Dougherty, since I'm the only one of us who knows anything about it and I'm going to talk about the mission for the same reason," and to my surprise, Marcie backed me up on both accounts.

Scott, still wanting to find a way of minimizing my impact of the news conference, said, "But you have to talk about the science and you can't talk about everything."

I answered, "There is no science to talk about — we will have just gotten into the mapping orbit a couple of hours before the news conference. We've talked about the science goals a hundred times already so there is no point in doing it again and there won't be anything to talk about scientifically for several weeks."

Scott didn't like that at all and continued to try to push me off as "just the Project Scientist" and promote himself, Ames, Marcie, and Lockheed, in that order, as being responsible for the mission.

The meeting ended with my being absolutely intransigent and Scott, the stinking SOB, had to give in. Scott said he would talk first about program "firsts" and then Dougherty was going to talk about how Lunar Prospector was managed — all of that was totally irrelevant at that point, the only thing that mattered was the spacecraft and how well it was performing. Regardless of how dumb it was, Scott wanted to have it that way, and then I would talk about the mission and the spacecraft for as long as I wanted. Because Scott also wanted to pretend that Marcie had something to do with running the mission, she was going to sit up there with the three of us, which, to her credit, she was not happy about — it was just plain stupid.

After that, I found out via Dougherty that Scott was having Marcie report the daily activities directly to him, without my knowledge. Scott didn't even have the guts to tell me what he was doing — as usual, he just kept sneaking around behind my back. I was going to get rid of that SOB just as soon as I had the time, i.e., right after Lunar Prospector was safely in its mapping orbit.

I had been working on the letter I was going to send to Wes demanding that Scott be removed from the mission, so I called Dave Weaver, whom I had asked to look at the draft letter from a lawyer's prospective, and he gave me a lot of good suggestions that would make the letter even more powerful.

Once I had (hopefully) gotten rid of fatso Scott, I intended to take on NASA for all the crap they had done. NASA had gotten so bad that, as John Gruener told me, Wendell Mendell and other NASA employees at JSC were appalled that NASA was simply ignoring me and all the years of work the JSC area volunteers and I had put into the mission and pretending that Lunar Prospector was just a NASA mission. First Scott, then NASA — somehow I would make them pay for what they were doing.

The only good thing about Scott's underhanded, cowardly, and self-serving ways was that the prick did not even say a word of congratulations to me about the success of the mission, and I was very happy about that.

Similarly, except for Frank, not one single Lockheed manager called me about the mission — what else does one need to know about Lockheed?

One other amusing thing was that the Lockheed PR guy who was working for Buddy had been doing a good job of trying to keep me in the limelight and he kept bitching that NASA was totally ignoring Lockheed's contribution to the mission and that NASA wouldn't give out the Lockheed PR material to the press unless he was physically there to see that NASA did so. I thought how ironic all that was — NASA and Scott were continually trying to screw Lockheed and visa versa, while all the time they were both screwing me!

Regarding the spacecraft's attitude and how Dan determined it, Dan came up with something that both of us should have thought of much earlier — given Dan's expertise in spacecraft dynamics and my astronomical background. In order to determine a spacecraft attitude, one needs two different measurements, because the attitude is defined by two angles. Thus, we had the Sun sensor that gave us one of the angles (the Solar Equatorial Angle or SEA) and the EM limb-crossing sensor to give us the second angle. However, as Lunar Prospector was coasting towards the Moon, Dan noticed that the SEA was slowly changing and then it hit him. Just as the Sun appears to move up and down the Earth's sky by $\pm 23.5°$ between summer and winter every year, Lunar Prospector's Sun sensor was so accurate that it was picking up the slow shift in the SEA as the Earth, and hence the Moon and Lunar Prospector, moved 1° around the Sun every day. Just like that, Dan knew he could use the data from the extremely accurate Sun sensor to determine the spacecraft attitude, all by itself, by noting the SEA (the first measurement) and the change in the SEA over a period of several hours (the second measurement) and could do so more accurately than he could using the less accurate data from the EM limb-crossing sensor! When he told me that, I was very pleased, and felt like hitting myself in the head for not thinking of it years earlier. I was just as sure Dan felt the same way about himself. Regardless of how dumb we felt, Dan had just made the mission better and easier to do and we were both very happy about that.

Also, Bill Feldman wanted to have me change some of the energy window settings on the GRS to peak it up and on the APS so he could figure out what was wrong with Face 5. He thought the energy response range of Face 5 had shifted during launch. He wanted me to reset the energy windows to check out that idea. Saying that something was not quite right with Face 5 of the APS was putting it mildly.

Finally, Dave Curtis had found that the ER had some noise at the highest voltage in its voltage sweep cycle and he wanted to run some tests to find the source of that noise. Also, he wanted to determine the zero offsets of the three axes of the MAG.

I got all the commands that Bill and Dave wanted me to send and added them to the Mission Profile for the evening, as well as the commands for the LOI burn attitude reor maneuver that Dan and I were going to do. When I was finished, I went through the usual series of checks with Bill, Dave, and Dan to insure that everyone agreed with the Mission Profile and that it contained no errors. That done, we were ready for the third commanding session.

My Ops Team, Dave Curtis, Bill, Marcie, Dave Lozier, Ken Galal, and I had all assembled in Mission Ops by 7:00 Thursday evening and I started commanding about 15 minutes later, at 001/23:48 MET. As Bill requested, I first reset the APS energy windows with a series of two commands and two executes, so he could watch the APS data for the 1½ hours it would take me to run through the various commanding sequences Dave Curtis wanted to have done for the MAG/ER, after which, I would finish Bill's set of APS test commands.

I got started on Dave's first sequence — the check of the MAG zero offsets — at 002/00:03 MET (gee, spacecraft turn-on had occurred just 2 days and 3 minutes earlier, a lot had happened in those 2 days) and I finished that set of 8 commands 21 minutes later, at 002/00:24 MET. Ten minutes later, I started Dave's second series of tests, which we finished at 002/00:48 MET. Again, after a 10-minute wait, we began the third and last MAG/ER test, which consisted of a series of 10 commands.

As was our standard and well practiced practice, as Paul uplinked each MAG/ER command, I read and verified the echo and then Dave did the same when the echo appeared on his screen. After we both had verified the 9th MAG/ER command in the last series, I was waiting to see "MTLOADB, 1, 5, 27" appear on my command screen, but instead I saw "GACSLO, 4," which was the first command in the final series I had prepared for Bill and not the last command in Dave's final series! I immediately said, "Stop, that's the wrong command. What's wrong?"

Paul quickly said, "I'm sorry. That's my fault. I accidentally skipped a command."

No harm was done. The "GACSLO, 4" command had not been execute, because I had caught it, and even if it had been executed, it would have only started the spectrometer sequence of commands before I was finished with Dave's MAG/ER test and that would have made no difference at all. However, I did not like the fact that Paul had been sloppy. He had not paid strict attention to what I was saying and hence, had not strictly followed the Mission Profile. While such a command sequence error, even if I did not catch it via my careful reading of the command echoes, would do no harm when commanding the science instruments, it could be fatal when I was commanding an engine burn or some other engineering subsystem. I was very unhappy that Paul had screwed up and told him to be much more careful in the future.

With that little experience behind us, I had Paul uplink the last MAG/ER command and we finished the MAG/ER tests at 002/01:26 MET.

When we were finished, Dave had found that the source of the ER noise was the MAG/ER heater circuit! Since the translunar coast phase of the mission was the coldest phase of the mission, and since neither the MAG heater nor the ER heater had turned on, they would never turn on during the rest of the mission. I told Dave that and I said we ought to consider just shutting off the heater circuit and not use it unless we found we needed it on once we were in lunar orbit. Dave agreed that was probably the correct thing to do, but said he would check everything out very carefully and we should make the final decision after he was sure about his conclusion. The downside to turning the MAG/ER heater circuit off was that I would no longer get the MAG/ER engineering data on my console screen, hence I would have to go look at the MAG/ER console to check the health of the instruments, which I could do with little trouble.

After waiting nearly 10 minutes to completely check out the spacecraft and the MAG/ER, I got ready to start Bill's command sequence by re-uplinking the GACSLO, 4 Command and then executing it. Bill said, "No, that's not necessary; the command is in the buffer and the buffer can be filled with several commands that can all be executed with one Spectrometer Execute Command (SECMDEXEC)."

Well that was news to me! That was not the way I had asked Bill to build the SES and it made the whole concept of having the SES Execute Command meaningless, because if we did uplink an incorrect command and I caught it when I checked it, it would still be in the damned buffer and we couldn't get it out. I told Bill to see if he could find a way to empty that damned buffer.

I did not like the fact that, except for the most important commands (basically the Turn-on and Turn-off Commands), I could not check the commands properly for both sets of instruments before the commands were acted upon by their electronics. In the case of the MAG/ER, most of the commands were executed immediately upon reception by the MAG/ER DPU (Data Processing Unit), and in the case of the spectrometers, most commands went into that damned buffer, so if we inadvertently sent an incorrect command, it would be executed without my being able to do anything about it. Happily, none of the instruments commands that could be inadvertently executed in those ways could hurt the instruments or, more importantly, the spacecraft. Nevertheless, that was not the way I wanted the instruments built and neither Bill nor the MAG/ER guys had understood what I meant when I had told them how I wanted the command electronics to be built in the beginning. Well, the instruments were built that way so, like the C&DH error that shut off all the engine heaters when I fired any one engine, I would have to set up my commanding tables to account for those irregularities.

I went ahead and executed the buffered "GACSLO, 4" Command and then finished uplinking the rest of Bill's command load. I finished that at 002/01:47 MET. Though Bill had originally wanted me to change the energy windows of the APS to help determine what was wrong with Face 5, he had concluded before the commanding session began that there was no shift in the energy response of Face 5 — something else was wrong with it! I only uplinked the GRS and NS commands, but the question remained, "What is wrong with Face 5?"

Goddard Nav reported the results of our 2nd mid-course maneuver and they were phenomenal. The first couple of solutions showed that our velocity was off by just 20 cm/sec, that we were arriving at the Moon 19 seconds late (out of a 105 hours translunar coast), and the periselene of the incoming hyperbolic orbit was just 11 kilometers low; so the trajectory was just right on the mark. The trajectory errors were so small that the 3rd pre-planned MCM, set for the following night, would at most be a tweak burn that would last a second or something like that, i.e., the absolutely minimum burn.

With that excellent news, Dan and I computed and compared our reor parameters and found that to make the 34.3° turn we needed to do to put the spacecraft into its LOI burn attitude, we needed to do a 93 pulse burn that would take 14.5 minutes, using our standard reor engines A1 and A4. Dan said the final SEA would be –1.7°. With the reor burn parameter file ready, Dan sent it to Paul and we ran through our series of verification checks. Starting at 002/02:39 MET, I had Paul uplink the standard A1 and A2 heater turn-on file, verified the echoes, and watched to see that the engines were heating up. When I had verified that they were, I told Paul to uplink the burn parameter and engine selection file, which he did and then Dan and I went through our careful parameter verification ritual as the command echoes came back from the spacecraft. That finished, I had Paul send the EXEC at 002/03:05 MET and for the next quarter of an hour, we watched the various engineering data tell us the reor burn was proceeding successfully and Dan read off the SEA as it slowly approached –1.7°. Finally, Dan said the burn time was up and I saw the A1 and A4 engine temperatures begin to drop — the maneuver was over and Lunar Prospector was in its LOI burn attitude. I immediately had Paul uplink the Engine Safeing Command File and then it was 002/03:21 MET and we had just finished sending our 248th perfect command to the spacecraft.

The spacecraft was behaving phenomenally. The power, the propulsion, and everything else were just rock solid. I could not fathom how perfectly the spacecraft was performing. The only slight flaw, of course, was the problem with Face 5 of the APS, but everything else was just perfect. And, I had used slightly less fuel than I had planned for that phase of the mission — I still had 91.2% of my fuel!

I left Mission Ops well after midnight, at about 002/05:00 MET and, because the spacecraft was in such good health, I decided to drive home to Gilroy, where Rebecca was, to get a good night's sleep in my own bed.

It was kind of cloudy when I got home, but the clouds were thin enough so I could see the gibbous Moon — it was a couple of days before full. I tried to sit back, relax, and think of what was really going on, because, up until then, the mission had been my computer screen and the data I was getting. As was necessary to do my job, I had intentionally suppressed my emotional connection with the mission — I was totally disconnected from the reality of it and I did not think of the spacecraft as a real entity that I loved and knew so well and that was about ¾ of the way to the Moon. But I was not in Mission Ops, so I wanted to regain the emotional realization that I had a spacecraft on the way to the Moon and it was physically out there, spinning away with its engines firing at my command. Even in Mission Ops, I had moved a model of Lunar Prospector to where I could see it from my console, so I could capture a little of the emotional reality of the mission, because it was a phenomenal thing that was going on. By seeing the beautiful Moon up there in the dark, cloudy night sky and knowing that Lunar Prospector was out there too, I totally regained the emotional connection with my spacecraft and my mission and I enjoyed that so very much.

Finally satisfied, I went to bed at about 2:00 AM.

Friday, January 9, 1998

002/13:30 MET through 003/03:00 MET: The 3rd MCM Canceled

I had had a good night's sleep and woke up at about 9:00 AM. Nevertheless, I had run out of adrenaline and really felt a deep fatigue in my body. It was phenomenal to see how my body was reacting to all the work and lack of sleep associated with what was the thrill of a lifetime!

When I got up to Mission Ops, the spacecraft was in perfect condition and then I got a call from a business financier magazine that Jim Benson had told to talk to me, so I gave the reporter the entire spiel about Lunar Prospector and the future of commercial lunar exploration.

About 3:00 PM Friday, Goddard gave us an update of our trajectory after the 2nd MCM and it was even better than their preliminary analyses showed. Our arrival time was 3.4 seconds late (out of 105 hours transit time), our velocity was 10 cm/sec off and our periselene was 4 km low! The corrections for those small errors were something like a ½ sec burn on the A1 and A2 engines and ½ of a pulse on the T1 and T2 engines, so trying to make such small burns was absurd and we all agreed that I should cancel the 3rd MCM originally planned for early Saturday morning — as we had expected would be the case from the beginning.

Though I was not surprised that we canceled the 3rd MCM, I was very surprised at the amazing accuracy of our burns, especially given that we had a simple blow-down propulsion system! My idea of having the spacecraft as simple as possible was paying off handsomely.

Besides trying to figure out what was wrong with Face 5 of the APS, Bill had been watching the performance of the GRS and NS, which were functioning perfectly. But he wanted to change the gains on the GRS and on Side 2 of the NS. He gave me the changes he wanted, I redlined my Mission Profile and we went through the checks to insure that everything was correct. Starting at 002/20:06 MET (about 3:30 PM on Friday the 9th), I had Ric uplink the two commands and two executes to first change the high-voltage of the GRS to 1572 v and then that of Side 2 of the NS to 1192 v (raising or lowering the high-voltage on the GRS and the NS is the equivalent of tuning your radio and was something we would have to do periodically during the mission).

After watching the GRS a little more, Bill wanted to change the energy response windows of the GRS, so I again redlined the Mission Profile and between 002/23:25 MET and 002/23:28 MET (nearly 7:00 PM), I had Ric uplink the four commands needed to make those minor changes to the GRS.

I stayed around Mission Ops until about 9:00 PM and then drove home to Gilroy to get some sleep. The next day was going to be a long one.

Chapter 4-3
LOI — Lunar Orbit Insertion

Saturday, January 10 through Early Sunday Morning, January 11, 1998

003/10:30 MET through 004/05:00 MET: The Prelude to Lunar Capture

Rebecca and I got up about 6:00 Saturday morning, got some donuts, coffee (for her), and a coke (for me) at the local donut shop and drove up to Mission Ops.

We got there at about 10:00 AM and I started getting everything ready for the 1st LOI burn — *the all important capture burn* — that was to occur in about 20 hours. The capture burn was the fourth and last of the critical missions events — the first three being launch, spacecraft turn-on, and boom deployment — since, if we did not get into a highly elliptical capture orbit, we would go sailing by the Moon and the mission would be lost. Once we got into the capture orbit, then, even if something went wrong, we had plenty of time to fix the problem and, if necessary, we could take weeks instead of two days, to get down to the 100 km mapping orbit. The critical 32-minute capture burn was the focus of our attention.

After seeing to it that everything was ready, I sat down at my console and watched the spacecraft. I noticed the MAG heater was on and using about 0.08 watts! Since we were thinking about turning the MAG/ER heater off because of the little bit of noise it caused, I called Dave Curtis and left a message for him to call me.

During the course of the afternoon, Goddard's trajectory determination was getting more and more accurate. Goddard's final solution was that the periselene was 10 km low instead of 4 km, but the velocity error was holding at 10 cm/sec. Basically, the slight differences in their solutions were not enough to concern us. And their solution for the ΔV required to put Lunar Prospector into its 12-hour capture orbit was 356.2 m/sec.

Dave Curtis returned my call and said he had looked through the MAG/ER data and found there was some bad data when we did the reor to LOI attitude the previous night. He wanted to know if any other instrument or subsystem had produced bad data during the burn and I said, "I don't know for sure, but I doubt it. I'll find out for sure." I looked at the MAG temperature data and said, "The MAG temperature started to drop when we did the reor. It had been holding at (a hot) 20° C and then it dropped down to (a still very warm) 8° C over a period of about 3 hours. Then the heater went on." We both found it very strange that though the MAG was warm, the ER and the MAG/ER DPU were so cold the heater went on!

Dave said, "Well gee, it sounds like the thermal blanket came loose or came off, but that doesn't make any sense."

I said, "Well, we changed the attitude of the spacecraft quite a bit to get it into the LOI attitude. Maybe it's just something weird like — like the sunlight shining on the magnetometer in a peculiar way and keeping it hot." We really didn't have any idea about what was going on — it was a minor mystery. The MAG temperature was not out of spec, but we just could not figure out why in hell its temperature suddenly dropped and why the ER heater turned on. We were going to have to look at all the data and get it plotted up, but since we were at the coldest point of the mission, we were not concerned, just perplexed.

Bill had been working with the spectrometers and wanted to make some changes in the energy detection windows of the NS. Then he wanted to run an APS test and turn Face 5 of the APS off, since it was not working. I thought we should keep Face 5 on to see if it worked after the LOI burns. If it still was not working, then we could turn it off.

I typed up a modification of the Mission Profile with all the changes Bill wanted. I was being very, very careful about the instrument commanding because of what I had learned from the previous instrument commanding session. Since it was true that instrument commanding could not endanger the mission, as could spacecraft commanding, I did not apply the triple (or more) check procedures I used for spacecraft commanding to the instrument commanding. But I did not like the fact that the instrument electronics had been built in a way that eliminated my ability to completely check all of the instrument commands via the command echoes before their electronics acted upon them. I carefully checked the spectrometer commands in the Mission Profile with both Bill and Ric before I started the uplink session shortly at 003/20:03 MET.

The first command was supposed to change the high-voltage level of Side 2 of the NS to 1145 v, but when I got the echo, I didn't recognize the command and said, "Stop, that's the wrong command." Then we checked it out and we found out it was the command to change the NS Side 1 high-voltage level. Bill had inadvertently given me the command for Side 1 instead of Side 2 and, despite our careful checks, we had missed it until I saw it in the echo (remember, all of us had had only a few hours of sleep per night during the previous five days and were at Mission Ops most of the rest of the time). I thought, *oh crap, there's nothing I can do about it now because of the damned buffer.* I had to go ahead and execute the command; then I redlined the Mission Profile and changed the Side 1 high-voltage right back to what it was.

That was our second instrument commanding error and I did not like it at all. I had caught both commanding errors, but because the SES wasn't built the way I wanted, I did not have the ability to write over the commands and I had to execute them — though in neither case did that make any difference, it annoyed me very much.

I continued having the remaining commands in Bill's APS test sequence uplinked. As we did, the DSN was going to pass us off from one tracking station to another (as it did about every eight hours), so we didn't think anything about it. All of the sudden, the DSN called up and said, "We are going to be shutting you down for this switch over in about 2 minutes."

Well, we didn't have enough time left to finish Bill's sequence. I executed the command that was in the SES buffer. Bill was looking at the APS detectors in pairs to see if there was any cross-talk between them and we had gotten half way through that series of tests. He said, "This isn't a critical test, so we can forget the rest of it, but I want to change the NS Side 2 high-voltage up another step to 1191 v." I just had time to command Faces 1, 2, 3, and 4 of the APS back on, but not the NS Side 2 high-voltage step before the DSN dropped us, so I planned to command the NS Side 2 high-voltage to its new setting just as soon as the DSN had locked us up again.

As soon as that commanding was done, I wanted to go to the motel, where Rebecca was trying to nap, and try to get a few hours sleep myself before starting the commanding session for the 1st LOI burn that would begin at about 2:00 Sunday morning. By that time, it was nearly 5:00 PM Saturday and I wanted to be in bed by 6:00 PM, so I could sleep until midnight. Well, we waited and waited and the DSN could not get their damn system going — they were having trouble with the ephemeris, couldn't get the right link, and blah, blah, blah. It just went on and on and at nearly 7:00 PM I finally said, "OK, I have to try to get some sleep and I'm not going to wait until I've changed the NS high-voltage. I'll do that when I get back," and I left for the motel. However, what the delay really did was it ended any possibility of my getting any sleep. When I got to the motel, neither Rebecca nor I could sleep, so we got up after resting about two hours and went back to Mission Ops!

I immediately started checking out the spacecraft and since I again had command capability, I changed the NS Side 2 high-voltage to 1191 v at 004/02: 32 MET (just before 10:00 Saturday night), even though Bill wasn't there. He was also trying to get some sleep — also without any success, but he did rest a couple of hours. None of us got any sleep — we were all too keyed-up about the critical capture burn.

While I was changing the NS Side 2 high-voltage, I noticed we had forgotten to reset the EM sensor threshold when we canceled the 3rd MCM. Somewhat later, when Dan arrived at Mission Ops, I pointed that out to Dan and asked him if he still wanted it changed. He answered, "Yes," so I went ahead and sent that command and executed it at 004/03:21 MET. Slowly but surely, we were working our way towards the capture burn.

Scott was giving all kinds of interviews to the press and of course, he hadn't been around Mission Ops except for one meeting where I briefly saw him. There was no interaction between us at all. I didn't want to see him and I had the feeling he was afraid to see me.

Visitors started showing up around midnight. Dougherty came in and brought some cake and other goodies. Sylvia brought some champagne and Sparkling Apple Cider to celebrate our expected successful capture burn.

Slowly but surely, the mood began to build up and my Ops Team and I had gotten everything honed down to a fine point for the burn. We discussed all the emergency procedures and I wrote the exact time of the beginning of the burn in the Mission Profile to an accuracy of a tenth of a second (usually the timeline was just timed to the nearest minute). We were slowly getting ready for the big one.

Early Sunday Morning, January 11, 1998

004/05:00 MET through 004/09:00 MET: The Capture Burn

Finally, at about 12:30 Sunday morning, a little more than 3 hours before the burn and about 2 hours before we were to start commanding, my Ops Team and I started to get ready in the Glass Room for the critical events ahead and I tried to get everybody outside the Glass Room to quiet down. The crowd was getting bigger and bigger. Dougherty had invited Henshaw to be there and there were several bigwigs from Ames and a lot of other people were coming in. Scott was giving press interviews, so he slithered in later.

Unfortunately, the bigwigs and all the other guests were blabbing to each other like they were at a cocktail party instead of in a Mission Control area. As I began to get my team ready to go, I told Marcie to tell everyone outside the Glass Room to be quiet. Though the guests did quiet down some — enough so we could work — they were not keeping their mouths shut as I wanted and as the situation required.

Just about 3 hours before the burn, the tank heaters turned on, so the load current jumped up to about 5 amps. Before that, the load current was running, as usual, at about 3½ amps and if the tank heaters did not gone off by the time the engines fired, the load current would be about 6½ amps during the burn. If so, I was pretty sure the spacecraft would have to draw some power from the battery, because I did not think the solar array would produce enough power to handle that load. That possibility was increased because I was sure the solar array would produce even less power as it got hotter due to the heat radiated by the Moon as the spacecraft got near the Moon. Also, I was pretty sure, as the tank pressure dropped from 361 psi to 214 psi during the long 32-minute burn (the burn would use 29.2% of our fuel, leaving us with 62.0% at the end of the burn), there would be adiabatic cooling of the helium in the tanks and that might keep the tank heaters on or make them turn on again during the burn. I wanted Woody to watch the power usage during the burn. I would be watching the power, too, but I wanted to make sure I knew if the battery was discharging. I couldn't be sure I would catch everything since I had so many things to watch during the burn. Similarly, I had each of the other support engineers watch their subsystems to make sure I missed nothing of importance during the critical capture burn.

Dan, the Nav Team, and I made our final checks of our calculations for the burn duration and timing and Dan checked his burn parameter files again. I had Marcie make sure JPL had our emergency burn parameter files at the Goldstone DSN station in case we became inoperable (earthquake, fire, sabotage, etc.) and Goldstone had to send up the critical capture burn commands. She reported that JPL and Goldstone were ready. Thus both the belt and suspenders were in place. I asked if, as planned, we were being tracked by both the Canberra (Australia) and the Goldstone (California) DSN stations and the answer was, "Yes." The safety pins were also in place.

Besides having two completely different tracking stations tracking us and having emergency command loads at Goldstone, our plan was to turn on the A1 and A2 engine heaters over an hour before the burn and uplink the burn parameter file with a 1-hour burn delay programmed into it. If we could not get that file uplinked for some strange reason (both DSN stations were down or the ground lines were dead), we had backup burn parameter files with 45, 30, 15 and 0 minute delays and we would try to uplink the appropriate file every 15 minutes until one got uplinked.

Finally, even if one of the files was properly loaded, but the burn did not start, we would try to uplink the 0-minute delay file over and over again until the burn started or until it was too late to do anything about the 1st LOI burn. Then we would initiate other emergency procedures to try to get Lunar Prospector captured by the Moon before it slipped completely out of the Moon's gravitational grasp in less than a day. Clearly, we were leaving nothing to chance with the all-important capture burn and, as such, the fact that the bigwig guests could not keep their loud mouths shut was a source of great annoyance to me.

About an hour before I was going to start commanding the burn, I started calling out how far Lunar Prospector was from the Moon and the various spacecraft engineering data, partially in an effort to try to keep the crowd interested in what was going on and partially because I would have done so even if the guests were not there. But they were not interested! All they did was yak, yak, yak, and Scott, when he did slither in, was blabbing more than the rest of them — trying to be the big shot. Rebecca, who was sitting in her usual position right in front of me outside the Glass Room, said Scott had been talking with Henshaw and he turned around, bobbed his head down, shook his hair like a woman does and then combed his hair to make sure he was all properly preened for his court. Then he pranced around and talked to everyone.

The guests were again talking so loudly that I looked around to see who was making all the damned noise. Marcie, whom I had asked to keep the people quiet, was as bad as the rest of them. In fact, she was one of the ringleaders doing all the yapping. Even Sylvia was yapping away all the time! I was disappointed and annoyed with everyone out there. Why were they there? It was not a cocktail party; it was Mission Operations for a spacecraft that was about to go into lunar orbit! Since Marcie was as bad as everyone else out there, I told everyone over my microphone to be quiet because we were about to command the burn. With that, everyone simmered down to a reasonable level, but they were still not completely quiet, as they should have been.

To top all that stupidity off, an Ames cameraman came, but without a camera! Wasn't that lovely. I was disgusted with the whole bunch of NASA and Lockheed idiots.

Finally, we got to the point where it was time to start commanding and Dan, Paul, and I got ready to start our formal checks of the heater turn-on and critical burn parameter files and to do the commanding.

First Paul and I checked the standard A1 and A2 heater file. When we were satisfied it was the correct one and had checked it, I said to Paul, "Please uplink the heater file on my mark at 004/07:09 MET and I soon started my standard countdown, "20 seconds, 10, 5, 3, 1 and 0."

Paul said, "File away."

And I waited for the echoes. Shortly thereafter, I saw the first echo and I said, "I have echo of 2-A-0-0-2-2, VCID of 0-6, which is correct for the A1 heater." Then, "I have Execute of the A1 Heater Command," and a frame later I said, "I have echo of 2-B-0-0-2-4, VCID of 0-6, which is correct for the A2 heater," and finally I said, "I have Execute of the A2 Heater Command," the file was correctly uplinked. I saw that the load current had increased with each execution by the expected 0.2 amps, and then I waited to see the first signs that the A1 and A2 heaters were heating up. As expected, the A1 temperature curve started climbing first, followed by the A2 heater curve — the engines were heating up, a fact I announced to the still all-too-noisy mob.

I turned to Dan and, as always, asked him to re-check the parameter file to be sure he had the correct one, then he called out its name and purpose and sent it to Paul's computer. Paul called the file up, read its name to Dan and me and asked if that was the correct file. Dan answered, "Yes." Paul opened the file, and with me watching over his shoulder and simultaneously looking at my Mission Profile, Paul read the numbers in the five registers out loud and Dan and I checked the validity of each number.

When we were satisfied the file and the parameters were correct, I asked Dan formally, "Are you ready to have the file loaded?"

Dan answered equally formally, "Yes, I am."

I then told Paul to uplink the file, which he did on my usual time mark, "20 seconds, 10, 5, 3, 1 and 0."

Paul said, "File away."

I watched my echo screen intently while waiting to start the strict file uplink verification procedure with Dan. Then, I saw the first echo and I said, "I have echo of DELAYSUN of 3-1-0-0-0-0, VCID 0-6. Is that correct, Dan?"

Dan answered, "Yes it is."

The next frame appeared on my screen and I said, "I have echo of LONGDUR of 3-2-4-B-4-6, VCID of 0-6. Is that correct, Dan?"

Dan answered, "Yes it is."

The next frame appeared and I said, "I have echo of HALFREV of 3-3-0-0-0-0, VCID of 0-6. Is that correct, Dan?"

Dan answered, "Yes it is."

The next frame appeared and I said, "I have echo of DELAYNUM of 3-0-F-0-0-1 (the 60 minute delay), VCID of 0-6. Is that correct, Dan?"

Dan answered, "Yes it is."

Finally I saw the engine selection echo and I said, "I have echo of 3-F-0-0-5-6, VCID of 0-6, which is correct of the A12LOI engine selection," and I then asked, "Dan, do you concur with the entire load?"

Dan answered, "Yes I do."

I said to Paul, who was to send the burn file EXEC Command in the Store-and-Forward mode so we would get it executed exactly on time, "Please set the send-time to 10:44:51.9 GMT," and then I asked Dan, "Do you concur with the send-time?"

Dan said, "Yes, I do."

Paul then read back the send-time and Dan and I confirmed it was correct. Then I said, "Paul, please send the Execute Command file on my mark at 004/07:20 MET and have the Set Command Register and Execute file ready to send at the end of the burn."

Paul answered, "Affirmative."

And we waited until I said, "20 seconds, 10, 5, 3, 1 and 0."

Paul immediately said, "Command away."

I waited one or two data frames for the verification echo that showed the file had been executed.

I saw the EXEC echo and I said, "I have Execute."

Shortly thereafter, Dan said, "DELAY, 59 minutes," the spacecraft had started its internal countdown to the capture burn. The load was in and the sequence had started (and the engines were getting hot). We did not need the belt and suspenders any longer, so at 004/07:25 MET, I told John to inform JPL that the LOI file at Goldstone should not be executed; he did that and confirmed it.

Dan continued counting down the time remaining to burn-initiate and I read off the engine temperatures that reached their equilibrium levels at about 140° C after about 30 minutes and the crowd noise got louder and louder as the guests continued their cocktail party behavior. As we got closer to the burn, I said over my mike, "OK, I want it quiet out there," at least twice politely. About three minutes before burn-initiate, they were all out there just yakking it up — Dougherty was guffawing around and Scott was prancing around talking to everybody. I had had it. I said very loudly over the mike that they had to be quiet, but since they were all talking so loudly and not paying any attention to what was going on in Mission Ops, they didn't even hear me! I shouted, "OK, we are coming up to the critical events and unless it is quiet out there, I am going to have the area cleared. I want it quiet and I mean it." That finally shut the bastards up. I would have thrown them out if they had not shut up and, in retrospect, I should have thrown them out and I should have done so much earlier.

While all the crowd commotion was going on, Bill told me the NS had begun detecting neutrons emanating from the Moon when the spacecraft was still a good two lunar radii away from the Moon and that was really great.

Then Dan (based on the clock time) said, "Burn initiate," and, about 17 seconds later, he called out "NUMTIME zero." The A1 and A2 engines should have begun firing and I was intently watching for the engine temperatures to rapidly increase, the tank pressure to drop to its dynamic value and the load current to jump up by about 1½ amps.

All of the sudden, I saw A1 heat up to about 800° C and then A2 jumped up to about 500° C. I called out the engine temperature increases, confirming we had ignition. I saw the tank pressure drop from its static value of 361 psi to its dynamic value of 345 psi and I called that out as Dan called out, "Increase in spin rate," and then I looked for the change in the load current. But, just about the time the engines fired, some other heaters, besides the two engine heaters, shut off, so I didn't see any change in the load current that was recognizable as being due to the engines turning on, i.e., the 1½ amp drop in the load current due to the engine heaters and other heaters turning off was offset by the 1½ amp increase in the load current by the engines turning on! Happily, even though the load current was well over 6 amps, we were not drawing power from the battery.

All that happened in 3 or 4 seconds and I then realized *that engine A2 was not heating up any more!* I thought, *uh-oh, do I have an engine that's not performing properly?* I would have just kept the burn going no matter what, but nevertheless, the critical question I had was — *do I have a bad burn going here?*

All of the sudden, as I was waiting to see if A2 was heating up beyond 500° C, I saw that A1 was still at 800° C and I realized I was not getting new data! I quickly asked, "Am I not getting updates?"

Paul, who was doing a fantastic job, answered, "No, we have lost telemetry on Station 24 (the station I was getting telemetry from)."

Since Dan was getting his data from the backup station, I asked, "Is Dan getting data?"

Paul answered, "Yes, Dan is still getting data, but it's intermittent."

My screen was dead! I was getting no updates at all! All I could see was the last readout showing that engine A1 was at about 800° C and that engine A2 was at about 500° C. I scooted my chair over so I could see Dan's screen, and even though he was losing data, I saw the next frame. About two or three frames later, I saw that both engines were at about 950° C and, very relieved, I said, "OK, we've got two good engines firing."

Then we began getting bad data most of the time, but I could see the tank pressure was dropping. Then we lost Dan's link, too! I said, "We've lost our telemetry." Almost immediately, we were told by JPL that the problem was that the ephemeris was not good, i.e., the predictions of the change in the transmitter's frequency due to the Doppler shift as the spacecraft's velocity decreased during the burn were not accurate enough so the DSN stations could keep a good lock on the Doppler shifted spacecraft signals. What a relief — it was not a spacecraft problem!

Knowing that the loss of lock was just due to the ephemeris, I knew the spacecraft was OK and since I knew the engines were burning and since I believed my spacecraft just worked no matter what, I correctly assumed we were not in trouble. I said, "The spacecraft is OK and we have a good burn going. We've just lost the link because the DSN can't track the Doppler shift properly."

About three minutes into the burn, we started getting data and I could see the engines were burning beautifully. They were just rock solid. The beautiful thing was that the spacecraft was hardly spinning up at all. Dan had thought that, based on the short burn we did using engines A1 and A2 during the 1st MCM, we would spin up by 3 rpm; in fact, we ended up with a spin rate of 13.2 rpm or with just a 1.2 rpm increase, which was fantastic.

Then I saw the adiabatic temperature drop in the tank temperatures, which was just fantastic. It turned out the temperature dropped from 23 to 18° C, a total of 5° C. Which was exactly what the thermal engineer had calculated when I had asked him the question about the adiabatic temperature drop as the pressure dropped during the long LOI burns.

After that, I saw, as I had expected, that the solar array was heating up as we came around the Moon. Then I asked Bill if he was seeing any effects of the spacecraft getting closer to the Moon and he said, "I'm getting lots of neutrons and lots of gamma rays. In fact, the flux is twice what I expected!" Everything was just going beautifully and I kept calling out the drop in the tank pressure and temperatures and the engine temperatures — I had a rock solid spacecraft!

Everybody was quiet outside the Glass Room and when we were 16 minutes into the burn I said, "We are now captured. We are nearing periselene, which is at an altitude of just 84 km."

Just a little bit later, Dan called out, "Periselene."

Since we had already achieved capture, as the burn continued, the period of the elliptical orbit the spacecraft would be in if the engines prematurely stopped for some reason, became shorter and shorter. I had the orbital period as a function of the burn time on a graph in front of me and I periodically called out those decreasing orbital periods, starting at several days and decreasing to 12 hours, as the burn continued. However, the engines did not stop prematurely, they just kept burning beautifully.

Also, once we had passed periselene and the spacecraft started moving away from the Moon, the temperature of the solar array temperature leveled off and then it started to drop — though that was what should have happened, I was surprised I saw the effect of the increase in the spacecraft's distance from the Moon's on the solar array temperature so quickly.

Dan had missed seeing the Moon come into the EM sensor's field of view because that happened when the DSN had lost the link. But, about a minute before the end of the burn, the Moon went out of the EM sensor's field of view and Dan called it out and added that he thought it was about a half a minute late.

Just after 004/08:52 MET, Dan called out, "NUMTIME zero," and I saw the 1½ amp drop in the load current as both engines cut off — the capture burn had ended on time. Then the engine temperatures began to drop and the tank pressure jumped to its static value — all signs that the burn had ended.

Some 3 or 4 frames later, as I was having Paul send up the SETCMDREG and EXEC file at 004/08:54 MET, and just a couple minutes after the end of the burn, the tank heater went off and the load current dropped back down to 3½ amps. I saw the echo of the EXEC and the registers all went to zero — we had successfully completed the critical 1st LOI, capture burn.

The instant the burn stopped, the adiabatic cooling stopped and the 18° C helium pressurant began to absorb heat very rapidly from the fuel, which was still at 23° C. I soon began to see the tank temperatures increase and, in about 20 minutes, the tank temperatures rose right back up to the pre-burn value of 23° C.

As we sat there, watching the spacecraft after the burn, we could see that the spacecraft was in good shape. We were absolutely certain we had had a good burn and the spacecraft's capture orbit was close to what we had wanted. *Regardless of what the exact orbit was, we knew that we had been captured!* Marcie stuck her head in the Glass Room and asked if we could come out for the champagne.

Later Sunday Morning, January 11, 1998

004/09:00 MET through 004/14:30 MET: Post-Capture Burn Activities

I hated to leave the Glass Room, in part because I really didn't want to have to accept the congratulations I was going to get from people like Scott, Dougherty, and other NASA and Lockheed managers who had made my job so hard and, in part because I really felt that having achieved lunar orbit after nine years of efforts was something I wanted to savor only with my trusted Ops Team and my sweet wife. I hesitated leaving the Glass Room, thinking, *how in hell can I get out of this?* — and hoping Marcie would bring the wine, sparkling cider, and goodies into the Glass Room so I could avoid the mob that had so aggravated me with its constant, loud yapping during most of the night's activities, but I obviously had to go out.

I finally did leave the Glass Room, but only after Marcie stuck her head in the door a couple of more times and said, "Come on out and have some wine, everyone wants to congratulate you."

Henshaw was the first to shake my hand, followed by Dougherty. I had to admit that Dougherty's congratulations were absolutely sincere — even if he is a bozo. Everybody came around and congratulated me. Scott, of course, came slithering up and shook my hand, but I thought he knew he was not exactly number one on my list (that is, the good list, not the shit list, on which he is number one) because he made no attempt to talk to me, except to say congratulations. Then his wife came up and said, "Congratulations, I am Susan Hubbard, Scott's wife."

I said, "Yes, I know; thank you," and thought, *unlike some people I know, I do know who my co-worker's wives are,* since Scott either did not recognize Rebecca, or intentionally snubbed her, as he did at the launch festivities at the Cape.

Everyone, especially my engineers, was really pleased with the success of the mission and that was gratifying. I got a lot of nice comments about the commanding, like, "Oh my God, you were so cool during all that." Finally, everyone noticed that I — a dumb scientist — knew what I was doing.

And Gerry Grismore, who had always been bitching about something, floored me by saying, *"You know, if you hadn't kept hammering on this stuff, this spacecraft wouldn't be so simple and easy to fly, it would have been a mess. You did it right."* I was truly floored and extremely pleased by what Gerry said. He had always been the most critical of the engineers, regarding the way I wanted to do the spacecraft, so his compliment meant more to me than anything anyone else said to me after the capture burn.

Sylvia came up to me and said "Congratulations," and turned to Rebecca and introduced herself to Rebecca.

Rebecca said, "Yes, I met you at the Galileo party."

Sylvia said, "Oh gosh, you've got a good memory."

Finally, Dan came out of the Glass Room (he was as reluctant to face the mob as I was, but, being second in command, he was able to hide in Mission Ops a little longer than I was). Dan and I toasted each other (with sparkling cider) and the spacecraft, and then I made a second toast to my command crew, who did a fantastic job, to the Ames and Goddard Nav Team, and to all the engineers and everybody who helped build Lunar Prospector — carefully not saying Lockheed engineers, just engineers.

By then, it was well after 5:00 AM, but it still amazed me how quickly the rats left the sinking ship. The place cleared out so fast they almost left a vacuum behind! Scott, of course, rushed downstairs to call Headquarters and to give all kinds of press interviews. My sweet Rebecca was really pissed off that Scott was giving all the interviews while I was doing all the work. I reminded her that everyone had said, "Alan has been working on this for 9 years, and this is his dream come true. Scott can say what he wants, but everybody knows it's Alan's project." However, before he left, Dougherty came over and gave me another good handshake; I felt good about that because, despite everything, he was very sincere about wanting the mission to succeed.

After all the visitors left, we went back into the Glass Room to watch the spacecraft return to normal and to wait for Goddard to tell us the results of the burn. I checked the MAG temperature and it was still at 8° C. The MAG/ER heater power usage had dropped down to about 0.04 amps and then came back up. We had to figure out what was going on with the MAG.

I got a call from the BBC and one from Florida asking for live interviews. Then Betsy Carter, a really nice Ames PR person, called to ask me if I had done the six or seven telephone interviews various reporters had requested. I answered, "No, I had a call from the BBC and one from Florida." She was quite puzzled and I thought there was something rotten in Denmark, i.e., that Scott had probably intercepted the reporters' calls. She told me I was supposed to go over to the auditorium at 9:00 AM for some TV interviews. By then it was after 7:00 AM; Rebecca had gone to the motel and, though I was dead tired, I had to stay up for the TV interviews.

Finally, we got the NAV report from Goddard, the capture orbit had a period of 11.60 hours, a little less than the planned 12-hour orbit, but that was OK. The post-burn orbital calculations also showed that our periselene was at 71 km (13 km lower than expected) and we had passed the periselene point just 33 seconds later than originally planned! Given those data, we clearly did not need to do the planned aposelene burn at 004/15:30 MET to raise the orbit's periselene, so I canceled it.

We tried to figure out why we had the slight over-burn of 4.3 m/sec (the burn was set for 356.2 m/sec, so the over-burn was just 1.2%) and we decided we had used too low a tank pressure in our calculations. Dan and I had calculated that the pressure at the end of the burn would be 213 to 214 psi and our calculated values were within 1 psi of each other. But the tank pressure, after the tanks had warmed back up, was 217 psi! I had thought that, because of the adiabatic cooling, we were going to have an underburn, so I expected that the orbital period was going to be over, not under 12 hours. However, since the engine calibrations were no better than 1%, and since the tank pressure had dropped from 361 psi to 217 psi, or nearly 40%, the engine thrust had decreased by nearly 40% during the long burn. Thus, a 1.2% over-burn was well within the burn uncertainties we had to expect, especially since the engines had performed over such a large dynamic range.

Nevertheless, we needed to understand the burn because we obviously wanted to do the final two LOI burns better; though the 2nd LOI burn was not critical, the 3rd LOI burn was very critical. Dan and the NAV guys were very nervous about the possibility of an over-burn on the 3rd LOI burn, because if we over-burned by 23.0 m/sec or by over 8.8%, we would hit the Moon! I didn't want to over-burn either, but there was no way we could have an 8.8% over-burn, given the performance of the engines up to that point in the mission. They wanted to chicken out and do a large under-burn on the 3rd LOI burn and I said we would talk about that after we saw how the engines performed during the 2nd LOI burn. Dan said, "I wanted a minimum under-burn of 10% and I'm going to put my foot down at anything less than 10%." I did not reply to that dumb remark, but I thought, *you can put your foot down all you want, but you don't run this mission. I do and I will decide how much of an under-burn we will have, if any*, and decided to wait until we saw what happened on the 2nd LOI burn before calling Dan on his impudence.

However, I was beginning to believe we were not going to be able to even calculate the 3rd LOI burn to better than 1%, so we probably wouldn't be able to burn all the way down to the 100 km circular orbit altitude. That would make no difference operationally; since the periselene of our original incoming trajectory was 10 km lower than originally planned, the periselene of the orbit after the 3rd LOI burn would be about 90 km, or 10 km lower than the circular orbit mapping we were ultimately going to reach. Thus, though I thought we would be close to circular, we would have to do a small ΔV burn to circularize the orbit a couple of days after the 3rd LOI burn, no matter what.

Shortly before 9:00 AM, I walked over to the auditorium and there was not a soul there. I thought, "Well, just like them. They've already done it and sent everybody home!" Then I saw a note from Betsy saying that Scott and I were supposed to go to the TV recording room. Though I did not want to see Scott, I went there and Betsy told me there were going to be two TV crews there, CBS, that was going to do a piece for the national TV evening news, and Channel 7. The Channel 7 guy just came with a camera; so Betsy was going to do the interview for him.

Finally the CBS crew came, as did Scott. Scott sort of slunk around and avoided getting into a conversation with me, which was fine with me — but very strange when you remember that we were supposed to be partners.

The first interview I did was for Channel 7. Betsy asked a lot of good questions and I was remarkably coherent, considering that I hadn't slept in 26 or 27 hours. In contrast to Scott, who was being interviewed by a really pretty blonde with CBS and who was well rested, well groomed, and in a nice suit and tie, I was tired, haggard, and disheveled in my work clothes. *It was a perfect example of what I had observed at NASA meetings my entire career; those attendees who were impeccably dressed and impeccably groomed knew nothing and did nothing except pontificate, while those who were poorly dressed and poorly groomed were the ones knew what they were doing and did all the work.*

While I was waiting to do the CBS interview, Harry McDonald, the boss of Ames came over and said, "I don't know if you know me; I'm Harry McDonald."

I said, "Of course, I know you."

He congratulated me and said, "You've done a marvelous job. The spacecraft is incredible and I am extremely proud you are working with Ames to do the mission," which was all very nice. Then I thought, *OK, Harry, you're going to find out all about Lunar Prospector*, since I wanted him to know that Lunar Prospector was neither a NASA, nor a Scott endeavor. I gave him the complete Lunar Prospector story, and as I was doing so, the CBS cameraman turned his camera on us and recorded the conversation.

Harry asked, "How is your institute?" and since he didn't quite understand my institute, I explained it to him.

Then the pretty blonde started to interview me. Her questions were also very good. She asked, "You are driving the spacecraft, aren't you? You are the one who is doing all the commanding, correct? Since this is your mission and you have worked on it for years, how does it feel to be in orbit now? Are you nervous and excited?" and so on.

I answered her questions one by one and explained, "I'm not driving the spacecraft, I am just doing my job as Mission Director and commanding it. No, I'm not nervous or excited. When I'm sitting there watching my computer screen and doing the commanding, it's not the time for emotions. There is no emotional connection with the spacecraft; it's just a lot of numbers and graphs on my computer screen. However, when I'm through commanding and I leave Mission Ops, I go out and look at the Moon and force myself to realize that I have a spacecraft up there and then I can visualize and enjoy it, but the rest of the time, it is a computer screen to me. I have to stay detached."

She asked about the future and I explained what LRI and Lunar Prospector were all about and that I wanted to do commercial lunar missions and help get man back on the Moon. I got to discuss everything about the mission's expected impact on the future of lunar and planetary exploration that I wanted to discuss.

While her interview was going on, Scott was making so much noise while he was being interview for Channel 7 that the lady and her cameraman had to stop and ask them to shut up. Despite that, the whole CBS interview was good. Finally, we were all finished and Scott just slithered away.

Then the long day was over and I went to my motel room where Rebecca was fast asleep. I went to bed at 10:00 AM (004/14:30 MET), so I had been up for about 28 hours. I slept three hours.

Sunday PM, January 11, through Early Monday Morning, January 12, 1998

004/17:30 MET through 005/09:00 MET: The 2nd LOI Burn

I got up at about 1:00 PM and went over to Mission Ops. Since the spacecraft was in perfect shape, and since I was dead tired from the lack of sleep, I went back to the motel room and slept for another three hours before going back to prepare for the 2nd LOI burn commanding session.

Dan, the Ames Nav guys — Dave and Ken — and I sat down to further evaluate the 1st LOI burn and effects of the adiabatic cooling, which was very definitely visible in the tank temperature data. We talked about the corrections we needed to make to our burn models since we had had the slight over-burn on the 1st LOI burn. Of the three models, my model came closest to correctly modeling the actual LOI burn; Dan's was too hot (he had not allowed for the adiabatic cooling); and the Nav model was too low. I decided we would use my calculated burn duration for the 2nd LOI burn, keeping the adiabatic cooling effect (which would be much smaller for the 2nd LOI burn than for the 1st) in my model and adding our estimates of the engine efficiencies based on the results of the 1st LOI burn. The calculated burn time was 27.08 minutes and that would bring the spacecraft down to its 3.5-hour, intermediate orbit. We would burn another 19.7% of our fuel, leaving us with 42.3%. When everyone agreed, I finished the Mission Profile and we got it ready to do the 2nd LOI burn.

The Ames TV crew was over to film the burn. I told them I was disappointed that the 1st LOI burn was not properly filmed and they agreed. They also agreed that NASA does a very poor job of PR and documentation.

With the exceptions that there were no visitors in Mission Ops, that we had no belt, suspenders, and safety pin backups at the DSN, that we used a 15 minute burn delay (rather than the 60 minute delay that we had used for the 1st LOI burn), and that the DSN did not lose contact with the spacecraft during the burn, the events of the 2nd LOI burn were essentially identical to that of the previous night and we conducted it like a well oiled machine.

As we were sitting at our consoles, getting ready to command the burn sequence, Dan, who had been using the Sun sensor data on the SEA and the rate of change of the SEA to determine the spacecraft's attitude with great accuracy, leaned over and showed me the graph of the spacecraft's SEA for the two orbits since we had burned into the 11.6 hour capture orbit a little less that 24 hours earlier. As expected, the graph showed that the SEA steadily decreased as the spacecraft, the Moon, and the Earth all moved together around the Sun by nearly a degree. But there was a little bump in the otherwise apparently straight SEA graph and that little bump (it amounted to just a few hundredths of a degree) was centered on the time of our 2nd periselene passage, 11.6 hours after we burned through our 1st periselene passage during the 1st LOI maneuver. Dan asked, "Do you know what this bump is?"

Astounded at seeing it, I answered, "Do you mean to tell me, that we are seeing the effects of the (lunar) gravitational gradient on the spacecraft?" (Except when the spin axis of the drum shaped Lunar Prospector Spacecraft was perpendicular to surface of the Moon [twice per orbit], one side of the spacecraft was closer to the Moon than the other side and hence the gravitational pull of the Moon on the far-side of the spacecraft was less than that on its near-side. This tiny, so called "gravitational gradient effect" caused Lunar Prospector to very slightly rock to and fro twice per orbit, an effect that was so small that we never expected to see it — but we did)?"

Dan answered, somewhat surprised that I knew, "Yes, we are! Isn't it amazing?"

I answered, "Yeah, it's more than amazing, but do you see the effect over the rest of the orbit (when the spacecraft was far from the Moon.)

Dan answered, "Yes, when you hold the graph up so you can look along the slope, you can see it's very slightly curved, rather than being straight," and he handed me the graph and I looked along it and, yes, it was very slightly curved!

I said, "Boy, I can hardly wait to see the graphs when we are in the 3.5-hour orbit and better yet, when we are in the mapping orbit," and Dan wholeheartedly agreed. That was really exciting.

After that exhilarating piece of news, I commanded the A1 and A2 heaters on starting at 005/07:08 MET (just after 2:30 AM). I executed the burn file at 005/07:18 MET and 15 minutes later, at 005/07:33 MET, the burn began. Along with the usual indicators of the burn that Dan and I monitored, I saw that the adiabatic temperature drop in the tank temperatures was, as expected about 2° C, i.e., much less than the 5° C for the 1st LOI burn. The burn ended at 005/08:00 MET and I was finished safeing the engines at 005/08:04 MET.

However, unlike the first LOI burn, we did a spin-trim burn after the main burn was finished, since the cumulative effects of the previous two sets of burns had increased the spin rate to 13.95 rpm, well above the range of 12±0.7 rpm we wanted to maintain. We did a 5.08 sec burn on the T1 engine at 005/08:38 MET and ended up with a 12.15 rpm spin rate (just 0.15 rpm high, but well with the 12±0.7 rpm range). The engine was safed by 005/08:40 MET.

We watched the spacecraft for a while and got the preliminary orbital data, which indicated we had achieved a 3.52-hour orbit; hence, we had an under-burn of only 1.7 m/sec or 0.6%, which was fantastic.

As I left Mission Ops at about 4:30 AM (005/09:00 MET), I thought, *everything is going perfectly, just one more major burn and we'll be there. I'm worn out and I need some sleep, but I'll get this baby into the mapping orbit and then I'll see if I can get rid of Scott and get into a regular day routine rather than this night routine. It's a great mission thus far and I am very pleased and proud.* Then I got to the motel and gratefully went to bed.

Monday, January 12, through Tuesday Morning, January 13, 1998

005/14:30 MET through 006/13:30 MET: The 3rd LOI Burn

I guess I got about four, maybe five hours of sleep and I was very tired — I was still running on adrenalin, but my adrenalin tank was getting very dry. Nevertheless, I was up and over at Mission Ops after a late breakfast or early lunch, depending on how you wanted to look at it.

Dave Curtis called and said he thought the MAG was running hot because we had a high SEA, so sunlight was shining on the MAG's bottom where there was no thermal blanket. He figured, when we did our reor a couple days earlier and went to the nominal, low SEA, the Sun would no longer shine on the bottom of the detector and it would cool down. I thought he was right.

Bill had come to the conclusion that the problem with Face 5 of the APS was that its delicate light filters had torn and, since the spacecraft was at a high SEA, sunlight was shining in through the torn filters and saturating the Face 5 detectors. Bill was convinced the filters had torn because, at my insistence for the safety of the launch, we had left the red covers off the APS detectors while the spacecraft was on the launch pad and hence the strong, cool airflow in the shroud had caused the filters to flutter so much they finally tore. I was equally convinced that the blast from one of the TLI Stage spin-up rockets and/or the 3000 psi nitrogen blast from one of the TLI Stage collision avoidance system rockets, both of which would have affected only the Face 5 filters, had done the filters in — but, of course, we would never know who was correct. However, as soon as I did the post-LOI reor maneuver and sunlight would no longer shine on Face 5, we would know if Bill's analysis was correct, because Face 5 should work just fine if he was.

In addition, Bill said, when he integrated the 20 minutes of GRS data that were collected around each periselene passage of the capture and intermediate orbits, the resulting spectrum already showed lines! That clearly indicated that we were going to get excellent compositional data from the GRS.

Dan had the SEA plots of the spacecraft's attitude for the five orbits since we entered the intermediate orbit early in the morning. As expected, the new SEA plots beautifully showed the slight wobbling of the spacecraft twice every orbit due to the effects of the gravitation gradient torques on it. Given the shorter, final 3.55-hour period of the intermediate orbit vs. the 11.6-hour period of the capture orbit, one could see the curve of the SEA plots during the three hour, aposelene legs of the plots almost as plainly as one could see the little bumps in the plots as the spacecraft passed quickly through the periselene of its orbits. That was a joy to see.

Since I was so tired, Rebecca and I went back to our motel after we had dinner and I took a one-hour nap. When I woke up, we watched the 10:00 PM CBS news, which had the interviews Scott and I had done the morning after the 1st LOI burn. Then we went over to Mission Ops to do the 3rd and final LOI burn.

When we got there, the big issue was how much of an under-burn would we do on the 3rd LOI burn. I was busy assessing the engine performance data from the 1st and 2nd LOI burns and making the burn calculations. Then Dan, Dave, Ken, Marcie, the Nav guys at Goddard (on the phone), and I had a burn conference to discuss our different opinions and to decide how big the under-burn should be.

My attitude was that we would determine exactly how the engines were performing, take that into account when we calculated the burn duration, and then do the LOI burn to get as close to the 100 km average orbital attitude as the engine performance data would allow. Given that our previous two burns had been no worse than 1.2% off and that we would have to have an 8.8% over-burn before we were in serious trouble, I saw no reason to consider a maximum under-burn of more that 1% or maybe 2% at the most.

Dan still wanted a minimum under-burn of 10% and was quite surly about it. Dan had called Irv, our propulsion engineer, to get Irv's opinion and that annoyed me. I knew more about the damned subsystems than the subsystem engineers did and if I needed their help, I would call them myself. But the damned engineers think that only engineers know anything and I was so sick of that attitude that I could have puked.

Well, in his infinite wisdom, Irv wanted us to do half of the burn, then a quarter of the burn and then an eighth of the burn, etc. on successive nights, until we had, after several days, slowly and ultra-cautiously worked our way down to the mapping orbit. That was just plain stupid. If that was all the faith Irv had in his engineering abilities to design a propulsion system, then he had no business being an engineer. I said, "That is just plain unacceptable. I'm not interested in even considering that."

When I said that, Dan became very sullen and would hardly talk. The Nav guys said they would be happy with a 3% under-burn and Marcie wanted a 5% under-burn. I said, "Look, I'll accept a 2% under-burn, throw away the adiabatic correction and the burn inefficiencies, as we know them. That gives a 3% under-burn, which is much bigger than the previous burn data indicates is necessary and much bigger than I like, but I would accept it." The Goddard and Ames Nav guys said they thought 3% was OK. Marcie said she kind of thought it was OK too, but she would still prefer 5%.

Dan got a bitter, frustrated look on his face and said, "I don't want anything less than 5%."

I asked Dan, "Dan, if you worked for me and not for Lockheed and if this was an LRI mission and not a Lockheed mission (in Lockheed's opinion), would you have any qualms at all about burning all the way down to circular, given the data we have on the first two burns?"

Dan said "No I wouldn't."

Well that did it, Dan's concerns had nothing to do with the real facts of the burns — he was just being a damned, gutless Lockheed engineer who was afraid of his company. I said, "I thought so. Well, since I'm not interested in having an under-burn at all and since I see nothing in any of our (burn) data to indicate there is anything wrong with us going with 3%, that's my decision. We go with 3%."

Dan said, "You mean 3% plus leaving off the adiabatic and engine performance corrections?"

I answered, "No, 3% total, with the corrections," and Dan was not happy.

The conference broke up and we all went to our cubicles to make our independent burn calculations. The burn duration was to be 27.03 minutes and we would use 17.4% of the fuel, leaving us with 24.9% to do the rest of the mission. The 24.9 % was a little bit more than I had expected at that point in the mission, so I was very happy.

Very shortly thereafter, Dan said he had called Irv again and Irv was pissed off at my decision and would not support the burn. Dan added angrily, "And I won't do the burn either."

I said, "Well, this is the way it is going to be done. If you won't do it, I'll pull John (Dan's poorly trained backup) in and I'll do the burn with him."

With that, Dan stormed out of my cubicle and I got pissed off at his childish and non-professional actions, so I followed him out and I let him have it. I said, "Look, this ultraconservatism is just plain wrong. This is the same thing that happened when you were overly concerned that the slag (in the TLI stage) would cause 30°s of nutation and we were going to have to plan an over-burn bias to correct for it and it was totally wrong. I told you in the first place you were wrong and then we got the data from Clementine that proved I was right and you were wrong. If we had done what you wanted, we would have already lost the mission with a big over-burn and this is the same kind of thing!"

I thought that at that point, Dan realized he had stepped way over his bounds and I was going to do the burn with or without him. Since he certainly wanted to be there doing his job (and I certainly wanted him and not John doing his job) and because Ken Galal said, "Hey guys, calm down; we've gotten this far all together, let's finish the job together."

Dan backed off and said he would do the burn. I replied, "Fine, let's get back to work."

Unknowingly, Dan had just crossed a bridge of no return with me as I thought, *well Dan, you just completely blew your chance of ever working at LRI with me on follow-on missions.*

I returned to my cubicle, where Rebecca had been reading and had witnessed the short skirmish and she said to me, "He's never going to work for us; we don't need that kind of a disloyal person in our Institute."

I replied, "You've got that right."

We all got our burn duration calculations done and compared our results. I finished the Mission Profile for the burn and went to print, copy, and distribute it. When I got back to my cubicle, I found Rebecca with her nose forcefully buried in her book and Dougherty, looking quite unsure of himself, was sitting next to her. Either Dan or Irv, or both, had called him and told him to come to Mission Ops to stop me from doing the burn my way.

I immediately took the initiative and said, "I know why you are here, but the burn is fine just as it is," and I briefly tried to explain to him that according to our previous burn results, no under-burn was necessary at all, that a 3% under-burn was more than conservative and that even though the under-burn was unnecessary, I had agreed to the 3% number.

As always, he had no concept of what I was talking about and, being afraid of something he did not understand, he asked, referring to Irv's ridiculous suggestion of doing several little burns over several days to get down to the mapping orbit, "Well why can't you do it slowly?"

I answered, "Because there is no rational reason to do that; there are no data that support Irv's suggestion. I'm not going to go any more than 3%, since even that is a waste of time. This is an executive decision and as PI and Mission Director, I am making it. I told you when it came to Mission Ops, nobody is coming in and telling me what to do."

Dougherty asked, "What do we do if it crashes?"

I answered, "It won't, but if it did, it would be my responsibility and my fault."

Not knowing what to say, he said, "Well you know, I'm just taking my expert engineers' advice, and you should, too."

I ended the conversation by replying, "Look, your expert engineers have known about the three burn LOI sequence for months. They reviewed the Mission Profile over and over and neither Irv nor Dan had any concerns about burning down to the circular orbit on the 3rd LOI burn during all that time and you yourself signed off on the Mission Profile. There is no reason for your and their concerns now, especially after we have seen how perfectly the spacecraft behaves and how well all the burns have gone." With that, Dougherty finally gave up, but he sat in my cubicle as I finished what I came to do, looking like a wet puppy dog, hoping, I thought, that I would change my mind.

When I left my cubicle, Dougherty went to talk to Dan, who certainly told him the same things I had told him, because Dan knew by that time that I was going to do the burn as planned. Then Dougherty talked to Marcie and everybody else and finally gave up and just sat around. I was sure he wouldn't have been there for the final LOI burn had it not been for the under-burn flap.

Since Dan had accepted the inevitable, we got down to the business of doing the 3rd LOI burn that would put the spacecraft into a preliminary mapping orbit. Because the DSN had a station change right in the middle of our preplanned commanding sequence and because the DSN had dropped us more than once during the station handovers, we decided to do the commanding an hour early and again have a 60 minute delay built into the burn parameter file. That way, the critical commanding would be done well before the station handover was to occur.

With that decided, we got started and Dan became much more cordial after we got going — I thought he knew he made a fool of himself. I started the A1 and A2 heater turn-on command and verification sequence at 006/07:02 MET and, as soon as I saw that the engines were heating up, we verified, uplinked, and verified the burn file, which I had executed at 006/07:13 MET. Then we waited. Finally, at 006/08:13 MET, the 27.03-minute burn started and Dan and I saw the burn indicators in the telemetry a frame or two later. At 006/08:40 MET the burn ended and I commanded the safeing of the engines at 006/08:41 MET. We were essentially down in the mapping orbit, since the final circularization burn, two days hence, was in nature and magnitude equivalent to an orbital maintenance maneuver (OMM), so it did not count as an LOI burn.

However, we still had to adjust the spacecraft's spin rate, which had crept up to 12.6 rpm during the 27-minute LOI burn. Between 006:08:53 MET and 006/09:47 MET, I commanded a 2.0158-second despin burn that resulted in a 12.01 rpm spin rate or just 0.01 rpm too high — Dan and I had really begun to understand exactly how the engines were performing, so our burn calculations were getting very accurate.

We started getting the burn report from Goddard and they said we were about 4% cold (under-burn). All the to-do was for absolutely nothing, as I had maintained. We should have burned all the way down to near circular the way I wanted to and we would have been well within the 100±20 km altitude range of the desired mapping orbit had we done so.

As I watched the spacecraft telemetry after the two burns, I again noticed that the tank pressure was a little higher than we had calculated at the end of the burn and I suddenly realized why the pressure was high, especially during the 1st LOI burn, when the high pressure had caused the 1.2% over-burn. Once the pressure began to drop, especially during the first long burn and then, to a lesser extent, during the final two LOI burns (the tank pressure at the end of all three LOI burns was just 145 psi), the helium that had dissolved in the fuel had started to absolve, just like the carbon dioxide dissolved in a can of coke comes bubbling out when you open the can, and also the tanks contracted after having expanded because of the initially high pressure. I should have thought of those two effects right after the 1st LOI burn, but I didn't, probably because so much was going on and because I was so damned tired.

Goddard got us the preliminary orbital calculations and we were in 91 x 153 km orbit, thus we were still too high to call it the 100±20 km altitude, mapping orbit. I said, "Well, we will call it a preliminary mapping orbit, because we got the three LOI burns done and we are down close to the mapping orbit." As a result, the tweak burn we had planned in two days would have to be a damned big tweak burn, which was totally uncalled for. I was not happy at all about any of that.

Though there was nothing wrong with that preliminary mapping orbit, I was very annoyed because I had been prevented by Dan, Dougherty, and Lockheed's stupidity from burning down to within ±20 km of the 100 km altitude I had always planned for the mapping orbit. Though it was a minor thing, it just topped off the months and months of frustrations and annoyances I had had with Lockheed, Dougherty, Scott, and NASA. Instead of having a 1% burn as I had wanted, I had had a sloppy 3.4% burn. What people want to hear is how good you are, not how sloppy you are. I had a sloppy burn because of the conservatism and cowardice of those guys. I had had it with them.

I got a congratulatory call from some guy at Headquarters! I told him how well we were doing and that the instruments were doing better than I had thought, so I thought we would produce much better data than I had promised. He said, "Well, everybody is really pleased, especially Dan Goldin and Wes are really pleased." I thought, *if they are really pleased, then when I tell them I want Scott off the program, maybe they will agree.*

By that time, it was close to 7:00 AM and we were about to leave Mission Ops to go to the press conference. As we left to go to the auditorium, Dan tried to smooth things over a bit more by saying that part of his concern was that I had hurt Irv's feel-

ings by not listening to him. I replied, "So what, Lockheed has trampled all over my feelings for two years and no one cares. And Irv was dead wrong, period."

Irv was off pouting, Dan was licking his wounds, and the spacecraft was not quite
in the mapping orbit I wanted. Nevertheless, we were close to the mapping orbit and the
mission was all down hill from that point on. I had already achieved essentially all the
programmatic and engineering objectives I had set out to prove over nine years earlier.

Rebecca and I left Mission Ops and went to the motel, where I changed into my
suit and tie for the press conference that was to start at 9:00 AM.

Tuesday, January 13, 1998

006/13:30 MET to 007/02:00 MET:
The Press Conference, Home at Last, and the Lockheed Party

I had prevailed at the meeting with Scott and Dougherty the previous Thursday;
the post-third LOI burn press conference was going to consist of Scott giving a brief
overview of the program, Dougherty talking about Lockheed's role in the program, and
I would give the details of the spacecraft and mission to date.

After David Morse introduced the press conference and the three of us, Scott led
off and announced, looking frequently at his notes, "Early this morning, the Lunar
Prospector Team successfully completed the 3rd Lunar Orbit Insertion burn and we are
now in our preliminary mapping orbit. With this success, we are taking a giant step
towards rediscovering the Moon . . . . " He then said a few words about the success of
the mission being due "in large part by going back to the basics," all of which was fine,
but delivered in Scott's stilted manner. Then he tried to get cute and, after looking at
his notes again, said, "we left on our 240,000 mile (284,000 km) journey, and in cosmic terms, that's relatively short, on the celestial golf course it might be a par three, but
we hit a birdie along the way. We only needed two mid-course maneuvers, rather than
three that were planned." I thought I would puke. Then Scott got serious and more
relaxed and gave an excellent review of all the nine significant "firsts" we had already
accomplished, including Lunar Prospector being the first peer reviewed, competitively
selected Discovery Mission, the first use of the Athena II rocket, the first use of the
Spaceport Florida launch facility, and, surprisingly, the first time the PI, a scientist, ran
the mission! That was followed by an equally excellent discussion of our success in
doing Lunar Prospector in the "Faster, Better, Cheaper" mode and what our success
should mean for the future of space exploration. Scott then briefly explained and laud-
ed the expected science return of the mission over the next 12 months. Finally he discussed the public interest in the mission and our desire for the public to participate in
the mission as much as possible. All in all, Scott did a good job after he settled down
and got serious.

Then Dougherty was on and he read a prepared text that was basically a TV ad for
Lockheed, in which he explained Lockheed's role in building the spacecraft and gave
credit to each and every subcontractor who had helped us build Lunar Prospector.

Finally, Dave introduced me as the PI and Mission Director and I intended to
make the most of it. Though I was in a suit and tie (Rebecca made sure that I looked
nice), one could see the dark circles under my eyes and though I was very tired, I was
still very peppy after having just put Lunar Prospector into its preliminary mapping
orbit. I started by giving a very detailed review of all the mission activities from launch,
a week earlier, through the final LOI burn that morning. I pointed out that within 10

hours of spacecraft turn-on, we had a completely functioning spacecraft that was performing so perfectly that the mission had already become routine. I said, with great emphasis, "Lunar Prospector simply responded absolutely perfectly to every command — it-did-what-we-asked-it-to-do." Then I explained I had turned to Dan a few hours into the mission and said, "This is beginning to look like one of our training sessions." After discussing the various mission activities, culminating in the morning's LOI burn and the upcoming tweak burn, I emphasized what a joy it was to fly Lunar Prospector and that it was "child's play" to do so because of its simplicity and reliability.

Then I discussed the science a little bit, pointing out how excited Bill Feldman was that, even though we had been close to the Moon only during the (ten) periselene passages of the capture and intermediate orbits and thus had only a few hours of integrated data, he could see the oxygen, iron, and aluminum lines in the GRS spectra and that the neutron flux was twice what he had expected. Given those spectacular results from the calibration data, we expected to produce much better data than we had promised NASA.

Similarly, I explained how well the MAG/ER were performing and that the spacecraft was so magnetically clean that we were detecting 1 nT magnetic fields, which, according to Mario, had never been done before.

Then I stated emphatically that if there were water ice on the Moon, we would find it, that we would map the composition of the Moon, and do the gravity and magnetic mapping, as well as find any gas release events.

I ended by saying, "The spacecraft is — is not just exceeding our expectation — I think it's probably one of the best spacecraft that has ever been launched and flown and the science payload is certainly among the best that I have ever seen." Then I turned the mike over to David who opened the press conference to questions.

We had about a dozen good questions: three about how we would find the water ice and the science mission; two about the public interest in the mission and its impact on follow-on missions; one each about the remaining amount of fuel (25%), where the LOI burns occurred (over the far-side, just around the eastern limb, at latitude +35°, i.e., just around from the northern rim of Mare Crisium as seen on the full Moon) and what kind of computer Lunar Prospector had (none, just a dumb C&DH); and four about the 3rd LOI burn and the need for the tweak burn.

Just as I had thought earlier, *what people want to hear is how good you are, not how sloppy you are.* As a result, one reporter asked why we were in a preliminary mapping orbit and not the planned mapping orbit? I covered up the real reason (cowardice on Lockheed and my Ops Team's part) and explained about the spacecraft's incoming orbit being 10 km low, the desire to be slightly conservative (not on my part) so we would not crash into the Moon and the fact that the gravity field would perturb the orbit from circular quickly no matter what we did.

I got a second question on that annoying topic, regarding the criticality of delaying the start of the mapping and I explained that a two day delay in circularizing the orbit made no difference, since we were collecting science data all the time and the orbit we were in was nearly the same as the mapping orbit.

A little later, a lady reporter asked pointedly, and in a condescending manner, why we were no where near the 100 km, circular mapping orbit we needed, i.e., why we did such an inaccurate 3rd LOI burn. Though I wanted to say, "Because I am dealing with gutless idiots," I explained again that we were just being conservative, that our burns were all very accurate, and I gave her the example that our last despin burn to 12 rpm was so accurate that we ended up at 12.01 rpm. Noting the hostility in her question, Scott added that, having learned from earlier missions that a tired Mission Ops crew can make disastrous mistakes (e.g., the Lewis fiasco), we had opted to be conservative since there was no rush in getting down exactly into the 100 km mapping orbit.

That led to the final question regarding how tired my Ops Team and I were and what effect having the tweak burn in two days had on the mission schedule. I again explained that the delay had no effect on the science mission, that the Moon's gravity field would immediately perturb the circular orbit, and that as long as we were in an orbit between 100 ± 20 km, we were happy. I also explained that, by delaying the tweak burn by two days, we could shift from a night to a day schedule and get some rest.

With that, Dave closed the news conference and we all left the Ames auditorium.

Rebecca and I went to the motel, checked out and headed for home, since for all practical purposes, we had reached the mapping orbit and everything about the Lunar Prospector Mission was all down hill from that point on. When we got home, at about noon, we took a long and much needed nap. Towards evening, we reluctantly got ready to go to Lockheed's celebration party.

Though we did not want to go to Lockheed's stupid party, we had no real choice. Nevertheless, it was kind of fun, because I had some nice conversations with some of my engineers before the BS started. As I was talking to Woody, Irv tried to tell Rebecca (literally, behind my back) that I didn't know what I was doing regarding the 3rd LOI burn in an attempt to justify the stupidity of his suggestion regarding it and his refusal to support the burn. I turned around and said, "Hey Irv, I've got to talk to you about the tanks." Then I explained that the pressure was 2 or 3 psi high.

He asked arrogantly, thinking I did not know why, "You don't know why, do you?" he had nicely fallen into my trap.

I said, "Sure I do, because both the helium that had dissolved in the fuel had absolved and the tanks contracted as the pressure dropped." Piqued and not saying a word, Irv turned around and walked away and I thought, *that fixes your wagon, you stupid SOB.*

Then Dougherty started the official Lockheed babble and there were three stupid parts to it.

The first stupid part was that — and I wasn't surprised — the *Lockheed higher-ups congratulated each other on everything*. And it was amusing: A) When Mike Coats jokingly said he was taking all the credit for Lunar Prospector — I felt like saying, "You might be joking, but your company certainly is not," B) that I was mentioned only in passing whenever they had to acknowledge there was a PI involved with the mission, and C) when Henshaw said, "it is great to have customers like Alan and Sylvia who listen to Lockheed" (they just never caught on).

Then Dougherty pointedly said me, "You don't want to say anything, do you Alan?"

To his dismay, I answered, "Yes I do," and I took the opportunity to give Dave Curtis and Bill Feldman high praise and I thanked the engineers, but not the corporation.

Then Larry Price was stupid enough to ask me, "Aren't you glad you were not on a Taurus?"

I answered, "You don't really want to hear my answer, do you?"

The third stupid part was when Tenerelli came barging up to the front of the crowd after Dougherty was stupid enough to ask if anybody else had any comments. In his typical, bombastic fashion, Dom started telling about the proposal effort he had led, how he did this and how he did that, and that he wanted to personally thank this person and that person. Dom tried to make it sound like he was responsible for everything and ended his diatribe by saying "and when I left the program, Tom took over." I was embarrassed that he has such a sick ego he had to take credit for a mission he was fired from.

I couldn't stand the BS after three-quarters of hour, so Rebecca and I left and we had some dinner at a nearby restaurant. Then we drove home and went to bed.

Wednesday, January 14, 1998

Day 007 MET

I went up to San Francisco and did a Channel 2 interview, which went pretty well.

Then I went to Mission Ops. The spacecraft was doing fine. I commanded some changes to the NS, GRS, and APS parameters that Bill had asked me to change between 007/16:10 MET and 007/16:19 MET (just before noon), and then my Ops Team and I discussed the circularization burn set for the next day. Also, Dan showed me the SEA plots and, since we were essentially in a circular orbit around the Moon, the SEA plot was essentially a perfect sine wave, caused by the gravitational gradient torques acting on the spacecraft, with two cycles per orbit. As we already knew, Dan had a perfect handle on the new method of determining the spacecraft's attitude and we were both very pleased.

Thursday, January 15, 1998

Day 008 MET

Rebecca and I went down to Salinas where I did two interviews for Channel 6 that went pretty well. Then I drove up to Mission Ops.

Scott brought Sam Venneri and some other NASA guys over to Mission Ops and I showed them around. Though Scott knew little about Mission Ops, he tried to be the big shot and impress his NASA buddies. I was really tired of him.

To top that off, Scott was having Bob McMurray ask Bill, behind my back, about the spectrometers and then Bob was relaying the information to Scott, just like he was having Marcie report to him on the spacecraft, behind my back. It appeared he wouldn't ask me anything about the mission any more. Because of that and because of his demeanor, I thought he was afraid to talk to me and I was very happy if that were the case. It was amusing to see what a weasel Scott is.

I was almost 100% certain that Dougherty was acting the same way and was having Dan watch me and make sure I didn't do anything wrong — like the 3rd LOI burn. As far as I was concerned, they were all a bunch of gutless weasels and I was glad not to have to deal with them very much anymore.

At about noon, we got ready to do the circularization burns. Goddard had an excellent solution for our orbit and gave us the velocity vectors for the two burn sequences that required only burns on the A1 and A2 engines, i.e., we did not need to do pulsed burns on the T1 and T2 engines, which was great.

The first axial burn would be near the 91 km altitude periselene and that would drop the aposelene from 153 km altitude to the desired 100 km. The second burn would occur nearly one-half an orbit later (49 minutes), near the new 100 km aposelene and that would raise the periselene to 100 km and we would be in our circular, 100 km altitude orbit.

Dan and I calculated that the first burn, whose ΔV was to be 12.06 m/sec, would last 76.7 seconds and the second one, whose ΔV was to be 2.6 m/sec, would last 16.4

seconds. Dan prepared the two burn files and, at 008/17:06 MET, I issued the order to Ric to uplink the A1 and A2 heater turn-on file. Then, following our well practiced procedure, we uplinked and verified the file for the first burn, which was executed at 008/18:18 MET. I again had Ric uplink the heater turn-on file at 008/18:41 MET to prepare for the second part of the circularization burn. Then we uplinked and verified the second file and executed it at 008/19:07 MET and then I safed the engines.

That done, we prepared to reor the spacecraft from its LOI burn attitude to its mapping attitude. Nominally, we had planned to have the spacecraft's spin axis perpendicular to the ecliptic, but since Bill had come to the conclusion that the APS's Face 5 light filters were torn, we were going to orient the spacecraft so its SEA was slightly positive, so the APS's Face 5 would always be in shadow. If Bill was correct, Face 5 would then work fine, except during that quarter of an orbit when moonlight could shine through the torn filters.

Dan had calculated that we needed to change the attitude by 31.37° and we had each calculated that would require a 139-pulse burn on the standard A1 and A4 reor engines. Dan then prepared the burn parameter file while I had Ric send up the A1 and A4 heater turn-on file at 008/20:07 MET. We started the 12.01-minute reor maneuver at 008/20:32 MET and safed the engines at 008/20:25 MET. We ended up with a +0.65° SEA and Face 5 of the APS immediately started to work! I watched the APS data for a full orbit and it was working as expected! That was great.

Shortly thereafter, Goddard reported their first orbit solution and it was 100±1 km! Later, the 4-hour solution was 99.9 km by 98.9 km — no one could have done better (but we really did do better) and I hoped the lady reporter who had been so nasty about our 3rd LOI burn results would find out how accurately we had circularized the orbit (I was still ticked off about the unnecessary 3.4% underburn and Dan's stupidity. We could have and should have come as close as possible to circular, but —).

Regardless, we were officially in the final mapping orbit, in the correct mapping attitude, and the spin rate was 12.074 rpm, well within our 12±0.7 rpm operational range. All the critical, major events of the mission were over! All we had to do was to sit back, watch the spacecraft, and collect science data. Within two weeks we would have produced the first accurate gravity map of the Moon and then we would know how often we would have to make an Orbital Maintenance Maneuver (OMM). Within four to six weeks, we expected to have the data to answer the polar water ice question. Life was great.

My next major task was to try and get rid of Scott. I would have my letter to Wes Huntress, demanding Scott's removal, ready by the end of the following week and that Friday, when Scott returned from a trip to Headquarters, I was going to drop the bomb on him.

Chapter 4-4
The Letter, the Confession, and the Gravity Map

Friday, January 16, through Monday, January 19, 1998

Day 009 through Day 012 MET

Since the spacecraft was functioning perfectly and the orbit was excellent, I took Friday and Saturday off to rest up after the long grueling week of intense activity. The monitoring controllers, who were then on duty in three 8-hour shifts, were continuing to watch over the spacecraft 24 hours a day and I was just a phone call and a 45-minute drive away from taking command control of Lunar Prospector — if an emergency arose.

Rebecca and I went up to Mission Ops Sunday to print out the letter for Wes and to check on the spacecraft and, of course, it was fine. I looked at the APS data and we were getting good data from Face 5. I also got the final orbit solution for our circularization burn — we had achieved a 99.18 km by 100.36 km orbit and you couldn't have asked for anything better.

Monday was a holiday, so I rested up some more.

Tuesday, January 20, 1998

Day 013 MET

I went up to Mission Ops. The spacecraft was doing fine. The β angle of the spacecraft's orbit (the angle between the plane of the orbit and the radius vector to the Sun) was still more that 73° and hence the spacecraft was in sunlight during its entire 118-minute orbit. However, we would reach $\beta = 71°$ in two days and then the nighttime passes would begin, just a couple of minutes at first, but they would rapidly build up during the following 72 days to their maximum of 47 minutes at $\beta = 0°$ (after which the nighttime pass durations would decrease for 72 days to 0 minutes, remain at 0 minutes for 38 days while β went through 90° and again decreased below 71°, then the nighttime pass cycle would start all over again). I was planning to spend a lot of time in Mission Ops come Thursday, to see how the spacecraft, especially the battery and the power subsystem, was responding to the cold, sunless nighttime passes.

We were still transmitting on the omni antenna. Though Alex was happy with the Doppler tracking data he was getting for the gravity mapping, we were having a little trouble getting good data when we were being tracked with the 26-meter antennas. That might just have been a problem with the Doppler predicts; if it were not, then I would switch to using the medium gain antenna to get the extra 7 dbs of signal strength.

I had finished the letter to try to get rid of Scott and was just waiting until he came back from his trip to DC. Funnily enough, he sent me an email saying he wanted to sit down like we used to do in the good old days and talk about the mission and the science results. I emailed him and said I would be at his office Friday at 11:00 AM (but not to talk about the mission and science).

Wednesday, January 21, 1998

Day 014 MET: The Nighttime Passes Begin

Dave Curtis wanted to send up a long series of commands to the MAG/ER to peak up their performances, since he had earlier determined the MAG offsets and had seen exactly how the ER was performing. He had sent me the list of 70 commands he wanted uplinked. I put together the Mission Profile for the commanding session and added the command to switch from the omni to the medium gain antenna at the end of Dave's sequences.

A Canadian TV crew from Toronto came and did a great 2-hour interview. I had a good time talking with them.

We started the nighttime passes! The reason they started a day early was that the lunar gravity anomalies had already pulled the periselene of Lunar Prospector's orbit down to about 83 km, while our predicts were based on a 100 km spacecraft altitude. The nighttime passes started with the spacecraft just skimming along the Moon's shadow, but never fully going into the shadow. The spacecraft just went into the shadow of a mountain or a crater rim for several seconds, only to reemerge into the sunlight streaming through an intervening valley or low area for several seconds. That occurred a few times during the couple of minutes that the spacecraft was skimming along the Moon's shadow, before its orbit carried it well away from the shadow.

Each successive orbit carried the spacecraft deeper into the Moon's shadow and the nighttime passes got rapidly longer (by the eighth nighttime pass, just 15¾ hours later — the nighttime pass was already 10 minutes long), so we "saw" the spacecraft alternatively going into a mountain's shadow and then reemerging into the sunlight only during the first couple of nighttime passes. What we saw in the engineering data was that the Solar Array current jumped back and forth between its full value and zero, the battery jumped between charging and discharging and Dan's Sun sensor alternately saw the Sun and then lost it. It was fascinating to watch all that for those couple of minutes per orbit.

Once the nighttime passes began, I began to carefully watch how the battery was discharging and recharging and I started plotting a graph of the drop in the battery voltage as a function of the computed depth of discharge (DOD) of the battery that would eventually tell me how the battery was behaving, when extended to the maximum 47-minute nighttime pass. We were also watching how the spacecraft was cooling down during the nighttime passes, e.g., Dan began building up a spin-up curve vs. time-in-the-dark, since, as the booms cooled and contracted, the spacecraft spun-up slightly, just like a spinning skater spins-up when he or she pulls his or her arms inwards. We were very excited to start see all those interesting physical effects, each one telling us something different about our little spacecraft.

Scott called and agreed to meet Friday. He was at Headquarters telling everybody how wonderful Lunar Prospector was and taking all the credit.

Thursday, January 22, 1998

Late Day 015 MET through Very Early Day 016 MET:
MAG/ER Commanding and Dinner

Rebecca (who wanted to enjoy the mission commanding activities as much as she could) and I went to Missions Ops at about 4:00 PM, to do the MAG/ER commanding for Dave Curtis. There were two reasons for us doing the commanding so late in the day: First, Dave wanted to do it towards the end of his normal workday at UC Berkeley and second, I had invited Dave and his lovely wife, Victoria, out to dinner to thank him for all the hard work he had put into the MAG/ER effort.

When Rebecca and I got there, the Nav guys told me that the perturbations of Lunar Prospector's orbit were less than Alex's old model had predicted, i.e., the model I had used to calculate Lunar Prospector's fuel load way back in the proposal days in the fall of 1994. We finally knew we would have to correct the orbit, i.e., do an Orbital Maintenance Maneuver or OMM, only once every two, or possibly even every three, months. I was ecstatic; I was going to have a lot of fuel for the extended mission and we had our first scientific result from the mission.

About an hour and a half after everyone was at Mission Ops, after we had checked the command files that Ric had set up and after we were sure everything was OK, we got started commanding — it was 015/21:44 MET. However, when Ric sent the first command, nothing happened — there was no echo — nothing. Ric quickly found that he had inadvertently put the wrong spacecraft ID in his file, so Lunar Prospector did not respond to the command. Ric quickly fixed his error (we, the Command Team, only checked the validity of the commands before the files were uplinked, we did not check the file headers — that was the responsibility of the uplink controller) and then the first command, turning off the MAG/ER heater that was causing the ER noise, was successfully sent, verified, and executed.

Uplinking the remaining 68 commands of Dave's long sequence was to take 3 hours and 14 minutes, including two 42-minute radio occultation periods when Lunar Prospector was behind the Moon. During the entire sequence, Dave and I would check the validity of each command after it was uplinked via its echo, first on my screen and then on his. We got started — on time — at 015/21:48 MET, uplinking the remaining commands and the uplinking was going perfectly. However, we kept noting that the received signal strength from the spacecraft was rather low and I began to worry that we might start losing data or commands. Since I had planned to command the switch over from the omni antenna to the medium gain antenna at the end of the command sequence anyway, I interrupted the MAG/ER commanding, moved up (redlined) the antenna switchover in the Mission Profile and commanded the switchover at 015/23:34 MET. The received signal strength jumped by the expected 7 db and that ended the concerns I had about losing any data or commands. Then I continued commanding Dave's sequence.

Because I had redlined the Mission Profile, we were three minutes ahead of the planned timeline and that meant I could get the last of Dave's commands uplinked before the second 42-minute radio occultation period occurred, and still have time for me to make a spacecraft safety check before the occultation began at 016/00:10 MET. That also meant that Rebecca, Dave, Victoria, and I could go to dinner an hour earlier than planned. The last command went up at 016/00:06 MET and we were finally done. I was very pleased that we had successfully commanded the entire load consisting of several files containing eight blocks of commands and 18 single commands, plus the two antenna switching commands and the two commands to turn off the MAG/ER heater, without error (Ric's ID error did not count as a commanding error). We had demonstrated our ability to command the spacecraft (engineering-wise) error free ever since it had been launched and we had just demonstrated that we could load a long and complicated science instrument command sequence as well.

As we prepared to leave Mission Ops, I reviewed in my head the performance of the spacecraft: It was doing well in eclipses; the battery was charging properly and quickly; we were learning more and more every day about the spacecraft; and everything looked just great.

Then Rebecca, Victoria, Dave, and I went out for a nice steak dinner at the Black Angus and we talked and had a good time. Rebecca and I got home very late and we were very tired.

Friday, January 23, 1998

Day 016 MET: Scott Gets His

I went to Ames to see how the spacecraft was doing, to work on the Mission Profile for the next day's reor burn, to drop off a copy of the Wes Huntress letter (Appendix 4-1, also see www.lunar-research-institute.org) for Ames's Director, Harry McDonald, and to drop the bomb on Scott. Rebecca had faxed the letter and mailed it to Wes after I left for Ames; I also sent copies to Jim Muncy and James Paul, the Congressional aides on the House Science Committee, and my LRI lawyers, Dave Weaver and Todd Greenwalt.

When I went in his office, he was smiling and just so happy to see me. I shut the door behind me to keep our conversation private and sat down. Scott started to say something about the mission and I said, "I didn't come here to talk about the mission, I came here to discuss my outrage at the way this mission has evolved." Then I handed him a copy of the infamous memo he had sent to Cathcart and that Maryann had given me and I asked, "Do you remember this little item?" He looked at it a little perplexed. I asked, "Do you know the consequences of this?"

He answered cautiously, "No."

I said. "I was locked out of Lockheed for a week, like a common criminal. This is just one result of the fact that you have simply taken over complete control of the mission. You and I have discussed the management of the mission more than once and I am outraged that you have taken over this program."

Scott said that he wanted to discuss any problems I had and I said, "There's nothing to discuss. I've written Wes to inform him that I want you removed from the project, period. Here is a copy of the letter, read it. I am leaving, goodbye."

Scott quickly said, "No, no, I want to talk about this."

I said, "OK, but there's not much to talk about."

He quickly skimmed the letter and asked immediately, "Has this letter already gone out to everybody?"

I answered, "Yes, it has."

He said, "Then I'm pissed off that you've blindsided me with this, without giving me a chance to respond before you sent the letter out."

I replied, "So what; do you think I care how you feel after you usurped the authority over my mission and pushed my position down to that of a project scientist? I've been annoyed about the way this has gone for some time and we've already had two discussions about it."

He asked, "Why didn't you want to come and talk to me? You should have come and talked to me about it."

I answered, "Why? As I said, I talked to you about the management twice and it's clear to me that you are going to do it your way; your attitude is that I'm subservient to you; and that is the end of it. I worked years on this to bring it to where it is today and I brought you in on it only at the end of the initial six years of effort. This isn't your mission, it's mine, and you don't know anything about how to do this or any other mission."

Scott tried to say I was mistaken and all he had done was to try to keep everything the way he thought it had to be done. I replied, "You don't know what in hell you are talking about and you've no business trying to run this mission. I'm older than you, I'm more experienced than you, and I'm smarter than you, and I know how to do this without you. As far as I am concerned, you've been mainly feathering your own nest. In principle, I don't have any problem with that — you and Ames benefiting from this — but not at my expense."

We returned to the letter and I told him that LRI's two lawyers had drawn it up. He was trying not to get mad, because he knew that was not the thing to do, but he did get mad once in a while and said, "You're pissing me off."

I replied, "I frankly don't care. Did you care if I got pissed off when you were screwing me?" and then he would calm down because he knew I had him by the short and curlies and his only chance was to convince me to withdraw the letter. I said, "This conversation is a waste of both of our time. That is my position. You can read it (the letter) carefully. Then you can react to it and defend yourself. That's fine. That's your right. And that is my position — I want you off this program, now."

He skimmed through the letter again and said, "I didn't know of any of the consequences" (e.g., like me being locked out of Lockheed).

I said, "That's really nice Scott; you don't even bother to follow up on what you start. You just do this sort of thing and let everyone else pay the consequences. Your email (to Cathcart) told me exactly what you considered me to be and that you are the Supreme Being here. You're a NASA God and I'm just a peon and I'm here to be lashed out at, whenever and for whatever you wish (just like everyone else under NASA management)."

Scott tried to get around my accusations by saying, "No, no, I know you've worked so hard on this and you've done 95% more than anybody else has ever done. Nobody (no scientist) has ever been allowed to work on a spacecraft and nobody has been allowed to command a spacecraft before."

I said, "I don't really care about that, my goals were to do this mission right. The whole purpose of Lunar Prospector was to keep NASA out of the picture and to demonstrate how to do these things correctly. I'm not interested in 95% — I'm interested in 100%."

Upon hearing that, Scott said, "Well, you don't want anybody in this position" (the position of the NASA Mission Manager).

I said, "That is exactly correct, Scott. I didn't want a NASA partner. I was forced by Lockheed to ask Ames to be my NASA Center Partner; otherwise Lockheed would not back my proposal. I've been around NASA long enough to know exactly what would happen if I had a NASA partner and that is exactly what has happened. I did not want Ames, I did not want you, and I did not want to have anything to do with NASA," and that surprised and shocked him.

He again tried to defend himself by saying, "Well you know, I was just following rules and regulations, being very careful to do everything legal."

The SOB — like far too many incompetent, self-serving bureaucrats, Scott was hiding behind the numerous and often conflicting, rules and regulations to justify his actions and to twist the issues around to his advantage — as I had seen him do many times before. I responded, "Scott, if that is true, then you are following the rules without having any concept or concern about the consequences, and what you were actually doing is just as bad as if you did it maliciously. What's the difference if you're maliciously doing it or you are just so incompetent that you can't understand the impact of what you are doing? Is this how you treat a Principal Investigator? And I am not just talking about me; I'm talking about everybody. This is exactly the way NASA treats its PIs, as well as everybody else; and that is what Lunar Prospector is all about."

Trapped, Scott asked, "What's your main point?"

I answered, as I had always done over the previous couple of years, "This is not what Discovery is all about — I didn't work for years for you and NASA to take over control. Since you've taken control of this program and you usurped all the authority, I want you removed."

Then I got back to the infamous email regarding my TV interview with the spacecraft. I asked, "How do you explain this?"

He answered, "Well, there was the problem of proprietary information about the spacecraft."

I retorted, "Scott, who are you trying to kid? We already had the news conference. The world saw the spacecraft. There is no proprietary information about the spacecraft since that point in time, period." He started to say something about what I said on TV and I cut him short with, "I know more about PR than you do. The PR on this program has been miserable, both at Headquarters and here (Ames). You guys don't have the vaguest concept of what good PR is."

By that time, since everything I said just shut him up, I thought he understood two things: First, I wasn't going to put up with any more of his BS, and second, I was right and he hadn't a leg to stand on. But he was desperately trying to maneuver out of my firing line, so he brought up what Headquarters thought about how he had run the mission. I said, "I really don't care what Headquarters says or thinks, they are as bad as you are." and that shut him up, too.

We then left the generalities and got to some of the specific charges I had in my letter, e.g., the LRI decal I wanted on the rocket. I said, "I was going to ask about having the LRI logo on the rocket when you got me locked out of Lockheed. I didn't pursue it right then because I was more concerned about my being locked out and the impact your actions would have on my ability to do the mission. Later, when I asked Sylvia about having an LRI decal on the rocket, she told me you said it was too late, which was a lie, as I found out down at the Cape," and I told him the details of what had happened at the Cape regarding the decal.

At first he lied, "Well, I don't know anything about the decal."

I said, "Scott, I was told directly that you told the Lockheed crew they were not to put the LRI decal on the rocket" (Sylvia had admitted that to me).

Then he admitted to part of it, but lied again, saying, "Well, yes I did, but you couldn't have a decal on there because you're a subcontractor (to Lockheed)."

I said, "Scott, that's BS and you know it. I'm the damned Principal Investigator of this program and your keeping my logo off had nothing to do with my being a subcontractor — look at the rocket, there were subcontractor decals all over the place. There was Primex (who built the engines for Lunar Prospector and for the Athena's orbit adjustment module), Thiokol (who built the two Castor 120s), Spaceport Florida, and the Lockheed Company that built the rocket — all subcontractors. You use every single excuse like that as a justification for doing what you want to do in order to make Lunar Prospector look like a NASA mission you run and to make LRI and me disappear."

Clearly caught in a couple of out-and-out lies and gross deceptions, Scott quickly left that topic, so I started another example, i.e., leaving LRI off the poster (and coffee cups, etc.). I said, "LRI was supposed to be on this stuff and it's not."

He said, "Well, next time it's printed, LRI will be on there."

I said, "It has already been printed the *next time*."

Trapped again, he asked nervously, "How do you know all these things?"

I answered, "That's none of your business. But it's very easy to get the truth out of people, Scott," and I felt like adding, "Because everybody who works for you hates your guts," but didn't, and thought further, *you would be appalled if you knew all the stuff I knew about you.*

Then I brought up his forcing Lockheed to change the Lockheed contract behind my back. He lied again, "Oh no, I didn't do that."

I said, "Oh yes you did, Scott, you had it changed to make you the Mission Manager."

Trapped again in a lie, he said, "But I did not encroach on your being the Mission Director in any way."

I said, "Regardless, you violated tort laws."

He said, "I don't know anything about that, I just do what my contracts people say."

I retorted, "That's BS. You told them to do it."

Having forced him to admit to everything and having no place to hide, Scott again asked, "Well, what do you want?"

I answered, "I want you off the program. I have no personal or professional confidence in you anymore. I don't trust you. There is nothing you can say that is going to change that."

Seeing no way out, he asked, "Who would run the program (from NASA's side)?"

I answered, "As far as I am concerned, Sylvia can continue being the interface (between NASA and me). She has done a good job and has done most of the work anyway. Besides, there is no real need for a lot of interfacing now. The spacecraft is where it belongs (in orbit) and is working well. I just want to be left alone and allowed to fly the mission and finish the job I started out to do without interference from you."

He said, "Well, I'm the Deputy Director of Space at Ames."

I retorted, "Scott, as far as I am concerned, they can make you the head of NASA. I couldn't care less what you think you are."

But he continued, "I have the right to bring people to Mission Ops and show them Lunar Prospector."

I said, "Fine, as long as you do not do it as part of the Lunar Prospector Team, you can come over as often as you want. I have no objection to you doing anything — except being part of the project."

Worried that he had been had, he then tried to work the sympathy angle. He complained about all the hard work he had done, that he was so hurt that I had called him unethical, that I was hurting his career and that I should be worried about what people would say about me because I wanted him off the project. I said, "Scott, my opinion of you is that you are unethical, whether you like it or not, just accept it. I don't care about your career, though this is not meant to damage it. For all I care, they can make you the head of NASA; I just want you to get the hell out of my program. And I really don't care what anybody says about me. I know what I can do and who I am. You and anyone else can call me anything you want — I couldn't care less."

Giving him credit, Scott handled himself well, in the sense that he didn't lose it and he made no threats, which surprised me. But he kept wanting to talk and I said, "Look Scott, this is a waste of time. I encourage you to read the letter in detail. You can defend yourself in anyway you choose, but I am adamant that you get off this program. I brought you onto this program and now I'm throwing you off of it. I'm sure Headquarters will be involved and there will be discussions about this. That is exactly the point of the letter." With that, I walked out of Scott's office and said sarcastically, "Have a nice day, Scott."

Pleased at having made the bastard admit to all the crap he had pulled on me, I left the administration building and went back to Mission Ops.

When I got there, Preston had called, so I called him and we had a good long chat. I told him to come on over some weekend to see Mission Ops and so we could go out to dinner.

Preston said Stu Nozette was continuing to raise hell about Lunar Prospector. Thus Preston had gone to his management at Lawrence Livermore Labs and told them what Stu was doing, i.e., that everything Stu was saying was a lie (Stu and Scott must be related), like Stu saying he was the originator of Lunar Prospector — a bald-faced lie. Preston also told them, "You've got to realize that Alan is writing a book about the mission and if this sort of stuff keeps up, it will be documented and you guys are going to have dirt on your face."

They said, "We have to stop Stu."

As a result of Stu's activities, he was being demoted over and over again, but Preston added that Lawrence Livermore Labs never fires anybody. I asked, "What will they do, shoot him?"

Preston laughed and answered, "They should."

Then I explained that a Lawrence Livermore official had called me to apologize for Stu's actions and had said, "Stu does not represent Lawrence Livermore Labs view of you and Lunar Prospector. But we are embarrassed and we are going to do something about it."

Monday, January 26, 1998

Day 019 MET: Tweak Burns, Screwed, and a Fancy Dinner

I got to Mission Ops well before 8:00 AM to prepare for the tweak reor and the tweak de-spin burns we had planned for the morning. We needed to tweak the attitude to keep the Sun off of Face 5 of the APS and while we were at it, we wanted to bring the spin rate down from 12.098 rpm to 11.93 rpm. By then, we knew that all the engine combinations we used for the various burns (all combinations except the A3/A4 pair, which we had yet to fire as a pair) spun Lunar Prospector up a little during each burn. Since our acceptable spin rate range was ±0.7 rpm (around the desired spin rate of 12.0 rpm) and since we then knew we could do much better than that, we decided to cut the spin rate range to one-tenth of the acceptable range, i.e., to ±0.07 rpm. Further, in order to minimize the number of spin correction maneuvers we would have to do (one does not fire engines any more often than absolutely necessary, because every burn is a potential catastrophic failure), we decided to bias the spin rate low, at 11.93 rpm, and let the spacecraft spin up a little bit each burn until it was at about 12.07 rpm and then drop it back down to 11.93 rpm.

Dan and I calculated the parameters for the 2.4° reor (12 pulses on engines A1 and A4, resulting in a +0.5° SEA) and the −0.105 rpm despin (0.56 sec burn on engine T1). I typed up the Mission Profile for the burns; we went through our rigorous checking procedures and I started the heater turn-on sequence for the reor at 019/13:27 MET and finished the reor sequence by safeing the engines at 19/13:54 MET. At 019/14:04

MET, we began the sequence for the de-spin burn and finished it at 019/14:30 MET. We achieved an 11.935 rpm spin rate, which was very good for such a short, ½ second burn.

After the successful commanding session, I went over to Lockheed to see where the LRI payment for December was. Maryann checked for me and found that our invoice hadn't even been entered into the system, even though I had delivered it by hand on January 6! I went over with a copy of the invoice to make the finance department give me the payment on the spot, which was what Maryann said they could do. Of course, nobody there could help me. I would have to try again the next day, when I turned in the invoice for January! Anyway, it was the same old Lockheed crap.

Similarly, as I walked by Bob McMurray's office at Ames, on my way to see Sylvia, I noticed he had a nice little model of Lunar Prospector in his office and then I went to see Sylvia and she had one too! I asked Sylvia, "Where's mine?" She didn't know and hadn't even thought about seeing to it that I had gotten one. It was the same old crap as at Lockheed. They just ignored the fact that I even existed — the only things that counted were that Lockheed and NASA got what they wanted and I could go to hell.

The editors and owners of *Space Daily* had invited me to dinner, along with a nice Lockheed PR lady, Buddy Nelson, Dougherty, and Dave Waller. When I got to the restaurant, the editors asked me a lot of questions about Lunar Prospector, so I told them about the spacecraft and the mission. But the really good part was after we ate. We got down to the nitty-gritty of the entire program and my interest in doing commercial lunar exploration missions after Lunar Prospector. I was pleased, because I was able to discuss every single point I wanted them to understand in great detail.

We also talked about the mission's poor PR and they agreed that neither NASA nor Ames knew how to do PR. It was an evening well spent, even though it was at a very fancy restaurant (they offered venison and the menu had no prices on it). The PR lady picked up the tab, which must have cost a couple hundred bucks. A little rich for my blood, but it was their choice.

Tuesday, January 27, 1998

Day 020 MET

I tried to call Wes in the morning to find out if he was going to let me get rid of Scott, but, of course, he wasn't around. I tried to find out where LRI's December payment was and found out we had not been paid because the idiots had not put any more money in the damned LRI contract account! They, Maryann and/or Garner, had only put $100,000 in the account in the beginning and they never bothered to update it. I finally got a hold of Maryann and she OK'ed adding more money to the account. By the time all that got done, the guy who was to give me the check was gone, so I would have to wait another day to get LRI's money. What a bunch of damned fools. Adding insult to injury, I was never able to get a hold of Wes. An annoying day — all the way around.

Wednesday, January 28, 1998

Day 021 MET: A Science Team Meeting

We had a Science Team meeting most of the day. We talked about the various data products we had to deliver to the NASA Archives. There was nothing spectacular about the meeting, except, of course, that we had been in low polar orbit for 14 days and hence Lunar Prospector had completed one mapping pass around the Moon. Thus Alex and the Nav guys had the first complete data set they needed to completely define the lunar gravity field and we knew for sure that we would need to do an OMM only once every two months. But the best part was that — for the first time in history — *we had the first complete gravity map of the Moon!*

After the meeting, Dave Curtis and I went to Mission Ops and, at Dave's request, I had Ric uplink a five-command file to the MAG/ER. The commanding itself took just two minutes and was over at 021/19:MET.

I still was unable to reach Wes!

Thursday, January 29, 1998

Day 022 MET

I went in to work just before noon, since I was to have lunch with Jack Boyle, Harry MacDonald's Assistant. Jack had asked me out to lunch because he wanted to know about the history and the success of Lunar Prospector and he wanted to know what LRI was all about. Part of his interest was, because NASA was always threatening to close down Ames (he said, "those bastards at Headquarters are always trying to close Ames down."), he was trying to find solid reasons for keeping Ames alive and thought that Lunar Prospector and LRI could help in that matter. He was very complimentary and talked about his helping me get political support for what I wanted to do in the future. We had a good, productive lunch, but I did not expect much to come of it.

Wes did call, but while I was gone. He promised to call in the morning.

Friday, January 30, 1998

Day 023 MET

I finally got to talk with Wes about my request to get rid of Scott. He said, "It's your team's decision. It is an inter-team matter. You, Lockheed and, Ames have to make the decision, nobody else." He obviously didn't like it that I had sent copies of the letter to the congressional aides, but screw him. Then he said, "The mission is going so perfectly. The data is perfect, everything is perfect, and we're sorry there is this problem in the team, but it is a team problem."

I asked, "OK Wes, is this my decision?"

He answered, "No, it's your team's decision, but you put the team together." Basically, he was giving me the responsibility of throwing Scott off. Nevertheless, I had to clear it with Lockheed, so I was going to talk it over with Dougherty. It looked like I was going to be able to get rid of the SOB. However, before I did anything further, I wanted it in writing from Wes.

Bill called and said that President Clinton was going to visit Los Alamos the following Monday and there was a possibility that we would be asked to explain how our search for lunar polar water ice was going. Bill wanted me to fly over the next day, so we could look at the two weeks of NS data we had, determine if we were seeing any evidence for the water ice or not and, if asked, present our results to Clinton. Since the Clinton/Monica Lewinsky scandal had recently broken and since there was no question that Clinton was lying and had violated a number of workplace, sexual harassment laws (and worse) that would have immediately led to the ouster of any corporative executive who was fiddling around with a young female employee, I did not like the idea of possibly having to interface with Clinton — but he was still the President. I made immediate plans to fly to Los Alamos the next day.

Chapter 4-5
Water, Water Everywhere, But...?

Saturday, January 31, through Wednesday, February 4, 1998

Day 024 MET through Day 028 MET:
A Trip to Los Alamos — The Water Question and a Remote Commanding Session

I flew to Albuquerque and drove up to Los Alamos on Saturday. Bill and I immediately got to work after I arrived at Los Alamos late in the afternoon. Though we had only one complete mapping cycle of data, plus a little bit of cycle two (as Lunar Prospector orbited the Moon and as the Moon rotated under it once every 27.32 days, the spacecraft mapped the entire surface of the Moon once every 13.66 days; hence we called each successive 13.66 days of mapping a mapping cycle and numbered them consecutively), the data was phenomenal. But before Bill and I had any time to really get into the details of the data, I got a call from Dan and Marcie — the SES had frozen up and we were getting no data from the spectrometers.

When I told Bill what had happened, he said that had happened a couple of times during their testing of the electronics (the SES) and spectrometers before they were shipped to Lockheed for integration into the spacecraft. All I had to do was to shut the spectrometers and the SES off and turn them back on. With Dan and Marcie on the phone, giving me the exact command information I needed, I wrote up the Mission Profile I needed to turn the entire spectrometer system off and back on, including turning on — and stepping up the GRS and NS high-voltages to their operational levels and resetting all the energy windows.

When I was finished, the entire sequence consisted of 38 commands and it would take 2 hours and 34 minutes to uplink it, in part, because there would be a 46-minute interruption when the spacecraft was out of radio contact behind the Moon. After having carefully checked the command list, with Dan acting as my second in command at my console and with Marcie monitoring the spectrometer console, so they both could verify all the commands and all the spectrometer's responses, and with Ric ready to follow my orders, I began the command sequence at 024/22:22 MET and finished it at 025/00:56 MET. When we were finished, the spectrometers were back on and happy, as were Dan, Marcie, Bill, and I that we had solved the problem. I was particularly pleased because that session proved that Dan was more than capable of taking over my responsibilities while I was absent from Mission Ops and that our careful command procedures worked perfectly, even under such extreme conditions.

The next day, Bill and I got down to the business of looking at the data; the GRS spectra were just beautiful, with spectral lines all over the place. The APS data looked pretty damned good too, but our main attention was directed at the NS data for two reasons: first, because the NS data would answer the water question, and second, the data were the first neutron spectral data ever obtained for the Moon — or any other planetary body. When Bill showed me the maps the day before, to my great surprise, the lunar maria (the dark, flat, lava plains) stood out like sore thumbs from the highlands (the bright, highly cratered areas) in the thermal (low energy) and fast (high energy) neutron flux maps.

Though Bill had expected that the neutron flux from the Moon would be sensitive to the compositional differences between the maria (iron- and sometimes titanium-rich volcanic rocks, i.e., basalts) and the highlands (aluminum- and calcium-rich, ancient crust), we were both taken aback by the magnitude of the effects — there are nearly factors of 4 and 1.4 in the differences in the thermal neutron fluxes and fast neutron fluxes, respectively, between the maria and highlands! Those new observations instantly showed two things: First, we had just discovered a new and a very sensitive way of mapping the iron plus titanium abundances of a body from orbit and second, the search for the water ice was going to be complicated by the sensitivity of the neutron data to even small compositional differences in the polar regions. In addition to having to allow for the composition differences, Bill said he would have to correct the thermal neutron fluxes for the effects of the temperature differences in the upper parts of the regolith (lunar soil) and for gravitational energy losses.

Given all that, we looked at the thermal and epithermal (intermediate energy) neutron data for any signs of water ice in the polar regions (Note: neutron data do not directly show the presence of water [H_2O] ice, rather they show the presence of the hydrogen in the water — the presence of water ice is only inferred from the maps of the hydrogen distributions over the Moon). We had expected to see relatively smooth curves when we plotted the neutron fluxes as functions of latitude, with dips over each polar region if water ice were present there. Instead, given that we had data from only one complete mapping cycle, that the fluxes are very sensitive to the composition and the subsurface temperatures, and that we hadn't yet corrected for gravity losses, the plots were very rough, with many dips and peaks at all latitudes. Even so, if the predicted maximum amounts of water ice — perhaps enough to fill Lake Erie — were there, we would have easily seen their signatures, despite the noisy data. We knew by then, positively, that the Moon's polar regions did not have anywhere near Lake Erie amounts of water ice in them.

Bill and I looked and looked at the various curves — some curves seemed to have polar dips of a few percent, while other, adjacent curves showed nothing. After a couple of days of analysis, we decided we had not detected any positive signs of water ice and if any ice were there, the dips in the flux caused by its presence had to be less than about 3%, i.e., any possible positive signal was still "in the grass (noise)" and that we would have to wait until we had more data and until we fully understood the effects of composition and temperature on the data, before we could be sure if water ice were present in much smaller amounts than predicted, or none at all. Regardless, it was very exciting to finally see some of the data we knew would eventually solve the water ice question.

Happily, since we had nothing positive to show, or just because the Los Alamos administration had better things for Clinton to do, we did not have to present our very rough findings to Clinton. I was very happy about that, since, given his lying ways and immoral activities, I did not want to have to address and shake the hand of Clinton, the man, but would have done so reluctantly, because he was Clinton, the President, no matter how much he was disgracing that office.

Thursday, February 5, 1998

Day 029 MET

LRI finally got paid for December!

Friday, February 6, 1998

Day 030 MET

The mission was a month old and the spacecraft and instruments were working perfectly.

I worked in my LRI office at home all day, partly because we had a bad storm, so I did not want to drive up to Mission Ops, and partly because there was little for me to do there. I talked to Bill a few times about the data and Scott called and was just as nice as pie. Scott, Sylvia, and David Morse wanted to know what Bill and I had concluded about the water ice question in preparation for a news conference on the topic we were planning in a few weeks. I told them we had found no indications of water ice, if any were there — it was below the 3% level or so, and by the time we had the news conference, we would have a fairly definitive answer to the question.

Though I still had to put up with Scott, I was hoping I would soon have the definitive letter from Wes on that topic.

Monday, February 9, 1998

Day 033 MET

Dan and I talked about the need for a reor maneuver. The SEA had come down towards zero faster than Dan had expected, so we decided to do a reor maneuver the next afternoon, at about 2:00 PM, when Paul was at Mission Ops.

Ledbetter and Piotrowski were visiting Ames from Headquarters, so Dan and I went downstairs (Mission Ops was in the penthouse on the third floor and the conference room is on the first floor of the building) to the meeting. I told them we had too little data for me to discuss the science in any intelligent way and they said they would wait until next week to hear our preliminary results.

Scott was, of course, at the meeting and there was a distinct coolness between us. I thought Scott might have been told he was not running the show any more, because Sylvia, rather than Scott, gave the pitch about how the mission was going, engineering-wise, to the Headquarters crew.

Since we were not going to talk about the science, I didn't expect to have to say much. However, Sylvia just didn't understand much about the technical issues, so I had to clarify things a lot more than I had expected. Ledbetter and Piotrowski congratulated me on the success of the mission, which was nice.

During a break, I took Ledbetter and Piotrowski up to Mission Ops to show them how we were running the spacecraft. As I did, it was really apparent that Sylvia was taking on Scott's role, which was fine with me, because Sylvia and I had always worked well together. It was interesting to see that Scott was either phasing himself out of the mission willingly, or that he knew the handwriting was on the wall, even if I didn't know it officially.

Finally, Sylvia dragged us back down to the meeting. As usual, to keep up the façade that I was not completely running the show, Sylvia had asked Dan and Marcie to give the status of the spacecraft and the mission. They both did poor jobs of it. Dan showed a series of viewgraphs indicating that the spacecraft had been successfully launched and turned on, that we had successfully deployed the booms and that we did mid-course maneuvers, etc. At that stage of the game, everybody with a brain in their head knew all that — it was old news! When he got to the important things they did not know, he did not put the facts into context. Instead of telling them that we had a 1-σ launch velocity error of 9.2 m/sec, he just said that the launch velocity error was 9.2 m/sec, so they did not know if that was good or bad. Similarly, he told them that we had used 70 m/sec of ΔV for the two midcourse maneuvers, but did not tell them that that was 10 m/sec less than the 80 m/sec I had budgeted! Well, Marcie and Dan are just engineers and it showed. As a result, Ledbetter and Piotrowski weren't really interested in listening to that blabber, so the meeting got over very quickly.

After that, I saw Dougherty, who was really gracious and nice. He asked me, "How're you doing?" just like we were old buddies. I asked him for Brashears's and Henshaw's addresses so I could write them letters thanking them for their support of the mission, and he was going to have Delores send them to me.

Sam Lu Chung, a freelance reporter came to interview me for an article he was doing for Hewlett Packard (HP), who had built the test consoles for us. Several things were interesting about our discussions.

First, Sam wanted to know the history of Lunar Prospector and I was happy to give him all the details.

Second, he wanted to know about the HP test consoles and I told him he needed to talk with Kim Foster and Dougherty about that, since they had done all the interfacing with HP.

Third, and most interesting, he asked about the NASA/Ames PR effort and I said, "You know, the way they do PR sucks."

He responded, "Boy, you're not kidding," and then he explained he had tried to get some information from Ames PR about doing interviews for CBS and other networks and about the details of the upcoming science press conference. Sam said, "I'm not going to mention any names, but I could not believe how bad he is (I knew he was talking about David Morse). I asked him, 'Did you contact anybody (about coming to the press conference)?' and he answered, 'Oh no.' Then I asked, 'Did you invite anybody?' and he answered, 'Well no.' I asked, 'Did you do anything to let the media know about the press conference?' and he answered, 'No.' Finally I asked, 'Do you want some lists of press people who should be coming?' and he answered, 'Well, OK.' I was appalled at how incompetent he is."

I said to Sam, "Well, thanks for your efforts." And then I told him that when David called the reporters on his list, he said to them, "We're going to have a press conference, *if you want to come, you can.*"

Sam just shook his head and I said, "Yah, I know, it's just pathetic. Just like not having real TV cameras in Mission Ops!"

Sam replied, "Yah, that Internet camera they have in there just shows the backs of your heads!"

Fourth, regarding an earlier HP article he was involved with, Sam said, "I tried to do as much as I could to get you in the article, but there are some big egos around here. I had to give Scott and Dougherty the main billing, but it's totally transparent to people who know the business that they don't know what they're doing and you do. Scott just sits around trying to be the big shot. He's pathetic." I was extremely pleased to hear his opinions on that topic.

And fifth, Sam offered to have HP give me an HP 32SII (scientific) pocket computer, and I gratefully accepted his offer.

Speaking of PR, Morton Dean of ABC News called my LRI office at home and Ned Potter emailed me; they wanted to know what was going on with our search for water and they said they had heard we had found rivers of water. I called and told them,

"We're not yet in a position to say anything about the water ice. But I appreciate your interest and call me anytime you want to." They were happy with my offer to have them call and I was happy with their interest.

Late in the afternoon, I went up to Stanford to give a talk that Bob Twiggs had set up for his students. Bob was always very gracious and nice. I talked for about an hour and a quarter. I told them chronologically how the mission went and tried to get them to understand how easy it was to fly a spacecraft when it was built as simple as possible. I told them, "I went down to the Cape the day after Thanksgiving and came back Christmas Day. When you have a simple spacecraft, it gets processed (for launch) quickly. We had all kinds of contingency time and every day we were done early. For example, the fueling took us four hours instead of the planned twelve. Look, if you guys are going to build spacecraft, then make them simple. Don't try to make them do everything." It was about 5:30 when I was finished. The students who could stay, stayed and asked a lot of good questions, and one guy, who had been Bob's assistant the previous year and hence had heard all my seminars, asked if he could come to Mission Control. I answered, "Of course you can, just come on over anytime you want. In fact, we're doing a reor burn tomorrow; if you want to be there for the burn, just come on over."

He said, "Gee, I can't make it."

I said, "Well come on anytime if you want to see how it works. It's your spacecraft, your money paid for it."

He said, "I would just love to work on this if there is anyway I can." Unfortunately, there was no way he could.

Tuesday, February 10, 1998

Day 034 MET: A Great Interview and a Tweak Burn

Sylvia came up to my cubicle in Mission Ops and told me Scott was not going to be involved with the mission much longer and if I had any concerns or objections, I should make them known. I said, "Believe me, I don't." I thought she knew something was up, but I didn't know if she knew all the details. I could hardly wait until I got the official letter from Wes so I could throw Scott out and then I could talk to her about all the issues and start getting things done right. Sylvia would be great as the NASA Mission Manager and she would not cause any problems. Then she said Headquarters was thinking that maybe the post-mission, data analysis phase should be done on a Lockheed contract, which I absolutely refused to do.

Then I got a phone call from someone telling me that the Las Vegas bookies were taking bets and put odds on whether Lunar Prospector would find water — I found that very amusing.

After that, a reporter, Jim Rendon, came from one of the local newspapers for an interview and later wrote my favorite article on the mission and me, called *Lunar Loner.* One of his questions was most interesting. He asked, "How do you feel about Lockheed and NASA taking most of the credit for the Mission?"

I answered that I was annoyed, both personally and professionally, by their doing so and, "that is not what Discovery is all about, the PI is supposed to be running the show and not have these people taking over." I was pleased that every reporter who interviewed me knew that both Lockheed and NASA were trying to take all the credit for a mission that they really had very little to do with.

After the interview, I showed Jim Mission Ops and told him he could stay in Mission Ops and watch our tweak reor burn. That worked out well, because he did a good job of using the burn as the background for his article.

As Jim watched, Dan, Paul, John, and I went through our well practiced routine of checking, rechecking, uplinking, verifying and executing a 12-pulse burn on engines A1 and A4, changing the spacecraft's attitude by 1.73° and setting the SEA at +1.0°. I started the sequence with the A1 heater turn-on at 034/19:04 MET and it ended with the engine safeing command at 034/19:30 MET. Jim was really pleased to be able to watch the reor burn, during which someone from JPL called to tell us that the BBC had reported that we had found water.

According to Jim's slightly exaggerated article, what followed was, "Binder jumps from his seat and presses the headset to his head. 'Hell no, we haven't found water!' he barks into the phone. 'The rumors are so rampant' (very true), he says to the caller. 'I even heard Las Vegas has odds on us finding water — I could make a killing,' he adds, cracking a smile as the group bursts into laughter." What Jim left off was that I added," — and then the mob would kill me." Regardless, Jim's article was an accurate reflection of my views of NASA, Lockheed, and the mission and he gave the reader a good feeling of what it was like in Mission Ops during a burn. I was very pleased with the article.

Wednesday, February 11, and Thursday, February 12, 1998

Day 035 MET and Day 036 MET

I stayed home Wednesday so I could get all the historical records of the mission pieced together. I was, of course, saving all the original Mission Profiles I used when I commanded and in which I checked off each command with a red pen as I verified the echo of each command and in which I redlined any real-time changes I had to make to the command sequence. I was also making a clean version of the actual Mission Profile with all the redlined change.

I went into Ames Thursday to show Mission Ops to Preston and his crew, who were visiting from Lawrence Livermore Labs and to reset some of the green, yellow, and red data limits.

I also sent a letter to Mel Brashears, telling him of Lunar Prospector's success, thanking him for his critical support when I proposed the mission to the Lockheed New Business Council in the fall of 1994 and (and this was the fun part) asking Lockheed to split its $4 million fee for the mission with LRI (Appendix 4-2, at www.lunar-research-institute.org). I did not believe in my wildest dreams for even a millisecond that Lockheed would do that, but I wanted to put Lockheed on the spot and make them say no to someone with a non-profit, tax-exempt, science based corporation, LRI, who had given them a multi-million dollar spacecraft design, brought in a $63 million program for Lockheed, and provided them with a completely successful, high PR value program. I awaited Mel's answer with great interest.

Friday, February 13, 1998

Day 037 MET

I stayed home and got a lot of work done (when I was at Mission Ops, I did very little except monitor the spacecraft, prepare to command it, or command it, so when I needed to get work done, I stayed at home to work in my LRI office).

I decided I had better go see Bill for two reasons: first, he had corrected the two mapping cycles worth of NS data we had for instrumental effects and still found no evidence for water, and second, I had made a good subsurface temperature model he needed in order to make the thermal correction to the thermal neutron data.

I talked to Sylvia and she said Wes was going to be at Ames the following Wednesday, so I wouldn't be able to leave for Los Alamos until Wednesday afternoon. She also said that Wes's letter concerning Scott was in the mail. She clearly knew a little about what was going on, but not much. Though she was taking over all the NASA/Ames management activities, she still had to ask Scott about everything, which, of course, I hoped to put an end to soon.

Monday, February 16, and Tuesday, February 17, 1998

Day 040 MET and Day 041 MET

I was home with the flu and I was not going to go see Bill until I got over it.

I got Wes's letter about Scott (Appendix 4-3, also see www.lunar-research-institute.org); the bastards at Headquarters weren't going to let me get rid of the SOB. Julius had forewarned me that he had heard that, though Wes believed the PI should have the right to run his team, Earle Huckins did not agree and wrote the letter for Wes to sign, in part, because Wes was resigning from NASA and was, in effect, a lame duck Associate Administrator. Though I was very disappointed and though I had hoped Headquarters would have enough integrity to back its PI when some little prick like Scott pulled the crap that he did, I had been around long enough to know that government bureaucracies, like NASA, protect their own, no matter what — in the same way the Democrats protected Clinton, no matter how much he lied and what he did. I would have to put up with Scott, but, since I believed my letter had at least caused Headquarters to shift the real responsibility over to Sylvia and leave Scott as the NASA figurehead, I hoped and believed I would not have to interface with the bastard very much. If nothing else, I had at least put the SOB on notice that I would not put up with any more of his backstabbing. However, it just confirmed that NASA consists of the same kind of asses that it always has since the end of Apollo — NASA would never change for the good.

Other than saying no to my request to get rid of Scott and extolling all his virtues, there was one particularly interesting sentence in Wes's letter. Instead of saying, as he always did in public "the PI is solely responsible for the success of the mission," Wes wrote that the PI was the central figure of the mission — the same phrase Scott had used in our discussions. Thus, typical of NASA's deceit, Wes said one thing about the role of the PI in Discovery Missions at press conferences and science meetings, but played a very different tune when dealing in a non-public forum. Even if Wes were not responsible for the letter, his two-faced behavior caused me to think even less of him than I did before.

Wednesday, February 18, 1998

Day 042 MET: Wes's Visit

I felt fairly good, but I would like to have stayed home and completely gotten over the flu. Had Wes not been at Ames, I would have done so. When I got to Mission Ops, I spent some time monitoring the spacecraft, which was doing splendidly.

I went to Wes's meeting and, of course, Scott and some other Headquarters wienies were there. I showed them our NS data and I told them there was no water ice we could find above the 3% level. That made Wes happy, because as he said, "I knew that the Clementine guys were wrong," — NASA hated Clementine because it was done by the Air Force to show Congress and the public just how bad NASA is (the same reason I was doing Lunar Prospector). But I warned Wes that the data were still noisy and that we would not know if there was water below the 3% level until much later in the mission (the precision of integrated data improves with the square root of the integration time. Since we had analyzed just one month's worth of data at that point in the mission, by mission's end — in 12 months — the data would improve by a factor of $\sqrt{12}$ or 3.5 and thus our measurements would be good to the 1% level). I showed them the data and how good it was and how well the spacecraft was working. They were excited about the quality of the data and the success of the mission. Wes was very complimentary, as he should have been.

Thursday, February 19, 1998

Day 043 MET

I stayed home to finish getting over the flu and I got dozens of calls about Lunar Prospector. I postponed my trip to see Bill until the following week, so I could get completely well.

Later in the evening, Buddy Nelson called to tell me that, despite the absolute embargo, demanded by NASA, that none of us tell anyone in the press or public about our water ice findings until we announced our results at the upcoming water press conference, *our NASA PR friends, starting with NASA's David Morse and followed by NASA's Doug Isbell, had leaked our initial finding!* I was pissed.

Friday, February 20, 1998

Day 044 MET

We tried to do a SIM (one per month was required by my contract) and couldn't get it done because we couldn't get the system to work. We had to figure out how to run a SIM while the real spacecraft was on line!

Bill had asked me to increase the high-voltage level of the GRS (as it aged, the gain of the GRS dropped a little, so Bill had me periodically increase the gain to compensate for that effect), so I sent two commands to the spacecraft at 0044/11:54 MET and increased the voltage to 1596 v. That was the first commanding that I had done in 10 days; Lunar Prospector was doing what it was supposed to do without any help from me.

Sylvia, Scott (ugh), and I had a meeting about the water ice press conference and the fact that the Ames and NASA PR people had leaked our initial finding. Right after that, Pat Dasch called me and said NASA had accused Julius and Pat of leaking the information and I told her it was David and Doug. What a dirty trick on NASA's part, trying to blame my close friends (whom I had told absolutely nothing) for something that NASA's own staff had done. I was going to raise hell about it, among other things. Since I was getting more incensed about the stupidity of NASA, I asked Pat to see if I remembered correctly that Discovery was supposed to be run by the PI and not by NASA. She agreed with me and agreed that NASA had just changed all the rules after we got started. How I hate NASA; every one of them should be arrested and put in jail — they are just bunch of lying crooks.

Sunday, February 22, through Friday, February 27, 1998

Day 046 MET through Day 051 MET: Los Alamos and the Water

I left for Los Alamos Sunday, and early Monday morning I went to Bill's office to start working on the NS data. When I got there, he said, excitedly, "I think we have the signature of water!" Then he showed me the neutron flux curves and they looked really good. Sure enough, there were dips of about 2½% over the poles in the great circle profiles of the epithermal neutron fluxes. Though the corrections Bill had applied had reduced the compositional variations in the profiles considerably, the profiles still showed those effects, but the dips at the poles were very distinct. Sure enough, there were dips at the poles. There was excess hydrogen there and that most probably meant we had found the water ice we were seeking.

We worked on the data the rest of the day and then, that evening we went to the Blue Window Restaurant where Bill's Danish wife, Margrethe, met us for dinner. Just as we got done with the meal, Bill said all of a sudden, "I don't feel well," and then 5 or 6 seconds later he said, "Maybe we ought to get going," and he started to stand up. As he did, he again said, "I really don't feel well at all," and he just started to slump down, so I grabbed him and eased him into his chair. He was totally out; he had passed out cold.

Margrethe immediately went to call 911. Very quickly (everybody in Los Alamos knows everybody else) the waitress, the owner, and everybody else in the restaurant crowded around Bill. Then he started waking up and was very groggy. By the time the paramedics arrived, he felt better, but they still checked him out. The paramedics said, "We're going to take you to the hospital for some tests."

Bill said, "That's OK, I'll go to the hospital myself."

All of us said, "No, get on that stretcher," and we made him do it.

I asked Margrethe, "Do you want me to come with you to the hospital?"

She answered, "Yes, please."

I replied, "Good, because I wanted to come. I just didn't want to intrude."

She and I took off to the hospital behind the ambulance. The nurse who was taking care of Bill is a friend of Margrethe and is Danish too. It is the same nurse who took care of Bill when he got hit by the car on his bike in early April 1997. The doctor began to check Bill out, as I waited in the waiting room. After some time, Margrethe came out and said Bill was fine, but they wanted to do an EKG on him, so she said, "If you want to go to your motel, that would be fine," so I did.

Bill had to go to the doctor again Tuesday and the doctor insisted he stay home Tuesday morning and that he slow down. It was a very serious matter, since the intense effort and long hours demanded by space missions like Lunar Prospector, spent over long periods of time — months to years — always take their toll in terms of health problems (remember that Tom's health was suffering to the point were, along with other factors, I had to remove him from the mission), e.g., heart attacks and deaths. Both Bill and I were very aware of that, so Bill took his doctor's advice, even if he did so reluctantly.

The doctor said Bill, who has low blood pressure all the time, probably just had a low blood pressure attack and passed out after eating a big meal. As far as Margrethe and I were concerned, it was a good sign for him to start behaving himself.

After Bill got back to work Tuesday afternoon, we worked very hard on the data, trying to understand it, getting ready for the water press conference and writing abstracts for the various papers we would soon be giving at various scientific meetings. We concluded we were really seeing 2 to 3% dips in the epithermal fluxes over the lunar poles. Since I wanted to get a better evaluation of the depth of the dips, Bill made calculations to correct the data for the geometry of the instrument's field of view of the lunar surface, i.e., of its spread function. We were also considering two models of how the supposed water vapor was delivered to the polar cold traps where it froze out as ice.

The first model is a thick atmosphere model, in which, each time a comet, which is mainly a big lump of water ice, hits the Moon, the water ice vaporizes and forms a so-called "thick atmosphere." Such a thick atmosphere is, in reality, nearly a vacuum, but it is thick enough so that tenuous water vapor winds can blow from the hot equator of the Moon to the cold polar areas, where the water vapor freezes out, forming ice deposits. Such a thick atmosphere would last only a few thousand to tens of thousands of years before most of it would be lost to space and some of it would have frozen out at the poles. In that case, we would expect the water vapor would be deposited in a millimeter to centimeter thick layer after each comet impact. Slowly, during the last 2 billion years, since the tilt of the lunar rotation axis became essentially zero and hence, polar ice deposits would be stable, successive comet impacts on the Moon would have built up significant layers of ice in the permanently shadowed floors of polar craters (ice deposits could not have formed before two billion years ago, because the Moon's axis was tilted and hence, the Moon had seasons like the Earth. The Polar Regions were alternatively dark and cold for six-months and then sunlit and warm for six months).

The second model is where the Moon never has a thick atmosphere after a comet impact (because most of the water vapor would be lost to space during the impact event) and the individual water molecules that do remain in the Moon's tenuous exosphere, hop around the Moon in ballistic trajectories and when, by chance, they land in a permanently shadowed, polar crater, the water molecules freeze to the cold surface. In this model, the ice would be in crystals that are mixed in the regolith and the ice-to-regolith mixing ratio would be very small — probably no more than a few percent.

We went through various calculations and found that the 2½% dips we were seeing could be explained by a wide range of models, from a pure ice layer model in a 35 kilometer diameter crater to a 1% mixing ratio, ice crystal model in a 55 kilometer diameter crater. We had a spectrum of answers, we just didn't know which one was correct.

I asked Bill, "What else might we see in the data to help us determine which answer is correct?"

Bill answered, "Well, you know, the fast neutron flux is not constant, it should vary just a little bit and it varies in a different way than that of the epithermal flux." Bill explained that the depth of the dip in the epithermal flux grows rapidly for small amounts of water (hydrogen in reality) and slower and slower as the amount of water increases, while the reverse is true for the dips in the fast neutron flux, i.e., the dips are insensitive to small amounts of water, but grow more and more rapidly as the amounts of water increases. If the mixing ratio was small, we should see a bigger dip in the epithermal flux than in the fast neutron flux and the reverse for large mixing ratios — at least, that was what we concluded.

Since the plots we had of the epithermal flux had dips and those of the fast neutron flux showed no signs of polar dips at all, I said, "Well OK, if we're not seeing any damned change in the signal of the fast neutrons, then we've got very little water there and it has to be in widely dispersed crystals (in the regolith). We need better plots and we have to look closer at the fast neutron flux to see if there are any dips at all. If there aren't, then we're really seeing virtually no water at all." We had Sylvest Maurice, a bright, young French astronomer who was visiting Los Alamos and who was doing most of the data reduction of the NS data for us, start plotting up all the data in five great circles going just through the highlands, to cut down the background noise.

Finally, we got the new plots and they were much cleaner than the first plots. I measured the new epithermal plots and found that the North Pole had about a 3.4% dip and the South Pole had about a 2.2% dip, confirming that there is more water ice in the North Polar Region than in the South. That was interesting, because everybody at NASA and in the press had been saying, incorrectly, that we were looking for ice at the South Pole, because the Clementine photographs had shown there is a lot more permanent shadowing in the south than in the north. Even in the original, less accurate plots Bill had, we could see there was a bigger dip in the neutron fluxes in the north than the south.

Then I very carefully measured the fast neutron flux plots and found that there appeared to be very slight dips, no more than about a ½%, at both poles. However, those ½% dips were at the noise level of the data and hence we were not sure they were real at all. However, real or not, the fact that the dips were very small, meant that we were dealing with dispersed ice crystals with a mixing ratio of 1% or less — maybe down to even less than 0.3%. After a while, we decided that the mixing ratio was most probably between 0.3% and 1%. Bill's models showed that for those mixing ratios, the ice would be in permanently shadowed areas measuring 3,000 to 6,000 km^2 near the North Pole and 2,000 to 4,000 km^2 near the South Pole and that there would be about twice as much water ice in the north as in the south.

When we were finished, we felt we had the right — though preliminary — answer, given the limited data we had at hand. We were not sure about the exact numbers, but we were quite sure there is hydrogen in small amounts at the poles, most probably as dispersed water ice crystals in the regolith. If correct — and we were convinced that as the mapping proceeded, we would have the data to know for sure — then we calculated the lunar polar regions contained some 30 million to 50 million metric tons of water ice in the outer 1 meter of the regolith (the maximum depth in the regolith the NS could probe), or enough water to fill a square lake about 10 m deep and about 2 km on a side — no Lake Erie as had been theoretically suggested, but a significant amount of water ice in terms of its utilization for life support and for rocket fuel in the future exploration and colonization of the Moon.

Given our preliminary results, it was time to inform Headquarters and their reaction ticked both Bill and me off. When I had briefed Wes and the rest of the NASA wienies the previous Wednesday at Ames, I had told them our search for the water ice was an evolving story, that we had found no evidence for water ice above about the 3% level and if any ice was there, it was in the "grass," below that level. Our story was consistent — we were now working down near the 1% level and we were seeing evidence for relatively small amounts of water ice. However, Doug Isbell, who, along with David Morse had leaked our initial finding that we saw no evidence of the water (above about the 3%

level), and who had got wind of our new results (probably via David Morse who probably got it from Scott, who probably had been kept informed of our progress by Sylvia) tried to tell our complex analysis to Wes and Carl Pilcher. Of course, Doug got our story all screwed up (since he understood nothing about what we were doing), so Carl and Wes got nervous and said, "Maybe we shouldn't have a news conference. This doesn't sound very clear." What a chain of typical NASA incompetence.

After Bill and I had a telecon with just Wes and Carl, we got the mess cleared up and explained to them exactly what was going on, i.e., how we had worked our way down into the "grass" and finally had a result we believed in. We explained we were not presenting an upper limit to the amount of water ice, rather a real value. I explained that everything I had told them earlier was true; that the signals we were dealing with were at — and below — the 3% level. Though they finally understood what we had done, Bill and I were disgusted with them and, like me, Bill didn't want Scott at the news conference.

We had a telecon with Ames and Headquarters Thursday morning to discuss the format of the news conference. Bill and I thought we (Alex, Bill, and me) should present the gravity map, the thorium data from the GRS, and then the NS water ice data. We thought that was the correct sequence because, if we talked about the water first, all the reporters would probably run out to get their stories in press, since that was what they were really interested in. Headquarters agreed, but Wes said that because the press was really only interested in the water ice and because the gravity map had to be discussed (because of its importance for navigation), he thought we should limit our presentations to the water ice and the gravity — and I agreed with him.

We started to discuss the details of the press conference. I suggested I would first give an overview of the gravity data and then turn it over to Alex to explain the details of the gravity mapping. Then I would give an overview of the water ice, explaining how much we saw, and then let Bill talk about the details. The reason for my wanting to do that (other than the fact that I am the PI and should give the overviews) is that Bill just cannot explain anything in terms that anyone, except a nuclear physicist, can understand. Bill lives in a world of electron volts, nuclear reaction, capture cross-sections, and the like, and even when talking to school kids, he uses such terms. Bill just cannot conceive that the vast majority of the people in the world do not live and work at Los Alamos, where the best scientists in the world developed the first atomic and hydrogen bombs. As such, I wanted to tell the press what we found and how we did it in simple, everyday terms, before Bill started telling our story in terms the media could not understand. Of course, I did not say that, because I did not want to insult Bill, but I also did not want the press to leave our most important press conference without the foggiest idea of what we had said.

Everybody at Ames and Headquarters agreed with the format, but they said, "We need Scott to say something."

Bill and I both said, "No, we don't see any reason for that. This is a science press conference."

Headquarters said, "We need to have an overview; we need to have this put into the context of the whole mission."

I replied, "I'm the Principal Investigator; I defined and developed this whole program and nobody knows this better than me and nobody can put it into the proper context better than me."

Well, they couldn't argue against that, but tried again, "Somebody has to put it into the context of the NASA programs."

Bill and I said, "This is not about NASA programs, this is about Lunar Prospector science."

Headquarters said, "Well, yes; that is correct and we agree with you, but —," and then they would try another tactic.

The person that always led off each new tactic was David Morse and I thought Scott put him up to it, because I was sure Scott didn't want to be the one to have to say, "Well, I want to talk."

David kept trying to find a reason for Scott to be in the press conference and Bill and I just kept saying, "No, this is about science, not NASA." Then I said, "Look, the context of this mission in terms of the payload, lunar science, and its impact on NASA has been discussed at the pre-launch science news conference. It was discussed during the news conference you guys had down at the Cape, and it was certainly discussed when we had the post-LOI news conference and now we are just presenting science."

Again they had to agree, "Well that's all true, but blah, blah, blah."

Then they tried, "We agree that Scott shouldn't speak first, but he should say something at the very end about how this ties in with the rest of the NASA Discovery program."

I said, "This is not about Discovery any more, this is about the Moon," and Bill said the same thing — he was just as vocal as I was, since he hates Scott as much as I do, but for slightly different reasons.

They just kept wiggling around and Bill and I just kept saying, "We just don't agree."

Carl Pilcher finally said, "Well, as a representative of Headquarters, I'm going to have to insist that Scott be up there as the 4th person and that he give a slight summary as to what this means for NASA programs."

I replied, "Well, this is a NASA news conference and you guys are going to do what you want to anyway. You know our opinions."

Of course, NASA didn't want to hear that; they wanted us to say, "Oh yes, yes, yes," but Bill and I would only say, "No, no, no." Scott was going to be up there and give a summary, no matter what we said.

I flew home Friday and stopped at Mission Ops to see how the spacecraft was doing — it was fine — and then I drove home.

Monday, March 2, 1998

Day 054 MET

I went to Mission Ops and monitored the spacecraft for a while and then I worked on the viewgraphs for the press conference. Because we were presenting very preliminary results and were unsure about the amount of water ice, Bill and I just wanted to say, "We found modest amounts of water ice. There is more in the north than in the south. The mixing ratio is very low. We don't know exactly how much, but there seems to be enough water ice there to be of economic importance for the future." We didn't want to get tied down to exact numbers, because we knew that the numbers would change as we got better data and understood the data better and better.

I got a call from London asking me about the water ice and I said I could not say until the press conference. I also got two emails from reporters saying they had deadlines to meet before the news conference. I told each one I was sorry, but I was not allowed to give privileged information (however, the SOB Scott leaked the answer in an interview the morning before the news conference — so much for his integrity and NASA's, remember the Isbell and Morse leak?).

Tuesday, March 3, 1998

Day 055 MET: Chatting with Sylvia

I had a nice chat with Sylvia. I suspected she had been told she was supposed to do all the NASA management work on the mission from then on, but that changed nothing, since she had done all the work all along. I assured her she and I could easily work together, that I didn't want her to be caught in the middle of Scott and me and I was really ticked off. I asked her if she had seen the letter I had sent to Wes and she answered, "No, Scott would not give it to me. But he was very upset the day you confronted him."

I said, "Good."

I told her the whole history of Lunar Prospector — how NASA had ignored us and had slammed the door in my face so many times in the early days and that there was no question in my mind that if there had not been a fair and equitable, external evaluation of the Discovery proposals, NASA would have never chosen the mission for flight. I said, "They (Code S) told me a dozen times they didn't want Lunar Prospector, so I'm really ticked off about NASA now taking all the credit for it and pushing me aside."

She said, "NASA and Scott never intended that the PI would be in charge. They were always supposed to be in charge, not you."

I replied, "Yeah, I know that now, but that was not how Discovery was sold to the public and the science community," and I told her Lockheed had forced me to ask Ames to be my NASA Center Partner. Then I explained to her some of the things Scott had done and what I had in my letter to Wes — like the business of my getting locked out of Lockheed. I told her, "I've no objection to Scott and Lockheed getting their share of the credit for this, there's plenty of credit to go around, but I refuse to let them simply push me aside and take all the credit." It was clear from her comments that she was aware of all that and that she respected my position. She knew the reason Lunar Prospector was selected for flight was that I had a complete mission and a credible science package long before I ever came to Lockheed and Ames.

She said her boss, Bob Hagen, who hates Scott (I had gradually found out that everybody at Ames hates the backstabbing, self-serving SOB, except those above him, whose asses he carefully and continually kisses) and who had often fought with him, wanted to get involved with the mission and what was going on. I quickly surmised that Bob, who knew I was raising hell about Scott, wanted to use my complaints about Scott against him. I did not want Bob to be able to use my battle against Scott against him too (that was an altruistic mistake) and I didn't want Lunar Prospector and me to become Ping-Pong balls for internal, Ames political battles. I wanted the mission to be done properly and for both Bob and Scott to keep their noses out of my mission. I said, "That (Bob's getting involved with the mission) is just totally unacceptable."

Apparently Sylvia agreed with my position because she complained, "They (Bob and Scott) give me all the work, but none of the responsibility. As a woman, I get all the crap all the time," a sentiment I wholeheartedly agreed with, just as I agreed with Maryann's plight at Lockheed.

I said, "I know just what you mean. You get treated like that because you're a woman and Lockheed treats me that way because I'm a scientist and Lockheed considers that scientists are a waste of time."

She told me what one of the Ames Project Managers had told her, i.e., "You ignore scientists. You don't give them a say in anything. You tell them what the engineering requirements are and that they have to stick to them. You don't let them anywhere near the hardware or operations." And NASA still felt that way, despite what Wes had said about Discovery. It was the same old crap.

What she told me indicated that, even though Scott wanted to have less to do with the mission's day to day activities, he would be back there pulling the strings, i.e., she had to have everything OK'ed by Scott. I did not want Scott involved at all, but since Headquarters was stonewalling me on the Scott issue, there was little I could do about it.

Having finished our mutual bitching session, we turned the rest of our conversation to the extended mission and data analysis program. Sylvia again said NASA wanted to have Lockheed run both the extended mission and the data analysis program, because it would be the easiest for NASA. I again said, "That is absolutely unacceptable. I will not do the data analysis through Lockheed. I do not want to and I do not intend to do the extended mission through Lockheed. I simply will not do it. They (NASA) are going to have to get me (LRI) a contract for the extended mission; if they want to, they can add the extended mission to the data analysis contract, but I am not working through Lockheed and I am not going to put up with Scott after the primary mission. I really don't care if NASA likes that or not. I really don't care, I am old enough to retire and NASA can go to hell."

Wednesday, March 4, 1998

Day 056 MET: The Press Conference Dry Run

At 2:00 PM, we (Bill, Alex, and I) went over to the Ames Auditorium for the practice session for the press conference. Lewis Peach (a really nice guy from Headquarters) was going to represent Headquarters at the end of the press conference, as was Scott. Clearly, Bill and I were not happy about that. Also, Headquarters wanted me to just give the introductions, but not the highlights, and let Alex and Bill give the result. Not only was I worried about that, but so was Los Alamos — they had sent a PR guy along with Bill to try to coach him through the press conference.

Just as I thought, after I did just the quick introduction, Alex and Bill blew it. When we were finished, the criticisms were basically that Alex and Bill (mainly Bill) were far too complex, they didn't get their points across and they didn't give sound bytes (Bill just doesn't know how to do that). As a result, the format was changed to the way I had originally suggested. I was to give the results and the highlights in the beginning, and then Alex and Bill would fill in some of the details.

After that, a guy from the BBC was in Mission Control and I did an interview with him.

Thursday, March 5, 1998

Day 057 MET: The Water Press Conference

I was surprised when I got to the auditorium to find all kinds of people there. Kent Joosten and Doug Cook were there from JSC. Frank Martin, Dougherty, Bob Garner, Steve Debrock, most of my engineers, and many others from Lockheed were there. Stu Nozette was there to be sure we gave credit to him and Clementine for having provided the first (though highly dubious) evidence for the water ice. Of course, there were a whole lot of reporters and cameras there. Finally Rebecca and Margrethe Feldman were sitting together in the middle of a row down near the front where I could easily see them.

David Morse introduced the press conference and introduced Bill, Alex, and me as the main speakers and then Scott and Lewis Peach, who were there to answer any questions that required an input from Headquarters.

I led off and gave the results of the gravity mapping, e.g., we had the first complete gravity map of the Moon and evidence for a small iron core, and we had found evidence for small, but significant amounts of water ice near each pole and there was more ice in the north than in the south. Then I turned the mike over to Alex who did a fairly good job of discussing the gravity results and then Bill started. He started off with a joke about the NS either finding water in the Atlantic or on the Moon and that, happily, we had found it on the Moon. From there it went down hill rapidly as Bill went off into his semi-private world of nuclear physics tech-talk. I thought, *oh no, he's lost everyone already,* and I looked at Margrethe and saw that she had buried her face in her hands and was shaking her head out of hopelessness, as her brilliant husband just babbled on and on, while the press and everyone else in the audience looked more and more bewildered.

Finally and mercifully, Bill was finished and the reporters started to ask questions. A couple of them tried to get an understandable clarification from Bill and Bill, who was equally puzzled as to why they did not get his simple explanation of nuclear physics, tried to answer their plaintive questions. Finally the reporter just gave up on Bill. Later, Al Tilley said, though he and the others had understood what Alex and I had said, the minute Bill started, everyone effectively asked, "What language is he speaking?"

Then a reporter asked the $64,000 question; "Is NASA planning follow-on missions to the Moon and when is NASA going to put man back on the Moon?"

Poor Lewis Peach had to give the standard NASA, semi-evasive, Clintonian answers that boiled down to, "No," and, "Never." Soon after that, the press conference came to its end and some of the reporters rushed out to tell the waiting world that Lunar Prospector had discovered water ice on the Moon.

As we began to break up, Lewis came over to me and privately said what he really thought, i.e., our discovery of lunar water ice was great; he hoped it would get us back on the Moon; he was soon retiring from NASA; and he would then be willing to do anything to help me in my future attempt to start doing commercial lunar exploration missions. Right after that, the reporters besieged me with more questions.

Before leaving Ames, I did ten TV and telephone interviews and I was asked to do a live interview on Channel 2 TV in Salinas in the early hours of the next morning.

When Rebecca and I got home after the press conference, Jim Muncy called and wanted the information so Congressman Rohrabacher could put out a press release. Then Jim disappointed me; typical of a politician, he grumped that I had sent him a copy of Wes's letter and that I wasn't getting along with NASA and Scott. That really ticked me off because he was the very person who had always cheered me on when I was raising hell with NASA.

That evening, the results given at the press conference were on all the national and local newscasts. Lunar Prospector was big news again.

Friday, March 6, 1998

Day 058 MET: The Day After the Press Conference

Rebecca and I drove down to Salinas very early in the morning and I did two live spots on Channel 2 TV.

All the morning newspapers carried stories about our finding the water ice and what it meant for the future exploration and the colonization of the Moon.

When I got to Mission Ops, I did a live radio interview via telephone for *National Public Radio*. *Newsweek's* Ronda Adel called for an interview, as did nine other reporters in the USA and one in Spain! Late in the afternoon, the *McNeil/Leher News Hour* staff called and asked if I could quickly drive up to San Francisco to be on their live nightly newscast. I said I could and then I quickly did.

Chapter 4-6
PR, Reor Maneuver Problems, and the LPS Conference

Saturday, March 7, 1998

Late Day 059 MET and Early Day 060 MET: The 1st OMM

I had already done a radio talk show via phone by the time that Rebecca and I drove up to Mission Ops to do our first orbital maintenance maneuver (OMM) of the mission, which was going to begin shortly after 7:00 PM.

After having obtained the first complete gravity map of the Moon, we finally knew exactly how the lunar gravity anomalies were perturbing our orbit. Thus our Ames and Goddard Nav Team could, and did, find the best way to keep Lunar Prospector's orbital altitude within the 100±20 km range I wanted and to minimize the number of OMMs we had to do. Their solution was to rotate the line of apsides — the line connecting the periselene (when it was near 80 km altitude) and the aposelene (when it was a the same time near 120 km altitude) by 180° once every 55 days, i.e., just switch the low and the high points of the orbit around. That was far better than, as previously planned, circularizing the orbit at 100 km, which, if we did that, we would have to do every 27 days.

After a burn sequence that rotated the line of apsides, the lunar gravity anomalies would gradually decrease the 80 x 120 km orbit towards a 100 km altitude circular orbit and then continue to change it into a 120 x 80 km orbit in a total of 8 weeks, i.e., the gravity perturbations would rotate the line of apsides 180°. If left uncorrected, the orbit would continue to evolve with the aposelene getting higher and higher (well above the 120 km maximum I wanted) and the periselene getting lower and lower, until the spacecraft hit the Moon in about 200 days. To stop that from happening, all we had to do was to rotate the line of apsides back to where it was 8 weeks earlier, forcing the orbit to start its 8 week perturbation cycle over again. Also, that allowed the Nav guys to time the burns so they would just be axial burns, with no tangential pulse burn component! That was great, because it greatly simplified the OMM sequences (two simple axial burns vs. two axial burns and two more complex, pulsed tangential burns), so I thought my Nav guys were really clever.

After everyone had arrived for the OMM, the Nav guys (Dave and Ken in Mission Ops and the Goddard guys on the phone) gave us the burn vectors and times and told us the ΔV vectors of the axial engines were in the –Z direction, so we had to use the A3 and A4 engine pair for the first time for a axial burn (up to that time, all the axial burns required the A1 and A2 engines and A4 was used with A1 for the reor burns, thus the A3 engine was the only one that had never been fired). The first burn, the periselene burn, had a ΔV of 7.36 m/sec and was to start at 060/00:24 MET. The second burn, the aposelene burn, had a ΔV of 7.26 m/sec and was to start at 060/01:28 MET. Dan and I calculated the burn times (46.5 sec and 45.9 sec, respectively) and then Dan created the two sets of engine parameter files, which we checked, as always, after he sent them to Paul, who was the uplink controller for the burn. In addition to Rebecca, Dan, Paul,

Dave, Ken, and me — John Kohli was there as the fourth (communications) controller, and Marcie was also there (as far as I was concerned, mainly to annoy me).

I started commanding the A3 and A4 heater turn-on for the first burn at 060/00:01 MET and safed the engines after the second burn nearly an hour and a half later, at 060/01:29 MET. The A3/A4 engine pair had worked just fine and we had completed, in our very routine and well-practiced manner, the 1st OMM of the mission.

Given what we then knew about the orbit maintenance requirements, we would use just 110 m/sec of ΔV to keep the spacecraft in its correct orbit during the one-year primary mission. That was just a tad less than the 120 m/sec I had calculated during the proposal effort over four years earlier. Since I had multiplied my number by a factor of three to take into consideration the very large uncertainties in the gravity models I had to work with back then, I had budgeted 360 m/sec of ΔV for orbital maintenance during the nominal 1-year mission. Thus I would have 250 m/sec of ΔV for the extended mission phase and, boy, was I happy about that.

As it turned out, the A3/A4 engine pair spun the spacecraft up more than we expected. We ended the burns with a 12.18 rpm spin rate. Also, that engine pair caused the spacecraft to reor a little, so we would have to do a tweak de-spin reor burn in a few days.

All in all, the OMM was very good and it was fun to do. I loved that spacecraft.

Monday, March 9, 1998

Day 061 MET

Rebecca and I went up to Oakland so I could do a live interview on the Bay Area TV morning show.

When I got to Mission Ops, Ken had left a message saying we were only a kilometer off in the new periselene and aposelene altitudes, so I knew we had done a really good OMM the night before.

Sky and Telescope magazine called for a telephone interview, as did a reporter for *Que Pasa* magazine in Santiago, Chile — so Lunar Prospector's ice discovery was still worldwide news.

Tuesday, March 10, 1998

Day 062 MET

I changed the GRS high-voltage to 1604 v at 062/11:30 MET, as Bill had requested, and I prepared the Mission Profiles for our first penumbra lunar eclipse that was going to occur late Thursday night and for the reor and de-spin burns we were planning for Friday.

Though, during the penumbral eclipse (from the viewpoint of the Moon and hence the spacecraft, the Earth would only partially eclipse the Sun, so neither the Moon nor the spacecraft would be in the full shadow of the Earth), just 65% of the Sun would be blocked by the Earth at maximum eclipse as seen from Lunar Prospector, the March 12 lunar eclipse would be our first since achieving orbit, and since most of the others we would have to endure later in the mission would be worse, we needed to learn how the spacecraft reacted, power-wise and thermally, to the diminished sunlight.

PR-wise, the *Sci-Fi TV* channel people came for an interview, which went really well. I had a luncheon with Gilroy school kids and I had a telephone interview with a Milwaukee newspaper. Things had gotten down to a dull roar in that department.

Bill was whining about getting a paper on our water ice discovery submitted for publication — even before we had all of the necessary data. I was getting a little bit annoyed with him and his continually wanting to prematurely publish while we had more important things to concentrate on — like running the mission!

Space News ran an article on me that again ticked off NASA, because I was (correctly) quoted as saying I wanted to do commercial lunar exploration missions after Lunar Prospector. NASA does not like the word "commercial" and liked it even less since I was successfully getting the word out to the press more and more. I was quite happy (both because of the PR and because I was annoying NASA — annoyance causes change).

I was getting more and more invitations to give talks at various international meetings and Rebecca and I were trying to figure out if we should make a grand tour to Melbourne, Japan, Moscow, France, and Germany to attend the meetings. I was worried about being on such a long trip — after all, I had a mission to run and that was much more important to me than running around giving the same talk at several different meetings to a lot of the same people!

Wednesday, March 11, 1998

Day 063 MET: National Geographic, Data Analysis Money, and Marcie

National Geographic came and I talked with them for over two hours. They were quite excited about the mission and the future of commercial lunar exploration. They were doing a two-hour special on the next millennium, i.e., on the things that would make the most impact during the coming millennium and on the people who were going to make them happen.

In addition to the *National Geographic* interview, I did telephone interviews with a Seattle radio show, an English TV show, the *Discovery Channel,* and a national junior high and high school newspaper. Interest in Lunar Prospector's discoveries was running very high.

I talked with Sylvia about the money we needed for the post-mission data analysis and found that NASA was doing what it always did. The first Discovery Announcement of Opportunity clearly stated that the Discovery Program was a data acquisition program, not a data analysis program, so the data were to be delivered to the NASA archives in nearly their raw form. To be sure that was correct, I had called Mark Saunders when I was writing the Discovery proposal back in the fall of 1994, since I did not want to get caught with my data-analysis pants down. Mark confirmed that the Discovery Program would only pay for getting the data ready for archiving at the very lowest level of processing and that the analysis of the data was to be done as part of a post-mission data analysis program.

Since then, after our mission contract had been written and after NASA had signed off on our data archiving plan, NASA had changed its feeble mind and decided we were supposed to archive the data in the high level forms, i.e., the forms scientists and the public could use. That was impossible; we had $5 million worth of numerical data reduction to do before the data were in the form of maps the science community and the public could use and there was no money in the original contract to cover that.

If, as NASA was saying, "Well, you just have to find the money in the contract to produce the fully reduced data scientists can use," Lockheed would have to give up all its $4 million profit, which Lockheed would never do, and even that wouldn't be enough to cover the analysis costs. NASA was pulling its usual tricks and was indifferent to the fact that, if we did not receive the money to numerically reduce the data to usable forms, the Lunar Prospector data, which cost NASA $63 million, would be useless! And you wonder why I hate NASA?

After we convinced them there was no money in the contract for data analysis, Headquarters said, "Well, then you'll have to submit a proposal to the standard data analysis program (NRA) and compete for the money." Now that was a brilliant suggestion; there were about 15 different NRA categories and each category would receive dozens of proposals; the NRA program probably had about $15 million and we needed $5 million — so you do the math! It was the same old song and dance NASA always does — they fly missions and then they have little money to do the data analysis.

My questions to NASA and Discovery were, "If you have no money for data analysis, then why did you pick two new Discovery missions? And, why did you pick missions that cost nearly the full cost cap of $250 million, rather than picking missions that cost less than half of the cost cap (like Lunar Prospector) as you said you were going to do in the beginning of the Discovery Program?" Unfortunately, I knew the answers; it was because the same types of fools ran NASA that had run NASA for decades and they were running it into the ground.

My Ops Team and I talked about the penumbral eclipse we were going to go through the next evening and I got even sicker of Marcie than I was before. She knows very little about spacecraft or space missions, but despite that, she thinks because she is a big NASA engineer, she knows everything; so she believes what she does not understand, no one could possibly understand — the typical NASA arrogance I had almost always seen during my entire 40 year career. As a result, she started hollering about the "catastrophic" eclipse and insisted we call in all the Lockheed engineers to get us through it (I had already asked Woody and Jim Schirle to come, mainly so they could enjoy seeing the thermal and power effect on the spacecraft as it went through the eclipse, not because I needed them to help get us get through such a minor event. Ken and Dave were also going to be there just for the fun of it, since there was certainly nothing for those two Nav guys to do during an eclipse).

As all my calculations showed, the 65% penumbral eclipse, while interesting, would not seriously stress the spacecraft, either thermally or power-wise — Lunar Prospector was built to take much worse. I knew my spacecraft and I knew how to run it and Marcie knew neither of those things. But fearful of an imaginary failure, she just kept hollering, "We can't let the spacecraft fail. I've got to understand this. I don't want something to happen to the spacecraft." She is just a hysterical, incompetent boob, who I would never have had on the program, if I had had any say in the matter. Needless to say, I just ignored her hysteria, even if I could not shut out the loud noises she continually made.

Since the eclipse was so benign (despite Marcia's hysteria), the only thing we considered doing, except watching the spacecraft during the eclipse (those of us in Mission Ops were the only people in the world who could see the effects of the penumbral eclipse from the vantage point of a spacecraft orbiting the Moon — all other human beings, if they even noticed that slight lunar eclipse, saw it from the vantage point of the Earth) was to shut off the primary heater circuit if there was a chance that the big propellant tank heaters would turn on during the eclipse. That would cause a several hour delay before the secondary tank heaters would turn on, because their set point was a few degrees lower than that of the primary heaters, and by that time the eclipse would be over. As long as the tank heaters didn't turn on, there would be no power problem. My Mission Profile for the eclipse was very simple; I had written in the commands to turn off the primary heaters and then to turn them back on after the eclipse was over, but I did not expect I would have to use those commands. Other than that, the Mission Profile just had the timings of the various events that would occur during the eclipse and thus had just 12 lines in it.

Thursday, March 12, 1998

Late Day 064 MET and Early Day 065 MET: The First Penumbral Eclipse

During the day, Allen Zeyher of *Star Date* called for an interview and I didn't go to Mission Ops until late afternoon, since the penumbra eclipse was not going to start until after 7:30 PM and I would be up until about midnight.

When I got to Mission Ops, I found that the last tank heater event had occurred at 064/05:05 MET. Since our data showed a tank heater event occurred about every 21 hours and 25 minutes, we expected the next heater event would occur after the main part of the eclipse was over — too late to cause us any power problems.

In the final analysis, as the spacecraft was orbiting the Moon and the latter slipped into the partial shadow of the Earth, the spacecraft would go into the Earth's partial shadow at 065/00:18 MET, reaching a maximum loss of sunlight of 65% at 065/00:50 MET. Five minutes later, at 065/00:55 MET and while still deep in the Earth's partial shadow, the spacecraft would slip into the Moon's full shadow for its normal nighttime pass for 46 minutes. It would reappear from behind the Moon at 065/01:42 MET into full sunlight. Forty minutes later, at 065/2:22 MET, the spacecraft would again enter the Earth's partial shadow and remain there for 26 minutes, reaching a maximum loss of sunlight of a scant 10% and exiting the Earth's partial shadow at 065/02:48 MET. At that point, the penumbral eclipse events would be over and five minutes later, the spacecraft would again start a normal 46-minute nighttime pass.

Given that sequence of the events, only the first, 65% dip into the Earth's partial shadow plus the overlapping 46-minute nighttime pass were of any concern — and concern is far too strong a word. The second, short, 10% dip into the Earth's partial shadow was of no concern at all. I had come to the conclusion that I wasn't going to turn the primary heaters off at all. I showed Dan the data and he agreed it would be silly to turn the primary heater off, because anytime you turn something off, there is a small chance that it might not turn back on. When Woody and Jim Schirle arrived at Mission Ops and Dan and I showed them my analysis and asked them for their opinions about shutting the primary heater off, they answered, "Hell no, don't turn them off." But, of course, Marcie was still worried about leaving the primary heaters on — who says that ignorance is bliss?

As my Command Team — Paul, John (who together had the normal nighttime monitoring shift anyway), Dan, and I — sat down at our consoles to get ready for the coming events, Paul said, "We've just lost command capability!" JPL had screwed up changing something at the DSN and we couldn't command the spacecraft! Since I did not expect to have to command, it made no difference, but it made Marcie very nervous to say the least.

Finally, things were about to begin. The spacecraft emerged from its final pre-eclipse nighttime pass at 065/23:44 MET and the battery began to charge up. Since the tank heaters had not turned on, the battery got fully charged up before the spacecraft started to dip into the Earth's shadow 34 minutes later — that was just perfect. As the spacecraft dipped into the shadow, the solar array temperature started to roll off and instead of reaching a maximum of 69° C several minutes later, as was normally the case, it only reached 65° C and Dan started seeing the effects of the eclipse in the Sun sensor data. The Sun sensor data gave the time of the crossing of the middle of the Sun through the detector. As the Earth began to partially cover the Sun, one side of it began to disappear and the middle of what was left shifted from the true middle of the Sun. As a result, the spacecraft's spin period appeared to change. Dan saw that effect within about a minute of the beginning of the penumbral eclipse and that was just amazing.

As the spacecraft got deeper and deeper into the Earth's partial shadow, getting ever closer to the maximum 65% shadowing, the solar array power output dropped slowly from its normal 6 amps to 2 amps — you could just see the solar array power output go down, down, down — and since the spacecraft needed a minimum of a little more than 2 amps to function, the battery started to discharge slightly. As I watched the solar array power output slowly decrease, I also looked for any thermal effects on the science instruments and the other spacecraft subsystems. Except for the most notable decreases in both the solar array temperature and its power output, everything else showed only slight or no thermal effects at all.

By the time the spacecraft was about to enter its nighttime pass, the battery had an insignificant discharge of only 1 or 2%. We were in excellent shape for the 46-minute nighttime pass. That was the part we were concerned about, because if the tank heaters had gone on any time during the previous hour, I would have had to turn off the primary heater circuit for the duration of the nighttime pass and the rest of the eclipse. When we entered the nighttime pass, the spacecraft was in perfect shape and man, it had been really exciting to watch the spacecraft respond to the penumbral eclipse during the previous 37 minutes.

Some 46 minutes later, the spacecraft emerged from its nighttime pass into full sunlight and the battery started charging up. It was fully charged before we started the second, very minor dip into the Earth's penumbra again. The effects of that 10% dip were negligible. The solar array temperatures reached 68° C, just one degree below its usual 69° C; and Dan saw just the slightest change in the apparent spin period of the spacecraft. If we had not known about the second dip, we would not have noticed its small effects on the spacecraft.

Well, the eclipse was over at 065/02:48 MET and it was such a hoot to watch, we were all looking forward to the future eclipses. Though it was getting late (10:15 PM), we all stayed for the following nighttime pass to see if everything was really OK with the spacecraft and it was — it was just like every other normal nighttime pass. Then I turned the spacecraft back over to Paul and John and the rest of us left before midnight. It had been a really fun evening.

Friday, March 13, 1998

The Rest of Day 065 MET: Tweak Reor and De-spin Burns

I was back in Mission Ops by about 10:30 PM and found out why the DSN had dropped us at such a potentially critical time, i.e., just before the eclipse. A JPL/DSN error had shut down the system and when they tried to reboot it, they used an older, incorrect program that did not work! When they found that out, they rebooted with the correct program and we were back on line. However, since we had reor and despin burns scheduled later in the day, I had the NOOP 1 command uplinked and executed at 065/15:34 MET, to see if we could really command the spacecraft and we could.

Then I looked at the spacecraft to see how it was doing and especially at the GRS temperature. The β angle of the spacecraft's orbit was down to 20°, so the spacecraft was passing over the hot, daytime part of the Moon. The temperature of the lunar surface where the spacecraft passed over the equator was about at the boiling point of water (100° C). In three weeks, when the spacecraft passed over the noontime point at the equator, the lunar surface temperature would be 6° C higher. The spacecraft and the instruments were receiving a lot of thermal energy from the dayside of the Moon and they were getting hot — as expected.

Though the GRS's temperature was being regulated and was supposed to stay in its thermal dead-band between –27.8 to –29.5° C, it was not doing so. For the past several days, for several minutes around the time when the spacecraft passed over the hot lunar equator, the GRS's temperature rose above the dead-band. By day 065/MET, the GRS temperature increased to as high as –18° C for the several minutes when the spacecraft was near the lunar equator. That was initially of concern, but since Bill saw no effect from the high temperature in the GRS data itself, we realized what was happening.

The thermister that was measuring the GRS's temperature was not very close to the actual BGO detector; rather it was on the graphite epoxy structure of the GRS. As such, we were measuring the temperature of the outer part of the lightweight structure rather than the temperature of the heavy BGO crystal. The former had a thermal time constant of only a few minutes and hence responded quickly to the temperature variation caused by the Moon's heat (on the dayside) and cold (on its nightside). Since the thermal time constant of the heavy BGO crystal was several hours and since the crystal was deep inside the thermally shielding structure, the BGO was not responding to the short heat pulses caused by the dayside passes. The measured temperature deviations above the dead-band were of no concern, though interesting to watch.

During the afternoon, i.e., between 065/17:34 MET and 065/18:26 MET, and following our well-practiced routines, we did a 1.67° reor and a 0.22-rpm de-spin to get the spacecraft back to where it was supposed to be. Preston, who had come over from Lawrence Livermore Labs, watched the burns.

Reporters from Brazil and Spain called for interviews about the lunar water ice and the mission.

When I got home, I found I had received a copy of a letter that Lockheed vice-president Coats had written to Wes, defending Scott against my request that Scott be removed from the project, praising Scott and NASA and stating that I had no reason for my charges (Appendix 4-4, also see www.lunar-research-institute.org). I had not expected Lockheed would stoop that low, but after seeing Coats's letter, I realized Lockheed would always take the side of NASA and Scott against (supposedly defenseless) me. Though I was used to Lockheed backstabbing me and ass-kissing NASA, I was really surprised that Coats did not have the guts to say no to Lockheed (or to Scott — there was a very good possibility Scott had asked Coats to write the letter). Here is an ex-military pilot and an ex-shuttle astronaut, supposedly a national hero, who wrote one of the most spineless, ass-kissing letters I had ever seen in my life. Though I had neither a good, nor a bad opinion of Coats before, his letter showed me he was a spineless worm who would do well in Lockheed's ass-kissing upper management, where competence and guts are not desired — just like at NASA. Not one to let such crap go unchallenged, I wrote Coats a letter regarding his letter (Appendix 4-5, also see www.lunar-research-institute.org).

Saturday, March 14, through Saturday, March 21, 1998

Day 066 MET through Day 073 MET: The LPSC in Houston

Rebecca and I flew to Houston Saturday so I could attend the annual Lunar and Planetary Science Conference. After going to our motel, she went to see her friends and I went to dinner with John and Barbara Gruener at our favorite German restaurant.

I had been told that Mike Duke had set up a meeting at 3:00 PM Sunday on the need to integrate all lunar science data, so I went there to find out what was going on. It turned out the meeting was really just a JSC Building 31 meeting about where lunar science should go after Lunar Prospector's success. Interestingly enough, though the meeting's theme was based on Lunar Prospector, Bill and I — the very people who had made the meeting possible — weren't invited! Despite Lunar Prospector's success — or because of it — many in the Building 31 crowd still hated my guts, though Mike himself was very nice and complimentary. The former was also apparent because many of the Building 31 crowd would not even say hello when they saw me. Similarly, Paul Spudis would not even look at me when we passed in the hall. I found all that amusing — success is truly the best revenge.

The conference started Monday morning and, as had been the case over the previous many years, the lunar science papers presented at the conference were very bad. Lunar science had gone to hell and needed a lot more data than Clementine had provided and lot more than even Lunar Prospector would provide in a year or two to get back on its feet. As such, the same old people, plus some young ones, were blabbing about the same old stuff they had been blabbing about since the Apollo data had gotten stale nearly a quarter of a century earlier. John Longhi and arrogant Tim Grove were the absolute worst of the worst. After listening to a few boring papers, I left and thought, *how in hell can they keep getting money for research that doesn't lead anywhere.*

Monday night, John and Barbara had a nice little party for a few of my old JSC friends (John Connelly, the Weavers, Kent Joosten, Larry Toups, and their kids were there, but unfortunately Bret Drake and his family weren't there) and us. Rebecca and I had fun with all my friends and colleagues.

Tuesday, I just visited with people and did not bother to listen to any more bad papers. Chuck Wood, Julius, and I went to lunch and that evening, Don Davis, Chuck Wood, Julius and Pat, and Rebecca and I had a nice dinner at a Luther's Barbecue joint.

The usual poster session, during which the various investigators stand around poster displays of some of their research results and talk to the scientists who come by to look at their work, was set for Tuesday evening. Bill and the Los Alamos crew had made posters of our GRS thorium map and NS water map. I went over there for a little while to see what was going on and I saw Wes Huntress milling around the crowd and I got the distinct impression that Wes was avoiding both me and our poster display. Finally, Bill and I decided just to go get Wes and we, almost literally, had to drag him to the Los Alamos poster area — Wes clearly did not want to interface with the guys who had a NASA supported spacecraft orbiting the Moon!

Since Wes wanted to get away from us a quickly as possible, Bill quickly showed him our latest results and Wes said, supposedly jokingly, "Well, you've got the gravity, water, and thorium maps, I guess we can shut you down now and save the rest of the money. Ha, ha."

As I said to Bill as Wes scooted away as fast as he could, "Unfortunately, he is not really joking," and Bill agreed. It was very clear that Headquarters had gotten all it wanted from Lunar Prospector — a pretty launch on TV and a few headlines — and would have loved to pull the plug on a mission they hated and a PI who would not put up with their BS, a conclusion that was supported by NASA's continual trying to find a way out of giving us the money we needed to numerically reduce the data and get it archived!

Wednesday morning, Matt Golombek, the Pathfinder Project Scientist, and I gave our invited talks on Mars Pathfinder and Lunar Prospector, respectively, to the JSC staff at the JSC auditorium. Given that the JSC staff should have been interested in the Moon and Mars and since JSC had posters telling about our talks all over the place, there were surprisingly few people there. I thought only about a 100 people were there, though the lady who ran the seminar said there were 300 people in the audience — if that were true, I would have been floored. On top of that, the seminar was badly set up because we, the speakers, couldn't see our viewgraphs from the podium — so it was difficult to explain to the audience what we wanted them to look at. Matt came dressed very casual, which I didn't think was right for the occasion and goofed around all during his presentation. All in all, I was disappointed in the supposedly big event.

The Discovery session occurred that afternoon and was even worse than the morning seminar. Doug Blanchard, one of the Building 31 crowd who ran the show, told us that the PIs of the missions in preparation would have 10 minutes to describe their missions and I would have 15 to 20 minutes to bring everyone up to date on Lunar Prospector — that sounded just fine. Wes got up first to discuss the Discovery program and, interestingly enough, said almost exactly what he said 3 years earlier about the PI being responsible for his or her mission. Both Rebecca and I were amazed that Wes would stand up there in public and say how Discovery missions were supposed to be run by the PI and then pull the rug out from under us behind the public's backs.

After Wes spoke, Gene Shoemaker's wife, Carolyn, got up and said some nice things. She was followed by Don Burnett, Genesis's PI, who talked for 30 minutes and went into great and glorious detail about his yet to be lunched mission. Doug never made any effort to stop him. Similarly, a representative of the Contour (Comet Nucleus Tour) PI got up and talked for more than 20 minutes. By that time, it was nearly 2:00 PM and the session was almost over, so I had just a few minutes to talk about a mission that was actually in flight and yielding results — needless to say, I was not happy with the way Doug ran the session. It was typical of the crap that the Building 31 guys pulled. To top that off, I had said something about Lunar Prospector producing some of the best lunar orbital data ever during my very short talk and Doug said snottily, "It's a little early in the mission to say that isn't it?" I just shook my head and thought, *what can I say to a Building 31 ass.*

I had invited the entire, original LEI Lunar Prospector core crew to a celebration dinner Wednesday night at Landry's in Kemah, on the shore of Galveston Bay. Mike Matthews, Brian Cox and his girlfriend, the Spratlins and their family, the Starcks, Andre Sylvester and wife, Graham O'Neil and wife, Rick Corbell and wife, Bill Feldman, and, of course, Rebecca and I were there. I had asked Tom Polette and Shelley (who were married and working at Lockheed) to come, but Tom did not want to, which was too bad, since he belonged there. Also, Todd Greenwalt and his wife didn't make it. He called later and said they had driven down to the restaurant, but they couldn't find us. Apparently nobody at the restaurant told them to go upstairs, where we were having our dinner party! That was really too bad, since I would have loved to have seen them. In any case, everyone had a great time. It was great to be able to thank the old LEI core group for sticking with me all those years until Lunar Prospector was accepted for flight by Discovery. As far as I was concerned, it was their success and their mission just as much as it was mine and I was very pleased to be able to buy them at least one dinner as a demonstration of my appreciation. It was a splendid evening.

I gave a couple of interviews Thursday morning and I talked with a number of people about future lunar missions. Alan Stern told me he was going to propose a Lunar Prospector follow-up mission to Discovery, using my spacecraft design with his instruments. He was going to have Lockheed build it and fly it from the Lunar Prospector Mission Ops at Ames, with Ames being his NASA Center Partner, i.e., basically a Lunar Prospector 2. He asked me to be an adviser on his proposal and mission. I answered, "I have no interest in participating in any way, shape or manner with a Discovery mission or with Lockheed again."

He just couldn't believe I wouldn't be an advisor and yammered, "But you have done it; you know how to do it."

I thought, *yes I do, but I am not going to tell you*, and then said, "There is no way that I will every work with Lockheed and NASA again, period."

Then Rebecca and I drove to San Antonio and had a great time Friday at the River Walk, where we had gotten so well acquainted on our third date. We drove back to Houston and then flew back to California on Saturday and got home very late.

Sunday, March 22, 1998

Day 074 MET

I went up to Mission Ops to check on the spacecraft and to look at a week's worth of emails and phone messages. Karen had called to invite me to go to a dinner at the Governor's Mansion in Florida on April 13, when and where I was to receive an award, and then to go before the Florida Legislature on the 14th, along with Goldin and the head of the Lockheed rocket division in Denver that had built my Athena II. I called her to let her know I would be there. Wayne had called and he was coming over the following Tuesday and Wednesday to work on LRI issues and to discuss the possibility of starting LEI up again, as a for-profit company, to do the commercial lunar exploration missions I wanted to do. Things were getting hectic and I was beginning to run out of steam.

Monday, March 23, 1998

Day 075 MET: A Backwards Reor and More NASA BS

I went to Mission Ops and the spacecraft was fine, but Dan had found out that, for some unknown reason, our last reor maneuver had apparently gone in the wrong direction! He was going to talk to Gerry Grismore about the C&DH, since we could not think of any explanation for the apparent error, except that something was wrong with the logic in the C&DH. It was a serious mystery. Thus, we planned a small reor burn for Wednesday (we delayed it until April 24) that would tip the spacecraft a little directly towards the Sun. We hoped that would tell us if the there was something going wrong with the delay-time part of the command load we used to tell the engines how long to wait after a Sun sensor timing pulse to fire each engine. Somehow we had to figure out what in hell was going on.

I talked to Sylvia. Headquarters was fussing about our data analysis program and wanted to have a meeting at Headquarters the week of the 23rd. Sylvia was afraid NASA had no money for the numerical analysis of the data, because the space station was way over budget and NASA was looking for money they could steal from other programs and she said further, "You're going to have to trade off the extended mission for data reduction money, its either one or the other." That was BS. There was only $2.5 million budgeted for the extended mission and since we needed $5 million to get the data numerically reduced and archived, using the $2.5 million from the extended mission would not do the job, so we would end up with no extended mission and half reduced data. Sylvia was even worried Headquarters was going to force us to shorten the main mission and use the money saved to reduce the smaller amount of data we would get! Typical NASA crap — fly a $63 million mission, but don't reduce the data, what a bunch of bastards and what a waste of taxpayers' money. But, they kept adding new Discovery missions, so they could do the same thing over and over again! I was so disgusted I was almost ready to quit.

Since I was so disgusted with NASA and since I was getting worn out from Mission Ops, fighting NASA, and travel, I decided that if I had to go to Headquarters the week of the 23rd, I would not to go to Florida the week before. I called Karen and told her I could not make it to the Florida Governor's dinner and she was disappointed.

Also, someone from the Melbourne meeting planning committee called and wanted to know why I had not submitted my abstracts to their meeting. I told him I was not sure that I would be able to go to the meeting because I had a mission to run and that I had too much travel already. He said the planning committee really wanted me to attend the meeting and present Lunar Prospector's results, so I said I would try to do so. However, I really did not feel like going to Australia, Japan, and the rest of the places that I had been invited to. It was just getting to be too much travel and I was really wearing out.

Tuesday, March 24, 1998

Day 076 MET: Wayne's Visit

Wayne and I had good discussions about LRI's future and how we would build up its staff. We also decided to restart LEI as the commercial partner to LRI to do commercial lunar exploration missions and to use the same name Preston and I had used for our original Texas, non-profit corporation back in the Early Years (Part One), since people still associated Lunar Prospector with the name LEI.

I was asked to give a talk in Aspen, CO, and I unfortunately said yes. To do so meant it would take a day to get there, then all day the following day to get back. I should have said no to that one and I decided I should start saying no to most invitations to give talks.

Wednesday, March 25, 1998

Day 077 MET: A Japanese Visit

Two Japanese guys from NASDA came to see me at Mission Ops and Wayne and I had a good talk with them. They were planning a huge spacecraft called "Selene" that would be ten times bigger than Lunar Prospector and would cost them about $2 billion. They wanted to hear all about Lunar Prospector and why it was so cheap and easy to fly. I tried to explain everything to them, but they just could not understand why Lunar Prospector was so inexpensive and why their spacecraft was so costly. I answered them with, "Because your science payload is as big the entire Lunar Prospector spacecraft." I asked them why they were flying some of the same instruments I was flying and they answered, "Because we want to learn how to fly those instruments." After they left, Wayne and I concluded they didn't have a clue as to what they were doing and they were not willing to do what was necessary to keep their mission inexpensive. They were just wasting their time and money.

Thursday, March 26, and Friday, March 27, 1998

Day 078 MET and Day 079 MET: An Aborted Trip to Aspen

I reluctantly took off from San Jose to fly to Aspen, with a plane change in Phoenix, to give the invited talk that evening. After I got to Phoenix, I found there was a snowstorm in Aspen and it was questionable that I would be able to get there. After some delays, the situation looked worse and worse, so finally, I called to tell the people at Aspen I could not get there because of the weather. Unfortunately, by that time, it was too late to fly back to San Jose, so I had to spend the night in Phoenix and fly home Friday morning. Thus, I shot two days on a useless trip. I decided right then and there I was not going to accept so many invitations to speak in the future — enough was enough. I had a mission to fly and I was running out of gas.

Monday, March 30, 1998

Day 082 MET

Dan and I decided how we were going to do the next reor maneuver considering that we thought there was a C&DH error during our previous reor maneuver.

Tuesday, March 31, 1998

Day 083 MET: A Reor

I went out to lunch with Steve Durst. He had been in China trying to drum up space trade over there. Steve said the Chinese wanted to invite me over for a lecture at the university in Beijing, so I was considering doing that and going to Japan and Australia at the same time. Everybody was interested in what I was doing, except NASA and Lockheed.

We did a 4.7° reor burn during the afternoon (between 083/19:08 MET and 083/19:34 MET) to make up for the reversed reor we had had trouble with a couple of weeks earlier. The burn went well.

A guy named Roger Lenard from the Sandia Labs in Albuquerque called and wanted to do a Discovery Mission with me and I said I would not be the PI, but that we could talk about some other arrangement.

Wednesday, April 1, 1998

Day 084 MET: Is the Spacecraft Playing April Fool's with the Reors?

Early in the morning, Dan called me at LRI (home) to tell me that we had again apparently gone in the reverse direction when we did our reor the day before! I immediately went up to Mission Ops. Dan said he was getting conflicting solutions when he used the SEA rate of change data as observed via the Sun sensor and when he used the EM limb-crossing sensor data to determine the attitude. Regarding the SEA rate of change data Dan was using, we were seeing the expected bi-monthly variations in the SEA due to the gravity gradient torques and Dan was using the mean value of those variations to get the SEA rate of change. Since that seemed to be the correct thing to do, we thought some other screwy thing was going on. For example, Dan thought maybe the mathematical models he was using were screwed up somehow. We just did not know, so we had a meeting with Marcie, Dave, Ken, and Bob Jackson to discuss all the possibilities.

The spacecraft itself was fine — there was nothing wrong with it and its attitude was OK. It was just that we didn't know exactly where in hell the spacecraft's axis was pointing (we knew where it was pointing to within a few degrees, but that was not good enough), or how we got there or what was going on with the reor maneuvers. Since we were getting excellent data and since the spacecraft was functioning perfectly (that is one of the nice things about a simple spinner — its safe mode is its normal operational mode; if Lunar Prospector had been a three-axis stabilized spacecraft, we would have been in serious trouble), we decided just to let it ride for a couple weeks to see what the attitude was doing and let Dan work through his calculations. Even if the attitude got so far out of whack that we could not get good communication through the medium antenna, I could switch back to the omni antenna and we would be OK. The mission was in absolutely no danger due to our little dilemma.

I didn't see how there could be something wrong with the spacecraft, i.e., something wrong with the C&DH, the engines, or the attitude sensors, so I had a sneaking suspicion there was something wrong with Dan's analysis. It was peculiar that the attitude determinations were right on until we got into the mapping orbit; after that, each tweak reor burn seemed to be wrong — very puzzling.

Thursday, April 2, 1998

Day 085 MET

I talked to Sylvia, who was getting grumpy and remorseful. I thought she felt caught in the middle of my battles with NASA (though I thought she disliked NASA and Scott as much I do), but she had to work for NASA, so there was nothing she could do.

She said NASA still wanted the extended mission contract and the data analysis contract done through Lockheed. Though I had accepted that NASA wanted the extended mission done on a Lockheed extended contract, since that was the easiest and — I had to admit — the most expedient thing to do, I absolutely refused to do the data analysis on a Lockheed contract. The data analysis is science and Lockheed knew absolutely nothing about science. She said, "You can tell Headquarters that when you go there."

Friday April 3, through Sunday, April 5, 1998

Day 086 MET through Day 088 MET: Berkeley and a Weekend Vacation

Friday morning Rebecca and I drove up to Berkeley to looked at the MAG/ER data and they were absolutely exquisite. They showed limb shocks in the solar wind (similar to the waves at the front and sides of a speeding boat) due to relatively big magnetic fields (big for the Moon, but very tiny compared to the Earth's magnetic field) on the lunar far-side in Mare Ingenii and in the South Pole-Aitken Basin. Clearly, the MAG/ER mapping was going to exceed our expectations.

Then Rebecca and I drove up to Point Reyes on the coast north of San Francisco and we had a wonderful weekend. The epicenter of the great 1906 earthquake that destroyed San Francisco was at Point Reyes and we saw the fence that originally ran straight across the fault line and whose two sides were moved laterally about 6 meters as the Pacific side of the San Andreas Fault moved north with respect to the America side of the fault. I had seen pictures of that fence in my geology textbooks and was thrilled to see in myself. We stayed at a beautiful hotel, took walks and hikes, looked at everything, and had a great time. We went home Sunday night.

Monday, April 6, 1998

Day 089 MET: Dan Begins to Understands the Reor Problem

Dan thought that he was finally figuring out what was going on with our attitude/reor problem. When he started using the rate of change of the SEA to provide the second piece of information to determine the spacecraft's attitude, Dan naturally assumed that the Moon was a sphere and that the gravitational gradient torques were just causing the spacecraft to rock back and forth twice per orbit, but that they did not actually change the spacecraft's attitude. He was beginning to believe that the torques were actually changing the attitude and if so, he was using incorrect values for the SEA rate of change in his attitude calculations. If he were correct, than that was why his solutions using the SEA data and the EM limb-crossing data were different from those he got using the SEA data and the SEA rate of change data. Anyway, I knew Dan would figure it out.

I went home (to LRI) and set up a trip to Washington, DC on the 20th through the 22nd, and then one to LA, followed by another to Albuquerque.

Jim Benson called and told me something that was unbelievable, since I knew from Wes, Mark Saunders, and Al Schallenmuller that Lunar Prospector was selected for flight because it was deemed to be the best mission by the hundred-person, external review board. Jim said he was talking with Wes Huntress, Mike Drake, and Carl Pilcher at Headquarters, when Mike accused Wes and NASA of not paying attention to the true science value of the missions (i.e., Mike was mad because Wes did not select the bigger, U of Arizona, lunar orbiter that Mike was part of), but just took the mission that was at the top of the list (Lunar Prospector) that was presented to Wes by the review committee (that was a stupid statement, science value was at the top of the list of five criteria on which the missions were judged). Defensively, Carl Pilcher had said, "That's not true, that is absolutely not true. There is a perfect example of where we overrode that and picked a mission for reasons of our own."

Mike had asked, "You mean Lunar Prospector?"

Both Wes and Carl had answered, "Yes."

I said, "Jim, that is a lie. It (Lunar Prospector) was picked because it was the judged to be the best mission in terms of the review board criteria. It was the one that met all the criteria and Wes just took the recommendation of the board and that was Lunar Prospector. Wes told me that himself and that was what he told the public at the Discovery Press Conference." I was amazed at how they just lied. I had given Wes more credit that that, but I guessed I was wrong.

Tuesday, April 7, 1998

Day 090 MET

Lunar Prospector had been launched exactly three months earlier and everything was going splendidly. Lunar Prospector was spinning away merrily as it orbited the Moon every 118 minutes, collecting science and engineering data and sending it down to us on the Earth. Except for the occasional tweak reor and spin-up burns, the OMM burns that would occur only once every two months and the occasional science instrument commanding, we did little on the ground except monitor the spacecraft 24 hours a day, seven days a week. As I had designed it to do and as Al Schallenmuller had so correctly said at our Ground Segment Review back on May 13, 1997 (Part Three) *"I realized this is a perfect example of a very simple spacecraft and very simple mission. I realized there is nearly nothing for you guys to do. This gets launched, it gets into orbit, it takes data, and transmits data and that is the end of it."* Lunar Prospector was doing exactly the job it was designed to do, with very little help from us!

I talked with Sylvia, mainly about my trip to Headquarters, but we discussed some other interesting topics. She said a number of things I knew, but it was interesting to hear an honest NASA person saying them. She said Headquarters was actively trying to bury the success of the mission and the importance of our discovery of water ice, because NASA had its sights set on Mars and they didn't want the public's attention being diverted to the Moon. I said, "Yeah, I've known that for years."

Sylvia continued, saying, "Everything is driven by politics at Headquarters," a fact everyone with more than one active brain cell knows, but it was amusing to hear her say it so honestly.

Since she knew of my opinion that everyone who is competent and honest can't stand it at NASA and they eventually leave, I complimented her in a backhanded way by saying, "You know, you're not going to last very long here — you'll leave." She wouldn't say yes, but she didn't disagree.

Then she told me the disturbing news regarding the devolution of Discovery: Headquarters had gone one step further down the path of taking over the responsibility of the missions from the PIs by making JPL and APL responsible for all Discovery missions — so the whole Discovery program had become a piece of crap. NASA was dismantling everything it had started and that I had been fighting for since Discovery started! Also, the fact that only JPL and APL could run Discovery missions pissed off Ames, because Ames had been pushed out in the cold and that made it more vulnerable to being closed (remember my January 29 lunch with Jack Boyle?). The ironic part of that was if Scott had not attempted to steal Lunar Prospector for himself and to make Ames look good at my expense, I would have been helping him to make Ames look good as I told him I would back on August 18, 1997 (Part Three). All he had done was to piss me off so I didn't give a damn what happened to Ames. The crux of the matter was that NASA was going down the same old path and the whole concept of Discovery was being destroyed — it was just the same old NASA crap.

Wednesday, April 8, through Sunday, April 12, 1998

Day 091 MET through Day 095 MET: A Meeting at Colorado Springs

Rebecca and I flew to Colorado Springs where I was to give a talk to an Aerospace Conference held there every year at the famous and fabulous Broadmoor Hotel. In my opinion, this annual conference is just an excuse for the big military brass and the big aerospace executives to be able to spend an all-expenses-paid, very expensive vacation at a four star Hotel in a beautiful setting.

Also, Rebecca had a cold before we left and she managed to give it to me. Then my cold turned into the flu by the final three days of the trip.

I gave my talk and I was very disappointed by the circumstances surrounding it. The people who set up that session had planned to have six people speak in one hour — Pathfinder's Donna Schirle, JPL's Director Ed Stone, The Planetary Society's Lou Friedman, The Mars Society's Zubrin, Apollo 17 Astronaut Harrison Schmidt, and me. As a result, none of us had enough time to discuss out topics properly, especially Donna and me, since we were talking about real missions. They should have had just three or four speakers in that session.

In addition to the poorly run session, I sat next to Lou Friedman and I could see that he was writing notes on a pad of paper as the others were giving their talks. He was writing what appeared to be his evaluation of our talks; among which was that there are no resources on the Moon; the Moon has no scientific value; man would never return to the Moon; and there would never be commercial exploration missions to the Moon or anywhere else. I thought, *what a stupid jerk.*

Harrison argued that our "water signature" could be due to enhanced solar wind deposits of hydrogen — which is possible since the NS only measured hydrogen abundances and not water. But he was pushing that theme so he could argue, if there were large hydrogen deposits at the poles, then there would also be more helium and hence, more ^{3}He at the poles. I assured him I always said we detected hydrogen and we interpret it as water, but his interpretation was also possible. Harrison said he would do anything to help get the money we needed from NASA to numerically analyze our data and get it archived.

Ron Humble came by (Rebecca and he met for the first time) and we had a good long talk about our mutual interests and later, Rebecca and I met Ron and his lovely wife, Judy, for dinner at a nice German restaurant.

Doug O'Hanley at Ames called me about the Melbourne, Australia meeting. Doug said Scott had submitted a Lunar Prospector abstract and the planning committee decided that Scott would give an overview of the mission and they would give me a half hour to talk about the science. I said, "Thanks, but no thanks. They can go to hell. If Scott is going to be there, I have absolutely no interest in being there."

Doug, who apparently knew Scott all too well and knew of my attempt to get rid of the SOB after talking with Earle Huckins, said he understood my attitude all too well. Doug asked, "Can somebody else give the science?"

I answered, "No. If NASA wants to pretend Scott is the head of this program, then they can do without us (my science team and me)."

He understood that, too, and indicated he was not happy with NASA either and could hardly wait to retire. He said, "NASA has never paid for my going to these meetings — meetings I help to organize — and they said this time if I put in an abstract for the meeting, maybe they would pay my way there. Well I did and then they said they couldn't pay and I should just take vacation and pay for it myself." He is as happy with NASA's backstabbing as I am.

I got the impression from Doug that Earle Huckins was on the review board of the meeting and that Headquarters had given Scott the travel funds to go to Australia and represent Lunar Prospector, because Huckins had told O'Hanley, "this is going to piss Alan off." My suspicion was that Headquarters was sending Scott to give the lead paper on the mission so it would sound like Lunar Prospector was a NASA controlled mission and I was just the Project Scientist, rather than a mission being run by the PI and hence, that it was my mission. I was, to say the least, sick and tired off NASA, Earle Huckins, and Scott's continual backstabbing and misrepresenting the mission in their favor. However, I was happy about not going on a long trip to Australia and the Orient (if I was not going to Australia, then I was not going to Japan and China either), so there is always a silver lining!

Though Rebecca and I were not feeling well, when the conference was over we tried to enjoy the weekend by going to some of the beautiful and famous Colorado Springs attractions, e.g., the Garden of the Gods and the Seven Falls, and by driving around in the Rocky Mountains.

Monday, April 13, and Tuesday, April 14, 1998

Day 096 MET and Day 097 MET

I was still sick with the flu, so I stayed home in bed.

Wednesday, April 15, 1998

Day 098 MET: The Reor/Attitude Problem Solved and a Big Surprise

When I got to Mission Ops, Dan said he had indeed correctly figured out what was going on with the attitude issue. He finally knew for sure that all our reor maneuvers had gone exactly as we had planned, but because he had not understood the effects of the gravitational torques on the spacecraft's attitude, he had been using the wrong SEA rate of change data in his calculations, so his attitude calculations were wrong, so we were performing the wrong reor maneuvers! In addition to not correctly understanding the SEA rate of change data, he had also found a small error in the textbook equations he was using for the attitude calculations. When he corrected for both sources of error, the attitude solution using the SEA and the rate of change of the

SEA was exactly the same as the attitude solution he got when he used the SEA and the EM limb-crossing data. Dan had solved the problem, as I knew he would do, and we finally knew our exact attitude and we could proceed making the correct tweak reor burns.

Dougherty called me and I was floored when he said, "Goldin is so ecstatic about Lunar Prospector that he has asked Lockheed and you to put in an unsolicited proposal for a follow-on lunar mission!" Dougherty said, "I assume you have plenty of suggestions as to what we could fly."

I replied, "Yes, let's talk about it." Dougherty said he would set up a meeting to discuss the issues in a couple of days.

Routine Mission Activities and the Data Reduction Money Issue

Thursday, April 16, 1998

Day 099 MET

Sylvia and I talked about the meeting at Headquarters regarding the data reduction money set for the following Monday.

After that, I went over to Lockheed to talk to Bob Garner. He said I was finally going to get the extra $40,000 to pay for the 2½-month delay in the launch and it was going through their system without any monkey business. I went home after lunch.

Once at LRI, I called Pat Dasch. She said Rohrabacher was ready to write a letter to NASA saying they had to give us the money for the data reduction if my meeting at Headquarters didn't work out well. Even better than that, Rohrabacher and some other Congressmen wanted Pat to get information from Jim Benson, David Gump, Harrison Schmidt, and me, so they could put in a bill to get money for commercial missions! They were considering a bill that required a certain percent of NASA's budget had to be used for commercial missions and another would give tax breaks for commercial space activities. I was extremely pleased that Lunar Prospector was beginning to help open the door to commercial space activities.

Friday, April 17, 1998

Day 100 MET: The Mission is 100 Days Old!

Knowing that NASA did not want to give us the $5 million we needed for the Lunar Prospector data reduction effort, I knew they would argue first, that we were supposed to have budgeted the money for the data reduction in the original proposal and since we had not, we would just have to use mission money to do the numerical reduction of the data. If that failed, they would want to show that the data themselves were no good, so they wouldn't have to waste money reducing bad data. One way or another, NASA was going to get rid of the mission.

I prepared for the meeting by making viewgraphs showing A) the section in the Discovery Announcement of Opportunity (the Discovery AO) where we were instructed to deliver the data at the lowest possible level to the archives, B) the fact that I called Mark Saunders as I was writing the proposal to be sure of what was in the AO as above, C) the parts of my Discovery proposal in which I had stated we would deliver only low level data products to the archives and D) the Archiving Document Headquarters had signed off on that defined the low level data products we would deliver to the archives. I figured those viewgraphs would end Headquarters' attempts to say we had to use mission money for the data reduction.

To show that our data were excellent, I asked all my Co-Is to be at the meeting to show the NASA bastards just how great our data were and that would destroy their second excuse for not getting us the needed money.

That would then leave them with only one possibility — saying what they really felt, i.e., "We don't want your damned Moon data (even though we spent $63 million having you get it)," and then I would rely on Congressman Rohrabacher and others in Congress to make NASA give us the money — a tactic of mine NASA hated with great passion.

Sunday, April 19, through Thursday, April 23, 1998

Day 102 MET through Day 106 MET: The Trip to Headquarters

I flew to Washington Sunday and we had our meeting Monday morning regarding the money we needed for the reduction of the Lunar Prospector data.

Scott was at the meeting, though there was no real reason for him to be there, except to show that he was still officially the NASA Mission Manager. Basically, I ignored him and he ignored me. We spoke to each other as little as possible and never in friendly tones, which I enjoyed very much. Other than that, Scott kept his big fat mouth shut and everyone else said I was doing a good job with the mission — I was pleased to hear that for a change.

In addition to Scott, Sylvia, and Marcie were there, Marcie was there for no apparent reason, except for Scott to keep pretending for Headquarters' benefit that she was playing an important role in Mission Ops (what a joke).

In an — as far as I know — unprecedented act, NASA had invited several lunar scientists to act as the jury for judging our data: GRS specialists Jack Trombka and Al Metzger were there, as well as (friendly) Ray Arvidson, (unfriendly) Roger Phillips, and (hostile) Paul Spudis.

On my side, representing the MAG/ER team, were Bob Lin and Lon Hood and, representing the spectrometer team, were Bill Feldman and Bruce Barraclough. We were loaded for bear.

I started out by showing NASA the viewgraphs that clearly showed we were supposed to deliver only very low level data to the archives during the mission and the analysis of the data was a post-mission issue. I told them I had followed the AO instructions implicitly and read off the parts of the AO to prove that. Then I went through my other viewgraphs and they had to agree I had done exactly what I was supposed to do. I had hit a homerun with that — they had to get us the money if we could prove that the data were good.

My Co-Is then got up and easily demonstrated how good the data were and what we were going to get out of the entire mission, including the low altitude mapping of the extended mission. They hit the second homerun.

I got up again and said, "You shouldn't screw up our doing the extended mission or cutting the nominal mission in any way, because if allowed to finish the mission as planned, we will to be able to complete the mapping of the Moon using these six mapping techniques (i.e., NASA would never have to fly these types of instruments again to complete the job that we started — if they let us finish the job). It would be wasteful not to allow me to finish two missions (the nominal one year mission and a second, six month extended mission of low altitude mapping) for the price of one and never have to do this stuff again."

In the end, NASA agreed they were going to have to come up with the money (whether they liked it or not). The meeting was successful (for us, not for NASA) and there was no ambush Sylvia and I had worried about.

Tuesday I went to see Davis Gump at LunaCorp to find out exactly what LunaCorp was all about. Of course, I had known for years about LunaCorp and what they wanted to do in general — land a rover on the Moon as a Disneyland attraction, but since the success of Lunar Prospector, Jim Muncy (yes, Congressman Rohrabacher's aide) and Rick Tomlinson, founding members of LunaCorp, wanted me to be LunaCorp's CEO. I was not really interested in the idea, but I wanted to find out more about LunaCorp to see if our two companies could work together towards our common goals — the future exploration of the Moon and the commercialization of those activities.

I met with David, who had been a journalist, and Jim Dunstan, who is a commercial communications satellite lawyer, and, as they admit, they don't understand anything about the science, the engineering, or the lunar environment side of what they wanted to do. However, they do understand the business side a lot better than I do and we decided we would fix up some arrangement so we could help each other, but not work for each other. Basically, if one company got something going in the near future, the other company would get in on it.

While I was busy with LunaCorp, Dan, acting as Mission Director in my absence, sent two commands to the spacecraft between 105/22:47 MET and 105/22:49 MET. The first commands, NOOP1 and its execute, were done to verify that the uplink system was OK and then Dan reconfigured the downlink, so we could read the temperature of one of the reor engines (A1 and A4) with 2 second resolution (instead of 8 second resolution) using the so called "tailbytes." Gerry had built into the C&DH the capability for us getting high time-resolution engineering data (when necessary for diagnostic purposes) from any engineering sensor on the spacecraft using a channel we called tailbyte. That would allow us to confirm that the engines were pulse firing when we were instructing them to do so, as a final check on our reor maneuver burns.

Julius, Pat (with whom I was staying — as usual), and I went out for a Mexican dinner that evening.

Wednesday I went to Orbital Sciences and met with Chris McKelvey and other staffers. I told them how Lunar Prospector was doing and we talked about the Taurus. I told them about my future plans to do commercial lunar exploration missions and asked if they would be interested in being part of a consortium that would conduct the missions. They liked both the consortium idea and the idea of doing future lunar missions with me.

After that, I went back to DC and Pat and I had a meeting with a Presidential advisor to discuss the possibility of getting legislation requiring NASA to have a data purchase program. He was not interested in legislation. The administration's problem was the damned space station and nothing else was going to happen until it was taken care of. Well that meant that nothing else would ever happen! Nevertheless, he believed what we wanted to do was correct — it was just that he didn't know how to implement it.

Then we went to see Dick Obermann over at the House Committee on Science Office. Dick liked the idea of a commercial data purchase program, but he did not like the idea of legislation either, because it would take too long. He would rather get NASA to do it voluntarily and both Pat and I said, "Well, we would too, but we don't believe that will ever happen. If this was Mars, it would be a different story, but they have no interest in the Moon. We are not capable of doing Mars commercially, but we are capable of doing the Moon commercially." Dick understood that I had proven the latter with Lunar Prospector and everyone gave me credit for that.

After we talked to Obermann, we talked to Jim Muncy, who is just a flake in many ways. First he encouraged me to raise hell with NASA, then he didn't want to be involved, then he wanted everybody to get along, and finally he wanted me to raise hell again. Jim is just too erratic to be of any use.

Finally it was Thursday and I winged my way home.

Friday, April 24, 1998

Day 107 MET: A Test Reor and a Low Extended Mission Mapping Orbit?

Though I was dead tired from the long trip, I went to Mission Ops very early. Dan and I did the one-pulse test reor burn between 107/11:05 MET and 107/12:08 MET and it worked exactly as expected. That was our first use of the tailbyte data and it showed us that the engines were firing in the proper sequence. We were ready to do the reor to get the spacecraft's attitude where it belonged the following Monday. I had fun doing the commanding — I missed doing it.

As I saw what the science data was showing us, I was leaning more and more towards doing the extended mission in a low (25 km altitude) circular orbit, so we could get really good MAG and gravity data over the entire Moon and get a lot of high resolution NS data on the water ice in the polar regions. I asked the Nav guys to see if we could pull that off. If we could, it would be fantastic.

I wanted to go as low as possible during the extended mission for three reasons. First, the resolution of spectrometers, the MAG, and the gravity mapping improved linearly (and inversely) with altitude. If I got down to the hoped-for 25 km mean altitude, i.e., 4 times closer than the 100 km altitude of the nominal mission mapping orbit, our surface resolution would improve by a factor of four, from 150 km to less than 40 km. Second, since gravity effects drop off with the altitude squared (or more), the gravity mapping would increase in sensitivity by a fact of, at least, 4^2 or 16 times. Third, since magnetic effects drop off with the altitude cubed (or more), the MAG mapping would increase in sensitivity by a factor of, at least, 4^3 or 64 times. Thus all those factors pushed me to want to lower the mean altitude as much as possible during the extended mission.

Monday, April 27, 1998

Day 110 MET: The Correct Reor Maneuver

We did the reor burn to put Lunar Prospector in the attitude we wanted and it went extremely well. It was a 40-pulse burn that took 6 minutes and 41 seconds, and that shifted the spacecraft's attitude by 8.54° and resulted in a SEA of +0.97°. I sent the first heater-on command at 110/11:00 MET and I finished safing the engines at the end of the maneuver at 110/11:44 MET. The burn verified that Dan was correctly interpreting the attitude data and it was really nice doing a full burn.

Also, that was the first time our new uplink controller, Cathy Culver, did the uplinking for me. She had just one small problem getting the engine parameter file uplinked because she clicked twice on something she should have clicked on only once, but that did not cause us to even get off the timeline and she did a really good job. I was very impressed with her performance; she is very dedicated and careful and she is a very nice person. Also, it was nice to have a female controller on my all male Mission Ops Team, excluding Marcie of course.

We started getting ready to do the SIM of the orbital maintenance burn we were going to do on Friday, but JPL could not get the command system up. The reason was that JPL had some people there who had never done it before, so they kept screwing it up. Since I was going to be on travel the next day, I told my team to do the SIM the next day if they could, with Dan being the Mission Director and me being on the telephone. I needed to get the SIM done to meet my contractual obligations and I wanted to make sure Marcie got some practice.

I talked to Steve Debrock, who had taken Dougherty's place on the mission after Dougherty had moved up in the Lockheed hierarchy, about Goldin's request that we submit an unsolicited follow-on mission to Lunar Prospector. Unfortunately, Dougherty had misunderstood what Goldin had said. What he really said was that he was interested in Lunar Prospector type missions — not lunar missions. I told Debrock, "I'm not interested in doing anything but the Moon," and that ended that. Then I added, "If people like Alan Stern can get a proposal together with you guys, using my model, that's fine." After talking with Debrock, it was clear he and Lockheed didn't know what in hell was going on at all.

Tuesday, April 28, through Saturday, May 2, 1998

Day 111 MET through Day 115 MET:
A Trip to Pasadena, Los Alamos, and Albuquerque and the 2nd OMM

I flew to LA and drove to Pasadena to give a talk on Lunar Prospector at Cal Tech and then one at an IAA meeting on Tuesday. Wes was there and gave the first talk in the session, followed by Mark Saunders, then came talks on Pathfinder and NEAR and some other missions. As soon as I gave my talk, I got out of there, because I had to fly to Albuquerque. Wes gave the same false story about the PI being solely responsible for the success of Discovery missions and blah, blah, blah. It was amazing that he and NASA consistently said one thing in public and then did the opposite in practice. NASA is just a living lie.

After arriving at Albuquerque that evening, I stayed there overnight. I met John Gruener, who was in Albuquerque for the *Space 98 Conference*, Wednesday morning and we drove up to Los Alamos together to talk to Bill and his staff about the spectrometer data. The GRS and NS data were looking better and better and Bill and his staff understood better and better how to interpret those data. The APS data also looked good, but nature was throwing us a curve. Unexpectedly (no one had ever flown an APS in deep space for a extended period of time before), the Sun was erupting large quantities of alpha particles as much as half of the time. When the Sun did that, the APS count rate went up from the expected lunar rate of a few counts per 32-second integration period to several thousand particles per integration period! A large fraction of the time, the APS was saturated with solar alphas. There was, of course nothing we could do about the Sun, except hope that solar physicists would find our APS data useful in their studies of the Sun.

John and I went back to Albuquerque that evening and I gave my talk at the conference Thursday. Jim Benson was at the conference and he had been talking to a reporter from *The New Yorker*. After I gave my talk, that reporter and I spent about an hour and a half on an interview. The reporter was pumped up about our commercial exploration missions after talking to Jim and me. He was going to go see Wes and Goldin the following week and he asked me what he should say to them. I told him to tell them about the value of commercial space missions. Then he said he was going to see Vice President Gore and asked me what he should say to him. I told him to tell Gore he should talk to Benson and me.

Then I went back to the meeting because I was on a panel Wendell Mendell ran. Wendell introduced each of us and asked us questions. It was fun. Wendell did a really good job of roasting each of us as he introduced us — I enjoyed his roasting me very much.

Friday morning, starting at about 8:00 AM, I commanded, via phone, the 2nd OMM, a tweak de-spin burn and a change of the GRS high-voltage, with Marcie sitting in my chair and passing on my directions to the command team. The commanding session started at 114/11:54 MET and ended at 114/14:17 MET. All three burns (the two OMM burns and the de-spin burn) and the GRS high-voltage change went without a hitch.

After the conference was over on Friday, I went to Sandia to meet Roger Lenard; our meeting went very, very well. Basically, Roger wanted to do a Discovery proposal for a lunar rover and he wanted me involved. I told him I wanted nothing to do with NASA and Discovery again, rather I wanted to do commercial lunar missions and maybe we could do the rover as part of my future activities. Roger agreed with all that, because he hates NASA, too (who doesn't), and then we quickly started discussing the commercial lunar base that is the penultimate goal of my efforts. Roger thought we (he wanted to be part of my efforts and I was happy with that) should get moving as quickly as possible on the commercial lunar base concept, work out its business plan, and have a workshop in the fall. The purpose of the workshop was to invite potential hardware vendors and potential customers, so we could find out A) what the former had to offer and at what cost and B) what the latter wanted to do at a commercial lunar base and what they would pay to be there. Our goal was to have the lunar base up and running a decade after we got started. We decided to try to get JSC's George Abby to say NASA needed a lunar base if NASA wanted to go to Mars and we discussed a number of other things we needed and/or should do to get the lunar base effort started. Our conversation lit a very hot fire under Roger and he was raring to go, but I had to remind him I had a mission to finish. Nevertheless, when we finished our discussions, I had the feeling we were going to get to the Moon and build a commercial lunar base and all that was starting with Lunar Prospector.

Since I had always wanted to go to the Moon (I applied twice to become an Apollo Astronaut), I told Roger, "If we build a lunar base, I'm going on the first mission and I'm going to stay there at the base."

When I went to my hotel room, I called Rebecca and told her about Roger and my conversation and I asked her, "Do you want go to the Moon with me to live in our lunar base in ten years?"

She answered emphatically, "No." Well, you can't have everything.

Monday, May 4, 1998

Day 117 MET: The Japanese and a Long Bitching Session with Sylvia

A delegation from the Japanese space program came to see Mission Ops and me during the afternoon. We talked about Lunar Prospector and their planned lunar missions for about 3 hours. It was difficult trying to say things so the non-technical translator would understand. It was a laborious discussion.

Bill called and told me that, after I had left Los Alamos and was at the Albuquerque meeting, Sylvia had called him three times. She was desperately trying to find me because she was told I wasn't going to go to Australia. She asked Bill why and he talked around the issue and said I had declined to go because of the travel costs and the time. Finally, during the third call, Sylvia asked Bill if he would go in my place and he also said, "No, I won't go either." Bill hates Scott as much as I do.

Shortly after that call, Sylvia came to my office to talk about the extended mission. When we were finished, I asked her why there was such a big flap about my not going to Australia. She said, "Huckins (the SOB who had decided to send Scott to the meeting) was very concerned that you have withdrawn all your papers, because they (NASA) wanted Lunar Prospector science presented at the meeting. The fact that you won't go to the meeting has them greatly concerned."

I had had it with Huckins and NASA's two-faced BS, so I didn't spare a thing; I said, "Well they can go fuck themselves. Pardon my French, Sylvia, but I was invited to give the paper on the Lunar Prospector Mission, but I hadn't made up my mind to go because I didn't know if I had the time and money for all the travel. Then someone from the planning committee called me and said I just had to come and give a paper on Lunar Prospector. I told him it was really not worth my time to make a long trip like that for a 15 or 20 minute paper on the mission and hence, I would like to give some of the science results. He said that would be fine and I should put in some extra abstracts on the science. I said I would do that. Then I got a call from Doug O'Hanley, who said Scott had put in an abstract, that he was going to give the lead talk on Lunar Prospector and I was supposed to follow him and only talk about the science. I said hell no. I'll be damned if I'm going to get up on the stage with that SOB. If NASA and Scott want to take all the credit for the mission and continually shove me down to the level of the Project Scientist, I won't help them do it by standing up there with that bastard and licking his boots the way they want me to. They can all go to hell." Sylvia understood completely, in part, because I thought she felt the same way about Scott as I did.

However, I was not finished ranting and I continued, "It's an insult to me that I have to put up with him (Scott). I have done my job. This is my program; everybody in the world knows that except NASA and Scott. I developed it and I made it work. I have no objections to sharing it with NASA and Scott, as I've told you before. But after what Scott did, he should have been removed from the program and it's an insult to me that NASA didn't do that. I don't care if they believe me or not (regarding Scott's misdeeds), the point is there is no working relationship between us anymore and they should have removed Scott, if for nothing else, for the good of the program. If they want the science discussed at the meeting, since they chose Scott to represent the mission, then let Scott get up and give the science."

She said, "But he's only going to talk about the management."

I replied, "I don't give a damn. First of all, it isn't even his damned management, it's the management scheme I set up. Second, they called each and every one of my Co-Is and they all said no (I had checked with my Co-Is before talking with Sylvia). They said they wouldn't do it. You know Sylvia, I'm not the only one who hates Scott. I'm very pleased the guys wouldn't do it. That lets NASA know how we all feel about Scott and the way NASA does things."

I said, "Sylvia, I want you to understand two things. First of all, I apologize to you because I know you are in the middle of this and I don't like that. This is not against you. I know damn well the reason you weren't officially put in charge of the mission when I raised hell with Scott — they just don't want to remove him when he is under the gun."

She replied, "Well, I think that is true."

I continued, "If Huckins is so concerned that I'm not going to go to the meeting, then why did he decide to send Scott, since he knew, as he told O'Hanley, that his sending Scott was going to piss me off. If they don't care how they treat me, then screw 'em."

I went on to my second point, "Second, I want you to understand that I do not hold you in any way responsible for this, because I have always worked well with you and I respect you and wanted you to take over for Scott."

She said, "Yes, I know; I've done 95% of the work anyway. At first I was upset about this (not being officially the NASA manager), because it would look good on my resume if I were the Project Manager, but then, on the other hand, I don't worry about it too much."

I said, "Anytime you need a letter of recommendation from me or need me to talk to somebody, I'll tell them what really happened and how you did all the work and Scott took all the credit."

She said, "Thanks, I appreciate that."

Tuesday, May 5, through Friday, May 8, 1998

Day 118 MET through Day 121 MET

The spacecraft was fine and everything was normal. I gave a talk at Palo Alto to the solar physics and space physics guys from there and from Stanford. Other than that, things were very quiet.

Monday, May 11, 1998

Day 124 MET

I had to go to court to be a jurist and the damn fool judge wouldn't let me go despite my explaining I was on 24-hour duty on a $63 million mission that was orbiting the Moon. They had a trial set for the following next week and I had no idea what was going to happen.

While I was doing my civic duty, Guenter Riegler was at Ames for a Mission Review and since neither Dan nor I were there, Sylvia and Marcie presented the status of the mission to Guenter.

Tuesday, May 12, 1998

Day 125 MET

I went to see Sylvia to find out what happened Monday. Since Guenter is very pedantic and very detailed, but he doesn't understand anything, he wanted us to have a Science Team Meeting to clarify the science and stupid Marcie wanted one for the same reason. Typical of NASA personnel, when they don't understand something (which is usually the case), they think that no one else can possibly understand it (after all, no one is smarter than a NASA employee), so they want a magic NASA committee meeting to clarify everything. Because, if they have a committee meeting and something still goes wrong, then none of them are to blame, because they had a committee meeting!

Needless to say, I was more than a little tired of Marcie thinking she was running the mission and wanting a science meeting every five minutes. I didn't need science meetings; I talked to my science guys frequently and went to see them at their institutes frequently. I knew my mission and the science and we were getting exactly what we expected — actually, a lot more.

The unfortunate part was that, since Sylvia has no science or engineering background at all, she relied on Marcie to tell her what was going on technically. And since Marcie knows nothing about science and very little about engineering, all she was doing was screaming that we had to have meetings and scaring Sylvia into thinking that, since she (Marcie) did not know what was going on, neither Dan nor I did either. I was going to politely tell Sylvia I really didn't give a damn what Marcie thought or said, because she is a damned idiot.

Given that background, I did not expect Sylvia was going to tell me anything positive about the meeting between Guenter, Marcie, and her — and I was more than correct.

Sylvia told me Guenter had several questions that neither she nor Marcie could answer (big surprise there), so she had promised him to get the answers from me and relay them to him. First she said Guenter was very disturbed by the fact that during the solar storms, the APS was saturated with solar alpha particles and he wanted to know why we hadn't properly designed the APS to exclude solar alphas. Now that was the dumbest question I had heard up to that point in my existence and I was astounded that Guenter was so dumb he asked it. Though we knew which face of the APS detected which alphas, what direction that face was pointing when it detected those alphas, and where in the orbit the spacecraft was when those alphas were detected (information that we would later use to sort out which alphas came from the Sun and which came from the Moon), that was it. Other than that, as Shakespeare said about a rose, i.e., "A rose, by any other name . . . ," — well, an alpha, by any other name . . . They don't have little signs on them saying, "I'm a solar alpha," and, "I'm a lunar alpha." Simply put, the APS just detected all alphas as long as they were in a certain energy range. I explained that to Sylvia and then she asked the second of Guenter's questions — and it was even dumber than the first.

Guenter seriously questioned why I had said the magnetic field strength dropped off with altitude cubed, when, as everybody knows, gravity drops off with the square of the altitude. Well Guenter, you moron, magnetic fields are not gravity fields and as anyone who has had high school science and has a brain in their head knows, magnetic fields drop off with distance cubed. Technically the answer is that gravity is a monopolar field and hence, its strength drops off with the square of the distance, while magnetism is a dipolar field and hence, its strength drops off with the cube of the distance, but if Guenter did not know what a high school science student knew, I could not have expected him to understand the technical reason. I was doubly appalled by his second question and could hardly wait to hear his third, which was similar in stupidity to the first.

He wanted to know why we had not properly designed the MAG to measure just the lunar magnetic fields and not the solar fields. I though, *did Guenter grow up in a world where physics does not apply?* At that point, I said to Sylvia, "Sylvia, we are talking about high school level science here and not even high school level physics. If Guenter does not even understand that level of science, then there is nothing I can say that he can understand, except that's just the way it is because I said so. I'm absolutely appalled at his level of ignorance."

Sylvia answered, "Well, I don't know any of that either."

I said, "I know, but you have no science background at all, so I don't expect you to know any of that." But what I did not say was, "However, Marcie is supposed to be an engineer and hence, does have a physics background — but she still doesn't know any of this stuff, because she is an idiot and an arrogant NASA idiot to boot."

More than frustrated and angry at having to put up with such ignorance on Guenter's (and Marcie's) part, I said to Sylvia, "He has no knowledge of any of this stuff.

What in hell is he doing up there (at Headquarters, running science missions) if he doesn't even understand basic physics? I'm just appalled. This is stupid beyond comprehension." She had no answer to that question for there is no logical answer to it — it's just NASA stupidity.

She then added insult to injury by saying, "Guenter wants another meeting with the review panel to discuss the science data sometime in August. And he wants to discuss the details of the extended mission."

I was so disgusted with NASA at that point that it would have been very easy for me to tell them to go screw themselves and quit. I was so sick and tired of dealing with NASA's incompetence, stupidity, and backstabbing, that I had just about had it. I thought, *this is a damned Discovery mission. I was given the responsibility of this mission. I know my business and I'm sick of people like Guenter Riegler and all the other NASA assholes who are deciding my mission has to be done in the old NASA way, where you have 27 meetings every time someone has to pee, to see if he should be allowed to pee, and to make sure if he misses the toilet when he pees, no one is held responsible for the pee on the floor.* To say the least, I was mightily pissed off at the entire bunch of damned fools who ran NASA.

As a result of my colossal frustration, I came up with a new saying about NASA — "If stupidity were a deadly disease, everybody at NASA would be dead"

Rebecca said, "NASA means Numerous Arrogant Stupid Asses."

And I added, "Where arrogance is overshadowed by stupidity."

Thursday, May 14, 1998

Day 127 MET: A Very Big Load, the Battery, Trying to Get Paid, and Scott Again

The highlight of the day was a commanding session that lasted nearly 3½ hours, from 127/13:20 MET through 127/16:45 MET. After some four months of operations, Dave Curtis knew exactly how the ER was performing and how to increase its data output. He had prepared a command list that was 283 commands long! I picked Day 127 MET to do the commanding, since there were no radio occultations during that day to interrupt the commanding — because, if there were, then the session would have taken another 1½ hours. Despite the length of the command session and the number of commands sent, we did not have any errors on the command side, but the DSN dropped us for a few seconds when we uplinked command number 31 and again at command 153, but we still did not miss a beat. Towards the end of the long sequence, Dave said he wanted to add four more commands, so I redlined the Mission Profile at the appropriate places, so we ended up sending 287 commands.

After we were finished and had all left, Dave called me at home and said he needed five more commands uplinked. I went back up to Mission Ops six hours later and, between 127/22:24 MET and 127/22:27 MET, uplinked the final five commands of the then 292 command load.

However, after the main commanding session, I became convinced (after suspecting it for some time) that the battery was not charging up as fast as it used to after the nighttime passes (which were back down to a having 42-minute duration after having reached the maximum duration of 47 minutes some 43 days earlier). I was hoping that the battery was not degrading and after talking to Woody about it, we suspected we had lost solar array capacity, but there was no proof either way.

Also, the number in a C&DH counter called the VMET (I had no idea what that stood for, nor did I care), after having never changed since the beginning of the mission, had begun to increase every once in a while when I was sending commands — for no apparent reason! Dan and I talked to Gerry Grismore about it and Gerry said, "As long as it's doing that only when you are commanding, it's OK, but if it does it by itself, then we have to start to worry." OK, I bought it.

I went to see Maryann to ask her if she had put the $40,000 in the LRI account, so we could get paid and she answered, "Well, I haven't gotten any instructions from Garner and I don't remember anything about it."

I went to Garner and he said, "Oh for pity sakes, I told her to do that. She totally forgot about it. She apparently is getting overworked (that was very, very true). I'll send her an email."

I said, "OK, and I'll check on it later," and thought, *next week, if I'm not on jury duty, I'll come back to check and if it isn't taken care off, I'll take him by the hand and take him over there and make him do it himself.*

I also talked to Sylvia about general things and the fact that the viewgraphs Ames had presented at Headquarters had a picture of Lunar Prospector and the Moon on the coversheet along with the names, NASA and Lockheed, but not LRI. I said, "Sylvia, you know, the next time I want LRI on the viewgraphs too,"

She said, "Oh, I don't know if Scott will allow LRI on anything."

I replied, "If Scott stops that from now on, there is going to be real trouble."

Monday, May 18, and Tuesday, May 19, 1998

Day 131 MET and Day 132 MET

Monday I reported for jury duty to find out the judge had reconsidered my being on the jury (I suspected she had checked to see if my fantastic story of having a spacecraft orbiting the Moon was true or not) and she dismissed me from jury duty. I went home and worked on the papers for the Preliminary Science Report we were going to soon submit to *Science* the rest of the day and all day Tuesday.

Wednesday, May 20, 1998

Day 133 MET

We did our contractual SIM and it went well, but it was boring because the SIMs were of no use any more.

I told Dan we needed to do a reor, so we set up a five pulse reor burn that would change the spacecraft's attitude by 0.86° and get the SEA back up to 0.97°, to keep Face 5 of the APS in shadow. We were going to do it at about 1:00 PM, but the DSN line of communication between the DSN and us wasn't working. We lost the first pass, so we had to do the reor burn between 133/18:41 MET and 133/19:43 MET.

Because Face 3 of the APS had begun to produce large counts, I commanded it off at 133/20:31 MET. Bill and I didn't know what the heck was going on with Face 3, but we thought that maybe some of the light leaking into the APS housing through the torn light filters on Face 5 was shining on the back of Face 3 and screwing it up. We were going to try to figure out what was going on with it over the next few days.

The real killer of the day was as follows: I took a letter Lockheed required regarding the $40,000 contract extension to Maryann and she was not at her desk. I left her a note and I called her later, saying, "OK Maryann, there's the damned letter and now I want to get that money transferred."

She said, "Well, you have to talk to Bob Garner."

I called Bob and I asked him about the business with Maryann. He answered, "The thing is, Sylvia, Scott, and Cathcart say you have to have some kind of deliverables for the 2½-month extension if you want to get paid."

I said, "Are you all nuts? First of all, my deliverables are all the extra work I had to do because you guys (the Lockheed launch vehicle people) delayed me for 2½ months. I could not deliver the other deliverables (those defined in the contract between Lockheed and LRI) that were due because of the 2½-month delay. Does this make any sense to you?"

Bob replied, "Well, we've got to discuss this because we have to have some measure of your performance." Clearly, Lockheed and NASA were going to try to screw me out of 2½ months of pay, using any excuse they could. Pissed, I said, "Look I'm going to come over to Lockheed at 1:00 tomorrow and we are going to settle this. My attitude is very simple; *you guys delayed me 2½ months, so it's your fault*. I did all the things necessary to keep ready for launch and that's that."

Then he said regarding my last invoice, "You shouldn't have put all the money (for the 2½ months) — the $38,000 — in your last invoice."

I said, "You signed it. I gave you guys a letter explaining exactly what I was doing. You guys signed it. If you didn't read it, that is your problem. That was the work I did; now pay for it," and they finally did without any more BS.

Thursday, May 21, 1998

Day 134 MET

I gave a luncheon talk to the local chapter of the AIAA. Dan was there, as was Jack Houle, Gus Guastaferro's Exploration Programs Manager, who had pulled the rug out from under me (with Gus's blessing) in November of 1990, by cutting the support Gus had given me in the Early Years (Part One). Despite Jack's negative attitude towards Lunar Prospector eight years earlier, he was happy with its success and, despite his negative role then, I was happy to acknowledge him, as well as Dan, when I gave my talk.

Friday, May 22, through Sunday, May 31, 1998

Day 135 MET through Day 144 MET:
A Very Long Trip to Milwaukee, Boston, Washington DC, and North Carolina

Friday, Rebecca and I flew to Chicago's O'Hare Airport and then we took the shuttle bus from O'Hare to Milwaukee, so I could attend and give a talk at the National Space Society's (NSS) annual meeting. It was cold and rainy and I caught a cold, but the meeting and my talk went well and I was given the NSS Scientist of the Year award. One of the entertainment events was a nice evening boat ride on Lake Michigan that was really fun. Also, Rebecca and I had dinner with my cousin Bonnie McGrew and her husband, Glen, who then lived in a suburb of Milwaukee.

After the NSS meeting Sunday, Rebecca and I drove down to see my mother in Chemung, IL, and then Monday we drove to O'Hare to fly off on the second major leg of our trip — to Boston.

Bill, his staff, and I gave a series of papers on the results of the GRS and NS mapping on Tuesday the 26th at the annual spring meeting of the American Geophysical Union and then Rebecca and I took the overnight train down to Washington, DC for the fun of it — we both love riding trains. Though we had a compartment, we did not sleep well and we arrived at the Union Station in DC early Wednesday morning the 27th feeling very tired. We took a taxi to Pat and Julius's, where we were going to stay for a couple of days.

I spent some time on the Hill, trying to get support for the commercial lunar science data purchasing program I was trying to get started, and I had a meeting set up with Joe Rothenberg, the Associate Administrator (AA) of NASA for Manned Space Flight, with whom I wanted to talk about my plans for a commercial lunar base. Unfortunately, he had been called to a meeting at OMB (Office of Management and Budget), but he made sure that one of his assistants was there to talk to me in his absence — unlike Wes (the AA for Space Science), who just found ways of not talking to me, period. Rothenberg's assistant said, "Yes, we are very interested in having commercial exploration of the Moon and a commercial lunar base we could also use." That meeting was encouraging.

After finishing my business in DC, Rebecca and I flew to Charlotte, North Carolina on the 29th to attend an Amateur Astronomy Meeting — the *Southern Star Annual Meeting* at Wild Acres in North Carolina. First they had an "Ask The Expert" session with me that Eric Douglass ran, a really great guy who was just getting over leukemia. After that, I gave the featured dinner talk and then, because it was cloudy and we could not observe, I was asked to give another talk; so I told them the personal side of what it was like to fly a spacecraft to — and around — the Moon.

Finally, we got home, dead tired, on Sunday, May 31, after a very successful and fun-filled trip.

Tuesday, June 2, 1998

Day 146 MET: Understanding the Solar Power Variations

Because of the problems that Face 3 of the APS had had before I turned it off, Bill wanted me to run some tests on the APS, turning various combinations of Faces 3 and 5 on and off. Between 146/10:59 MET and 146/17:17 MET, I ran a series of 4 turn-on/turn-off tests of those two faces. No matter which face I turned on or off or in what combinations, those two faces produced bad data. It was quite apparent that the light leak was affecting Face 3, as well as Face 5, and I ended the command session by turning both of those faces off, leaving just Faces 1, 2, and 4 on. I was beginning to think that Face 4 was going bad, too. Bill and I thought the thermal working of the thin light filters, that Jim Schirle had been concerned about before launch, was slowly but surely degrading and ripping them.

Also, I finally got the plots of the battery voltage and the maximum solar array current that I needed in order to see if the battery and the solar array were degrading with time. The plot of the maximum solar array current showed all kinds of unexpected variations. First there was a general decrease in the current by about 0.3 amps as a function of time since launch. Second, there was a broad maximum of about 0.8 amps center on β angle $= 0°$. Third, there was a 4-week periodicity of about 0.7 amps.

At first, I was puzzled by the solar array current variations and I was worried because the greatest depths of discharge (DOD) of the battery had occurred between

β = 30° to 40°, instead of around β = 0°, as I expected. I was wondering if the solar array was degrading, since the battery seemed to be OK. I set out to see if I could understand what was causing the solar array current variations.

The first thing I remembered (still being an astronomer at heart) was that we had gone into our mapping orbit on January 15, just 11 days after the Earth was at the perihelion of its orbit around the Sun (on January 4). That being the case, the Earth, the Moon, and the spacecraft were all then 1.5% closer to the Sun than on average, so the output of the solar array would have been 3% higher than on average (the intensity of light depends on the square of the distance). Similarly, when the Earth reached its aphelion on July 3, the solar array current would be 3% lower than on average. When I corrected the solar array current data for the variations due to the differing distances of the Earth/Moon/spacecraft from the Sun as a function of the time of year, the general decrease of 0.3 amps in the solar array current over the pervious five months vanished. That explained the first of the three types of variations.

Again, given my astronomical background, I immediately thought the second variation was due to the variations of the amount of sunlight reflected off the Moon (moonlight) as a function of β angle, since the moonlight shining on the solar array was clearly helping to generate electrical power, as I had expected. The simplest astronomical model that describes the amount of light reflected off a body assumes the body is Lambertian (after the physicist who first defined the model), in which the reflected light varies with the cosine of the angle of reflection, i.e., in our case, with the cosine of the β angle. I put in a cosine correction to the data and, bingo, the 0.8 amp β angle variation disappeared.

After making those two long-term corrections, I was left with a plot with a strange 4-week variation of 0.7 amps. Then it dawned on me what it was, but first, I checked to see if the 4-week period was actually a 27.32-day period, i.e., the sidereal rotation period of the Moon and hence, the time the Moon required to rotate once under the orbit of the spacecraft, and it was. The 27.32-day variation was clearly a result of the fact that most of the dark lunar maria are on the lunar near-side and the lunar far-side consists almost exclusively of bright highlands. Since the maria have albedos (the percent of light reflected off a surface) as low as 5% to 6% and the highlands have albedos as high as 15% to 18%, the spacecraft was getting 0.7 amps more power from the reflected sunlight, i.e., moonlight, when it was daytime on the far-side than when it was daytime over the near-side, during the Moon's monthly day/night cycle.

With that, I fully understood the solar array current variation and could easily predict them in the future. Better yet, after I had applied all three corrections, the data showed that there was absolutely no degradation in the power output of the solar array. Though I was absolutely certain of the correctness of my analysis, I wanted to see if the power output varied as I expected over the full, one-year perihelion/aphelion cycle of the Earth's orbit and the full six month period of the β angle cycle (and they did).

Further, it appeared that the battery had not degraded either — both of those things made me very happy.

Wednesday, June 3, 1998

Day 147 MET: The COMPLEX Meeting in Irvine, CA

I had been invited to the COMPLEX (COMmittee on PLanetary EXploration) meeting in Irvine, CA, on Wednesday to tell its members how Lunar Prospector was doing. I flew to LA Wednesday morning, drove to Irvine, and gave them my presentation about midday. Everyone thought I had a great mission going and I had done a good job. Best of all, all the initial skepticism about the quality of the science data we would get from such an inexpensive mission was just washed away. I talked to Larry Haskins, who is one of the guys who was initially very skeptical about the GRS data. He said, "Man, you know, we were all wrong and you were right." That was especially nice to hear from Larry, because he is one of the lunar scientists I most respect.

After the COMPLEX meeting, I met Rick Tumlinson for dinner to discuss both the commercial lunar base workshop Roger Lenard and I wanted to set up and the arrangement Rick was trying to promote between LRI and LunaCorp.

Regarding the workshop, I wanted to get LunaCorp and the Space Frontier Foundation involved. Rick was very interested in the Space Frontier Foundation participating and wanted it to co-sponsor the meeting. Then we talked about getting Pat Dasch and the NSS involved. Rick had no problem with working with Pat and we both thought the NSS should also be a co-sponsor of the workshop.

Then we talked about LunaCorp and Dave Gump. LunaCorp wanted to again put in a proposal to the Discovery program for their lunar rover mission, which, instead of being a Disneyland rover, would mainly be a science rover going to one of the craters that has enhanced hydrogen deposits in it according to our NS data. The purpose of the mission would be to determine if the hydrogen there was in the form of water ice or as solar wind implanted hydrogen. Of course, they wanted me to be involved and I said I would help them. Dave had given me a draft of the proposal, which was a rewrite of their earlier Discovery proposal and I was not impressed with it for a large number of reasons. Rick and I discussed the proposal and I said, "When I read this thing, I see huge holes in it big enough to drive a truck through."

Rick said, "That's what we are all afraid of, but you can fix it."

I replied, "I'm not going to take this over, I don't have the time," and thought, *why should I take over a floundering effort, when I had something going that is doing extremely well?* We left it at that. Nevertheless, Rick and I had a good dinner and productive discussions.

Thursday, June 4, through Sunday, June 7, 1998

Day 148 MET through Day 151 MET: The Preliminary Science Report Papers

I finished working on the Preliminary Science Report papers and then Rebecca and I went to Ames and printed them out. While at Ames, I monitored the spacecraft and the science instruments for a while and it did look like Face 4 of the APS was getting noisy, too.

Monday, June 8, 1998

Day 152 MET

I was at Mission Ops most of the day checking on the spacecraft and instruments. At 152/17:22 MET, I increased the high-voltage of the GRS by one step — up to 1623 v — as Bill had requested. Face 4 of the APS was getting noisy every once in a while, but it was still OK most of the time.

I called Roger, who had done a good job of setting up a straw-man schedule for the lunar base workshop, so everything was moving along.

Wednesday, June 10, 1998

Day 154 MET: An APS Test

I conducted a test on the APS between 154/10:30 MET and 154/12:25 MET to find out what in hell was going on with it. I turned one face on at a time. What I found was that, just like Face 5, Face 3 was bad only when the spacecraft was over the sunlit northern hemisphere of the Moon, i.e., when moonlight was getting into the APS through the torn Face 5 light filters, but they were both OK when the spacecraft was over the sunlit southern hemisphere, i.e., when Face 5 was looking at the black of space, and when the spacecraft was over the night side of the Moon. It appeared that the tears in the Face 5 light filters were getting worse and letting more and more moonlight into the APS housing and causing major problem for Faces 3 and 5 and some problems for Face 4. I left Faces 1, 2, 4, and 5 on and kept 3 off to verify all that, but I thought we would probably get more APS data by just leaving all the faces on and just letting each one stop producing good data when it wanted to. I was going to talk to Bill about doing that.

I arranged to get my Preliminary Science Report papers transferred to *Science* by mail and by computer.

Thursday, June 11, 1998

Day 155 MET

I went to Mission Ops and turned Face 5 of the APS off at 155/11:20 MET.

After getting back home to LRI, I called Israel Galvan in Houston. Israel was very excited about our plans for a commercial lunar base and the workshop. He said he would set up a meeting for us with his good friend and JSC Director, George Abbey. Israel also said both Goldin and Abbey wanted NASA to get back into the Moon business and to have a commercial lunar exploration program and they had the money to support it. That sounded good, but I was skeptical.

Mike Duke called me shortly thereafter with a similar story (so maybe what Israel said was true) and I explained to him what we were doing. Apparently things were really beginning to rock and roll.

Friday, June 12, through Early Thursday, June 25, 1998

Day 156 MET through Mid-Day 169 MET:
A Trip to Tucson to Find a Lot and Then on to Huntington Beach

Rebecca and I got up very early and, at 4:30 AM, we got into her car and started to roll towards good old Tucson to look for a lot where we would build our new house after the mission was over.

While in my beloved Tucson, we drove all over the place looking for just the right lot to build the house I had designed and to have room for my observatories. Originally, I wanted enough land so I could have a small landing strip for an ultra-light airplane (I wanted to start flying an ultra-light again when Lunar Prospector was over and I would again have the time to do so), but I found that inflation had taken a bigger jump than I had thought, so I was going to have to forget my ultra-light airstrip. After several days of going from one side of Tucson to the other, we finally found a one-acre lot on the far eastern side of the Tucson basin that suited our needs and our pocketbook — our search was ended.

Besides looking for a lot, I gave a talk at the Lunar and Planetary Lab (where I studied and worked as a graduate student in the 60s) and I met Carolyn Porco for the first time in my life. Unfortunately, she took me by surprise after my talk, which she had not been able to attend, and I was unable to tell her exactly what I thought about her getting Gene Shoemaker's ashes on Lunar Prospector.

What happened is as follows: As I was walking out of the auditorium to meet Rebecca, Debbie and Doug Johnsen (our niece and nephew), and their son, Luke, who had attended my talk, a very sweet and attractive young lady came up to me and, without introducing herself, started raving about Lunar Prospector and thanking me for carrying Gene's ashes to the Moon. Not knowing who she was, I was more than bewildered by her comments and cautiously said NASA had put Gene's ashes on the spacecraft and I had nothing to do with it. Then she rattled on about Gene and it finally hit me, *this must be Carolyn Porco, who I want to strangle for getting Gene's ashes put on my spacecraft and for causing us all kinds of problems when we were trying to get the spacecraft ready for launch.* However, by that time in the nearly one-sided conversation, it was too late to try to strangle her. She appeared to be very naïve about all the issues involved (though Sylvia believes that is just an act to help her get her way) and was so very proud of herself, because she had gotten Gene's ashes to the Moon. I kept saying I had no choice in the matter, but she just never caught on to what I was politely trying to say to her. I was taken aback by her apparent naiveté and I just couldn't tell her I wanted to strangle her because it would have been like trying to strangle a poor little kitten (I love cats and would never hurt a kitten) who would just look up trustingly and say meow!

After we were finished in Tucson, we started on the road back to California, but stopped in the Phoenix area, so I could thank Spectrum Astro for building me such a good C&DH and to give them a talk on the mission. They gave me a very nice little memento, it was the first page of the code hardwired in the C&DH with all the workers' signatures in a nice plastic casing, and I really appreciated it.

Then we drove on to Huntington Beach near LA, where I gave an invited talk to AIAA on Wednesday.

Because we had the 3rd OMM planned for Thursday afternoon, Rebecca and I got up at 1:00 AM (after getting to bed at 11:00 PM) and left our hotel at 2:00 AM to drive from the LA area to Gilroy. We got to Gilroy at 8:00 AM and I slept for an hour and went up to do the OMM.

Thursday Afternoon, June 25, 1998

Late Day 169 MET: The 3rd OMM

After arriving at Mission Ops before lunch, my Ops Team and I prepared everything for the 3rd OMM, which would consist of a 44.2 second periselene burn on engines A3 and A4, followed by a 43.5 second aposelene burn on the same engines an hour and 3 minutes later. We were also planning a 0.48 second burn on engine T1 to bring the spacecraft's spin rate back down to 11.95 rpm.

I started the commanding session by turning on the A3 and A4 heaters starting at 169/17:47 MET and ended the successful set of burns at 169/20:08 MET. Our commanding of the spacecraft and its responses had reached a high state of perfection and was more fun than you can imagine. I frequently said, "I have the best computer game in the world!"

Friday, June 26, 1998

Day 170 MET

Alex sent his paper on the gravity mapping off to *Science* and Bill was getting close to having the GRS and NS papers finished. The Preliminary Science Reports were all getting done.

Ed Guinness called and said he was finished testing the Level 0 data we had delivered, so those data would soon be archived

The spacecraft was fine and the commercial lunar base and my commercial lunar exploration mission plans were coming along very nicely. Life was very exciting.

Wednesday, July 1, 1998

Day 175 MET: Sylvia Starts Down the NASA Path

We had an anomaly meeting about the APS. Sylvia, Marcie, Dan, Bob Garner, and Ralph Fullerton, Lockheed's QA guy, were all there. I explained what was going on with the APS. Though I was happy that Sylvia had, in effect, taken over the responsibility of the mission for NASA, there were three problems: First, she had to put up with Guenter Riegler, who does not understand anything technical (but keeps extensive notes in a little book to make up for it); second, Sylvia does not understand anything technical, so she relied on Marcie; and third, Marcie understands very little that is technical. Sylvia and Marcie, who wanted to be assured that everything was fine with the APS, that we were doing everything right, and that we had done the appropriate tests, could not be assured of anything because they had no concept of what in hell was going on and that really annoyed me. Yet, because they are NASA, they sat there and expected that I explain things to them they simply are not capable of understanding. In stark contrast, Ralph, who really knows his job, asked reasonable questions and quickly came to the exact conclusion that I had come to when I did the tests and said, "Well, you've done everything you can do."

It was a shame to see somebody like Sylvia, who is a nice person, begin to turn into a NASA ass, just because the system requires they do that to survive. As soon as someone has any real responsibility in NASA, they just follow the NASA line of BS to stay alive. I hated to see Sylvia start down that road, just as Scott had done when he got promoted and became a big shot — he turned from being a reasonable person to work with into a self-serving NASA asshole. It is disgusting and disturbing that NASA is just NASA and there is nothing you can do about it, except get rid of it.

Friday, July 3, 1998

Day 177 MET

Jim Muncy, Rick Tumlinson, and I had a telecon, because they really wanted me to become the CEO of LunaCorp and take it over. I just didn't think that was the right thing to do, either for me personally or for David Gump, who I would be pushing aside and I did not like that idea, even though David had said he didn't mind if it helped their cause.

Saturday, July 4, 1998

Day 178 MET

Rebecca and I went to Steve Durst's annual meeting that was held in a nice hotel just south of the San Francisco Airport and I gave a talk on Lunar Prospector. Steve's meeting was interesting, but I did not see it was leading to anything.

On the way back home, we stopped at Mission Ops so I could see my baby, which was just fine. Late that afternoon, the spacecraft's orbit went through $\beta = 90°$, so we were beginning our second β angle cycle. Ever since we had gotten above $\beta = 72°$, 19 days earlier (June 15), the spacecraft was in full sunlight during its entire 118 minute orbit and it would continue like that for another 19 days, until β was again less than 72°. As such, the spacecraft's temperatures remained essentially constant all the time and even the temperature sensitive solar arrays showed only a couple of degrees of variation over the orbit. Watching the spacecraft was kind of boring.

Sunday, July 5, through Wednesday, July 8, 1998

Day 179 MET through Day 182 MET: The Abby Meeting

I flew to Houston Sunday to have the meeting Israel had set up with George Abby and to see Doug Cook and the exploration office guys I had worked with. I got down to the JSC area about noon and then got something to eat. Later, I went to see the Weavers and had a really nice time with them and their kids, who were uncharacteristically yelling and screaming a large part of the time; nevertheless, we had a great time. I stayed until about midnight, since Dave and Laurie wouldn't let me leave come hell or high water.

I met with Mike Duke Monday morning and brought him up to date with Lunar Prospector and my plans to try to do commercial lunar exploration missions and eventually build a commercial lunar base. He thought my plans sounded really quite good. He liked the idea of the lunar base workshop and was very positive about all my ideas. He also said I hadn't missed a thing by not going to that lunar meeting in Moscow, so I was glad Rebecca and I did not go on that long world tour.

After I met with Mike, Roger Lenard arrived, since he was going to go to the rest of the meetings with me. We headed off to see Israel and, as I expected, that went very well, except for one thing. Roger, who is a very fundamentalist Christian and a very far-right Republican (he is so far right, he even makes me look like a middle-of-the-roader), doesn't know when to shut his mouth. Here we were, meeting with Israel, who wanted to help us and who is a very big time Democrat, and Roger had to go into a tirade about what a scumbag Clinton is!

Despite that major blunder, as Roger and I went over the lunar base and workshop plans with Israel, he became convinced that what we wanted to do could work. We spent part of the morning, lunch, and the early afternoon with Israel, during which he said Goldin was really interested in the Moon, but he just didn't want to get into a mess like he had with the space station.

Finally we went over to JSC for our meeting with Abby. As usual, John Young, the Apollo 16 astronaut, for whom I have a lot of respect, was there, as well as Abby's deputy, who was an astronaut on flight status (Abby liked to be surrounded by astronauts). Roger and I went through the whole pitch and we had a good discussion — Abby only fell asleep twice and was called out for phone calls only about half of the time! They understood the purpose of the workshop was to determine if a commercial lunar base was economically feasible. They thought we had a great idea and they especially liked it when we said that JSC (not NASA) was our natural customer.

I said politely, "NASA has no interest in the Moon, because it's focusing on Mars and we, the commercial exploration world, can fill that gap, just as the commercial world has taken over the utilization of near-earth space and geosynchronous orbit for weather, communication, and remote sensing satellite after NASA had developed the technology. We are going to take the next step beyond geosynchronous orbit as NASA moves further out into the solar system. This is all doable commercially, since our going from Lunar Prospector to a commercial lunar base is a much smaller step than the giant leap from Shepherd's sub-orbital flight (May 5, 1961) to Kennedy saying three weeks later that we were going to put a man on the Moon by the end of the decade (and doing it on July 20, 1969). At that time, we knew almost nothing about the Moon and how to get there, but now we have an enormous amount of experience, knowledge, and most of the hardware needed for a lunar base." That went over very well.

They asked me how I had done Lunar Prospector, i.e., how I was able to keep it on track, on schedule, and on budget and I answered, "By keeping it simple and by having no bureaucracy," and then I filled in the details.

That impressed the pants off everyone, especially Israel, who was somewhat irate that I was not getting the recognition he thought I should have gotten and who said, "You should be on the cover of *Time* magazine for what you have done."

We left the meeting with Abby being very positive about our idea and our approach and, of course, the astronauts were all for it.

Monday evening, July 6 — we had launched 6 months earlier and we were half way through our 1-year nominal mission!

Tuesday Roger and I talked to Doug Cook, Hum Mendell, and Ken Joosten and gave them and the rest of the exploration guys the same pitch. As expected, they were very positive.

Wednesday, we each headed home, feeling we had made a good step towards our ultimate goal of building a commercial lunar base.

Thursday, July 9, 1998

Day 183 MET

I called Rick to let him know how the JSC meeting went and he said that FINDS (Foundation for the International Development of Space that Rick runs) had given LRI $10,000 for the workshop, so everything was falling into place.

Chapter 4-8
Planning for the Extended Mission, the Flip, the Leonids, and Eclipses

Friday, July 10, 1998

Day 184 MET: A Frustrating Meeting

I went to Mission Ops to monitor the spacecraft, which was fine, and to go to a useless meeting Sylvia wanted to have with Marcie and Ken Galal, about the low altitude mapping of the extended mission. Unfortunately, none of them understood anything about the spacecraft, the science and the mission — even Ken — and I had to go over it and over it and re-justify and re-justify the need to go down to 25 km altitude. No matter how many times I discussed what was going on, they asked over and over, fearful of an imagined failure, "Well, what are the risks? What are the benefits? Don't we need a science team meeting to discuss this?" The trouble always started with Marcie, who doesn't understand anything and then she would get Sylvia worried. As much as I like Sylvia, she just does not have the background to understand the issues. Since she and Marcie didn't understand anything, they assumed I didn't either; since I could not make them understand what was going on, they did not want us to make a decision about the extended mission. They insisted everything had to be done the NASA way — by consensus. Everything had to be done the NASA way — by committee. They always came back with, "Don't you need a science team meeting to discuss the science?"

I kept telling them, "I know the science; I know every one of these experiments and I know that everyone on my science team wants to go as low as possible." They were slowly but surely driving me mad with their incompetence and their NASA ways.

Wednesday, July 15, 1998

Day 189 MET

Lisa called and said a group of teachers had come to visit Mission Ops, so I went up to give them the tour. There were about 27 teachers in Mission Ops and more standing in the hall while I was talking. It was a good group and I got the biggest chuckle out of what one teacher, who was so in awe of what I was doing, that she asked, "Does the secret service guard you 24 hours a day?"

I answered, "No, they have better things to do," but it was quite a compliment.

Monday, July 20, through Saturday, July 25, 1998

Day 194 MET through Day 199 MET:
A Trip to Los Alamos, Albuquerque, and Tucson

I left Monday to go to Los Alamos and worked with Bill, mainly, on the APS data. I spent most of two days there and we made good progress at starting to understand the data.

I went back down to Albuquerque to meet with Roger at Sandia Wednesday morning, to discuss the lunar base effort and the workshop with him and Rick, who was flying in later that morning. I went to pickup Rick at the airport, but unfortunately, Rick's airplane was stuck in Phoenix, first because of a problem with the airplane and then because of a thunderstorm. As I waited, I had lunch at my favorite Mexican Restaurant in the airport. Finally Rick arrived and we drove back to Sandia.

Rick, Roger, and I spent the rest of the afternoon and most of Thursday working on the outline for the workshop and discussing lunar base issues. We had a good session.

I flew down to Tucson Thursday afternoon and went to the University of Arizona Science and Technology Park to see about renting space there for LRI after the mission was over. I talked to a guard and he gave me the telephone number of Marshall Warden, who ran the park. I called and set up a meeting with Marshall for the next day.

Friday morning, Marshall told me all about the park and I told him about LRI, Lunar Prospector, and my plans to, hopefully, expand in the future and have LEI there, too. I concluded the park was an ideal location for LRI, since there was plenty of room to expand and to have our own building, complete with spacecraft assembly facilities and mission operations centers.

I checked on the lot and found that it was just right for the house and then left for home Saturday; we were one step closer to buying the lot.

Monday, July 27, 1998

DAY 201 MET: A Tweak Reor and the Leonid Meteor Shower

We did a 27 pulse, tweak reor burn, changing the spacecraft's attitude by $5.6°$ and the SEA to $+0.36°$. Also, at Bill's request, I increased the GRS high-voltage to 1622 v. The whole commanding session lasted from 201/12:05 MET to 201/12:55 MET and went perfectly.

We had a discussion about the November Leonid Meteor Shower. NASA had put out a warning to all Mission Ops teams that they needed to have procedures in place to protect their spacecraft(s) from impacts by the high velocity (71 km/sec) meteoroids of the Leonids — one satellite had been lost and two damaged in previous Leonid showers. The only thing we could do to protect Lunar Prospector was to point its insensitive bottom in the direction of the incoming meteoroids, i.e., do a $78°$ reor, and leave it in that attitude for the several days of the shower. That would protect the delicate solar cells of our solar panels. Also, I said I would stay in Mission Ops all the time (except for sleeping in a neighboring motel and eating) so, if we did get hit, I would be there to do something immediately — remember, since Lunar Prospector had no computer, my Ops Team and I were the eyes, ears, nose, fingers, and brains of the spacecraft and it was up to us to take care of it.

Other than that, I was appalled at how little Sylvia knew about anything related to space exploration. She thought the spacecraft would not have as much power during the meteor shower because the meteoroids would block the Sun! Despite my liking Sylvia very much, she is a perfect example of NASA personnel — they don't know crap about what they are supposed to be managing (and you wonder why I am frustrated with — and hate — NASA).

Tuesday, July 28, through Wednesday, August 5, 1998

Day 202 MET through Day 210 MET:
Grand Forks, ND, Green Bay, WI, and St. Louis, MO

Rebecca and I flew to Minneapolis and then to Grand Forks, ND to see my good old friend, Chuck Wood, to give talks to his students and the public and to participate in a review of their Masters Program Group Projects, whose theme was the design of a lunar base. After we got there and got set up in our hotel, we had a nice dinner with Chuck and Vera, his wife, after which I gave a public talk on Lunar Prospector.

We spent all day Wednesday listening to and evaluating the Lunar Base Study presentations and that evening we attended a Masters Program Celebration Dinner, at which I gave a second talk.

Thursday we flew to Green Bay via Minneapolis to visit George French and Moonlink. George picked us up at the airport and we had a great time. George is really a nice, generous guy. We first went to lunch with the entire Moonlink staff, after which they showed us the Moonlink facilities and I gave them a talk on the mission. Then George took us to his country club for dinner and Rebecca and I stayed at his house that night. Before going to bed, he gave me the keys to his BMW so we could drive up to his luxury hotel near the end of the peninsula that sticks out into Lake Michigan to the NNE of Green Bay, where we were to stay for the duration of our visit!

Saturday, Dan Goldin was there for the formal opening of the NEARlink, the educational program George had patterned after Moonlink for NEAR (Near Earth Asteroid Rendezvous Mission), but before that got started, George asked me to give a talk to the students who were there and to run a Moonlink simulated mission with those students, which I did and which was fun.

A little later, when I was sitting next to NASA Administrator Dan Goldin on the stage as George was introducing the program, Dan leaned over to me and said, "This is the kind of thing I keep telling my staff at Headquarters we need to be doing, but they won't ever do what I tell them to do," which reminded me of what Goldin had told someone about how NASA worked, "I tell my staff what I want done and they go and do what they want to."

More interesting than that, when Dan was leaving, he walked up to Rebecca and me and said, *"You know, I'm trying to get rid of all the bad bureaucrats in NASA, so just keep on bitching."*

I was floored and Rebecca said to me, "Boy, I wish I had the tape recorder to record that."

I said to her, "That's right. Boy, I'll get rid of that SOB Scott, one way or another."

Sunday we flew down to St. Louis, MO, to spent the next couple of days with Rebecca's daughter, Stephanie, and her family. I also gave a talk at Washington University.

Finally, Wednesday we got up at 5:00 AM to go to the airport and the plane was two hours late in taking off! We missed our connection in Minneapolis by ten minutes and we had to stay all day — until 8:40 PM — in Minneapolis for the next flight to San Jose. Then that flight was delayed, so we didn't get home until midnight.

Friday, August 7, 1998

Day 212 MET: The Second, Very Minor Penumbral Eclipse

I gave a talk to a group of teachers that was visiting Ames in the morning and that night there was a penumbral lunar eclipse. The eclipse was so minor (the spacecraft and the Moon dipped only about 14% of the way into the Earth's partial shadow) that we made no special preparations for it, but Dan and I were in Mission Ops, along with the regular Monitoring Controllers who had the night shift, and we never noticed a thing, as expected. However, we were looking forward to the next, much bigger penumbral eclipse coming in one month.

Tuesday, August 11, 1998

Day 216 MET

We started planning the 4th OMM that was to occur on the 17th and I looked at the power profile for the next penumbral eclipse of the Moon that was to occur on September 6. I talked to Ken Galal to find out how accurate we were doing our OMM burns and he said we were only a fraction of a second off in the orbital period of the spacecraft after each burn. We could easily change the orbital period by 8 seconds when we did the next OMM in six days and that would slowly shift the phasing of the orbit during the following three weeks, so the spacecraft would spend a minimum amount of time in the Earth's partial shadow during the eclipse.

Wednesday, August 12, 1998

Day 217 MET: Goldstone

Giving credit where credit is due, Marcie arranged for the entire Ops Team (except one controller who volunteered to stay behind to watch the spacecraft) to fly down to the Goldstone DSN Station in one of the NASA airplanes. It was like a school field trip and we all enjoyed seeing the giant antennas that helped track Lunar Prospector all day, every day, and I had the opportunity to thank the men and woman who ran the facilities for all their good work in supporting my mission.

However, just before we left to go the few blocks to the Moffett Field runway, but after we had all assembled at Mission Ops, I was sitting at my desk working. As I did, I dropped a piece of paper and as I leaned over in my chair to pick it up, I had a sudden woozy feeling and I thought for a split second something was wrong with me, but then a split second later, I realized it was not me, rather an earthquake had hit just as I had bent over and the woozy feeling I had felt was really the swaying of the chair, the room and the building due to the earthquake. I shouted, "Did you guys feel that?"

And everyone answered, "Yes."

I immediately reached for the phone to call Rebecca when it rang — it was Rebecca, who said, in a keyed up voice, "We just had a big earthquake and some stuff got broken."

Well, the epicenter of the magnitude 5, San Andreas quake was in Hollister (the earthquake capitol of at least California), just 25 kilometers from Gilroy. I was disappointed I was not at home for the quake, but Rebecca wished she had been somewhere else. A few things broke in our house, worst of all, my big, hand-made model of the Saturn 1 rocket was damaged and the books on our bookshelves had moved. The stores in Gilroy and Hollister suffered the most, their goods (cans, bottles, etc.) were thrown from their shelves and were strewn all over the aisles.

Thursday, August 13, 1998

Day 218 MET

Sylvia was fussing about the extended mission contract, which NASA hadn't prepared, because they didn't seem to understand what we were going to do during the extended mission. That really pissed me off, because Sylvia and I had talked three times about what we were going to do. She was simply too insecure to take the answers I had given her and say to her management, "This is it, let's get the contract done." I was really getting disturbed, because she didn't understand what was going on and she relied on Marcie who also didn't understand the mission. It was the blind leading the blind — typical, arrogant NASA procedures. I felt sorry for Sylvia, she was simply out of her element and the NASA hierarchy plagued her — so she was caught in the middle between it and me.

Friday, August 14, 1998

Day 219 MET

I talked to Bob Garner about the extended mission funding. There was only $2 million for it! That was what Lockheed was going to get! It is amazing that NASA always does things backwards. Instead of finding out from us what we needed, they simply gave us what they had, based on the earliest, pre-mission estimates.

There were two big reor maneuvers coming up. The first, as I had always planned, was a 180° flip of the spacecraft half way through the mission. The flip was required because no omni directional instrument is absolutely equally sensitive in all directions. For example, the GRS anti-coincident shield (ACS) was asymmetric with respect to the BGO detector because A) there was no ACS shield on the end of the 7 cm diameter, 7 cm long cylindrical BGO crystal where the photomultiplier, which detected the flashes of light caused when a gamma-ray or a cosmic ray hit the BGO detector, attached to the crystal; B) the opposite end of the ACS was thickened from 1 cm to 7 cm so it could serve as a fast neutron detector as well as an ACS, and the ACS photomultiplier was attached to the free end of the ACS; C) the ACS surrounding the cylindrical part of the BGO crystal was only 1 cm thick; D) the entire GRS was attached to the tip plate of its boom on one side of the GRS assembly by a metal tip-plate; and E) the spacecraft was at the other end of the GRS boom, so it and the tip-plate attenuated the gamma-rays that were coming from that direction. Even though the GRS theoretically detected gamma-rays from all directions, the response of the detector to gamma-rays coming end-on into the GRS and from the side facing the spacecraft were different from all the rest of the directions and we needed to know the "instrument response function" to properly correct the data for those differences.

Similarly, each of the other instruments had their own response function and we needed to know all of them. The simplest way of getting those instrument response functions was to tip the spacecraft upside down and do the second half of the mission with the +Z direction pointing to the south ecliptic pole, rather than towards the north ecliptic pole, as had been the case since launch. Since most of the asymmetries in the instrument response functions were along the Z-axis, doing the second half of the mission "upside down" or inverted would give us most of the data we needed. I was planning a 180° flip at the midpoint of the mission and given that we were definitely going to have an extended mission, ending near the end of July 1999, the midpoint of the entire mission was early October.

In addition to doing the 180° flip, we would also get important data on the instrument response functions if we first did a 90° reor into what we called the "roll mode," where the spacecraft's spin axis was parallel to the lunar surface, and so, if one imagined that the spacecraft were on the lunar surface, it would appear to be rolling along the surface. We intended to leave the spacecraft in the roll mode for a couple of days, and then do another 90° reor, to complete the 180° flip.

In addition to the 180° flip planned for mid-September, we also had to do a 78° reor in mid-November to point the bottom of the spacecraft in the direction of the incoming Leonid meteoroids, leave it there for a few days, and then reverse the 78° reor to put the spacecraft back into its inverted attitude.

Since, except for our initial, post-launch reor from the spacecraft's launch attitude to its cruise attitude, all our reors were quite small, and because I had to fulfill my contractual obligations, we did a SIM of the first 90° reor of the flip and it went quite well.

With that behind us, I started to think about the September penumbral eclipse that was going to be fairly severe compared to the first two we had gone through. The maximum immersion of the spacecraft into the Earth's partial shadow was going to be 87% and the whole affair would last 2½ hours. I decided the best way to get through the eclipse was to leave the primary heater circuit on and turn it off and go to the secondary heaters only if we needed to delay a tank heater event until after the eclipse was over — just as we had planned to do for the first penumbral eclipse on March 12. If, instead, we went to the secondary heaters before the eclipse even started, the entire spacecraft would cool down about 10° C lower than normal. Then, when we came out of the eclipse and turned the primary heaters back on, every heater would turn on, i.e., all the fuel line heaters, all the electronic unit heaters, just everything, and that would require an extra 5 to 6 watts. We would be draining the battery, even if we were in full sunlight, and that would not work. Leaving the primary heaters on and turning them off only if absolutely necessary was the way to go.

However, Dan had other ideas that we had to spend time discussing and, because Lockheed had certainly told him he was responsible for the mission and he had to keep me from doing something wrong, he kept thinking he was really running the mission. He and Lockheed just didn't quite get the fact that I was running the mission, so I was getting more and more annoyed with Dan's attitude, which always came to the fore when there was some event that might put the spacecraft in jeopardy. Then Dan became ultraconservative, rather than being rational as he usually was.

We had had a big discharge of the battery during one of the tank heater events, thus I was getting all the battery data plotted up for the new β angle cycle, so I could figure out what was going on.

I received word from the editor of *Science* that our Preliminary Science Report articles, after having been reviewed and revised, were accepted — so that was done.

The mission was getting much more interesting, since we were getting away from the routine OMM phase and moving into a more active phase of spacecraft maneuvers and events. Thus, we were looking forward to the coming penumbral eclipse — it was going to be fun.

Monday, August 17, 1998

Day 222 MET: The 4th OMM

We did the 4th OMM and a tweak de-spin burn starting at 222/12:39 MET and ending at 222/14:37 MET, with our well practiced procedures of checks and verifications. The only difference in that OMM compared to the earlier three was that we changed the orbital period by 8 seconds, thereby changing the phasing of the spacecraft's orbit during the upcoming eclipse in order to minimize the time the spacecraft would spend in the Earth's partial shadow. Just before I left Mission Ops, Ken said, "It looked like a really good burn and we are probably very close to having changed the period by 8 seconds," so, mission accomplished.

Tuesday, August 18, through Thursday, August 27, 1998

Day 223 MET through Day 232 MET: A Vacation in the Cascades and a Visit to Primex

Rebecca and I left Tuesday morning for a vacation in the Cascades and to visit Primex (previously Olin) to thank them for making me six excellent engines and to tell them how the mission was going.

Unfortunately, we took Rebecca's car (because she hated my little, reliable Ford Fiesta) and it broke down near Sacramento. We found a repair shop and had to spend the night in Sacramento. We left late Wednesday morning to continue our vacation to the Cascade volcanoes.

One of our main destinations was Mt. St. Helens, since I wanted Rebecca to see it and since I had been there twice since its spectacular explosion at 8:29 on May 18, 1980, and I wanted to see how it had changed. We had a great day, Thursday the 21st, hiking and seeing the majestic beauty of Mt. St. Helens. As we were heading down the mountain late in the afternoon, Rebecca's car broke down again — in the wilderness. After a several hour wait, an AAA tow truck finally arrived and took us to the nearest town, where we could get the car fixed and rent a car, so we could get to Seattle for our visit to Primex.

The next day, we rented a car, did some sightseeing over the weekend, and went to Primex on Monday, the 31st, where everyone was thrilled about the success of the mission. That evening, Primex took Rebecca and me out to a nice dinner and then I gave an evening talk to the Primex workers, their families, and the public. We had a great time at Primex.

After the Primex visit, we did some more sightseeing and then drove back to where Rebecca's car was finally fixed and was waiting for us. We turned in the rental car and headed for Gilroy before something else happened to her car. We made it home Thursday afternoon, but we did have to stop once more just north of Sacramento to see if the car was OK, before driving the rest of the way home!

Monday, August 31, 1998

Day 236 MET: Another Long Talk with Sylvia

When I got to Mission Ops, I took a long look at the spacecraft and it was, as expected, perfect. Interestingly enough, the APS seemed to be working properly for some strange reason, a fact I was not going to complain about. Then, at Bill's request, I increased the GRS high-voltage by one step to 1632 v at 236/13:32 MET.

After finishing with the spacecraft, I looked through my mail and there was a memo indicating that Scott, as of September 1, was no longer involved with Lunar Prospector! He had become a big cheese at Ames, so could not be bothered with Lunar Prospector anymore and Sylvia was officially the NASA Mission Manager. Both things made me very happy.

Sylvia had sent me an email regarding Guenter Riegler's quarterly meeting set for September 8 and about a Science Team meeting that had been set up. I had not set up a science team meeting and the fact that she (and Marcie?) had set one up behind my back pissed me off.

I also had an aggravating email from Marcie, who had a list of 10 to 12 things she wanted the engineers to look into regarding the upcoming eclipse and that really pissed me off. The moron just never gave up sticking her nose into things that she knew nothing about and because she didn't understand them — like all NASA idiots — she expected that we spend all kinds of time and resources answering her stupid questions which really required only a high school level of understanding of the issues, which she does not have.

Between Sylvia's email and Marcie's, I had had it and so, when Sylvia came in, I had a little chat with her.

First, I congratulated her on officially becoming the head of the program. Then I said politely, "I'm surprised to see that a Science Team meeting has been set up."

She responded, "I thought you understood that. We talked about that."

I said, "No, what I understood was that Bill and Dave were coming down. They were going to be here for the eclipse and some other instrument related things, but we were not having a full-blown team meeting. I didn't expect to have a full team meeting and that is encroaching on my authority. I'm really getting a little tired of this stuff. You know I don't want to get into a tussle with you. I like you and respect you, but this is my responsibility, as you well know."

She replied, "Well you know, the team (Marcie) has all these questions and I feel they have to be answered and I want to make sure we get the right answers."

I responded, knowing Marcie was behind all that BS, "Marcie is not half as good as you guys think she is. She doesn't understand the spacecraft and she doesn't understand the mission. And she thinks because she doesn't understand anything, nobody else does, either. But I do."

Sylvia responded, "I know you know this stuff, but I still want the meeting."

I tried to couch my response in terms that would not be confrontational and said, "I'm getting a little tired of this whole NASA attitude. I know you are caught in the middle and the one who is really the problem is Guenter. He doesn't even know basic physics and I keep being questioned on what I am doing because he, and others like him, simply do not know anything about anything."

Sylvia said, "Well, that applies to me, too," which it did, but she is smart enough to know that and that is why I like and respect Sylvia — she did not try to cover up her lack of experience and knowledge with the usual, "Well, I'm NASA, so what I say goes."

She argued, in an attempt to back up her desire for a NASA type committee consensus, "But Alan, if something goes wrong, we don't want you to be the only one who stands up and says that it's your fault."

I said, *"That is exactly what I would do; that is exactly my job; and I don't want it any other way. It's not your responsibility. It's not Lockheed's responsibility. It's my responsibility."* She well knew, from our past discussions, that I was not kidding about my taking full responsibility for both the success and the failure of the mission, but we both agreed that was somewhat hypothetical, since Lockheed did have the contractual responsibility to NASA, even if the contract did say the PI was responsible for the success of the mission. Nevertheless, she knew I was, as always, trying to keep Discovery the way it was proposed, i.e., keep NASA out of the loop and keep the PIs in charge.

Later, Marcie called me because she still didn't know how we were going to do the extended mission. There was still uncertainty about whether we could go down to 25 km or just 30 km mean altitude and if we would have to do an OMM every two weeks or every four weeks. I said, "Look, I've said a hundred times to everybody I want to go to 25 km and do a burn every two weeks. But, if we find we can't handle that, we will obviously go back to 30 km and do a burn once every four weeks."

Marcie said, "You can't do that; we can't wait two extra weeks because we would hit the Moon in two days if we didn't get the burn done."

Clearly, Marcie, as usual, did not understand what I had said, so I said, "Marcie, if we find we can't handle the 25 km orbit, we will immediately do a burn to bring the orbit up to 30 km and then start doing a burn every month." Typically, she had not understood what was going on and thus had gotten quasi-hysterical about the whole issue. Man, how I hated having to deal with that woman.

I then spoke to Sylvia about Marcie's concerns and said, "I'm not going to change anything just because she is petrified that things are going to go wrong and her career with NASA is in jeopardy and all that crap."

Sylvia replied, "I know you would have liked for them (Headquarters) to have given you the money and let you do your job and stay out of your hair."

I answered, "That's absolutely right. It's the way to get it done properly." And I thought, *this damned NASA bureaucracy. I just hate NASA. I can hardly wait until this mission is over — I am so sick and tired of this crap.*

I was also sick and tired of Lockheed's crap and since I had received no answer to my February 12, 1998, letter to Mel Brashears in which I thanked him for his support of Lunar Prospector and asked him to split Lockheed's $4 million fee with LRI, I sent him a follow-on letter, expecting the same result.

Wednesday, September 2, 1998

Day 238 MET

I took Rebecca to the airport so she could fly to St. Louis to see her new baby granddaughter. Since our Preliminary Science Reports were going to appear in the September 4 issue of *Science,* the embargo for the science papers was to be lifted on the 3rd, when *Science* appeared, and the news media was already asking for interviews. I did a couple of telephone interviews, one with a reporter in Germany and interviews with CBS and CNN, with the proviso that the pieces not appear until the next day.

Thursday, September 3, 1998

Day 239 MET: The Preliminary Science Reports Appear

I had eight or so phone interviews in the morning and a number of TV interviews at the Ames TV facilities in the afternoon. The PR about Lunar Prospector was very good.

The highlights of the Preliminary Science Reports are as follows: Using the gravity data, Alex and his crew had discovered three new gravity anomalies or mascons (mass concentrations) on the lunar near-side and partially mapped four new ones on the far-side (which was previously thought to be impossible to do). They had also provided very strong evidence for the existence of a small lunar iron core with a radius of 220 km to 450 km, containing 0.5 to 2.2% of the lunar mass (for comparison, the Earth's iron core contains some 30% of the Earth's mass).

The MAG/ER team showed there are relatively strong magnetic fields (but a thousand to ten thousand times weaker than the Earth's magnetic field) in the areas antipodal to the Mare Imbrium and Mare Serenitatis impact basins, and those fields are strong enough to form miniature magnetospheres.

Using the GRS data, we presented the first complete maps of the thorium and potassium distributions over the Moon, confirming the earlier concept that KREEP (a lunar material rich in potassium [K], the rare earth elements [REE], and phosphorus [P], as well as thorium, uranium, and other trace elements) had been excavated from a KREEP-rich layer at the base of the lunar crust by the Imbrium impact and strewn around the entire Moon. We also had two papers on the distribution of iron plus titanium over the Moon, as defined by the new technique of using the thermal and fast neutron data that we had discovered for mapping these two elements.

Finally, we had a paper on the water ice, as defined by the NS data. As our data and analysis of the NS data had gotten better and better, we had changed our water ice interpretation a little. The small dips over the poles in the fast neutron data I thought might just be visible during late February, turned out to be illusionary. The only way Bill could explain our seeing the dips in the epithermal neutron fluxes over the poles, while seeing no dips in the fast neutron fluxes, was to assume that the water ice was buried under about 40 cm of regolith. Given that model and assuming that there was a solid layer of ice about 1½ m thick below the layer of regolith, our data indicated that there might be as much as 300 million metric tons of ice at each pole — or about ten times more than we had estimated at the water ice press conference on March 5.

Friday, September 4, 1998

Day 240 MET

Extrapolation of the tank heater event data showed that the heater events which would occur on Saturday night and Sunday morning were going to bracket the penumbral eclipse, so we did not expect to have any trouble with the power.

The BBC called for an interview, as did CBS in Los Angeles.

Later Saturday Night, September 5, through Early Sunday Morning, September 6, 1998

Day 242 MET: The Third Penumbral Eclipse

After having a 2-hour nap in the afternoon, I went to Mission Ops at about 8:00 PM Saturday, many hours before our pre-eclipse activities were to start just before 1:00 AM. I took one of my telescopes with me, so we could watch the eclipse when the spacecraft was in radio occultation and hence, when we were getting no telemetry from the spacecraft. However, it turned out that it was frequently cloudy, so there was little to see.

By the time my Command Team, Marcie, and I were ready, Jim Schirle, Woody, Kim Foster, and John Kohli (who had worked the earlier monitoring shift but came back to watch the eclipse activities) were also there to watch the fantastic event of the eclipse as seen via the spacecraft engineering data and it was beautiful to watch.

The pre-eclipse commanding session started at 242/04:28 MET, just after we simultaneously came out of radio occultation and the nighttime pass at 242/04:25 MET (12:50 AM). At that time I increased the GRS high-voltage by one step, to 1641 v, as Bill had requested. Then to save 0.2 amps of power (every little bit, even 4%, helped), I turned both the pressure transducer (that measured the fuel tank pressure) and the EM limb-crossing sensor off between 242/04:31 MET and 242/04:32 MET. Those three things done, we were ready for the eclipse that was still well over two hours away.

At 242/05:38 MET, the spacecraft went into its last 45-minute nighttime pass and radio occultation period before the eclipse started and emerged from behind the Moon at 242/06:23 MET. The battery was fully charged (after discharging during the nighttime pass) by 242/06:52 MET, approximately as expected, and just six minutes later, at 242/06:58 MET, the spacecraft entered the Earth's partial shadow — the eclipse had started for the spacecraft and the fun had just begun.

Within about 5 minutes, the spacecraft was already 10% into the shadow and Dan and I began to see the effects of the partial eclipse on the spacecraft. The solar array temperatures began to show the effects of the failing sunlight and the solar array power output began to drop precipitously. By 242/07:15 MET, the solar power output was below 2½ amps and we began to draw power from the battery. The spacecraft hit its maximum immersion in the Earth's shadow (87%) at 242/07:30 MET, just 5 minutes before it went into its normal radio occultation/nighttime pass period. The battery had a depth of discharge (DOD) of 8% by the time the spacecraft went into the Moon's shadow.

When the spacecraft emerged from behind the Moon 45 minutes later, at 242/08:20 MET, it was in full sunlight — but just for 34 minutes. It again dipped into the Earth's partial shadow for a second, maximum emersion of only 15% at 242/08:54 MET. Because of the greater DOD of the battery, caused by the fact that the battery already had an 8% DOD before it started its normal nighttime pass and the fact that more heaters were on because the spacecraft was cold, the battery had not fully charged up before the spacecraft again entered the Earth's partial shadow. However, because the second dip into the Earth's shadow was only 15%, as expected, the battery did get fully charged by 242/09:12 MET, i.e., well before the spacecraft left the Earth's shadow for the last time at 242/09:28 MET, and well before the spacecraft went into its next radio occultation/nighttime pass period at 242/09:33 MET. Thus, as preplanned, I commanded the pressure transducer and the EM limb-crossing sensor back on between 242/09:25 MET and 242/09:26 MET. We were back to our normal configuration even before the eclipse was completely over.

However, the spacecraft was really cold, essentially everything (the C&DH, the SES, the science instruments, etc.) had dropped 4 to 5° C below their normal temperatures and it took an orbit or two before the temperatures were completely back to normal.

Finally, well after 7:00 Sunday morning, we left the spacecraft in the good hands of the early morning spacecraft monitoring shift and all went home to get some sleep. It had been a beautiful eclipse that everyone enjoyed. And since the spacecraft had gotten good and cold, it was clear that the penumbral eclipse that was coming up in January was going to be very interesting — especially since we would be in the lower, extended mission mapping orbit.

Monday, September 7, 1998

Day 243 MET: Figuring Out How to Get through the Tank Heater Events and the 1999 Eclipses, When the Spacecraft Would Be in its Low Mapping Orbit

Lunar Prospector had been designed to operate in a 100 km altitude mapping orbit, with a 118-minute period, with a maximum nighttime pass of 47 minutes and a minimum daytime pass of 71 minutes to charge the battery, as well as to survive penumbral eclipses. As of September 7, 8 months after our launch, we had easily gotten through all three penumbral eclipses of the nominal mission and ⅔ of the way through the nominal mission itself. And we had no concerns about the spacecraft's performance during the remaining four months of the mission.

However, Lunar Prospector was not designed to work efficiently in the 25 km altitude mapping orbit I wanted to use for the extended mission mapping. The issue was simply that the period of a 25 km altitude orbit is 110.7 minutes and the maximum nighttime pass is 49.4 minutes, leaving a minimum of 61.3 minutes of daytime pass to charge the battery minutes at $\beta = 0°$. Thus, the discharging of the battery and its recharging during the big tank heater events was going to stretch the capabilities of the spacecraft.

Similarly, the penumbral eclipse at the end of January 1999 was going to push the limits of the spacecraft in its low orbit and the partial umbral lunar eclipse towards the end of July was expected to kill Lunar Prospector. The spacecraft was not designed to survive umbral eclipses, so we had always considered that that eclipse would be the end of the extended mission.

However, with the experience gained during the Sunday morning penumbral eclipse and knowing how well the spacecraft was performing, I devised a strategy to keep the spacecraft happy in the low mapping orbit, during the January penumbral eclipse, and perhaps even during the July umbral eclipse.

First, it was clear the battery would not survive the 3-hour tank heater events when we were in the 25 km orbit, since the 61-minute daytime period was too short to get the battery properly charged up during the long heater events. However, right then, we still had 20%, or about 27 kg, of the fuel left. After doing the October and December OMMs, the 180° flip in early October, the two 78° reors for the Leonid Meteor Shower in November, and then going down to the 25 km orbit in early January, we would have only about 12% of the fuel left and the tank heater events should have shortened to about two hours, since there would then be only about ⅔ as much fuel to heat up. If the tank heater events were no longer than two hours, the battery would not discharge to the point where the mission was in jeopardy — and, of course, the shorter the tank heater events were, the better. Thus, I was considering burning some fuel off to improve the situation even more, since, thanks to my conservative fuel planning, we were going to have 7 to 8 kg of fuel left at the end of the mission. Thus, if I got rid of that extra fuel, I could reduce the tank heater event durations down to about an hour and that would be just great.

The next problem I considered was the January penumbral eclipse, during which the spacecraft would dip nearly 100% into the Earth's partial shadow, and hence was going to spend a lot of time in the darkest part of the penumbra. That problem was compounded by the fact that, because we would be in the low orbit, the nighttime passes were going to be relatively long. However, since I had the 7 or 8 kg of fuel I wanted to get rid of, instead of just burning it off, I could use it to raise the aposelene of the orbit high enough so the spacecraft would not pass through the Moon's shadow, i.e., there would be no nighttime passes during the eclipse, and to phase the orbit so that the spacecraft would spend only 50 to 60 minutes in the partial shadow of the Earth. Thus, the January eclipse would be about the equivalent of a normal nighttime pass, which the battery could easily handle. After the eclipse, we would drop the aposelene back down to 25 km and continue with the 25 km altitude, extended mission mapping.

Thus, I could kill two birds with the one stone: I would use up the extra fuel to shorten the length of the heater events and insure we survived the January penumbral eclipse!

The kicker was that we could use the same strategy to survive the July 28 partial umbral eclipse at the end of the mission and that would be a magnificent engineering and operational feat.

Tuesday, September 8, 1998

Day 244 MET:
Sylvia and Marcie's Science Team Meeting and the Quarterly Meeting

We had the Science and Quarterly Meetings that Sylvia and Marcie had called; needless to say, I was not pleased. Joe Boyce was there for both the Science Team Meeting and the afternoon Quarterly Meeting and Guenter was there for the latter. Of course, Scott had to come so he could announce that he was no longer the NASA Mission Manager. He explained arrogantly, "I have been given so much responsibility in the Ames administration," and he rattled off all his new responsibilities, "that I just don't have any time to manage Lunar Prospector, so Sylvia is going to take over." He is such a pompous, self-serving ass; he nearly made me puke, as he made sure that everyone fully understood how important and wonderful he is.

The science meeting started with a discussion on the extended mission, which, as I expected, led to nothing beyond what I had already planned — it was a total waste of time. Then we discussed the quality of the data and Joe understood how good it was. But when I brought up the $5 million we needed for the data reduction and archiving, he began to waffle. Clearly, Headquarters was not going to give us the money if they could help it and I was going to have to force the issue one way or another. Sylvia and Marcie's Science Team Meeting was useless and I was disgusted with Sylvia for forcing the issue and having a useless Science Team Meeting.

At the Quarterly Review Meeting, I described my idea about raising the aposelene of the orbit to get through the January and July eclipses, thereby also getting rid of the extra fuel to shorten the duration of the tank heater events. Guenter, Sylvia, and Marcie didn't have a clue as to what I was talking about. Dan, of course, understood my reasoning. Nevertheless, because Dan and Marcie really believed they were running the mission, they both said very snottily, "Well, we'll have to look at those suggestions and then we'll decide if we should do them." I thought, *you won't decide anything you arrogant SOBs; I'm the PI and Mission Director, not you, you bastards*, and I regretted ever having had the slightest thought of having Dan work at LRI. The sooner I had nothing to do with those people, the better.

Shortly thereafter, the Nav guys expressed their concerns about my wanting to change the orbit, so we could easily survive the eclipses. Given that my scenario would require major changes to the orbit within a day or two of each other, they did not feel they would have the tracking data to support their orbit and burn calculations, nor the time to do so. Unless there was no way to survive the eclipse(s) without doing the orbital maneuvers, they recommended I put my idea on the back burner. Respecting those guys as I did, I accepted their comments and let the issue go (we never had to use it — so that was the end of it).

We talked about the extended mission and nothing was accomplished because, of course, Headquarters wanted to have independent verification of our plan and insisted they sign off on the plan before we could go down into the low orbit — NASA makes me sick.

The entire day was just a complete waste of time and money. I could have kicked Sylvia in the butt for setting up those useless meetings and I could have done a lot more to Dan and Marcie.

Wednesday, September 9, through Friday, September 11, 1998

Day 245 MET through Day 247:
LunaCorp, National Geographic, and Carnegie Mellon

Wednesday, I flew to Washington to go with David Gump to a meeting he had set up with *National Geographic* and to go to Carnegie Mellon in Pittsburgh, PA to see Red Whitaker, who was to build the LunaCorp rover. *National Geographic* was considering a deal for $5 to $15 million for the exclusive TV and press rights to document the Luna-Corp rover mission and I was asked to help close the deal. The idea being that, having proven my expertise with Lunar Prospector, I would be Mission Manager and Mission Director of the LunaCorp rover that would explore the polar ice deposits Lunar Prospector had discovered — an arrangement we hoped *National Geographic* could not resist.

I met with David, Jim Dunstan, and a computer guy named Steve early Thursday morning and we all drove to Carnegie Mellon. Since the trip lasted nearly four hours, we had plenty of time to discuss the technical and financial issues of the LunaCorp mission and to get better acquainted. The main reason for our going to Carnegie Mellon was that *National Geographic* wanted to have an independent review of what Red and LunaCorp were planning to do before they put money into it. As soon as we got there and met Red, we had a 2½-hour telecon with the engineering group in Los Angeles *National Geographic* had hired to conduct the review. Between Red's world-renowned expertise in robotics and my expertise in lunar science, spacecraft engineering, and mission operations, we easily convinced the LA group that we knew exactly what we were doing (and they convinced us that they had very little knowledge about what they were doing).

Then I gave a talk to Red's class and finally I gave a seminar to the entire engineering facility. The seminar was rather well attended and was a lot of fun. At the end,

Red seriously asked, "Do you want a job?" and explained that the Dean had asked Red, when he read about my coming to give the seminar, if I wanted a job — it is nice to be wanted.

On the drive back to DC, we talked about how we could work together, that I was not going to be LunaCorp's CEO, and that I would run the mission in my usual dictatorial fashion — as is necessary if a mission is going to be successful (the lack of my having total dictatorial powers over Lunar Prospector was the root of all the battles I had been fighting with NASA and Lockheed). It was clear I would have to do so and they knew that was true and were very happy about it.

Friday morning, we went to *National Geographic* and had a very good three-hour meeting. *National Geographic* was convinced that I knew what I was doing and I would run the mission. We all thought they were going to give us the money. We started to seriously talk about how to work out the arrangement between LRI, LEI, and LunaCorp.

Once back in DC, we stopped in to see Jim Muncy to tell him about our progress with *National Geographic*. As we walked into Jim's office, Jim said, "I'm happy to see you (David and me) both together. Are you the CEO yet?"

I answered, "No, but we're working on alternatives."

Jim pointed to an article about Lunar Prospector in *Space Week*, in which Scott had been quoted and Jim asked rhetorically, "What is that fat slob still doing there?"

I answered, "Look, I tried to get rid of him, don't blame me." Jim hates Scott, too.

Finally, Jim said Congressman Rohrabacher was going to write a letter to NASA about the Lunar Prospector data reduction money. Hopefully I would get the money with Rohrabacher's help.

After that, Dave drove me to the airport and I winged my long way home. It was a very, very good trip, but it was very exhausting.

Saturday, September 12, 1998

Day 248 MET: The Oakland Astronomy Club Meeting

Late Saturday afternoon, I drove up to Oakland, had dinner with David Rodrigez, and gave a talk to the astronomy club that was well attended. We saw an Iridium flash, i.e., when the sunlight flashes off an Iridium satellite's solar panels for about a minute. The flashes are very bright, many times brighter than Venus and that was the first time I had even seen one — it was beautiful. Then we observed with the telescope there and I didn't get home until after midnight, but I had a really good time.

Chapter 4-9
The Degrading Battery

Monday, September 14, 1998

Day 250 MET: The Battery Crisis

I went to Mission Ops where, after checking on my spacecraft, I was told there had been a red limit, low voltage event while I was on travel. The battery had discharged too much during a tank heater event and Marcie was, of course, having a conniption fit. Also, Woody had left me an email saying, after hearing about the event, the battery people were getting concerned about the low voltage. I asked to have the engineering data plotted up during the red limit event, so I could find out what the DOD and battery voltages really were and to see if there was anything really wrong.

I wrote a useless APS anomaly report and gave it to Sylvia. I grumped about having to write the useless thing and she sympathized with me about such a useless piece of NASA/Lockheed crap.

Then I went over to Lockheed to give a copy of the report to Maryann and Bob Garner. A little later, one of them gave it to Dan and Dan came running over to Mission Ops and wanted some more information about the APS I did not have in the report. Who in hell did he think he was, asking me about the APS (the answer was that Lockheed had told him he was in charge of the mission, so he thought he was)? I was really disappointed that, despite his being a very smart and competent engineer, he was just too damned arrogant and self-serving to remember I was the PI, the Mission Director, and the Project Scientist. He just did everything Lockheed asked of him like the Lockheed ass-kisser I had realized he was, ever since the 3rd LOI burn confrontation.

Between Marcie's hysteria and arrogance, Dan's arrogance, and poor Sylvia's panic, my return to Mission Ops after such a good trip to DC was disgusting.

Then we had a second red limit battery event during a tank heater event and we were clearly having a problem!

But first, a little background about the battery. Ever since we had started the nighttimes passes of the first β cycle (Day 021 MET, β = 71°), I had made a plot of the drop in the battery voltage as a function of the depth of discharge (DOD) of the battery. The initial graph covered the entire first β cycle, going through β = 0° (Day 084 MET), when the nighttime passes had their maximum duration of 47 minutes and then back down to zero minutes at β = 72° (Day 158 MET). I had that graph taped on the right-hand side of my computer monitor, because that was my reference to see how the battery was doing, as I watched the battery data on my screen.

I had, of course, started adding the data for the second β cycle, as soon as the nighttime passes started (Day 200 MET, β = 70°). As of that date, we were back down to β = 19° and the nighttime passes were 45 minutes long (almost at their maximum again). However, I had quickly seen that the slope of the main part of the voltage vs. DOD curve for the second β cycle was slightly steeper than that of the first cycle. As soon as I saw that, I asked Woody why the slope of the second graph was different from the first and Woody, who really did not know why, answered it was just the battery wearing a bit, but it was OK.

However, when he heard about the red limit discharge, he had informed the battery people and then he left me the message saying the battery people were really concerned. They thought we had a 95% DOD (why, I didn't know; but I suspected Marcie had screamed something like that) and if that were the case, then we were in real trouble and about ready to fall off the dreaded DOD cliff, i.e., reach the DOD where the voltage dropped rapidly and irrevocably to 0!

Despite my having asked Marcie days earlier to get me the engineering data on the tank heater on-times (so I could figure out the relationship between the amounts of propellant in the tanks and the heater on-time and hence, figure out how we were going to run the spacecraft during the extended mission eclipses) and earlier in the day to get me the data on the red limit, low voltage event, she had not done so — despite her hysteria over the low voltage. I forcefully got it across to her that I needed those data right then and there. Marcie just didn't get it; all she could do was to scream and holler that something was wrong, but she did nothing to help resolve the situation. She is really pathetic. I was really looking forward to being finished with the mission and being far away from her and the other NASA and Lockheed idiots I had to deal with on a daily basis.

Tuesday, September 15, 1998

Day 251 MET: Solving the Battery Crisis

Given the events of the previous day, I woke up about 2:30 AM and left for work about an hour later. Happily, Troy had gotten me the much-needed data over night, so I plotted it up and I began to try to make sense out of it. Other than the known differences in the slope of the battery voltage vs. DOD graphs for the two β cycles, there was nothing that showed anything was wrong.

George Collins from BJ Link arrived. Dick Seeley had called and asked if George could come and make a second video for his class and, of course, I had said yes. George arrived at about 8:00 AM and he videoed for about 2 hours.

About 10:00 AM, I went over to Lockheed to talk to Woody and to show him what I had. He didn't think we were in real trouble, but he said again the battery people were really concerned. Unfortunately, they couldn't meet with us until 1:30 PM, so I went back to Mission Ops and kept busy until it was time for the battery meeting.

I told neither Marcie nor Dan about the battery meeting. I wanted to get the information I needed quickly and without any interference from Marcie's ignorance and hysteria or Dan's arrogance and his Lockheed first/Lockheed kiss-ass attitude. The meeting was just between Woody, the battery engineers, and me and we quickly got things done.

I learned a lot about the battery, things I should have been told when we were designing the power system, but things that Woody apparently did not know. The most important thing was, despite what I thought, the battery was not fully charged when its voltage had reached its maximum (usually around 32.5 v) and the solar array current began to drop (as long as the battery was charging, the power system drew all of the available current [up to 7½ amps] from the solar array, but when the battery reached its maximum voltage, the solar array current dropped to the 2 to 4 amps used by the spacecraft itself). At that point, the battery automatically was switched from full charging to "trickle charging," which was — as I had been led to believe — just supposed to maintain the battery at full charge.

However, the battery engineers said that was not correct. They explained that when the battery first appeared to switch to trickle charge, it still had a DOD of 10 to

15%, so the solar array was still pumping energy into the battery for several more minutes. Thus the switch over to trickle charge was a gradual event that started when the battery voltage hit its maximum of 32 to 33 v, but lasted for several more minutes, as the battery continued to charge. I had always noticed it took the solar array current 15 to 20 minutes to settle back down to its normal mode of varying after both the battery voltage had max'ed out and the solar array current had dropped down to equal the load current — and I always wondered why. Finally I knew why — the battery was trickle charging like hell. A lot of the time I thought the battery was fully charged — it wasn't!

The battery guys explained why the slope of the battery voltage vs. DOD curve of the second β cycle was different from that of the first β cycle I had asked Woody about. That was very simple. The battery characteristics had changed because of the numerous charge/discharge cycles of the previous β cycle and the battery was running hotter, i.e., the battery had just aged, but was not degrading. They explained to me that the battery voltage told me the DOD directly, so I should use my original discharge curve from the first β cycle to determine what the DOD really was and to forget the second cycle curve I was generating. Thus, when the battery voltage was below 24 v, we had more than an 80% DOD and we were maybe even pushing 90%, depending on which curve you want to believe.

Given that, we had to find the proper response to the red limit, low voltage events of the past couple of days, since the situation would only get worse as the nighttime passes increased to their maximum of 47 minutes and as the battery continued to age. We discussed all the "ifs, ands, and buts" about turning the science instruments off part of the time, but that would not save enough power and I was not willing to lose the science data, especially for a partial solution.

I said, "Well, we can burn off fuel. I've made the calculations and it would shorten the heater on-times to a couple hours or even an hour and a half, if we got rid of the excess fuel. That way, the heaters would not be on long enough to cause the battery to discharge too much." Then I reluctantly said, "If that isn't enough, the other alternative is to turn the transmitter off during the occultation periods when the heaters are on." That would easily work, since the transmitter drew about 1¼ amp or about half of the normal bus current load. Since the tank heaters drew a little over 1½ amp, if we shut off the transmitter that would nearly cancel out the effect of having the big tank heaters on. Also, since the transmitter would only be off during radio occultation periods, we would not lose science data because we would get that portion of the data from the delayed part of the data stream 59 minutes later. The only thing about that was — I did not like the idea of turning the transmitter off and on! Every time you turn something off, there is a chance that it won't turn back on! However, those were our only alternatives and we needed to decide which was the correct solution and do it fast.

As soon as the meeting was over, I found Dan, who was peeved when he learned I had the meeting without him (like I cared if he was peeved — it was my mission not his, despite what he seemed to think) and explained to him the two alternative solutions to the low voltage problem. Dan, despite his loyalty to Lockheed, is very sharp and caught on immediately to what I was telling him. We both agreed that the best thing to do was to burn off some fuel, because neither one of us liked turning off the transmitter.

There was also an operational problem with turning the transmitter off to save power. Tank heater events occurred roughly every 22 to 23 hours, neither Dan nor I could be in Mission Ops every day of the week for a few hours around the expected time of the heater events to do the commanding (remember, I was the only person with command authority, except when I turned it over to Dan in my absence, e.g., Dan had commanded the pressure transducer off at 247/01:01 MET to save a little power after the first red limit power event, because I was on travel). Like it or not, *we would have to rely on the monitoring controller to identify the heater events and turn the transmitter off and back on at the appropriate times during each event, activities they were not trained for!* If we had to do that, we would have to develop failsafe procedures for the controllers to follow.

We both agreed, if the situation worsened, I would cancel my upcoming trip to Houston and Tucson, since the mission always came first.

We also decided we might do a fuel burn-off burn the next day by just firing the T1 and T2 engines continually for 36 seconds at a time — the maximum time we could fire them with one command file. Since the tangential engines fired in the same direction and since the spacecraft spun with a 5 second period, firing the T1 and T2 engines in that way would have no net effect on the spacecraft, assuming both engines were perfectly aligned and had exactly the same thrust. Of course, neither of those conditions were exactly true, so the burns would disturb the orbit and the spacecraft's spin period a little, both of which we could easily correct later. However, we would be able to burn off the 7 kg of excess fuel and that would result in the shorter tanker heater on-times we needed to solve the power problem — if things went the way they were supposed to go.

I went to Mission Ops and told Ken Galal that Dan and I might do a fuel dump burn the following day. He was taken aback and asked, "How can you make a decision like that in just two hours."

I was surprised at his question and I realized he just did not understand that I spent most of everyday thinking about the spacecraft, how it was performing, and what I could do to fix any problem that might arise. Did he think I was taking a nap when I sat in front of my control console for an orbit or two everyday? But I answered, "I haven't made any decision yet," and that calmed him down. Then I said, "I want you to look at the orbit perturbations the fuel dump burn could cause, they must be tiny, but that's why I came to talk to you."

About then, Marcie came in, so I brought her up to date. She was actually pretty good about the whole thing, which both surprised me and made me happy.

I was really enjoying the situation. Once we had gotten down into the mapping orbit, flying the spacecraft had become routine — even Dan's little attitude determination problem was no threat to the mission, just a small hiccup — but the power issue was something we had to solve or we would be in big trouble. I knew we would get around it, but it was challenging and fun.

I told everyone, "We will all meet here tomorrow morning at 8:00 to discuss the two alternatives."

I told Marcie I would be in very early the next morning and she was to make sure that Troy had the data on the duration of the tank heater events, starting at the beginning of the mission, ready for me when I came in. I wanted to determine the empirical relationship between the amount of fuel remaining in the tanks and the heater on-time. I knew the theoretical answer, but I wanted to see what the actual data showed in case reality did not follow theory. She said Troy would get on it and she made him start getting it right then and there.

As it turned out, I was at work all day (from 4:30 AM to 7:30 PM), since Rebecca was flying home from visiting her daughter and her new baby granddaughter and I was going to pick her up at the San Jose Airport at 8:00 PM. I just stayed there, bugged Troy for the data I needed, kept working on the issues, and began discussing with Marcie and the controllers what we would have to do if we were going to shut the transmitter off and on to save power during the tank heater events.

Then I sat and watched the engineering data from the spacecraft as a tank heater event occurred. The problem was that not all tank heater events would cause the battery to discharge too much. At that time in the mission, the tank heaters were on for almost exactly three hours, or 1½ orbit. If the tank heaters turned on when the spacecraft was in the daylight part of the orbit, then the heaters would be on during the following nighttime pass and turn off during the next daylight pass and the battery would be OK. But if the heaters turned on during the nighttime pass, they would stay on through the following daylight pass and the next nighttime pass, i.e., the spacecraft would spend most of the time without solar power, the battery would not get fully charged and we would end up with a low voltage event. And even that was not clean cut, because the ability of the battery to charge up properly depended on the exact time in the day or night part of the cycle that the heaters turned on. It was complicated and, unless I was sitting there, monitoring each heater event, there was no way of knowing *a priori* if we would have to turn the transmitter off or not. We were going to have to watch the heater events very carefully from then on.

While I was sitting there, watching the spacecraft, trying to figure out how we could best teach the monitor controllers when it was necessary to turn off the transmitter and when it was not, Troy brought me the data I needed and boy was I surprised at what I saw.

Based on straight thermodynamics and the facts that the tanks had a total mass of only 14 kg, that the thermal inertia of the tanks was small compared to that of the fuel, that we initially had had 137 kg of fuel in the tanks, that we had 27 kg of fuel left and that the tank heaters were on for roughly 3 hours at that time, the heater events at the beginning of the mission should have been about 15 hours long. However, the data showed that the *early tank heater events were only about 3½ hours long*! The very first one was about 5 hours long, but once the spacecraft reached thermal equilibrium after launch, the heater events were all 3½ hours long and they had only decreased by about a half an hour in duration, despite the fact that we had used 80% of the fuel!

Upon seeing those data, I knew exactly what was going on and I was surprised as hell. First, one has to know that the heaters are at the bottom of the tanks (bottom as defined by the artificial gravity vector caused by the spinning of the spacecraft) where the fuel was and the thermisters and thermostats that controlled the heaters were at the top of the tanks where the helium pressurant was. When the heaters turned on, the heat was conducted from the heaters, right along the highly conductive titanium tank walls to the thermostats and the fuel received very little heat, i.e., instead of heating *all of the fuel* each time there was a heater event, the heaters were mainly heating the tanks and the fuel remained essentially at the same temperature. That was OK, since all we were concerned about was that the fuel did not freeze — but that was not the physical model we had used when we built the tank heater system nor that I was using to make my calculations about the effects of doing a fuel dump burn on the heater on-times!

I immediately called Jim Schirle and explained to him what I had just found, i.e., that we were mainly heating the tanks, rather than the fuel. He thought about it a minute and said, "Gee, you're right, that has to be correct." I was floored — why did I keep finding out things the engineers never thought of? How in hell did they design spacecraft that worked?

Well, that little discovery meant that burning off the excess fuel would not help the heater/low voltage problem very much at all. Like it or not, we were going to have to turn the transmitter off and on during the tank heater events for roughly the next 6 to 8 weeks, i.e., until the nighttime passes got below 45 minutes again. During heater events, we would turn the transmitter off for 50 minutes at the beginning of the radio occultation period during the two parts of each month when radio occultations occurred, and during the two, radio occultation free periods per month, we would turn the transmitter off for 50 minutes when a nighttime pass started. We could and would work around the problem.

After having resolved the issues, I thought about the engineering aspects of the problem. Clearly, if I had chosen a bigger battery (as nearly everyone had wanted me to do, but for which there were no real arguments) we would not have had the low voltage/large DOD problem. However, the battery guys did not complain about the size of my little battery, they said the battery was holding up very well, but it was aging — not degrading, just aging as the battery engineers kept saying. I guessed the difference between aging and degrading is that during aging, the charge/discharge characteristics change — just like wearing in a pair of new shoes, while when a battery degrades, it looses its ability to hold a charge or even get fully charged.

The other possibility was that we could have used thermostats with a smaller thermal dead-band to control the tank heaters than we did. If Jim had used thermostats with 2° C dead-bands on the heaters, instead of those with 5° C dead-bands, we would have been OK — the heater events would have been 40% as long, i.e., 1½ hour long, and would have occurred 2½ times more often, but that would have been just fine. Actually, when I talked to Jim about that, he said he had originally planned to use thermostats with 2° C dead-bands, but didn't because Lockheed did not have any that were reliable, so he used the very reliable 5° C dead-band thermostats — too bad.

Finally, I went to Lockheed to ask about the dangers of turning the transmitter off and on a couple of times a day — still my main concern. As I already knew, our transmitter was designed for use on CRSS, but what I did not know was that CRSS's normal mode of operation was to turn the transmitter on for just 10 minutes out of its 95 or so minute orbit and then turn it off, i.e., it was designed to be turned on and off 14 or 15 times a day, every day for years! There was absolutely no problem with us turning our "CRSS" transmitter off and on a couple of times a day for a few weeks or, at most, a few months. I was very relieved, but I still did not like to have to do it.

Finally, it was 7:30 PM and I left to go to the airport to pick up my sweetheart. It was a long day, but an exciting and fun-filled day. There was nothing like a spacecraft problem to liven up the otherwise routine activities of the mission.

I picked up Rebecca; we drove home and jumped in bed. Both of us were very tired.

Wednesday, September 16, 1998

Day 252 MET: The First Transmitter Turn-Off Event

I went to Mission Ops at about 4:30 AM. I got everything ready for the first transmitter turn off/on event. I had laid out a standard one-page Mission Profile sheet with no dates or times, but with the XMTOFF, EXEC, XMTON, and EXEC Commands and their hexadecimal echoes all laid out. Whoever was on duty when a tank heater event occurred, could just follow the command sequence and fill the dates and times. Ken, Marcie, Jim, and Dan arrived later in the morning and we discussed the various issues and agreed on the procedures that the controllers would use to determine when they needed to turn the transmitter off and back on, when Dan or I were not there to do it.

Then we took our places in Mission Ops and waited for the next heater event to occur. We called the DSN and told them that we were going to be turning the transmitter off and back on a couple of times within the next couple of orbits, so they would know what to expect and properly link up with the spacecraft when we turned the transmitter back on. We had calculated that the heater event would start at about 8:00 AM (252/11:35 MET), but it didn't start until just after 10:30 AM (252/14:05 MET) — and therein lay one of the problems with having the monitoring controllers commanding the turn-offs and turn-ons — there was a couple of hours uncertainty in the times when the heaters would turn on!

However, even though the tank heaters had not turned on by 152/13:30 MET, our next window to turn the transmitter off was rapidly approaching and we decided to go ahead and turn it off, since it was a test anyway. We checked everything and I checked with Jim and then we told the DSN exactly when we were going to turn the transmitter off and back on.

We were pretty confident everything would be OK, but the transmitter had never been turned off since it was turned on over 252 days earlier at spacecraft turn-on, right after launch. I felt like I was about to throw my eight-month-old baby into a lake to see if it could swim!

Well it had to be done; so at 252/13:40 MET, I had the XMTOFF Command file uplinked and a frame or two later I read the echo, "I have echo of 1-D-0-0-9-A, VCID of 0-6, which is correct of the transmitter off command." Eight minutes later, at 252/13:48 MET, the EXEC, which was in the command file, was automatically uplinked. Immediately, as expected, the downlink data stream stopped (there was no echo of the execute because the transmitter was off before the C&DH could send the echo down). There was deadly silence from the spacecraft.

Though we were normally going to have a standard 50 minute transmitter-off-time, we decided to leave the transmitter off for just 40 minutes, first because the radio occultation right then was just 30 minutes long and Jim was worried that the transmitter might get too cold if we left it off too long (the transmitter burned 38 w, of which only 5 came out as radio frequency energy — so it was a good heater itself).

At 252/14:28 MET I had the XMTON Command file uplinked, which had in it, after a 2-second delay, the EXEC. To our relief, the transmitter came right back on and the DSN locked right up on the spacecraft without any trouble. The transmitter had cooled only about 5° C, though Jim had feared it would have cooled 15° C. The spacecraft didn't seem to be too affected at all. The tank heaters were on, as we had expected, and everything was OK.

Since everything was OK, I decided to go on my trip to Houston and then to meet Rebecca in Tucson, so we could buy our lot and get the house started. Since I would be leaving the next day, I had a number of things to do to get ready for the trip, so I left Mission Ops and turned the command authority over to Dan.

The heater was still on during the next pass, so Dan turned the transmitter off for the second time and left it off for the standard 50 minutes, everything was working perfectly again.

Thus, we had a good procedure worked out and we just had to make sure the controllers could do it properly. I was not too concerned about that, but it was too bad that I had to go on a trip for the next 6 days.

Thursday, September 17, through Wednesday, September 23, 1998

Day 253 MET through Day 259 MET: Houston and Tucson

I flew to Houston on Thursday and went to a meeting about the Moon that was set for Friday, Saturday, and Sunday morning. The meeting was OK; it had its good points and its bad points, but I really didn't enjoy it very much. I eventually left. I talked to Mike Duke and Kent Joosten about my lunar plans and I saw the old LEI guys, the Weavers, and John Gruener. But basically, I was bored to death and I was happy to leave Sunday to fly to good old Tucson and meet Rebecca there.

We bought our lot and talked to our architects, Jay Hanson and Matt North, and got the house going. Then we went to the University of Arizona Science and Technology Park and looked it over. We found it was the perfect place for LRI and later LEI. It is only 21 km from the lot we bought for our house. It is a beautiful place, with beautiful grounds. I asked about renting a single, small office, so we could officially establish LRI there, before we actually moved to Tucson after the end of the mission in July.

With everything accomplished in Tucson, Rebecca and I flew back to California, arriving about noon. After I took Rebecca to Gilroy, I went back up to Mission Ops, partly because I was going to be interviewed by a Japanese reporter and, more importantly, to see how things were going with the spacecraft. It was, as always, OK and the guys had been doing a good job of turning the transmitter off and on. Happily, that was working well, so the battery crises had been solved. We were back to routine operations, albeit with a new twist, but nevertheless, even the new twist had fast become routine.

Friday, September 25, 1998

Day 261 MET: Sylvia and Marcie Slowly Drive Me Nuts

We did a SIM of the first 90° segment of the 180° flip during the morning. It went well, but it took a long time. Then I went downstairs to talk to Sylvia.

I asked her how the extended mission contract was coming and, instead of answering me, she asked me, "Have you decided how to fly it yet?" That blew my mind! How many times did I have to define it for her? Clearly, she was not up to the job of being the NASA Mission Manager and was panicking (with a big push in that direction from good old Marcie). After I explained again that we were going down to the lowest possible circular mapping orbit, she said, "I want to talk to you about something. If you're going to be moving to Tucson before the mission ends, we should make Dan the Mission Director."

I said, "Whoa, back up the cart there. First of all, I have no intention of leaving before the mission is completely finished. As I told you, the only way we would move early is if the house (that we were renting in Gilroy) is sold out from under us; then we would have to move, but that isn't going to happen." Then I said, in a very threatening way, "Don't even start thinking about that. This is my mission and I'm flying it to the end." Despite my liking and respecting Sylvia a lot, the woman was totally petrified. If she didn't calm down and quit that crap, I was going to start raising hell about her.

Then we got back to the extended mission contract; of course, Ames had done nothing about it because NASA had given them only $2 million for it, Ames didn't know if it was enough money and Ames was afraid that Headquarters was even going to take the $2 million away! It was the same old NASA crap. As Guenter Riegler said once, "Well, you know, if people are crabbing about money, I just let them crab." Those people are so incompetent. They just don't care. Why don't they do things right? NASA should be put out of our misery.

After my little talk with Sylvia, Marcie came up to Mission Ops and said we had another useless meeting to prepare for the equally useless Extended Mission Review

Meeting Guenter wanted (not her words, but mine). I said, "This whole damned meeting is a sheer waste of time."

Marcie replied, "Oh no, it's good to go through the issues. This forces us to think about the issues and make sure we are doing everything right."

I nearly puked and you do not want to know what thoughts went through my mind, except that at that moment, I was really looking forward to Lunar Prospector's end and my never, ever having to see any of those idiots again. Right then, I wouldn't even have minded if Lunar Prospector got destroyed during the November Leonid Meteor Shower. It would be a nice, glorious end to the mission and I would be free of those bastards in two months. I was absolutely disgusted with Marcie and NASA.

When I got home, I found I had finally received a reply to my two letters to Mel Brashears in which I had asked Lockheed to donate half of its Lunar Prospector $4 million fee to LRI and, as fully expected, I got a NO. But I was told to contact Dale Von Haase, who administered Lockheed funds for research (Appendix 4-6, see also www.lunar-research-institute.org), about my request. Surprised, but with little hope for success, I decided to write Dale, but, as expected, nothing came of it.

Wednesday, September 30, 1998

Day 266 MET: More Aggravation

Rebecca and I went up to Mission Ops in the afternoon — we were going to have dinner with Don Davis and his son-in-law, Ian, who were again at Ames doing ice-body impact studies.

I had a telecon with Marcie, Dan, and Goddard about the 180° flip maneuvers and the low altitude mapping orbit. As usual, Marcie didn't understand anything. As we were talking about the emergency burn procedures to get us out of the low orbit in case we were in trouble, I said, "All we have to do is do a burn with the axial engines when the spacecraft is over the equator" (since the axial engine would be firing exactly along the spacecraft velocity vector at those two points in the orbit and we could raise the orbit with two quick burns without any preplanning).

Mystified at the simple celestial mechanics involved, Marcie asked, "Well, how do you know that's the right place to do it? How do you know this?" My silent answer was, *because I have at least two functioning brain cells in my head and you don't,* but I answered sarcastically, but truthfully, "Because it's basic orbital mechanics. If you don't believe me, ask Goddard."

She simply knew nothing about any facet of the mission and when she doesn't understand something, which is almost always the case, her mode is always to say, "Well, I don't agree with this," and then she makes a big stink about it to cover her stupidity.

My frustration level of having to put up with her on a daily basis, compounded by Sylvia's panic, NASA's overall incompetence, and Lockheed, etc. was rocketing skywards. It was a good thing the spacecraft basically took care of itself and I only had to go to the Ames and Lockheed madhouses every couple of days or —.

I called Bill to talk about money and other mission issues, one being that there had been a MagStar explosion detected on August 27. The MagStar, a neutron star with an unimaginably strong magnetic field, had a magnetic event — a starquake — and it bathed the Earth in enormous amounts of gamma rays and x-rays, so much so that the nightside ionosphere was completely ionized to dayside ionosphere levels. All the gamma ray detectors on all the spacecraft in the solar system detected the gamma rays, as did our GRS.

I was at Mission Ops when the gamma ray burst hit Lunar Prospector. We were already in the middle of a huge solar storm when the burst hit and suddenly the GRS, NS, and APS just went bonkers. As a result of the burst and the solar storm, Bill wanted to have me delay the flip and roll maneuvers by two to four weeks (we had to do the maneuvers at new Moon or full Moon, as well as near $\beta = 0°$, otherwise the geometry would not allow us to simultaneously have solar power, communications, and the GRS and spacecraft "rolling" along parallel to the lunar surface during the roll phase, so we could not do the flip and roll just any old time). Clearly, if the spectrometers were overloaded when we did the maneuvers, we would not get the roll calibration data we were after, but that would not be the end of the world — the flip was the main thing and we could do that at anytime. However, if we delayed the maneuvers for two to four weeks as Bill wanted, there was no guarantee there would not be another solar storm the next time we planned the maneuvers, and worse, we would be moving farther and farther away from $\beta = 0°$, so I was going to go ahead and do the maneuvers on October 5 and 7, when β was within 1° of 0°.

I also talked to Sylvia about the amount of money we were getting for the extended mission and I was going to have to bitch at NASA — we were about $500,000 short. I was getting very sick of these SOBs.

Thursday, October 1, 1998

Day 267 MET

I gave a talk up at Palo Alto that went very well.

I got an unintelligible letter from NASA in response to my trying to make sure that NASA had enough money for the reduction of our data (Appendix 4-7, see also www.lunar-research-institute.org). In the letter, George Withbroe danced around the issue, but basically he said they weren't going to give us any money for data reduction!

However, that message was so buried in NASA gobbledygook that nobody could understand it who was not used to NASA. Neither Rebecca nor Wayne could figure out what the letter meant. But Pat Dasch and I had a good laugh about it over the phone, because we were used to NASA letters that mean nothing. I was going to have to find a way to get money for the data reduction, because the NASA bastards weren't going to give us any.

Saturday, October 3, 1998

Day 269 MET

I went to Mission Ops and increased the high-voltage level of the GRS to 1650 v at 269/13:48 MET.

Chapter 4-10
The Flip

Monday, October 5, 1998

Day 271 MET: The Reor to Roll

I had become concerned over the weekend because Troy, when he was on duty, was simply turning the transmitter off and on three times around the expected time of each heater event, rather than noting when the event started and then turning the transmitter off and on only once or twice, as needed. Either he was not paying attention to the downlinked engineering data or he did not understand it. I mentioned that to Marcie, whose limited job was to manage the monitoring controllers and, of course, she got extremely defensive. There was just no way I could interact rationally with her — she was always confrontational as she tried to cover up her own incompetence.

The solar storm had abated and the GRS and NS were back to normal, β was less than 1°, and we had a nearly full Moon (no, it had nothing to do with vampires) — it was time to start the flip sequence.

Since Dan had turned the pressure transducer off to save a little power on Day 247 MET, I had to turn it back on for the reor burns and I also had to switch from the medium gain antenna to the omni antenna before we started the reor maneuver to insure we could get downlinked data from the spacecraft when we were out of its normal attitude.

Dan and I had both computed that the 90° reor would require 429 pulses on the A1 and A4 engines; hence, the maneuver had to be broken up into two segments. The first segment would have 255 pulses, the maximum we could command in one uplink file, and that would cause a 53.8° reor. The second segment would have 174 pulses and reor the spacecraft an additional 37°, resulting in the 90.8° reor that was necessary to keep the SEA positive, i.e., we were shooting for a +1.2° SEA. That break in the maneuver would also allow Dan to reset the delay time parameter (DELAYSUN) that controlled the firing of the first pulse of each pulse pair (one pulse on the A1 engine and the second on the A4 engine) with respect to the Sun pulse (derived from the Sun sensor) and the time delay (HALFREV) between the firing of the first and second pulses of each pulse pair. That was desirable because the spacecraft would very slightly spinup during the pulse burn and that would slowly throw the timing of the pulses off just a little bit. Correcting DALAYSUN and HALFREV part way through the maneuver would reduce the error in our reor.

In addition to the main reor maneuver, I had written into the Mission Profile a tweak reor burn to correct for any errors in the final attitude, if required.

At 7:00 AM, we were ready to go and 11 minutes later, after going through our standard and very thorough file checks, I had the first file uplinked that turned on the pressure transducer (271/10:46 MET) and switched to the omni antenna (271/10:47 MET). There was the immediate and expected drop of 6 dB in the strength of the signal received from the spacecraft when the spacecraft switched from the medium gain antenna to the omni antenna. Then I had the A1 and A4 heater turn-on file uplinked and those commands were acted upon at 271/11:41 MET and 271/11:42 MET, respectively.

As the A1 and A4 engines began to heat up, we uplinked and verified the first engine parameter file, which I had executed at 271/12:41 MET. The 255 pulses took 21 minutes and 15 seconds to complete. As soon as it was over, Dan corrected the DELAY-SUN and HALFREV in the second file for the very slight spinup, I had it uplinked, we verified it, and the second segment was executed at 271/13:19 MET. The 174 pulses took 15 minutes to complete, so the entire maneuver was completely over and the engines were safed at 271/13:36 MET. The reor burn had been very accurate; we were off by only 0.89°, so I canceled the tweak reor. The two-day roll part of the sequence had begun.

Tuesday, October 6, 1998

Day 272 MET: Rolling

The spacecraft was rolling along, collecting the desired calibration data as nice as could be.

I canceled the planned, second tweak reor and tweak despin burns, because the attitude was close to what we had wanted and the spin rate was OK. Also, Dan was having a little trouble determining the attitude because there were some strange gravitational torques acting on the spacecraft in the roll mode we didn't expect. Nevertheless, Dan said we were very close to the desired attitude and rather than making the tweak burn and forcing him to start all over with his attitude determinations, I wanted to leave the spacecraft where it was for the full two days. That way, Dan could get a really good measure of the attitude and then we would have the best possible data for the final 90° reor maneuver that was set for the following day.

Wednesday, October 7, 1998

Day 273 MET: Finishing the Flip

Preston and an Air Force guy were there for the final 90° maneuver. The sequence of events for the two burn segments, a 255-pulse burn segment followed by a 179-pulse burn segment, were essentially identical to that of the first 90° maneuver two days earlier. We started the command sequence at 273/10:40 MET and finished with a safed spacecraft in its inverted position at 273/12:42 MET. As was the case two days earlier, the maneuver had been so accurate, I canceled the planned tweak reor burn. Operationally, that event marked the halfway point of the mission.

I again started my campaign to get money for the data reduction. The NASA announcement requesting research proposals had arrived and there was no money in there for data reduction. I called Brad Jollif, Bill, George French, and everyone else I could think of in our community who might be able to help put pressure on NASA to get us the money that we needed to get our data into the archive in forms the science community and the public could use. The data reduction money issue was a big headache.

Thursday, October 8, 1998

Day 274 MET

I canceled the planned tweak reor and tweak despin burns because we hit our attitude to within 0.64° and the spin rate was still OK. It was amazing how well we controlled the spacecraft — a 0.89° error on the first burn and a 0.64° error on the second; that was amazing, we had less than 1% errors. Also, the Sun had remained calm during the entire roll portion of the sequence, so we got perfect calibration data.

Friday, October 9, through Sunday, October 11, 1998

Day 275 MET through Day 277 MET:
The Space Frontier Foundation Meeting in LA

Rebecca and I flew down to LA for the SFF meeting on the 9th — my 59th birthday.

The SFF meeting was very productive for me. I gave a talk on the mission and I was given an award. But almost everyone who was there, alive or dead, got an award, so the award was nearly meaningless.

Greg Maryniak was there; it was nice seeing him and talking with him about the mission that he had helped get going — and, of course, he got an award for Lunar Prospector, too!

Joe Rothenberg, from Headquarters, was there and I brought him up to date on the progress I had made towards getting a commercial lunar exploration program and a commercial lunar base going. I suggested that maybe we could meet at JSC when he was there sometime, so we could have a good discussion about my efforts. He thought that was a good idea.

I had a nice talk with Alan Ladwig, also from Headquarters. I told Alan about my commercial data purchase program and I said, "I really would like to see Code M (Rothenberg's Division) take over the Moon, since Code S is so bad and hates the Moon."

Alan, replied, "Well maybe when Wes goes, things will get better."

I said, "I doubt that."

Alan asked, "The problem is Carl (Pilcher), isn't it?"

I answered, "Yes. I don't see any way to change Code S until Carl is gone." Alan wanted to get back to the Moon, as did Rothenberg and Abbey. I was very optimistic I could pull off getting a commercial lunar exploration program started.

Wayne Stevens and I had long talks with David Gump, about how our three companies could work together on lunar missions. We all agreed that we weren't going to merge and that LRI/LEI would have the absolute responsibility for all the technical aspects of all joint missions.

I met some of the guys from Rotary Rocket and they definitely wanted to talk to me about launching my future missions.

Since I was going to do the next OMM — the last OMM of the nominal mission — on Monday, I invited David Gump, Jim Dunstan, and one of the Rotary Rocket guys to come and watch the burn — and I was hoping George French would be there, too.

Monday, October 12, 1998

Day 278 MET: The 5th and Final OMM of the Nominal Mission

I got in very early and tried to get caught up with everything that was on my desk and I had a long telephone interview with the writer from *Scientific American*.

By 10:00 AM, my Ops Team and I were ready to start our 5th and final OMM of the nominal missions. David Gump, Jim Dunstan, a guy who worked with Rotary Rocket, and then another guy who worked at Ames were there for the burns.

The OMM was to consist of a 7.22 m/sec, 45.5 sec periselene burn on the A1 and A2 engines, starting at 285/14:47 MET; a 6.50 m/sec, 40.9 sec aposelene burn on the A1 and A2 engines, starting at 285/14:47 MET; and possibly a tweak reor burn and a tweak despin burn.

After having gone through our standard checks and rechecks of the various command files, I issued the command to send the engine heater turn-on file at 278/14:16 MET and the engines were safed an hour and 34 minutes later at 278/15:50 MET — we had accomplished the two burns of the OMM.

Dan quickly determined that we had not disturbed the spacecraft's attitude, so I canceled the tweak reor burn, but the spin rate was 12.14 rpm, so I issued the commands to turn on the T1 engine heater at 278/15:53 MET and, 16 minutes later, we did a 0.55 sec despin burn, bringing the spin rate back down to 12.0 rpm. The engine was safed and the command session was over at 278/16:11 MET. Needless to say, David, Jim, and my other two guests thoroughly enjoyed watching the command session.

Tuesday, October 13, through Friday, October 16, 1998

Day 279 MET through Day 282 MET: Thanking the Vendors

Rebecca and I left Gilroy Tuesday morning to drive down to southern California, so I could thank some of the vendors who had built subsystems for Lunar Prospector and tell them how the mission was proceeding, as I had promised them I would do early in Phase C/D. We drove all the way down to San Diego and the smog was just as thick as soup once we got into the LA area, and it extended all the way down to San Diego — we did not see how people could breathe there.

Wednesday morning we went to Loral, which built the transponder, in San Diego and I gave them a talk and thanked them. They were appreciative, but not very enthusiastic.

Wednesday afternoon, we went to Vertigo in Lake Elsinore (between San Diego and LA) and talked to those guys about the inflatables. Roger had found we could buy habitation modules (tin cans, as I called them), that Boeing had developed for the space station for NASA at great cost, for only $5 to $10 million per can and that was what we had discussed using to build the lunar base. However, Vertigo had developed an inflatable structure NASA was also considering for use on the space station. However, after Vertigo developed the technology, NASA decided that they would build the unit themselves, leaving Vertigo out in the cold and that really pissed Vertigo off. I wanted to explore the use of Vertigo's inflatables for the lunar base, instead of the Boeing tin cans. They were excited about the possibility and I got a lot of good information from them. They said that each inflatable could provide three to four times the volume of a Boeing tin can for $1 million! That sounded very good.

Rebecca and I drove the rest of the way to the LA complex, found a Holiday Inn next to the freeway for the night and had a nice dinner at Tony Roma's — our favorite barbeque restaurant.

The next morning, Thursday, we went to PSI, which had built the fuel tanks, and they really were happy to see us. I gave them a nice talk and everybody was really pleased with the mission and my visiting them to thank them.

Next we drove up to JPL (Pasadena, CA), so I could talk to the DSN staff about my extended mission tracking requirements and they wanted to hear some of our science results, so I gave them a talk too. When I was finished, I was sure I was going to get almost the same 97% coverage for the extended mission we had been getting during the nominal mission (remember, NASA had promised us only 70 to 90% coverage, but the DSN had been giving us an amazing 97% coverage — that was unbelievable).

After we left JPL, we drove out of the LA basin and out of the unbelievable smog. We reached Santa Barbara (which Rebecca loves), where we stayed the night. We had a great Mexican dinner and stayed in a nice hotel on the beach and just walked around.

Friday morning, we went to Able Engineering and saw Bob Crawford and the guys who had built the science instrument booms. I gave them two short talks, about a half hour each. I told them about my future plans and gave them a very brief rundown on the mission. They were very enthusiastic about my future plans and said they would be happy to do the types of booms I would need for the lunar landers.

Then, we took off and drove the rest of the way back to Gilroy. It was a very good trip. I enjoyed thanking the vendors for helping make Lunar Prospector a success and they appreciated my doing so.

Saturday, October 17, 1998

Day 283 MET

David Gump had sent me a fax while we were on our trip. He said that *National Geographic* was concerned and scared about the LunaCorp rover mission and Dave wanted to know if *National Geographic* could come out to Ames, so I could show them Mission Ops to calm them down. I called Dave to say yes, but in the meantime, it turned out that the head of *National Geographic* wasn't interested in the mission, so I thought the *National Geographic* connection was going down the drain.

David told me we should visit Anthony Zuppero, who worked for the Department of Energy in Idaho and who wanted to get the Department of Energy involved in buying data from the LunaCorp mission. We were going to pursue that.

Tuesday, October 20, 1998

Day 286 MET: More NASA BS

I talked to Sylvia, who said Guenter had complained to her that he was not getting enough information about the science results, so she asked him if he had read the monthly reports, which, of course, he had not! She said he had then crabbed at Lockheed and then, of course, I had gotten a stupid letter from Lockheed, saying they wanted more science detail.

I was sick of that NASA crap. First, Guenter did not even read what he was sent and second, if the SOB had looked at the contract, he would have seen that we were funded only to produce Level 0 and Level 1 data products and we had delivered everything we were contractually obligated to deliver. Nevertheless, the SOB was trying to get more than NASA paid for.

Sylvia said, despite our having been at Headquarters on April 20 and having shown their damned science review committee that our data were much better than we had promised, Guenter was griping to somebody that our data were no good. The SOB was again trying to find a way out of putting any money into the data reduction program and trying to degrade the value of the whole mission.

It was clear to me NASA was doing everything that it could to get rid of the mission and to avoid putting any more money into it. Sylvia thought Guenter was trying to put so much pressure on the extended mission as to make it impossible. I was really sick of that crap, so I called Israel who said Goldin, who had given a speech at Rice University, said, "We (NASA) are not interested in the Moon; we've been there and done that." Israel didn't want to bring up the Lunar Prospector data reduction money to Goldin, rather he went to Abbey and he wanted me to talk to Abbey.

I called George French and George already had talked to Sensenbrenner's people who said, "Hey, we can't make NASA do anything, all we can do is to gripe."

I said to George, "I understand that, but that is exactly what I need to have done." Well, if I was going to succeed in getting our data reduced and into the archives, I was going to have to fight for it and fight hard. If the NASA bastards weren't willing to have the data reduced to useful forms and archived, so scientists and the public could use it, why did the bastards ever give us the $63 million to do the mission — a good question, huh?

Finally, Sylvia said that she was getting ready to prepare the recommendations for the NASA Awards for the mission and wanted to know a couple of things. First, she wanted to know who should be listed in the group awards for the science teams and the engineering teams. We went through that list. Then she said, "I know that you don't care about awards, so if you don't want a NASA Gold Medal for being the PI on the mission, I won't bother to recommend you for an award, since it requires a lot of paperwork."

Well, I saw no value in getting a NASA Gold Medal Award, especially since someone like Dougherty had one for his work on the Hubble Telescope — if NASA gave a gold medal to someone who knew as little about engineering as he did, the medal couldn't have much meaning. I answered, "No, don't bother. Besides, NASA would never, ever give me an award anyway." But then I thought a second and said, "Yeah, put me down for a gold medal — I'm curious to see if NASA would give me an award." Though I really didn't want Sylvia to waste her time and I did not believe for a second NASA would give me an award, I wanted NASA to have to say to me, "No, you don't deserve a gold medal for all your work as PI on Lunar Prospector." I chuckled at the thought.

Thursday, October 22, 1998

Day 288 MET: Another Confrontation — the Extended Mission

I went up to Mission Ops early in the morning. I was going to talk to Sylvia, but I got everything done quickly, so I went home to work at LRI. I made numerous calls to various colleagues, trying to garner support for my getting the money for the data reduction. Everyone was willing to write letters to NASA to make them stand up and face the issue.

I got a fax from Sylvia, who was pissed because I hadn't stayed at Ames to talk with her — she had several questions about the Extended Mission Review. I went back up to Ames.

When I got there, she was grumping and again said something about my not being Mission Director during the extended mission and added, "You're never here; you're always on travel."

I said, "I want to keep this friendly, Sylvia; but I'm telling you, if you try to do that, I will raise so much hell, that the hell I raised about Scott will look like nothing. Believe me Sylvia, just back off."

She said, "Well, I have my concerns and you're not around and we can't reach you. Some of the other people are concerned, too, that you are never here."

I asked, "Who are they? What's the problem?" but I got no answer.

Rather she said, "I feel I have to do my job, so I wrote another letter to Lockheed."

I said, "I'm really getting tired of this stuff. If you have something to say to me, come and tell me."

She replied, "Well I do, whenever I think that's applicable, but sometimes I think I have to go through Lockheed. In any case, you're never here when I need you."

I retorted, "Sylvia, I have plenty to do running this mission and trying to get the money for the data reduction and for the extended mission. Do you think I'm just going to come up here and sit next door, waiting to answer your question?"

She answered, "Well no."

I felt sorry for Sylvia; she had been given a job she was not equipped to handle. She had no background in science or engineering whatsoever and she was relying on Marcie, who is, at best, a third-rate engineer and who hardly knew more than Sylvia did about any of the technical aspects of the mission. Sylvia was really trapped in the middle between Guenter, who also knew nothing about the technical aspects of the mission, and me. Giving the devil his due, at least Scott had a physics background and understood exactly what I was doing. If Sylvia had had Scott's technical knowledge or if Scott was a decent person like Sylvia, instead of being a backstabbing, self-serving SOB, Lunar Prospector would have been 100 times easier to do. But neither was the case, and I somehow had to get Sylvia to calm down and stop listening to Marcie's hysteria.

I said, "Sylvia, the main problem that's causing all these issues is that you are doing this in the typical NASA way, not the Discovery way, and not my way. As you freely admit, you don't have the background to understand this mission, so you don't trust what I am doing. There is no way I can make you, Guenter, and Marcie understand what you don't have the background to understand. Marcie and Guenter want piles of documents and procedures, just like on a *normal* NASA program. But you yourself know that half of the cost of a *normal* NASA program is spent on useless paperwork, so people like Marcie and Guenter and the others at Headquarters can pretend they have all the information they need to protect their butts if something goes wrong. And you know just as well if we had all that paperwork, this mission would have cost $120 million instead of $63 million. You can't have it both ways. Either you trust those of us who know what we are doing and let us do it cheaply, or you require all the useless paperwork and double the cost — which would mean there would never have been a Lunar Prospector."

Knowing all that was absolutely true, Sylvia said, "I am trying to avoid having procedures written out and things like that."

I replied, "I know that, but that's what the others want and that's what I'm fighting against. We are 180 degrees apart on this."

She said, "Well, yes, but NASA has ownership of the mission, since they selected your mission."

I said, "No, I don't agree with that. If the AO was written in a different way — if it had said this would be a NASA mission if we select your mission, I would agree, but that's not what it said. It said it was to be run by the PI. It is his responsibility. And Wes stood up there (at the initial Discovery Selection News Conference) and said that in the past, these were NASA missions with community support, but these (Discovery missions) are community mission with NASA support. If Lunar Prospector is a NASA mission now, then you guys have changed the damned rules. And that is what I am fighting against."

The conversation continued and I could see she was just going to continue as she had been doing — she would continue to listen to Marcie's stupidity and they would want procedures and everything written down. They wanted a schedule. They wanted to know where I was at all times. I said, "Look, I'm going to be there during the extended mission, as I have always been. You can't tell me where I have to stand or sit."

Sylvia again said, "Well, you are never here."

I said, "That's what telephones are for."

But she wouldn't back off, because her way of doing things was to follow procedures — just follow the NASA way. I said, "You know, this is exactly what I hate. This is why you guys do everything so badly."

She replied, "Well, we need the procedure, because there have been miscommunications, people don't understand."

I replied, "The reason they don't understand is because they are not very damned good. They don't pay any attention to what I say, because they are arrogant NASA employees and NASA people think they know everything, when in reality they don't know anything."

She said, "You know, the thing is, this is a very difficult extended mission and there is a lot of uncertainty." That was clearly Marcie talking, even if it was Sylvia's lips that were moving.

I replied, "That's not true. For example, we are going down to 40 km to verify the gravity field before going down to 25 km" (Though Dave Folta thought the orbital tracking was accurate enough for us to go that low, he wanted us to go down to a 40 km altitude orbit for one mapping cycle, before we went down to 25 km, so they could verify the gravity model before we got down so low. That made sense, since the lower we were, the more sensitive we were to the higher order harmonics of the gravity field, and of course, the higher order harmonics were less well defined than the lower ones, as long as we were in the 100 km altitude orbit. Though we knew the lunar gravity very well after more than nine months in orbit, we did not want any little surprises when we got down to within 10 km of the Moon. Since the irregularities in the gravity field would cause the 25 km mean altitude orbit to vary by ±15 km during the two weeks of a mapping cycle, the spacecraft would get as low as 10 km above the mean lunar sphere — but the topography on the lunar far-side is more than 5 km high, so there was little room for error).

Sylvia said, "Yes, I know to re-map it."

I shook my head in disbelief, she simply had no concept of what we were doing and I said, "No, we are going down to verify there is nothing unexpected in the higher order harmonics. We have already mapped the gravity field and know what it is," but she remained unconvinced.

At that point, I didn't know whether she and I were going to get along much longer, but if they wanted to start playing that game, I could play it too. I was at Mission Ops almost everyday when I was not on travel and I was usually there by 5:00 AM. If I had to be present and accounted for everyday, then the day would start for everyone at 5:00 AM, not at 9:00 or 10:00, and all meetings would started at 7:00 AM and we would have a damned meeting every damned day.

I like Sylvia. She works hard and I understand it is hard for a woman in NASA. But she did not understand anything about the mission, she had no business running it, and worse, she relied on Marcie who also doesn't know anything at all. Between them, they just sat there and got panicky.

I came away from that meeting, hoping Lunar Prospector would get slammed during the Leonid Meteor Shower, so the whole mess would be over in a month and I would be free from all that insanity. There I was, I had a mission that was working perfectly. There had never been a serious problem. There had been no errors. The spacecraft worked perfectly. Why in hell couldn't Sylvia and NASA accept all that and just say, "Well gosh, it's working, let's keep our mouth shut?"

The only hope I had to keep my sanity was that they would fuss around until we got into the extended mission, then the extended mission would go well and then they would calm down — just like after launch.

Monday, October 26, 1998

Day 292 MET: The Roots of Sylvia's Concerns

I went up to Mission Ops, got caught up with everything on my desk and watched a tank heater event. The heaters went on just after the spacecraft came out of the nighttime pass, so I stopped Ric from turning the transmitter off and the battery did not discharge beyond its normal limits.

Ric had turned the transmitter off during the previous tank heater event at the wrong time, since the heater didn't turn on until after the spacecraft had come into the sunlight, but the battery hadn't discharged anymore than it would have under normal circumstances. The controllers still did not understand when they were supposed to turn the transmitter off and when they weren't, despite Marcie's written procedures, and happily, most of the heater events did not lead to an excessive DOD of the battery and the resulting low voltage.

I was a little annoyed with the former fact (but happy with the latter) and it just proved two things I had told Sylvia a few days earlier. First, having procedures written out, as Marcie insisted, does *no good* if the people trying to follow the procedures do not have the background and training necessary for them to properly follow the procedures. Second, Marcie, whose job it was to teach the controllers how to do their jobs, did not know enough herself to even teach the controllers how to follow the simple procedures, i.e., she is incompetent and useless.

After watching the spacecraft for a while, I talked to Sylvia and I found there was more to her being mad the day before than met the eye. Her problem seemed to be that Ames's Hogan and Cathcart and Lockheed's Bob Garner expected her to go through Lockheed and not talk directly to me. They all felt that was the contractual lineage and hence she had to let Lockheed know what was going on before discussing any issue with me. That was just bureaucratic BS, and even though it was stupid beyond comprehension, I didn't really care (mainly because I did not care what Ames and Lockheed did, because I have no — and I mean zero — respect for either organization or the people who run them), as long as she didn't blindside me. However, as was correct and rational, she preferred to talk directly to me, despite her catching hell about it. When that became apparent, I felt even sorrier for her than I did before — she was caught in the middle while trying to do things correctly.

We talked about the extended mission and her concerns that I was not at Mission Ops enough to suit her. Interestingly enough, Sylvia said Marcie had said I didn't need to be there that much — well good for Marcie, sometimes she was a help rather than a hindrance. Then I said, "The thing that bothered me is the fact that we discussed this issue a couple months ago and I made it clear then that during the extended mission I was going to be here most of the time — that I was going to minimize my outreach and educational travel. I thought I had made that clear." She said she understood that. I said, "Well then, tell Garner to back off and not to get all excited about this."

I thought and hoped that everything between us was back on track. We had a very nice conversation and I assured her, if that was what they were grumping at her about, I didn't really care if she had to inform Lockheed every time we talked and, "We should just let them go their bureaucratic way. It won't change anything, because you and I will still talk the issues out and it is between you and me and not between Lockheed and Ames."

It was really too bad that the pressure Ames and Lockheed were putting on Sylvia had caused our rather confrontational discussion of the previous day, because Sylvia and I had a really good working relationship (except she relied on Marcie far too much). But, other than her learning to ignore the idiots, there was little I could do, except to assure her that what Ames and Lockheed did made no difference to me as long as it did not cause problems with the actual running of the spacecraft.

Tuesday, October 27, 1998

Day 293 MET: The Leonid Reor SIM

Dan, Ric, and I did a SIM of the reor to turn the spacecraft's bottom into the Leonid Meteor Shower. The circumstances of the reor were going to make it a very long procedure. At the time of our Leonid reor, the nighttime passes would be 42 minutes long and 180° out of phase with the radio occultations that would be 46 minutes long. Since the spacecraft had to be in sunlight to do the pulsed burns (because the firing of the pulses was controlled by the Sun pulse from the Sun sensor) and since we could only do pulsed firings when we were also in radio contact with the spacecraft — by mission rules — we would have two, short 15-minute periods to upload and execute the reor files during each orbit! Thus, we had to break up the reor into six, 9-minute segments, each with just 55 pulsed burns on the A1 and A 4 engines, that would shift the attitude by just 11.3° and a seventh, 8-minute segment with 49 pulses to shift the spacecraft the final 10.2°, ending up with the required 78° change in attitude.

In addition, since it took longer than 15 minutes to uplink and verify a full engine parameter command file and execute it, we devised a plan in which we would uplink and verify the command file for a burn segment during the nighttime pass, when we had radio contact, and then execute the file when the spacecraft came into the sunlight and still have enough time before the beginning of the radio occultation period to determine if the spacecraft was OK. During the occultation period, we would then prepare the simple execute file for the next segment. As soon as the spacecraft came out of occultation, we would use the new execute file to re-execute the previous engine parameter command file. As soon as that was done, Dan would note the change in the spacecraft's rotation rate and then he would build a new engine parameter command file with corrected DELAYSUN and HALFREV parameters. We would then uplink the corrected engine parameter file during the next nighttime pass in preparation for the next two burn segments of the maneuver. It was a good time saving strategy; otherwise, it would take us twice a long to do the reor that would require nearly 7 hours to complete, even with the time saving strategy!

Thus, the Leonid reor was going to be complex and long and the SIM was very useful in preparing for it. For example, Dan noticed during the SIM that he had given me some incorrect information on the burn times and sequences when I was preparing the Mission Profile for the reor maneuver, so I corrected those errors. Also the SIM reor went in the wrong direction, by just a little bit, because Dan forgot to change one of the parameters in the parameter file. The SIM was very useful in preparing for the real thing.

We had a telecon about the extended mission with Dave Folta at Goddard, who said we could go down to 25 km altitude as far as he was concerned.

Then I drove back to Gilroy just before lunch to have lunch with — and give a talk to — the Gilroy Rotary. It was a waste of time, because they were fooling around with their jokes and stuff and I ended up with only about 15 minutes to talk, so I just talked about the commercial aspects of the mission, since they were all commercial people.

Wednesday, October 28, 1998

Day 294 MET: What a Day

I didn't sleep well and I had a dull headache, so I got up late. I left to go up to Mission Ops at about 6:30 AM and the traffic was fierce. It took me an hour and a half to get up to Ames.

Dan Green from Channel 8 in Salinas was going to interview me at 9:30 and then I had a talk at San Jose University. When I got to Mission Ops, I checked out the spacecraft at my console and it was fine. Then I went over to the instrument consoles and I found that the GRS wasn't downlinking any spectra, the NS spectra were no damn good, the APS data seemed to be OK on one screen, but the other screen was blank!

I immediately called Bill and told him what I had found. We discussed it, but we didn't know what it meant. I then told Sylvia and Marcie we apparently had a bad anomaly, but it was too early to tell. I called Bill a little bit later, after he had time to analyze the data, and he said it was clear from the diagnostics that the spectrometers were fine. He thought maybe there was a problem in the C&DH. If that were the case, then we had a very big problem because the C&DH was the brain (albeit, small and dim-witted) of the spacecraft.

I called Gerry Grismore and left a message for him, warning him that something might be wrong with the C&DH.

I looked closely at the MAG/ER data and the MAG data looked kind of screwy. I thought, *oh-oh, we really have a severe problem.* I tried to call Berkeley, but nobody was there. Bob Lin was in Europe. Dave Mitchell wasn't around and neither was Dave Curtis, so I left a message for Dave Curtis, indicating I had to talk to him ASAP.

I looked at the MAG data again and I realized that what I was seeing was just the gain switching automatically. The only trouble was, the gain was switching every time at exactly the same point in the spin cycle, so it looked very weird. I watched it for some time and decided it was actually OK and that suggested the C&DH was not screwing up, it was probably something in the spectrometer electronics, probably in the SES itself.

In the meantime, Bill had determined that we were getting data from both the APS and the anti-coincident shield of the GRS, but no gamma-ray spectra from the GRS itself and that the NS was generating data, but it just was not being downlinked in its primary mode! The NS data was downlinked in two ways, directly as raw data and after it had been histogramed. The latter was what I normally saw on the NS console screen and that was what was missing.

Also, Bill had contacted Dave Black at Southwest and asked him what could be wrong with the SES. Dave thought it sounded like the SES timer that controlled the histograming of the GRS and NS data was not working. If so, and if we could not fix it, we would continue to get NS and APS data, but we would lose the GRS spectra! However, Dave thought it was not a hardware problem, rather a software problem. But Bill said he would have to wait until Dave Black got back from lunch to really find out what was going on.

Dan Green was late — it was about 10:30 before he and his camera crew got there. I did the interview. It was a really good interview. I enjoyed it very much. Dan Green is a very nice guy and we talked for a good hour about the polar water ice, its implications for the future exploration and utilization of the Moon, as well as what it meant scientifically. It was really a lot of fun.

By then, it was time to go to San Jose. I drove down to the university and gave them my seminar. The staff and students really enjoyed it and then I hurried back to Mission Ops.

I got back at about 1:45 PM and by that time, Bill and Dave Black had figured the problem out and I thought I also knew what was going on. Given what we were seeing in the raw data and, since Dave thought it was a software problem, the only logical explanation was that we had had a bit flip, either a bit flipped by itself or it was a single event upset, caused by a cosmic ray hitting the SES and flipping a bit in its logic. If so, then all I had to do was turn the SES and the spectrometers off and turn them back on and everything would be fine. I said, "All right, we'll go ahead with that."

I wrote the Mission Profile for the shutdown and turn-on sequences, which together had 34 commands. Marcie and I checked it very carefully and then I faxed it to Bill to have him check it. He faxed it back and said everything was OK. Then we checked it again. Finally, just before 5:00 PM, we were ready.

I shut down the SES and the spectrometers by first turning off the GRS and NS high-voltages (at 294/20:33 MET), so the instruments would not be damaged and I watched the high-voltages bleed off as they were supposed to do. Then I turned off the SES at 294/20:37 MET. I watched everything for the standard 5 minutes to see if the turn-off had caused any problems with the spacecraft, especially with the power sub-system. Everything was OK, so I started the turn-on sequence by turning the SES back on at 294/20:42 MET. Again, I checked all the systems and at 294/20:48 MET, I had the command file, which contained 14 commands, uplinked that turned on all three spectrometers, but not the high-voltage supplies of the NS and GRS. That went well and the science data from the APS was normal, as were the engineering data from the SES and all three spectrometers. That being the case, I started turning on the NS and GRS high-voltage supplies and turning up the voltages, stepwise, to the operational values at 294/20:59 MET. The turn-on commanding was completed at 294/21:10 MET, 37 minutes after we had started commanding and all the spectrometers were churning out data in their normal fashions. The spectrometer mini-crisis was over and it was fun.

Later, Dan asked Marcie why he hadn't been informed about the spectrometer anomaly. I found that funny, because Lockheed had him believing — or he believed it on his own — that he had to be in on everything and that he was running the show, rather than me. It was the same thing that had happened when we had the problem with the tank heater/battery low voltage events six weeks earlier — he wanted to know why I hadn't had him at the battery meeting. I decided if he said anything to me directly, I would just say, "Dan, you weren't in the line of fire, so I didn't need you. I needed to talk to Gerry. I know you are interested, but I am not going to chase you down when I have other people I need to chase down."

Of course, I came home late, after a 13-hour day (gee, and Sylvia was concerned that I was never at Mission Ops). It was a long hard day, but it was fun finding the problem and getting everything back on line. However, I was disturbed the monitoring controllers had not noticed that all the spectrometers were out and I had to discover that obvious fact when I arrived at Mission Ops at 6:30 AM, once again, proving to Sylvia that what I had said in our conversation on the previous Thursday was true. Marcie's precious procedures do little good when the people who are supposed to follow them don't know what they are doing.

Thursday, October 29, 1998

Day 295 MET

I went up to Mission Ops in the morning. Everything was fine with the spectrometers. Bill wanted me to change the gain on Side 2 of the NS, which I did at 295/12:50 MET.

Monday, November 2, 1998

Day 299 MET

I went up to Ames and talked with Sylvia. Part of her concern about the extended mission financing was that she thought we only had $1.2 million, but it was really $2.2 million, which made it a lot easier.

I got the Mission Profile ready for Leonid reor. Dan checked it and I made the corrections and we were ready to go.

I went home to LRI and spent an hour on a phone interview, as well as time on numerous other calls.

Tuesday, November 3, 1998

Day 300 MET

I went up to Mission Ops to get some work done there and to get caught up on the historical records of the Mission Profile.

Dan was working on the viewgraphs for the Extended Mission Review that was set for the 10th. I considered the review a total waste of time, but Dan and Marcie thought it was very important and wanted all kinds of additional information in the viewgraphs. I said, "OK, just go ahead and do it, if you want to." It was not worth arguing about it, because Lockheed, Ames, and NASA only know one way of doing things and that was to have all kinds of superfluous detail — but that way, they felt like they were doing their jobs.

Wednesday, November 4, through Monday, November 9, 1998

Day 301 MET through Day 306 MET:
The NSS Board of Governors Meeting in Orlando

Rebecca and I flew to Florida Wednesday for a little vacation and to attend the National Space Society's Board of Governors meeting, since I had been asked to be a board member. We got there about 4:00 PM and stayed at the Hyatt in the Orlando Airport, where we also had a nice meal.

The next morning, we went to Epcot Center and had a great day. We had German food at the German pavilion and enjoyed all the attractions at Epcot. That evening we drove to the hotel in Coco Beach and got a good night's rest.

The next morning, Friday morning, we didn't do a lot of sightseeing, rather we went to the Dinosaur Shop where I bought a beautiful piece of amber from the Miocene (14 million years ago) with a fossilized bee, leafhopper, and beetle in it.

At 3:00 PM, the NSS activities started with a meeting of all the Governors who were there. Bruce Boxleitner, the actor from the Star Trek spin-off series, was there — without his actress wife, Melissa Gilbert, much to Rebecca's disappointment. We met Bob McCall, the famous artist from Phoenix, and Ed Finch, the Ambassador, and several other people. Of course, Pat Dasch, our good friend and the Executive Administrator of the NSS, was also there.

We then went to Spacehab, the company that did the processing of the Spacelab that went into to the Shuttle's equipment bay and the pallets that were used for resupply. The guy who ran the place, Shelly Harrison, ran it the same way I ran Lunar Prospector and, like I had done with Lunar Prospector, he had cut the costs to a tenth of what NASA would have spent on the same program. It turned out that Spacehab was the company that had bought Astrotech, so I had used their facilities to process Lunar Prospector for launch without knowing it.

Saturday morning, we were driven out to the VIP viewing stand to watch the Shuttle return from orbit. I saw Goldin, who didn't remember me, so I said, "I'm Alan Binder."

Goldin said, "Oh yeah, you're the guy taking us to the Moon."

After returning from watching the Shuttle land, we started the Board of Governors Meeting and discussed a number of NSS issues.

The second day, Sunday, I gave a talk on the mission, the history of Lunar Prospector, and how the NSS had helped with the mission from the beginning. I discussed my goal of starting the commercial exploration of the Moon, leading up to a commercial lunar base. Then Buzz Aldrin, the second man to walk on the Moon, talked about his Share Space Program that was meant to give the average American citizen a chance to ride in the Shuttle.

During Sunday afternoon, we had an open discussion and finally, the meeting broke up and people started drifting away, while some of us went to dinner. After that, Rebecca and I drove to the Orlando Airport again and stayed at the Hyatt for the night and then flew home Monday morning.

After arriving at San Jose, we drove to Mission Ops before going home. The Review Meeting was all set up, but Sylvia and the guys had turned the stupid meeting into a full-blown Review with 100 viewgraphs — it was sickening.

Tuesday, November 10, 1998

Day 307 MET: The Extended Mission Review Meeting

I woke up very early and went to work at 4:00 AM. I got caught up with the historical mission records, my email, and all that junk. Then the meeting started.

There were a good 30 people there! Al Schallenmuller and Chris Russell (from UCLA) were there, as was just about everybody who had even the slightest thing to do with the mission, including all the guys from the JPL/DSN tracking group, Dave Folta and one of his sidekicks from our Goddard Nav group, and, of course, Bob Lin and Bill Feldman from the Science Team. And to my surprise, the meeting was actually fun!

At 10:00 AM, Sylvia started the meeting. I talked about the science we had already achieved, what we would achieve during the low altitude mapping of the extended mission, and how well everything was going with the mission. Then Dan gave a good review of the spacecraft, followed by a talk by the Nav Team about the low altitude orbits.

When I started planning to fit the entire mission — nominal and extended — into the 22-month period between September 16, 1997 and July 28, 1999, that was free from umbral eclipses way back in early August of 1995, the mission was to end just before the July 28, 1999 eclipse. The whole rationale behind limiting the mission window to that umbral eclipse free period, was that I could build the spacecraft with a smaller battery and a less robust thermal system — thus saving money and mass. Lunar Prospector was not designed to survive the July 28 umbral eclipse. Nevertheless, rather than ending the mission on July 27, I wanted to attempt to get Lunar Prospector through the eclipse as a test of the spacecraft's engineering and end the mission a day later. Everyone thought that would be an excellent engineering exercise. If the spacecraft died during the eclipse, we would lose nothing, but if it survived, then we would learn valuable engineering information. I was pleased.

Everybody was really pleased with the whole mission and when they summed it up, Chris Russell said, "Well, we should say in the report that Alan and his team should be complimented for doing a great mission." All of them were appalled that NASA hadn't set aside the money for the extended mission and the data analysis. They were also going to write in the report that it was the official position of the Review Team that the money should be made available for the extended mission (Sylvia was still short $95,000) and for the data reduction and further that "this is a great mission; the team knows exactly what it is doing; the mission has been extremely well done; it is a perfect mission; and it is producing excellent results. Hence, all the Lunar Prospector Team can do is to get more and better science during the extended mission."

It was a long day. We didn't get done until well after 3:00 PM. Then I took everybody up to Mission Ops, which they loved, and I didn't get to leave until about 5:00 PM. It was a very successful day. Actually everybody said, "Wow, we had a great time. This was not really like a normal (boring) review. This was very good." I thought we would end up getting our money for the data analysis, as well as the money we needed for the extended mission, without any trouble.

Thursday, November 12, 1998

Day 309 MET

I went up early and watched the spacecraft and a heater event. I was quite annoyed because, when I got there, I saw that the heater was already on and the controllers didn't even know it. They just followed the instructions instead of looking to see if the tanks were heating up or if the load current had jumped up, indicating that a heater event was underway. We just didn't have the right people to watch the spacecraft and Marcie was no help at all, despite all her precious procedures crap.

Bill called and asked me to change the gain on the GRS again; so at 309/13:11 MET, I had the command uplinked to increase the GRS high-voltage to 1659 v.

Then I went home and worked on the proposal for the data analysis money.

Friday, November 13, 1998

Day 310 MET: The Final SIM

I woke up at 2:00 AM! I went up to Mission Ops, got everything ready to go for the SIM we were going to do and watched the spacecraft. Later, we did a SIM of the first couple of burns of the Leonid reor.

There was a big solar storm that saturated the spectrometers. But the GRS and NS had calmed down by the time I left for home and LRI, though the APS still had high counts.

Chapter 4-11
The Leonid Meteor Shower and the End of the Nominal Mission

Sunday, November 15, 1998

Early Day 312 MET through Early Day 313 MET:
The Leonid Reor and the Beginning of the Leonid Watch

In addition to rotating the spacecraft so its relatively insensitive butt was facing the incoming Leonid meteoroids, I was planning to stay at Mission Ops during the entire four days of the shower, except for sleeping at a nearby motel and eating at the Ames cafeteria, during which times Dan or Marcie would watch the spacecraft. That was necessary because if we got hit, there would not be enough time for the monitoring controllers (even if they noticed the spacecraft got hit) to call me in Gilroy and for me to get up to Mission Ops to try to save the spacecraft.

I got up very early Sunday morning and went up to Mission Ops. When I arrived, I got everything ready for our Leonid reor burn. Just before 7:00 AM, everyone was there and we were all set to go. At 312/11:35 MET, I had the commands uplinked to switch from the medium gain antenna to the omni antenna we would use during the entire Leonid Meteor Shower event. Then at 312/11:41 MET, I started commanding the reor sequence and finished with the engine safeing commands at 312/18: 20 MET, nearly 7 hours later.

Since the spin rate of the spacecraft had not increased above 12.07 rpm, I canceled the pre-planned tweak de-spin burn, so we were finished with the maneuver just before 3:00 PM. Though the long and complicated set of burns went very well (and was a lot of fun to do), Dan had made an error in calculating the gravity gradient effects, so we ended up about 8 degrees short of our 78° reor. But, since we had planned a tweak reor burn for the next day anyway, we would easily correct for the error at that time. Regardless of that minor blip, I was very pleased that the uplink crew and I worked so well during such a long commanding session — we had uplinked 69 commands, error free, as always.

Then I began the spacecraft Leonid Watch. A couple of hours later, during one of the 46 minute long radio occultation periods, I walked over to the McDonald's on Moffett Field, bought a hamburger, fries, and a coke for supper and got back to Mission Ops to eat my gourmet repast while sitting in front of my computer console — all before the spacecraft came out of occultation. I stayed there until nearly midnight and then I went to my nearby motel room for a couple of hours sleep.

Monday, November 16, 1998

Early Day 313 MET through Early Day 314 MET:
The First Full Day of the Leonid Watch and Rebecca's Birthday

I slept about three hours and was back at Mission Ops shortly after 3:00 AM to monitor the spacecraft and to occasionally go outside to look for Leonid Meteors (I didn't see any). I watched the spacecraft all day, getting lunch from the Ames lunch wagon that came around about noon.

Shortly before 5:00 PM, we got ready for the reor burn to correct for the 8° error in our attitude. Because of the interspersed nighttime passes and radio occultations, the 6 minute and 20 second pulsed reor burn sequence lasted nearly an hour — I started with the uplink of the heater turn-on command file at 313/20:56 MET and finished with the engine safeing commands at 313/21:49 MET. When it was over, we were within 1.2° of our target attitude — close enough.

I watched the heater events and one started exactly when the spacecraft came into the sunlight, so it was not necessary to turn off the transmitter — though had I not been there, the controllers would have done so, because they blindly followed the procedures. Since I didn't like having the transmitter turned off any more frequently than absolutely necessary, that had to come to an end, ASAP.

Rebecca came to Mission Ops and she and I went to Tony Roma's for a nice barbeque rib dinner to celebrate her birthday. After dinner, we went to the motel so I could get a few hours sleep.

Tuesday, November 17, 1998

Early Day 314 MET through Early Day 315 MET:
The Second Full Day of the Leonid Watch

I woke up really early — around 2:00 AM and went to Mission Ops. We had nearly a 3-hour break in tracking because other missions needed the tracking time.

I saw one beautiful Leonid meteor and a couple small ones, but there was nothing spectacular. I began to think that maybe the shower wasn't going to be very good.

I watched the spacecraft most of the day and, of course, nothing happened.

Rebecca went back down to Gilroy.

Wednesday, November 18, 1998

Early Day 315 MET through Early Day 316 MET:
The Third Full Day of the Leonid Watch

Since I was getting only about 3 hours sleep a night, I was beginning to get very tired. But I watched the spacecraft all day and we heard no reports of any really big meteor showers. It turned out that the maximum count over the Pacific was 1,000 counts per hour, which was no big deal.

Thursday Morning, November 19, 1998

Most of the Rest of Day 316 MET:
The Final Day of the Leonid Watch and the Reor Back to the Inverted Attitude

Finally, we were out of danger from the Leonids and there were no reports of any damage to any spacecraft. But like a good mother hen, I had watched over my little chick during its time of danger and, though I was really tired after having slept only 3 hours a night for the last four days, I had really enjoyed watching the spacecraft perform flawlessly during that entire period.

Then it was time to do the reor back to our nominal, inverted attitude. Like the Leonid reor four days earlier, the pulsed burns of the reor had to be broken up into segments, but because the timing was a little different, we could do the reor in four segments, rather than seven, and it took only 6 hours, instead of 7. I started the commanding at 316/13:56 MET, by having the A1 and A4 heater turn-on command file uplinked and finished at 316/17:38 MET by commanding the spacecraft to switch back to the medium gain antenna. Dan said that we were within 1.2° of our target attitude and our spin rate was OK, so I canceled the tweak reor and de-spin burns preplanned for that day, as well as the tweak reor planned for the next day, thus ending our Leonid activities.

I went home to Gilroy to finally get some rest.

Late Thursday, November 19, through Monday November 23, 1998

Late Day 316 MET through Day 320 MET: Albuquerque, Los Alamos, and Tucson

I flew to Albuquerque Thursday evening and then drove to a motel near Roger Lenard's home. I met him Friday morning at his house to further discuss our commercial lunar base plans.

I drove to Los Alamos to work with Bill and David Lawrence, who was doing most of the GRS data reduction for Bill and me, on the data reduction proposal and to discuss the data reduction itself. The GRS data analysis, especially the thorium and iron mapping, was coming along very nicely. After that, Bill and I discussed the APS data, which was in its earliest stage of analysis, and the fact that we saw no evidence of radon or polonium lines in the APS spectra.

I met Bill Saturday morning at about 8:00 AM to further discuss the APS. Then I drove down to Albuquerque and flew to good old Tucson to check on the progress being made with our house.

That evening, I went to our lot and it was all staked out. Then I went on a nice hike in the Saguaro National Monument just down the road from where our house was soon to be built.

Sunday, I went on a nice hike on my favorite trail in Sabino Canyon. Then I went back to the hotel, took a nap, watched the football game, and then met our niece and nephew and their son (Debbie, Doug, and Luke), for dinner at a great Mexican restaurant.

Monday, I met with our architects, Matt North and Jay Hanson. In order to keep the costs of the house down, Matt suggested that his dad, Bill North, who builds houses for labor and materials, do it. That sounded good to me, but it would mean that, rather than our having a house to move into when we moved to Tucson after mission's end in July 1999, the house would not even be started until June 1999. That would also mean that we would have to live in an apartment for several months and store most of our household goods, while the house was being built, but the cost saving made it worth it.

I stopped at the university to see Lon about the data reduction proposal we were writing and to talk about the MAG data he was working on.

I went to the University of Arizona Science and Technology Park to get the keys to our (empty) office and the mailbox and then I got my badge — the first LRI badge, LRI 001. When Rebecca got her badge it would be LRI 002 and Wayne's would be LRI 003.

I really enjoyed getting our Tucson LRI office started — even if it was empty, it was the beginning!

Finally, I went to the airport and flew home.

Tuesday, November 24, 1998

Day 321 MET

I went up to Mission Ops to checkout the spacecraft and to get caught up with everything. The situation with the battery/tank heater events had improved since the duration of the nighttime passes was down to 39 minutes and would soon be below 38 minutes as β continued to increase towards 90°. I felt we didn't need to turn the transmitter off any more and so did Dan. To be sure of that, I watched the heater event that had come up. The tank heaters turned on about 20 minutes before the spacecraft went into the nighttime pass. The DOD went down to 70% at the end of the 39-minute nighttime pass and then the battery got completely recharged and started to trickle charge about 5 minutes before the spacecraft went into the next nighttime pass — and the heaters turned off at about the same time. It was clear from that heater event that we did not need to turn the transmitter off anymore, since the nighttime passes were short enough to prevent a red limit/low voltage event. That is to say, we would not have to turn the transponder off and on again until the nighttime passes again got long enough to cause a problem during the next β angle cycle, i.e., during the extended mission, when the problem would be exacerbated by the longer nighttime passes and shorter daytime passes we would have in the lower orbit.

In addition to the shorter nighttime passes, the tank heater on-time had decreased because of the decrease in the fuel resulting from the burns we made during the flip and the Leonid reors. The on-time had decreased by about 6 minutes for every kilogram of fuel that we used. Dan and I decided to burn off 3 to 4 kg of excess fuel in a fuel dump burn and we would use a couple of kilograms getting down to the 25 km altitude, extended mission mapping orbit. We thought that the heater on-time would be less than the orbital period of 1 hour and 51 minute when we were down at 25 kilometers. I was glad of that and that we could stop turning the transmitter off, because the controllers simply never understood when it was necessary to turn the transmitter off and hence, they were doing it far too many times. It was a sorry state, if you asked me.

Wednesday, November 25, through Saturday, November 28, 1998

Day 322 MET through Day 325 MET: Thanksgiving Vacation at Point Reyes

Wednesday morning, Rebecca and I first went to Mission Ops to check on the spacecraft, which was fine. Dan and I watched a heater event and it went off without any problem. Both Dan and I fully agreed we didn't need to turn the transmitter off any more — so we stopped that nonsense.

Rebecca and I went up to Berkeley to see David Mitchell and Bob Lin about the MAG/ER data and the data analysis proposal we were writing.

After that, we drove to the Point Reyes Seashore Lodge, one of our most favorite hotels in the world, for Thanksgiving.

Thursday, we had Thanksgiving dinner at a fancy restaurant across from the hotel, but the food wasn't too great, given that it was Thanksgiving Day. Nevertheless, we enjoyed ourselves immensely — we rested and hiked and had a great time. It is a wonderful hotel and Point Reyes is a wonderful place to visit.

We drove home Saturday, but, of course, we stopped in at Mission Ops so I could check on my beloved spacecraft — which was fine.

Monday, November 30, 1998

Day 327 MET

I went to Mission Ops and the spacecraft was happy. Dan and I talked about the fuel dump burn. We decided we should probably just burn off 2 kg, because there was about a kilogram uncertainty in the amount of fuel in the tanks, with one of them possibly having a kilogram more than in the other two. As a result, if we burned off 4 kg, as we had originally wanted to do, that would leave just over 1 kg in each tank at the end of the mission and we could end up venting helium pressurant during the last burns — not a good thing. We thought we would keep a little margin for the end of the mission. We were both in total agreement about the fuel dump burn and the need for it.

Wednesday, December 2, 1998

Day 329 MET

I went up to Mission Ops early and the spacecraft was fine. The ER guys wanted to get some high-resolution data on a specific area of the Moon, so Dave Curtis had sent me two commands that would set up the ER for what they called the "burst mode." The first command set up the ER for the burst mode and the second told the ER when to collect the high-resolution data. I got the Mission Profile ready and had the two commands uplinked at 329/13:30 MET and 329/13:35 MET, respectively. That done, the ER would collect 12 minutes of high-resolution data at about 9:30 PM or about 330/01:00 MET.

I talked to Sylvia and she said everything was going quite well at Headquarters — the paperwork was getting done, so we could do the extended mission as we had presented it to the review committee.

After that, Dan and I talked about doing the fuel dump burn Friday. Then Marcie called and said, "You can't do it (the fuel dump). It's unacceptable to do it, we don't have everything properly planned yet."

The stupid bitch! There was nothing to plan; Dan and I could do that burn in our sleep. All I had to do was to write up the Mission Profile and we were ready to go. Though Marcie is too dumb to understand it, the burn would have no significant effect on the spacecraft's orbit, spin rate, or attitude — it would just burn fuel. However, in her typical NASA way, she wanted a meeting to discuss what she did not understand. I said, "OK, let's have a telecon tomorrow," in the expectation that would shut the stupid bitch up.

David Gump called and said we had a meeting in DC with the President of the *National Geographic* on Friday the 18th. That being the case, I also set up a meeting with Alan Ladwig and I started trying to get one with Joe Rothenberg.

When I got to LRI, Maryann called and said LRI had taken more money out of the contract than was in there. I had no idea what she was talking about, so I said I would see her the next day to find out what the problem was.

Thursday, December 3, 1998

Day 330 MET: Much Ado About Nothing — Times Two

Apparently I had underestimated Marcie's ability to stir up trouble and get Sylvia and Lockheed worked up to a fever pitch over nothing, as well as Dan's intense desire to kiss up to Lockheed every chance he had — at my expense. As a result, December 3 was a day of great aggravation and increased my hatred of certain NASA and Lockheed personnel — and those two institutions themselves — to new heights.

We had the telecon with Lockheed Marcie was whining about in the morning and it really pissed me off, because it was the same crap as usual. Debrock, who had taken over Lockheed's management of the mission from Dougherty and who is even dumber than Dougherty (if that is possible) was highly concerned that I was doing something (that he had absolutely no understanding of) to risk the mission and asked. "Why risk anything when we are this close (to the end of the nominal mission)?" All he and Lockheed cared about was their damned $4 million fee. I tried to explain to the idiot that burning off a couple of kilograms of fuel would reduce the risk to the mission caused by our having to turn the transponder off and that firing the engines was something we did all the time, but to no avail. Everyone was up in arms.

Marcie admitted she didn't understand anything about the fuel dump, but was nevertheless against it because it was a "big risk." Sylvia, of course, had no concept of it all, but because Marcie said it was a "big risk," she just followed along. Dan, who well knew that what I was planning was no more risky than any other engine firing we did and that reducing the heater on-time by dumping fuel would reduce the risk to the mission caused by having to turn the transponder off and on so often during the extended mission, sided with Debrock, i.e., sided with Lockheed, as he always did when it would get him brownie points with Lockheed.

I carefully went through all the arguments about the real risk we had, i.e., turning the damned transmitter off and on, and that depleting the fuel to get the heater on-time down would reduce the number of times we would have to do that during the extended mission. When the telecon ended, no one could find any real reason for me not to proceed, so Sylvia reluctantly said, "Well, apparently everybody here (at Ames) agrees to do it, because there are no real arguments against it."

I said, "OK, let's get this thing planned."

But she said, "I don't think Debrock agrees."

I said, "So what."

Sylvia said, "Well, he's concerned about his fee and he's concerned we are so close to the end of mission that we shouldn't do anything risky."

I reminded her, "I'm directing this mission, not Debrock, and I really don't care about Lockheed and its damned fee. I care about getting this mission done right and getting the science done, but if it will make you feel better, I will go talk to Debrock."

She said, "Yes, that would be good."

I drove over to Lockheed, but when I got there, Debrock was in a meeting until 11:00 AM, so I went and talked to Maryann. I had my laptop with all the LRI payment records with me, so when she said, "You've been overpaid," I was ready.

I said, "Well, let's see." We compared her records and mine, and it was clear that LRI had received the correct amounts of money every month. Then she checked Lockheed's records and it turned out that Lockheed had double booked the August check! They had paid LRI $14,972 and then their records showed they had issued the same check (or the same check number) again, but we had neither received nor cashed a second check, otherwise Maryann's records would show a $14,972 deficit! It was Lockheed's error and their problem; they would have to find out if they really did issue a second check and find out where it was, if they had done so. What a company!

Debrock wasn't back at 11:00, so I went and found him and he said he would be out of his meeting in a few minutes. I said I would have lunch and meet him after that.

After a quick hamburger at the Building 107 cafeteria, Debrock was finally in his office and Bob Garner joined us. Of course, Lockheed can't have a one-on-one discussion; they have to have two, three, or more against one. I said to Debrock, "I understand you have some questions about my dumping the fuel."

He said, "Yes," and thus began a long and aggravating conversation.

I explained to him in detail the reasons for my doing the fuel dump. Not understanding a thing I said, he said, "This is a big risk you're taking. This is a risk to the mission when we are almost finished. Why risk the mission when we are within a few weeks of being done? If something goes wrong, it would hurt Lockheed's reputation and we could lose our fee (that was BS, Lockheed already had almost all of its fee by that time in the mission). Dan told me he didn't see any reason for you to do this and it is a risky thing." Either Debrock was lying, since Dan and I had been in total agreement about the burn when we discussed it Monday, or Dan had played on Debrock's stupidity and fears to gain brownie points for himself. I was not pleased with Dan's absolute lack of character, despite the fact that he is a very good — and a very smart — young engineer.

Debrock asked, "Why can't you wait until after the nominal mission is over and do it just before or just after you are down in the low orbit?"

I answered, "As long as we are at 100 km, the small perturbations caused by the burn are of no consequence, but if we do it just before lowering the orbit to 40 km or after we are down at 40 km, then the perturbations do make a big difference. The Nav guys don't want us doing anything within 3 days of the burns to lower the orbit. Also, this is the appropriate period to do the dump — we are in an occultation free period and we don't want to do maneuvers except during the occultation free periods." Despite his not understanding them, Debrock argued about those points and then he brought up Dan's supposed concerns again.

I was starting to get annoyed, but I was being polite. I said, "Look, I have a lot of respect for Dan, but Dan doesn't know everything about this mission."

He again said, "We can't have bad PR."

I said, "Well, you have already had bad PR because of Dan," and I told him about the 3rd LOI burn confrontation and the fact the press jumped all over me because we hadn't gone down all the way to the circular orbit and said we didn't know how to run our spacecraft — so I got my point across.

Debrock replied, "Well, we are not saying Dan is your equivalent in any way."

I thought, *yeah, BS; then why do you bastards ask Dan to report every time I go to the bathroom?* But I did say, "Look, I don't work for you. You guys work for me. If you look at the contract, you will find that you work under my direction, not the reverse," a point that they would not acknowledge. I then said, "This is my mission. I designed it. I understand it. What you guys are doing is throwing up hypothetical problems and basing your decisions on the lack of knowledge and panic. I don't work that way."

Finally, after some more discussion, Debrock understood all the reasons and he understood I was mitigating problems that would come up in the extended mission. Garner then said to Debrock, "Well, you know, the (nominal) mission isn't over until the 6th (of January), but we're already going down (to 40 km) on the 19th (of December), so we are already in transition." Still trying to protect his damned company, Debrock asked Bob, "Can't we make NASA say the transition starts when we do this fuel dump?"

Bob answered, "They aren't going to buy that."

Still not willing to give up, Debrock said to me, "But your team doesn't like this?"

I replied, "I don't really care what my team likes or doesn't like. This is my mission; I understand it and they don't. I don't take the advice of people who don't understand the spacecraft or the mission or the science and I don't take a vote on how to do things with people who don't understand what's going on. Besides, when the telecon was over, everyone at Ames was in agreement with the dump, but Sylvia said you were not in agreement, so it's not my team, it's you and no one else."

Debrock was still was not going to give up unless NASA gave Lockheed a waive and he said, "OK, if NASA will make sure we are not in any trouble if something goes wrong and blah, blah, blah."

He called Sylvia and she said, "We are in agreement with what Alan is doing."

Still not finished, Debrock said, "Well, I guess we're ready to do it, if Dan doesn't have any objections."

I said, "Fine, let's get Dan in here right now."

I wanted to have Dan in there right then, right in front of me, so Dan could not tell Debrock any more BS behind my back and stick the knife in any deeper than he already had. Dan was call to Debrock's office and then Debrock summarized what I had said for Dan's benefit — I always hate it, when some idiot like Debrock tries to tell someone else what I have said, especially when they hardly understand any of it. Then he said, "Alan wanted to make sure you are in agreement with the fuel dump." What a bunch of BS, I didn't give a damn if Dan was in agreement or not, I just wanted Dan to know I had caught him in his little spiel and I expected him to keep his mouth shut from then on. Debrock asked Dan if there were any technical reason for not doing the fuel dump.

Dan answered, "No, there are no technical reasons for not doing it."

Then Debrock asked Dan, "Are you in total agreement with it?"

Dan answered, "No."

Surprised, Debrock asked, "You're not in agreement with this?" and added, "I don't understand — you just said you had no technical reason against doing it. Why are you objecting to doing it?"

Dan showed his true colors by answering, "I'm concerned about the managerial considerations," i.e., the SOB was worried about his ass-kissing at Lockheed.

But Debrock said, "No, don't worry about that. Is there any technical reason?"

Dan then answered, "Oh no, of course not. Alan is totally correct. There is nothing wrong with this. It's the right thing to do and he's doing it the right way."

That really pissed me off, the little weasel had done just what he did when we were getting ready for the 3rd LOI burn, the SOB was putting his personal interests at Lockheed ahead of the mission and was panicking over a contrived managerial problem. I was totally disgusted with Dan and his behavior — despite his technical competence, Dan had shown me too many times he could not be trusted.

After leaving Lockheed, I went back to Ames to look for Sylvia. I heard Marcie's shrill voice, followed it, and found Marcie and Sylvia were in Bob Jackson's office. Bob, who is Marcie's boss, Sylvia, and Marcie were talking about the events of the day. I went in and sat down.

As I did, Sylvia said, "Come on in, we want to talk to you."

Bob, who is very good and very experienced and one of the people at Ames I really respect, said, "I know you don't want to hear this, but we are very concerned that you are not properly communicating with your team and with Lockheed and NASA about what you are doing." He had a very stern look on his face and he was trying to be very serious.

I didn't respond to his statement in any way. He said something else in the same tone as I was thinking, *what in hell am I supposed to say to this BS? Where do I start telling him what a bunch of idiots I have to work with? Which of my tirades does he want to hear?* But basically, I said, "OK, I understand you guys feel that way, but that's not the real problem. What this really boils down to is that Marcie is, as usual, in a panic. She is worried about the extended mission, because she does not understand what is going on and she wants things done the way she is used to — the NASA way — and I won't do them that way. There is never enough coordination or communication for her. And now she's got Sylvia worried over nothing."

I enjoyed the ensuing conversation very much, because I got to lay out all my issues to someone who would actually listen. Then I gave him my usual speech, "Here is how I view this. This was my mission. NASA gave me the responsibility to do it and I'm doing it in the Discovery mode. It's being done so NASA can learn how to do things in a better way — in more efficient and more cost effective ways. And I have done that — we're flying a nearly perfect mission and this has worked extremely well. The thing that annoys me is this began fairly well — in the sense that NASA left me alone and let me do my job as they said they were going to do in the beginning. But that has been eroding all the time and NASA is going back to the old way of doing things where NASA has control of everything and everything has to be done by committee, just like now. This morning we had a big telecon that accomplished nothing — as usual. I don't work that way. This was set up with me in charge. That was the way it was supposed to be done and all I see is that everything is just getting worse and worse."

When I got done, my voice showed just how annoyed I was. Bob had listened to everything I said and his tenor changed completely. He said, "I agree with you in many ways and with 95% of what you have said." I was floored! Then he said, to my astonishment, *"I consider that the way NASA has treated you is absolutely inexcusable and shabby."* He continued with, *"Your concerns were the same concerns a lot of people have and you are right. The whole Discovery program has been screwed up; it has gone away from what it was supposed to be doing and I'm very concerned and very annoyed about that.* But, the thing is, we work for NASA and we have responsibilities to NASA and we have to do what NASA requires. What we have to do is certainly opposite to what you want to do."

I said, "Of course, I understand that. Clearly you guys have different ways of doing things than I do. You guys are trapped by the system."

Bob said, "Yes."

Marcie started blabbing about her concerns — she needed schedules and procedures to feel secure in what she was doing. She complained, "We don't have meetings, we don't have enough communication."

I replied, "This is my mission and this is the way I am doing it — I don't have meetings, I go talk to the individual I need information from or who needs to know something. I don't need a room full of people to get things done. My experience, and the way I view the world, is that the more people in a room, the less gets done and the

ALAN BINDER

less happens." Bob agreed emphatically with that. In fact, they all kind of agreed, but of course, that isn't the world Marcie lives in. She just couldn't let go of her NASA world.

But Bob said, "Nevertheless, I'm concerned because you announced the fuel dump burn with very little warning and nobody knew what was going on, but all of a sudden, it was happening."

I said, "Bob, look let me explain something to you. I know my spacecraft. I designed it and in a certain sense, I built it. I know everything about it. I wrote the manuals. I wrote the procedures. I wrote everything about the spacecraft. The only person who even knows anything about the spacecraft besides me is Dan Swanson. When Dan and I talk about something and we agree, as far as I am concerned, it's a done deal."

Bob said, "OK, but that leads to you getting lax with time."

I replied, "No, quite the contrary, Bob. The team has become sharper and sharper. We do the commanding by the book. We have procedures I laid out and we follow them so strictly that if I don't say exactly the same words every time, Dan tells me I didn't say exactly what I always say. We are sharper and better than we ever were."

Marcie said, "Yes, that is quite true."

Bob said, "I'm surprised at that, because usually, it's the other way around."

I responded, "Well, not on my mission, Bob."

I said, "There are different levels of complexity in the commanding of the spacecraft and let me go through them. Clearly, an orbital maintenance burn is a very serious thing, because we are changing the orbit, and I want everybody on exactly the same page. I want everything done exactly according to the procedures I have laid out. We have all four controllers in there and follow the procedures exactly every time. Also Bob, our checking and verification procedures are so strict that we have never, ever sent a wrong spacecraft command to the spacecraft. The other end of the spectrum is when I am commanding a gain change for an instrument. It is a trivial thing; if it's done wrong, it doesn't hurt anything. I don't feel like bringing in four people in and having a big discussion about one simple command. In the beginning, when we were doing that, we made a couple of mistakes, but the procedures have gotten tighter and we haven't made a mistake in months. This particular burn, the fuel dump, is so benign that I don't consider it to be of any concern at all. It is a matter of just going in and doing it and getting it done and not making a big deal about it. That is my decision, not Marcie's or anybody else's. It is my decision as to when I need the full team involved and not, and it's irrelevant to me whether anyone agrees or not. This is my responsibility and I am telling you this maneuver is of no consequence. There is nothing that can happen to this spacecraft because of it. There is nothing that can happen to the orbit. It is a small event and it is simply so far down in the pecking order that it does not deserve any of the attention it is getting. It has gotten completely blown out of proportion by you guys and Lockheed — it's benign." Bob accepted that and the fact that I knew enough about the spacecraft to run it properly, that I was the PI and hence, that it was my decision, whether they liked it or not. That finally finished that part of the conversation.

But Marcie said from her standpoint, everything had been getting worse and worse. I said, "I would like to understand why you have these concerns about the meetings and getting everything done three or four days in advance? First of all, I thought we were doing this most of the time. On the other side of the coin, there have been times when I haven't been given the information early enough, too. There was at least one time when I was given the information I needed so I could do the Mission Profile one hour before we were supposed to do the burn. I don't like that either, but that happens every once in a while. The point is that we have had no problems. Everything has been working fine. So what is the problem?"

Marcie answered, "But there is so much more to do" (in the extended mission).

I replied, "Marcie, as far as I am concerned, all the stuff you do is useless. You follow NASA procedures. But this mission is about doing things differently, without all the wasted effort. Let me give you an example. All the documentation we did at Lockheed (during Phase B and C/D) was of no use. We did it because the damned review committee said they wanted to see certain documents signed off. Both Dougherty and I had the stupid documents written, but we never looked at them, we never read them, we just signed them off. They had no effect. Nobody ever used them. It was a sheer waste of time, but the review committee was happy because they saw a stack of signed documents! Similarly, everything you have put on my desk and all the things you want from me, are of no use to anybody. I'm the one who knows how to run the spacecraft. I'm the one who has the procedures in my head. Everything you have asked me to do — because you want all this stuff written down — serves no purpose. I'm not saying that what you've asked me to do is useless from your standpoint. What I am saying is I was given the responsibility by NASA to run the mission my way, not your way or NASA's way."

Marcie asked, "Do you mean you don't think I do anything useful?"

I answered emphatically, "That is exactly right."

I got a little more general, "The point is, we are trying to find new ways of doing missions and you guys are dragging me back to the old NASA way. You guys have to realize I am not crabbing about the mission or the science, they were never the objectives. Lunar Prospector was always about how to do things right. That is what I was asked to do. That is what the Discovery program is all about. I'm trying to do that and all that is happening now that we are successful, is that NASA is mad because I am not doing it NASA's way. NASA can't stand my doing the mission my way. When Scott and I were on the same side of the fence, both Scott and I were annoyed with the fact that, there we were doing the mission properly — it was on time, on budget, and there were no questions about the spacecraft in terms of its development, and yet NASA said it was never going to do a mission that way again. Here we are, we have a perfect mission, as perfect as you can get, and all that is happening is that everybody is bitching about it. Nobody looks at the fact that it's working perfectly the way I'm doing it. Just leave me alone and let me do my job."

The discussion was finally winding down, so I reminded them, "Before launch, everyone said the mission was going to be so hard and we were going to have all kinds of problems. I never believed that. I knew this would be an easy spacecraft to fly because I designed it that way and I never agreed with all these criticisms and concerns. It has been exactly the way I said it would be and I will tell you right now, eight months from now, when we are done with the extended mission, it will have been just as easy to do as the nominal mission was. We understand what we are doing and the spacecraft does what it is supposed to. This is all just a tempest in a teapot and you guys are just getting into a panic about nothing."

Sylvia and Marcie said somewhat defensively, "We're just concerned. You're probably correct and there probably is no issue, but we're just concerned, that's our jobs," to which I thought, *well BS*.

The second long discussion was finally over and I went up to Mission Ops and called Dan, who came over so we could get everything ready for the fuel dump the next day. I told Marcie I wanted to get the fuel dump done the next day and she said, "Well, let me call Goddard to see if they are going to be around."

They were going to be there, so I said, "OK, we will do it tomorrow."

Sylvia said that she would check with Cathcart (why, I did not know) and let Debrock know.

Hearing that, I asked, "Are we going to get bogged down again?"

She said, "Just go ahead and do it, unless you hear differently from me."

She sent Debrock an email and, of course, kiss-ass Dan had called him, too. When Dan did, Debrock wanted to see him. I thought, *oh no, that's trouble.* I found that Sylvia had gone home by that time, so I called Sylvia at home and said, "Call Debrock and make sure you tell him about this."

I went to Marcie's office to give her the Mission Profile for the dump and we chatted a little bit. It was kind of interesting, because she said, "I feel I can talk with you about this, because we really do communicate. I want you to know I'm just as proud of this mission as you are and that's why I come to all the burns. I know I serve no purpose there, but I like being there and I hope my being there might be useful if something happened, but I realize I have really nothing to do." Then she said, "Even though I disagree with what you say when we have a discussion like we had, in reality when you're not around and I get into discussions with other people about this, I defend everything you are trying to do." I was surprised, but it was a good conversation.

Friday, December 4, 1998

Day 331 MET: The Infamous Fuel Dump

At 8:00 AM we were ready to do the fuel dump. The procedure was to fire both the T1 and T2 engines simultaneously, so the spin-up effect of the T2 engine would cancel out the spin-down effect of the T1 engine — except for the slight imbalances in their thrust levels and the slight engine misalignments — for periods of time exactly equal to 7 spin periods, i.e., about 35 seconds (the maximum period we could fire the tangential engines with one computer load was 36 seconds). That way, the fuel dump burns would affect the orbit by the least amount. Then we would do a spin trim burn to get the spin rate back to 12 rpm, if necessary.

I started the procedure by having the file to turn on the T1 and T2 engine heaters uplinked at 331/11:52 MET. Then at 331/11:53 MET, I uplinked the first master engine parameter file and I executed the first, 34.797 sec burn at 331/12:18 MET. Dan noted the slight change in the spin period, calculated the new burn-time based on the new spin rate and I uplinked the new, 34.398 sec burn-time. Then I executed the second burn. We repeated that procedure two more times and then we were finished with the fuel dump — having burned 1.8 kg of fuel. Then Dan prepared the engine parameter file for the despin burn on T1 we needed to perform, since, as expected, the spin period rate had increased to 12.8 rpm. We did a 2.41 sec despin burn at 331/13:06 MET and the engines were safed at 331/13:08 MET. After having spent nearly a full day fighting with Lockheed and Ames, the fuel dump lasted just 1 hour and 16 minutes! That was also the last burn of the nominal mission, which was rapidly coming to its end.

As soon as we were finished, Dan quickly and uncharacteristically snuck into my office (he did not have an office in Mission Ops — he just used mine when necessary). As I walked into my office, he, with a "the cat who was caught eating the canary" look on his face was trying to call Garner to tell him the burn went well. But Garner was not in, so he had to call Debrock in my presence and tell Steve that everything went OK. I thoroughly enjoyed watching Dan squirm in embarrassment, as he had to tell his mommy that everything was OK in front of me — it was good for the bastard. Despite all the BS surrounding the fuel dump, it was fun — as were all burns.

I asked Dan to stay to do a SIM, the last one we had to do to fulfill my contractual obligations, but he said no because he had to get back to Lockheed — he had a lot of work to do. However, when I told him a film crew was coming to film the SIM, all of a sudden, his work at Lockheed was not important and he could stay (I chuckled to myself about his sudden change of heart).

Then the film crew came to film the SIM, so they would have some film that looked like a real burn. It was a blast. It took them quite a bit of time to get set up and we had trouble getting the SIM going. Finally they got their cameras rolling, but then it was time for lunch. They wanted to buy us lunch, so they sent someone to McDonald's to get some hamburgers and fries, but it took the guy almost an hour to get lunch and get back.

Finally we got going. It was amazing because when we finished it up, they applauded! Then they wanted to know if they could get another take. Dan had to go, so we did it again with Troy sitting at Dan's console. Then they wanted another take and finally they were done and that was also the end of the SIMs. Then they did a long interview with me and finally they left.

I left Mission Ops at about 4:00 PM and drove home. That evening, Rebecca and I went to dinner at the Cutting Horse Restaurant in San Juan Bautista for our 4th anniversary.

Tuesday, December 8, 1998

Day 335 MET: Another Guenter Visit

NASA had agreed with our extended mission plan and we were ending the nominal mission about three weeks early. We were going down to 40 km altitude on December 19. I went in early and got the Mission Profile for the 19th finished and ready to go.

Then Guenter arrived for his site visit. It was a typical stupid, useless site visit. I was amazed at just how dumb Guenter is. He couldn't follow anything we told him and he remembered everything incorrectly. It is sad that many of the people who run NASA programs have no technical skills.

In addition to my having to put up with Guenter, Scott came over to the meeting, just to put in an appearance — the pompous, fat little prick made me want to puke.

A few days earlier, Bob Lin had told me they were putting up a tracking antenna at Berkeley to track another mission they were doing and that the German tracking facilities, which were already tracking Lunar Prospector for their own purposes, were also available for tracking. Bob had the idea that, after we had completed the extended mission in July 1999, Berkeley and Germany could track Lunar Prospector for another six months. That way, Bob could get additional high-resolution ER measurements after the mission was officially over at very little cost.

Prior to Bob's suggestion, I had always planned to de-orbit Lunar Prospector at the end of the mission and cause it to crash at some predetermined place. There were two reasons for doing that: First, no matter what we did, the lunar gravity perturbations would eventually cause Lunar Prospector to crash, and second, since it was going to crash anyway, we could get some additional information about the Moon by crashing it in the right place. Bob's proposal gave me an alternate way of getting more data from the spacecraft after the end of the mission.

I told Guenter we could put Lunar Prospector in a frozen orbit (an orbit with a specific initial eccentricity, inclination, and mean altitude that responds to the gravity perturbations in a cyclic way and is therefore stable) and if Berkeley wanted to track it, all we would have to do was to find the little bit of money needed to get the data tapes put into the archives, so we could get some nearly free science. To my amazement, he asked, "What's the advantage of all this?" I tried to explain to him more about the science windfall and the fact that the frozen orbit would take us very low over the North Pole, so we could get even higher resolution NS mapping data on the water ice deposits. Again to my amazement, Guenter said, in a disinterested tone, "I don't really see a zinger here."

I replied, "I have a perfectly functioning spacecraft and rather than just crash it, we can get six more months of data from it at essentially no cost!"

Guenter responded, "Well NASA is really concerned about its image and that there is no negative PR."

I asked, "What could be negative about using a fully functioning spacecraft to get free data?"

He answered, "Something could go wrong."

What an idiot and what a bunch of idiots at Headquarters! At Headquarters, out of fear, the glass is always half empty, it's never half full! Their first questions asked about everything are always, "What are the drawbacks?" and "What could go wrong?" I was so disgusted with him that I could have spit nails.

Dan got up and clacked about the spacecraft. Dan was trying to explain how we calculated the remaining propellant using his model and my model. Guenter could not follow what Dan was saying and asked, in a confused tone, "You say you use the pressure and temperature to compute the amount of fuel remaining?" Dan tried again to explain, but it was useless.

Finally Marcie got up and, just like a typical NASA person and just like Dougherty, she went through her viewgraphs she really didn't understand, so she got more and more muddled. Despite the fact that she became less and less clear and more and more incoherent, Guenter just sat there, writing her crap down, assuming it meant something. But since he did not understand anything anyway, what difference did it make if his notes did not mean anything either? What a joke!

Wednesday December 9, through Friday, December 11, 1998

Day 336 MET through Day 338: Another Trip to DC to See National Geographic

I flew to Washington on the 9th. I spent the night at Pat and Julius's and we had a good time chatting, though Pat was ill.

Thursday morning, I had an appointment to see Rothenberg, the Associate Administrator for Manned Space Flight, but he had been called to another meeting, so I met with one of his staff. He wasn't the right guy to talk to, so the meeting was a waste of time.

After leaving NASA, I went to LunaCorp to meet with David in preparation for our meeting with *National Geographic*. David was concerned because the President of *National Geographic* had bowed out of the meeting! Jeff Hughes, from Rotary Rocket, was there and we got acquainted. Jeff, David, a Japanese astronomer from Goddard, and I were going to represent LunaCorp and LRI at the *National Geographic* meeting. I was concerned about that, because I don't like meetings with four or five people, they are ineffective.

By that time it was lunchtime, so I went to lunch with David and Jim Dunstan, the lawyer who works with David, and then David and I went to see Alan Ladwig back at

NASA Headquarters. The meeting with Alan went perfectly. I did most of the talking, but David is no slouch and did well too. We told Alan what our commercial programs were and I said what was needed was a data purchase program funded at, at least, the $200 million level per year. Alan liked the whole idea.

Thursday evening, David, Jeff, and I went to dinner together and we had a good time discussing Rotary Rocket and Lunar Prospector.

Friday morning, we had breakfast together and then we went to *National Geographic* and had a very good meeting. Unfortunately, the President's attitude, as related to us, was that *National Geographic* is supposed to concentrate on the Earth and how to save the Earth ecologically. Thus his question to us was, "What does lunar research have to do with the Earth?"

We all answered, "Everything!" and then ran through the numerous examples of how the future utilization of resources and power from the Moon could relieve the Earth from the pollution caused by power production, mining, and industry.

When we were done with our long list of possibilities, they said, "That's really good. Now we can tell the President this is really important." Thus ended what we thought was a very good meeting.

Dave took me to the airport, where I had lunch as I waited for my plane. Finally I got home to end a long, but a good trip.

Tuesday, December 15, 1998

Day 342 MET

I worked on the proposal for the data reduction money.

We had our planning meeting for the burn down to the 40 km altitude orbit we were going to do on Saturday the 19th.

I commanded a GRS gain change — *the last science commands of the nominal mission* — at 342/14:22.

I got everything ready to go to a meeting in Idaho.

The disgusting, immoral President Clinton was about to be impeached.

Wednesday, December 16, and Thursday, December 17, 1998

Day 343 MET and Day 344 MET: A Useless Meeting at the DOE in Idaho Falls

Wednesday morning, I went to Mission Ops to see how the spacecraft was doing and then I flew up to Idaho Falls. Anthony Zuppero, a Department of Energy employee, had set up the meeting in an effort to try to get some money out of their director for a study of a nuclear rocket that would use water — the lunar ice water that we had discovered — as fuel. The idea being that, by using such rockets and the lunar water for fuel, it would be economically feasible to start using the Moon to provide energy for the Earth. In the shorter term, Anthony hoped the DOE would be interested in buying commercially available data — data David and I could supply — on the Moon to further those longer-term goals.

When I got to the DOE, I found that they were the most disorganized bunch I had ever seen. They had six of us come — David Gump, three guys I didn't know, Stu Nozette (unfortunately), and me.

We had some very interesting debates on Thursday. Then their director came to the meeting and the conservatism of the higher ups is always amazing. He didn't know anything about the Moon, the water ice, power satellites, lunar power, lunar resources, etc. But we did some good for Anthony.

I flew home, got in very late and found I had received word that I was a semi-finalist in the *Discover Awards* given by the *Discover* magazine — I had a chance of winning $100,000!

Friday, December 18, 1998

Day 345 MET: The Last Full Day of the Nominal Mission

I went up to Mission Ops in the morning and worked on the proposal for the data reduction money. It was almost done; the only things missing were Bill's technical discussion and his budget.

I checked to see that everything was ready for the burn the next day and that the spacecraft was OK, since Saturday was the big, historic day when the nominal mission was over — when we burned down to 40 kilometers, and later, even closer.

Chapter 4-12
Transition to the Extended Mission and a Critical Penumbral Eclipse

Saturday, December 19, 1998

Day 346 MET: Impeachment and the Burn to 40 km

Two great events marked the day. First, President Clinton, who had disgraced the Presidency, lied to the American public, and almost certainly did a lot more that would have gotten any executive in the country removed from his position and probably put in jail, was happily impeached by the House on two counts. Though it was doubtful the Senate would convict Clinton, if there were any justice in the world, Clinton would be removed from office and NASA would be forced to reform, but — .

Second, 346 days, 14 hours and 46 minutes after spacecraft turn-on, or just 18 days, 9 hours and 14 minutes before the originally contracted end of the one-year nominal mission, I fired the A3 and A4 engines — an act that operationally ended the nominal mission and began the extended mission of low altitude mapping. Saturday, December 19 was truly a historic day — at least for me.

The day started for me when Rebecca and I got up early and drove up to Mission Ops to prepare for the burn activities that were to start at 10:40 AM. The burn sequence would put the spacecraft into an intermediate orbit with a mean altitude of 40 km. However, to account for the evolution of the orbit during the following six weeks, the initial orbit would be 25 km by 55 km.

In addition to Rebecca, Dan, Ric, John, Ken, Dave, Rick, Marcie, and me, who were at Mission Ops, I had invited Jeff Hughes and Phil Chapman from Rotary Rocket to watch the burns. We got everything checked and verified and were ready to begin by 10:30 AM, (365/14:05 MET). I issued the first command to uplink the A3 and A4 engine heater turn-on file at 346/14:15 MET — *the final act of the nominal mission was under way*. After our standard checks and cross checks of the engine parameter file for the aposelene burn, I had Ric uplink it and Dan and I verified the parameters as I read the echoes as they appeared on my screen. Then, *at 346/14:46 MET, the nominal mission ended and the extended mission began* when, after I had issued the command a few frames earlier, the A3 and A4 engines began to fire for 46.8 sec and changed the spacecraft's velocity by 7.30 m/sec. The burn lowered the periselene from 77.5 km to 50.5 km — we were getting down there!

As soon as the aposelene burn was finished, Dan prepared the file for the periselene burn and, at 346/15:15 MET, I had Ric uplink the A1 and A2 heater turn-on file. We then uplinked the file for the periselene burn on the A1 and A2 engines — a 150.4 sec burn that would decrease the spacecraft's velocity by 24.02 m/sec. The periselene burn began at 346/16:13 MET and lowered the aposelene from 122.5 km down to become the new periselene and moved the ascending node of the orbit so the new periselene was at 25 km. When we were done, the reshaped orbit was 25 km by 55 km and we were in our initial, 40 km mean altitude, extended mission mapping orbit.

The spacecraft's attitude was OK, so I canceled the preplanned tweak reor burn and proceed with the planned spin trim burn we had to do.

At 346/15:53 MET, I issued the command to turn on the T1 heater and at 346/16:13 MET, we did a 0.65 sec burn on the T1 engine that decreased the spin rate from 12.16 rpm to 11.997 rpm. And the engines were safed by 346/16:15 MET. Just like that, in just under two hours, we had transitioned from the nominal mission orbit to the extended mission intermediate orbit.

Given that we were as close to the Moon as 25 km, or over three times closer than we had ever been, the strengths of the lunar magnetic fields we were flying through had increased by a factor of up to 30. For the first time, we started seeing 20 nT fields on the MAG data screen, where we had previously seen only 1 or 2 nT fields!

Dropping down to the lower altitudes had several other immediate effects. The spacecraft got a little cooler. Also, even though the β angle had gotten greater than 70° just 5 days earlier (Day 341 MET) and hence, the nighttime pass had stopped, the nighttime passes immediately started again with a duration of 27 minutes! That would decrease rapidly to zero in a few days. Then, after about three weeks, the nighttime passes would start up again.

The tank heaters came on just after I finished the commanding and the damned things stayed on for 2¾ hours — a lot longer than was usual, especially after our fuel dump. But Dan and I had long believed that when we did a burn, the vibrations caused the fuel to slosh around and mix the different layers of fuel that were at different temperatures. As a result, the first tank heater event after each burn required longer than usual to heat the tanks.

It was a great day. The nominal mission was over and I made a little speech, in which I thanked everyone for their great work during the nominal mission. Lunar Prospector was just wonderful and I was very happy.

Monday, December 21, 1998

Day 348 MET

Wayne was at LRI and we worked out the budget for the NRA proposal for the data reduction. The budget was at $3.9 million, but we still did not have the final budget numbers — we were waiting on Bill. Wayne and I got everything done and were ready to finish it up when Bill's stuff finally arrived.

Wednesday, December 23, 1998

Day 350 MET

I went up to Mission Ops and the spacecraft was fine. Then I noticed (but no one else had) that we were still having nighttime passes, even though they should have stopped that morning. I asked Nav what in hell was going on, so we spent some time discussing it. The orbit calculations were just fine, but the nighttime pass calculations were based on the radius of mean lunar sphere (1738 km) and did not take into consideration the topography (which is not well known anyway). At that point in time, the spacecraft was going into the moon's shadow behind the far-side where the mean elevation due to topography is 5 or 6 kilometers higher than the mean sphere and that was the reason why we were still having short nighttime passes, rather than missing the Moon's shadow all together.

Thursday, December 24, 1998

Day 351 MET: Christmas Eve Day

I worked most of day getting the proposal done. It had taken more time than I had wanted, because Bill and Bob kept dribbling stuff in, rather than getting it to me when I had asked for it. But finally it was done and I would be able to send it off after Christmas.

Friday, December 25, through Sunday, Dec 27, 1998

Day 352 MET through Day 354 MET: The Christmas Weekend

Rebecca and I enjoyed a relaxing Christmas holiday weekend.

Monday, December 28, 1998

Day 355 MET

I sent the proposal for the data reduction money off to NASA via Federal Express — it was finally out of my hair.

Thursday, December 31, 1998, through Monday, January 4, 1999

Day 358 MET through Day 362 MET: New Year's Weekend

New Year's 1999 — the end of a fantastic year and the beginning of another seven months of fantastic mission activities. Despite the numerous aggravations with NASA and Lockheed, 1998 had been the most exciting and rewarding year of my life. I had succeeded — *AGAINST ALL ODDS* — in pulling off Lunar Prospector in essentially the way I had hoped when we started the mission over a decade earlier. However, never one to look back, I was looking forward to the rest of the mission and beyond — to the commercial exploration of the Moon and to its utilization for the benefit of humankind.

Tuesday, January 5, 1999

Day 363 MET: 25 km or 30 km — A Question of Topography

Since we were down at 40 km, we would know in a few weeks if there were any problems, gravity-wise, with us going down to 25 km — though we did not expect any. However, given a mean altitude of 25 km and with a ±15 km monthly variation in the actual altitude, the spacecraft would be within 10 km of the mean sphere of the Moon at various times during the month! And that brought up a couple of interesting points. What little is known about the topography of the lunar far-side shows that the mean topographic elevation there is 5 or 6 km higher than the mean lunar sphere. Hence, the spacecraft would be frequently getting within 4 or 5 km of the mean surface of the lunar far-side, which in itself presented no problem. However, because of our ignorance about the far-side topography and because local topographic variation on the Moon frequently reaches 5 km, there was a good chance that some of the mountains and crater rims on the far-side are high enough that Lunar Prospector could hit one of them — if we went all the way down to a mean altitude of 25 km. The question was, 25 km or 30 km?

Given that the unknown topography could have a grave impact (pun intended) on the rest of the mission, we had a telecon with Goddard in the morning and we all agreed we didn't think that the topography was well enough known for us to go down to 25 km. To be sure, we decided to call the Clementine people to get the latest information from their topographic data. Unless the Clementine data gave us a really clean bill of topographic health, we were going to stay up at 30 km.

Since one of the main reasons for getting as low as possible was to get the best MAG data possible, the difference between the 25 km and 30 km altitudes is only about a factor of 1.7 when it came to the magnetic field strengths that we could measure. However, when I looked at the MAG data, I was already seeing 37 nT fields and we were still at 40 km mean altitude! We were clearly getting excellent MAG data at 40 km and by going down to 30 km we would get another factor of 2.4, so I didn't think the added data quality we would get by going down to 25 km, was worth the risk caused by the unknown topography. Besides, even at 30 km mean altitude, we would sometimes be within 15 km of the mean surface on the far-side, so that would result in another factor of 5 in the magnetic field strengths over what we were getting in the 40±15 km orbit.

Also, at 25 km, we would have to do an OMM every two weeks to avoid hitting the Moon, while at 30 km we would have to do one only once every 4 weeks.

Everybody agreed that unless the Clementine topography people told us a different story, we were just going down to 30 km and that would mean we would have a more relaxed mission. That meant we would have a much safer mission, too, because by doing a burn only every four weeks instead of every two weeks, we would not be so overworked and run the risk of fatigue errors that could end the mission. While there was no problem mapping at 30 km, there was also essentially no room for error. For example, while we were in the 100 km mapping orbit, we had months to do an OMM before we would hit the moon, but at 30 km, we had just two days to get the OMM done! There really was no room or time for error.

Wednesday, January 6, 1999

Day 364 MET: Lunar Prospector's 1ˢᵗ (and only) Birthday

Happy Birthday to Lunar Prospector! I brought a cake to Mission Ops and we celebrated the one-year anniversary of the launch and turn-on on January 6, 1998 — what a year!

We had our second telecon with Goddard, but this time we had the Clementine topography people on the phone. I had known that the spacing of the Clementine Laser Altimeter measurements on the lunar surface was 18 km, which was bad enough, but I did not know that their data recovery rate on the lunar far-side was an amazingly low

19%! There were gaps of up to 100 km or more in the topographic profiles of the critical far-side. That did it; we were staying at 30 km. That decision was final, period.

Thursday, January 7, through Sunday, January 10, 1999

Day 365 MET through Day 368 MET: Tucson

Rebecca and I went to Tucson to get our operational office space for LRI selected. We saw the available space at the University of Arizona Science and Technology Park and tentatively selected a small suite with 4 or 5 rooms. We also got our house plans more or less finalized. We were looking forward to our new home, our LRI office, and our new lives in beautiful Tucson.

Monday, January 11, 1999

Day 369 MET: The Pull to the Far-side

I got data from one of Alex's coworkers showing that if we lowered the orbit to 30 km in four or five days, as planned, and then did an OMM every four weeks, the lunar gravity perturbations would quickly pull the periselene over to the southern hemisphere on the far-side, where the topography is high, after each OMM and the periselene would stay there. I did not like that, because we would get asymmetric data sets in which the best data would be limited to the southern far-side. However, if we waited another two weeks, until Day 387 MET to go down to 30 km, then the periselene would stay over the near-side and give us much more uniform data sets when we considered the topographic variations. Then, half way through the extended mission, we could do an OMM in two weeks and shift the periselene over the far-side to even out the coverage. That way we would be able to use the gravity perturbations to our advantage, rather than having to fight them. It was a good plan I would discuss with Dan and the Nav guys the following day.

Tuesday, January 12, 1999

Day 370 MET

I went up to Mission Ops and we all agreed to delay lowering the orbit to 30 km by two weeks in order to keep the periselene over the near-side and then to shift it to the far-side three months later. We were going to get really great data sets from the 30 km orbit and I was very pleased.

Friday, January 15, 1999

Day 373 MET: A Tweak Reor Burn

We did a tweak reor burn to shift the spacecraft's attitude by of 4.16°, so the SEA would stay positive as the Earth, Moon, and spacecraft continued on their yearly journey around the Sun. I sent the commands to turn on the A1 and A4 engine heaters starting at 373/12:49 MET; we started the 22 pulsed reor burn sequence at 373/13:19 MET, and the whole thing was over and the engines safed at 373/13:21 MET.

I talked more with Sylvia about the possibility of having Berkeley track Lunar Prospector after the extended mission was over, since the issue was far from dead, despite Guenter's lack of interest. But before we could proceed, we had to have Berkeley do the communication link margin calculations to see if it would even work.

Sylvia told me that Ames was discussing Lockheed's fee and I suspected that fat ass Scott and even fatter assed Cathcart didn't want to give Lockheed the rest of the fee for the nominal mission until all the Level 0 and Level 1 data were archived — a process that would take several more months. Well, it was nice to see Lockheed and NASA annoying each other instead of me for a change.

Tuesday, January 19, 1999

Day 377 MET

Bill had asked me to increase the gain on the GRS again. Before I did that, I checked the spacecraft and found that the load current was 3 to 3½ amp, which was an amp higher than when we were at 100 km. I assumed the spacecraft was a lot cooler because of the longer nighttime passes, so more heaters were on, but it still surprised me.

I checked the instruments and found, to my surprise, that Face 3 of the APS was saturating, while face 5 was fine! At 377/16:41 MET, I increased the GRS high-voltage to 1677 v and then, at 377/16:46 MET and 377/17:44 MET, I sent commands to turn just Face 3 and Face 5 on, respectively, so I could see what they were doing. Satisfied that I understood what was going on, I turned Faces 1, 2, 4, and 5 on and left Face 3 off at 377/17:58 MET.

Wednesday, January 20, 1999

Day 378 MET: Preparing for the January Penumbral Eclipse

Dan and I had a meeting with Woody and Jim about the January 31 eclipse, which was going to be much more difficult to get through than the previous penumbral eclipses. It was deeper, 88%, and we were going to be in the 30 km altitude orbit. Woody had calculated that if we had a tank heater event at the beginning of the eclipse, we would have to turn off the primary heaters and go to the secondaries. However, because of the longer nighttime passes at our low altitude, we could not recover and get back on the primary heaters until we got back close to $\beta = 90°$, five months later. But Jim said that should be OK.

Other than that, both Woody and I thought the power was degrading and we all thought that the spacecraft was getting colder. Jim said he would take a careful look at the temperature histories of the various electronic units and the viscous damper. All that was most interesting.

Friday, January 22, 1999

Day 380 MET

Face 5 of the APS was saturating, so I turned it off at 380/17:00 MET, leaving just Faces 1, 2, and 4 on. However, the APS problems were affecting the NS via cross-talk between the two instruments (remember, both the APS and NS were in the same housing and on the same boom). Bill and I began to discuss the problem and since the NS data were of much higher priority than the APS data, we started considering turning the APS off, so it would not foul-up the NS data.

Sunday, January 24, 1999

Day 382 MET

I drove up to Mission Ops in the morning to see how things were going. The tank heater events were lasting only two hours and there were no high DOD/low battery voltage problems. I was hoping that, after we used more fuel getting down to 30 km, the tank heater on-time would be short enough so we would not have to start turning the transmitter off again to save power.

There was another big solar storm that was saturating all the spectrometers.

Monday, January 25, 1999

Day 383 MET: The SES Freezes Up Again

When I got to Mission Ops, I found that the spectrometers were not working, i.e., we had had another bit flip in the SES like the one three months earlier on October 28. And once again, Marcie's monitoring controllers had not noticed a thing! Almost certainly a solar cosmic ray from the solar storm that was occurring had caused a single event upset. After conferring with Bill, we decided to leave the APS off, so it would not foul-up the NS data any longer, and just turn the GRS and NS back on with an abbreviated procedure I quickly set up in the Mission Profile. I started the commanding at 383/14:20 MET and was finished just 14 minutes later, at 383/14:34 MET. When I was done, we were again getting good data from the GRS and NS and the APS was off.

The minute I told Dan I had turned the APS off, he ran to the phone as fast as he could to snitch to Lockheed. It was funny — he was doing that as soon as anything at all happened — he had become such a wienie.

Dan and I talked to Woody about the power usage during the upcoming eclipse. Woody had been working on more power models and it was apparent we might have to turn the transmitter off during part of the eclipse, as well as switch to the secondary heaters, if tank heaters turned on at the wrong time. It could get really ticklish if the damned heaters did turn on at the wrong time. I hated the idea of turning the primary heaters off, but Woody thought we could recover and switch back to the primaries, if we didn't leave them off too long. We would just have to wait and see.

After that, I drove up to San Francisco for an interview on KPEQ Radio, which was fun.

Tuesday, January 26, 1999

Day 384 MET: Final Preparations for the 30 km Orbit Burn and
Getting Ready for the Last Penumbral Eclipse

We had our pre-burn meeting and got everything prepared for the burn down to 30 km that was set from 10:00 PM Thursday through 2:00 AM Friday.

I talked to Woody again about the penumbral eclipse on Sunday and he was going to do some more calculations because the tank heaters were turning on very frequently (less fuel meant a shorter heater on-times, but also quicker tank/fuel cool down times), so the chance of us having a heater event during the eclipse was very great. He was working up several models, each depending on when the damned tank heaters came on, to determine what we would have to do to keep from having a power problem.

We were nearly ready for the two major events that were to occur towards the end of the week — going down to 30 km and getting through the last penumbral eclipse of the mission. It was going to be an exciting few days, because once we were down at 30 km and once we were through the eclipse, then it was home free to the end of July and the end of the mission. It was very exciting and we were having a great time.

Thursday Evening, January 28, and Early Friday Morning, January 29, 1999

Day 387 MET: Going Down to 30 km

Marcie just amazed me. We had been talking to Woody early Thursday evening about how we could handle the power during the upcoming eclipse. Marcie just didn't believe (in reality, did not understand) any of it! It was always the same thing with her. She didn't understand the problem or the solutions, so the solutions could not be correct. She just dealt from ignorance and fear that something would go wrong. I said, "This is what the calculations show, so we will be fine." She was concerned about the 8 amps that the spacecraft would draw if we went to the secondaries for a short time and then turned the primary heaters back on. Jim agreed that if we went to the secondaries and stayed there for a while, it would be no big deal — we had a completely failsafe backup. But Marcie was just Marcie and she didn't understand it and you couldn't make her understand it — so she just bitched. The last day that I would see Marcie Smith would be a great day.

We assembled to do the burns to take the spacecraft down to 30 km at about 10:00 Thursday evening. The burn would actually put us into a 15 km by 45 km orbit and the perturbations would do the rest.

I started the commanding session at 387/03:04 MET, by having the A1 and A2 heater turn-on file uplinked. Immediately after that file was uplinked, verified, and the engine temperatures began to rise, I turned the APS back on (at 387/03:10 MET), so we could see if we could get some good data from it.

Dan and I went through our check and verification routine for the aposelene burn that would last 40.4 sec and decrease the spacecrafts velocity by 6.34 m/sec. I had that uplinked and I verified the engine parameter echoes. The burn was executed at 387/03:30 MET. Step one was done.

We prepared the second burn and I ordered the A1 and A2 engine heaters turned on again, starting at 387/04:05 MET. After the usual checks and verifications of the engine parameter file, I had the file for the periselene burn executed at 387/04:19 MET. The second burn, which lasted 71.6 sec and changed the spacecraft's velocity by 11.27 m/sec, finished putting us into our 15 km by 45 km orbit. *We were down at 30 km mean altitude!*

Between 387/04:40 MET (A1 and A4 engine heater turn-on initiate) and 387/05:01 MET (safeing the engines), we did an eight pulse reor to shift the spacecraft's attitude by 1.54° and to get the SEA at +1.5°, to see if that would help the APS by shading Face 5 and stop the APS from fouling-up the NS.

Because we only spun up to 12.092 rpm (i.e., we hadn't gotten over the 12.1 rpm limit we had reset), I canceled the preplanned spin trim burn. We were done with the sequence to put Lunar Prospector into its final mapping orbit by 1:30 Friday morning.

Interestingly enough, when I first turned the APS on, it was a mess. There were a lot of transients that really mucked up the NS for quite sometime. But slowly the APS settled down and finally, after the second burn, it was OK and was not affecting the NS anymore. I concluded that there must have been a loose contact in a plug on the boom and that the cross-talk was occurring somewhere in the long lines on the boom — but who knew for sure.

Daytime Friday, January 29, 1999

The Rest of Day 387 MET

The nighttime passes had already reached 39 minutes in duration and as of early morning (387/11:25 MET), the controllers had to shut the transmitter off to save power during a tank heater event — there went my hopes that the heater on-time would be short enough so we would not have to start turning the transmitter off until much later in the β angle cycle.

When I arrived at Mission Ops in the morning, I talked to Bill about how the APS had behaved the previous night and we tentatively agreed that, rather than a contact problem in one of the plugs, the thermal foil on the instrument housing was probably shaking during the burns and was periodically touching the APS detectors on Face 5 — thus causing the noise. Regardless of the cause of the noise, there was something mechanical, rather than electronic, going on with it.

Sunday, January 31, 1999

Day 389 MET: The Final Penumbral Eclipse

I woke up at 2:00 AM and was at Mission Ops by 3:00 AM. The eclipse was going to be tough — the spacecraft would enter 88% of the way into the Earth's partial shadow and, via a combination of nighttime passes superimposed on the eclipse, the spacecraft would be in partial to total darkness for just 4 minutes less than 3 hours. Worse, it was clear that the tank heaters were going to go on during the eclipse. There was just no question about it. We decided we would turn the transmitter off for most of the time, and just turn it on for short periods in order to see what was going on — we did not want to go through the entire eclipse not knowing if we were getting in trouble or not.

The predicted chronology of the eclipse was as follows:

The spacecraft would enter a normal nighttime pass at 389/11:38 MET (7:03 AM).

Nine minutes later, at 389/11:47 MET, the Moon and the spacecraft would enter the Earth's partial shadow.

At 389/12:20 MET, the spacecraft would exit from its nighttime pass, but it would be 84% of the way into the Earth's partial shadow.

Ten minutes later, at 389/12:30 MET, the spacecraft would be at its maximum depth into the Earth's shadow — 88%.

At 389/13:17 MET, the spacecraft would exit the Earth's partial shadow.

But just 12 minutes later, at 389/13:29 MET, the spacecraft would start its second nighttime pass.

At 389/13:51 MET, the spacecraft — while still in the shadow of the Moon — would enter the Earth's partial shadow for the second time.

And the spacecraft would emerge from its second nighttime pass at 389/14:12 MET, while 30% deep into the Earth's partial shadow.

At 389/14:25 MET, the spacecraft would be at the maximum depth of its second orbital loop in the Earth's partial shadow, i.e., 40% of the way into the Earth's partial shadow.

Finally, at 389/14:46 MET, the spacecraft would leave the Earth's partial shadow for the last time.

But 34 minutes later, at 389/15:20 MET, the spacecraft would enter its next, 42-minute nighttime pass. As I said, it was going to be a tough penumbral eclipse.

I, of course, had a Mission Profile all laid out, but by the time the eclipse was over — it was blazing red with all the changes I had to red-line into it — it was an exciting morning to say the least.

As preplanned, I had Ric turn the transmitter off at 389/11:35 MET — three minutes before the spacecraft simultaneously entered radio occultation and its nighttime pass at 389/11:38 MET. Just before I had the transmitter turned off, the three tank temperatures were 23° C, 21° C and 21° C — sure signs of an eminent tank heater event — and the load current was 3 amps.

The penumbral eclipse started 9 minutes later at 389/11:47 MET.

I had planned to keep the transmitter off until the spacecraft was back in full sunlight at 389/13:17 MET, but I issued the command to turn it on 2 minutes early, at 389/13:15 MET. We had expected that the tank heaters would turn on at about 389/14:00 MET, so we thought everything would still be OK when we started getting the downlinked engineering data.

But we had been having trouble with the DSN all morning. Of course, when the transmitter came on, the DSN had trouble locking up on the spacecraft and we didn't have a whole hell of a lot of time (just 14 minutes from the time I issued the turn-on command) to see what was going on before the spacecraft went into the second radio occultation period and we lost the signal (LOS).

Five minutes passed and still no link and no data, but just then, at 389/13:20 MET, just 6 minutes before Ric had to uplink the command to turn off the transmitter at 389/13:26 MET, we got data! The load current was varying around 5 amps and the battery voltage was 31 v, both pieces of data suggested that the tank heaters were on. However, the battery was charging at about 1 amp and the tank temperatures were 23° C, 20° C and 21° C, so it was not clear if the heaters were on or not — and I had only a few more minutes to determine if they were on or not. If they were on and I did not turn the primary heater circuit off, we could have problems — but I did not want to turn the primary heaters off unless it was necessary.

I watched the battery voltage and the battery current and it appeared they were dropping and just then, the temperature of Tank 3 increased — the heaters were definitely on — I had to get those tank heaters off by uplinking the command to turn off the primary heaters as fast as possible. But it was 389/13:26 MET and Ric, as he was supposed to do, had just started to uplink the transmitter off file!

I immediately told Ric, "Abort the transmitter off file and send the primary heater off file (that we had ready and waiting) as quickly and as many times as you can in the next two or three minutes and then get the transmitter off file uplinked again, at least a minute before LOS (at 389/13:29 MET)!"

Ric sent the abort command for the transmitter off file and then sent the primary heater off file three times before the downlink stopped at 389/13:26 MET — *the abort had not gotten in early enough*, so the transmitter had turned off on schedule. Nevertheless, we still expected that the primary heater off command file had gotten uplinked, since uplink commanding had nothing to do with the transmitter being on or off — because the receiver was always on. However, the minute the DSN saw the transmitter was off, they dropped the uplink too (!), so we couldn't command, i.e., the DSN never sent up the primary heater off commands to the spacecraft! Though we did not know that at that time, we thought that the primary heaters were off!

The transmitter was off, but the primary heaters were on — gobbling up over 1.5 amps of power and Lunar Prospector was again in the dark! Well, though I did not know it at that time, I would find out in 48 minutes just how good my spacecraft power system was!

I turned the transmitter back on at 389/14:14 MET, just as soon as I could after the end of the nighttime/radio occultation pass period (389/14:12 MET) — and sure enough the battery voltage was low, 25 v, and dropping fast, the tank temperatures had risen about a degree and we were still on the primary heater circuit (I knew then we had failed in our attempt to turn it off some 50 minutes earlier). We were still in the Earth's partial shadow (but no more than 40%) and would remain there for another 30 minutes (until 389/14:46 MET).

The tank heaters were definitely on and we watched the battery voltage drop for a minute or two and then it hit the yellow limit of 24.5 v. I said, "That's it, primaries off." Ric got the command uplinked at 389/14:17 MET, I saw the echo and then the primary heater circuit went off, the load current dropped from nearly 6½ amps to 3½ amps and the battery switched from discharging at −1 amp to charging at ½ amp — even though we were still close to 40% into the Earth's partial shadow. Then, knowing we were going to be OK, I issued the transmitter off command at 389/14:18 MET.

At 389/14:40 MET, 6 minutes before the spacecraft left the Earth's partial shadow for the last time (at 389/14:46 MET), I had Ric uplink the command to turn the transmitter on, so I could evaluate the state of the battery and the spacecraft — everything was cold, but OK. I watched the engineering data for 14 minutes and then had Ric uplink the command to turn off the transmitter at 389/14:54 MET. I left it off for an hour and 10 minutes, i.e., until we had completed the next nighttime pass. That way, the battery could get charged back up in preparation for my turning the primary heater circuit back on.

When we came out of that nighttime/radio occultation pass (at 389/16:03 MET) and got the transmitter back on (at 389/16:04 MET), the spacecraft was OK and the battery was charging rapidly — it was clear that we were out of the woods. I watched the spacecraft for about 10 minutes and then, at 389/16:14 MET, I issued the command to turn the primary heaters back on. The beauty was that I knew when I turned the primary heaters back on, there would be an enormous jump in the load current because all the heaters would be on. When I had the command executed, the load current went to 8.4 amps. But instead of staying that high for several minutes, it started to drop right back down to 6 amps within 4 minutes, and then slowly, but surely, it drifted down to its normal value of 4 amps. It was really beautiful to watch and the spacecraft did everything we thought it would do.

I had turned the primaries off and I did all kinds of things I never would have done during the nominal mission. But because we were in the extended mission, I could take those "so called" risks and every time I did, the spacecraft just worked fine.

It was close to lunchtime and someone went to McDonald's to pick us up some lunch. Also, Woody had brought banana nut bread and I had three slices of it. It was a good lunch for a good day.

As we ate, we watched the battery charge, and then I turned the transmitter off at 389/17:09 MET for the next nighttime/radio occultation pass (from 389/17:11 MET to 389/17:55 MET) and turned it back on at 389/17:57 MET. With that, the spacecraft was back to its normal daytime/nighttime thermal and power cycling and I watched the battery charge up. When it hit trickle charge, I left for home — it was 2:30 PM, I had been in Mission Ops for nearly 12 hours and I had enjoyed every minute of those 12 hours.

We had gotten through the worst penumbral eclipse of the mission and the spacecraft was fine. It had gotten really cold. The GRS had dropped all the way down to its red limit at –40° C! The viscous damper got cold (1° C, normally it varied between 7 and 8° C) and hit its yellow limit and the transmitter got really cold (–15 ° C, normally it varied between 14 and 22° C). Though it would be very tough, I was certain we could also make it through the partial umbral eclipse in July — the eclipse that was to mark the end of the mission, since Lunar Prospector was not designed to survive an umbral eclipse. Regardless of what would happen during the July eclipse, we had just been through the last hurdle of the mission. The rest of the mission was going to be just more of the same, with an OMM every month. It had been a great day and I had as much fun as I had had since launch.

Once I got home, I watched the Super Bowl.

Chapter 4-13
The Extended Mission
Becomes Routine

Monday, February 1, through Friday, February 5, 1999

Day 390 MET through Day 394 MET: Albuquerque, Los Alamos, and Tucson

Monday, I went to the University of New Mexico in Albuquerque to see Horton Newsom and Jim Papike to seek their help in forcing NASA to give us the money we needed for the data reduction and archiving program and to give a seminar on Lunar Prospector to the geology and planetary science faculty and students.

Tuesday, I went up to Los Alamos to talk to Bill and his crew about the data reduction. The GRS and NS data analyses were well advanced. They were working on the APS data and getting to the point where they were going to be able to soon make some sense out of it. But, we had a suspicion there was nothing to see in the data, though we would know that for sure only when they got through with the analysis.

I went back down to Albuquerque on Wednesday to go to a conference that Roger had asked me to attend and we gave our joint papers on Lunar Prospector and the commercial lunar base.

Thursday and Friday, I was in Tucson, seeing about the house and our loan. Then, I flew home.

While I was on travel, David Gump had published a letter to the editor in *Space Week* about the Moon, commercial missions, and the lunar base meeting that LunaCorp, the Space Frontier Foundation (SFF), and the National Space Society (NSS) were helping me set up. David called it a Space Frontier Foundation meeting with co-sponsors LRI, NSS, and LunaCorp! All of a sudden, the LRI workshop had been taken over by the SFF and they had turned it into a completely different type of meeting than Roger and I had wanted! I was not happy with the turn of events and intended to get to the bottom of it.

Monday, February 8, 1999

Day 397 MET: The Berkeley Plan and More Stupidity from Carolyn Porco

I woke up very early, so I went up to Mission Ops very early and started getting caught up. The spacecraft was in good shape.

Bill sent me an email — he wanted me to turn the spectrometers off, turn the NS and GRS back on, but leave the APS off, so we would get a month of good clean NS data before turning the APS back on. Also, he wanted me to run a NS calibration test during the turn-on sequence. I wrote up the Mission Profile and I started commanding the sequence at 397/13:12 MET and finished it at 397/15:28 MET.

I then talked with Sylvia about Bob Lin's proposal to track Lunar Prospector after the end of the extended mission. I said, "The way I look at it, it's a great idea, but it doesn't come free — we have to archive the data. We can't just collect it. I figure that the archiving will cost about $200,000. Clearly, this is a good thing to do, but I told Bob I don't know if it can even be done. We first have to get the link margin calculations before we know. I called Joe (Boyce) and told him I would like to be able to do this, but if it was going to cost any real amount of money, I wasn't going to push it. We've gotten so much out of this mission I was not going to stand up there and say we have to do this. Joe understood and said he would rather put the $200,000 into the data reduction program and I tended to agree." Sylvia and I discussed it a little further, and we both thought we would probably not agree to Bob's post-mission tracking idea — not for $200,000. It looked like the mission was going to be over at the end of July — in less than six months.

Sylvia told me something really stupid. Carolyn Porco had called NASA and said she wanted to have Lunar Prospector crashed on the Moon on the 20th anniversary of the Apollo 11 landing on the Moon, i.e., on July 20, 1999. Sylvia said Porco claimed she had discussed it with me and I agreed. But Sylvia said, "I didn't believe her. I couldn't imagine you being willing to crash the spacecraft when you are collecting science data."

I said, somewhat astonished and pissed, "I saw her months ago and she mentioned that to me, but I said no, but I guess she thinks no means yes" (like Clinton).

I said I would call Porco and set her straight. Sylvia said, "Why don't you wait; we don't know what the real story is." Sylvia was trying to make sure the situation didn't get out of hand and I didn't get too pissed. To add fuel to the fire, Sylvia said it was Porco who had released the story to the press that Gene's ashes were on the spacecraft, not NASA! Sylvia did not trust Porco, who projects an image of innocence, naiveté, and child-like enthusiasm. Sylvia's opinion is that Porco uses that as a façade to manipulate people and I began to agree with Sylvia.

The Laurels issue of *Aviation Week* (February 8, 1999) came out. The laurels piece said, regarding Lunar Prospector being chosen for laurels, "Principal investigator Alan Binder of the Lunar Research Institute, mission manager G. Scott Hubbard of NASA's Ames Research Center, project manager Thomas A. Dougherty of Lockheed Martin Missiles and Space and the science team of the Lunar Prospector, for achieving a textbook example of a cheap-to-build and quick-to-launch scientific spacecraft program. Since its launch last year, Lunar Prospector has succeeded in its science mission with quiet precision. It not only confirmed the presence of water ice at the North and South Poles of the Moon, but found evidence of vast sheets of ice that will change scientific thinking. Lunar Prospector also has mapped the surface of the Moon for key elements and analyzed its gravity and magnetic fields more completely than any previous mission." I feel the piece is beautifully phrased — I especially like the part about the mission being done ". . . with quiet precision," an apt description of the way we had conducted the flight. I must say, the little article touched me.

Tuesday, February 9, and Wednesday, February 10, 1999

Day 398 MET and Day 399 MET

I was home in bed for two days with the flu.

Thursday, February 11, 1999

Day 400 MET: Pat and Dave Took the Ball and Ran with It

Still at home with the flu, I got a call from Israel Galvan that woke me up from a nap. Israel said that, as requested by David Gump and Rick Tumlinson, he had set up a meeting with Doug Cook and George Abbey at JSC and Israel wanted to talk to me to find out what this was all about, since he had been told I was involved. I said, "I didn't know. This is the first that I've heard about it."

He said, "The only reason I set the meetings up was because I thought you were involved," and he was a little peeved. I told him I would make a couple of calls and find out what was going on in my name!

I called David and explained to him what Israel had said about his setting up the meetings and that both Israel and I were concerned about what was going on. Dave said that he and Pat, not Rick, had been talking about how to get things moving and they decided that the best thing to do was to talk to Doug Cook in order to get JSC involved and to try to get support from the Houston community. Then someone had the bright idea to call Israel and see if he would help, because Israel knows everyone there. Then the question of seeing Abbey came up and the whole thing just snowballed. Since Israel thought I was the one trying to set everything up, he went ahead and set up the meeting.

I explained to David that Israel was quite concerned and quite ticked off about the whole affair; Israel is a great ally and not someone we should get pissed off. I also pointed out that Rick was not very high on Israel's list, so we had to be very careful about all that.

David said he understood the meeting was open to the community at large. I said, "No, that's not why we set this up. This was to validate our business plan." Then Dave said Pat and Rick had told him that, as non-profit organizations, the NSS and the SFF could not champion for-profit businesses efforts, so they made it an open meeting. We discussed it further and David was concerned that I was stepping on the SFF and NSS charters too much — if the meeting was to focus on LRI's business plan, then maybe we were doing something that was not illegal. I suggested that the four of us sit down and make damned sure we were not working at cross-purposes. Clearly that had to happen and soon.

After we finished our phone call, I quickly got a flight set up to Houston, which cost $1700, because of the short notice. Nevertheless, I had to get there because I couldn't let them meet with Doug and Abbey to discuss my program without my being there.

Tuesday, February 16, 1999

Day 405 MET

Dave Curtis called and asked me to send up three commands so he could run a MAG/ER diagnostic test. Very late in the afternoon, I prepared the Mission Profile and at 405/19:00 MET, I started having the file uplinked and the uplinking was finished at 405/19:03 MET.

Wednesday, February 17, and Thursday, February 18, 1999

Day 406 MET and Day 407 MET: An Aggravating Trip to Houston

I flew to Houston Wednesday morning for the meeting Pat, David, and Rick had initiated. Pat and Dave were late arriving from DC, because one of their flights was canceled, so they missed their connection. Rick didn't get in from LA until that evening because of poor connecting flights, and then he got sick on the food he had eaten at the Dallas Airport.

Pat, Dave, and I had our meeting with Doug and my old co-workers from the Exploration Office late in the afternoon. I gave Doug Cook reprints of our Preliminary Science Reports that had appeared in *Science* and then John Young, the Apollo 16 astronaut, saw the reprints and took them from Doug, which pleased me to no end. The meeting with Doug went well; he was very supportive of our efforts. However, I was somewhat disappointed in David Gump's performance — he had done well at *National Geographic*, but when we were with Doug, David was out of his element. Similarly, I didn't quite realize that Pat didn't have as much access to material and information as I thought she did. Even though Pat did a fairly good job, I was a little bit disappointed in both of their performances and to find out that they really did not have access to the people we needed to help us. Worse, it was clear that the NSS and LunaCorp had very different agendas than mine — while that was no surprise, I was surprised at how strongly we diverged. Though we all want the same thing in general, our approaches as to how we get there were radically different.

After the meeting with Doug and the Exploration Office guys, we met Israel for dinner, during which we had a good long talk. Israel surprised me; knowing how much of a yellow dog Democrat he is, how pro-Clinton he was, and how much he supports and defends NASA, he said things about Clinton and NASA that just floored me. Regarding our randy President, as Israel called him, he said, "Well, I don't want to see him quit or get impeached, but I'm really disgusted with him," and then he rattled on about Clinton's numerous transgressions. Then, regarding NASA, he said, "Well, you know, we don't want to get rid of NASA *yet*. We need NASA, but we've got to help it get better." That was the first time I had ever heard him talking about getting rid of NASA!

Thursday morning, after breakfast, we (Pat, Rick [who was feeling better], David, and I) went to see Israel and then all of us went to meet Abbey. Like our meeting with Doug, the Abbey meeting went well and Abbey was pleased with the idea of a Lunar Base Meeting being held at Houston. However, it was again clear that the SFF, the NSS, and LunaCorp were going in a very different direction with the conference than Roger and I had planned for our workshop.

After we left the Abbey meeting and said, "Thanks and good-bye," to Israel, Pat, Rick, David, and I talked a little bit before I took off for the airport. I said I was not pleased that they had turned the workshop into a typical NSS/SFF meeting and as a result, the meeting was going to be useless. Their attitude was, *that's just tough*, and my attitude was, *OK, you go your way and I'll go mine.* I had learned, much earlier in my life, that when you get in bed with other organizations, it just dilutes your efforts because the horses never pull in the same direction. In that case, the NSS, the SFF, and LunaCorp were trying to make capital off of Lunar Prospector's success and ride on its coattails towards their individual goals — regardless of whether that helped or hindered my efforts and goals. Though I was very used to that type of behavior (by Lockheed, Scott, NASA, SSI, etc.), I was very disappointed to see that Pat, Rick, and David were so willing to behave that way. Well, the problem had started because I had neither the time nor the money to set up the workshop that Roger and I needed and hence I had asked for Pat and Rick's help. The workshop had become one of their usual clambakes and I decided just to let it play out and then to never work closely with any of those organizations again.

Another disappointing aspect of what was happening was that, especially Rick and the SFF, both of whom had been staunch opponents to the incompetent way NASA tried to do business, were adopting the very methods that were killing NASA. Rick wanted to have inputs from everyone, select the best ideas, integrate them into a common lunar base plan, get a consensus of opinions and build a coalition — exactly what an organization does when it does not know what it is doing and exactly the way NASA had been doing business — and failing — for the decades since Apollo. I tried to point out that Lunar Prospector was successful because I had dictatorially laid out the mission plan, payload, and spacecraft and then done it with the minimum number of people, i.e., you have to know what you are doing, get a few good people who know what they are doing, and just do it, period.

Thus, I was not a happy camper as I flew back to California — the trip had been one big aggravation and a waste of time and money.

Monday, February 22, 1999

Day 411 MET

I went up to Mission Ops, got caught up on everything that had happened during my abortive trip, and prepared the Mission Profile for our 1st OMM of the extended Mission. The spacecraft was, as always, fine. The nighttime passes were 47 minutes long (and were still getting longer) and the monitoring controllers were doing a good job of turning the transmitter off during the tank heater events.

Very Late Wednesday Evening, February 24, through Early Thursday Morning, February 25, 1999

Day 414 MET: The 1st OMM of the Extended Mission

I got up shortly before midnight and drove up to Mission Ops to do the OMM that was scheduled to start shortly before 3:00 AM.

The only excitement was that the downlink telemetry was ragged — we were getting data dropouts, though not all the time and not enough to bother us, so we could proceed.

I started the command session at 414/07:20 MET, by having Paul uplink the A1 and A2 heater turn-on command file. Then we went through the checks and verification of the engine parameter file for the aposelene burn that was to be for 43.5 sec and was to change the spacecraft's velocity by 6.86 m/sec. The file was executed at 414/07:51 MET.

We repeated the procedure for the periselene burn — a 46.52 sec burn, causing a 7.34 m/sec change in the spacecraft's velocity — and I had it executed at 414/08:31 MET. The OMM was finished just like that — strictly routine.

We then did a 7 pulse, 1.20° reor burn that started with execution of the A1 and A4 heater turn-on command file at 414/08:40 MET and ended with the execution of the reor burn itself at 414/09:19 MET.

The entire command session ended with an 0.62 sec despin burn that started with the T1 heater turn-on command file's execution at 414/09:24 MET; the burn was executed at 414/09:37 MET; and the engines were safed by 414/09:39 MET. It was just after 5:00 AM, so Dan and I left the spacecraft in the hands of the monitoring controllers and went to our respective homes to get some sleep.

Friday, February 26, through Monday March 1, 1999

Day 415 MET through Day 418 MET: The Rotary Rocket Rollout

Rebecca and I had been invited to the Rotary Rocket Rollout at Mojave, CA — the presentation of their single stage-to-orbit, reusable rocket to the press and the public. But, before we left Friday morning to drive down to Tehachapi, CA — about 26 km west of Mojave — where we had our motel room for the weekend, I had to go to Mission Ops. Bill needed me to increase the GRS gain to 1695 v. I got to Mission Ops by 7:45 AM, prepared the two commands and sent them at 415/12:34 MET. The voltage step counter on the spectrometer console changed from 214 to 215, indicating that the command had been executed and the voltage had increased, but the voltage still read 1686 v! I had the commands sent up a second time at 415/12:43 MET and the voltage just stayed at 1686 v! Perplexed, I watched the readout of the GRS voltage as I tried to figure out what could be wrong, when the voltage suddenly changed to 1695 v and then quickly flipped back to 1686 v. Then I realized that the 9 v increase caused by switching from step 214 to step 215 was insufficient to push the digital readout up to the next readout step, i.e., to 1695 v, and I was just seeing bit flipping. The GRS was OK and I left Mission Ops, drove back down to Gilroy to pickup Rebecca and then we drove on down to Tehachapi.

We went sightseeing in the Mojave Desert area Saturday and had a nice hike in the Red Rock Canyon Park north of Mojave — the rock formations there consists of really beautiful, red volcanic ash deposits.

Sunday, we went to the Rotary Rocket facilities to setup our little Lunar Prospector display and to be part of the "Pre-press-conference, Family and Friends Rollout of the Rocket." Before the rollout, Jeff Hughes took Rebecca and me to show us the rocket that was to be piloted and was to be flowing to and from orbit. The rocket was really quite impressive. But the most interesting part of the story for me was that there were two seats in the vehicle — one for the pilot and the second for the payload technician, i.e., whomever the company that had bought a launch wanted in the second seat! If, as Rotary Rocket and I were discussing, I were to use the Rotary Rocket to launch my future lunar missions, I would be in that seat whenever I wanted to be! Jeff asked, "Do you want to climb in?" — he did not have to ask twice. As I sat in the second seat, I had visions of the future.

Also, Rick, who was to be the Master of Ceremony for Sunday's rollout, came over to me and said, because he was feeling guilty for having taken over the workshop and making it into a SFF/NSS meeting, he was having FIND give LRI $10,000 so I could hold the workshop Roger and I wanted at a later date. I found that very interesting — $10,000 is a lot of guilt in my book!

The next day, Monday, was the press rollout, which was anticlimactic after the previous day's events. Also, it was very cold and windy, so everyone froze.

Right after the rollout was over, Rebecca and I started driving back to Gilroy. It had been a fun weekend.

Tuesday, March 2, 1999

Day 419 MET

I went up to Mission Ops to check on the spacecraft, which was, of course, OK and got caught up on everything that was on my desk.

Bill called and wanted the GRS gain increased to 1704 v. I prepared the commands and had them uplinked at 419/14:00 MET, but the DSN did not get the command uplinked. I had to repeat having the commands uplinked at 419/14:17 MET and then everything went OK.

Wednesday, March 3, 1999

Day 420, MET: A Big MAG/ER Load

Because we were in the lower orbit with a shorter orbital period, Dave Curtis needed to reprogram part of the memory of the MAG/ER DPU. Dave came down from Berkeley just before noon and I had the Mission Profile prepared and ready to go. The loads consisted of one file with 42 commands, a second with 29 commands, a third with 7 commands, and the last one with 2 commands. But as we were loading, Dave added 3 more commands. The entire load consisted of 83 commands and it took us 2 hours and 7 minutes to uplink it. We started at 420/15:20 and were finished at 420/17:27 MET.

Thursday, March 4, 1999

Day 421

I went up to Mission Ops late because I first had to write a press release about the mission for NASA — since they would just screw it up if I didn't write it.

Just as I arrived, a tank heater event started, so I watched it and modeled it. The β angle was 29° and the duration of the nighttime passes was already 48 minutes and would increase to 49 minutes as β reached 0° in a month. The conditions were not going to get significantly worse and I was pretty convinced we could stop turning off the transmitter during the heater events. I asked Woody to cross check my findings to hopefully verify that we could stop turning the transmitter off.

Friday, March 5, 1999

Day 422 MET: A Blue Day

I left for Mission Ops just as the sun was rising and as I drove to the east along the short dirt road on which we lived, the sun was in my eyes. A few hundred meters to the east of our house is a little horse ranch with big trees shading the road and just as I drove into the shadows of those trees, the Sun stopped blinding me and an old pick-up truck suddenly backed out of the driveway — directly in front of me. I did not even have time to hit the brakes and my beautiful, little, blue Ford Fiesta, slammed into the back of the pickup, which had a ½ m long trailer hitch sticking out the back. There was no damage to the pickup, but the trailer hitch and the massive steel bumper of the pick-up dealt my beloved blue car a fatal blow. After we both ascertained that neither of us was hurt, the driver of the pickup truck got the hell out of there as fast as he could and I was able to drive my mortally wounded blue car the few hundred meters back home. Rebecca, who always hated my little blue car, had mixed feelings about the event. I spent the rest of the day, first seeing if the damage was repairable — it was not — and then junking it. Bye-bye blue car.

Saturday, March 6, 1999

Day 423 MET

Woody and I agreed there was no reason to continue turning the transmitter off. I monitored another tank heater event later in the morning and the modeling I was doing was quite accurate, so I really thought we were OK. But I was still going to watch a few more heater events to be absolutely sure, since we were close to reaching the yellow limit on the battery voltage during the worst of the events. To be on the safe side, I turned the pressure transducer and the EM limb-crossing sensor off at 423/10:51 MET and 423/10:52 MET, respectively, just to give us that little edge.

Sunday, March 7, 1999

Day 424 MET: A Midnight Heater Event and More

A tank heater event was going to occur between 12:00 AM and 2:00 AM. I got up in the middle of the night and called Troy at Mission Ops to ask him to tell me exactly when the event started, when the nighttime passes started, what the battery voltages were, etc. I also had my computer model of the heater events on my computer at home and so, with Troy's help, I went through the heater event via the phone.

The tank heaters turned on at 424/04:58 MET (12:23 AM), 31 minutes after the nighttime pass ended (and 31 minutes before the next nighttime pass started) and my worst case calculations showed the battery would not get fully charged up and go over to full trickle charging before the next nighttime pass. Sure enough, though the battery voltage reached its maximum of 32.5 v with seven minutes to spare, the battery did not reach full trickle charge. Thus my modeling was quite accurate.

Later in the day, I went up to Mission Ops to watch the next tank heater event at 3:00 PM. I was going to make absolutely certain it was OK to leave the transmitter on all the time, before I canceled the turn-off commanding.

Monday, March 8, 1999

Day 425 MET: More Tank Heater Events

I went in to Mission Ops and watched the heater event, which was fairly benign.

Tuesday, March 9, 1999

Day 426 MET: Another Middle-of-the-Night Heater Event

As I had instructed the monitor controllers to do, Howard Wilkinson called me at 1:00 AM because the tank heaters went on. I got up and drove up to Mission Ops because the heater had gone on ten minutes before the nighttime pass started, so that event was the one I had been looking for — the worst possible case. I drove up to Ames in about 45 minutes; just in time to see the spacecraft come out of the nighttime pass. The DOD of the battery was 75%, so the question was, "Would the battery get charged back up to 32 v and start trickle charging before the spacecraft went into the next night-time pass?" It did, but just barely. The battery voltage reached 32 v just 3 minutes before the nighttime pass began and even though there wasn't a sign of trickle charging, I decided it was OK and I did not have Howard turn the transmitter off. When the space-craft came out of the next nighttime pass, the DOD was just 55% and that told me we were really OK and we did not need to turn the transmitter off during tank heater events anymore.

I drove home, went to sleep for a little bit, and went back up to Ames because I had an interview at 11:00 AM for the Challenger Day celebration.

At 3:30 PM, the Palo Alto guys and the Berkeley guys came down to Ames so we could discuss the Berkeley post-mission tracking proposal. We found nothing techni-cally wrong with the Berkeley proposal.

In addition to the Berkeley proposal to do passive tracking after the end of the extended mission, I had received a call from David Goldstein, an engineer from the Uni-versity of Texas at Austin, a couple of days earlier with another proposal. Dave asked me if I could crash Lunar Prospector into one of the craters that we thought contained water ice at the end of the mission and I answered, "Yes."

He then explained that his group had calculated that Lunar Prospector, which would have a mass of about 160 kg at the end of the mission and would be traveling at 1.7 km/sec, had enough energy to vaporize sufficient amounts of water ice so the Hubble telescope and various ground based telescopes could detect it. If we could do that, then we would know for sure that the hydrogen deposits mapped by the NS were truly water ice deposits. I said that that was a good idea. He said, "Good, we'll contin-ue with our calculations and start seeing about getting the Hubble and other tele-scopes to participate."

I said, "Fine," but I told him about the Berkeley proposal and the possibility that we might not be crashing the spacecraft at the end of the mission, as well as the fact that NASA would have to approve any plans for the end the mission, regardless of what I might say.

I told Sylvia about the University of Texas impact experiment and said, "If we can't do Bob's tracking and have to crash it at the end of July, we should attempt to do the experiment with the University of Texas guys. But let's see what Bob can really do."

The big question was, "Would the Berkeley antenna really give us the signal-to-noise that we needed to track Lunar Prospector?" and to answer that question, Bob was going to have the antenna vendor do some tests. All in all, there were numerous ques-tions that had to be answered about both the Berkeley and the UT proposals, both of which offered us exciting possibilities.

I took a look at possible impact sites based on our map of the hydrogen deposits and quickly settled on a 50 km diameter crater located 70 km from the South Pole, the middle of a row of three craters that had the highest concentrations of hydrogen and supposedly water ice. A quick check with Dave Lozier showed we could impact in that crater on July 30 or 31, i.e., two or three days *after the July 28 umbral eclipse*! Thus to do the impact experiment — we had to survive the eclipse! However, I thought we could survive the eclipse after our experience with the last penumbral eclipse in January. But, that did add another dimension to both the impact experiment and the July 28 umbral eclipse preparations!

David Lawrence sent me a copy of the high-resolution (60 km or 2½ time better than the 150 km resolution that we had promised NASA in the original Discovery proposal) map of the thorium distribution over the Moon we had obtained from the low altitude GRS data and it was just exquisite. You could see that the modest sized craters, Arago, Aristarchus, Aristillus, Kepler, and Mairan, had re-excavated KREEP from below the lava units and ejecta blankets that had buried parts of the original deposits of KREEP in the Imbrium Basin ejecta around Mare Imbrium. The map also showed that, despite its size and proximity to Mare Imbrium, the crater Copernicus did not excavate any KREEP — the map was just absolutely exquisite. I was just floored at how good the data were!

I waited around Mission Ops until the next heater event started about 5:00 PM. The heaters turned on 40 minutes before the next nighttime pass started, so I left for home. When I got home, I called Mission Ops and, as I suspected, the battery had reached full charge and was trickle charging some 15 minutes before the next nighttime pass started. Basically, we were out of the woods, even though the heater on-time had gone up from about 1 hour and 55 minutes to 2 hours because the nighttime passes were longer.

Wednesday, March 10, through Thursday, March 18, 1999

Day 427 MET through Day 435 MET: DC, The Lunar and Planetary Science Conference in Houston, Tucson, and a Countermanded Order

I flew to Washington on Wednesday the 10th to attend a meeting on Thursday that Alan Ladwig had invited David Gump and me to. It was a much bigger meeting than I thought. There were a large number of NASA people there from all over the agency. I was happy to see Mark Craig, who at one time ran the Space Exploration Initiative at JSC when I worked supporting that effort, and Doug Cook was there from JSC.

Alan Ladwig said he did not know what to call the meeting, but its purpose was to try to figure out how to orchestrate all the elements, inside and outside of NASA, that could help in the exploration of space. We were not there to develop a plan to go to Mars or to the Moon or elsewhere. Alan pointed out that NASA was finally realizing it was in trouble and needed the help of artists, writers, philosophers, the commercial world, etc. to get the agency doing something productive. The meeting was open to all suggestions and ideas. That sounded very good to me.

Mark Craig started off with some very good viewgraphs about commercializing space exploration and how NASA should remove the barriers it had against commercialization, encourage it, and help it grow. With that great introduction, I gave my talk on the success of Lunar Prospector and my approach to commercializing the exploration of the Moon and the development of a commercial lunar base. David was up next, but it was already was quite late (I was supposed to have started my talk at 9:15, but it was 10:00 before I even got up there) and I had several other appointments, so I had to leave. I was happy to see that NASA was beginning to wake up, but unfortunately, it was only Alan who was awake at Headquarters and his efforts soon died.

My next meeting was with Joe Boyce and Guenter Riegler. I showed them our new, high resolution GRS thorium map that was so spectacular and they thought it was very good. Then I explained to them the two end-of-mission scenarios, the Berkeley plan and the UT plan, and how far we were in investigating both of those possibilities. I said we saw no showstoppers for either one. They wanted to know if both could be done. I answered, "It doesn't look that way. The reason is that we won't be able to command the spacecraft from Berkeley and we can't afford to keep Mission Ops in working condition at Ames after July."

Then I went up the Hill and saw Eric Sterner, Congressman Sensenbrenner's aide, and I told him how things were going, both with the mission and with my efforts to get a commercial lunar data purchase program started. He emphasized two things, that I was aware of, which presented big problems. First, NASA cannot obligate money more than one year in advance. If I were to fly a mission that took two or three years to build and fly, NASA could not set money aside when I started the development of the mission to pay for the data when I delivered it two or three years later. Rather, NASA would have to ask Congress for the money to pay for the data the year it was delivered — a tricky proposition! Second, even if Congress allocated money for data purchase, NASA could swipe that money for something else (as they were doing to keep the space station alive — facts I was well aware of) unless there were somebody in NASA who was in charge of the data purchase program and who could keep track of the money to make sure that it was used to purchase data. Eric was skeptical, because he doesn't trust NASA — but then who does trust NASA? Then, as Alan Ladwig had already mentioned, Eric said I should go talk to Dan Tam, who was at JPL, but who was actually a Headquarters person. Tam was then the head of NASA's effort to commercialize space activities.

After meeting with Eric, I went back to NASA for a meeting with Joe Rothenberg. Joe was very enthusiastic and positive about my commercial lunar data purchase ideas and the commercial lunar base. Joe said, because he didn't have the time, the guy I really should be talking with was Darrell, the guy with whom I originally talked, when Rothenberg had to bug out to the OMB the first time I went to see him. Actually, Darrell was at the Ladwig meeting, so he had already heard my pitch and I was pleased about that. Joe agreed with me that what I was doing was really supporting Code M and that Code M, rather than Code S, should be supporting what I wanted to do. That was music to my ears, since Code S hates my guts.

Then it was back to Alan Ladwig's office and we had a good chat about the progress I was making.

Friday, I was back on the Hill talking to the aides of various Arizona Congressmen and Senators, trying to get their support for my efforts, since LRI would soon be in Arizona. I got the usual enthusiastic response from the aides, but enthusiasm is not real support.

Late Friday, I flew to Houston and when I arrived at my motel, there was a message that Dan, Sylvia, Marcie, and Woody had wet their panties about the battery and had countermanded my order to stop turning the transmitter off. They thought, because the battery voltage had dropped to the yellow limit once or twice since I had left, the voltage would soon hit the red limit if we did not restart turning the transmitter off.

I was as pissed as I had ever been. I had not gotten up in the middle of the night several times to follow and model the heater events just to have those twits countermand my order as soon as I was out the door. As far as I was concerned, their actions were a direct challenge to my authority as PI and Mission Director. If I had the authority, I would have fired Dan and Marcie on the spot. I was so sick of those two SOBs and their eternal efforts to run the mission that I could —.

I assumed that Dan and Marcie had gotten Sylvia in a tizzy and then they had pushed Woody into a corner, since he had reached the same conclusion I had regarding the battery and agreed with me that we should not be turning the transmitter off.

I was fuming when I got to my room, but I knew there was nothing I could do to fight Lockheed and Ames's stupidity as long as I was on travel. I immediately called Dan and, despite my anger, I politely asked Dan what was going on and he said Woody was concerned because they were seeing evidence of a roll off (i.e., when the battery voltage starts to drop ever more rapidly, indicating that the end is near). I knew that was a load of BS, since we had always seen an increase in the load current towards the end of a nighttime pass as more and more heaters went on, and that always made it look like a battery voltage roll off was occurring. I was dealing with idiots and I did not believe Woody was the source of the problem.

Also, Dan said, because he needed 12 hours of lunar limb-crossing data, he had turned the EM limb-crossing sensor back on just after Wednesday noon (427/17:01 MET) and then turned it off again just after midnight (428/05:01 MET), which I said was fine with me.

I also had a call from David Curtis, who wanted to have another burst mode set up, so I arranged for Dan to send the burst mode set of commands on the coming Wednesday.

I was tired and annoyed, so I slept a lot Saturday and I spent Sunday with John Gruener.

The Lunar and Planetary Science Conference started Monday. The meeting was pretty good, better than usual. My guys did a fantastic job — we had such phenomenal data. I talked to a lot of people, including Jeff Taylor and Brad Jolliff, about my doing sample return missions, trying to get everybody on the bandwagon for new lunar missions.

Bill and I talked to Joe Boyce and Joe said NASA had not put any more money in the NRA. It had just $3.1 million for 3 years for everybody and our numerical data reduction proposal was $3.9 million alone! However, I decided I wasn't going to cause a stink right then; I would just call the Senators and Congressmen's aides that I had talked to the previous week and get them to put pressure on NASA.

Wednesday, between 434/17:48 MET and 434/18:06 MET, Dan uplinked the ER burst mode commands and turned the EM limb-crossing sensor back on. The next day, after getting the 13 hours of data he needed, Dan turned the EM limb-crossing sensor back off at 435/07:06 MET.

Thursday afternoon, I flew back to San Jose and home, still very annoyed about the countermanding of my order.

Friday, March 19, 1999

Day 436 MET: Discussing the Battery Issue

I went to Mission Ops early to catching up on everything and to do a TV interview with the *Discovery* crew from England. I also had calls from the BBC and some other reporters who had read the NASA press release and had various questions, and I watched a tank heater event.

Later in the morning, Dan, Woody, and I got together and talked about the battery. Woody said we would be in danger of losing the battery if we got below 22 volts. Well, we hadn't been below 24.5 v (the yellow limit), but he thought he was seeing the beginnings of the voltage roll off during the worst tank heater events. I responded,

"That always looks that way because more heaters are turning on toward the end of the nighttime pass. But when you correctly plot the battery voltage against DOD, there is no sign of the roll off. I just don't see any evidence of a roll off." Finally, he agreed there was no problem (and hence, there was absolutely no need for the aggravating counter-mand) and, even though the tank events would frequently push the voltage down close to the yellow limit of 24.5 v, the battery was OK. Also, since the β angle was 14°, the nighttime passes were within a few seconds of their maximum duration of 49 minutes, so the situation was not going to get any worse. But, just to keep the nervous Nellie's happy, I agreed to keep having the transmitter turned off during the tank heater events until the next OMM burn, which was just in a couple days. That would knock the heater on-time down some more (it was usually running 2 hours, but sometime it was up to 2 hours and 6 or 7 minutes). After the burn, the turn-off crap was coming to an end.

Sylvia and I talked just a few minutes and she had done a very good thing. Ed Weiler, the new Associate Administrator for Space Science, who had replaced Wes Huntress, wanted another peer review of the extended mission. Sylvia had raised hell about it, saying they had asked for one and we had given them one, so they weren't getting a second one — and Weiler backed off! I was proud of her.

I finished the Mission Profile for the 2nd OMM of the extended mission, set for the following week.

Chapter 4-14
The Eternal Question —
Who is in Charge?

Monday, March 22, 1999

Day 439 MET: The Same Old Conflict

As was my habit, I watched another heater event because the monitor controllers were still turning the transmitter off twice per event since they still could not tell when (or did not pay attention) the heater events were happening. They had already turned the transmitter off once — for no reason — when I came in, so I stopped them from doing it again as I watched the event.

I was told that the day before, the controllers had to send the turn-on commands three times before the transmitter turned back on! Kathy said the first two sets of commands had been uplinked — with no response — and that sounded to me like the transmitter simply didn't turn on until the third try and I did not like that!

Disturbed and still annoyed that the nitwits had countermanded my order not to turn the transmitter off, I went to talk to Bob Jackson. I had had it with Marcie, Sylvia, Dan, and Lockheed interfering with my authority and questioning my judgment about how to run the spacecraft — especially since they were always wrong. I told Bob, "We are getting to the point where turning the transmitter off and on might end the mission," and, "Unless I'm allowed to run the spacecraft without interference, we are going to get into real trouble." He said Sylvia had talked to him about the same issue, i.e., who was in charge of the spacecraft, but from her perspective. He said he couldn't talk about it right then, because he had to go to a meeting. I said we could do so the next day, because I wanted Sylvia there anyway.

I went back up to Mission Ops, just as Ric came in and he was of the opinion that what had happened the day before was as follows: The DSN had started to sweep before the spacecraft had come out of occultation and hence, they hadn't really locked up on the spacecraft, even though they thought they had. The first two sets of commands didn't get to the spacecraft. Then, when they swept again and got a lock, the third command got in the spacecraft. I hoped he was right, but it still could have been that the transmitter had not turned on. Regardless, except for Dan, Marcie, and Sylvia's fears, there was no rational reason for turning the transmitter off and running the risk that it would not turn back on, period.

Just as I was about to leave Mission Ops, Sylvia came in. We sat down and had a nice long chat. I told her that I was not happy about their countermanding my order for two reasons. First, it was the wrong thing to do, i.e., continuing turning the transmitter off and on, and we discussed it politely. Her problem was, of course, she simply didn't understand what was going on — it was over her head. I knew she was trying to do the best she could, but stupid Marcie was continuing to give her incorrect information.

Then, my second and usual point, "Who in hell is running the mission, you guys or me?"

She started with the usual, "Although I try to respect your running the mission, we also don't want the mission to go bad, and blah, blah, blah," it was the same old tune from both of us.

I kept saying, "I'm in charge of the this, that is what the contract says."

And she kept saying, "That's your interpretation of who is responsible and that isn't necessarily what NASA meant."

I responded with, "That's BS. That's a copout. Lockheed works for me, I don't work for them."

She said again, "That's your interpretation."

We again looked up the original contract and, of course, it said the work was to be done *under my direction*. But then she found a modification of the original contract — modified for the extended mission or perhaps when I retired from Lockheed — *that I had never seen, nor was aware of, nor signed!* The NASA bastards — almost certainly led by Scott — had snuck in and changed the contract behind my back to say the mission was to be done via "consultation with the PI." Well, they could pull all that kind of sneaky, backstabbing BS they wanted, it didn't make any difference to me, it was just BS. Screw'em.

When I got home, I found that the *Discover* award gala was going to be in Orlando at Epcot. That was going to be fun, if we got to go. Then I got a lot of calls from Spain, England, Germany, and elsewhere regarding the NASA press release.

Tuesday, March 23, 1999

Day 440 MET: A Continuation of the Same Old Conflict

I got everything ready for the OMM burns the next day, including turning the pressure transducer and the EM limb-crossing sensor back on. The file was uplinked at 440/13:15 MET and both sensors were back on by 440/13:17 MET. Then we had our pre-burn meeting.

After the meeting, we talked to JPL about the possibility of periodically commanding the spacecraft from JPL after the end of the extended mission, if Berkeley were to track the spacecraft for another six months. They said, "Yes, you can do it here." That opened the possibility of doing both the Berkeley tracking and the UT impact experiment. Despite those two excellent possibilities, Marcie was so damned negative about all of that, I could have kicked her butt. She is just worthless — her only function was to cause trouble.

After that, Bob Jackson came up to Mission Ops and asked me to come down to his office to finish the conversation we had started the previous day. To my surprise, he had told Sylvia not to come, because he wanted to talk to me alone!

As he requested, I began to explain to him my main concerns. I said, "We've discussed the facts that I'm trying to demonstrate how to do missions correctly (a main goal of Discovery) and that I believe I've been given the sole responsibility to do it. Thus, I'm greatly concerned that I kept seeing my authority and that (Discovery) goal eroded."

He said several things that were very interesting. First, "Everyone — Scott, Sylvia, Marcie, Lockheed, and me — is concerned that the mission is coming to its end and we are all afraid that something will happen to wreck it so close to the end — that your people and you will get lax or something like that. Everybody wanted Lunar Prospector to be a perfect mission."

I felt like saying, "Well, since I've directed a perfect mission to date, why don't you trust me to finish the job?" But I did not want to interrupt him, so I let it go.

Second, and I found that the way Bob put it was very interesting, Bob said, "Marcie and Sylvia feel you just go and do what you want and they are left to pick up the pieces — they are always having to catch up."

Third, he said, "I am concerned that one man has so much responsibility and nobody likes that."

I replied, "My attitude is, so what, it works! NASA gave me those responsibilities and now they've decided they were just kidding! I'm really annoyed about that. As I have said over and over, this mission was never about science, it was always about what NASA wanted and that was a demonstration about how to do things Faster, Better, Cheaper, and that's what I'm doing. I'm more interested in the programmatics than anything else. I'm really annoyed that the lessons learned are being ignored and pushed aside. As far as I'm concerned, NASA is shooting itself in the foot about this — the very things that NASA needs to learn from Lunar Prospector are just being ignored."

Bob responded with, "Well, then you need to get people at Headquarters on your side." I explained to him that Alan Ladwig and Joe Rothenberg were on my side.

Bob returned to Marcie and Sylvia's concerns and I replied, "OK, I understand they are concerned, I accept that, but I don't agree they have any basis for their concerns, but I don't want to get personal about it."

He said, "No, go ahead, get personal." And that was when I realized why he did not want Sylvia there; he wanted to hear what I had to say without any inhibitions — like Sylvia's being there would stop me from saying what I thought anyway.

I started, "OK, in my opinion Marcie is a third-rate engineer. She does not understand anything about the spacecraft or the mission. She may understand the DSN and that's good, but she does not understand this spacecraft. She is so rigid that she is incapable of looking right or left. She sees a yellow limit and she goes ballistic. First of all, we've never actually went yellow (during that β cycle). We've hit 24.5 v, but the battery voltage has to go below 24.5 v before it goes yellow. This whole to-do is about nothing. Also, Bob, I set those limits and I know what their sensitivities are and, as you well know, yellow simply means caution and red means that something is getting serious. Clearly, it's a matter of an arbitrary definition and it (the battery voltage) has just been on the fence — so her screaming that we had yellow limits is simply not true and is irrelevant. But she just goes ballistic, she panics and then she flails around. I'm sorry to use a sexist word, but she does get hysterical. She doesn't know what is going on, so she flounders around and raises a big stink and then there is a big to-do about nothing. I really cannot stand her. I knew that from the beginning, because she has all these rules and regulations that she blindly follows, none of which are useful. She comes in and insists I have procedures laid out every time we have an eclipse or whatever. I write up the procedures and they just lay there — nobody uses them. They are totally useless, a total waste of time. I have the information in my head and I'm always there. I understand that makes you guys nervous, since you don't have a backup for me. If something happened to me, you could lose the mission — but I doubt very much that will happen. But, if you are going to do cheap programs, what choice do you have? You have to take that risk."

Getting back to Marcie, I said, "The minute I interfaced with Marcie after Scott had put her on the program, I knew she was not going to work out. I asked Scott to get rid of her, but he wouldn't do it. Though I agree there are certain things she does well, when I weigh those things against her drawbacks, she is a negative influence on the program and I really did not want her around. After having asked Scott to get rid of her more than once, I considered asking you to reassign her, but I didn't do it, because I figured Scott would overrule you if you did what I asked. I've been stuck with her and all the trouble she causes." Having somewhat vented my spleen on Marcie, I turned to Sylvia.

I said, "In contrast to Marcie, I really like Sylvia and respect the job she is doing — the part of it that she can do. She does a good job of managing the money, keeping Headquarters happy and all that sort of stuff, but when it comes to the technical stuff, she is in over her head — she doesn't have the background. She doesn't have any physics. She doesn't understand it."

Bob said, "Well, that's the problem, they complain that you don't communicate with them."

I replied, "I can't communicate with them on the technical issues. I tell them something and they forget it. They don't understand it; so they didn't get the message. Marcie likes to work with email and I don't. I go tell people personally what I want them to know so there is no miscommunication — but Marcie wants her emails. Clearly we have completely different ways of working and that is part of the disconnect. Regardless, it doesn't do any good to tell either one of them anything, they never understand — they are just technically incompetent. I don't expect Sylvia to be technically competent and I do respect and like what she does in the other areas. But I am really floored that NASA gives someone with no technical background responsibilities they can't handle. I am not crabbing about Sylvia, because I really think she is doing a good job, but why do you put her in a position that she can't handle?" There was no answer to that question.

Bob did not contradict any of the things I said about Marcie or Sylvia. Rather he reiterated everyone's concern that the mission could get fouled up so close to its end. I responded, "That bothers me tremendously — when you tell me that everybody is so concerned about this mission failing at the end. First of all, the spacecraft has performed flawlessly. I have run it flawlessly. I know what I am doing. We could walk away from that spacecraft and after six months it would still be working flawlessly. It works just like clockwork. I watch it. I know how it acts. Why don't you guys have any confidence in me and in the spacecraft? Why do you assume I am going to fail or the spacecraft is going to fail, when everything has been perfect to date?" Again there was no answer to that question.

I continued, "Look, you're part of a dying organization that is desperately trying to learn how to do things Faster, Better, Cheaper. I'm doing it, but NASA is ignoring it. That's why I am annoyed and frustrated."

Finally Bob said, "Well, this is interesting, because I get everything second and third hand — I've only listened to their side of the story."

I felt like saying, "Well, why in hell didn't you come and ask me much earlier? What kind of managers are you guys?"

Bob continued, "I now see this in a different light. I see that for you this mission has a fresh new start every single day. It's not getting old. It's not getting sloppy."

I replied, "That is right and that is an interesting way of saying it. Interestingly enough, when we started the extended mission, Dan and I were discussing the very same thing and we both agreed that our team was better, sharper, and crisper than we ever were, even in the beginning." I explained that the only mistakes we had ever made in commanding were just on the science side and only in the beginning, and that I had changed the procedures and there hadn't been a mistake since then. Then I said, "What bothered me was when Sylvia and Marcie looked at the low orbit of the extended mission, they panicked. They just knew we were going to crash the spacecraft and all that sort of stuff. To me, it is the same exact thing as the nominal mission, the same procedures, the same everything — we were just going to be closer to the Moon."

Finally our conversation died down. I told Bob I appreciated sitting down and talking to him and that we had had a good conversation.

I went to see Sylvia to let her know she was OK.

Wednesday, March 24, 1999

Day 441 MET: Commanding Problems During the OMM

A few days earlier, I had met Désirée Karge, a reporter for the German magazine *Bild Der Wissenschaft*, who wanted to do an article on Lunar Prospector and I had invited her to watch the OMM burn before we did the interview. The commanding was to begin just after 9:00 AM and Désirée came a few minutes early, as we were getting ready for the burns. I gave her a copy of the Mission Profile and explained that we were going to do four burns, a 43.78 second burn at aposelene on engines A1 and A2 that would change the spacecraft's velocity by 6.87 m/sec and a 47.10 second burn at periselene on engines A1 and A2 that would change the spacecraft's velocity by 7.39 m/sec, after which we would do a tweak reor burn and a tweak de-spin burn.

As we sat down at our consoles, we were getting a lot of data dropouts in the downlink, which I did not like at all. But, since we had to do the OMM or hit the Moon in 48 hours, I started the commanding at 441/13:39 MET, by having Ric uplink the A1 and A1 heater turn-on file. I saw, read, and verified the echoes of the A1 heater turn-on command, its Execute, and the A2 heater turn-on command — but there was no EXEC echo for the A2 heater command! I waited a little over a minute and it became clear the spacecraft had not received the second EXEC. I had Ric send a second EXEC at 441/13:42 MET and I saw its echo — the spacecraft had accepted the second EXEC. I grumped about the dropouts and the bad signal-to-noise, but we had to proceed with the OMM — regardless.

Knowing that we were having communications problems, we paid very strict attention to the uplink and verification of the engine parameter load, but it went up OK and the burn started at 441/14:05 MET and went perfectly.

Still concerned about the data dropouts, I issued the command to send up the A1 and A2 heater turn-on command file for the periselene burn at 441/14:14 MET and it went up OK. That was followed by the uplink and verification of the second engine parameter file, which also went up without incident. Then at 441/14:46 MET, the second burn started and went off without a hitch. We were relieved since the OMM was successfully behind us and the spacecraft's orbit was good for another 4 weeks, but I grumped more and more about the poor communications link — by then we were even getting CHECK-SUM errors on the instrument readouts and I did not like that one bit.

To add to the problems, the DSN had an equipment problem, which delayed us by about 10 minutes.

At 441/15:04 MET, I had Ric uplink the A1 and A4 heater turn-on file to start the reor burn sequence and there was no echo for second EXEC — the spacecraft had again not received the command. Just like the first time that happened — 1½ hours earlier, I waited a little bit and then I had Ric uplink an EXEC. I got the echo of the EXEC and the A4 heater began to heat up.

Cautiously, we started to load the engine parameter file. I saw, read, and verified the DELAYSUN, SHORTDUR, HALFREV echoes, *but there was no DELAYNUM echo*, and then I got the echo for the A14REOR engine selection! I said, "That's it. I'm canceling the rest of the burns until we find out what is going on." I had Ric send a STOPFIRE

Command at 441/15:33 MET to insure the engine did not fire, immediately followed by the SETCMDREG Command to safe the engines at 441/15:37 MET and then the CAT-SOFF Command at 441/15:43 MET to turn off the A1 and A4 engine heaters. With that, I had safed the spacecraft and said, "OK, we're done for now."

I turned to Désirée and said I was sorry, but we had to break off the commanding session because of communications problems and we would have to do the interview at a later time. She understood it was time for her to leave. We said, "Auf Wiedersehen."

Dan and I immediately started looking at the data and Dan found, from one of the pieces of engineering data we never normally look at, that the first EXEC that had failed had been *received and then rejected* by the spacecraft. The command had apparently become garbled. Either the command had not been properly transmitted from the DSN or the spacecraft had screwed it up and we didn't know which. We checked with the guys at the DSN and they said, "No, we had no problems, no errors, no error flags, and no nothing. The (orbital) predicts were good and there were no problems here."

As soon as possible, Dan snuck off to the telephone and called Steve Debrock to snitch to him what had happened. I had lost all respect for Dan as a person since, as Lockheed's spy, he reported every move I made to Debrock, just like the little lap dog he had become. Despite my annoyance with Marcie, at least she acted out of fear and stupidity, rather than personal gain. But Dan was just shamelessly brown-nosing Lockheed to ingratiate himself with the company for his personal benefit — he disgusted me.

When Dan had Debrock on the phone, I could hear Dan answer, "Yes, Alan is here and yes, Alan was doing the commanding." I was amazed at how dumb Debrock is, since he did not even know how I ran Mission Ops, i.e., that I was always there and that I always did the commanding, but he was still ready to try to tell me what I had to do. Apparently, Debrock was saying I must have done something wrong, because Dan said, "Well, he is here. Do you want to talk to him?" but gutless Debrock didn't, which did not surprise me. Then Dan just said, "OK," and hung up. Whatever was said, I knew it was a reflection of the fact the Lockheed considered that I was in the way of their running the mission and I was a problem — but Lockheed and Debrock could kiss my ass.

However, I was really annoyed with Dan; I have the greatest respect for his technical capabilities. Dan knew the C&DH and he knows a lot more about dynamics and computers than I do, but he always tried to take over. In one sense, I didn't mind, since I believe in delegating responsibilities and I expect that the person to whom I give responsibility should take over in that area, but it bugged me the way he took over, i.e., like I was an idiot, and the way he so slovenly ran to Debrock. In contrast, later, when he left, he said respectfully, "If you don't need me any more, I'll go home." He had a strange combination of arrogance and humility that befuddled me.

After Dan's kiss-ass call, he and I spent a lot of time looking at the engineering data. We plotted up the downlink signal-to-noise as a function of time and found that the uplinked commands that did not get into the spacecraft were sent right when the signal-to-noise was worst. That didn't make any sense, because the signal-to-noise of the downlink has nothing to do with the signal-to-noise of the uplink! I thought, *what in hell does that have to do with the data going up, unless there is something wrong in our system?* But I just did not think there was something wrong with the spacecraft.

Nevertheless, I had seen for quite some time that the signal-to-noise of the downlink varied as a function of where the spacecraft was in its orbit. The signal-to-noise was bad during the nighttime passes — it started getting bad while we were still on the dayside, but approaching the nightside; and then it started getting good again as we were approaching the dayside. I thought maybe there was something in the spacecraft's

Communications Subsystem that was responding to the thermal variation between day and night and causing the increase in the noise when it got cool.

Dan kept saying, "Maybe it's ephemeris; maybe the DSN is not doing it right."

I replied, "But since we always have the same periodic changes in the signal-to-noise as a function of spacecraft's orbit position, you can't tell me the ephemeris errors are always the same for every orbit. The only things that repeat themselves the same way every orbit are the temperatures. I think there is something going on in the spacecraft in response to the orbital temperature changes." But who knew? Dan and I kept brainstorming, trying to find an explanation for what we were seeing.

Regardless, the commanding problem was not a catastrophe. I had written in the Emergency Procedure part of the Mission Operations Document years earlier that, if the spacecraft does not accept a command, send it again, until it is accepted and that was, of course, exactly what we had done.

Thus ended an interesting day. That was the first serious commanding anomaly we had. We had things that we had called anomalies before, but they were all small things that didn't have any consequences for the spacecraft. The command anomaly was the real thing and we had to figure out what in hell was going on. We set up a meeting at Lockheed at 9:00 AM the next day with Woody, Gerry Grismore, and whoever else could help. We would all have to put on our thinking caps and figure it out.

Thursday, March 25, 1999

Day 442 MET: The Anomaly Meeting

I went up to Mission Ops early and watched a tank heater event, which was fine (as agreed to six days earlier, we had again stopped turning off the transmitter, but I still checked the heater events to make sure the battery was OK).

We had our command anomaly meeting at 9:00 AM. We went through everything we knew. Marcie brought some data she had plotted up from the last time we were in the radio occultation free period, as we were during the previous day's commanding, and we saw the same orbital variations in the signal-to-noise. Since, during the radio occultation free periods, the spacecraft appeared to go around the edge of the Moon and never behind it, it was possible that when the spacecraft had the correct geometry each orbit, the radio waves not only traveled directly to the Earth, but they also bounced off the Moon surface and were reflected to the Earth. Since the reflected waves would take a microsecond or two longer to reach the Earth than the direct waves, the two sets of waves could interfere with each other and cause the signal-to-noise of the down-linked signal to drop and — and that was the important point — the same thing would happen to our uplinked signal! Gerry was going to check a number of things about the antenna and the direction it was pointing with respect to the Moon to see if the interference idea made any sense. However, none of the things we discussed seemed to clarify the issue. But since Bill had seen noise in the NS and APS data that was orbit position dependent, it was possible that, since we were making such sensitive measurements, we were seeing unexpected secondary effects.

Since we could find no reasonable explanation for the command anomaly and since Gerry knew the C&DH inside and out, he agreed with us that the only thing we could do was to follow my procedure, i.e., if I didn't get a valid echo of a command, I would repeat uplinking the command until the spacecraft accepted it and sent back the correct echo. We also decided to relax our acceptable range of spin rate and attitude drift, so we would have fewer tweak burns to do and do anything else that would reduce the number of commands we had to send to the spacecraft. Not that we were in any trouble, but the less we had to do, the better.

However, if the anomaly was due to something degrading in the spacecraft (remember Lunar Prospector was designed for a 1-year mission lifetime at 100 km altitude and we were well into our 15th month of operations and at very low altitudes), we could get to the point where we couldn't do much commanding, but I didn't think that would happen. In any case, we would find out during the next couple of months.

The command/signal-to-noise anomaly also meant that Bob's wanting to track Lunar Prospector after the extended mission came to an end, might not work. Since it was already questionable if Berkeley could track the spacecraft, if the signal-to-noise got really bad, then Berkeley wasn't going to be able to get a decent signal most of the time. I was getting skeptical about that anyway and we would soon have the answer to that question. Thus, the impact experiment was looking more and more interesting. If the Berkeley plan had problems, I would just kiss it off and go straight for the impact experiment.

Monday, March 29, 1999

Day 446 MET and Early Day 447 MET:
A Tweak Reor Burn and a MAG/ER Sequence

Shortly before noon we started the command sequence for the reor I had canceled the day of the command anomaly. The reor consisted of 11 pulse burns on the A1 and A4 engines; we changed the spacecraft's attitude by 1.89° and the SEA became 1.5°. I started the command sequence with the A1 and A4 heater turn-on file that was uplinked at 446/14:05 MET, the reor burn started at 446/14:35 MET, and the engines were safed by 446/14:39 MET.

Since Bill wanted the GRS gain turned up two steps, to 1710 v, I had inserted those commands into the burn sequence at 446/14:15 MET while we were waiting for the engines to heat up. The entire sequence went perfectly — there were no commanding errors.

Monday evening at about 7:30, I went back to Mission Ops to command a data collection sequence that would allow the ER to collect a special set of data when the spacecraft was in the Earth's magnetic tail (the geomagnetic tail) with Dave Mitchell and to turn off the pressure transducer and the EM limb-crossing sensor, since the battery voltage had hit the yellow limit during the previous tank heater event, so I wanted to save that little bit of power. The ER file contained 14 commands and we started uplinking it at 447/01:10 MET. The spacecraft did not accept the 4th command that was uplinked at the exact time when the signal-to-noise was very low! When I saw that I had no echo of that command, I asked David if we could uplink the lost command after the rest of the file was uplinked and he answered, "Yes, it makes no difference when the command is uplinked." At 447/01:19 MET, I had the 4th command uplinked again, the spacecraft accepted it, and I got the echo.

Between 447/01:21 MET and 447/01:23 MET, I had the file uplinked to turn off the pressure transducer and the EM sensor. Also, since our last OMM, the tank heater event durations were below 2 hours, but still not down to 1 hour and 51 minutes or one orbital period. The last heater event was 1 hour and 56 minutes.

Wednesday, March 31, 1999

Day 448 MET

I went to Mission Ops because I had an interview with Robert Irion, a local free-lance reporter who was writing an article on Lunar Prospector for *Astronomy* magazine.

Thursday, April 1, 1999

Day 449 MET

I went up to Mission Ops, mainly to do the interview with Désirée Karge for *Bild Der Wissenschaft*, which I enjoyed very much because I had a chance to speak German.

Friday, April 2, 1999

Day 450 MET: Commanding and More Lockheed BS

I went up to Mission Ops fairly early to check on the spacecraft and to do the commanding to turn on the EM limb-crossing sensor, so Dan could collect some attitude data, and to return the ER to its normal operation mode after the end of the geomagnetic tail pass. I had the EM limb-crossing sensor commands uplinked at 450/11:09 MET (6:34 AM) and then I had to wait nearly 3½ hours to return the ER to its normal mode. That procedure consisted of uplinking two files, the first at 450/14:35 MET with four commands, and the second at 450/14:38 MET with ten commands. I was finished with the commanding by 450/14:45 MET or 10:10 AM.

Friday was also the day we passed through β = 0°, so we had the longest possible nighttime pass duration, some 49 minutes. Very slowly, over the next three months, the nighttime pass durations would get shorter and shorter and the tank heater events would become less of a problem — but very, very slowly.

Dan told me Debrock was going to have some guy from Mission Success coming over the following Monday or Tuesday to help insure we successfully ended the mission! It was all I could do not to blow my top. I was fed up with all the Lockheed and Ames stupidity and incompetence I had to deal with on a daily basis and I did not need Lockheed telling me how to run the mission. It was just the same BS over and over. I had just had a long talk with Bob Jackson about the mission and satisfied him that everything was OK and then stupid Debrock was starting the same thing over again. Why, oh why do stupidity and incompetence always win out over competence? The answer is — because most Lockheed and NASA managers are incompetent and there are so many of them! Were they trying to drive me nuts so they could get rid of me by having me committed? Wouldn't it have been easier just to have me shot in some alley or, as so often mentioned in the past, killed in a freeway accident (by a NASA van)?

Late in the afternoon, at 450/20:40 MET (4:05 PM) and while at home at LRI, I commanded the EM limb-crossing sensor off via telephone, since Dan had all the attitude data he needed.

Monday, April 5, 1999

Day 453 MET

I went up to Mission Ops at about 10:00 AM. The spacecraft was fine. The battery was OK. I would be glad when the next several weeks were behind us, so the nighttime pass duration was at least down to 48 minutes. By then, we wouldn't be hitting the yellow limit on the battery voltage anymore.

Andre Sylvest, his wife, and a friend came for a visit and I showed them Mission Ops.

I got a message from the mission success guy Debrock was sending over, Mohammad something, he wanted to see us (Dan, Sylvia, Marcie, and me) individually. Needless to say, I was not happy about that BS. The whole concept of having a mission success review at that time was an insult and annoying. Nevertheless, I would have to put up with it and get through the next three weeks and the final three months without blowing my top. Lunar Prospector was far too important to me to let Lockheed and NASA's annoying crap wreck what I had worked to accomplish for over ten years. Once the mission was over, NASA and Lockheed could all go straight to hell.

Rebecca flew in from St. Louis at about 12:30 AM and it was about 1:30 AM before we got home and in bed.

Tuesday, April 6, 1999

Day 454 MET

I went to Mission Ops late because Rebecca had flown in from St. Louis so late.

Mohammad called and he actually sounded like a nice guy. We talked briefly, but we really needed to sit down together for a long discussion, so we agreed to meet the next day at 8:00 AM.

I talked to Sylvia later and she said she had told Mohammad he had better talk to me and find out what I was up to before he talked to anybody else, with the implication that, otherwise, he might screw up. She had done a good job and I really appreciated the fact that she, too, knew the whole mission success exercise was stupid and a waste of time.

Sylvia said she knew Mohammad from some classes she had had and he is really a sharp guy who has a lot of experience in Mission Ops over at the Blue Cube. Though I was certainly not happy about Debrock forcing his damned mission success review on me, I was actually looking forward to talking with Mohammad. Perhaps, as I had done with Bob Jackson, I could make Mohammad understand what was really going on with Lunar Prospector and finally get Lockheed to back off.

Wednesday, April 7, 1999

Day 455 MET: A Conversation With Mohammad

I went up to Mission Ops mainly to talk with Mohammad, who turned out to be a very nice guy. He had asked me to meet him at McDonald's, so we could talk privately. After taking a look at the spacecraft, I went to McDonald's. After greeting each other,

I said, "I would like to explain the whole program to you, since you need to know that in order to understand what is going on." I proceeded to explain to him the entire history of the program — how it got started; how I had asked Lockheed to be my industry partner; how I was trying to show how to do missions Faster, Better, Cheaper; how Discovery missions were to be run, i.e., by the PI, and that if I had been at my own institute or at a University instead of at Lockheed, I would have had the main contract and Lockheed would have been my subcontractor. He understood Lockheed's having the main contract was the main part of the problem.

I told him the history of the spacecraft's performance and how I ran Mission Ops. Because he seemed most interested in things related to the transmitter turn-off issues, I went through its history. I explained why I did not want to turn the transmitter off and that I had telephoned or had come in every time there was heater event, day or night, for the ten days before I decided to stop having the transmitter turned off. I explained the fuel dump debate and that Debrock knew nothing about this spacecraft or the problems — that Debrock had just inherited the project from Dougherty and he was sitting there, knowing nothing about the program or me, being a stupid jerk. I ended by saying, "I have no respect at all for Lockheed and the way it does things."

I explained about Marcie and her hysteria when she saw a yellow limit — even though I had set the yellow and the red limits and hence, I knew exactly what they signified. Interestingly, Mohammad said, "Well, in the Blue cube, we don't even pay any attention to the yellow limits and if it goes red, then we might ask the engineers to come and look at it." He thought all that was silly crap.

I said, "I don't like her. She's not a good engineer. She's just a pain in the butt."

I said, "Dan is very good, but he is a company man and he always takes the Lockheed's conservative side to protect his own self-interest."

Regarding Woody, I said, "I get along well with Woody, but Woody will never give an answer because he knows better than that; that way he is not responsible for any problems and he keeps out of trouble with Lockheed. I get along well with Woody because he knows when I need information and he gives it to me, I'll take the responsibility for the results and I don't try to blame him if something goes wrong. That's why, when Debrock asked Woody for an answer about turning the transmitter on and off, Debrock couldn't get an answer from Woody, even though Woody was in agreement with me."

Regarding how I ran the mission, i.e., as a dictatorship where I had the only vote, I told him what Jim Martin said after we — the Viking Landing Site Selection Team — had voted on the Viking landing sites back in the early 70's, i.e., "That's not the answer I want, let's vote again. When you get the right answer, then I'll agree with you."

At that point, Mohammad finally got to the core of the matter — he said, "That's the thing, they want to be able to vote." That was it, Dan and Marcie were whining that they wanted to vote on how the mission was run — well screw 'em.

Knowing that we had finally gotten to the bottom of the BS, I said, "I knew Dan was unhappy about something, but I didn't know what."

Mohammad said, "Well, that and the fact that you didn't ask him, or at least inform him, when you turned off the EM limb-crossing sensor a month ago (Day 423 MET) to save power." I was more than astounded at that statement! Dan's feelings were hurt because I did not ask his permission to turn off the EM limb-crossing sensor or, at least, inform him I was going to do so! Well, with that, I had heard everything. I was the damned PI and Mission Director, not him. I did not need his permission to do anything and turning off the EM sensor was such a trivial thing, there was no reason to try to reach him somewhere on vacation to inform him of my action! What a crybaby!

I responded to Mohammad's astounding statement with, "Dan only uses the EM data as a backup to the Sun sensor data. Besides, I asked him before he went on vacation if he needed EM data more than once a week and he said no. Why should I have had to discuss it with him further?"

Mohammad finally said, "I understand all that. You are right, you are doing a good job running the mission."

Then I showed him Mission Ops. He was very impressed. I showed him the Mission Profiles and explained how we did our triple checks and verifications of every engineering command that went to the spacecraft and how Dan and I talked everything out before I wrote up the Mission Profile. I emphasized, "Dan and I always discuss everything and we check each other over and over and over."

Mohammad said, "Those are the right things to do and the things I wanted to hear."

When Mohammad got ready to leave, he said that he wanted to speak to me privately again. We went outside Mission Ops and he said, "I would like to have a meeting with all of you together. It is clear you guys have a textbook perfect mission. This is a perfect example of mission success. There is no reason to question anything you are doing. Everything is being done properly, but I would like to have a meeting with all the people to discuss the issue that some of the people's feelings are hurt and they want to be part of the decision making process."

I said, "As far as I am concerned, that is a waste of time, but if that is what has to happen to keep Lockheed out of my hair, OK."

However, I was sick of that kind of crap — I had just had a similar discussion with Marcie, Sylvia, and Bob Jackson and then a second one with Bob. How many times did I have to prove to those asses that the mission was going perfectly and would continue to do so? So what if they were upset because I didn't let them vote on every move we made? That is not how successful missions are flown or how successful businesses are run. We discussed everything and I got their inputs — what the hell did they want? The answer was, "They did not want to vote; Dan and Marcie wanted to run the mission."

Well, BS, I didn't question the Nav guys' work. They gave me their data and I assumed it was correct (and it always was) and then I went and did my job. I didn't question the way Marcie ran the Mission Ops personnel (her only real job). Though I would have liked to have known why, every time I came in at 5:00 AM, there were never more than two and frequently only one controller on the night shift and then, at shift change over at 6:00 AM, we had four or five controllers there for the morning shift? And I certainly didn't question Dan's dynamics work and he and I checked and cross checked and discussed everything together. But he was still upset, because I didn't confer with him while he was on vacation, about a trivial matter we had discussed before he left on vacation! I was sick to death of these damned crybabies.

As all that was happening, I was amused at Dan's behavior. He had been at Mission Ops in the morning before I went to meet Mohammad at McDonald's and was about to go back to Lockheed to do some testing on his subsystem on another spacecraft when I left, saying I had a meeting with Mohammad. An hour and a half later, when I came back to Mission Ops with Mohammad, Dan was still there! And Dan stayed there all the time that I was showing Mohammad Mission Control and while Mohammad and I had our final private conversation just outside of Mission Control! Clearly, Dan was hanging around so he could do his Lockheed spying for Debrock, since he had plenty of other important things to do at Lockheed. When I came back in after Mohammad left, Dan asked, "What was that all about?"

Clearly, in addition to needing information on my every move for his report to Debrock, the whiney little Lockheed snitch felt left out, so I simply answered, "I showed him everything because he is really interested in the mission," and I laughed to myself at Dan's childish behavior. Then Dan left for Lockheed to do the testing he was supposed to do and to run over to kiss Debrock's butt.

Friday, April 9, 1999

Day 457 MET: A Meeting with Dan Tam

Dan needed some EM limb-crossing data for his attitude determinations, so I turned the EM limb-crossing sensor on at 257/09:39 MET, i.e., at 6:04 AM.

When Dan came to Mission Ops, he said Mohammad wanted to have a two-hour meeting with Sylvia, Marcie, Dan, and me. Neither Dan nor I could understand why he needed a two-hour meeting. I was a little bit puzzled and a little bit wary. I didn't think that I had misjudged Mohammad, but he did work for Lockheed! He knew the mission was being done properly, so what could he tell us we didn't already know? I was very wary.

As both Eric Sterner and Alan Ladwig had suggested on my last trip to DC, I had called Dan Tam and arranged for him to come to Mission Ops so we could talk about my plans for commercial lunar exploration, and so I could show him Mission Ops. Dan is a very young oriental guy and I quickly found out he has a tendency not to listen.

I showed him Mission Ops. Then I explained to him what I wanted to do and about my discussions with Ladwig, Rothenberg, the Congressional aides, etc. He agreed that my plan was the right thing to do and had many questions and many suggestions. Happily, I had already done almost everything he suggested I do to get support for a lunar data purchase program. We had a very interesting and productive discussion and I was pleased that Dan wanted to see my plans come to fruition and was willing to help me as best he could.

After Dan left, I went to see Sylvia and she told me that our considering the UT impact experiment at the end of the mission had gotten all the way up to Dan Goldin. Dan was going to have a say — probably the final say — in it. That was how important the end of the mission had become and that was fine with me, because that meant Lunar Prospector was getting some good exposure.

At 2:20 PM, before I left for home, I turned the EM limb-crossing sensor off at 457/17:55 MET.

Sunday, April 11, through Friday, April 16, 1999

Day 459 MET through Day 464 MET: Caltech and Disneyland

Rebecca and I drove down to LA Sunday in a very, very bad storm — we saw three or four accidents on the way!

I had been asked to give a seminar at Caltech on Monday and it was a very interesting experience. When we got there, the faculty had arranged for Rebecca and me to have lunch with them at the faculty lounge. As we were chatting over lunch, I was exposed to the typical Caltech arrogance, i.e., "We know everything better than you, because we are Caltech and you are common as dirt." However, after I gave the seminar on Lunar Prospector, they were all whistling a completely different tune. Both Rebecca and I got a big kick out of their change of attitude.

After leaving Caltech, we went to Disneyland for a nice vacation and took a boat trip to Santa Catalina Island, which we found enchanting.

While I was on vacation, Dan was in command control of the spacecraft and between 462/16:55 MET and 462/17:11 MET, he uplinked the commands for another ER burst mode and turned the EM limb-crossing sensor on. The following day, at 463/04:27 MET, he turned the latter off.

Monday, April 19, 1999

Day 467 MET: Mohammad's Big Meeting

Mohammad came to meet with Sylvia, Marcie, Dan, and me. The meeting, which was the kind of touchy-feely thing that happens on the Oprah Winfrey Show and that I hate, was a total waste of time. But, by that time, I had found out from Mohammad how that particular brouhaha had gotten started — and Dan was the focal point. It started when crybaby Dan's whining got Sylvia going and then Sylvia got stupid Debrock going. Knowing that, I was just waiting for Mohammad to get started.

Mohammad started off by saying, "This a great mission, totally successful, nothing is really wrong with it. You guys know your stuff and blah, blah, blah. But I was given the job to make sure that everything is OK."

He continued, "However, there are some issues we have to discuss," and he turned to Dan and said, "Dan, I understand you have some concerns."

That was beautiful, whiney Dan was put on the spot and he was clearly humiliated. Dan stuttered a bit and than said, looking at me, "Well, I came back from vacation and I found out Alan had turned off *my* sensor and had stopped turning off the transmitter. In principal, that was the right thing to do, but I felt that I should have been informed."

I looked at Mohammad and asked, "Am I supposed to respond or how is this supposed to work?"

He answered, "No, no this is not supposed to be confrontational. We are just trying to discuss the concerns everyone has" (enter Oprah stage left).

Mohammad asked Marcie what her concerns were and, of course, she wanted more information and she felt left out of things.

Sylvia was next and she brought up this business about the yellow limits, which she still didn't understand. But to her great credit, she had a technical concern and was not whining about hurt feelings like Dan and Marcie.

Then he mistakenly asked me what I thought and I said, "As far as I am concerned this is a tempest in a teapot. It is a total waste of time. But, since you asked — Dan and I always talk over everything in great detail before we do anything. But Dan was not here when I needed to shut off the EM sensor. He was on vacation and I saw no reason to bother him while he was on vacation. I would have told him if he had been here, but I knew he did not need the EM sensor on all the time, since we had discussed it. I didn't say I was going to turn it off before he left on vacation because I did not know I would need to. Turning it off is no big deal. Everyone understands I don't like turning the transmitter off, especially since more than 80% of the time it is being turned off for no reason at all. I am obviously concerned — and everybody, you Mohammad, Dan, and everybody agrees — that every time we turn it off, we are taking a risk and I wanted to minimize that risk. It was obvious to me, and pretty much to everybody, that we didn't need to turn it off. Since I was going to be on vacation and since the controllers were turning if off three times in a row, because they were missing the heater turn-on times, I was getting very concerned. I was up here, or called in, for every heater event for ten days — day and night — to check on it, so I knew exactly what was going on. Then I did exactly what Dan and I had done the previous times when we needed to save power — I shut the EM sensor and the pressure transducer off. I did nothing we hadn't done in the past. It was my decision based on my watching the system and my discussing it with Woody. I felt that Lockheed was informed because Woody is the responsible engineer, but I still told Garner what I was doing. I also had Ric write it up and that should have taken care of the paper trail for Marcie. Finally, when Dan got back from his vacation, I told him. What more do you want?"

We went around and around again. Mohammad just kept going over and over each complaint Marcie and Dan had — it was a sheer waste of time — a tempest in a teapot. Tiring of the useless repetition, I said, "Look, when you guys (Dan, Marcie, and Sylvia) reversed my decision, I didn't like it, but I left it because it wasn't going to kill the spacecraft, and I said we would handle it when I got back. So what's the big deal here?"

But that did not stop the merry-go-round, so I said, "OK, what I'm annoyed about is that Lockheed management keeps getting mixed up in something they don't know anything about and monkeying around in things they shouldn't be involved in. This is my responsibility, both as PI and Mission Director, and I am certainly within my rights to do whatever I feel is necessary, without consulting anyone, but that's not the way I prefer to do it. In the case in question, Dan was gone, so we couldn't go through normal procedures."

Mohammad said, "This is an example of not communicating."

I responded, "How could we communicate, when he was not there?"

Mohammad said, "Well, you could have called Dan. He does have a beeper."

I replied, "It was not that big of a deal. I didn't feel like disturbing him on vacation with something I knew the answer to and that he knew the answer to, too. There was no impact on the spacecraft."

Dan said, "Well, I would have preferred that you called."

I thought, *well, screw you, you whiney little ass*, but I replied, "I would have, had it been something important."

Still not finished, Mohammad brought up our procedure for firing the engines. He said, "You have one of the best procedures I have ever seen. You guys have never made a mistake. This is ideal and other people should use it. Why don't you use that procedure for everything?"

I answered, "Because it's not necessary for the science instruments — it's a matter of complexity and whether the command in question could hurt the spacecraft. Regardless, in all cases, we have the Mission Profile. Everything is done following the timeline — that's our procedure."

Mohammad said, "But you still need to communicate."

I said, "We do. Everything you are asking us to do, we do — every time. That's what the Mission Profile is for. The procedures are there. We do it and it works every single time. What more do you want?"

He shifted to Marcie again and her desperate need to communicate (where is Oprah when you need her?). I responded with, "I don't write emails. I communicate directly by talking to people. I don't like email. Don't expect me to write emails to you (Marcie), because I won't do it." Then Mohammad pointed out again that Marcie felt left out, because Dan and I actually do most of the work in Mission Ops. I responded, "That's because she doesn't know anything about the spacecraft or the mission and she has no responsibilities in those areas," and that sort of ended that.

Sylvia said, "But I keep hearing about yellow limits."

I said, "They don't make any difference. They are just yellow limits that say we need to watch it. Don't forget, I set the limits; I know what they mean."

Since Mohammad believes that yellow limits are meaningless and only red limits are of even slight concern, he finally got it across to Sylvia that the yellow limits were no big deal. He said, "Alan does it right. Alan has done everything right and all his decisions are right. All you really have is this communication problem."

I had to ask myself, *how can you communicate with morons?*

The circus went on for a couple of hours and was a total waste of time — a fact I kept reminding Mohammad of. Finally, he summed it up by saying, "I hope some good will come out of this and you will communicate more."

To which, ironically enough, Sylvia said, "You know, Alan and I communicate all the time. We have great communication. *And I guess I agree with Alan, this is just a tempest in a teapot." Hurray for Sylvia, she was catching on!*

I said, "What I hope comes out of this is that you will tell Lockheed management to butt out. This mission is, as you have already said, a perfect mission. It is an exemplary mission. It is an absolute success. We are doing everything right. All the decisions have been right. So tell them to keep out of my hair," and mercifully, that was the end of it.

After Sylvia, Marcie, and Mohammad left, Dan said to me, "You know how this got started don't you? Sylvia was concerned about these things and said it is Lockheed's contractual obligation to take care of them." The whiney little weasel was trying to push the blame off on Sylvia and Debrock, when he was the one who started it — what a gutless wimp.

I was really pleased with Sylvia and had even more respect for her. She was beginning to understand that all her concerns were baseless and that the mission was not only a success, but would continue to be a success to its very end. She had stopped falling into the NASA trap of making ass-saving, conservative decisions based on ignorance and incompetence once she had the responsibility of the mission, rather, she was beginning to see that what I had been saying from the beginning was correct. Sylvia had turned the corner to start becoming a rarity in NASA — a good manager. As she had finally recognized, most everything "is just a tempest in a teapot."

Despite the wasted morning, the afternoon was great. Joe Boyce called and said I was getting $3 million over 4 years for the data reduction program! Then the guy from *Discover* called and said, "You are one of the three finalists for the *Discover Award*!" He asked me to write up a little story about my work. What a way to end a day that had started off so poorly!

Chapter 4-15
The Tank Heater Event/ Battery Problem

Tuesday, April 20, 1999

Day 468 MET: The 3rd OMM of the Extended Mission

I went up to Mission Ops very early to get everything prepared for the OMM.

Then Wayne came over from Auburn to go with me to Rotary Rocket and to watch our 3rd OMM of the extended mission. We drove up to Rotary Rocket's office and discussed their projected costs for a launch. Their rocket was going to be more expensive than I had originally thought because they had told me the cost of a launch to low Earth orbit, not to a translunar trajectory. We wanted to knock their price down, but, in any case, they would have enough launch capacity so we might be able to launch two spacecraft at a time, which would be very cost effective.

After that, Wayne and I went out to an early dinner because the pre-burn activities were going to start around 5:00 PM.

I started our commanding activity for the OMM at 6:01 PM, i.e., at 468/21:36 MET, by having a file uplinked that turned the EM limb-crossing sensor and the pressure transducer back on. Then at 468/21:41 MET, I had the A1 and A2 heater turn-on file uplinked, followed by the engine parameter file for the 45.2 sec aposelene burn that would change the spacecraft's velocity by 7.10 m/sec. The burn was executed at 468/22:08 MET and the engines were safed at 468/22:10 MET.

At 468/22:12 MET, I started the same sequence of uplink events to prepare the spacecraft for the 45.3 sec, periselene burn that would change the spacecraft's velocity by 7.12 m/sec. That burn started at 468/22:49 MET and the engines were safed at 468/22:51 MET.

With the OMM behind us, I had the A1 and A4 heater turn-on command file for a 4-pulse reor burn uplinked at 468/22:53 MET, the reor burn was executed at 468/23:33 MET, and the safeing was done at 468/23:36 MET.

Next came the T1 heater turn-on at 468/23:37 MET for a 1.1 sec despin burn, which was executed at 468/23:54 MET, and the final engine safeing was finished at 468/23:56 MET.

Finally at 468/23:57 MET, I had the commands uplinked to turn the pressure transducer off, but I left the EM limb-crossing sensor on, so Dan could get his attitude data. By then it was nearly 8:30 PM and the commanding activities had lasted nearly 2½ hours.

There was no problem with commanding at all. I had watched the signal-to-noise very closely, because Alex Konopliv had sent me an email a day or so earlier, confirming our suspicions that we were getting reflections of the radio signals off the Moon and that was almost certainly what was causing the command and downlink problems we had encountered during the previous OMM.

The burns were great. They were the kind of burns we really enjoyed — it was just a perfect sequence. We were doing great. Three more OMMs to go.

Wednesday, April 21, 1999

Day 469 MET

I went up to command the EM limb-crossing sensor off. The commands were uplinked at 469/12:35 MET and I got the correct echoes, but the sensor did not turn off! I had the commands sent again at 469/12:39 MET and the sensor turned off. Why it did not turn off the first time was a mystery.

Thursday, April 22, 1999

Day 470 MET

I checked out the spacecraft and it was fine.

I called Dave Mitchell to ask about the amount of MAG/ER data we would really be getting if we did the Berkeley tracking. Since we would be in very low orbits only at the very beginning and at the very end of the 4 or 5 month period when Berkeley would be tracking the spacecraft, we would only get a few weeks of really good data from the MAG. The rest of the 4 or 5 months would be spent at mean altitudes above 75 km, i.e., so the MAG data would be no better than what we had gotten during the nominal mission. My question was, "What was the ER going to produce under those circumstances?" Dave told me, to my surprise, that, while we had completely mapped the Moon with the ER at the high energy end of the spectrum, we had mapped only 6 or 7% of the Moon at the low energy end of the spectrum, i.e., at 5 km resolution and that would take 7 or 8 years to get the high resolution mapping completely done! Similarly, we had mapped only 5 or 6% of the Moon during the magnetically quiet geomagnetic tail pass periods, though they might be able to double or triple those numbers when they got further into the data reduction phase of the program.

Those statements killed my interest in letting Berkeley do the post mission tracking. If they had completed 70%, or even 50% of the high resolution ER mapping, then getting another 20% mapped during the Berkeley tracking phase would be worth it. But since they were only 6 or 7% complete, getting another 1 or 2% done was not worth the expense. I would rather do the impact experiment since it was clearly the more promising of the two and it cost no money. If that were the final decision, then we would probably impact the spacecraft on July 30 or 31.

I went to talk with Sylvia about the end of the mission scenarios. She said Headquarters wanted our answer to that question ASAP.

Then she told me Carolyn Porco was pestering her again because she, Carolyn, wanted to have Gene's ashes on the Moon on a certain date. I had really had it with that stupid twit — Gene's ashes continued to be an annoyance to us.

Finally, Bill called and asked that I turn the APS back on. It had been 73 days since we had turned it off and Bill felt we had enough good clean NS data so we could turn the APS back on. At 470/11:10 MET (mid-afternoon) I turned the APS back on and then I checked Faces 1, 2, and 4, reset the APS energy window, and at 470/11:20 MET, I turned all the faces on. The APS was back in business.

Tuesday, April 27, 1999

Day 475 MET

We decided we were going to do the impact experiment on July 30 or the following day — it depended on the Hubble telescope's availability — and forgo Bob's attempt to track Lunar Prospector after the official end of the extended mission.

Since we were only going to get $3 million, instead of the $3.9 million we needed to do the numerical reduction of the data and archive them, Joe Boyce asked me to submit a revised budget and revised work statement, since we could not do all the proposed work with the budget I was getting. Thus, some of the higher-level products could not be done, but I hoped to be able to get the rest of the money the following year to finish the job. I wrote the new work statement and new budget and sent them to NASA.

The big news was that Lockheed finally attempted to launch CRSS on the second Athena II launch *and the launch failed!* I trust that everyone remembers all the problems that NASA and Lockheed caused us during the two years leading up to our January 6 launch on the first Athena II launch — NASA insisting that we wait for CRSS to be launched because NASA did not want Lunar Prospector on the first Athena II launch and Lockheed lying and saying that CRSS would be launched in December of 1997. *Well, CRSS was launched 16 months late and the second Athena II failed!* So much for NASA wisdom and Lockheed lies. If we had waited until CRSS launched on the first Athena II, Lunar Prospector would have been canceled because of the 16-month delay and/or ended up on the bottom of the ocean, as did CRSS. The cause of the failure was the shroud did not separate, so the Athena II never reached orbit.

Wednesday, April 28, 1999

Day 476 MET

I called Dave Folta to get better ground tracking information for the end of July, so I could start planning the details of the impact experiment, i.e., determine exactly where I wanted the spacecraft to impact.

At 476/11:35 MET (8:00 AM), I issued the command to uplink the standard file with 14 commands we were using to prepare the ER to collect the special geomagnetic tail pass data set. I was a little bit peeved because I had told David Mitchell to be there for the commanding, but he had a seminar he was going to give that afternoon, so he didn't want to drive down from Berkeley. I said, "OK, but be there (at your office) at 8:00, so I can call you and get your verifications over the phone," and he said he would be there. Of course, he did not get to his office until after 8:00, so I couldn't have him check the commanding. Dave just did not take the running of the spacecraft seriously enough to suit me. It was not that I was worried that I could not get the load uplinked properly, but I expected the MAG/ER guys would verify that everything was OK with their instruments — verification was the lifeblood of the commanding — so I told him he had better be there the next time.

Nearly two hours later, at 476/13:15 MET, I had the EM limb-crossing sensor turned on.

Shortly after that, we had a yellow limit tank heater event! The duration of the heater events was down to 101 minutes to 108 minutes, much less than the period of one orbit. But the nighttime passes were still 48 minutes long, so we were still hitting the yellow limit on the battery voltage every once in a while. I had thought that would have stopped by that time, but I was wrong. I was still keeping the pressure transducer off and I kept the EM limb-crossing sensor off, except when Dan needed attitude data. I was hoping we could stop turning them off after the next OMM burn set for the following week. By then, the nighttime passes would be below 47 minutes and the heater on-time would be a little shorter, since we would have used more fuel.

Nevertheless, everything was going fine. The following week, when we did the next OMM burn, we were going to move the periselene of the orbit from the near-side to the far-side, and that would be the last modification of the orbit in the extended mission — so just three more months to go!

Joe Boyce wrote me an email regarding the revised budget and work statement for the numerical data reduction program, informing me that what I had sent him was on the right track for what he needed, but that I was supposed to put most of the money into reducing all the GRS and NS data, do as much as I could with the rest of the money to reduce the MAG/ER data, and do nothing with the APS data — what a waste of data.

Saturday Evening, May 1, 1999

Late Day 479 MET through Early Day 480 MET: A Red Limit Battery Voltage Event

Around 7:00 Saturday night, I got a call from Troy, who said he and John had just seen in the data playback from Friday night, and there had been a red limit event on the battery voltage (23.8 v at 479/2:07 MET)! I immediately drove up to Mission Ops and got there somewhat before the next heater event was to occur.

The story was that the tank heaters had turned on about six minutes after the spacecraft had started the daytime pass and stayed on during the rest of that daytime pass, all of the next nighttime pass, and turned off two minutes after the next daytime pass had started. The problem was that the spacecraft was over the Maria during the daylight part of the orbit, so the solar array current was down about ½ amp, because the dark Maria reflect less sunlight back to the spacecraft, as compared to when the spacecraft was over the bright highlands. As a result, the battery did not get charged up and we buzzed right through the yellow limit and went to and then below the red limit!

The following heater event had started Saturday morning at 479/12:09 MET, but happily, the battery voltage never got below 24.6 v, so, even though no one had noticed, everything was OK.

Needless to say, I was not happy that the controllers on duty Friday night had not noticed a red limit event and that I was informed about it nearly a day later — where was Marcie when it was her turn to have an effective line of communication she was always bitching about? Nevertheless, I was relieved that Troy and John had caught the red limit event the next evening.

The next heater event started about an hour after I arrived at Mission Ops. The heaters turned on at 480/00:25 MET, just two minutes after the spacecraft started its daytime pass. John and I watched it and the battery did not get fully charged before the next nighttime pass began — the battery voltage was only 32.2 v, nearly a full volt below the 33 v that was the normal maximum at that time. It was clear we would have a low voltage/red limit event if I did not turn off the transmitter. At 480/01:26 MET, two minutes before the spacecraft went into radio occultation, I had John uplink the transmitter off command. Then at 480/02:17 MET, I had John uplink the turn-on command, but the DSN was having a problem, so I had John repeat the uplink at 480/02:22 MET and the transmitter came back on. Since the timing of that heater event was even worse than the one that had gone red the night before, we would have definitely gone red and dropped well below the 23.8 v of the previous red limit event, had I not turned the transmitter off. Also, the load current was abnormally high during that heater event, so that would have added to the problem.

Since we were in the worst of conditions, i.e., the nighttime passes were still 48 minutes long and the daytime passes were over the Maria — so the solar array current was low, I was hoping that, as the conditions improved over the next few days and we had the next OMM, we would not have to turn the transmitter off any more.

I left Mission Ops shortly before midnight to drive back home.

Sunday, May 2, 1999

The Rest of Day 480 MET through Early Day 481 MET:
Watching the Battery and Commanding the MAG/ER

I slept very badly, just a couple of hours, was up by 5:00 AM, and drove back up to Mission Ops to change the ER back to its normal mode after the geomagnetic tail pass and to watch the morning heater event that was to start shortly before 9:00 AM.

Since the monitor controllers did not know when it was necessary to turn off the transmitter and when not to, I was going to have to go up to Mission Ops every 12 hours to watch each heater event and determine if and when it was necessary to turn the transmitter off.

I started commanding the ER load at 480/11:35 MET and we were finished by 480/11:45 MET. I kept a watchful eye on the tank temperatures and the load current the entire time we did the ER commanding.

Then, 32 minutes later, at 480/12:17 MET (8:42 AM), the next heater event started. But we got through it without any difficulty, even without turning the transmitter off. I had modeled the event, as it was happening, to make sure it was OK.

I then drove home and both Rebecca and I slept during the morning, because she too did not get more than three hours of sleep. Then, after supper, I went back up to Mission Ops for the next heater event. That event started at 480/23:52 MET, 11 minutes after the beginning of the nighttime pass. Though the battery did not get fully charged — it just reached 31 v — based on past events and my modeling, I decided I did not need to command the transmitter off. The event looked benign, because the heaters were to go off shortly after the spacecraft was to go into the next nighttime pass, which they did, just 9 minutes after the nighttime pass started. But the damn battery voltage just kept dropping, ever more rapidly — it hit yellow and then red and dropped down to 23.66 v, which was deep red. That was the lowest voltage I had ever seen. The problem was that the load current, after dropping down to 2.5 amps when the heaters went off, went right back up to 4 amps, as all of the other smaller heaters started to go on! Though we still had some margin in the battery, I was going to have to watch the heater events like a hawk.

I knew that the next couple of days — until the OMM burn Wednesday — were going to be hard, and if the burn did not drop the heater on-time significantly, I was going to have to watch the heater events for the entire week, if not longer — until the daytime passes were over the brighter far-side in a week and/or until the nighttime passes got significantly shorter than 48 minutes. I hoped that would not be the case, because I would be dead if I had to go to Mission Ops every 12 hours for a week or more. But I was not going to let the monitor controllers just turn the transmitter off randomly, the way they did in the past, and screw things up. I refused to do that. I would rather go up to Mission Ops every 12 hours and get little sleep. Also, I had to understand the battery, which I thought was degrading, since we were really punishing it in the low orbits, otherwise the mission could get screwed up.

Monday, May 3, 1999

Day 481 MET

I spent the entire day, from the early morning heater event to the late evening heater event, at Mission Ops because I had a long interview in between them with a reporter from Britain.

I had to have the transmitter turned off only during the morning heater event.

Tuesday, May 4, 1999

Day 482 MET

As result of going to Mission Ops every 12 hours, I was getting very little sleep, a few hours per night, and I was getting very tired.

Then I got some more information about the *Discover Awards*, though I was 1 of 3 finalists in my category, there were 27 finalists in 9 different categories. Though I had 1 chance in 3 to win my category, I had just 1 chance in 27 to win the $100,000.

Wednesday, May 5, 1999

Day 483 MET: The OMM That Put the Periselene Over the Far-side

We did the 4th OMM of the extended mission, starting a little after 10:00 AM, and put the periselene over the far-side. I started the commanding at 483/13:42 MET with a file that turned on the EM limb-crossing sensor, the pressure transducer, and the A1 and A2 heaters in a three-minute period. Then Dan and I did our usual checks of the engine parameter file for the first burn — a 25.5 second long burn resulting in a ΔV of 4.01 m/sec — and I had it uplinked and verified the echoes. The first burn was executed at 483/14:10 MET. A few seconds after I saw the echo of the EXEC, the engine temperatures started to increase and Dan saw the nutation, *then the damned DSN link stopped!*

The DSN had a problem getting the data from the tracking station to us. It took about 7 minutes before we got data back. Happily, Goddard could confirm that the burn ended while we were in the dark at Mission Ops. It was no big deal, but the data dropout sure as hell occurred at the wrong time. But we were all happy that it didn't happen just before the burn started, because then we wouldn't have known what in hell happened, i.e., if an engine had exploded and wrecked the spacecraft or something similar. As soon as I again had command capability, I safed the engines — at 483/14:19 MET.

We proceeded with the second burn — a 26.0 second burn with a ΔV of 4.08 m/s. I had the A1 and A2 heater turn-on file uplinked at 483/14:22 MET. The burn was executed at 483/15:08 MET and the engines were safed at 483/15:10 MET.

There was no need for the preplanned tweak reor and despin burns, so I canceled them and the 4th OMM was over without further incident.

Friday, May 7, 1999

Day 485 MET: A Cold Spacecraft

I went in very early Friday morning to watch the morning heater event. The one that occurred Thursday night had passed the yellow limit, which surprised me since it was a very benign heater event. Then the one I was watching, which was even more benign than the one the previous night, went yellow and almost red. I quickly decided that what was happening was, since the nighttime pass duration was still nearly 48 minutes long, the spacecraft was getting cooler and cooler — we had a very cold spacecraft. The regular heater loads were up. The only way I could model the power usage properly was to use a 2½ amp load current, which was up from the normal 2¼ amps. I had no choice but to turn the transmitter off during the nighttime passes when a heater event was occurring. Also, turning the transmitter off during the radio occultation periods no longer helped, the transmitter had to be off when the spacecraft was pulling the maximum load current, i.e., during the nighttime passes. Though the heater on-time was down to 100 to 104 minutes, that was just not helping and neither was the fact that the nighttime passes were down 47.5 minutes — the spacecraft was cold and was just using a lot of power for the heaters. For the next month, we were going to have to turn the transmitter off during the heater events — there was just no choice.

Some Japanese reporters came and I had a nice interview with them.

I talked to David Goldstein about the impact experiment. Our angle of impact was going to be just a few degrees, so I was getting skeptical that we were going to see much, but we would do the best we could.

Monday, May 10, 1999

Day 488 MET: Guenter's Visit

I went in to Mission Ops really early because I woke up very early and I wanted to be there well before the morning heater event started, which was to occur around 7:00 AM.

Guenter was at Ames for an 8:00 AM meeting with Scott and some other Ames people regarding a number of programs at Ames. Happily, Guenter stopped over at Mission Ops at about 6:00 AM (9:00 AM Headquarters time in DC) to look around; so I had a chance to talk with him about the revised statement of work and the new proposed budget for the data reduction program. I showed him the original work statement based on the original budget of $3.9 million and the data products we had hoped to deliver to the archives for that amount of money. Then I showed him the budget for the $3 million Joe said I was getting and the proposed work statement in which I was proposing that I would get the MAG/ER, GRS, and NS data all reduced to Level 3, but not to the higher levels. I said, regarding that proposed statement of work, "I know that Joe told me that I was to reduce only the GRS and NS data at the expense of the MAG/ER data, but I really hate to do that. It screws those guys (the MAG/ER guys) and really leaves them with barely any money to work with. Besides, the (MAG/ER) data are of great interest to the community." Then I repeated Bob Lin's argument he had given me as ammunition, "They (my same guys were on the Mars Observer Mission) found this neat stuff in the Mars magnetometry. The data show banded magnetic strips in the Martian crust and they might be the equivalent of the banded magnetic strips in the Earth's crust that are caused by plate tectonics. They're getting some tremendous results from Mars and here we have all this glorious data from the Moon and we don't know what is in it. We could have some great stuff in there and not even know it. We've already proven the theory about how the magnetic fields form at the antipodal points to the lunar mare basins. It just doesn't make any sense if I cannot go to Level 3 with all the data. If I do, then I will have broken the back of the reduction of the MAG/ER, NS, and GRS data sets."

He said, "I agree that's the thing to do and maybe we can shift funding around a little bit to make it happen. Go talk to Joe about it."

I then told Guenter I would be late for his meeting, because I had a heater event coming up and he understood it was much more important for me to watch the spacecraft than to be on time for a NASA meeting. He left Mission Ops somewhat before 7:00 AM. Unfortunately, Sylvia couldn't go to the meeting, which was over at Scott's new place, but Marcie was going to go and, of course, since she didn't know anything about the spacecraft, I knew she would stand up there and tell Guenter a bunch of baloney.

Right after Guenter left, I emailed Joe and said I would be in DC shortly and we could discuss the new statement of work. Joe emailed back that that would be OK. I was pleased.

Just a couple of minutes before 7:00 AM, the heaters turned on. I was right in the middle of the heater event when I got a panic note from Marcie saying, "Please come over to the meeting." Well, I was not about to leave my spacecraft, especially when Guenter knew I was in the middle of a heater event, so I continued monitoring the spacecraft. I didn't need to turn the transmitter off, but the battery voltage did go yellow because the load current went up at the end of the nighttime pass, as usual. But the battery was fully charged before the spacecraft went into the next nighttime pass. There was no question the load current was high during the nighttime passes, because the spacecraft was cold.

I decided to turn the pressure transducer and the EM limb-crossing sensor off to save a little power. I called Dan to tell him and he said, "Sure."

I said, "I would really like to leave the EM off."

Dan replied, "I really need it on for at least 12 hours a week."

I said, "That's fine, but the only concern I have is that if you or I are not here doing the commanding and checking it, they (the controllers) will screw up. Thus you or I have to be here to do the commanding, rather than doing it via phone." Dan agreed. Then I left Mission Ops for the meeting.

I walked into the rather small meeting room and there were a number of Ames people there, including Dave Morrison, Scott's boss. Scott was sitting at the head of the table and there was a seat right next to him and a seat further down. I was going to walk down to the seat that was as far away from Scott as possible, but it was crowded and kind of hard to get there, so David Morrison said, "No, go sit over there." I had no choice but to sit next to Scott — but I ignored him as much as possible. Since they knew I was busy at Mission Ops, they got right to Lunar Prospector and Scott said very little.

When I came, Marcie was blabbing about the battery and the heater events, neither of which she understood. Finally, I had to interrupt her and explain what was really going on. Immediately after I had clarified that issue, Guenter, who — like the rest of NASA — assumes, since Marcie is an engineer and a NASA person, she knows everything, turned to her and asked her another question. She did not know the answer and said, "You'll have to ask Alan." I answered the question. Then, Guenter turned to her again and asked another question and she again responded, "I don't know, you'll have to ask Alan." That little scene repeated itself a couple of more times, but Guenter never caught on that she didn't know anything — after all, she is a NASA employee and they know everything and I am just a dumb scientist!

I was both amused and annoyed at that crap. Amused because any normal idiot could see what was going on except the NASA idiots and annoyed because they simply refused to accept the fact that a non-NASA person, worse a scientist, rather than an engineer, could possibly know anything about a spacecraft and how to run it. I was also annoyed, as usual, at Marcie because, since she doesn't know much, she just makes up crap. She doesn't understand it, so she just blabs, since she wanted to play a role in the mission. If I had had the authority, I would have fired her so fast that it would have scared her to death. Happily, I was able to leave that useless NASA clambake very quickly.

I went back to Mission Ops and at 488/13:55 MET, and had the file uplinked to turn off the pressure transducer and the EM sensor.

I called Bob Lin and Lon Hood to tell them I had rescued a lot of the money for the MAG/ER data reduction and they were very happy about that. But, I said, "You know, until I've got a contract, I'm not going to believe this," and they agreed.

I was very tired, since I had gotten up so damned early. I drove home to take a nap. After Rebecca and I ate an early supper, I went back up to Mission Ops for the evening heater event.

I got through the 5:00 to 7:00 PM heater event without any trouble. It started in the middle of the nighttime pass, went through daytime pass and ended during the nighttime pass. The battery's DOD was 60%, which was OK.

Tuesday, May 11, 1999

Day 489 MET

I got up very early and was in Mission Ops by 3:30 AM, so I could watch the 4:00 AM heater event, which went well. Then I went home and slept. I was not going to drive up to Ames for the next event, rather I was just going to follow it by phone, but Lockheed sent me the final contract for the extended mission! Since I had to sign it and take it to Lockheed, I went up to Mission Ops in the late afternoon for the evening heater event and to take the signed contract to Lockheed.

Marcie came up to Mission Ops and was bitching about my not being there when she was, i.e., from 9 to 5! She was also bitching because I had not provided her with the new procedures the controllers were supposed to use to determine when to turn the transmitter off — so I showed her the procedures, which were laying right there on the table! Then, because she did not (and could not) understand the procedures, she asked, "Well, have you covered all the options and blah, blah, blah." The woman was driving me nuts.

Wednesday, May 12, through Thursday, May 13, 1999

Day 490 MET and Day 491 MET: A Quick Trip to DC

Wednesday I flew to Washington, but my meeting with Alan Ladwig on Thursday morning was canceled because Alan was sick! I did get to see Dan Tam, but nothing came of it. None of the congressional aides were available because they were all doing committee work. It was a bust.

I went to my meeting with Joe and Guenter, but Guenter was on vacation in his homeland, Austria! Joe felt I should really spend all the data reduction money needed to fully reduce the NS and GRS data and spend whatever was left on the MAG/ER data, despite what Guenter had agreed to on Monday! I still I didn't know what in hell was going on.

The trip was a total waste of time and money. I shouldn't have gone, I should have known better than to trust Guenter, but I wanted to get the data reduction program started off right.

Friday, May 14, 1999

Day 492 MET

When I got back from DC, the spacecraft was fine. The controllers didn't have to turn the transmitter off anytime during my trip, in part because the nighttime passes were finally down to 47 minutes. However, by the rules, Howard should have turned the transmitter off during one event, but he didn't think it was necessary and the voltage got rather low, but it was OK.

David Goldstein called because the American Geophysical Union (AGU) PR guy wanted to have a press conference about the paper on the impact experiment Dave was presenting at the spring AGU conference. But Ames's David Morse was all bent out of shape because he didn't want the AGU to have a press conference that preceded an Ames press conference! I told Goldstein to tell everybody involved to coordinate with Lisa, so if anybody had a PR issue, she could keep track of the mess. As far as I was concerned, I was sick of dealing with that petty crap and the NASA PR people could go screw themselves.

Saturday, May 15, and Sunday, May 16, 1999

Day 493 MET and Day 494 MET

Rebecca and I went to Mission Ops and watched a heater event after we had a nice dinner at a French restaurant. Dick Seeley had sent me a voucher for the restaurant to show his appreciation for my doing the videos and Q&A telephone sessions for his BJ Link video classes and for having him at the high school teacher's lunar science seminar. Though neither Rebecca nor I particularly like French food, we enjoyed the dinner and appreciated the kind gesture.

Also, Rebecca and I started getting the garage cleaned and started to pack for our move to Tucson. That weekend was the beginning of the end for us.

Monday, May 17, 1999

Day 495 MET

Sylvia, Marcie, Dan, and I had our final review of the command anomaly and concluded that it was most probably caused by interference because the radio signals were reflecting off the Moon.

Dan was digging out the information on the tanks and decided we could probably go down to just having 2 kg of fuel left in the spacecraft before we would run the risk of venting helium pressurant during the final kamikaze burn. That meant we could have a 6° angle of impact, but no greater.

I shut the transmitter off during the 8:00 PM heater event, because the battery voltage was getting too low — it probably would have been OK, but I shut it off.

Wednesday, May 19, 1999

Day 497 MET to Early Day 498 MET

Dan needed EM attitude data, so I turned the EM sensor on from 497/14:59 MET to 498/01:01 MET.

Thursday, May 20, and Friday, May 21, 1999

The Rest of Day 498 MET and Day 499 MET

I went over to see Wayne in Auburn, CA, to work on the LRI and LEI business plans.

The solar array current was down because we were getting to that point in the β angle cycle where we were getting less reflected sunlight from the Moon, but, because of the very low orbit, the nighttime passes were still very long, more than 45 minutes! The battery was not charging up properly during the heater events and we still had to turn the transponder off during every heater event. It was going to be well into June before we could stop that nonsense. That was too bad — it was a major concern of mine and a major pain in the butt.

We were getting a lot of press coverage. There was an article about the mission in the Gilroy *Dispatch,* but it was terrible and very inaccurate, though the pictures were good. However, there were good articles in *Space News* and *Scientific American.*

Monday, May 24, 1999

Day 502 MET: Turning Off the APS

The APS was getting noisy again and beginning to affect the NS data, so Bill and I decided to turn the APS off permanently. At 502/10:39 MET, I started the shut down sequence for the spectrometers and then at 502/10:42 MET, I began turning the GRS and NS back on and to bring their high-voltages back up to their operational levels. The entire series of 16 commands took 12 minutes to uplink and the GRS and NS were back on line and the *APS's mission had ended. That was the first step in terminating the Lunar Prospector Mission!*

We still had to turn the transmitter off almost every single heater event since A) the solar array power output was down because of the lessening amounts of energy reflected from the Moon as the β angle increased, B) the nighttime passes remained long (they were still more than 45 minutes long), and C) more energy was required to keep the spacecraft warm. It was cold for the same reason that the solar array power was down. And it was still three weeks before I expected things to get better.

A big to-do about the impact experiment press conference was going down and I stayed out of it.

I tried to call Joe Boyce, without success, to let him know I had sent off the materials he needed to finalize our funding for the data reduction program. I hoped we could finally get that straightened out.

I had a number of calls from reporters, including one from England and one from Germany.

Buddy Nelson and I went to Lockheed to make the little video I was asked to do for the *Discover Awards* event that was just two weeks away.

Rebecca was working really hard getting everything ready for our move to Tucson.

Wednesday, May 26, 1999

Day 504 MET: Did Lockheed's Incompetence Save the Day?

I read an article on the failure of the Athena II shroud to separate during the CRSS launch. There are two steps in the shroud separation sequence: First, an explosive zip cord at the base of the shroud explodes, separating the shroud from the Orbit Adjustment Module of the rocket; second, a second explosive zip cord splits the shroud into two clamshell like pieces, which then fall away from the rocket. What had happened was, when the first zip cord exploded, the entire shroud jumped up from the rocket for a fraction of a second, and during that fraction of a second — just when the electrical signal was being sent to explode the second zip cord — the electrical plugs connecting the shroud to the rocket disconnected for a fraction of a second and the second signal never got to the zip cord. The clamshell shroud never opened and hence, stayed on the rocket, causing the failure.

As I read that, it immediately dawned on me that, when we had finished encapsulating the spacecraft just before launch in December 1997 (Part Three), the plugs between the shroud and the rocket didn't match because they were offset laterally from each other. Denver then sent down a patch kit that consisted of an S shaped little piece of cabling, 5 to 8 cm inches long, with plugs at each end that would form a bridge between the two offset connectors. It was clear to me that that might have saved our mission! When, on our launch, the zip cord exploded and the shroud jumped up, the slack in the S part of the patch cable would have accommodated the jump and the second signal would have reached the second zip cord, causing it to explode and finishing the shroud separation sequence. If so, then the Athena II crew's incompetence, i.e., their not fit checking the connectors before shipping the equipment to the cape, may have saved my mission!

Whatever the cause of the Athena II failure, there was a big and well-deserved shake-up at Lockheed. Henshaw was moved back to the east coast and whoever was the head of the Athena program was out, and so on, and so forth.

We still had to turn the transmitter off during many, but not all of the heater events. I was hopeful that by the time we got down to a nighttime pass duration of 42 or 43 minutes, we could stop turning the transmitter off.

I talked to Alex Konopliv because Dan and I were going to have to use every bit of fuel in the spacecraft we possibly could to get the impact angle up to 6°, so we were going to spin the spacecraft up so the centrifugal force would be high enough to keep the fuel at the fuel-outlets of the tanks when the spacecraft was being accelerated during our last, kamikaze burn. After that final spin-up burn, we were not going to do any more spin trims. I called to ask Alex if that was OK, i.e., if it would hurt his Doppler gravity data and he said, "No, that won't hurt my data and besides, I have enough anyway."

I also told the MAG/ER guys, when I commanded the ER to change over to the geomagnetic tail sequence towards the end of July, I was not going to change it back at the end of the geomagnetic tail pass, since there would only be one more day remaining before the impact on July 31.

Slowly but surely, I was preparing to shut the science instruments down in order to get it ready for the impact. Like the coming of spring or fall, you could feel the end of the mission was near. It was a nostalgic feeling.

Thursday, May 27, 1999

Day 505 MET: A Meeting with Dan Tam

I flew down to Burbank, CA, early in the morning. Wayne picked me up and we drove to JPL. We first stopped to say hi to Alex. He showed me his latest gravity map and I was astounded. He had mapped all kinds of mascons on the far-side — something everyone had said you could not do without a sub-satellite or a relay satellite in lunar orbit with you. But Lunar Prospector's Doppler data were so good that Alex could map the gravity anomalies just from the harmonic analysis. I was pleased as punch, since we had a spacecraft and a mission that were so good we had done the seemingly impossible. It was just amazing what we were getting out of the spacecraft.

Then we went to our meeting with Dan Tam. It turned out that David Gump had a meeting with Dan just before we did. David said, "Do you want to do a joint meeting?"

I answered, "Nope." He went in to see Dan.

When Dave came out of Dan's office, Wayne and I went in. Dan poked holes in everything we said about commercializing lunar exploration and the proposed lunar data purchase program, but that was what we had expected. Nevertheless, it was a good meeting, but trying to get anywhere with NASA is like trying to run the 100 yard dash in a vat of molasses.

He wanted to know about Lunar Prospector's crash. He asked, "Is there going to be a TV camera in Mission Ops? Are you going to be able to see anything?"

I answered, "No and No. I wanted TV to be in there in the beginning, but NASA would not let me."

Dan said, "Well, they should have let you. I'll help you get it in this time. I want to have TV coverage of your doing the end of the mission."

I say, "Hey, fine, thanks. But why don't you come on down and see the final commanding yourself?"

He said, "OK, I think I'll do that."

Wayne then took me back to the airport and I flew back to San Jose and then I drove to Mission Ops, because I had to command the EM sensor back on and configure the ER for the next geomagnetic tail pass. I started the commanding at 505/19:55 MET and was done at 505/20:09 MET, or shortly after 4:40 PM. Then I drove home for supper.

Friday, May 28, and Saturday, May 29, 1999

Day 506 MET and Day 507 MET: A Wasted Trip

I went to the annual National Space Society (NSS) conference in Houston, which was a total bust. I really did not have the time to go, but Pat, the Executive Administrator of the NSS, wanted me there for three reasons: First there was to be a big press conference that was supposed to highlight Lunar Prospector; second, there was to be a meeting about the NSS's Lunar Science Institute — a NSS program set up to fund small lunar science studies — that Pat had asked George French, Apollo 17 Astronaut Harrison Schmitt, and me to help direct; and third, I was asked to give a talk on Lunar Prospector. I decided to make a quick trip to Houston and leave to fly home the minute my talk was finished early Saturday afternoon.

First of all, when I got there Friday, I found that the conference was being held in a dumpy, second-rate hotel, a fact I did not like and one that Pat was very unhappy about (the NSS conferences are set up nearly autonomously by the local NSS Chapters, so Pat had little to say about the matter).

Second, the minute I got there, I found out that Rick Tumlinson had told Pat they ought to cancel the Lunar Base Conference (the conference that was originally the Lunar Base Workshop Roger and I had wanted set up and that Rick, Pat, and David Gump had turned into their Lunar Base Conference) because it was going nowhere. I said, "Yes, I agree, kill it," but, Pat wanted to keep it alive since she didn't want the NSS to lose face and also because the NSS had already made commitments and spent money on the conference.

Third, Pat, Apollo 11 Astronaut Buzz Aldrin, a couple of other NSS people, and I went to the press conference room and there was *exactly one reporter there*! The conference committee had done absolutely nothing to promote the press conference! The reporter quipped sarcastically, "This is the only press conference I have ever been to where there are far more presenters than reporters." Pat was embarrassed and pissed. The single reporter didn't really want to ask any questions of the rest of us, all he wanted to do was to interview Buzz. The press conference was a total waste of time.

Fourth, the next morning, Saturday morning, we were supposed to have the Lunar Science Institute meeting to decide how to proceed. But neither George French nor Harrison Schmitt were at the meeting, so we were supposed to have a telecon with them. Well, the NSS organizing committee couldn't even set up a damned telecon in their second-rate hotel. That meeting was a bust — two strikeouts and one to go for the inning to be over.

Fifth, my talk was supposed to be at 1:00 PM, right after lunch — always a bad time. When it came time for my talk, I was told it had been slipped from 1:00 PM to 1:30 PM. Bob Zubrin was the luncheon speaker and as usual he was droning on and on about his Manned Mission to Mars Program — the same talk he had given a hundred times to the same audience, but they loved hearing his evangelical pipe dream. Unfortunately, Bob will never shut up and NSS conferences are never on schedule. I told Pat I had a plane to catch and if I did not get started by 1:30, I would have to leave.

I was taken to the meeting room where I was to give my talk on Lunar Prospector. It was down a dingy hallway with garbage cans lined up along the wall — it was the hallway that led to the room where the hotel staff went for their lunches and to smoke and to the back door of the kitchen. The guy who was to head the session I was in and who was leading me down the back hall was embarrassed and I was pissed. I thought, "This is what they think of Lunar Prospector? Everybody else has a decent place to give their talks and I am supposed to talk about lunar Prospector next to garbage cans!"

Since Zubrin was still clacking away, there were only a couple people in the room. I went back out to cleaner air and told Pat that enough was enough, I was leaving. She said, "Please stay, Zubrin is about finished."

I said, "It's getting well past 1:30 and if this doesn't get off the ground by 2:00, I have to leave to catch my plane."

At about 1:45, a guy came out of the luncheon and said, "Zubrin has at least 20 minutes to go."

I said, "That's it, there is no reason for me to stay."

Pat asked, "Can't you at least give a 15 minute summary of Lunar Prospector?"

I answered, "No, Lunar Prospector deserves more than 15 minutes," and I turned to leave.

But just then, Peter Kokh wanted to donate $500 in my name to the Lunar Science Institute and he wanted to have a little ceremony so he could give me the check and then I would give it to Pat. Reluctantly, I said, "OK." We went down the garbage hall to the meeting room that was about half filled with people. Pat asked me again if I would give a 15-minute summary and I again said no. Then we had the little ceremony and Pat explained to the audience that, because Zubrin was running late and because I had to catch my plane to get back to take care of Lunar Prospector, my talk was canceled.

The audience was very disappointed and one nice lady came up to me and said, "That's too bad, but we understand you have to go take care of Lunar Prospector." Strikeout three, the game was over and I left, highly pissed that I had wasted my time and money on a totally useless NSS meeting.

Sunday, May 30, 1999

Day 508 MET

I went up to Mission Ops in the morning and got caught up with what had happened while I was on travel. I was appalled to find out that David, who had no idea about what he was supposed to do, had turned the transmitter off during every single occultation — five times — the previous night! I was really worried because some of those guys just did not know what in hell they were doing. Some job Marcie was doing with her controllers!

Monday, May 31, 1999

Day 509 MET: A Cold and Tired Spacecraft

I went up to Mission Ops to make sure everything was OK and get caught up on the historical records of the mission. I found we were getting load current spikes of about ¾ of an amp that lasted up to 3 frames (96 sec) and that occurred every five minutes. I called Jim Schirle and he suggested it might be the battery heater. I checked the battery temperature, which was at about −1° C, and sure enough we were getting the corresponding spikes in its temperature. Jim and I discussed what I was seeing and he thought the battery thermostat might be failing. We would just have to wait and see, since there was nothing that we could do about it — again, *remember, the spacecraft was designed for one year of operations in a 100 km altitude orbit and we were beating the hell out of it in a 30 km altitude orbit after 17 months of operations.*

I called up Woody and Woody was concerned that if the spacecraft got too much colder, the secondary heaters would also turn on and the battery would not be able to handle that. He also agreed with me that the real problem was, since the controllers really did not understand anything about the spacecraft, if the secondary heaters went on along with the primaries, the controllers wouldn't catch it and the battery would drain before I was told about it and could do something about it. I was very concerned. Woody and I discussed it and agreed it might be prudent to do a pre-emptive strike and turn off the primary heaters and just go on the secondaries until β was greater than 80°, i.e., until the spacecraft was in sunlight during the entire orbit and therefore much warmer; then I could go back to primaries, so we would be ready for the eclipse.

I called Jim Schirle back and talked to him. He thought a pre-emptive strike was probably OK, even though my original plan was to go on the secondaries, only to insure that we got through the partial umbral lunar eclipse on the night of July 27/28. Nevertheless, I was really in favor of going to the secondaries right then to insure we didn't have a problem because of the controllers.

I talked to Dan and we decided when we had our OMM meeting the next day, we would decide what to do about the heaters.

The next day was going to be interesting, since we had to figure out what to do with our cold baby.

Tuesday, June 1, 1999

Day 510 MET: The 5th OMM of the Extended Mission

I went up to Mission Ops for what became a long day. I first got caught up with the historical records and then I prepared the Mission Profile for the day's commanding sessions. I then went to Lockheed for a meeting about the battery heater flipping on and off every three to five minutes. Jim Schirle thought it was OK, but stressed that we needed to watch it. It appeared that the cause of the rapid switching of the battery heater was that the dead band had somehow narrowed to a fraction of a degree, probably because the spacecraft was so cold. We also decided if the battery heater got stuck on, we would have to turn off the primary heaters and go on the secondaries.

We also discussed the fact that the spacecraft was sucking up a lot of power just to keep warm. We still had to turn the transmitter off almost every single tank heater event and they were occurring every 7½ hours. The nighttime pass duration was down to 43 minutes, but it had to get down several more minutes before we would be out of that mess.

I went back to Mission Ops to command the ER from its geomagnetic tail pass mode to its normal mode. I started the commanding at 510/13:00 MET (9:25 AM) and finished at 510/14:11 MET.

After that, we had our telecon about the OMM burn that was set to start at 4:23 PM and about the impact. The Nav guys said we were going to have a very accurate impact, much more accurate that we originally thought. The uncertainties in the impact point would only be about 8 km if we had a 10% under- or over-burn! Since our burns were almost always better than 1%, the uncertainty in the impact point, with respect to the assumed topography, would be less that 1 km. Thus, the real uncertainty was in the topography, not our trajectory. The End-of-Mission sequence was going to be: 39 hours before impact, we would spin the spacecraft up to 23 rpm; 29 hours before impact we would raise the aposelene up to 234 km; 36 minutes before impact we would do the Kamikaze burn and then the impact would occur.

We also went over the ephemeris for the partial umbral lunar eclipse we had to survive on the night of July 27/28, even to get to the impact sequence. The spacecraft was going to dip into the penumbra and out again on its first orbital loop, then dip into both the penumbra and the umbra on its second loop and stay in the penumbra for its third loop. That, plus the first nighttime pass, would result in the spacecraft being in the Earth's and/or Moon's shadows for 5 hours and 6 minutes, with a 44-minute break in full sunlight early in the sequence. Lunar Prospector was not built for that (that eclipse was originally supposed to end the mission, but we needed to get though it to do the impact experiment). I was going to shut the GRS and NS off, permanently, before the eclipse to save power. It was going to be tough, but I thought we would get through the eclipse.

I had asked Sylvia somewhat earlier if I could have the engineering model of the C&DH as a keepsake and she said she would find out if I could. Well, Scott, of course, took the C&DH for NASA — the fat little prick!

However, Lockheed was going to let me keep my Mac computer, but only until the data reduction program was finished — that was really big of Lockheed since I had brought them a $65 million dollar program that had earned them more than $4 million dollars in fees — fees they would not share with my non-profit institute!

Finally, it was late afternoon and we began the 5th OMM of the extended mission. I sent the file with the turn-on commands for the pressure transducer and the A1 and A2 engine heaters at 510/19:50 MET. Then, as usual, we uplinked the engine parameter file and the first burn, a 45.7 sec burn with a ΔV of 7.22 m/sec, started at 510/20:15 MET and the engines were safed at 510/20:17 MET.

The heater turn-on command file for the second burn was sent at 510/20:55 MET, the 45.1 sec, 7.12 m/sec ΔV burn was executed at 510/21:26 MET and the engines were safed at 510/21:28 MET.

I canceled the preplanned tweak reor, and since we were going to increase the spacecraft spin rate before our kamikaze burn, we just left the spin rate, which had increased to 12.12 rpm, as it was. Since that was the next to the last OMM, we had the strong feeling the mission was coming to an end.

Thursday, June 3, 1999

Day 512 MET: Sad News

I went in very early because I woke up early. Shortly after I got to Mission Ops, I got an email from JSC — Bill Huffstetler had died of a heart attack at 6:00 AM CDT. I was really very sorry to hear that. I liked Bill a lot and owed him a lot, since he had done so much for Lunar Prospector during the Early Years (Part One).

I watched some heater events and waited for some British guys to come from York Films. When they arrived to discuss future filming, we had a really good discussion. Also, a little later, Channel 4 came for a TV interview.

The tank heater event I was watching while I was talking to the York guys was so bad that the load current was 5 amps — because the spacecraft was so cold. The spacecraft was drawing so much heater power during the event that the battery was actually discharging in the sunlight! I had to shut the transmitter off for 30 minutes during the nighttime pass.

The β angle was 60° and the nighttime pass duration was still 41 minutes. Three weeks until we had a β angle greater than 80° and we were in full sunlight — but it was amazing how tough the power/cold crunch was right then. The spacecraft was so cold we were hitting yellow limits on the NS/APS and the viscous damper, neither of which made any difference. It was a good thing the mission was about over, because poor little Lunar Prospector was huffing and puffing because of the tough circumstances it had to endure in the low orbit, though the spacecraft itself was in good condition. Also, even though the battery heater was still cycling every 3 to 5 minutes, it seemed to be stable and OK.

Friday, June 4, through Wednesday, June 9, 1999

Day 513 MET through Day 518 MET: The Discover Awards

Rebecca and I went to Epcot in Florida on Friday for the *Discover Awards* Gala. We had a great time being wined and dined up to and during the evening of the award ceremony. I did not win in my category, nor did I win the $100,000 (see the July 1999 issue of *Discover*, page 90) — but we had a ball. We stayed a couple of extra days at Epcot and Disney World, and then Wednesday, we flew back to California to finish the mission.

While we were in Florida, I called in the commanding of the two commands needed to set up the ER in its burst mode as requested by Dave Curtis. The commands were uplinked at 516/21:45 MET and 516/21:49 MET.

Thursday, June 10, 1999

Day 519 MET

I went up to Mission Ops and a German TV crew came for an interview, which wasn't all that hot.

I worked on the preparation for the eclipse that was coming up on the morning of the 28th and talked to Dan. I was hoping we would be able to stop turning the transmitter off in a couple of days.

Friday, June 11, 1999

Day 520, 1999

Bill needed to have the GRS gain turned up one step to 1722 v, so I did that at 520/16:40 MET.

Saturday, June 12, 1999

Day 521 MET

The nighttime pass duration was down to 35 minutes and the β angle was 68°. Finally, we were out of danger of killing the battery during the tank heater events. I was finally able to order the cessation of the transmitter turn-offs during the tank heater event. I was relieved — the tank heater/battery problem was finally over for good.

Chapter 4-16
Transitioning

Monday, June 14, through Thursday, June 17, 1999

Day 523 MET through Day 526 MET: Getting Set Up in Tucson

Rebecca and I flew to Tucson Monday, where we were going to meet with Wayne and Tad Theno. Tad worked for George French on Moonlink and was planning on being a graduate assistant at LRI and start graduate school at the U of Arizona. We were going to get the LRI offices picked out and rented, furniture and computers picked out, an apartment rented for Rebecca and me to live in while our house was being built, and get everything all set up for our move to Tucson — right after the impact.

We got to Tucson Monday around noon and we found an apartment and rented it just like that. Then we met Tad and went to supper. The next morning, Wayne, who had arrived late Monday night, joined us for breakfast. We all went down to the University of Arizona Science and Technology Park and talked to Marshall Warden. Marshall showed us some offices on the second floor of Building 9040 that were available. One, with windows and a great view, was big enough to be split into two adjacent offices for Rebecca and me. The other office was just down the hall and Tad could use that. We quickly decided that those were the offices we wanted and started the process of renting them, starting August 1, 1999 — the day after the impact.

George had agreed to donate $8,000 to LRI for the furniture and computers (thanks George), so we then went to look for furniture, the computers, insurance companies for health insurance, and all the other things we would need to become a fully functioning company. Then we were done with LRI's business.

Wednesday morning, Rebecca and I met with the Bank about our house loan and with Bill North, our builder, to get everything finalized for the building of our house. We took Bill out to our lot and showed him exactly where the house was to be built.

After lunch, I had a telecon with the Ames and NASA PR people and everybody else who was involved with the impact. I said I wanted a pool camera in Mission Ops and pre- and post-impact news conference so we could sum up the mission in the first one, using the impact as a hook to get the reporters and TV to come, and then after the impact, tell the press what happened at mission's end. Doug Isbell, the PR guy from Headquarters, of course, argued against all that. Since Doug had squashed each and every attempt I had made to get Lunar Prospector good press and good TV coverage, he and I got into it. Doug said, "We've discussed you wanting a pool camera in Mission Ops before and the answer was no and still is no. No one is interested in the Moon or Lunar Prospector."

I replied, "You were wrong then and you are wrong now," and I told him how the national TV media had come to me after our first launch attempt and had asked me to let them have a pool camera in Mission Ops for the second launch attempt.

Idiotically, Doug said again, "I said nobody is interested in this."

And I said, "Well they are, because that is what happened."

But facts are of no interest to NASA idiots like Doug; his job was to keep the lid on Lunar Prospector, so it would not interfere with NASA's hoped for plans for a manned

Mars program by creating interest in the public for a manned return to the Moon. He stonewalled the pool camera and the second press conferences. All we were going to end up with was a press conference about the impact two days before the event and all I was going to be able to tell the press was what the final events were going to be and ask them "to stay tuned," in the hopes we would have some coverage after the impact.

I was annoyed, stupid Isbell and the other people at Headquarters just didn't want any good press for Lunar Prospector — it was just supposed to disappear. Though the hour and a half telecon was a complete waste of time, I did enjoy being able to tell Doug politely, but firmly, that he is an idiot and that he doesn't know anything about PR (a few months later, Doug was removed from NASA).

That kind of shot the day. Wayne left for home and Rebecca and I had a nice dinner with Debbie and Doug, our niece and nephew.

Thursday morning, we left good old Tucson for Gilroy and Mission Ops.

Friday, June 18, 1999

Day 527 MET: Sylvia Throws Off the NASA Mantel

I went up to Mission Ops early in the morning. The spacecraft was OK, but the battery heater was cycling as frequently as every two minutes. I called Jim Schirle and he said, "Well, it may be trying to fail, but it is still OK. Just let it roll," and that was what I did.

I called Joe Boyce and we worked out how the money for the data reduction was going to be dispersed: We were going to get $922,000 for what was left of FY (Fiscal year) 1999, $1,659,000 for FY 2000 and $390,000 for FY 2001, with most of the money going for the NS and GRS data reduction, what little remained was for the MAG/ER and there was nothing for the APS! Joe had already sent the paperwork to start the process of getting the contract written at Goddard, so I hoped we would get the money on time, i.e., starting on August 1, 1999, or in just 6 weeks.

I had a long chat with Sylvia about a number of minor issues, but the most interesting and important thing was that she was continuing to evolve away from the, "I am a NASA person and I have to do everything the NASA way" — a degenerate philosophy Scott embraces like a hot mistress — and returning back into an intelligent human being, a process she had started at our infamous meeting with Mohammad.

Before she got the job running the extended mission, she and I had gotten along really well. Then when she got that responsibility, there was a little bit of friction between us, because she felt she had to do what NASA wanted her to do and was listening to Marcie's hysteria. In the last few weeks she had swung completely over to my side. She said, regarding one of the issues Headquarters had screwed up, "You know, you're right, this is all crap. They made this mess and I'm not going to spend my time and my few resources fooling around with this." I was very proud to be finishing the mission with her.

Saturday, June 19, 1999

Day 528 MET

Saturday morning, at about 9:00, I started to drive up to Mission Ops to check on the spacecraft. I was on the freeway and I was just about to San Jose when all of a sudden the engine of Rebecca's car (after my blue car had been demolished, I was reduced to driving her car) blew in a cloud of blue smoke. I pulled off the freeway and called for help. Needless to say, I never made it to Mission Ops, rather I spent the rest of the day getting the car towed back to Gilroy, renting a car (we were down to zero cars) and calling one of the Bay Area charities that take disabled cars to make money. On top of everything else, we had to start thinking about buying a new car!

Monday, June 21, 1999

Day 530 MET

I watched the spacecraft during the morning. The nighttime pass duration was down to 25 min and the heaters were only on for 1½ hours, but we were still getting down to 25 volts during the tank heater events. Taking those data and assuming that my calibration curve for the voltage vs. DOD was still valid, we were still getting large DODs and the battery capacity had decreased from 5 amp-hr to something around 3.5 amp-hr. The battery heater was still cycling erratically, between once every 2 or 3 minutes to once every 7 or 8 minutes — that seemed to be its steady state characteristic! Clearly, the spacecraft was wearing out fast in the low orbit.

In three days, on Wednesday, the nighttime passes would stop for 23 days and the spacecraft would be in sunlight all the time — and that would help the situation a lot. But if the battery capacity was as low as 3.5 amp-hr, we were going to have a tough time getting through the eclipse on the night of July 27/28.

As a result, I talked to Dave Lozier about phasing the spacecraft's orbit so the spacecraft would spend less time eclipsed, but Dave said that would screw up the Hubble observing time. Dave gave me the plots showing the orbital loops through the umbra and penumbra and the way it was, was just about the best we could do. We would just leave the spacecraft's orbit as it was and not go screwing up the Hubble timing.

The spacecraft was clearly wearing out and was cold, but it had done its job and was still doing it — but we were clearly getting towards its end.

Tuesday, June 22, 1999

Day 531 MET

I did an interview over at the Ames Visitor's Center with *Discover News, ABC* that was quite good. I couldn't help but notice that the entire Lunar Prospector Display at the Visitors Center made it sound like Lunar Prospector was solely an Ames program with no mention of the PI or Lockheed — I wonder who could have had it set up that way?

We had our telecon about the impact and the final OMM that was scheduled for the following week. We were trying to get the exact time of the impact settled, since there was still a question, within plus or minus 5 minutes, as to the exact time when the Hubble would be observing the Moon. Other than that, I thought everything was OK and I was getting ready to prepare the Mission Profile for the last little bit of the mission. We had just 1 month, 1 week and 1 day left of the mission.

Wednesday, June 23, 1999

Day 532 MET

I put the final Mission Profile together, but it would have to be updated when we got the final ephemeris. I had a lot of phone calls and more interviews. People were getting really interested in Lunar Prospector again.

The β angle had finally gotten above 80° and the spacecraft was in sunlight all the time, so it was warm and had plenty of power.

Thursday, June 24, 1999

Day 533 MET

I went up to Ames three times during the day. First, I got a call at 1:00 AM and went up to Mission Ops because the battery temperature was yellow. I went up to make sure that everything was OK and it was. Then I drove back down to Gilroy and went to bed again.

After getting up in the morning, I went back up to Ames to give a talk at noon to students who were at Ames for the summer; that went very well and I had lunch with them.

Then I drove back to Gilroy to pick up Rebecca. We went back up to Sunnyvale, since I was the speaker at a dinner of the Northern California Science Writers Association. We enjoyed the evening.

Friday, June 25, 1999

Day 534 MET

I stayed home and worked all day on getting packed. We had a telecon about the impact and I had a telephone interview with a lady reporter from Switzerland.

Saturday, June 26, 1999

Day 535 MET

Five weeks and it would be all over. Rebecca and I worked very hard packing and I did the preparations for the burn Tuesday.

Rebecca and I left for Mission Ops at about 6:00 PM to put the ER into the geomagnetic tail pass mode. Since David Mitchell didn't get there in time (as usual), Rebecca became a mission controller and gave me the echoes from the MAG/ER console as I did the commanding between 535/22:55 MET and 535/23:07 MET. Thus she played an official role in the mission and that was really nice.

Tuesday, June 29, 1999

Day 538 MET: The Final OMM of the Extended Mission

Rebecca and I went into Mission Ops at about 6:00 AM for the 6th and final OMM of the extended mission. Laura Lewis, from Ames PR, came over with a crew to video-tape the OMM. The commanding began at 538/11:21 MET, when I had the A1 and A2 heater turn-on file uplinked. Then we checked and verified the engine parameter file for the 47.3 second, 7.51 m/sec ΔV first burn and uplinked it. That file was executed at 538/11:46 MET and the engines were safed at 538/11:49 MET.

The process was repeated for the second burn, a 46.9 second, 7.47 m/sec ΔV burn, with the heater file being uplinked at 538/12:30 MET, and the burn file being exe-cuted at 538/12:57 MET. The engines were safed at 538/12:59 MET.

As usual, I then canceled the preplanned tweak reor burn and, as preplanned, we left the spin rate as it was. *The final OMM and the final nominal burn sequence of the mission were finished — another milestone in the termination of the mission was reached.*

After the burn was over, Laura interviewed me, asking a number of questions about the end of mission sequence.

Later, in the afternoon, a reporter from the *San Francisco Chronicle* interviewed me.

Wednesday, June 30, 1999

Day 539 MET: Commanding Problems

Rebecca and I went up to Mission Ops to command the ER back to its normal mode at the end of the geomagnetic tail pass, but we had trouble. The commanding of the standard MAG/ER commands began at 539/11:05 MET (7:30 AM). However, I had had Cathy split the standard command file into two files and Cathy and I forgot to put the standard 32-second delay (one frame delay) between the commands of the new, sec-ond file, so when the second file was uplinked, its 10 commands were uplinked in a fraction of a second, so I could not read their echoes to verify that the commands were correct (which they probably were — but I did not take chances). Cathy corrected our error and uplinked the second file again at 539/11:15 MET, but the echo of the first com-mand in the file (MEEWEON) came back as AA2442, which stood for MEEWEOFF! I had her abort the file and start uplinking again at 539/11:24 MET. The echo for the com-mands were OK on my screen, but Rebecca, who was again the MAG/ER controller, said the MAG/ER console screen showed that commands 2 and 4 were erroneous, so I had Cathy abort the uplink again. Then we checked everything out and everything seemed to be OK. That being the case, I had Cathy uplink the file for the 4th time at 539/11:34 MET. That time all the echoes came back correctly on my screen and on the MAG/ER screen. Finally the ER was back in its normal mode.

I went down and had a nice chat with Sylvia, who was getting to be more and more like me — she was getting tired of NASA. She said there was some confusion as to what the final news conference was supposed to be about. At that point in time, it was supposed to be about the End-of-Mission plus a very quick review of the science I would do and then somebody who represented the science community was to say something about Lunar Prospector. I did not like that at all.

Rebecca and I bought a 1999 Saturn to replace our two kaput cars.

Thursday, July 1, 1999

Day 340 MET

The last month of the mission. The highlight of my day was finding an article on the aerospace crisis in the June 21, 1999 issue of *Aviation Week* (pp. 63–66) which detailed everything that is wrong with the aerospace industry and echoes everything I had been saying for many years — so much so that some of my acquaintances asked if I had helped write the article!

We had another telecon about the impact and it was getting finalized. It was going to occur at 2:52 AM on July 31, 1999.

Friday, July 2, 1999

Day 541 MET

We went up to Mission Ops and checked the spacecraft out — it was, of course, fine. The β angle passed through 90°, so we started the next β angle cycle and the night-time passes would be starting again in two weeks.

Rebecca and I went to the Saturn dealer and picked up our new car.

Sunday, July 4, 1999

Day 543 MET

Rebecca and I were getting things pretty well packed up at home. We were enjoying our new car and we drove it up to Mission Ops in the afternoon to do the burst mode commanding for the ER. I sent the two commands at 543/18:45 MET and 543/18:51 MET.

Then we went to see the famous Winchester House in San Jose — it was very interesting.

Tuesday, July 6, 1999

Day 545 MET

Rebecca sent off our paperwork to good old Arizona to get LRI's for-profit, sister company, Lunar Exploration Inc., incorporated. After various discussions, Wayne, Rebecca, and I were finally ready to start the commercial company we needed to do the commercial lunar exploration missions and the commercial lunar base.

Thursday, July 8, 1999

Day 547 MET: The NASA Awards

I went up to Mission Ops very early, because I was supposed to get a call from *Good Morning America*, but it never happened. Then I was supposed to call Kathy

Sawyer from the *Washington Post,* but she was not in, so I left a message and she didn't call back for a long time. I talked to Sylvia while I waited for Kathy to call back.

Sylvia and I were chatting about this, that, and other things and then she said, "I assume you're not going to stay around for the Lockheed awards on the 3rd (August)."

I replied, "No, I am not, but what awards are you talking about?"

She answered, "The NASA Gold Medal Awards. Scott is getting the Gold Medal Award for Outstanding Technical and Programmatic Leadership. Dougherty is getting the Public Service Gold Medal Award for Outstanding Leadership. I'm getting an Exceptional Achievement Gold Medal Award (she was the only one of the three who deserved a Gold Medal, because she did 95% of Scott's work and he took all the credit). The Lockheed Team and the Science Teams are getting Group Achievement Awards." Then she hesitated, and said, *"But your Gold Medal was turned down."*

I laughed and said, "Gee, why am I not surprised?"

Sylvia said, "The thing is, when you tilt at windmills the way you do, they just won't give you an award," which is true, but pathetic.

I was highly amused at NASA's refusing to giving me a Gold Medal, despite it being just one more, albeit expected, slap in the face. It was amusing because NASA just can't take criticism. Either you kiss their ass or you are out. I was, however, touched when Sylvia said, "Dougherty tried really hard to make sure you got the award." Despite everything, Dougherty had always tried to see that I got what I was due and I appreciated that. Anyway, I had proven my point, NASA was never going to give me anything but a kick in the butt for proving you can do missions "Faster, Better, Cheaper" — but only if you keep NASA out of the picture, and that pisses them off!

After that, I was supposed to have an interview with Channel 2 at 10:00 AM and they never showed, so I left for home at 10:30. It turned out they weren't late; rather Laura Lewis at Ames PR was late getting them over to Mission Ops. When I got home, Rebecca told me Channel 2 was driving down to Gilroy and wanted to meet me at Christmas Tree Hill Park to do the interview there. It was fun.

Sunday, July 11, through Saturday, July 17, 1999

Day 550 MET through Day 556 MET:
A Long Trip to Albuquerque, Los Alamos, and Houston

I flew to Albuquerque Sunday night and spent Monday morning with Roger Lenard and some of the people at Sandia, discussing lunar rover designs and missions. Then I picked Wayne up at the Albuquerque Airport. We had lunch at the Mexican restaurant I like in the airport and then drove up to Los Alamos to meet with Bill and to discuss the subcontract between LRI and LANL on the data reduction program with the LANL contracts people.

Tuesday, Wayne and I met with our main contract contact, Kim Sherwood, a really competent and very attractive blonde, and another lady to discuss the subcontract. Our first step was to call Joe Boyce, who still hadn't done anything with the LRI/NASA contract — even though it had been a month since we had reached agreement on the work statement and budget. Joe said the paperwork had gotten lost! I told him he had to get it done, because Kim told us that Los Alamos required 3 months worth of funding up front, before they would even begin work on a new contract. Thus, if we didn't get the contracts done by August 1, Bill and his people would simply have to stop working on the analysis of the Lunar Prospector data and go work on some other program.

If there were a two or three month delay before we got the LRI and LANL contracts done, then, of course, it would be even longer before Bill and his crew could get back working on Lunar Prospector. And that would delay our getting the data products archived and the whole contract would get screwed up.

The situation was serious enough that Wayne even offered to fly out to DC to help get everything done with the LRI contract. Joe said that was not possible in a federal agency and laughed a little bit at the suggestion. Wayne said, "This isn't a laughing matter," and Joe got a little miffed, but then he said he was sorry. Then Joe said he was going to be off the following week, so apparently nothing was going to get done for a couple of weeks!

I was frustrated and said to Joe, "I have two concerns. One is that if the contract is delayed past August 1, we won't get the (data) products in (to the archives) and that will delay getting Lunar Prospector's data out (to the science community). Second, we are still trying to prove Faster, Better, Cheaper and here I am being stymied by a bunch of bureaucratic junk." Joe said he would get on it. He also told us Jim Becker at Goddard was his liaison, so we could work directly with him. However, we were skeptical NASA would get the contract done on time.

After that frustrating conversation, we sat down with Kim and the rest of LANL contracts people and worked out as much of the LANL subcontract as we could. Then Wayne and I went out for a nice steak dinner.

Wednesday, we talked to Bill and his crew about the science and data analysis and then Wayne and I drove to the airport — he flew home and I flew to Houston for a conference.

The meeting at Houston was a waste of time. I was on a useless panel about the commercialization of space activities, but then there was a nice party toasting Lunar Prospector, during which I gave a talk on the mission. Roger talked to a lot of people and we had some good interviews — one with a Japanese lady and a freelance lady reporter, Joël Brenner, who worked for the *Washington Post*. Then I took Roger to the airport and I stayed at a motel near the airport Friday night and flew home Saturday morning.

While I was in Houston, Wayne called Jim Becker at Goddard and found out they had the paperwork, but it did not have any priority. Friday, I called Wayne and then we had a three-way call with Guenter Riegler. I told Guenter what was going on and he said he would tell Goddard to put the Lunar Prospector Contract paperwork on the top priority list.

After arriving at San Jose late Saturday morning, I went to Mission Ops to see how the spacecraft was doing. Everything was OK. The nighttime passes had begun again — I missed the first one, but saw the second one, which lasted seven minutes.

Sunday, July 18, 1999

Day 557 MET

Rebecca and I continued packing in preparation for our move to Tucson and then we went up to Mission Ops. The nighttime passes were already 18 minutes long and getting longer rapidly. Though we had less than two weeks to go, I wanted to know if the battery had degraded any more, so I checked the voltage vs. DOD as the length of the nighttime passes rapidly increased. I found that the voltage was a good volt below my standard calibration curve derived during the first β cycle 18 months earlier. It appeared that we had lost about half of the capacity of the battery. If that were the case, and I was not certain it was, I didn't think we would get through the eclipse the morning of the 28th. I was going to have to watch the battery over the next several days. If the battery had a capacity of only 2½ to 3 amp-hrs, then I would have to shut off the spectrometers to keep the spacecraft alive once we got into the longer nighttime passes. The next day, the nighttime passes would be up to 25 minutes and I would have a better idea of the battery's condition. Regardless, there was a good chance we were not going to make it through the eclipse. If that were the case, then the mission would be over 3 days early and we wouldn't have the final big splash (pardon the pun).

Monday, July 19, 1999

Day 558 MET

I stayed home all day and Rebecca and I got a lot of packing done. I had a million calls. I did an interview with Dan Green from the TV station in Salinas in the evening.

Tuesday, July 20, 1999

Day 559 MET: Apollo 11 and Viking 1 Landing Day Anniversaries

July 20 — the 30th anniversary of the Apollo 11 landing, the first manned landing on the Moon, and the 23rd anniversary of the landing of Viking 1, the first unmanned landing on Mars. I was home most of the day packing. I had a telecon about the burns and I did a TV interview.

Wednesday, July 21, 1999

Day 560 MET: Getting Ready for the Killer Eclipse

I went up to Mission Ops and did an interview with Channel 3 of Sacramento.

Dan and I talked about the preparations for the eclipse. I worked through my power model, so I had everything set up for the eclipse and then I worked out the commanding sequence for the Mission Profile.

Lisa called and sent me the fax of the press release she was preparing. Of course, there was no mention of the PI, just Ames and NASA. I was really sick of Scott, Ames, and NASA pretending that I didn't exist and rewriting the history about how the mission was done. I asked Lisa to change the press release, knowing that would probably not happen.

Thursday, July 22, through Saturday, July 24, 1999

Day 561 MET through Day 563 MET: Checking the Battery

I had been up to Mission Ops frequently to check the battery and it was holding up OK. It didn't get below 26 volts during the nighttime passes, which were up to 33 minutes long; so it looked like the battery was going to be fine until the eclipse and I thought we would successfully get through the eclipse.

I called Dave Curtis and told him I wanted either him or David Mitchell to be at Mission Ops by 6:00 the next morning because I was going to put the ER into its geo-magnetic tail pass mode for the last time.

I talked to Lisa and she was reluctant to make the changes I wanted regarding the role of the PI in the press release. I also told her that I had fired Scott from the Science Team and to correct that in the press release. I seriously doubted Scott would let her make any of the changes I requested. He is such a crook.

Rebecca and I got almost everything ready for the move to Tucson.

Monday, July 26, 1999

Day 565 MET: LEI is Official and a Final Trim Burn

I woke up at about 12:15 AM, but managed to stay in bed until about 2:00. Then I got up and went up to Mission Ops to do the trim burn the Nav Team had set up so that we would impact the Moon at the correct time, since we finally knew exactly when the Hubble Telescope was going to be observing the Moon. The impact was set for Saturday morning, July 31 at 2:51:01 or at 570/06:27 MET.

The trim burn sequence began when I had the A1 and A2 heater turn-on file uplinked at 565/10:11 MET (6:36 AM). Then Dan and I checked the engine parameter file, I had it uplinked, and we verified the parameters for the 9.0-second burn that would change the spacecraft's velocity by 1.44 m/sec. The burn was initiated at 565/10:36 MET and the engines were safed at 565/10:39 MET.

Despite my having called Dave Curtis the day before, telling him or Dave Mitchell to be at Mission Ops for the ER tail pass commanding, neither of them showed up and I was more than a little annoyed about that. I went ahead and sent the two files need-ed to set up the ER for the tail pass, starting right after the trim burn at 565/10:40 MET and I was finished at 565/10:49 MET.

I had a bunch of interviews — CNN, Channel 11, two calls from the San Jose *Mercury News* (one was about the impact and the other was for a series of articles they were writing called "365 Artists, Politicians, Scientists, and Leaders Opinions" or something like that, who they were asking, "What were the greatest events of the last century and where will we be at the end of the next century?").

LEI was officially incorporated in Arizona — we were ready to try to start the com-mercial side of our efforts to get humanity back on the Moon.

Tuesday, July 27, 1999

Day 566 MET

The movers came in the morning, packed up the bulk of our household things and, at about 4:00 PM, started them on their journey to Tucson, where they would be put in storage until our house was finished in 6 to 8 months. What was left, i.e., LRI's office things and the minimum Rebecca and I needed for the apartment in Tucson, would go into a Ryder truck I would drive to Tucson after the impact.

After the movers left, Rebecca and I drove up to the good old Maple Tree Inn, checked in for the next few days, and took a nap. We went to Mission Ops at about 9:00 PM to get ready for the killer eclipse.

Chapter 4-17

The Last 75 Hours of the Mission

Midnight through Mid-afternoon Wednesday, July 28, 1999

Day 567 MET: The Partial Umbral Eclipse

The circumstances of the partial (40%) umbral eclipse for the spacecraft were as follows:

The spacecraft would enter a 35-minute nighttime pass and radio occultation period at 567/05:12 MET (1:37 AM).

While in the nighttime pass/occultation period, the spacecraft would start its first orbital loop in the penumbra (partial sunlight) at 567/05:37 MET.

The spacecraft would exit the nighttime pass/occultation period at 567/05:47 MET, while in the penumbra and reach a minimum incursion into the penumbra of 14%, before looping out of the penumbra at 567/06:05 MET. Thus, the first loop into the penumbra would be of little consequence for the power and thermal state of the spacecraft.

The spacecraft would stay in the full sunlight for 46 minutes — long enough for the battery to get fully charged after the next nighttime pass if the tank heaters were not on, and then reenter the penumbra for the second time at 567/06:51 MET.

The spacecraft would move 26% of the way into the penumbra before the second nighttime pass/occultation period began at 567/07:03 MET.

While in the second nighttime pass/occultation period, the Moon and the spacecraft, doing its second orbital loop, would enter the umbra (no sunlight) at 567/07:27 MET.

The spacecraft would exit the second, 35-minute, nighttime pass/occultation period at 567/07:38 MET while in the umbra and stay in the umbra until 567/08:11 MET. Thus, the spacecraft would be in total darkness (in the Moon's shadow and then in the Earth's shadow) for a total of 1 hour and 8 minutes (Lunar Prospector was designed for just 47 minutes of total darkness).

After emerging from the umbra, the spacecraft would slowly complete its second orbital loop fully within the penumbra — starting at 100% immersion and ending at 24% immersion at 567/08:54 MET, when the spacecraft entered the third, 35-minute nighttime pass/occultation period.

The spacecraft would exit the third nighttime pass/occultation period at 567/09:30 MET, while 46% immersed in the penumbra, looping down to 63% immersion in the penumbra, and then looping back out, leaving the penumbra at 567/10:18 MET. The eclipse would then be over, but the spacecraft would have been in total darkness and partial darkness for 3 hours and 27 minutes, during the second and third orbital loops — and that could easily kill the battery and spacecraft, since neither was designed to take that kind of punishment.

After only 29 minutes of full sunlight and while still very cold and certainly with a partially discharged battery, Lunar Prospector would enter its next 35-minute nighttime pass/occultation period. If we were OK after that nighttime pass, we would be out of the woods.

Given the harshness of the eclipse, the survival strategy was to reduce the power requirements as low as possible and turn the transmitter off most of the time. With the Mission Profile all laid out and with hope in our hearts, my Ops Team and I were prepared for the eclipse that was supposed to have ended the mission, but which we had to survive in order to do the impact experiment in just over three days.

One very nice thing was that a tank heater event was going to occur before the eclipse started. It actually started at 567/03:13 MET and ended at 567/04:51 MET, just 16 minutes before the first nighttime pass of the eclipse sequence started, but the battery *was not fully charged* before the spacecraft entered the Moon's shadow, which was of concern. The expected start of the next tank heater event would be during the final penumbral phase of the lunar eclipse. That was going to be pretty good.

I started the command sequence at 567/04:00 MET by having the file to turn the pressure transducer and the EM sensor off uplinked. Then I started turning off the GRS, NS, and SES. Though I never expected to turn them on again, I carefully went though the shutdown procedure. I first turned off the NS and GRS high-voltages at 567/04:03 MET and watched their high-voltages bleed off to zero over a couple of 32-second frames. Then I had the file uplinked to turn the spectrometers and the SES off at 567/04:07 MET, and at *567/04:08 MET the compositional mapping, using the GRS and NS, was ended* (the APS had been permanently turned off two months earlier on Day 502 MET). Together, that saved nearly 13 watts of power (the MAG/ER took less than 4.5 watts and it would not make much difference, so I chose to leave them on).

Since the tank heater event was behind us, we decided not to turn off the primary heater circuit and go to the secondary heaters at that time, though we had planned to do so, if necessary — so I canceled that set of commands. But since the battery had not fully charged up after the tank heater event, I turned the transmitter off at 567/05:07 MET, five minutes before the nighttime pass that started the eclipse sequence and during which the spacecraft and the Moon would enter the penumbra.

When we came out of that nighttime pass, at 567/05:47 MET, we were still slightly in the penumbra, which we left 18 minutes later and the battery quite easily and completely charged up in the full sunlight. That was a relief and I thought, *OK, this is just about what I expected (from my power modeling). So far so good!*

At 567/06:51 MET, the spacecraft reentered the penumbra and started its second nighttime pass/occultation period of the sequence at 567/07:03 MET. Everything looked normal and I turned the transmitter off at 567/6:58 MET, the standard 5 minutes before the occultation period began, during which the spacecraft would enter the umbra. We had started the critical period!

The spacecraft exited from the next nighttime pass/occultation period at 567/07:11 MET — deep in the umbra. I waited to turn the transmitter back on until two minutes before we passed out of the umbra and into the penumbra at 567/08:11 MET. I turned the transmitter on at 567/07:09 MET and, of course, there was no sunlight as expected, i.e., there was no Sun sensor signal and no solar array current. As we crept out from the umbra into the penumbra, the battery voltage was 25 volts, exactly what I had calculated for the calculated DOD of 50%! I thought, *OK, this is good*. We watched the spacecraft's engineering data as we crept further and further out of the penumbra and we were about 75% of the way out before the next nighttime pass started.

During that time, when we were deep in the penumbra, the battery continued to discharge and then, as we got further and further out of the penumbra, the battery started to charge up — just as Woody's model and my model had predicted. Everything looked good and we started to get ready to go into the next nighttime pass and the third loop in the penumbra. We knew the tank heaters were going to turn on sometime after the end of that nighttime pass, so I turned the transmitter off at 567/08:41 MET as planned, and I decided to leave it off somewhat longer than usual, to give the battery some relief.

When we came out of the nighttime pass at 567/09:30 MET, we were still deep in the penumbra (45%) and getting deeper (to 63%). I turned the transmitter on at 567:09:48 MET AND WE HAD YELLOW AND RED LIMITS ALL OVER THE PLACE! Every temperature was extremely low. The transmitter had dropped down to –17° C, which was 3° C above its supposed absolute lower limit. The load current was over 6 amps, because the spacecraft was freezing to death and every damned heater was on. Worse, the battery voltage was really bad — it was only 21½ volts and JUST AS RED AS HELL! Immediately upon seeing my computer screen lit up like a Christmas tree and seeing the voltage was well below the 22 volts minimum we expected for the roll-off — I knew we were in the roll-off and the battery was quickly going towards oblivion. I immediately ordered the pre-prepared command uplinked to shut the primary heaters off (567/09:50 MET); the load current dropped from 6 amps to a little over 4 amps and the battery immediately began to charge, even though the spacecraft was still receiving only about 40% of its normal sunlight! That took care of the immediate problem, but to get the spacecraft in a safer condition, I had the command to turn off the transmitter uplinked at 567/09:51 MET. Just 3 minutes after transmitter turn on, i.e., less than 5 frames, I had the spacecraft back in a safe condition and I thought we were OK — power-wise.

However, Jim Schirle, Woody, Dan, and I were concerned that everything was so cold that we could not let them get any colder, or they might fail. Though it made no difference because it was off and was never to be turned on again, the GRS was down to minus 37° C, which meant it was about at the temperature where the circuit boards for its pre-amps might crack and be damaged. The MAG/ER was, of course, on during the whole time and the MAG's temperature had dropped to –28° C and was red as hell, but it was OK.

It was a tight walk between discharging the battery to the point where it was destroyed or freezing the spacecraft, because we didn't have enough energy to keep it warm. Nevertheless, we had to leave the transmitter off or the battery would die, so I left it off well after we left the penumbra (at 567/10:18 MET) and were again in full sunlight and were ready to go into the next nighttime pass.

I turned the transmitter on for 10 minutes at 567/10:29 MET. The spacecraft was still cold, but the battery was charging. As expected, the battery was not fully charged by the time we started the next nighttime pass, but that was OK. Jim was very concerned because the transmitter was down to –20° C, which was, in his mind, the absolute lower limit, below which we could lose it.

I turned the transmitter off at 567/10:39 MET for the next nighttime pass and when we came out of that nighttime pass, at 567/11:22 MET, the spacecraft had stabilized and had started slowly getting back to normal.

We watched the spacecraft through that daytime pass and decided the battery was not getting fully charged up, so I didn't turn anything back on, i.e., the pressure transducer, the EM sensor and the primary heaters.

By the next day/night cycle, the battery was finally getting fully charged. As soon as it was clearly fully charged and trickle charging, I turned the EM sensor, the pressure transducer, and the primary heaters back on (from 567/13:53 MET to 567/13:56 MET). When the pressure transducer came back on, I could see that, because the temperatures of the tanks were so low, the pressure had dropped from 127 to 124 psi. When I turned the primary heaters back on, the load current jumped because all of the primary heaters turned on. Though I had expected an 8 or 9-amp spike, the load current only got up to about 7 amps, but it took about 15 minutes to start to drop back down to its normal levels.

By then, it was about 10:30 Wednesday morning (567/14:00 MET) and we had done our job. The spacecraft had survived a very exciting eclipse — one that was supposed to have killed it and terminated the mission — and the spacecraft was recovering thermally, though it was still quite cold. The tank heaters were on, but the tanks had not showed any visible change in their temperature. I turned the transmitter off (567/14:22 MET) again during the next nighttime pass and I turned it back on in the daylight (567/15:06 MET). The spacecraft was still cold as hell, but the battery had a reasonable charge — about 28.8 volts when the transmitter came on, but it was not charging up! I watched the charge cycle for several minutes and decided it just wasn't going to reach full charge before the next nighttime pass, so I turned the transmitter off at 567/15:50 MET for a full orbit and then back on after the nighttime pass at 567/17:36 MET. Finally that did it, the battery had reached full charge and the spacecraft, which was still cold, was finally getting fairly warm.

All during that time, the battery heater was going bonkers. It was cycling on and off almost once a minute! There was nothing we could do about it, so we just decided that was it — we were ready to go home.

It was after 2:00 in the afternoon (567/17:40 MET) and I had been up for well over 24 hours, with just a 1-hour nap shortly before I came to Mission Ops at 9:00 Tuesday night. I left Mission Ops, went to the Maple T ree Inn, and tried to take a nap.

Late Afternoon, Wednesday, July 28, 1999

Late Day 567 MET

I immediately fell asleep, but about an hour later the maid called and asked, "Do you want any service today?" That woke me up and finished my nap. Rebecca was getting some sleep, but not doing too well either. She had gone to the motel at about 8:00 AM and had tried to get some rest while I was waiting for the spacecraft to warm up and for the battery to get fully charged. But she was also very tired.

I got up, took a shower, and went back to Mission Ops. I wrote the Mission Profile for the following morning's 8:00 AM spin-up burn. Then I checked the spacecraft and everything was more or less back to normal. The fuel tanks were nearly back to their normal temperature range. Their set point had shifted; it was slightly lower for some reason. By the time I had left that evening, everything was at equilibrium, but it had taken nearly ¾ of a day to get back to normal. Poor little Lunar Prospector had really frozen during the eclipse.

Well, the spacecraft had made it. We had really pushed it and it was nip and tuck. Had I not turned the transmitter on just when the battery voltage was at 21½ volts and found that I had to turn off the primary heaters, the battery might have died in just a few more minutes and taken the spacecraft with it. Regardless, we had pushed the spacecraft well beyond what it was designed for, but Lunar Prospector had come through beautifully.

Sylvia had called up a couple times during the night and Marcie had kept her informed. But I went to her office and gave her all the details. It was very nice, because she congratulated me on getting Lunar Prospector through the killer eclipse. In fact, everybody congratulated me for getting the spacecraft through the eclipse and that was really kind of nice.

Lunar Prospector had survived its last hurdle of the mission. The stage was set for us to do the next three events over the next 57 hours, starting with the spin-up the next morning. Then, at 1:00 AM the next night, we would raise the aposelene and then impact!

Thursday, July 29, 1999

Day 568 MET: The Spin-Up and the Last Science Command

We did the spin-up burn starting just after 8:00 AM. After all the usual file checks, I had the T2 heater turn-on command uplinked and executed at 568/11:42 MET. Then, at 568/11:45 MET, I uplinked one MAG/ER command — MTLOADW 2, 4, 4410 — at Dave Curtis's request; *that was the last science command I sent to the spacecraft!* Dan and I then checked the engine parameter file; I had it uplinked and Dan and I verified each parameter as the echoes came back down. Then I had the EXEC uplinked at 568/12:07 MET and the 4.05 second T2 engine burn began and quickly ended, spinning the spacecraft up from 12.18 rpm to 23.392 rpm — our target was 23.7, but that was more than good enough. Then I safed the engine at 568/12:09 MET and *we finished our last spin maneuver of the mission.*

CBS *Nightly News* was there to film the spin-up burn and Joël Brenner from the *Washington Post* was also there. In addition, I had several other interviews during the day, including ones for the Associated Press and a Toronto newspaper.

Late Thursday Night, July 29, through Early Morning, Friday, July 30, 1999

Day 569 MET: The Aposelene Burn

Rebecca, my Ops Team, and I assembled at Mission Ops after supper on Thursday evening for the penultimate burn of the mission — raising the aposelene up to 234 km (leaving the periselene at 17 km), so we would have the steepest angle of impact possible — 6°, given the amount of fuel we had remaining. Since the time of the impact was so critical in terms of the Hubble Telescope being available and in the right position in its orbit, an on-time execution of both the aposelene burn and the final kamikaze burn the following night were of even greater importance than for all our other burns. As such, I also decided to have Dan put a 10-minute delay in the engine parameter file so we would have time to recover if something went wrong with the initial commanding.

Shortly before midnight, we were prepared for the aposelene burn and I told Paul to uplink the A3 and A4 heater turn-on file at 69/03:23 MET. After verifying the echoes, I watched the A3 and A4 engine begin to heat up. Then shortly before the 47-minute radio occultation period began at 569/03:34 MET, Dan and I went through our careful check of the engine parameter file, I had Paul uplink the file, I verified each echo, and then Dan agreed that the load was correctly uplinked. The 4-minute and 16.3-second burn would increase the spacecraft's velocity by 40.47 m/sec.

When the spacecraft came out of occultation at 569/04:21 MET, JPL had an equipment failure and could not achieve a lock — *so we did not have any downlink!* I knew we could uplink commands, but I wanted to know if JPL could verify that the commands got to the spacecraft, so I asked Paul the question. Paul answered that we would have verification from JPL that the command went up, but that would be it. I said, *"Well, if we don't get (downlinked) data in five minutes, I'm going to have to send the (engine selection and EXEC) commands in blind, because if we miss the timing on this, then we'll lose a lot of the data on the impact, because Hubble won't be able to see some of it."* Though everybody was very tired, the failure of the DSN to provide us with down-linked data at such a critical time really woke us up!

I could tell by the look on Dan's face that he was extremely uncomfortable. His expression reminded me of when he didn't want to do the 3rd LOI burn 19 months earlier. Regardless of how uncomfortable he felt, I thought Dan knew there was no way out of the situation except for me to command in the blind.

There was still no downlink after the five minutes, so I had Paul uplink the A3 and A4 engine selection command — A34VEC — in the blind and then I had Paul uplink the EXEC file in the blind at 569/04:38 MET that would cause the burn to start at exactly 1:02:54.3 sec PDT. I asked Goddard if they could see the burn on Doppler and they said they could, though there was about a 3-minute delay in their Doppler data. The commands were sent to execute the burn in 10 minutes and we sat there and waited and waited with no data!

Just a minute before the burn was to start, we got our data! Boy, were we relieved! I saw the tank heaters, that had been on when we started, were off again and that the engines were at 140° C. Everything looked normal. We saw that the timer was counting down to the burn, but it seemed to be late by 13 or 14 seconds! But was the timer late, or were we just seeing the effects of the various time delays in the 32-second mainframe of the C&DH? I thought it was the latter, but Dan thought that the delay was real.

I looked at the clock and saw we still had 30 seconds to burn initiate, even though it was past the time the engines should have fired! We saw no indication from Doppler or anything else that the engines were firing. Then, all of the sudden, we started getting the normal indications that the engines were firing — the A3 and A4 engine temperatures went up — so we had at least gotten the appropriate engine selection command in during the blind commanding. Obviously, the EXEC had gotten up in blind. Then I saw the tank pressure drop to its dynamic value and an increase in load current — all indications that the engines were firing. Dan called out that we had some nutation and that we were spinning up a little bit. Then Goddard reported they were seeing a Doppler shift. I told Goddard, "The burn might have been late; can you say anything about the timing?"

About that time, the engines should have shut off and I saw that the engine temperature started to drop, the dynamic pressure returned to its static value and the load current dropped. The burn was over. I went ahead and safed the engines at 569/04:53 MET. We knew we had had the burn; the Doppler was about right, but what about the timing? Goddard said they thought that there was a 6-second error in the timing.

After everybody settled down in Mission Ops, I fully checked out the spacecraft and it was OK, including the battery that had fully charged up after the last nighttime pass and just before all that happened.

We discussed the burn and why it might have been late. Obviously, if there were an error in the timing of the burn, it would screw up the orbit. We discussed that and what could be done. With no obvious resolution to the critical questions and because everyone was dead tired, I decided to sleep on it and Rebecca and I left for the Maple Tree Inn to get a little sleep — it was about 2:00 AM.

When we got to the motel, I called Dan because it had dawned on me that maybe he had translated the hexadecimal number incorrectly in the engine parameter file. Dan did not think that was the case, since it would not account for a 6-second error.

Early Friday Morning, July 30, 1999

Day 569 MET: The Timing Error

I woke up at about 6:00 AM, after just about 3 hours of sleep and immediately went to Mission Ops.

Dan, who had stayed at Mission Ops, said he had looked at the tail byte data (which had a 2-second resolution) and had found that the engines had started getting hot within 3 seconds of the intended burn time. That told me we had an on-time burn and the apparent 6-second error in the timing had something to do with the Doppler data and not with the spacecraft.

There was no timing error; rather Dan had gotten so uptight when I had to command in the blind that he misinterpreted the normal delays in our reading the real-time data due to the 32-second mainframe of the C&DH. Dan is just not one to do things under pressure, even though he does everything extremely well.

Satisfied, and with only 20 hours left in the mission, I went back to the motel to get some more rest.

Friday Afternoon, July 30, 1999

Day 569 MET

I got the Mission Profile and everything else ready for the kamikaze burn Saturday morning. Then Rebecca and I slept a little bit in the afternoon. After the nap, we got some food and then we were ready for the final act of the mission.

Friday Night, July 30, through 3:00 AM, Saturday Morning, July 31, 1999

Day 570 MET: IMPACT and the End of the Mission!

We went to Mission Ops at about 11:00 PM and, after all the final preparations were finished, visitors started to come in. Kelly Beatty from *Sky and Telescope*, Joël Brenner, Dougherty, Scott, Sylvia, and others started wandering in. I told Marcie to keep all the visitors at bay and that no one, absolutely no one but Dan, Paul, John Kohli, and I were allowed in the Mission Ops Glass Room. *Then the four of us went into the Glass Room for the last time to take command control of the spacecraft.*

The circumstances of the spacecraft were just perfect; it was in full sunlight since we had raised the aposelene, the battery was fully charged at 32 volts, all the temperatures were, of course, a little high because of the full sunlight.

We watched the spacecraft's entry into its penultimate radio occultation at 570/03:34 MET and when it came out of the occultation at 570/04:19 MET or 12:44 AM Saturday morning, we were ready to start the final act of the mission.

I had someone call the astronomers at the Hubble telescope and the various observatories to see if they were ready and to let them know we were getting ready for the de-orbit burn.

After that was finished, and as we had done so many times during the previous 19 months, Dan sent the engine parameter file to Paul's computer and they verified that

Paul had received the correct file. Then Paul read each parameter and Dan and I verified that each was correct.

I had Paul verify that he had the correct A3 and A4 heater turn-on file prepared. About 30 seconds before that file was to be uplinked — at 570/04:40 MET, I said to Paul, "Uplink the heater file on my mark," and I began my standard count down, "20 seconds, 10, 5, 3, 1 and 0."

Paul said, "Command away."

A frame later I said, "I have echo of 2-C-0-0-2-6, VCID 0-6, that is correct for the A3 heater." A frame later I had the echo of the EXEC and I said, "I have echo of Execute." Another frame passed and I said, "I have echo of 2-D-0-0-2-8, VCID 0-6, that is correct for the A4 heater." Another frame later I had the echo of the EXEC and I said, "I have echo of Execute. Both heaters are on." I watched the engine temperature graphic on my console and saw that both engines were heating up and said, "I have a temperature rise on both the A3 and the A4 engines." I had also seen the load current jump by 0.8 amps as each heater had turned on.

I turned to Dan and asked, "Will you verify again that Paul has the correct engine parameter file? Also, please verify that you have a 60-minute delay in the execution of the burn."

Dan answered, "Yes, I will, and yes I do." And then I queried Paul about the file name. That done, I asked Dan and Paul if they were ready to uplink and verify the engine parameter file and they both answered in the affirmative. I then told Paul to uplink the file at his convenience and he immediately did so.

I watched my echo screen intently, waiting for the one or two 32-second data frames to pass and waiting to start the strict file uplink verification procedure with Dan that we had already done 83 times during the 19-month mission. Then, I saw the first echo and I said, "I have echo of DELAYSUN of 3-1-0-0-0-0, VCID 0-6. Is that correct, Dan?"

Dan answered, "Yes it is."

The next frame appeared on my screen and I said, "I have echo of LONGDUR of 3-1-0-A-D-8, VCID of 0-6. Is that correct, Dan?"

Dan answered, "Yes it is."

The next frame appeared and I said, "I have echo of HALFREV of 3-3-0-0-0-0, VCID of 0-6. Is that correct, Dan?"

Dan answered, "Yes it is."

And the next frame appeared and I said, "I have echo of DELAYNUM of 3-0-F-0-0-1, VCID of 0-6. Is that correct, Dan?"

Dan answered, "Yes it is."

Having seen that all four engine-firing parameters were correctly echoed back from the spacecraft, I asked, "Dan, do you concur with the entire load?"

Dan answered, "Yes I do."

I said to Paul, "Please verify that you have the A34VEC command ready for uplink," and he verified that he had the correct engine selection command. Then I said, "Uplink the A34 engine selection command."

Paul said, "Command away."

I watched my screen and soon called out, "I have echo of A-3-4-V-E-C, VCID of 0-6. That is correct for the A34 engine selection. Dan, do you concur with the engine selection and the entire load?"

Dan answered *for the last time in the mission*, "Yes I do."

I told Paul to send the EXEC as a Store-And-Forward command with an Execute time set for 08:15:53.1 GMT and asked Dan to verify the Execute time and he did. I said to Paul *for the last time in the mission*, "Uplink the Execute on my mark," and I began my *last command count down*, "20 seconds, 10, 5, 3, 1 and 0."

Paul said, "Command away," for the last time in the mission.

The Execute, which would start the 60-minute clock that would initiate the burn when the spacecraft was in radio occultation over the far-side of the Moon, was uplinked at 570/04:51 MET. *It was the last command I would ever send to Lunar Prospecto*r and the first and only time we did a burn in the blind, behind the Moon.

I saw the EXEC echo and called out — *for the last time*, "I have echo of Execute."

Dan said, "The timer is counting down from 60 minutes." That verified that the commands were in and that the spacecraft was counting down to its final, kamikaze burn.

Having heard Dan say that, I said, "I am canceling the commanding of the engine parameter files with the 40 and 20 minute delay times," and I redlined them out in my Mission Profile.

As we waited for Lunar Prospector to disappear behind the Moon for the last time, Dan continued the countdown to the burn and I kept everybody quiet.

At 570/05:34 MET, Lunar Prospector went behind the Moon — if everything went correctly, that would be the last time I would ever hear from my beloved spacecraft.

Dan continued the countdown to the burn and at 570/05:51 MET Dan said, "Expected burn initiate," and Lunar Prospector, all alone over the lunar far-side, began firing its A3 and A4 engines for 4 minutes and 37.6 seconds, a burn that slowed Lunar Prospector down by 44.26 m/sec and sent it on its death plunge to the Moon.

Dan started the countdown to impact. Had the de-orbit burn not occurred at all, the spacecraft would have reappeared 8 minutes before the predicted impact time. When Dan's count got below 8 minutes and we had not picked up Lunar Prospector, we knew that the burn had occurred. However, if we had an underburn, the spacecraft would fail to impact at the chosen site. Instead, it would have impacted tens or hundreds or even thousands of kilometers down range and the spacecraft would have appeared from behind the Moon before impacting and we would have heard it for up to a half an hour before it the impacted. It was really thrilling as the time before impact got shorter and shorter and we still did not hear from Lunar Prospector. It was clear everything had gone as planned.

Dan continued the countdown until one minute to impact and that was when I took over. I had a plot of the final 30 seconds of the trajectory in front of me and I said, "Impact minus 38 seconds — we are passing over the South Pole. Impact minus 22 seconds — we are passing over the southern rim of the crater at an altitude of only 450 m to 1400 m (depending on just how high the rim was), 10 seconds to impact, 5, — (predicted) impact at 2:52:00.8 AM PDT!"

I asked everybody to stay quiet because I wanted to be sure I could hear the DSN personnel if they picked up the spacecraft again and secondly, I wanted to hear if the astronomers saw any trace of the impact. I waited a few minutes after the predicted impact time to be certain we were never going to hear from Lunar Prospector again and then, shortly before 3:00 AM PDT, I said, "Well, it's clear that we have had impact."

After nearly 11 years of effort, THE COMPLETELY SUCCESSFUL LUNAR PROSPECTOR MISSION WAS OVER — AGAINST ALL ODDS.

EPILOG

The Lunar Prospector Aftermath and Payoff

July 31, 1999
and Beyond

Shortly Before 3:00 AM Saturday Morning Until Saturday Night, July 31, 1999: Lunar Prospector Was Over

Immediately after I declared that Lunar Prospector had impacted, everyone in Mission Ops applauded, Dan and I shook hands and than we each shook hands with Paul and John. The four of us just stayed in the Glass Room for another 20 to 30 minutes, enjoying the end of an extremely successful mission, sitting and chatting in front of blank screens — blank for the first time in 570 days, 6 hours and 27 minutes, — blank not because Lunar Prospector was in occultation or the transmitter was turned off or the DSN was not tracking the spacecraft, but blank because Lunar Prospector was dead, its parts strewn across the frigid floor of a crater near the Moon's south pole.

As we sat in the Glass Room, the rest of the Ops Team, as well as Rebecca, Sylvia, Tim Bridges, Tim Maloney, Kelly Beatty, and Joël Brenner came in and we all talked about the Mission; they congratulated me on Lunar Prospector and I thanked them for all their work and congratulated them on the great job they had all done.

As I had hoped and expected, Scott, David Morrison, and Dougherty stayed out of the Glass Room; so I didn't have to talk with them and thus didn't have the moment spoiled. Happily I had not noticed, but Rebecca said later that Scott had pranced around like Little Lord Fauntleroy, congratulating himself on his success.

When I finally left the Glass Room, I went into my office to do some telephone interviews with the news media and to correct the final operational Mission Profile and integrate it into my historical records.

When I was finished, I came out of my office and had a nice talk with Louis Peach, who was there from Headquarters. Louis was just ecstatic about Lunar Prospector and what I was trying to do commercially beyond Lunar Prospector. He said he was leaving NASA and would therefore be able to help on the private front more than he could as a NASA official.

Dave Lozier, who was nearing retirement, pulled me over and said, "I want to thank you for giving me a successful end to my career; it started with Pioneer and it's ending with Lunar Prospector and Lunar Prospector was a great mission." Dave's comments made me feel even better than I already did.

By then, it was past 4:00 in the morning and most of the people had begun to drift away. Before I left, David Morse had me do a video for the NASA historical records and then he did the same with Scott.

By that time it was going on 5:00 AM and I was dead tired. Rebecca and I left Mission Ops and went to the good old Maple Tree Inn. We slept for 4 or 5 hours and got up in time to go to the Cattleman's Restaurant near Ames, where I treated all the Mission Controllers to a "thank you and farewell" lunch. We all had a nice time; they were all loyal and dedicated to me and to the success of the mission and I was going to miss them.

Rebecca and I left the restaurant and went back to Mission Ops to pack up my things. When we walked into Mission Ops, it was very strange — it was totally dark and no one was there! That was the first time I had ever seen it dark and empty since we had started working there nearly two years earlier. I had the strong and strange feeling that it was lifeless and abandoned. That room had been both the focus of my life for the previous two years and the electronic lifeline to my spacecraft orbiting the Moon some 384,000 km away — and then, like my spacecraft, it was dead and abandoned. After a short pause, while Rebecca and I absorbed those feelings, I broke the spell by turning on the lights, we went in and got my computer and my other things packed up, said, "Goodbye," to Mission Ops, and carried everything down to the car.

We then drove over to the Ames Public Museum, where I did live TV interviews with CNN and NBC starting at 3:00 PM.

After the interviews, we drove down to Gilroy, got the rental truck, and parked it at the house, so we could load it first thing in the morning. Then, exhausted, we went to the motel in Gilroy, where we were going to stay, checked in, and slept.

Sunday, August 1, 1999: Getting Ready to Leave

We got up about 8:00 AM, after a pretty good night's sleep. Nevertheless, we were still tired after the last several days and nights of intense end-of-mission activities. After donuts, coffee (for Rebecca), and a coke (for me) we went to the house and spent several hours loading the Ryder Truck. During the afternoon, we took much needed naps and relaxed.

Despite the fact that NASA and the aerospace community had ignored the success I had in showing how to do "Faster, Better, Cheaper" missions correctly, I was happy. The Lunar Prospector Mission had been a complete success in every respect. I had accomplished everything we had set out to do over a decade earlier. I had defined and built as perfect a spacecraft as one could ever hope to build, I had flown an essentially flawless 19-month mission and, though we did not know the full extent of it at that time, I had produced lunar mapping data sets that were far superior to anything we, or anyone, could have expected — and all for $65 million. It was marvelous, just absolutely superb. As we prepared to go to bed for the last time in Gilroy, Rebecca and I were happily closing the most significant chapter in our lives and we were getting ready for our next chapter.

Monday, August 2, and Tuesday, August 3, 1999:
On the Road to Arizona

After turning in the rented car, Rebecca and I left Gilroy at 7:40 AM in the loaded Ryder truck. We had really been looking forward to leaving California and starting on our new life in Arizona, so we were excited and happy to finally be on our way to Tucson. The drive went well and by evening we had reached Indio, CA, where we spent the night.

We got an early start Wednesday morning and crossed the Colorado River, leaving California and entering my beloved Arizona, a couple of hours later. Though I had told a Tucson newspaper reporter that, after crossing the border into Arizona, I intended to stop, get out of the car, and kiss the Arizona ground, we just kept driving towards Tucson after we crossed the Colorado.

We arrived at the apartment that we had rented in Tucson at about 2:00 PM, found Tad Theno, who had arrived a day or so earlier to help set up the LRI office, and he and I unloaded the household goods from the truck Rebecca and I wanted in the apartment. Then we picked up our car that had been delivered to our niece's house a couple of days earlier. After a nice dinner with Tad, Rebecca and I retired for our first evening in our new, but temporary, apartment in Tucson.

Wednesday, August 4, through the Middle of August 1999: Getting LRI Set Up

The lease on the three-room suite we had rented at the University of Arizona Science and Technology Park started on Sunday, August 1, and the furniture we had bought with part of the $8000 that George French had donated to LRI had been delivered on Monday. Happily, Tad had already started assembling the office furniture. Wednesday morning, while Rebecca was unpacking our household goods at the apartment, Tad and I went to the office to unload the LRI things from the truck and to continue assembling the office furniture.

By the middle of August, with Tad's considerable help, we had a functioning office (we were also settled in the apartment and Bill North had a good start on building our house), so I could turn my attention to getting our contract for the Lunar Prospector Data Reduction Program pushed through the NASA bureaucracy — not an easy task — and to garnering support for my commercial lunar exploration plans from the Arizona Congressional delegation (Senators McCain and Kyl and Tucson Congressmen Pastor and Kolbe — we live in Kolbe's district and he was on the all important Congressional Finance Committee) and the Arizona State Government.

Middle of August to Early November 1999

I got started with my political activities by calling the Tucson offices of McCain, Kyl, Kolbe, Pastor, and Arizona Governor Hull and setting up meetings with their technical staffers, in the hopes that I would eventually see the Senators, Congressmen, and the Governor themselves. Except for Hassan Hijazi in Kolbe's office, I found I was dealing with people with no technical knowledge, though they all found what I was doing was very interesting. In the case of the Governor's office, I did not even get an answer back when I asked to meet with Steve Jewett, who was the head of the Governor's Tucson Office. I came away from that several weeks' effort concluding that my time was better spent talking with the staffers in the Washington, DC, offices of the Senators and Congressmen, than with their Tucson staffers. I left it at that and decided to do my politicking every time I had to go to NASA headquarters.

Regarding my other top priority, i.e., our money, I had finalized the revised Budget and Statement of Work with Joe Boyce on June 18, six weeks before our proposed start date of August 1 (the day after the End-of-Mission). Joe was aware that we needed to go right from the Mission Contract activities to the Data Reduction Contract work without a break: First, because we could lose critical personnel, especially at LANL, to other programs if we could not pay them to get started on the Lunar Prospector Data Reduction Program, and second, because LRI had accumulated only enough cash reserves from the Mission Contract to last about two months. Since the proposed start date of August 1 had already come and gone two weeks earlier and since I saw no progress in getting the contract negotiated and signed, I was getting concerned — especially since I did not trust NASA to do anything even close to on time (or right). Thus, Wayne and I started to harangue Headquarters daily to get the contract finished.

After a few calls to NASA/Goddard, we found that Jim Becker, Joe's contact there, was going to be responsible for our contract. We quickly established a friendly rapport with Jim after we explained to him that we understood his plight as a contracts officer and would not hold him personally responsible for all the dumb regulations that were going to cause us problems. As such, Jim was ready to try to help us. Nevertheless, there were many such problems and they were as follows:

A) Since the new Fiscal Year was about to start (on October 1), the contracts people were supposed to do all the renewal contracts first and then start on new contracts. That meant Jim would not even get started working on our contract until after October 1, or at least three months after our proposed start date! I made a few calls to Joe Boyce and Guenter Riegler, during which I reminded them of the urgency of us getting started and that part of my job in continuing to prove that "Faster, Better, Cheaper" worked, was to get the Lunar Prospector data in the archives on time. The calls eventually worked and Jim was told to get started on our contract right then.

B) However, Jim never received the paperwork from Headquarters — it had been lost a second time! The paperwork was supposed to have been sent electronically, as well as by hardcopy in the NASA mail. However, for some mysterious reasons, neither the electrons (which normally travel at the speed of light) nor the envelope were able to get across the few 10s of kilometers that separate Goddard from Headquarters! As the days ticked by, I kept calling Jim and Joe to find out where the paperwork was. I got annoyed enough to again suggest to Joe that Wayne fly to Washington, pick up the paperwork, and hand carry it to Goddard — a suggestion that Joe again said would violate all kinds of federal regulations. Finally, after several tries, Jim got the authorization paperwork and began to work on the contract.

C) We needed to have a contract, not a grant, between NASA and LRI, and we needed to get money upfront (as absolutely required for LANL and for LRI, since we needed to keep LRI solvent — though NASA did not care about LRI's situation), but Jim said both things were impossible. He explained that the government did not make contracts with universities and non-profit corporations, rather they gave such institutions grants and, as such, we would get "reimbursed" quarterly and only after we had submitted each Quarterly Report. That would mean we would not see any money for at least four months (assuming they got us a grant within a month) and LRI would always have to carry at least four months worth of charges (about $400,000 between LANL and LRI — money LRI simply did not have). Clearly that was not acceptable to LANL or to LRI (we had about $30,000 worth of resources and that would cover only about six to eight weeks of LRI charges alone). Wayne looked up the government regulations and found out, "Yes," NASA could write a contract with us — in fact NASA could only have a contract with us, because we had to produce "deliverables," i.e., the data that were to go into the NASA archives, and that could only be done under a contract and not under a grant! We then called Jim, who checked the right paragraphs in the regulations and found that Wayne was correct. Jim said he would look into our getting a contract and then call us back. When he did, he said that though a contract was required, they never did that and if they did, he would have to get signatures from seven different levels of bureaucrats and that would take a few more weeks (it was already September and so, at best, we would not have a contract until October — at least two months behind schedule)! After a couple more calls to Joe and Guenter, Joe told Jim to do a contract regardless of the bureaucratic BS and get it done ASAP.

D) In an effort to be helpful and to get the ball rolling, Jim countered with the idea that he could quickly get grants to LANL, UC Berkeley, and the U of Arizona, so they could start work and get a contract to LRI later (Jim did not know it, but that would have sunk LRI, because we would not have had any income for several months) and I said, "No, if you do that, I'll have no control over my Co-Is or their institutions, and I'll have no way of running the program or insuring that the deliverables are delivered on time. I successfully ran the mission by having financial control over my sub-contractors and

I'm not about to try to do the data analysis program any other way." Jim still thought his suggestion was the way to go, so I called Joe again and he agreed with me and informed Jim there was to be only one contract, it was to be with LRI and I was to be in charge of all the work.

That finally settled all the issues. Jim got to work on the contract and we finally signed it on October 8, 1999 — by which time, we had already lost 10 weeks of time and that was not the end of it. Obviously, Wayne and I could not start negotiating the sub-contracts with LANL, Berkeley, and U of Arizona until we had our contract with NASA signed. Though we got started immediately (remember, we had to deal with university bureaucrats, so all was not well), it took Wayne and me until the beginning of November before all the subcontracts were negotiated and signed and until we finally got started on the data reduction work. Also it took nearly three weeks after the October 8 signing before we actually got money transferred from NASA to LRI and by that time we had depleted all of the meager financial reserves LRI had had at the end of the mission three months earlier!

I was annoyed. It had taken nearly five months for NASA/Goddard to get us a contract for $2.9 million and start transferring the money. In contrast, it had taken just a month for NASA/Ames to get a $63 million contract with Lockheed done and money transferred, so we could get started on the Lunar Prospector Phase B work. How could NASA ever become "Faster, Better, Cheaper," if that was the way it continued to work?

To add insult to injury, the contract we had spent so much time getting through the system was just for the $922,000 we were to get from the FY99 budget and it would last us for only five months, or until the end of March 2000. I told Jim we had better get started on "Option 1" of the contract, i.e., the $1.6 million we were to get from the FY2000 budget. Jim said, "Don't worry, it takes only a few weeks to get the contract modified so you can get the FY2000 money," — famous last words.

While Wayne and I were fighting those bureaucratic battles, an event took place on September 23 in the upper atmosphere of Mars that would eventually play a major role in my efforts to get NASA and Congress to recognize the value of Lunar Prospector in showing how missions should be done "Faster, Better, Cheaper." *Instead of doing a propulsive maneuver and going into orbit around Mars, the $125 million Mars Climate Observer orbiter spacecraft burned up in the Martian upper atmosphere when arriving at Mars!*

That costly error occurred because the Denver Lockheed Martin engineers who had built and helped fly the spacecraft on its way to Mars, had used English units (e.g., ft/sec) instead of the metric units (e.g., m/sec) that they were supposed to use. The JPL managers had asked the Lockheed Martin managers several times if their engineers were giving JPL the navigation data in metric units and Lockheed Martin managers had always said, "Yes." The JPL engineers and flight controllers, who were doing most of the navigation and who were preparing to take over the spacecraft, had assumed in their trajectory calculations that all the data were metric. As a result, instead of coming in just above the Martian upper atmosphere for the orbit insertion burn, Mars Climate Observer's trajectory was several 10s of km low — well inside the Martian atmosphere!

Though the tracking data of the last couple of days of the approach to Mars had indicated that something was not quite right, JPL had ignored those signs of impending doom and hoped for the best! Mars Climate Observer went behind Mars and should have done its orbit insertion burn while out of radio contact — but when it was expected to reappear from behind Mars, it didn't — it had burned up in the Martian atmosphere!

That costly and, to say the least, embarrassing and stupid management and engineering mistake was the result of the general reluctance of most engineers to stop using the English system and to use the vastly superior metric system and, more importantly, *the fact that no one person, neither a NASA person, nor a JPL person, nor a Lockheed Martin person, was truly in charge of — or fully responsible for — the program.* The left hand simply did not know what the right hand was doing!

While NASA, JPL, and Lockheed Martian had to take the blame, the failure started a landslide of criticisms of the "Faster, Better, Cheaper" approach to missions, an approach the engineers, the aerospace companies, and NASA middle management did not like anyway (they thought it was too hard to do) and finally they had a failed mission to prove their point. I was not happy about those unfair attacks, especially since NASA had done its best to ignore the success of Lunar Prospector in showing how "Faster, Better, Cheaper" missions should really be done, but there was still more to come.

Early November 1999, through Thanksgiving, 1999: The Early Scientific Results

Once we got the sub-contracts signed and the money from NASA, work on the Level 2 GRS, NS, MAG, and ER data products began in earnest in early November. Though we had never actually stopped working on the data reduction while I was trying to get the contracts negotiated, my Co-Is (especially Bill) could not hire the new personnel they needed to get into high gear without the new funding. We finally got moving in high gear and, in order to see exactly where we were as a team and what we had already found out from the data, I started planning a Science Team Meeting to be held at LRI just after Thanksgiving, on November 29 and 30. Though the data reduction program had hardly begun, the Lunar Prospector data had already begun to yield remarkable things about the Moon, some of which we had published in our Preliminary Science Reports which had appeared in the September 4, 1998 issue of *Science.*

On November 15, as I was in the midst of planning the Science Team Meeting, I received a call from Laim Sarsfield of the Rand Corporation. He invited me to tell my tale about Lunar Prospector and my experience with "Faster, Better, Cheaper" at one of three meetings that Tony Spear had set up to evaluate the "Faster, Better, Cheaper" concept most people were complaining about. Tony, who was the JPL Project Manager for Mars Pathfinder and who had retired from JPL after Pathfinder's success, had been asked by Dan Goldin to find out what the people involved with "Faster, Better, Cheaper" missions thought of the concept. That request was prompted when, to Goldin's surprise, Tony responded to Goldin's question about how he (Tony) liked doing things "Faster, Better, Cheaper," by answering it was far too difficult and all the engineers had bitterly complained about having to do Pathfinder that way. Not liking Tony's answer, Goldin asked Tony to set up a series of meeting to get other people's opinions on the topic and to write a report on the results.

The Spear Meetings were underway and Laim asked me if I could come to a meeting in Pasadena on December 2 and 3 to give the Lunar Prospector story, since everyone recognized that Lunar Prospector had been a great success! Since that was the first time that NASA had shown any real interest in Lunar Prospector's success, I was more than happy to do so, but I said I could not attend the entire meeting. Laim said he would set up a time for me to talk at 9:00 AM on December 3 and I said that would be just fine. I was really pleased to finally get a chance to let NASA know how Lunar Prospector was really done without Scott and Lockheed filtering the real story for their benefit.

Monday, November 29, and Tuesday, November 30, 1999: The Science Team Meeting

After a nice Thanksgiving (Rebecca and I rented a cabin in the Santa Rita Mountains south of Tucson and had a great time), we had our Science Team Meeting.

Unfortunately, Alex Konopliv was ill and could not attend our meeting, but Alex sent me his viewgraphs and they were remarkable. In order to get good data on the lunar gravity field, we had to determine the spacecraft's velocity, via the Doppler measurements, with an accuracy of 1 mm/sec. However, Alex's data were nearly five times better — we had 0.22 mm/sec data! Also, because Lunar Prospector was a simple, spin stabilized spacecraft that did not maintain its attitude by automatically firing attitude jets, an activity that messes up Doppler measurements, and because we usually did not fire the engines to change either the attitude or the spin rate between the orbital maintenance burns that occurred only once every 56 days (nearly 700 orbits of the Moon) during the nominal mission, Lunar Prospector provided long periods, or long arcs, of undisturbed Doppler gravity data. Those long arcs of data, plus the amazing 0.22 mm/sec accuracy, yielded gravity maps of unprecedented accuracy and detail. That was well demonstrated by the fact that, in addition to more accurately mapping the known Mascons on the near-side of the Moon and discovering many new ones on the near-side and around the lunar limb, where previous missions had provided only scant data, Alex had mapped several Mascons on the lunar far-side — a feat that was thought to be impossible without a relay satellite or a sub-satellite co-orbiting with the main spacecraft!

Further, using the gravity data, Alex had obtained a value for the moment of inertia factor of the Moon of 0.3932 ± 0.0002 (the 0.0002 error being 5σ or 5 standard deviations) or some 20 times more accurate than ever before. That result indicates the Moon really does have a core and its radius, if the core is pure iron, is between 220 and 450 km and it contains between 0.5 and 4% of the Moon's mass (for comparison, the Earth's large iron core contains 30% of the Earth's mass). In addition, Lon Hood had used the MAG data to measure the radius of an electrically conducting (iron?) core and derived values between 250 to 430 km, values that are in total accord with the gravity results. Finally, as we had learned earlier in March at the XXX Lunar and Planetary Science Conference, J. G. Williams and his colleagues had used our gravity data and their lunar laser ranging data to show that the Moon does have a core and its radius is 352 km, or less, if composed of iron and 374 km, or less, if the iron contains some sulfur — values smack in the middle of our results and values that yield a core mass of about, or less than, 1.9% of the lunar mass. Thus, Lunar Prospector's data finally answered the important question about the existence of a lunar core in the positive and indicates its radius is most probably between 300 and 350 km and its mass is probably between 1.2 to 1.8% of that of the Moon — a very important result needed for unraveling the origin, differentiation, and early evolution of the Moon.

The MAG/ER results were equally impressive. We had expected to get good data when the Moon and the spacecraft were passing through the magnetically quiet magnetic tail of the Earth (about 5 days per month) and we had hoped to get good data some of the time when Lunar Prospector was in the Moon's own solar wind wake, and maybe even once in a while when Lunar Prospector was in the free streaming solar wind. However, it was clear that we had lots of good wake data and even quite a bit of good data in the free streaming solar wind. By the time of our Team Meeting, Bob, David Mitchell, Lon, and Mario had the first complete magnetic map of the entire Moon. That map clearly shows that the small, weak, local magnetic fields of the Moon are concentrated and are strongest in the areas 180°, or antipodal, from the major Maria Basins, e.g., the basins of Mare Imbrium, Mare Serenitatis, Mare Crisium, Mare Orientale, and that magnetic fields are absent or, at least, very weak in the Mare Basin areas themselves.

Those results conclusively show that the rocks in the impact area were demagnetized during a giant basin forming impact. Then, as the impact ejecta swept around the Moon, moving in all directions toward the impact's antipode, the plasma in the ejecta (formed from vaporized rock) swept up the preexisting magnetic fields and concentrated them at the antipode. In the presence of those concentrated magnetic fields, the hot, shocked rocks in the ejecta that were crashing into the antipodal area, became thermally and shock magnetized. Thus, the Lunar Prospector MAG/ER data resolved the question about the origin of the majority of the lunar magnetic fields, though the question remains concerning the origin of the original magnetic fields that were near or around the Moon when the giant impact basins formed.

When we published our Preliminary Science Results in *Science*, we only had data from the nominal Mission when Lunar Prospector was in the 100 km altitude orbit and we had seen the signature of hydrogen only in the low-energy or epithermal part of the neutron spectrum. That had perplexed Bill since he was sure we should have also seen the signature of hydrogen in the high-energy or fast neutron part of the spectrum. Because we did not, his modeling suggested, if we had detected water ice, it was buried below about 40 cm of regolith — a result that was possible, but puzzling. By the time of our meeting, Bill and Sylvestre Maurice had been able to analyze the data from the low altitude (30 km) Extended Mission phase of the mission and those data confirmed what Bill had expected, but had not seen in the high-altitude data — the fast-neutron flux also showed hydrogen signatures at the poles. Finally, the NS data were making sense. Bill found through new modeling that the reason we had not seen the signature of hydrogen in the fast-neutron flux from the 100-km data was that the patches of suspected ice were much smaller than the 150 km resolution of the NS at that altitude and hence, the hydrogen was not detectable until we had the 60 km resolution data from the 30 km altitude orbits. Though we still did not know if we had discovered water ice deposits or if we had discovered enhanced solar wind hydrogen deposits, the data showed what we expected — the hydrogen containing deposits extend from the surface to at least 1 m deep in the regolith (the neutrons we measured came from no deeper than a meter). If the deposits were water ice and if the deposits extended to about 2 m depths, as we expected on theoretical grounds, then the inferred amount of water would be a few 100 million metric tons.

As Bill and I discovered when we saw our first maps of the thermal neutron flux from the Moon, the mare basalt units stood out like sore thumbs. That is because the basalts are rich in iron (Fe) and titanium (Ti), both of which have large neutron capture cross sections. As a result, we had found an exciting new way of mapping Fe and Ti from orbit.

However, Rick Elphic, who is a member of Bill's group at LANL, had taken that discovery a step further. In an effort to understand how to properly apply the thermal neutron data to mapping Fe and Ti, Rick had compared our data with the maps of Fe and Ti produced by Paul Lucy and his colleagues using the Clementine spectral reflectance data, since we had a lot of work to do before we could get Fe and Ti abundances from our GRS data. The Clementine Fe and Ti maps were developed using empirical equations based on laboratory measurements of the spectral reflectivity of — and the laboratory-measured amounts of Fe and Ti in — the regolith samples obtained during the Apollo Program. Though that technique provides valuable information, it is limited in accuracy because we have regolith samples from only nine lunar sites, and more importantly, because the samples give the composition of the regolith on the centimeter scale, while the orbital spectral reflectivity data have resolutions on the 100s of meters scales — so an absolute comparison is not possible. Thus the question remains, "How accurate are the laboratory spectra of the returned samples for calibrating the orbital spectral measurements?"

That question notwithstanding, when Rick used the Clementine data to subtract out the effects that Fe and Ti had on the thermal neutron fluxes, he found there was a strong residual signature that had exactly the same distribution over the Moon as thorium (Th, as defined by the GRS data discussed immediately below) and hence, KREEP (a petrologically extremely important residual material rich in trace elements, especially potassium [K], the rare earth elements [REE] and phosphorus [P], from which KREEP got its name). As such, the answer to the question, "What is causing the residual signature in the neutron flux?" was immediately obvious and very exciting.

Though KREEP is rich in the REE's, their abundances in lunar materials are really very, very low, generally only from 0.1 to a few 10s of parts per million! However, two of the REE's, Gadolinium (Gd) and Samarium (Sm), have exceptionally enormous nuclear cross sections and hence they have a great effect on the neutron fluxes, despite their very, very low abundances and thus Gd + Sm are causing the residual signature in the neutron flux! Thus the thermal neutron data gave us a way of mapping the distribution of Gd + Sm (they are mapped together, since there is no way of telling them apart using the neutron data) over the Moon!

That was exciting, first because it added two important trace elements to our list of detectable elements (no one in the world would have guessed that we would have been able to map the Gd + Sm abundance over the Moon using the Lunar Prospector NS) and second, we had four, count them, four independent ways of mapping the distribution of KREEP over the Moon — since Th, uranium, K and Gd + Sm are all enriched in KREEP and between the GRS and the NS, we mapped all four!

Like the NS data, the GRS data sets had been greatly improved by the low-altitude, high-resolution data of the extended mission. While the first global map (with 150 km resolution) of Th we published in *Science* had proven the earlier concept that KREEP had been excavated from the crust-mantle boundary by the Mare Imbrium Basin Forming Impact and distributed over the Moon's surface, our new high-resolution data went a step further. Our new maps showed that Th was also concentrated around the 30 to 60 km diameter, post-Imbrium craters Kepler, Aristarchus, Mairan, Aristillus, and Arago, all of which are near the rim of — or somewhat outside of — the 1000 km diameter Imbrium basin. Thus the high resolution Lunar Prospector data clearly show that after Th-rich KREEP had been excavated by the Mare Imbrium Basin Forming Impact and deposited around the basin, those KREEP-rich ejecta deposits were partially buried by later mare basalt lava flows and the ejecta from other large impact events. Then, the smaller impacts that formed the 30 to 60 km sized craters re-excavated the buried KREEP-rich materials and re-deposited them on the lunar surface immediately around those craters. Thus, the new GRS data were showing us a second step in the distribution of the all-important KREEP over the Moon.

As our Science Team Meeting ended, we were all ecstatic about the results we had already obtained and we were looking forward to what further work on our beautiful data would bring — and I was looking forward to the Tony Spear meeting in Pasadena.

Thursday, December 2, and Friday, December 3, 1999: The Tony Spear Meeting and Another Disaster at Mars

I arrived in Pasadena, CA, for the Tony Spear "Faster, Better, Cheaper" meeting Thursday evening, December 2. The flight from Tucson to LA was geologically and meteorologically very interesting because there were very high winds blowing from the west, winds that were picking up dust at numerous places in the desert. The dust from each of those sources was blown to the east in long narrow plumes that extended up to several kilometers before turbulence caused the dust to billow out into an ever-expanding cloud. I was fascinated with nature's display in the desert far below.

Having been told that the meeting would start with my talk at 9:00 AM, I arrived at the meeting shortly before 9:00 only to find that it had started at 8:30 and that a relatively young man was telling the committee about his experience as a PI on a "Faster, Better, Cheaper" mission and it was not pretty. He explained how it had stressed everyone out, that people had gotten sick and had heart attacks, that he had had so little time for his wife and family that he and his wife divorced, but happily, after the mission was over, they got back together and remarried! He said while "Faster, Better, Cheaper" was very, very hard to do, it had its good points and that he would tell anyone who was about to be a "Faster, Better, Cheaper" PI to be very sure he or she knew what he or she was getting into before signing up. I found his comments very interesting.

Also as I walked into the meeting, I was very happy to see that Jim French was there. He got up and came over to me to say, "Hi," and we walked into another room and had a nice chat. Jim was very pleased with what I had done with Lunar Prospector and said that I had finally proven what he had been saying for years about how missions should be done. I was pleased with Jim's compliments — they meant a lot to me because Jim is one of the few engineers for whom I have total respect — and I was very pleased to see him again.

We then went back into the meeting and I was given a viewgraph package of what had already been presented. I leafed through it and was dismayed at what I read. The first thing that caught my eye was the statement, *"the PIs have not taken their responsibilities seriously."* That was followed by the recommendation that more money, more time, and more NASA management of the programs were required for success, i.e., "Faster, Better, Cheaper" was to slide back to "business as usual," if those guys had their way. Between the negative comments of the PI who was still talking and the dumb things I had just read, I was loaded for bear.

As soon as the previous speaker was finished, I was introduced. I got up and as I walked to the podium, I said, "I strongly disagreed with what I just heard and read."

But before I could say another word, several people, who knew full well how I had done my job as PI on Lunar Prospector, said, "Yeah, we know you disagree with the statement about the PIs not doing their job."

I replied, "Damned right," and everybody laughed.

With that as a good start, I told them about how I had done my job as PI; that I was involved with every phase of the mission, that I knew my spacecraft from one end to the other and that I knew how to fly it. I said further, that unlike the speaker before me, all my team members — all the engineers, my Ops Team, my Nav Team, and my Science Team — had fun doing Lunar Prospector and had thoroughly enjoyed being solely responsible for their subsystems or tasks, rather than just being a cog in a big, impersonal wheel. I told them what I had said to the engineers at the beginning of the program, i.e., "Lunar Prospector is supposed to be an interesting and fun program to work on. If you are not having fun, then go find another program to work on that is fun," and that to a man, at the end of the mission, they all said they had fun, that was the only way to do missions and they were all unhappy to have to go back to other programs. I also said, "In contrast to the previous speaker's experience, we had no heart attacks, no serious illnesses, and no divorces; in fact, we even had one marriage between two of my team members." I then said, "The PI has to be a fulltime PI; he has to be in residence where the spacecraft is being built and tested and he has to be the Mission Director." At the end, everyone seemed to agree with me, so when I left, I felt as though I had finally made an impact with Lunar Prospector's success and my approach to doing "Faster, Better, Cheaper." I left the meeting feeling good and headed for LAX and home.

The flight home was as interesting as the flight to LA. The dust storm had continued to build and when Rebecca picked me up at the Tucson Airport early in the afternoon, the air was so thick with dust that you could not even see the mountains around Tucson.

However, in addition to the dust storm that was in full force as I was winging my way home on December 3, another, far more important storm was brewing on Mars that would quickly spill over to Earth.

Because of the catastrophic loss of the Mars Climate Observer just 71 days earlier, the world was watching as a nervous NASA and an equally nervous JPL guided the $203 million Mars Polar Lander — the sister spacecraft to the Mars Climate Observer orbiter — on its approach to Mars for its aerobraking maneuver and its 1:01 PM MST landing near the south polar cap of Mars. *Another failure was unthinkable. But after the Lander shut off its radio in preparation for the atmospheric aerobraking and landing sequence, it was never heard from again!* NASA and JPL kept up a deathwatch for five days, hoping against hope to hear from the Lander and the two small, independent penetrator probes it had carried along to Mars, but to no avail. On December 8, NASA had to announce to a stunned world that it had lost its second Mars mission in ten weeks!

The following investigation concluded that the probable cause of the failure was a premature shutdown of the landing engines when the landing legs explosively extended while the lander was still high above the Martian surface — leaving the spacecraft to crash to the surface. Pre-launch tests had shown that the shock caused when the legs extended could cause the spacecraft's computer to think that the spacecraft had touched down on the Martian surface, so it would, of course, shut off the engines. *However, the software change the JPL engineers had made to correct for that possible fatal error was NEVER TESTED to see if it functioned correctly before launch!* There were several other serious issues about the construction and testing of the Lander and the two penetrator probes and about the management of the entire program, e.g., there were engineers working on the mission, who did not even know who was in charge!

Though JPL and NASA management were at fault for those failures, the opponents of "Faster, Better, Cheaper" were screaming. Letters to the Editors of *Aviation Week and Space Technology* and *Space News*, totally ignoring the complete successes of Mars Pathfinder and Lunar Prospector, decried the concept as a total failure and claimed that no science had ever come from a "Faster, Better Cheaper" mission and, of course, Congress began to ask Goldin, NASA, and JPL some very pointed questions.

NASA, of course, set up a committee to investigate the NASA/JPL/Mars mess and put Lockheed manager Tom Young in charge (Tom was the Deputy to Viking Project Manager, Jim Martin, so I know Tom well and have the greatest respect for him). Clearly things were wrong with JPL and NASA and Tom was supposed to find out what, but as far as I was concerned, it was the same problems as always — incompetent management, poor engineering, decision by committee, so no one person was ever to blame for anything, and no one person was in charge of or responsible for anything.

The very reason we wanted to do Lunar Prospector in the first place was to demonstrate how to manage missions correctly and to do them reliably and at low cost. We had succeeded and I hoped against hope that those two, expensive and unforgivable failures (plus the $900 million Mars Observer failure 7 years earlier) would finally give me the opportunity to make NASA and Congress recognize what I had accomplished with Lunar Prospector and use Lunar Prospector's success as a model for future missions.

The Remainder of December 1999

As 1999 approached its end, things were looking good. We had LRI up and running efficiently, the data reduction work was going well and Bill North was doing just fine building our dream house. Rebecca and I were enjoying the fruits of the mission and I was hopeful I would be able to press home both the Lunar Prospector message and the need for a funded data purchase program, so we could get back into the Moon business and I could get LEI up and running.

January through Early March 2000

January 1, the year 2000 had arrived and the computers of the world did not crash, so we successfully made it into the new millennium (at least, that was what most people thought the year 2000 meant, but as more and more people were beginning to understand, the new millennium would not begin until January 1, 2001) and everything continued to go smoothly.

In order to keep everything going smoothly and foolishly taking Jim Becker's assurances that it would only take a few weeks to get the $1.6 million, FY2000 money for the data reduction program to us, I sent a letter to Joe formally asking for the FY2000 money on February 1, noting that we needed the new allocation no later than the end of March, when the FY99 money would run out. Then a day or two after I sent that letter off to Joe, NASA threw a monkey wrench into the works.

I received a letter from Joe Boyce dated January 27, 2000, in which Joe informed me that due to a congressionally mandated, across the board NASA budget cut, Code S was cutting everyone's FY2000 budget by 5.8% or $98,000 in our case. I called Joe and told him, if the cut was across the board, i.e., if I had to cut Bill and the MAG/ER guys, then we could deliver neither the GRS/NS Level 4 data nor the MAG/ER Level 2 data to the archives. Alternatively, if I only cut the MAG/ER budget, then Bill could get the GRS/NS data in, but the MAG/ER guys would be dead in the water. Joe understood and said I needed to write Guenter Riegler a letter and let him decide what I was supposed to do.

However, before I wrote that letter, there was another twist. I got a call from Mario Acuña. The Goddard and Ames budget people had just informed him he had $160,000 left over from the Lunar Prospector Mission Contract and Ames was going to take it back! Of course, he wanted to keep the money, so he wanted me to find out what was going on. I called Sylvia Cox at Ames and she explained the situation (basically, Mario has so many pots of money he can't keep track of them) and the Ames budget people were going to get the money, but I had another idea. If Headquarters took the residual $160,000 and gave it to me, it would more than make up for the 5.8% cut and we would again be OK.

After all that was clear, I wrote Guenter on Feb. 18 and gave him three options: 1) cut everybody by 5.8% and then I would not be able to deliver the GRS/NS Level 4 data and the MAG/ER Level 2 data to the archives; 2) just cut the MAG/ER budget and kill all that work; or 3) restore the 5.8% by taking it from Mario's $160,000 residual funding and we would be back on track. Happily, Guenter agreed with the last suggestion and we eventually (May 4) got the $98,000 restored — one more bureaucratic battle won!

By that time, I had decided it was time to start bugging NASA about giving us all the money we had asked for in the NRA proposal ($3.9 million, not just the $2.9 million they gave us), so we also could reduce the APS data and produce all the higher level MAG/ER data products. I started calling various colleagues to have them help me put pressure on Headquarters to give us all the money we needed to get all the data into the archives. Interestingly, when I called Jim Papike and Ron Greeley, both of whom had been on the NRA proposal review committee, they had assumed NASA had allocated all the money to us we had requested and were surprised and concerned that that was not the case. They and the others were ready to pressure NASA into giving us the money we needed to get all the Lunar Prospector data numerically reduced and into the archives, so the lunar science community and the public could start using them.

Mike Drake, who was then the head of NASA's Solar System Exploration Subcommittee (and the Director of the Lunar and Planetary Laboratory at the U of Arizona, my old stomping grounds when I was a graduate student under Dr. G.P. Kuiper) also wanted to help and suggested I write Carl Pilcher at Headquarters. Knowing Carl and how uninterested he was in the Moon and Lunar Prospector, I questioned the value of Mike's suggestions. Nevertheless, I wrote Carl on February 21 in the vague hope that Carl might agree that we should get the $900,000 we needed to finish the data reduction tasks.

Also, by February 21, I had become concerned that nothing was happening about our $1.6 million, FY2000 funding, so I emailed Joe. I hit both the FY2000 funding and the extra APS and MAG/ER funding issues in an email to Joe and thus began a series of emails and letters to Headquarters in which I was trying to get our FY2000 funding done on time and to get the extra $900,000 we needed to finish the data reduction tasks.

Towards the end of February, Wayne and I called Mike Chobotov to get his advice about how to get LEI up and running and how to find investors, since he had successfully got his small engineering company in Santa Rosa, CA, on its feet. Mike said the first thing we had to do was to get a good, big law firm behind us so that investors would know we were legitimate. I called Todd Greenwalt and asked if Vinson & Elkins (V&E) might consider take on LEI on contingency — he said, "Probably yes!" I told Todd I would be in Houston in a couple of weeks for the Lunar and Planetary Science Conference and we could discuss the details then and he agreed that would be great. I also reminded Todd that my good old (actually young) friend, ex-Lockheed co-worker and ex-NASA engineer, but by then, a lawyer, David Weaver, was back with V&E in the Austin, TX office and that David would certainly want to be involved if V&E took LEI on as a client. Todd said he would call David (as would I) and discuss the issue with him. February ended on a very high note and March began with great promise.

Sunday, March 12, through Wednesday, March 15, 2000: The XXXI Lunar and Planetary Science Conference

I left Tucson for Houston to attend the conference on Sunday, March 12. Bill and the rest of my team were presenting a number of papers at the conference, but my main objectives were to see Todd about V&E backing LEI and cornering Joe Boyce and Guenter Riegler, so we could discuss the FY2000 Funding and, more importantly, the $900,000 we needed to finish the data reduction work we had originally proposed.

Also, by that time, we had found that the MAG/ER, GRS, and NS data sets were far better than we thought when we wrote the NRA proposal a year earlier. Thus, it was clear that we could get even higher-level products out of the data than we were currently funded for. Hence, we needed to write a follow-on proposal for the money to do so and I wanted to let Joe and Guenter to know that too.

After the conference got underway, I found Joe and asked him about getting Headquarters started working on the contract option for our FY2000 funding and about having a quick meeting at the conference with him, Guenter, Bill, Lon, Bob, Mario, and me, so we could discuss first, the need for Headquarters to restore the $900,000 we needed for the APS and the MAG/ER Level 3, 4, and 5 products and second, the fact that our data were so much better than we had thought that we wanted to put in a follow-on proposal for even higher level products. Shortly after that, we all met and Guenter was surprisingly supportive of both of our requests. We all decided to have a meeting at Headquarters on March 31, so we could present our cases to the Code S staff. The meeting with Joe and Guenter had gone very well, so I was optimistic we would get what we needed to finish our work on the data.

I also had a good meeting with Todd. He was enthusiastic and quite positive about the possibility that V&E would take LEI on as a client on contingency. To my surprise, Todd had talked to ex-Congressman Mike Andrews (Democrat) about LEI and Mike was extremely enthusiastic about my trying to develop a real commercial lunar exploration capability. I had met Mike in the Early Years (Part One) of the Lunar Prospector effort, when he was the Congressman from the district in which JSC is located and I had asked him for his support for Lunar Prospector. Mike was interested, but there was little he could do to help our private effort at that time. While in Congress (Mike served six terms), he had been a member of the Space Sciences Committee and an avid supporter of the space program. After leaving Congress, Mike had joined V&E in its Washington office and remained in close contact with his ex-colleagues on the Hill. I was extremely pleased when Todd told me Mike wanted to be a member of the LEI V&E Legal Team.

As I already knew from my discussions with David Weaver, Todd said David (who is an Intellectual Property Lawyer) was also on our team and that, because neither he (Todd, who is a Non-profit Corporation Lawyer), nor David, nor Mike are Corporate Lawyers, he was looking for a young Corporate Lawyer in the Houston office who could fill that position in our LEI Legal Team. That all sounded just great.

When I left Houston for home on Wednesday, the 15th, everything was looking good for both LRI and LEI.

Thursday, March 16, through Wednesday, March 29, 2000: A Letter to Goldin

When I got back to the office on the 16th, the Tony Spear Report had appeared and it was clear that my going to his Pasadena meeting on December 3 had *zero impact* on the report. There was no mention of the role of the PI in the report and the report concluded the control of the missions had to be returned to the aerospace and/or NASA mission managers and more money and more time were required for mission success. *Thus Tony wanted to return to "business as usual" and kill "Faster, Better, Cheaper", by making it "Slower, More Bureaucratic, More Expensive".*

I was annoyed, annoyed with Tony and his committee, annoyed with all the negative letters to the editors and annoyed with all the incompetent NASA and incompetent aerospace bureaucrats who just wanted to go back to big, costly, failure prone, no-risk-to-them-personally programs and to hell with the exploration of space, as long as they made money.

I had had it; I sat down and wrote a letter to Dan Goldin (dated March 21, 2000, Appendix E-1, also see www.lunar-research-institute.org), who was catching holy hell from Congress and everybody else, reminding him of Lunar Prospector's success, expressing my views on the topics and telling him I would be at Headquarters on March 31 and I would like to have the opportunity to share my views with him at that time.

Also, nothing had happened at Headquarters or Goddard about getting the FY2000 contract option ready, so I sent another email to Joe. I was mad because we were going to run out of money in a few weeks and LRI did not have the reserves to keep us going for very long without the FY2000 money. To say the least, I was frustrated at NASA's inability to do anything right or on time (what was new?).

Just a few days later, on March 24, Margaret Roberts, Dan Goldin's Special Assistant, called and left a message saying Dan had received my letter, he was extremely pleased and delighted with it, he had taken it to Congress, and he had read it to the Committee (whose members were eating his butt) and he definitely wanted to talk to me. I immediately called Margaret and made an appointment for 12:30 PM on the 31st. That brightened my day. Then I called and set up a meeting with Floyd des Champs in Senator McCain's office in another effort to get McCain interested in helping get the lunar data buy program started.

When I started to prepare my viewgraphs for the meetings with Goldin and Guenter, I called Bill, Bob, Mario, and Lon to find out what their budget needs really were to do the APS and MAG/ER Level 3, 4, and 5 work. Guenter had said, if NASA granted us the new money for the work, it might take them until October to get us the money, rather than by June as we wanted. If so, then we would have to extend the existing NRA contract an extra three months to get the new work done. That extra three months, plus the well-known fact that when a contract is stretched out, it costs more to do the same amount of work, because of the inefficiencies the stretch-out causes, meant we would require more than the $900,000 they had short changed us in the beginning. When I got all the information from my Co-Is, the proposed contract extension budget turned out to be $1.4 million! By not fully funding our data reduction program in the beginning, it was going to cost NASA and, more importantly, the American taxpayer, an extra $500,000 for the same work — would NASA never learn to do things right the first time?

Thursday, March 30, and Friday, March 31, 2000: DC and Headquarters Meetings

Well prepared for both meetings, I flew to Washington on Thursday, March 30. Because Pat was ill, I didn't stay with Julius and her as usual, rather I was booked at the Holiday Inn Capitol near NASA Headquarters and the Smithsonian Air and Space Museum (the Smithsonian had asked me to give a talk on Lunar Prospector on June 14, as part of their summer lecture series and that was the hotel the Smithsonian was going to put Rebecca and me in when we came to DC to give the talk — so I thought that I would try it out on that trip).

The next morning, the 31st, I went to the NSS office and talked to Frank Sietzen, who had been on Senator McCain's Presidential Campaign Staff and discussed with him my efforts to get a data purchase program going and how to get McCain to help.

After that meeting, I walked over to the Hart Building and talked to Floyd des Champs in McCain's office. That went well as usual. Floyd wanted my opinions on the "Faster, Better, Cheaper" and the Mars failure problems and he wanted to know if I thought NASA could be reformed and if so, what needed to be done. I told him what I thought about first two issues and that I didn't think NASA could be reformed and, as a result, a commercial data purchase program was absolutely necessary. I asked him to help me get in to see Senator McCain sometime soon and he agreed that he would try to do so.

After the meeting with Floyd, I went over to the Air and Space Museum to wait for the 12:30 meeting with Goldin and, even though I wasn't very hungry (I had pancakes for breakfast at the hotel), I had a bite of lunch.

I went to Goldin's office and was very surprised because he had Weiler, Huckins, Mary Kerwin (his congressional liaison), and three other staffers there! They all said they were, "just so happy to see you," which, in the cases of Weiler and Huckins, I doubted very much.

Goldin said he only had a half hour because, as he said, "I have to go back to Congress and get my ass chewed by another Congressman at 1:00 PM." Goldin said he really appreciated my letter, that everybody was on his ass with one-sided arguments, so he was really pleased with what I had written in defense of "Faster, Better, Cheaper." Because of the very limited time, I rushed through my arguments — just hitting all the high points. When I was through, Goldin said it was the scientists who had screwed up the missions! I disagreed and I was certain he didn't want to accept the fact that it was mainly NASA and the aerospace companies that had screwed everything up. Other than that, Goldin and the rest of them were very pleased with what I said and he again said how really annoyed he was at the unfair attacks and emphasized that by saying, referring to Congress, "They served me this turd and I had to sugar coat it and eat it, but I did." I chuckled over that, but clearly Goldin was catching hell.

We all began to discuss a couple of my main points in a little more detail. Regarding the role of the PI, I said, "You know, turning back the clock to having more NASA control again isn't going to change the situation at all — you really have to give the PIs the authority to run the missions and they have to be willing to do it full time. They have to be in residence where the spacecrafts are built and flown, as I was."

Someone said, "Well, we don't quite agree with you because there is only one Alan Binder and we can't clone you to run all the missions right."

I replied, "I don't believe that. I know several other guys who are just as capable as I am to run missions end to end. But if you don't give them a chance, how will they ever learn to do it? The point is, the PIs you pick should know exactly what they have to do and they have to be required to devote full time to it and not let someone else take over most of the responsibility. They have to have — and accept — the full responsibility of their missions." They still would not accept what I said and continued to argue that I was the exception, not the rule, which was just pure BS to me. As far as I was concerned, they just weren't ready to let go of the control of the missions and were just trying to flatter me into shutting up — a tactic that has never worked on me, especially when I know that their flattery is plain BS.

I then brought up the fact that Goldin had originally wanted the Discovery Missions to cost $1/3$ to $1/2$ of the cost cap, but that with the exception of Lunar Prospector, all the Discovery Missions were near or at the $250 million cost cap. I said I was very disappointed that NASA kept selecting expensive missions and, "If I were in charge of Discovery and if there were no low cost missions proposed in response to an AO, I would just say, sorry — no winners, try again with inexpensive missions if you want to win, and then send out another AO."

Before Goldin could even say a word, Weiler immediately responded, "If we didn't select the missions, we would lose the money!" Flying expensive missions was more important than holding the line and getting the costs down! Nevertheless, Goldin agreed with me and asked Weiler and Huckins to find out how they could write the next AO to reflect the requirement that inexpensive missions had to be proposed or else. We went around and around on that topic, but it was clear to me that no matter what Goldin and I said, Weiler and Huckins were not about to force the science community to propose Lunar Prospector-like, inexpensive missions.

That was just another example of what Goldin had once said about how NASA worked, i.e., "I tell my staff what I want done and they go and do what they want to."

Then Goldin changed the topic and said he wanted me to go with him to Congress to testify and to show them everything wasn't one-sided against "Faster, Better, Cheaper." He asked if I could fly back to DC the following week to go to Congress with him Thursday (April 6) to testify — I was ecstatic, that was the break I had been looking for! Then I remembered to my dismay that I was to leave Tucson on travel Thursday to go to Purdue University, where I was going to give a talk and participate in their "Mars vs. Moon" debate on Friday, April 7, after which I was going to drive to northern Illinois to see my 92-year-old mother (as it turned out, for the last time) who was failing fast. I reluctantly answered, "I can't Thursday, I fly to Purdue on Thursday (dummy, I could have flown to Washington on Wednesday, testified on Thursday, then flown from Washington to Indiana and still made it to Purdue by Friday — but I am never one to think very quickly on my feet). I then added, "But I would be glad to come back at any other time and do anything I can."

Goldin said, "Good, I want you there and I want you to tell them what you want to say — not what I want you to say. I just don't want to repeat what you have said; I want you to tell them in your own words. I don't agree with you 100%; I agree with you 90%, but I want you to give Congress your opinion, not mine."

I said, "I'll be there."

Goldin added, *"Good, you're the only one who isn't afraid to say what you think, even if I don't completely agree with you."* That was the second time Goldin had commended me for my continued criticisms of NASA and the aerospace companies — and I must say each time Goldin said it, I felt I was not banging my head against a stone wall for nothing. Finally Goldin told Mary Kerwin to see to it that I was invited to testify to Congress as soon as possible and then Goldin hurried off to get his "ass chewed by another Congressman," and I left to go to the 2:00 meeting with Guenter Riegler.

When I got to Guenter's office, Joe Boyce and Bill were there and Guenter told us where the meeting room was. We went to the room and Lon, Bob, and Mario soon showed up. In addition to Joe, Guenter had asked Ed Weiler to sit in, but he couldn't, as well as Carl Pilcher, who — to my surprise — did attend!

I started the presentation by reviewing what we had originally promised NASA and then pointed out that what we had actually achieved was far beyond that which we had promised and reminded them we had not received the full amount of funding we needed to reduce all the data. I finished by stating our objective for the meeting was to prove to them that they should allocate the $1.4 million we needed to finish all the numerical reduction work we had proposed in our NRA proposal. I added that we also wanted them to know, once we had started getting into the data, we found it was far better than we had thought when we wrote the NRA proposal a year earlier. As such, there were additional, higher level data products we could produce and we would be submitting a second proposal to do so in about a year. Then I turned the presentation over to Lon, Bob, Mario, and Bill, who went into detail about what we had accomplished with the money at hand and what we could accomplish if they restored the money we needed to finish the APS and MAG/ER data reduction work that we had originally proposed.

When we were finished with the presentation, Guenter, Joe and Carl exchanged a few comments on what we had just presented and then Carl said to Guenter, "Find a way to get them the money they need." Just like that — to my great surprise and that of my Co-Is — we had succeeded in getting the $1.4 million we needed. Though I had been fairly confident we would be successful (but I would never have guessed they would have made the decision on the spot), the others, especially Mario, who believed we had no chance of getting the money at all, were basically stunned at our success. We all said a very heartfelt, "Thanks," and left (before they changed their minds).

Early April 2000

I flew home the next day, Saturday, April 1. Bill North was finishing up our new house and we were planning to move in on May 1, so Rebecca and I had a lot to do to get ready for our move and I had two trips coming up immediately. The first was the trip to Purdue and to see my mother and the second, to a Discovery PI Lessons Learned Meeting in Oxnard, CA.

However, first thing Monday, I tried to call Mary Kerwin to find out if and when I was going to testify to Congress with Goldin. To make a long story short, nothing ever came from Goldin's request for Mary to set up a time for us to testify. I had the distinct feeling that her apparently not making any attempt to set up my testifying was another case where the staff simply ignored what Goldin wanted and did what they wanted, but I would never know if that was the case or not.

I called Francisco Andolz; he and his Rebecca were living near Washington and since they were both Purdue graduates, I hoped they might be able to go to Purdue (where his sister-in-law, Rebecca's younger sister, was getting her undergraduate degree), so we could have dinner and they could hear some of the Lunar Prospector results. When I called, he said he would love to and than maybe Rebecca would be able to come, too. That was great, I was looking forward to seeing them again.

About that time, the Young Report on the Mars failures and "Faster, Better, Cheaper" came out and, like the Spear Report, Tom and his committee had decided that more money, more time, and more NASA management and oversight was needed to ensure mission success, i.e., it was back to business as usual. That was BS, no one cared about Lunar Prospector's success — they all wanted to go back to the old, expensive and ineffective NASA way of doing missions and as far as I was concerned, that would just lead us down the path to oblivion.

Thursday, April 6, through Wednesday, April 12, 2000: Purdue, My Mother, and Oxnard

I left Tucson for Chicago's O'Hare Airport early Thursday, April 6. I got my rental car and drove down to Lafayette, IN, to Purdue. The next morning, at breakfast, I met Pascal Lee, a smart, young, personable planetary scientist from Ames who was my "opponent" in the "Mars vs. Moon Debate" set for that evening. We were shown around campus, had lunch, and then Pascal and I gave our afternoon talks to the engineering students. Afterwards, Francisco, Rebecca, and her sister showed up and we had a nice time. That evening, Pascal and I had our debate — which of course resolved nothing, but it was fun and I hoped informative for the students.

The next morning, Saturday, Francisco, Rebecca, her sister, and I had breakfast and then I drove off to see my mother and brother and sister-in-law in Chemung and Harvard, IL, respectively. When I got to Chemung early Saturday afternoon, it was very clear that my mother was fast approaching her death from old age. Over the rest of the weekend, my brother and I discussed what we needed to do to prepare for the inevitable and I said, "Goodbye," to my mother for what turned out to be the last time.

I left Chemung Monday morning and flew to LA, from where I drove to Oxnard. Happily, Sylvia Cox was there and it was her birthday! I took her out to dinner and we had a good chat.

The Lessons Learned Meeting was OK; I listened to Tony Spear tell about Pathfinder and the others tell about their missions. I gave them the full story of Lunar Prospector and my recommendations that the PI be given full authority to run their missions, but I doubted anything I said had any effect. Except for seeing Sylvia, the meeting was a waste of time and I was happy to leave for home. I flew back to Tucson and Rebecca on the 12th and was very glad to be home after nearly a week's travel.

Rebecca and I got very busy getting ready to move into our lovely new house.

Thursday, April 13, 2000: The Call From Congress

Though Goldin's staff had not arranged for me to testify to the Congressional Committee on Science, the Committee did! Lucky April 13; Sharon Hays, one of the Committee's staffers, called and said the Committee wanted me to testify on May 10 or 11 about the Mars failures and "Faster, Better, Cheaper." I said I would be honored to do so. Sharon told me I had to submit a two or three page written statement before the meeting, which I would be given five minutes to summarize at the beginning of the meeting and then the Committee members would ask questions. She explained a few other formalities and said she would email me the exact schedule and other information shortly. I was finally going to get my chance to tell Congress about Lunar Prospector. I was delighted and I got busy preparing my testimony.

Early May 2000

May started out well. First, Rebecca and I moved into our new house and I began to spend a couple of hours before going to LRI and after leaving LRI working on our library shelves, restoring the desert, and rip-rapping around the house and along the driveway, among other such things — a series of tasks that would take a full year!

Second, Option 1 for the $1.6 million, FY2000 money was finally signed — over three months late — on May 4, just in time before we ran out of money — or so I thought. When we tried to get money transferred from our NASA contract account to our LRI account, there was no money in our NASA account! Wayne began to track down the problem — with no success. Every time he called, he was told the money was in the NASA account and every time he tried to get money transferred to our LRI account, there was no money in the NASA account! To keep a long story short, after several more weeks, during which we had to borrow money from our meager LRI reserves to pay our wages and keep the doors open, we finally found out NASA had transferred our $1.6 million into some other NASA account! When that was finally discovered, the error was quickly corrected and finally, five months late, we got our Option 1 money — again, I asked my eternal question, "Why can't NASA do anything right?"

Tuesday, May 9, through Thursday, May 11, 2000: Off to Congress

I flew to Washington on May 9, all prepared for my congressional testimony on the 11th. I had set up meetings with Frank Sietzen at the NSS, Jonathan Fellows in Congressman Kolbe's office and, of course, with Floyd des Champs in Senator McCain's office on Wednesday the 10th, all of which went well, but really did not move my commercial lunar exploration agenda forward at all.

Thursday, the 11th, arrived and I was all prepared for the 10:00 AM Committee Meeting. I got to the Rayburn Building early and found the Committee Conference Room. Then, to kill time, I walked around a while and went back to the conference room at about 9:45, only to find a sign on the door stating that the meeting had been postponed! I immediately went down to the committee staffers office, found Sharon Hays, and asked her what had happened and when the meeting would be rescheduled. Sharon said the meeting was canceled because the Congressmen had to go for a floor vote (I was told later that the son of one of the Congressmen had committed suicide and that was the real reason for the postponement — maybe both stories were correct), she was very sorry for the inconvenience and she would call me as soon as she had a firm date for the Committee Meeting. Thus, $1100 of LRI's travel funds had been wasted on a useless trip to DC.

Saturday, June 10, through Wednesday, June 21, 2000:
The Smithsonian, My Congressional Testimony, and a Lot More

As it happily turned out, when Sharon Hays got back to me, the Committee Meeting had been rescheduled for 1:00 PM, Tuesday, June 20. That was great, because my Smithsonian lecture was on June 14, so I could take care of both events on one (albeit long) trip. Also, since the Smithsonian was paying for my airfare (and food and hotel for three days) that helped makeup for the $1100 I had wasted on my first attempt to testify to Congress. Further, because of the Smithsonian talk, Rebecca was going to accompany me on the first part of the trip, so we could also have a little DC vacation. Finally, since I was going to be in DC for such a long time, I set up meetings with a number of people who might be of some help getting commercial lunar exploration going — including a meeting with Dan Goldin.

Rebecca and I flew to Washington on Saturday, June 10. Francisco and Rebecca, with whom we were going to spend the weekend, met us at the National Airport and drove us to their new home half way between DC and Baltimore. We had a great time with them.

Monday morning, Rebecca and I took the metro from Francisco and Rebecca's down to DC and checked into the Holiday Inn Capitol where the Smithsonian was putting us up. After we got checked in, we went to visit LunaCorp to see what David Gump was up to. David said Radio Shack had invested $1 million in LunaCorp and they were having a news conference on Thursday, which David invited me to attend. That was great news, I was happy for David and LunaCorp.

Rebecca and I went to meet Mike Andrews at V&E to have lunch. The DC office of V&E is located in the Willard Office Building immediately adjacent to the famous and historical Willard Hotel. After meeting Mike at his office, he took Rebecca and me to one of the Willard Hotel restaurants where we had a fine lunch. During lunch, I brought Mike up to speed on what I was trying to accomplish. Mike was extremely enthusiastic about my efforts to do commercial lunar exploration and promised to help in every way possible. I was very pleased with his support and also enjoyed being in the historical hotel where some 150 years earlier, President Lincoln had started assembling his cabinet and staff before being sworn in as the new president. Rebecca also enjoyed the lunch, in part because Mike is very good-looking and very personable. Before saying goodbye, I asked Mike if he had received the invitation to the pre-lecture dinner at the Air and Space Museum of the Smithsonian and the co-sponsor of the Lecture Series, Space.com, was giving me and about a dozen others on their staffs. Alan Ladwig, who was then at Space.com and who was going to be at the dinner, had told me that, in addition to Rebecca, I could suggest someone else to be invited, so I had suggested Mike. Mike answered that he had received the invitation, that he would be there and that he was looking forward to the dinner and my lecture. On that happy note, Rebecca and I left Mike to spend time in the Smithsonian Museum of Natural History, looking at rocks, minerals, and fossils. Then at 4:00 PM, I met with Jonathan Fellows in Arizona Congressman Kolbe's office to further our discussions of commercial lunar exploration.

Tuesday was a play-day; Rebecca and I continued to visit the Smithsonian Museums and to see other DC sights. We ended the day by having dinner with Pat and Julius.

Wednesday was a busy day. First, as requested, we went to the Air and Space Museum so Jane Pisano, the lady in charge of the evening events, could tell us what was going to happen and then we were given a VIP tour of the inner workings of the Museum.

At 11:00, I had a meeting with Greg Finley at the Department of Commerce to discuss my trying to commercialize lunar exploration. Immediately after that I went to NASA to talk with Dan Goldin about my efforts.

Dan had asked Ed Weiler to be in on the meeting. As I had already known, Dan's views on commercial lunar and planetary exploration and mine did not coincide, even though Dan was pushing for commercial activities in general. Dan insisted that NASA should never be the main customer for commercial ventures; in fact he believed NASA should be a minor customer. I do not agree; NASA is the only customer for science data on the Moon and planets and will be for years to come — you can't sell science data on the street corner. Though Dan applauded my efforts (and my success with Lunar Prospector), he was not in a position to do anything about them. As he said, until the November election was over, the new administration was in power, and a new NASA administrator was selected (Dan figured he would not be called upon by a third administration to run NASA), Congress and NASA would not be in a position to start and fund the type of data purchase program I was pushing for. Though I agreed it was a tough time to push my idea, I did not intend to sit idly by for six to eight months and wait for the political dust to settle. Anyway, the meeting with Dan and Ed was cordial, but nonproductive. After the meeting, I went back to the hotel to get Rebecca for lunch and more sightseeing.

At about 4:00, Rebecca and I went back to the Hotel to get ready for the Smithsonian Dinner and Lecture. We walked the block to the Air and Space Museum and were escorted to a lovely dinner setting in one of the display galleries. Mike Andrews and Alan Ladwig arrived and we met the other dinner guests. At 5:30 we started a delicious, catered dinner among the rockets, airplanes, and other display items of the museum — it was a great setting and a great dinner. Soon it was 7:30 and time for my lecture, which was held in the Einstein Planetarium of the Museum. The talk was well attended and there were so many questions after I was finished that the museum host had to tell everyone it was time to leave — which we all did. Thus ended a perfect evening.

Thursday was another vacation day for us, except that I went to the LunaCorp press conference.

Rebecca flew back to Tucson early Friday morning and I spent the rest of Friday, the weekend, and part of Monday tromping around DC. The highlights of which were going to the Ford Theater to see where Lincoln was shot and then to the boarding house across from the theater to see the tiny room in which — and the tiny bed on which — Lincoln died. Given all the time I had, I really did a thorough job of seeing DC for the first time in all the years that I had been going there — and I thoroughly enjoyed it. Also on Monday afternoon, I had a useless meeting with the director of the US Chamber of Commerce.

Finally it was Tuesday and I was ready to testify. I went over to the Rayburn Building and up to the meeting room. Unlike the first time, there was a line of people waiting at the door to get in to see the proceedings, Pat Dasch being one of them. Pat and I chatted a few minutes and I asked her who else was testifying. She answered, "Goldin, Stone (the director of JPL), and the guy who had headed up Clementine, (Retired) Colonel Rustan." I had expected Dan Goldin and Ed Stone to testify and was pleased that Clementine was represented — though I had never met or heard of Rustan before. Shortly thereafter the doors opened and in we went. I found my seat at the table in front of the bench were the committee members were to sit. I must say that, uncharacteristically for me, I was impressed with the pomp and splendor of the room. I had, of course, seen such Congressional Committee Rooms on TV newscasts many times, but it was something else to be there in person and to be getting ready to testify — I knew I was going to enjoy the next hour or so.

Dan sat on my far right; on his immediate left was Ed, then Rustan and finally I was on the left side of our table. Rustan and I got acquainted a little as the committee slowly came in and took their seats. Congressman Sensenbrenner was the chairman and sat in the middle of the bench in front of us. To his left were the Democratic members of the committee and on his right were the Republican members. The gallery behind us was full of spectators, including a number of Goldin and Stone's staffers.

Sensenbrenner gaveled the proceedings open and then made an excellent introduction, in which he reviewed the need for the hearing, what he wanted to accomplish and admonished Goldin and Stone not to gloss over the problems as they had done in the first hearing several weeks earlier, rather he wanted them to give substantive answers to the Committee's questions. Finally, he thanked Rustan and me for appearing and giving our expert testimony. Then he asked Goldin to give his five-minute statement. In turn, Goldin, Stone, Rustan, and I gave our statements.

I was not particularly impressed with what Goldin and Stone said; they were properly contrite, but they still gave the usual NASA party line answers. In contrast, Rustan told it like it is and, given Clementine's success, said that unless NASA changed its culture, nothing would change and the failures would continue.

I had my say (Appendix E-2, also see www.lunar-research-institute.org) and then we were ready for questions.

According to protocol, each committee member asked one question and it quickly became apparent that the hearing was just a political show. Instead of asking Rustan and me about why we were so successful and how we would change things at NASA, all the questions — none of which were really probing — were directed to Goldin and Stone, who continued to give their pat answers. At the very end, the committee wanted Rustan and my opinions on a general question, but by that time, we had very little impact on the meeting. Except for Rustan and me getting our testimonies into the Congressional Record, the hearing resulted in nothing except to let NASA and JPL know (what they already knew) that Congress was disappointed at the loss of some $300 million worth of hardware.

Rustan was clearly as disappointed as I was about the hearing, since he wrote a letter to *Space News* a few weeks later with all his main comments and I wrote Sensenbrenner a letter expressing my disappointment (Appendix E-3, also see www.lunar-research-institute.org).

Regardless, I was pleased to have been able to testify and to let Congress know how Lunar Prospector was really done. And I was impressed to have been there, in the Committee Room, telling our political leaders what I had accomplished and what I thought needed to be done to improve the mess NASA and JPL had made. Also, I regarded my testimony as the first step in what I hoped would be other opportunities to testify, specifically about the need for a commercial lunar exploration program. I left the Room and the Rayburn Building feeling satisfied with what I had accomplished and very, very ready to go home. I was tired of being on travel for 11 days.

Late June, July, and Early August 2000

Once back in Tucson, Wayne and I turned our attention to getting the $1.4 million added into our contract. Clearly, our hopes that NASA would get us the money by June had been dashed and I was concerned that, given our bad experience getting the main contract and Option 1 through the NASA system and given the pace at which things were happening concerning the $1.4 million at Headquarters and Goddard, the addition to our contract would not be finished until well after our start date of Oct. 1, 2000! Wayne and I started calling and emailing Joe Boyce and Jim Becker on a regular basis — but still nothing seemed to move forward.

Sadly, but totally expected, my mother died a peaceful death, due to old age, on Monday, July 10, just 3 days after her 93rd birthday. Rebecca and I flew to Illinois the next day to help my brother and sister-in-law with the funeral arrangements and to help settle our mother's estate. We returned to Tucson on Wednesday, the 19th.

Thursday, August 10, and Friday, August 11, 2000: Vinson & Elkins

A couple of weeks earlier, Todd had called to tell me that he had found a young, V&E corporate lawyer, Matt Strock, who wanted to join our legal team. Thus, it was time for us to meet to discuss the details of the venture, so V&E could decide if they wanted to represent LEI on contingency. We set up the meeting and Wayne and I flew to Houston late Thursday.

The next morning, we went to V&E and were directed to Todd's office. Todd took us to the meeting room and then left to find Matt. When they came to the meeting room, Todd put in a conference call to Austin and Washington, since, respectively, David Weaver and Mike Andrews were going to "attend" our meeting via phone. Once the introductions of Wayne and Matt were over, Todd asked me to review the history of Lunar Prospector, the progress that I had made with NASA and Congress in promoting a commercial lunar exploration program, and my expectation about what it could lead to. I went through the whole ball of wax. When I was finished and when we had discussed the various issues, Todd said that V&E's corporate position was that if the four of them wanted to take LEI on, on contingency, it was their choice. Todd, David, Matt, and Mike all agreed that what I was trying to do was well worth supporting, it held great promise and, yes, they were more than willing to become our legal team. Great!

Todd then explained that V&E would allow us to charge up to $50,000 of their time, but LEI would have to pay for such things as postage, phone calls, reproduction, any trips that any of them would have to make on LEI's behalf, etc., and that after the $50,000 limit was reached, or say, six months' time, V&E would review their commitment to see if they were wasting their resources on LEI, before dropping us or committing to further contingency support. Also, as part of the V&E legal services, they would help us find investors, support any meetings we would have with investors, NASA, and members of Congress (Mike would be a big help with that task) and, of course, do all our contract work. Todd said further that he would get a contract between V&E and LEI to me in a week or two. Boy, all that sounded great — that was a big and important step in the development of LEI and establishing LEI's business credibility beyond the technical credibility I had already achieved via Lunar Prospector.

Matt then said the first thing we needed to do was to change LEI from an Arizona Corporation to a Delaware Corporation. I asked, "Why?" Matt explained that Delaware had the best, most well-known and most respected corporate regulations of all the states and hence that most big corporations were incorporated in Delaware. If LEI remained an Arizona Corporation, most potential investors would not know how to interface legally with LEI, but if we were a Delaware Corporation, they would feel comfortable with us and be much more willing to become financially and legally involved. I said, "Fine, what do Wayne and I have to do?"

Matt said, "Nothing, I'll take care of everything — all you have to do is to sign the various documents when they are ready."

I said, "Great, have at it." Shortly thereafter, the meeting broke up and Wayne and I got ready to fly back to our respective homes.

A few weeks later, on August 31, I signed the V&E agreement and V&E officially began to represent LEI. Two months later, on Oct 27, LEI became a Delaware Corporation.

Wednesday, September 6, through October 2000:
The Extended Contract

On September 6, Jim Becker finally sent us the contract modification for the $1.4 million for my signature. I immediately signed it and faxed it back to Jim. Then Wayne and I got busy with the sub-contracts to the U of Arizona, LANL and UC Berkeley, so we could get them signed, and so we could get started using the new money on October 1.

At last, I finally had all the money that we needed to do the data reduction job that we had originally proposed in our NRA proposal and, because NASA had not gotten us the contract by June as we had asked, the original contract would run to the end of 2001, rather than being done on October 1, 2001, but that was OK. The main thing was that we had the money.

With that out of my way, I began to think about the new proposal we needed to write for NASA to get support for the higher-level data products we knew we could produce. Also, I began to plan a second Science Team Meeting, again to be held just after Thanksgiving, to discuss the results of the first year of data reduction work and to start getting the information I needed for the proposal.

During the first year or so of operations, Wayne had proven to be a great asset to both LRI and LEI in his capacity as their Chief Financial Officer. However, Wayne is a great procrastinator and he was generally too busy with other (too many other) commitments, e.g., his other two businesses (the ones that paid his bills — a factory in Pakistan and a small restaurant chain in LA) and the reconstruction of his house in Auburn, CA, to attend to the financial needs of LRI and to come to Tucson when I needed him to do so. As a result, Rebecca had to take over Wayne's monthly duties of getting LRI's contract money transferred from NASA to the LRI account and of doing the payroll. Also, because Wayne was not keeping the LRI accounting up to date, I asked Valerie Pulos, a very dedicated and very competent lady who handled our business and personal accounts at the Wells Fargo Bank and with whom Rebecca and I had become friends, if she wanted to work a couple of days per month to keep our books straight and to do the NASA Quarterly Financial Reports. Valerie liked the idea and joined our staff in October. As of October, Wayne's only responsibilities were to help me get new money for LRI and to help me develop LEI into a successful business.

November 2000 and Beyond: The Election Fiasco

Since most of my efforts to get a lunar data purchase program started were political in nature, I was a captive of the November elections. Until we knew who was the new President, which party controlled Congress, who the new NASA Administrator would be, and what the new administration's space policy was, it was essentially impossible for me to make any more progress in getting political and NASA support for commercial lunar exploration activities. Thus I was eagerly awaiting the outcome of the November 7 election.

A few weeks earlier, with Todd's help, I had contacted the Bush Campaign's science advisors with the hopes of starting a pre-election dialogue about commercial space exploration, assuming Bush won. The Bush staff directed me to ex-Congressman Bob Walker (Republican), who was their advisor on space questions. I had met Bob in the summer of 1995 when, as the then head of the Congressional Committee on Science, he and another committee member toured Lockheed, where I showed them the Lunar Prospector Model and explained the mission to them. After leaving Congress, Bob had been working for a Washington Lobbying Firm. When I reached Bob, he said there was nothing anyone could do until the election was over. However, after the election, if Bush won and if he (Bob) had any role in the new administration, he would be happy to try and help me. There was nothing to do but wait.

As November 7 approached, I was ready to hit the road running. Then the election occurred and the endless recounts and endless legal activities started. I, like the rest of the country (and perhaps world), had to sit and wait, and wait, and wait until the election was finally over.

Thursday, November 30, and Friday, November 31, 2000: The Second Science Team Meeting

While we were all waiting for our political and legal systems to decide who was the next President, my Science Team and I had our Second Science Team Meeting.

Our science results had not changed much since our last meeting, but we were, of course, much farther along with the numerical data reduction work, so we had basically refined our earlier conclusions. As such, we spent more time discussing the impact of our mapping on the lunar science community's understanding of the origin and evolution of the Moon than we did during our first meeting. However, the most important things we discussed were the new tasks we were going to put in the new proposal. There were four new things that I found especially exciting.

First, our work with the GRS data had already yielded a thorium (Th) abundance map with 60 km resolution and Bill expected that we would also achieve 60 km resolution for potassium (K), iron (Fe), titanium (Ti), oxygen (O), and silicon (Si) (vs. the 150 km we thought we would get when we wrote the original Discovery proposal six years earlier) by the time we had finished our funded work. However, Bill expected, with more money and with new processing techniques, we could produce a 15 km resolution map for Th and 30 km resolution maps for the others elements — and that was very exciting.

Second, the GRS data Bill and his LANL team were analyzing were the so-called "accepted" spectra, which consist of spectral lines that are analyzed to obtain the elemental abundances. The primary purpose of the GRS instrument was to obtain the accepted line spectra. However, in addition to the accepted spectral data, the GRS also provided us with so-called "rejected" spectra and those data contain information on the Compton Continuum that contains additional elemental abundance information. Bill was proposing that we might be able to get a second, independent set of elemental abundance maps using the rejected spectra — again, an exciting possibility.

Third, Solar-Energetic Particle (ESP) events had occurred several times during the mission and Bill had set aside the spectra taken during the ESP events because they were, of course, different from the normal spectra. When he had finally taken a look at those data, he found that the energetic particles had caused great increases in the gamma-ray production rates, especially at the higher energy end of the spectrum and, as a result, those "abnormal" spectra had heightened sensitivity to light elements (Al, Mg, and Ca) that are normally hard to detect and measure. Thus, the SEP event spectra had opened up a new and unexpected window for mapping the elemental abundances of the light element — and that was also very exciting. Bill said that SEP event data covered about 20% of the moon's surface and so, with additional funding, we could add considerable new information for our elemental abundance mapping.

Fourth, as we had known a year earlier, the ER data had shown that, in addition to solar wind electrons being reflected by the moon's tiny magnetic fields, electrons were coming from the Moon itself. That meant that electric fields were being generated on the Moon and that was a new phenomenon we had to understand in order to correctly reduce the ER data and, of course, a new phenomenon to understand in its own right — again, an exciting new discovery.

Thus, it was clear we had important new tasks for our new proposal and, when the meeting ended, we all went away knowing that Lunar Prospector had produced data that were far better than we could have ever dreamed of and we had discovered several new ways of mapping and studying the Moon.

December 2000 through Early March 2001

During that period, I gathered the information and budgets from Bill, Lon, Mario, and Bob for the new proposal and got it written. The budget for the proposed two-year analysis program was $3.5 million and I was optimistic we would get the money, given the job we had done on the mission, the job we were doing on the numerical data reduction program contract, and the exciting new tasks we were proposing.

The only fly in the LRI ointment concerning the proposal was that I had asked Wayne to come to Tucson to help put together its budget, a matter of considerable concern given that we were trying to get $3.5 million. However, when I called Wayne (who lives in California) and asked him to come to Tucson, he said that he had to go Pakistan to take care of his factory there and couldn't come to Tucson. Since almost every time I had needed him at LRI to handle the financial issues that were his responsibilities, he had to go to Pakistan, or to LA or somewhere else — he was seldom available when I needed him. I was annoyed that LRI was always the last on Wayne's list and I was concerned that even though I had to give all of Wayne's monthly duties to Rebecca and Valerie, he still could not find the time to do the remaining, critical things I had hired him to do. Wayne and I had a serious talk about his work in both companies and Wayne assured me that, as soon as his house was finished and he and his brother had sold their chain of restaurants, he would have more time to help me get LEI on its feet and keep LRI running smoothly. I let it go at that, but I expected things to get better — or else.

On the political front, the election had been finally decided by mid-December with Bush becoming the new President and the Democrats becoming very angry. Because of all the election delays, the transition to the new administration was delayed and I knew I would have to wait even longer before I could start pushing my commercial lunar exploration program with the new administration and the new Congress. That delay in my activities was exacerbated further by the fact that no one wanted to become the new NASA Administrator (i.e., no one wanted to take over the hopeless mess we called NASA). Dan Goldin wanted very badly to stay on as Administrator, but that was really out of the question, given his very long time at that thankless job. Others, like Jack Schmitt and Bob Walker, both of whom would have been a great help in getting my commercial lunar exploration program going, refused to take on the job when asked or begged to do so. Until the new NASA Administration was named, there was little I could do.

However, the Bush Administration had named Courtney Stadd as the new NASA Chief of Staff and White House Liaison and, as far as I knew, Courtney was very pro-commercial space. George French knew Courtney well, since both of them were in the Aerospace States Association, so I asked George to call Courtney to introduce me to him and to let him know I would be calling for an appointment and seeking his help in developing a commercial based lunar exploration program. As usual, George immediately did what I asked and then told me Courtney was well acquainted with my Lunar Prospector success story and my commercial aspirations. I began to call his office to try and set up a meeting with him.

My plan was to try to set up meetings at about the same time with Courtney and with Guenter Riegler (with Guenter, so my team and I could deliver our proposal to him and to make a presentation to him in support of our request for the $3.5 million — as we had so successfully done a year earlier, when we were after the $1.4 million), so I would only have to make one trip to Headquarters. I also wanted to have the meeting just before or just after the XXXII Lunar and Planetary Science Conference in Houston, so I could combine both trips into one long trip — thereby saving both time and money. After some fiddling around with schedules, I finally got the two Headquarters meetings set up on Monday and Tuesday, March 20 and 21, during the week following the LPSC. That meant I would have to spend the weekend in Houston, but that was OK.

Monday, March 12, through Wednesday, March 21, 2001: The LPSC and Headquarters

As I was preparing to leave on my long and important trip, I was not feeling very well. I had been to LANL on February 14 and 15, where, having forgotten my coat in the car at the Tucson airport (Tucson was nice and warm), I had frozen and caught a cold or the flu or both. Unfortunately, I had not completely gotten rid of whatever LANL had given me as I entered the airplane to Houston.

When I got to Houston, the weather was fair, but some combination of the Houston air pollution and various pollens was causing a lot of people, including me, to have sore throats and watering eyes and that, of course, made my existing condition even worse. I spent a lot of time resting in my hotel room, hoping I would not be too sick to do a good job when I got to Washington.

My team gave a number of papers on Thursday and David Lawrence presented the first calcium abundance map of the Moon, a result I had not seen before and I was very pleased. All in all, our results were getting more and more impressive and the lunar science community was really beginning to understand how much Lunar Prospector had accomplished.

I saw Joe Boyce at the conference and told him I had set up a meeting with him and Guenter at 8:30 AM the following Monday to pitch our proposal. That was a good thing, because a little later, I got a message from Rebecca indicating that Guenter's secretary, Debra Price, had called to tell me that Guenter was going to be on personal leave and that Joe would have to take care of the meeting. I called Debra to let her know I had gotten her message, that I had already spoken with Joe, and, in the absence of Guenter, I needed someone at his level or higher to be at the meeting. She said she would try to get David Bohlin to be there and I said I would greatly appreciate that.

I flew to Washington Sunday, where it was quite cold. I felt even worse than I did in Houston and my voice was getting very hoarse.

I went to Headquarters at 8:00 AM and found Joe Boyce in his office. I gave Joe the copies of the proposal and the submission letter. Then I briefly told him what we were proposing to do and that the proposal was for $3.5 million. We discussed various aspects of the proposal and Joe did not give me the usual "we have no money" routine, rather he seemed fairly optimistic about our chances of getting the $3.5 million.

We were informed that David Bohlin would be late because his car battery was dead and, worse, he had a 9:00 AM meeting. We would have very little time with him. Joe responded by immediately leaving to find some other people with the authority to get us the money and I went to the conference room where Bill, Tom Prettyman (who worked with Bill on the GRS data), Lon, and Bob had gathered.

Immediately thereafter, Bohlin showed up and explained he had made it in on time despite the battery problem, and that his 9:00 AM meeting was canceled, so he could stay until his 10:00 meeting. Perfect! Then Joe came in with two additional NASA guys and we got started.

Joe gave a brief introduction to the meeting and then I went into my pitch, showing what we had originally proposed six years earlier and how much better the data were than we were delivering under the contract we were then working on and, more importantly, what we could deliver if we received the additional funding we were requesting for the new program. I then outlined the new things we were proposing to do and said we had found four new ways of mapping the Moon.

I also had a viewgraph indicating my belief that Lunar Prospector had successfully showed how missions should be run, i.e., that the PI should run things as I did and NASA should do science missions my way.

When I was finished Bohlin said, "You're a great salesman. If you ever quit being a scientist, you should go into real estate." That sounded very encouraging. Then I turned the floor over to Bob.

Bob did a good job, but, as I feared, he went into too much detail and ran well over his 15 minutes. Finally I had to stop him so Lon could speak; but Lon said Bob had covered most of the MAG/ER points and I should let Bill start on the GRS, NS, and APS parts of the presentation.

Like Bob, Bill (and as I really feared) ran over so much that Tom Prettyman had just a few minutes to add to the GRS story. By that time it was about 9:45, so I wrapped it up quickly. Bohlin congratulated us on what we had accomplished and added, "This is the first time I have enjoyed myself since coming to Headquarters!" He and the other NASA staffers said some other nice things about what we had accomplished with Lunar Prospector and said they would process our proposal as quickly as possible. As the meeting broke up, we all had the feeling we had sold our case and we had an excellent chance of getting the next $3.5 million.

Later that afternoon, at 2:00 PM, I met with Mark Morehouse in Congressman Kolbe's office and then at 3:00 I had a good meeting with Floyd des Champs in Senator McCain's office. Floyd and I re-discussed the commercial issues and Floyd decided that maybe they should start thinking about putting "data-buy" money into the FY 2003 budget and I wholeheartedly agreed (it did not happen).

Monday evening, Pat and Julius came to my hotel and we had a nice dinner at the hotel restaurant, since I was too sick to go out.

Finally, it was Tuesday afternoon and time for my 3:00 PM meeting with Courtney Stadd — and my voice was nearly gone. On my way into NASA, I met a young guy by the name of Randall Correll, who had followed my success with Lunar Prospector and was well aware of my pushing for a commercial lunar exploration program. Randall worked in the executive suite, i.e., behind the "Glass Doors," and, as such, escorted me to the waiting area therein. Since I was a bit early and since Courtney was a bit behind schedule, Randall and I continued to get acquainted.

Shortly thereafter Courtney came out, saw Randall and I talking, said to come into his office and extended the invitation to Randall, saying our meeting should interest him. Randall, not wanting to intrude, backed off, but I said, "Yeah, come on in," and Courtney again asked Randall to join us, which he then did.

To make a short (30-minute) meeting even shorter, we had an excellent meeting. Courtney was in agreement with what I wanted to do and would support my efforts. However, he said there was little that could be done until the new NASA Administrator was named and until the Bush administration was really settled in. He said further the new science advisor to the White House had just been named and it would be a month or two before any meetings with him would be meaningful. Despite, those unavoidable delays, it was clear that the ball was finally rolling downhill. Courtney's interest in supporting a commercial lunar exploration program and Floyd's statement that maybe it was time to consider putting $200 to $300 million for data purchase into the FY 2003 budget really sounded to me like I had finally succeeded in pushing the ball up to the top of the hill and it was, at last, starting to roll downhill. Nevertheless, it was clear the ball would need considerable help if it was going to successfully reach the bottom of the hill.

After we left Courtney's office and with what voice I had left, Randall and I spent another 30 to 40 minutes talking about various issues since Courtney had asked Randall to look into some of the problems we might run into. I left for the airport and home.

I arrived in good old, warm Tucson in the late afternoon. Rebecca had made a doctor's appointment for me, since I had been sick for five weeks and it was clear I was never going to get well without help.

A couple of days later, the doctor said I had acute bronchitis and prescribed a strong antibiotic that knocked the bronchitis out of me in just three or four days.

Tuesday, March 27, 2001: An Astounding Event

Early in February I had received a letter from Goddard stating that Ms. Lavern Harris had replaced Jim Becker as our Contract Administrator. Shortly thereafter Lavern called to say I needed to sign a contract modification regarding the deletion of the Level 2 GRS deliverables from our contract (by then we had planned to go directly from the Level 1 to the Level 3 data products, skipping Level 2 and Joe Boyce was in agreement with that plan). She said she would fax me the agreement, that I could sign it and fax it right back and then she would send a hard copy via the mail for my formal signature.

Lavern had sent the contract for signature just before I went on travel. Not knowing I was on travel, Lavern wondered why it was taking so long for my signed copy to get to her, so she called on Tuesday. I told her I had been on travel, but I had signed and mailed the contract on Thursday and she should be getting it shortly and she said, "Fine."

I said I was going to call her anyway, because I wanted to have her get started on Option 2 of my contract for the FY 2001 money. To my amazement, she said Headquarters had already sent over the paperwork, it was being taken care of as we spoke and I should get the paperwork in a couple of weeks! I was nearly speechless. I said something to the effect that I was amazed; that the next time I was in DC, I would come to Goddard to meet her to see for myself how she had gotten Option 2 done without my spending months calling Headquarters. She seemed quite happy with my compliments and understood my frustration with the past performance of Headquarters and the Goddard contracts office.

To say the least, Lavern made my day, so much so that I called Wayne, who also found her performance amazing.

Monday, April 9, 2001: A Second Astounding Event

The signed Contract Option for the $390,000 — i.e., for the FY 2001 money — arrived in the mail! Lavern had come through exactly as she had said and I was grateful to have the last increment of money for the contract signed off without me having to make one single call or sending one single email. I hoped, assuming Headquarters decided to give us the $3.5 million we had just requested, the new contract would be processed as fast and efficiently as the last Option had. I reached Lavern a couple of days later and thanked her again for the great job she had done.

The Second Half of April 2001: LRI and LEI Board Meetings

Having come away from my Washington trip with the feeling that the commercial ball was finally beginning to roll down hill, I decided to start looking for money for LEI. There were two reasons for my doing so: First, if we could get even a few million dollars in investments, we could design the landers and orbiters I wanted to fly in a commercial lunar exploration program, thereby getting real cost numbers for the commercial missions and second, if I could get investors, I would then have more leverage with the politicians to get them to fund a NASA lunar data purchase program.

Since it was the time of year for our LRI and LEI Board Meetings anyway, and since George French was going to be in Tucson for a week visiting his mother in Tubac (just south of Tucson), I set up our Annual Board Meetings. Wayne, Rebecca, George, and I were, of course, all on the LRI Board, but only Wayne, Rebecca, and I made up the LEI Board. That was because, when I had asked George about being on the LEI Board a couple of years earlier, he said that was not a good idea, because I needed to save the positions for financially heavy hitters — a sentiment echoed by our V&E lawyers. That good advice notwithstanding, George knew people with lots of money and I needed George's help getting LEI financially off the ground. After discussing the issue with Wayne and Rebecca, we decided to ask George to be on the LEI Board and to help us find some seed money.

When I called George and asked him to be on the Board, he agreed, but said he would step down when we started finding big investors — a position I was not comfortable with and I said so. However, rather than resolving our minor difference of opinion right then, we left George's future Board membership up in the air and agreed that we would have the Board meeting on Friday, April 20.

Friday the 20th came and we — Wayne, George, Rebecca, and I — had the LRI Board Meeting, conducted all the LEI business, adjourned, and then Wayne, Rebecca, and I started the LEI Board Meeting. The first piece of business was to officially elect George to the Board. He then joined us in the meeting (he really never left the room, he just pretended not to listen) and we discussed the LEI issues, of which the most important were finding money and getting more political support. As he already knew I would, I asked George to try to find $10 million for seed money, or better yet $100 million, so we could actually start the first mission and he said that he would try. We then adjourned the LEI meeting with all of us feeling that we might be getting somewhere.

Early the following week, after George was back in Green Bay, he called and said that instead of spending so much time trying to get to Senator McCain, I should try to get a meeting with Kyl, the junior Arizona Senator, who would not only be easier to get to see, but was also on the all important Congressional Finance Committee! I had tried without success to get to Kyl when we came to Tucson nearly two years earlier and had put that effort on ice. However, heeding George's good advice, I immediately called Kyl's Tucson office and asked for a meeting with the person who was responsible for space and technical issues. The receptionist said that would be Dr. Hank Kenski and she found he had some free time on Tuesday, May 1, and I said that would be fine.

Tuesday, May 1, 2001: Meeting With Dr. Kenski

Shortly after I arrived at Kyl's office on Tucson's far-NW side, Kenski came into the room where I had been asked to wait for him. He was about my age and, after I asked, he said he had a PhD from the U of Arizona in Communications and he had been with Kyl ever since their student days at the U of A. After a little bit more "getting acquainted talk," I gave him my Congressional Testimony, the LEI Business Plan, and backup material about Lunar Prospector and me. Then I explained to him what I was up to and that I was trying to get political support from everyone possible, including Kyl.

Hank was impressed and very interested in what I was trying to do. He said he would get me a meeting with Kyl and he would help sell Kyl on my program. He then asked if I had tried to talk with Arizona Congressman Kolbe (from my district and a member of the House Budget Committee) and Arizona Governor Hull. I explained about my attempts to do so and also about my attempts to get to Senator McCain. Hank said he could get me a meeting with Kolbe, but that McCain would be a tough nut to crack, because of his well-publicized national agendas. However, Hank added that if I could get to McCain and make him understand I would be cutting government waste and helping the American taxpayer, he might support my efforts. Hank said further he would call the Governor's Tucson office to get the ball rolling there and I should call Kyl's Phoenix office to ask the scheduler, Ashley Winkler, to set up a meeting for me and Ashley should talk to him about the importance of my seeing Kyl. When I left Hank, I thought I was finally going to start seeing the political figures who could help me get the commercial lunar exploration program off the ground.

Wednesday, May 2, 2001

Sure enough, late in the afternoon of the very next day, Hank called to say he had talked Steve Jewett in Governor Hull's Tucson office (the same Steve Jewett I had tried to meet with two years earlier) and that I should call him to set up a meeting. I did and we arranged a meeting for Wednesday, May 30, the week after Rebecca and I were to return from a week's vacation (from May 11 through May 18) on a Holland American Cruise Ship traveling up and down the Alaskan inner passage looking at glaciers, mountains, bears, killer whales, mountain sheep, and lots more.

Wednesday, May 23, 2001: Getting Started With Congressman Kolbe

Not wanting to wait for Hank Kenski to get me introduced to Congressman Kolbe, I had called his office a couple of days after Rebecca and I had returned from our Alaskan cruise. I spoke with Hassan Hijazi, Kolbe's aide with whom I had discussed my efforts nearly two years earlier. I told Hassan about the progress I had made, about my meeting with Kenski, and said I wanted to meet with Kolbe, ASAP. Hassan had not forgotten our earlier meeting and said I should email Pam Harrington, Kolbe's scheduler, to ask for a meeting and send him a copy. I said, "OK," and also that I would drop off my Congressional Testimony and the LEI Business Plan at his office the following Tuesday, the 29th — the day after Memorial Day. As it turned out, our email was down, so I told Rebecca we would hand deliver my request for the meeting with Kolbe to Pam when I took the back-up material to Hassan after Memorial Day. Also, since Kolbe's office is just a couple of blocks north of our favorite Mexican restaurant, we could have Mexican lunch afterwards and she agreed.

Tuesday, May 29, 2001

Rebecca and I arrived at Kolbe's office at about 11:00 AM and I asked to see Pam Harrington and Hassan. Hassan was in a meeting, so just Pam came out to greet us. I gave her my letter requesting a meeting with Kolbe and asked if she would give Hassan his copy, as well as the Business Plan and my Congressional testimony. She said she would and then I began to explain to Pam why I wanted to see Kolbe. She was very interested in Lunar Prospector and my plans to develop a commercial lunar exploration capability; so we sat and discussed the topics for at least a half an hour. Pam said I was doing great things and she would make sure I got a meeting with Kolbe the next time he was in Tucson, which might be on, or around, June 18. Rebecca and I left Kolbe's office with our mission accomplished and headed for Molina's restaurant for a great Mexican lunch.

Wednesday, May 30, through Friday, June 1, 2001: Lots of Activity

Early Wednesday morning, I drove to downtown Tucson where the Governor's Tucson office is located to meet with Steve Jewett. As I had done with Hank and Pam, I went through my story and gave him my backup materials. Like the others, Steve was interested and impressed and thought Arizona and the Governor should get behind me. I also told him of my desire and earlier attempt to be on the Arizona Space Commission and the need for Arizona to rejoin the Aerospace States Association. Steve also thought I should be on the commission and he asked me to email him my resume so he could send it to Phoenix. I left Steve's office feeling I had just made another good step forward.

The next day, I emailed Steve my resume and to Rebecca's and my surprise the very next day, Friday, I got an email from the governor's office requesting that I fill out an application form to be found on the governor's website and mail it in. Steve and the Governor's office were finally not letting grass grow under their collective feet.

Also Thursday, I called Mike Drake at the Lunar and Planetary Laboratory to again ask for his help in getting things moving from the science side, since, if the science community did not want lunar data, then NASA would have no reason to buy commercially available lunar data. That episode had actually started back in March at the Lunar and Planetary Science Conference where Jim Head, from Brown University, had laid out a stack of form letters he had written for people to sign and send to Ed Weiler, the Head of Code S at Headquarters. Jim's form letter asked NASA to restart the exploration of the Moon and begin sending exploration missions there, e.g., sample return missions. I had taken one of Jim's form letters, signed it, and sent it off to Ed and then more or less forgot about it, since I assumed it would be put in a file and that would be that. However, to my surprise, a few weeks later, I got a reply from Jay Bergstrahl indicating that (as I already knew) lunar exploration was not high on NASA's list of things to do and if I thought it should be, I should try to sell my case to NASA via their advisory committees. Since Mike Drake was the Chairman of the Solar System Exploration Subcommittee of the Space Science Advisory Committee, I called Mike to ask him if I could address his subcommittee. Mike said the next meeting was on July 18 at Headquarters and I should write him a short summary of what I wanted to tell the committee. He would then let me know if the committee agreed to let me present my case for a commercially based lunar exploration program. I did so and sat back to wait to see if I would be able to speak to the subcommittee or not.

I got a call from Pam Harrington in Kolbe's office saying she had set up a meeting for me with Kolbe at 2:00 PM on Monday, June 18 as promised. Finally I was getting somewhere.

On Friday I reached Ashley Winkler, the scheduler in Senator Kyl's Phoenix office. I had been trying to reach her for several days and it was not until Friday that the receptionist remembered that Ashley was pregnant and was working from her home, since her doctor had ordered bed rest for her. The receptionist said I could leave a voice mail message and then Ashley would call me back. I did and she responded within an hour. I told her Hank Kenski said to call her and I explained why I wanted a meeting with Kyl. Ashley said she expected that Kyl would be in Phoenix sometime during the second half of June or in July and she would let me know as soon as she could when I could see Kyl.

Monday June 18, 2001: Disappointment and Progress

Having heard nothing from Joe Boyce about our $3.5 million proposal, I called him to see what was up. Joe said he had emailed me a week earlier — an email that I told him had never arrived. He told me the reviewer's recommendations were to give us funding only for the GRS. There was to be no more money for the MAG/ER, the NS, or the APS. All in all, we were only going to get $900,000 spread over three years. Also, the proposal recommendations were still in budget review, but Joe thought we would get the $900,000 without any trouble. Unfortunately, most of the money would go to Los Alamos, so there would be little left over for LRI.

Despite that early morning disappointment, the rest of the day was great. I had my 2:00 PM meeting with Congressman Kolbe to discuss my commercial efforts. Kolbe was impressed and said he would try to convince his House Budget Committee colleagues to support the idea of a lunar data purchase program at NASA to the tune of $300 million per year starting with the FY 2003 budget. Needless to say, I was pleased. He then asked that I send him (via Mark Morehouse, with whom I had talked the last time I was in DC) a one or two page statement explaining exactly and clearly what I wanted and why, so that he could use it to persuade his Budget Committee colleagues from the House and Senate to support the funding of a lunar data purchase program. I said I would do so as soon as I returned from a few days vacation my brother and sister-in-law (Norman and Charlene, who were visiting us for two weeks from Illinois) and Rebecca and I were taking in northern Arizona.

I left Kolbe's office feeling very good about the meeting and then Rebecca, Norman, Charlene, and I drove off for the Grand Canyon and other sites in northern Arizona for that little vacation.

The Rest of June and Early July 2001

After we got back from our little vacation on Monday, the 25th, I called Todd Greenwalt to tell him about my meeting with Congressman Kolbe and my expectations about going to DC on July 18 to talk to the Solar System Exploration Subcommittee to get the science community behind a commercial lunar exploration program. As a result of Kolbe's support, I felt it was time to start seriously looking for big money to get LEI underway. It was clear to me that we could not wait until Congress had allocated money for a data purchase program because that would not happen until 2002, i.e., only one year before the FY 2003 money would become available. Since it would take at least two years to build our first lunar lander, we would have to get investors involved at the $100 million level *before* Congress had allocated the money for a FY 2003 data purchase program — a dicey proposition at best! But that was the only way to do it if I was going to be able to deliver lunar samples to NASA to get paid in FY 2003. Todd agreed it was time to start looking for potential investors, probably big companies that would eventually benefit from a commercial lunar program. He said he would inform the rest of our V&E Team and we would then decide just what the next step should be, besides my hopefully going to DC on the 18th.

On the 27th, I got an email from Carle Pieters from Brown University, indicating that a meeting was being held on July 13 in DC at the National Museum of Natural History (one of my favorites, with plenty of beautiful fossils, minerals, and rocks) to get the lunar and planetary science community's inputs for lunar, Mercury, and Venus missions. I decided that would be a good forum for me and I would attend both Carle's meeting and Mike's on one long trip.

I called Mike to see if I was going to be able to speak at his meeting and found that the answer was, "No." Carl Pilcher refused to let me address the Solar System Exploration Subcommittee Meeting. No surprise there, since Carl had always done everything possible to stop commercial exploration activities from getting started! Once again, NASA middle managers were protecting their little fiefdoms and personal power bases at the expense of progress and competence. Since Carl was blocking my discussing commercial exploration with the subcommittee, I would just do it at Carle's meeting.

Having decided to attend Carle's meeting on Friday, July 13, I emailed Carle to let her know I would be at the meetings and then I got busy writing the two-pager for Congressman Kolbe and calling DC to set up meeting with various congressional aids. Clearly I needed to see Mark Morehouse to discuss with him what I was writing for Kolbe. I got a meeting with Mark setup for early morning on Thursday the 12th. Then, since I had found out that Arizona Congressman Pastor (whose district covers the west side of Tucson and southwestern Arizona) was also on the House Budget Committee and since George French was already working with Pastor to get Moonlink and George's other education programs into the Arizona school system, I wanted to try to get Pastor behind my efforts. A call to his DC office led me to Richard Patrick, his aide for technical issues, and we set up a meeting for the 12th. Then, in order to cement my hoped for meeting with Senator Kyl, I called his office and talked with Christy Clark, with whom I also made an appointment on the 12th. I, of course, wanted to see Floyd des Champs (though I had begun to give up on Senator McCain), so I arranged a meeting with him in the late afternoon that would round out the 12th.

Then I called Mike Andrews to bring him up to date and to see if we could meet on Friday, July 13. As usual, Mike was most gracious and enthusiastic about the progress I was making and said to come on over to the V&E offices in the Willard Building on Friday morning.

Finally, I called Julius to see if I could stay with him and Pat and, as usual, I could.

Rebecca began setting up the airline reservation for what I thought was going to be an important trip. Since I had to stay over the weekend in DC to get an inexpensive airfare ($700 vs. $1800), I had toyed with the idea of stopping in Houston, so I could meet with Todd and Matt face to face on Monday the 16th, to discuss my progress and to discuss how to best proceed with the acquisition of hundreds of millions of dollars of investments on a wing and a prayer! However, Rebecca and I decided I had enough of long DC/Houston trips, so I called Todd and said I would not be stopping over in Houston, though Todd had thought that was a good idea when I had mentioned it to him in our earlier phone conversation. Todd said he would set up a telecon with Mike, Dave Weaver, Matt, him, and me the Monday after my DC trip and I said that would be great. Everything was set and the ball seemed to be rolling.

Wednesday, July 11, through Sunday, July 15, 2001: A Great Washington Trip

I arrived late Wednesday afternoon at Julius and Pat's. We had a light supper and then went for a walk along the Potomac to the famous old Fish Market. After returning to the apartment, I called Rebecca to find that Mark Morehouse had reset our meeting from Friday morning to late Friday afternoon. Then I went to bed.

Because Mark had postponed our early Thursday morning meeting to Friday, I had time to kill, so I went with Julius to NASA Headquarters to poke around a bit, but there was no one to poke. Finally it was time to see Richard Patrick in Pastor's office in the Rayburn Building. The meeting went very well and Richard promised to see to it that I got to see Pastor in Tucson.

By then it was lunchtime and since I like the Rayburn cafeteria, I had a light lunch (a piece of pizza and a coke) there and then stopped by to see Eric Sterner in the Space Science Committee Office in the Rayburn basement (near the cafeteria). I told Eric what I was up to and gave him a copy of the two-page piece I had prepared for Kolbe. Eric liked what I had written (I was glad of that, since I had little idea of what a Congressman might need to convince other Congressmen of anything, let alone a $300 million budget request). Eric thought what I was trying to do would be hard, but was possible. Then he added that if the new NASA Administrator (whoever he might be) were to embrace the idea and put the $300 million into the FY 2003 budget himself, then it would be a sure thing — an opinion I was, of course, in agreement with. But, as I replied, "Until I see NASA on my side, I will continue to assume I will have to get Congress to force NASA to accept a data buy program and I will proceed accordingly."

I appreciated Eric's positive comments and then left the Rayburn Building to go to the Hart Building to meet with Christy Clark in Kyl's office. That meeting was also successful and then I went to see Floyd. I told Floyd I was getting the impression I was wasting my time trying to see McCain and Floyd agreed. He said McCain was too busy with his political agenda (Campaign Finance Reform, Patients Bill of Right, and annoying the Republican Party), so much so that he was neglecting all other things, including keeping his staff informed of what he was doing. Though McCain would be of no help, Floyd said he would do what he could to continue helping me.

Floyd's new temporary office was in the Russell Building, immediately adjacent to the Hart Building and only a few blocks from the Union Station. Since Julius's (69th) birthday had been a few days earlier (Monday, July 11) and I had missed it, I told Julius and Pat to meet me after work at the Union Station and I would take them out for a belated Julius Birthday Dinner at one of the many great restaurants there. They did, I did, and we had a nice dinner and a nice evening.

Friday morning at 9:00 I went to see Mike. After bringing him up to date, we decided the next time I came to DC, hopefully to again see Courtney Stadd, the new NASA Administrator (if the Bush Administration could even find someone to take the job), the new Bush Administration Science Advisor (if Congress approved the Bush nominee), and some of the Congressmen and Senators I was courting, Mike would accompany me to see those people to officially and visibly throw his weight, as a former Texas Congressman and V&E lawyer, behind my efforts to get a lunar data purchase program funded and implemented.

I had plenty of time before the meeting at the Natural History Museum, so I decided to see what I could do without appointments on the Hill. I knew Florida Congressman Weldon, a key Congressman for space related issues, from the District in which the Kennedy Space Center and Cape Canaveral are located. He is also a friend of Karen Ramos and I had met Weldon at a Kennedy Space Center Dinner that Karen had invited me to when I was at the Cape with my engineers getting Lunar Prospector ready for launch. Also, Weldon, who was a member of the House Space Sciences Committee, was there when I testified to the Committee regarding the Mars Mission failures a year earlier. When the hearing was over, Weldon had come over to talk with me a bit before we left the Committee Hearing Room. I figured I had a chance to see Weldon for a few minutes without an appointment and went to his office in the Cannon Building, close to the Rayburn Building.

When I got there, I asked to see Congressman Weldon or his technical aid. The receptionist said I could talk with Brendan Curry, who shortly came out to the reception area and I started to tell him what I was doing. Just then, Congressman Weldon came out of his office to go to some committee meeting and he stopped to see what I wanted. I briefly told him about my $300 million data purchase request and asked for his support, saying I would get the details to Brendan. Weldon gave a hurried, but positive response and then took off. Brendan and I continued the conversation a little while longer and then he said I should also go see Arizona Congressman Hayworth, who Brendan said was a space-nut.

I went back to the Rayburn Building, where I talked Jill Henriques, Hayworth's aide, who confirmed that Hayworth was pro-space and said she would help me get a meeting with Hayworth in Arizona during the upcoming August Congressional break. With two home runs in, and since I was in the Rayburn Building, I decided to try for a third and went to see California Congressman Rohrabacher's new aide, Rubin Mitchell, to see if I could finally see Rohrabacher face-to-face. Since Rohrabacher had been one of the original supporters of Lunar Prospector a decade earlier and since he was a long-standing member the Space Science Committee, Rohrabacher knew me or certainly knew of me.

Since we had never met before, Rubin did not at first recognize my name, but quickly recovered when I said I had done Lunar Prospector. When I said I needed to have a face-to-face meeting with Rohrabacher, Rubin said he would make sure it happened the next time I was in DC. My sojourn back to the Hill had been very fruitful.

By then it was afternoon and I went to Carle's meeting and presented my commercial lunar data purchase story to the members of her subcommittee and the other attendees. As expected and as typical, my colleagues, who are far too used to waiting for NASA to give them their grants and to set the tone for lunar and planetary research and missions, were somewhat timid and skeptical about the idea of a full scale, commercially based, Congressionally supported Lunar Exploration Program not initiated and not run by NASA — but one should remember they also didn't think Lunar Prospector would ever succeed and would not produce any good data either. Nevertheless, they were willing to give my proposal a chance and, though rather subdued, raised their voices to tell NASA we needed to get back in the business of exploring the Moon. One small step for — well, commercial lunar exploration, anyway.

Then it was back to the Rayburn Building for the meeting with Mark Morehouse. I gave Mark the new support material that Kolbe had requested and we discussed the various points. Mark made it clear that, though Kolbe was supporting my efforts, he might not be able to spearhead the effort and suggested I get additional supporters (as I was already doing), as well as see if any of them might be willing to take the lead. Kolbe was backpedaling (not unexpected, but annoying). My thought turned to Congressmen Rohrabacher and Weldon, who were the real space supporters and who might spearhead the effort — only time would tell. On the more positive side, Mark asked me to send him a page or two on the benefits to the taxpayers from the use of lunar resources and lunar activities. I said I would get the material to him as soon as I returned home.

Though slightly disappointed about the backpedaling, I left Kolbe's office feeling I had accomplished a lot in the last two days. I really felt the ball was finally rolling down hill, to be sure — very slowly and on a very shallow slope, but I was no longer pushing it uphill, and though I would have to keep pushing to keep it rolling, it was at least going downhill.

Again, since I was not far from the Union Station and, since Pat would not be home for dinner, I told Julius I would take him to a German Restaurant a couple of blocks from the Union Station we had frequented in the past. We met there and had some good German food.

Saturday was spent sight seeing and then early Sunday I flew back to good old Tucson, thus ending a very productive trip.

Tuesday, July 11, through Tuesday, July 24, 2001: The Vinson & Elkins Telecon

While I was in DC, Todd had setup a telecon for Tuesday the 17th. Mike Andrews had a conflict and could not participate, but since I had just met with him in DC, that was OK. Matt, Dave, Todd, and I had a good telecon and decided we would pursue trying to get contacts at Schlumberger, Fluor, Bechtel, investment banks and the like, so I could present our case for them investing in LEI, and that Wayne and I would get a high quality sales package and video made to support our efforts. I was pleased because the V&E team really seemed to think we had a good chance of succeeding in such a difficult venture. I reminded myself that when we started Lunar Prospector so many years earlier, it was a very long shot and yet I had pulled it off, so maybe I could pull off the commercial lunar exploration program.

The next few days were spent getting the short paper together about the utilization of the Moon and its resources for the benefit of humanity I had promised Mark Morehouse; putting together information packages and sending all that off to the Congressional aides I had visited in DC, checking with the schedulers to see if meetings had been setup with Kyl, Pastor, and Hayworth during the August break, and setting up a second meeting with Steve Jewett in the Governor's Tucson Office, so I could bring him up to date on a number of issues and to see if there was any way that I could get Arizona State funding for LRI and/or LEI.

Wednesday, July 25, 2001: The Second Meeting With Steve Jewett

The meeting with Steve was very fruitful. I first asked him about my application to the Arizona Space Council since I had heard nothing and he said he would check on it (the next day he called to say that my application was being processed — albeit slowly. However, I never heard from the state about that application). Then I told him of my progress in getting political support of a $300 million/year commercial lunar data purchase program and what that would mean for Arizona. I also reminded him of the facts that there were three Arizona Universities, the USGS Branch of Astrogeology in Flagstaff, the Planetary Science Institute, and my two companies in Tucson that were involved in space research, that Arizona had the second largest (second only to California) amount of NASA funding for lunar and planetary research, and it provided most of the instrumentation and science support for the Mars Missions. In other words, Arizona had tremendous assets the politicians were hardly aware of and that Arizona was neither supporting nor building on those assets. I then told him California supported its space science community with state funding and Arizona should do the same. I also told him about the efforts of the National Coalition of Spaceport States (NCSS) to get Arizona involved it its efforts via me and that the Aerospace States Association (ASA) wanted Arizona to again be a member and have me represent the state.

Steve was convinced of the value of what I was trying to do and what I could do for the state and we discussed how I might get state support, the best way being from the Economic Development Council.

Monday, August 6, through Monday, September 10, 2001: Firing Wayne and Getting Nowhere with Arizona Politicians

As soon as I got to work on Monday, I called Wayne and told him that we had to get the LEI Business Plan in tip top shape, since I would need it to start talking with potential investors. I wanted Wayne to come to Tucson the following week, arriving on Sunday the 12th, and to stay as long as it took to get the job done. Wayne was enthusiastic about our prospects, but said he had to go to Oregon before he could come to Tucson, probably on the 12th or the 13th, at the latest, and that he would call me towards the end of the week to let me know when he would arrive in Tucson.

However, as the week ended and then the weekend passed without a word from Wayne, I knew he was not coming. I began to try to track him down, starting Monday the 13th, but he was never at home and his kids didn't know where he was (not an uncommon occurrence). Finally at mid-week, I reached Peggy, after she had gotten home from work, and she told me Wayne was still in Oregon, where he was setting up a new company with some friend of his.

That was it; Wayne had dumped LEI and LRI for the last time. It was clear I could not rely on him, no matter how important the issue was, because everything else in Wayne's life was more important than LRI and LEI. Moreover, Wayne's past performance had clearly shown me he would have no time at all for LRI and LEI for some time to come, while he was building their new company in Oregon, period — end of story. There was no way I could build LEI into a successful company with Wayne as my partner, so Wayne was out.

Peggy had given me a telephone number in Oregon where I could reach Wayne. When I reached him, I gave him the easy way out by asking for his resignation from LRI, LEI, and their Boards, and asked that he write me a letter to that effect. Wayne reluctantly agreed to do so, but — as usual — did not write the letter, he was too busy doing everything else to even take the easy way out. Rebecca, George French, and I had a Telecon-Board Meeting and removed Wayne from both Boards and both companies. I then sent Wayne a letter, dated September 10, informing him he had been fired from both companies and taken off both their Boards.

I was annoyed at that turn of events, first because Wayne has a lot to offer, especially to LEI, and second, Wayne had been part of Lunar Prospector since late 1989 and it would have been great to have Wayne be part of the follow-on efforts, as I had planned when I asked him to become part of LRI and LEI in 1997.

Since I had fired Wayne, I had to find a new engineering partner who I knew was the best and whom I trusted. I quickly came upon the idea of asking my good old friend Ron Humble if he wanted to partner with me or if he knew someone whom he could recommend for the job of LEI's Chief Engineer. I called Ron in mid-August at the Air Force Academy and told him what was up and within a day, Ron said he was very interested in being my partner. Great! I asked Ron to come down to Tucson as soon as it was convenient, so we could discuss the details and determine how we might proceed with his joining LEI. Ron had some other business in Tucson and said he could come down on Thursday, September 13 and leave on Saturday the 15th. We were all set and I was looking forward to the possibility of Ron joining LEI.

While all that was going on, Chris Español, the undergraduate student who worked with us, and I began to upgrade the LEI Business Plan and get it ready for printing. Chris, as always, did a great job of adding pictures, background, and information bullets. Also, Matt Strock, our V&E Team corporate lawyer, went over the Business Plan with a fine-toothed comb to make sure it was a good plan, both business-wise and legally. In the end, the finished LEI Business Plan was a very impressive document.

Simultaneously, I met with Don Rhodes of WBC Imaging and hired him to turn some of the TV coverage of the Lunar Prospector news conferences and interviews into a LEI PR video, and Rebecca, Chris, and I started making a LEI PR package out of the various newspaper and magazine articles about the Mission.

Finally, though I had made several follow-up calls to the schedulers of Arizona Senator Kyle and Arizona Congressmen Pastor and Hayworth to try to get meetings set up with them during the August break, I was unable to get any meetings scheduled. That annoyed me greatly, since the Arizona politicians seem to have time for everything except discussing commercial space exploration. Similarly, I tried to reach Steve Jewett in the Tucson Office of the Governor and Steve never returned my calls, which I found strange since we had a couple of very productive meetings! Clearly, the Arizona politicians, at all levels of government, were not the least bit interested in talking with me about the development of a commercial lunar exploration capability in Tucson, so I reluctantly accepted I would have to find the political support I needed outside of my home state — a testament to the quality of Arizona politicians.

Tuesday, September 11, 2001: A Day of Infamy

Rebecca and I had just returned from our early morning walk and I turned on the TV to see the Fox News before getting ready for work. The scene that came on the TV screen was of a burning World Trade Center Tower and then all of a sudden, there was a fiery explosion coming from the second Tower. As we soon learned, we had missed the live events and what we saw were the reruns of the attacks on the Twin Towers and America. Then the Fox reporter said there were reports of a plane crashing into the Pentagon and a little later that a plane had crashed in Pennsylvania. As we watched the horrific events following the terror attacks unfold, I knew my plans to get political support and budgetary funding for a commercial lunar data purchase program and to seek investors for LEI were going to be on hold, or a least considerably slowed down, for quite some time to come.

Wednesday, September 12, through Wednesday, October 17, 2001: Goldin Resigns

Because of the events of 911, there was no rush to finish the business plan and Don Rhodes was too busy making videos of the terrorist attacks for the local TV stations to get my video done. Also, because air traffic was halted and then only slowly restarted, Ron had to cancel his trip to Tucson. As I had expected, everything slowed down. The only real activity was my getting prepared for the Space Frontier Foundation Meeting in LA in mid-October.

However, I heard on the news on September 17 that Dan Goldin, the longest serving NASA Administrator, had officially resigned. Though I believed Dan had done many positive things at NASA during his tenure, it was time for a new Administrator and since Dan's and my views on commercialization differed in one critical point (I believe that in the beginning, NASA would have to be the only customer for commercial science data, while Dan insisted that NASA had to be a minor customer), I was happy to see that the transition to a different NASA had finally begun. I only hoped the new Administrator would accept my concept of commercial lunar exploration.

Thursday, October 18, through Saturday, October 20, 2001: The Space Frontier Foundation Meeting in Los Angeles

The main reason I went to the LA meeting was to attend a one day seminar the firm Citron and Deutsch, P.C. (a firm that helps several entrepreneurs set up their new companies every month) was giving on how to develop a business plan and to meet the Venture Capitalist and Angle Investors who were supposed to be present at the meeting.

The seminar was very useful, though it was geared to companies that needed no more than a few million dollars of investments. Since LEI needed at least $100 million to start doing lunar missions, I had a number of questions about how I should proceed. As I discussed the issues I had with the various presenters at the seminar, they agreed with the strategy Matt, Dave, Todd, and I had come up with during our telecon on July 17, i.e., that I should approach the big resource companies that might make big money in the future from the utilization of lunar resources and lunar derived energy — companies like Schlumberger, Fluor, and Bechtel and the energy companies.

In addition to the information I gained at the seminar, I was very pleased to find that the Deutsch brothers (one is a lawyer and the other is the co-founder of SpaceHab and Kistler Rocket), who ran the seminar, thought my idea for getting lunar data and selling it to NASA was the correct approach to starting a viable commercial space exploration capability and I had a good chance of getting the kind of money I needed, despite the fact that LEI needed very large investments! As I returned home on Saturday, I felt like I was really on the right track.

Monday, October 22, through Wednesday, November 14, 2001: Ron's Visit

Based on the response I had at LA, I started to think about finding my way into Bechtel, Fluor, and Schlumberger. As I was thinking about whom I might know who could get me an introduction to the upper management of those companies, I thought of Brad Roscoe in Schlumberger in Connecticut. I called Brad and explained what I was doing and asked him if he knew anyone I might talk to at Schlumberger. Brad said the guy who ran his branch was a great person for me to start with and that if he liked what I was doing — and Brad was fairly certain that he would — he would take me to the corporate higher ups.

Brad suggested he tell his boss about our conversation and that I come to Connecticut to give a seminar on Lunar Prospector and my commercial lunar exploration plan and to meet with his boss. I said that was an excellent idea and that, as soon as there was a new NASA Administrator and I could get a meeting with him, I would send Brad the LEI Business Plan and other information and then let him know when I could come to see them. Brad said that would be fine. I had a good start at Schlumberger.

Since I had not heard from Joe Boyce concerning the $900,000 we were still hoping to get for further work on the GRS data, I called Joe to see what was going on (as if I didn't know — all of NASA's money was going into the black hole called the International Space Station, since it was, by then, $5 billion over budget and President Bush said NASA was getting no extra money for the Space Station). Joe said that until the new NASA budget was finished, he would not know if we were going to get the $900,000 or not. I assumed we would not get the money and I wasn't worried about it either way. First, almost all the money would go to Los Alamos and thus the $900,000 would do LRI little good. Second, I was spending most of my time and resources pushing the commercial exploration theme and I was not concerned about doing additional work on the Lunar Prospector data analysis program — Bill and my other Co-Is were doing a great job of that.

After the delay due to the terrorist attacks on 911, Ron finally came to Tucson on Thursday, October 25 and left on the 27th. We had a very good discussion about LEI, what I wanted to accomplish, and how I wanted to accomplish it. Ron, who had known me since the mid-eighties, knew what to expect from me, and since we are of the same ilk, Ron was ready to join LEI. We decided that, if and when I started getting investors, we would work out the details of his employment at LEI, but by the time he left Tucson, Ron was LEI's Chief Engineer.

On October 30, I got an email about Ex-Congressman Bob Walker, the head of The Commission on the Future of the United States Aerospace Industry, and I decided that, when I went to Headquarters, I would try to go see his committee and ask for their support for my commercial lunar data purchase program.

Thursday, November 15, through Christmas, 2001: Enter Sean O'Keefe

The November 15 morning newspaper announced that President Bush had nominated Sean O'Keefe, an OMB (the White House Office of Management and Budget) senior staff member, to be the next NASA Administrator. Given NASA's catastrophic space station budget overruns and all the other budgetary problems NASA continually had, the idea of having a NASA Administrator with a solid financial background was absolutely sound and offered the possibility that maybe, just maybe, O'Keefe could pull NASA out of its fatal tailspin before it hit the ground. Also, given what I had read about O'Keefe, he was in favor of the commercialization of many of NASA activities.

I emailed Courtney Stadd on November 19 to let him know I was beginning to look for investors and, if O'Keefe was the new Administrator, I wanted to see them both as soon as was possible. Then I started trying to reach Courtney by phone — a difficult task — to discuss my plans further.

Over the next couple of weeks, it appeared that Congress would confirm O'Keefe as the next Administrator; in fact, Congress put his hearings on the fast track. As soon as it looked like O'Keefe was going to get the green light, I Fed-Ex'ed him a letter asking for a meeting to discuss my efforts to get a commercial lunar data purchase program started, the LEI Business Plan, my testimony to Congress, the rationale for the data purchase program I had prepared for Congressman Kolbe, and other backup materials. That package went out on December 5.

As I had told Brad Roscoe at Schlumberger, as soon as it looked like I was going to get to see the new NASA Administrator, I would send him the LEI Business Plan and my backup materials, so he could get things moving at Schlumberger. I called Brad and told him that I was sending him the package and Rebecca and I Fed-Ex'ed it to him on December 6.

The Senate confirmed O'Keefe as the new NASA Administrator on December 20. It was time to get into high gear.

I started trying harder to reach Courtney by phone and finally succeeded the day before Christmas. I brought him up to date about my activities and told him I had sent

O'Keefe a letter asking for a meeting. Courtney said, given O'Keefe's schedule of visits to the various NASA facilities and the like, it would be late February or early March before such a meeting could be arranged. I also said, when I was in Washington, I wanted to talk to Walker's commission. Courtney agreed that was the right thing to do and told me to call Paul Pisciopo, who took care of all the day-to-day activities of the commission.

I immediately called Paul, only to find that he had already left for the Christmas break. I told the secretary I would send Paul my Business Plan and the backup materials immediately and I would call Paul right after New Year's.

Wednesday, December 26, through Sunday, December 30, 2001: The Christmas Break

Rebecca and I were going to spend four days at Lake Havasu to see the London Bridge, to see the sights and just relax between Christmas and New Year's. As we started to drive to Lake Havasu, we stopped at the office to prepare a letter for Paul Pisciopo, the package of the LEI Business Plan, and the backup material, and Fed-Ex'ed the package off to Paul. Then we drove on and had a nice time at Lake Havasu.

Also, after Joe had told me in October that we might get $900,000 for more GRS data reduction, I decided it would be a waste of money and my time for me to administer that small contract, since almost all of the money would go to Los Alamos anyway. Bill, Joe, and I decided I would keep out of it and Bill would put in a separate Los Alamos proposal for the $900,000 and he did.

Monday, December 31, 2001: The Official End of the Lunar Prospector Program

Monday, December 31, the Lunar Prospector Program came to its formal end after 13 years, one month, and a week or two after it had started in late November 1988 — the contract for the numerical reduction and archiving of the Lunar Prospector data came to its end. The GRS, NS, APS, and MAG data had been delivered to the NASA archives on time and the final touches were being put on the ER data.

Though the contract was formally over, Bill and his team at Los Alamos were giving the GRS, NS, and APS data a final going over that would take a month or two and Bob and Dave Mitchell at UC Berkeley didn't send off the MAG/ER final products to the archives for a couple of more months. However, even after delivering the data products to the archives, the archiving itself took several months to complete, so my Co-Is still had to answer any questions and resolve any issues that came up during the validation of the data before the data were finally put into the archives. Even though Lunar Prospector had formally ended, there was, as always, some cleanup work to do.

Thus, as 2001 came to an end, so did Lunar Prospector. All that I had to do was to write the final report in January and send it to Headquarters by the 15th (I was a week late, but so what). The mission had been a complete success in every respect. The science data were far better than we had ever dreamed possible and it had already begun to greatly enhance our understanding of the Moon, its evolution, and its resources — especially the polar water ice deposits. Though the numerical reduction and archiving of the data were effectively finished, the decades long phase of the interpretation of the Lunar Prospector data had just begun.

Lunar Prospector had brilliantly demonstrated that "Faster, Better, Cheaper" really works — when one knows what one is doing — and, more importantly, the "commercial feasibility of lunar exploration missions." Thus Lunar Prospector gave me the credibility to continue seeking philanthropic support for the LRI (I am trying to build up a $10,000,000 endowment for LRI, through philanthropic contributions from individuals and/or corporations, to continue LRI's studies of the Moon and its resources), seeking corporations that will invest the $100,000,000 or so LEI needs to begin building a commercial lunar exploration capability, and pushing NASA and Congress towards a true commercial lunar exploration program — tasks that are clearly going to take much more time that I had hoped — but that is another story!

As 2001 and Lunar Prospector both officially ended, I was not sad to see Lunar Prospector come to its end, rather I was looking forward towards the future that Lunar Prospector had opened the door to. My dream is that, when historians of the 21st Century write the history of humanity's colonization of first the Moon, second Mars, and then the rest of the solar system and finally, its expansion beyond our solar system to the stars of our Milky Way Galaxy, that little Lunar Prospector will be recognized as the spark that rekindled the interest to start that expansion, after the flames started by Apollo were smothered by a backwards thinking NASA.

THE BEGINNING?

APPENDICES

Articles, Correspondence, and Photographs

Note

The first digit of the Appendix or Photograph reference number corresponds to the book section.

NASA
National Aeronautics and
Space Administration
Lyndon B. Johnson Space Center
Houston, Texas

Vol. 28

August 4, 1989

No. 3

Space News Roundup

Good prospects

A group of local engineers and scientists are working on a private unmanned Lunar Propector mission. Story on Page 4.

Back to a base

Concepts for a lunar base are discussed in excerpts from a new Advanced Programs Office report. Story on Page 3.

JSC Photo

The proposed private Lunar Prospector probe would search for ice hidden in permanently shadowed areas of the Moon.

Lunar Prospector group seeks engineering help

A group of local engineers and scientists is looking for professional engineers to help them fly a low-cost private Lunar Prospector mission in 1991 or 1992.

The Lunar Prospector is seen as an inexpensive way to map lunar resources needed to support a lunar base and further space exploration. Cost of the 330-pound spin-stabilized satellite is estimated at less than $5 million because of a reliance on contributions of time, equipment and material by individuals, organizations and companies.

Project Scientist Alan Binder and Project Engineer Preston Carter, both Lockheed Engineering and Science Co. employees at JSC, are working with the Space Studies Institute (SSI) of Princeton, N.J.

Binder said a six-month design contract for the spacecraft will start in October, with construction expected to be complete by the summer of 1991. A donated launch is hoped for, he said.

Lunar Prospector would carry a gamma-ray/neutron spectrometer for global mapping of the lunar surface layer and searching for ice in permanently shadowed areas, an alpha particle spectrometer to map the distribution of radon gas release sites, a magnetometer/electron reflectometer to map magnetic fields, and a gravity experiment to map the lunar gravity field.

Anyone interested in volunteering should contact Binder at 283-5316, or Carter at 333-6755.

Appendix 1-1: The article that appeared in the JSC/NASA Space news Roundup, announcing the Lunar Prospector Project and asking for volunteer help in developing the spacecraft and doing the mission (also see www.lunar-research-institute.org).

12602 Ponderose Dr.
Dickinson, TX 77539
Aug. 15, 1989

Professor Gerard O'Neill
Space Studies Institute
Princeton, NJ 08542

Dear Professor O'Neill:

As Lunar Prospector's Project Engineer and Project Scientist,
we are writing you due to the serious concerns we have about
the project's leadership as represented by Gregg Maryniak and
Gay Canough.

If you check our resume's (which Gregg has), you will find
that we are experienced and knowledgeable professionals who
are quite capable of bringing the technical side of the Lunar
Prospector Program to a successful conclusion. Since
starting work on the program, we have defined the mission
objectives and spacecraft hardware requirements in our
respective areas of responsibility. These mission objectives
and requirements were used as the basis for the RFP we
prepared for SSI in June. We have also recruited mission
experienced colleagues for the science and engineering teams.
All of the science team members chosen to conduct the five
Lunar Prospector experiments have flown experiments on
missions and most of them are currently science team leaders
or team members on Voyager and Mars Observer. Similarly, some
thirty Johnson Space Center area aerospace engineers and one
astronaut have been recruited to work on the engineering
team. We have, in our respective areas of leadership, the
personnel needed to carryout the technical side of the this
program.

We have recruited professionals since it was always clear to
us that the project could only be carried out with
professionals and in a professional manner. In contrast, both
Gregg and Gay have their roots in the amateur community and
still have very close ties with it. Because the amateur
community is needed to create interest and support for the
program, we accepted some of the inherent risks associated
with its members participating in Lunar Prospector and, in
Gregg's and Gay's cases, leading the program. However, given
the serious errors of judgement Gregg and Gay have made in
the last few weeks, the loss of time and credibility these
errors have cost the program, and the potential legal
difficulties they may have caused SSI, we no longer accept
this risk.

If SSI has any expectations that the Lunar Prospector Program
will come to a successful conclusion, we see no alternatives

except the following:

1) Gregg and Gay must be immediately removed from their present positions of leadership in the program and replace by a competent Project Manager. Since finding a qualified Project Manager will take some time, we suggest that Bettie Greber act as the interface between us and SSI in the interim.

2) A three and a half month delay, as announced by Gregg and Gay, is unjustified and has serious impacts on the project. We must discuss this problem and determine if, and by how much, the delay can be shortened.

3) We request that SSI have an executive meeting at Princeton in the very near future. At this meeting we must discuss how we can recover from the current situation and what the future of the project is. Since we do not yet have Lockheed or project support for our efforts, we will need SSI travel funds for this trip and the meeting will have to occur on a weekend.

Sincerely yours,

Dr Alan Binder
Project Scientist

Preston Carter
Project Engineer

Appendix 1-2: The letter Preston Carter and I wrote to the Space Studies Institute (SSI), expressing our concerns about the poor performance of the SSI members of the Lunar Prospector Team and the need to replace them with competent personnel (also see www.lunar-research-institute.org).

CONTRACT CONTACT RESPONSIBILITY

Gregg, I consider this exercise of writing down my points as to why I want Carter to be the point-man on the contract(s) to be a total waste of my time. I doubt very much that you will read this and that if you do, you will simply attempt to do exactly what you want for your purposes. I would be very happy if I am wrong and would then believe that our chances of success were greatly improved.

There are four main points why I want Carter to direct the Phase B (and Phase C) contract(s). The first is philosophical, the second is proceedural or perhaps practical, the third is historical, and the fourth is financial. All of these points not only reflect on why I want Carter to be the contract point-man, but also reflect on why I want the project to be run by a Consortium of equal pertners with equal say.

Point 1

As I think we all agree, our efforts are being made in large part because the NASA way of preparing for and doing missions has become very ineffective. As such, I think we agree that one of the major goals of the Lunar Prospector Project is to demonstrate a quicker, less costly and better way of doing lunar (and planetary) science missions.

My experience as a Viking PI and with other NASA (and ESA) missions with which I have intimate knowledge is that, although the mission goals are science objectives, the programs are administrated by engineers who have a superficial understanding of the actual mission drivers, i.e., the science. It is this approach which has lead in large part to the current inefficiencies in the NASA way, i.e., people who do not really know what the mission is to do, do not do an efficient job of running it.

While this engineering approach was certainly correct in the earlier days when a successful mission to the Moon or Mars, etc. was basically a technical challange, this is no longer the case. Space technology has advanced to the stage where scientists who not only have the scientific credentials, but also have a good understanding of systems engineering should be running or, at a minimum, should have a dominant role in running lunar and planetary missions.

If, as you propose, Jim is cast in the role of the classical Project Manager and contract point-man, we will be preserving the old, ineffective NASA top-down/engineer management approach in which science is subordanant to engineering. If Carter is the contract point-man, the science will not be subordanant. Carter and I work closely together, both because we are geographically close and because we work and think along the same lines. In effect, science would have the direct input into the design study and construction phase that is needed if the program is to be efficiently run. Our success in doing this will demonstrate that there is a better way to do missions than the NASA top-down/engineer dominated way.

Point 2
As both Carter and I have said several times, the fact that he and I, along with our engineering and science teams, will generate essentially all of the mission requirement and changes there of during the course of Phase B and Phase C of the project. As Jim has agreeded earlier and I think he will still agree, the transmission of our requirements to him and then his transmission of the requirements to OMNI will incrase the number of misunderstanding dramatically. It has been demonstrated over and over in every program I have ever been associated with that, the longer the chain of communications, the worse the results are. The only sensible way of doing this is to have Carter (and me indirectly via Carter) be the point-man on the contract(s).

Point 3
When this program started, it did not have a project manager since Gay had neither any experience nor any capability as a project manager. Since her position was cosmetic, I accepted her playing the role of Project Manager until it bagan to compound the problems you and she cause this summer. The main reason why I accepted her in the beginning was that with Carter as Project Engineer and me as Project Scientist, we did not need a real project manager. The position was a superfluous remnant of the NASA way of doing things discussed in Point 1. You might even recall that, when you, Carter and I had our first telecon to discuss how to recover from the problems you caused this summer, I pointed out that we did not need a Project Manager.

Though I welcome Jim's participation in the project and believe he adds considerably to our pool of talent, I feel that his role as Project Manager has little meaning (except for fund raising), because he is geographically too far away from Houston where the science and engineering work is done. As I initially pointed, he is near OMNI and can easily act as a monitor, reporting to Carter and me what is going on, but that is far different being the point-man. Also, I question how much time Jim really has for the project, given his current schedule of trips. While this is no reflection on Jim's capabilities, I suspect that the time and especially distance factor add up to the post of Project Manager being more cerimonial that substantive.

Point 4
Gregg, I really do not buy your argument that this is

11
day

SSI money that is being spent and therefore you want SSI
personnel to be responsible for it. First, since you are only
underwriting the contract, you do not intend to spend any SSI
money at all. You expect the project to return all the money
and/or you are hoping that the project will get the $75,000
before SSI has to pay. In either case, it is project money
that is being spent, not SSI's and it therefore does not make
any difference whether Jim or Carter is the point-man.

Secondly, $65,000 of the $500,000 Lockheed support I
have is being spent in direct support of the Phase B
contract. As such I have as much responsibility to Lockheed
for this work as you would have to SSI if you were truely
spending $75,000 of SSI's money. Given that the latter is not
really the case, I can use your argument and say that I am
the one to chose the point-man since I am resposible to
Lockheed for the $65,000 that they are spending on the Phase
B study.

① We are letting Gregg get his way
   Cuts off discussion when goes against him
   & pospones it or delay tatik
    Did not discuss point-man w/ Jim or us -just
   do it his way
② omitting arguments is delay tatik

Appendix 1-3: A draft of the memo that I sent to Gregg Maryniak at the Space Studies Institute regarding the need for Preston Carter to be the point-man between the Lunar Prospector Project and OMNI Systems Inc. during the Lunar Prospector Spacecraft Design Study that OMNI was to conduct.

Note in the 1st paragraph of Point 1, I stated, ". . . one of the major goals of the Lunar Prospector Project to demonstrate a quicker, less costly and better way of doing lunar (and planetary) science missions." Several years later, NASA announced the Discovery Program that was to determine how to do lunar and planetary missions "Faster, Better, Cheaper" and Lunar Prospector was selected as the first pear-reviewed, competitively selected Discovery Mission in February 1995.

Also see www.lunar-research-institute.org.

September 7, 1990

Gerard O'Neill, President

Gregg Maryniak Exec. VP

~~SSI, P.O. Box 81414~~ Space Studies Inst.

Princeton, N.J ~~08540~~ P.O. Box 82

08540

Dear Gregg,

SSI Fax (609/ 921-0389

This letter is to make you aware of several problems that have arisen in the administration of the Lunar Prospector Project . Dr. Alan Binder and Preston Carter of Lunar Exploration Inc., a member institution of the Lunar Prospector Consortium, have brought to my attention what they consider to be several ongoing violations of the Consortium Agreement of May 25, 1990, which are potentially catastrophic to the project:

1 - The contract entered into with NASA in August of 1990 for the use of the gamma-ray spectrometer was with Space Studies Institute exclusively, instead of with the Consortium as stipulated in Section 2.2.1 of the Consortium Agreement. It was verbally agreed on by representatives of both member institutions that, at minimum, a preamble to the contract stating that SSI was acting as an agent of the Consortium, which included LEI, would have at least fulfilled the spirit of the Agreement, if not the letter of it. Such a preamble is not present in the final NASA/SSI contract.

2 - In July of 1990, negotiations regarding the launch of the Lunar Prospector were held in the Soviet Union among the space agency, NPO Energia, and representatives of SSI and LEI. During these talks, your representative repeatedly presented the Lunar Prospector Project as being the exclusive effort of SSI, rather than the Consortium. This is a violation of Section 7 of the Consortium Agreement.

3 -The disregard for the proper identification and representation of the member institutions of the Consortium in the article in the September 1990 issue of Discovery, which is a violation of Section 7 of the Consortium Agreement. This is the most recent in a series of similar articles, both during the negotiation and after the initiation of the agreement, which violate the letter and/or spirit of said agreement.

These violations seriously undermine the efforts of Lunar Exploration Inc. to carry out its obligations to the Consortium. These obligations represent

To conduct the program and

the vast majority of the work necessary to obtain the financial, manpower and hardware resources to carry out the Lunar Prospector Project. The ramifications of these violations manifest themselves mainly as follows:

1 - The lack of SSI's public recognition of LEI's leadership role in the Lunar Prospector Project jeopardizes funding from major aerospace and non-aerospace companies with which LEI is negotiating. This is particularly damaging; at this critical juncture in the Project, the only funding efforts to show potential for success are those of LEI.

2 - The credibility of the Lunar Prospector Project is based almost exclusively on the engineering and scientific skills of LEI's membership. Without prominent recognition of LEI's role in the Project, the Project's credibility is significantly reduced, especially within the aerospace community upon whom we are dependent for major contributions of funding, personnel, hardware and facilities.

3 - The cumulative effect of these violations on LEI volunteers, upon whom this program is critically dependent, is profoundly negative. The only public acknowledgment these dedicated men and women receive is the media coverage of the Project, which is being denied by repeated SSI's misrepresentations of the Lunar Prospector Project as the effort solely of SSI. If left unchecked this demeaning and demoralizing situation will lead to the loss of LEI's, and the Project's, major asset: its volunteers. This will destroy LEI's ability to carry out its Consortium duties.

Given that this is a highly critical moment in the evolution of this project, LEI believes that an immediate face-to-face meeting with you is needed, here in Houston, on or by Sept. 12, 1990, to address these issues and LEI's concerns regarding the integrity of the Consortium agreement. According to Texas State law, the alleged SSI breaches of the Consortium Agreement can be considered grounds for nullification of said agreement. However, LEI has indicated that it would prefer not to pursue this option at this time. After identifying all legal options available, in the best interest of the Project, LEI has opted to rewrite several sections of the Consortium Agreement in order to insure that violations of these types will no longer hinder the progress of the Project. It is imperative that the discussions regarding these amendments be completed and the new agreement be in place by Sept. 12, 1990. In order to expedite your acceptance of these amendments, we are enclosing a draft of the agreement for you. Should the amended agreement not be in place by Sept. 12. 1990, LEI will pursue other options to protect its interest and insure the success of the Project.

Appendix 1-4: Because of various Space Studies Institute (SSI) violations of the Consortium Agreement, which served as the basis for the cooperation between SSI and Lunar Exploration Inc. (LEI) on the Lunar Prospector Project, I wrote this draft of a letter to SSI, demanding changes in the Consortium Agreement that would rectify the situation. The draft was sent to Jay Cuclis, LEI's pro bono lawyer at the firm of Vinson & Elkins, so he could prepare it as a legal document and send it to SSI (also see www.lunar-research-institute.org).

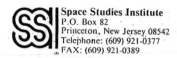

Space Studies Institute
P.O. Box 82
Princeton, New Jersey 08542
Telephone: (609) 921-0377
FAX: (609) 921-0389

Gerard K. O'Neill
President

Thursday

Dear Friend:

I'm writing to ask your help for a very quiet organization that does a great deal of good, the Space Studies Institute.

SSI is unique-- it conducts hard-science research aimed directly at developing space resources for human benefit. SSI works to achieve humanity's breakout from the planet Earth to the unlimited resources of free energy and materials in space.

The Institute is in its twelfth year, having completed scores of research projects. It is currently funding projects in two areas.

One is the materials processing area. SSI is developing glass-glass composites. These materials will be the building blocks for space construction. They are durable, yet light-weight and can be made entirely from lunar soil. SSI is also exploring ways to separate the useful elements from lunar soil.

The second major area of research is space exploration. SSI is currently designing a space probe to orbit the Moon. This probe, the Lunar Prospector, will chemically map the entire surface of the Moon, providing a comprehensive chart of resources for future use. The probe is scheduled for completion in 1992.

All Space Studies Institute Research Projects are designed to utilize space resources for humankind within our lifetimes and to reduce the pollution of environments, in space and on Earth.

The Institute plans to carry out the research and development necessary to provide all the technical verification for an action plan to develop an industrial system in space.

A company, a nation, or a consortium can then implement SSI's plan over the following five years, with a total investment comparable to what was spent on the Alaska Pipeline.

Opening large-scale industry in space will be the first step toward space colonies, (such as the one featured in the enclosed brochure) extending humanity's ecological range throughout the solar system and ultimately to the stars.

Will you help us by becoming a Member with a tax-deductible gift of $500, $250, $100, $50 or even $25? Your membership gift will help further SSI's research. And in return, for gifts of $25 or more, I will see that you are kept abreast of our important work through SSI's excellent newsletter, "Update."

Our work is building a free, peaceful, exciting future both for our country and for the world. I would be honored by your joining me in that great endeavor.

Sincerely,

Gerard K. O'Neill

Gerard K. O'Neill
President

P.S. With a gift of $50 or more, I will send you an SSI lapel pin, and with a gift of $100 or more, I will send you a signed copy of my book The High Frontier.

CLIP AND MAIL

Space Studies Institute
P.O. Box 82
Princeton, New Jersey 08542
Telephone: (609) 921-0377
FAX: (609) 921-0389

Membership Reply

☐ **YES,** I want to help make the dream of space colonies and space manufacturing a reality. Count on me as a Sustaining Member of the Space Studies Institute. To further the Institute's critical research work here is my tax deductible gift of:

☐ $200 ☐ $100 ☐ $75 ☐ $50 ☐ $25 ☐ Other _____

Please make your check payable to "Space Studies Institute."

Master Charge   Visa   Exp. Date _____   Card No. _____

Signature _____

Name_____

Address_____

For your membership donation to SSI you will receive the Institute's excellent bi-monthly newsletter "Update," an SSI membership card and decal.

For gifts of $50 or more, you will receive an SSI lapel pin.

With gifts of $100 or more, you will receive a signed copy of Dr. O'Neill's book, The High Frontier.

For our records, may we have your telephone number?

Home (____) _____

Appendix 1-5: The solicitation letter the Space Studies Institute (SSI) sent out in September 1990 that was sent to Preston Carter and me, by a friend, a couple of days after I drafted the letter reproduced in Appendix 1-4. This SSI letter again portrayed the Lunar Prospector Mission as solely an SSI venture, rather than a cooperative program between SSI and Lunar Exploration Inc., and confirmed that SSI had not lived up to its duties defined in the Consortium Agreement. Instead of starting to solicit the several million dollars we needed for the construction of the spacecraft in the fall of 1989, so we could start construction immediately after the completion of the design study in June 1990, SSI was starting a halfhearted attempt to solicit the money nearly a year late. That fact added to the concerns Preston and I had concerning SSI's ability to support the project (also see www.lunar-research-institute.org).

This lunar mapping mission is brought to you by ... Oct 18 1990

BY MIKE YUEN
OF THE HOUSTON POST STAFF

For months, Houston aerospace engineers Alan Binder and Preston Carter wondered how they could inexpensively fulfill their grand ambition of launching the first lunar science mission in two decades.

The talk in the international space community was that the mission, the complete mapping of the lunar surface, couldn't be done for less than $500 million.

Well, Binder and Carter believe it will cost them much less — only $11.7 million in contributions, donated time and material for technical and administrative support and not much more for liftoff.

Their solution? Turn to corporate donations and volunteer brainpower that join capitalism and science in an unusual space-age marriage.

Their project, which also has gained contributions from the American and Soviet space agencies along with donated work from moonlighting engineers, will bring the advertising-filled look of the Indianapolis 500 race track to the launch pad.

Prominently emblazoned on the sides of the Soviet launch rocket that is to carry the Lunar Prospector satellite into space will be the name of a major sponsor for the first corporate-sponsored, privately organized mission to the moon.

Coca-Cola or McDonald's perhaps? Jon Reed and Michael F. Lawson of Space Marketing Concepts of Atlanta, who are promoting the launch, won't say.

Reed does believe, however, that the promotional possibilities are seemingly endless. A corporate spon-

☐ NASA budget may hinder
space station plans/**A-31**

sor could hold "an educational promotion" where an American youth winning a contest linked to the launch could be flown to the Soviet space complex at Baikonur in the central Asian republic of Kazakhstan to push the button that blasts off the Lunar Prospector.

Corporations that might sponsor the lunar mission have more in mind

Please see **MISSION**, A-31

MISSION: Moon-mapping trip to be financed by corporations

From A-23

than increasing their name recognition, Reed said. With President Bush pushing for the establishment of a lunar base as a stepping stone for a mission to Mars, the astronauts manning the base will have to have a food supply and other services.

Possible corporate sponsors of the Lunar Prospector, Reed said, "want to provide those services on the moon."

A corporate logo will also be placed inside the Lunar Prospector. "So it will be accurate to say that the spacecraft will be carrying the name of its sponsor," said Binder, the mission's project manager who is on leave from Lockheed Engineering & Science Co.

Binder, Reed, Lawson and others associated with the project insist that the marketing of the mission won't overshadow the scientific benefits from the Lunar Prospector's mapping mission. The data from the satellite should prove useful in determining where to establish the lunar base that is a centerpiece of President Bush's moon-Mars initiative, Binder said.

The probe, scheduled to be launched in 1992 on a yearlong mission, will be using a gamma-ray spectrometer to search for deposits of "water ice," possibly enough to fill Lake Erie. The instrument was left over from the Apollo program of the late 1960s and early 1970s and is on loan from the National Aeronautics and Space Administration.

"I think, as everyone knows, water is obviously necessary for life support," Binder said. "Water can be broken down into oxygen and hydrogen for both breathing and rocket fuel — most of our rockets have liquid oxygen and liquid hydrogen as their propellants. So if we go there and find this water ice and if we can commercially utilize it, we can cut the cost of the lunar base. It would have enormous impact on the economics of lunar exploration."

The Lunar Prospector would also search for iron and titanium, which could be used to build the moon base, Binder said.

The 291-pound spacecraft, which resembles an oil barrel with three long toothpicks sticking out of it, would also produce the first

Gaylon Wampler/The Houston Post

Project director Alan Binder adjusts the lunar mockup.

complete map of the lunar gravity field, providing the information that will allow follow-up missions to save fuel when soaring over a particular region, Binder added.

"This is a private mission," Binder said.

Preston Carter, the Lunar Prospector's project engineer who is employed by Space Industries Inc.

in Webster near the Johnson Space Center, said Lunar Exploration did explore having a U.S. commercial space firm provide the launch vehicle for the moon probe.

But project leaders decided to accept the Soviet offer for launch services to make the project international and a symbol of East-West cooperation.

Appendix 1-6: A newspaper article that appeared in the Houston Post as a result of the Lunar Exploration Inc. Press Conference that was held on October 17, 1990 (also see www.lunar-research-institute.org).

Space Studies Institute
P.O. Box 82
Princeton, New Jersey 08542
Telephone: (609) 921-0377
FAX: (609) 921-0389

Gerard K. O'Neill
President

Gregg E. Maryniak
Executive Vice President

October 23, 1990

Dr. Alan Binder
Mr. Preston Carter
Lunar Exploration, Inc.
3027 Marina Bay Drive
Suite 110
League City, TX 77573

Re: Lunar Prospector Project

Gentlemen:

        Statements and activities surrounding the recent LEI
Press Conference in Houston have come to our attention which
violate both the spirit and letter of agreements between LEI
and SSI. More to the point, these statements and activities
threaten to destroy the work we have done to date in building credibility for the mission and mission concept and
could make it impossible to secure launch services and
other critical support for Lunar Prospector.

        The most serious damage to the project arises from
statements in the press release and quotes which you gentlemen apparently made to United Press International regarding
Soviet launch of the spacecraft. As you well know, negotiations and discussions in this area are delicate and ongoing
in nature. In good faith we have kept you apprised of these
discussions, including sending you a copy of the letter of
intent procured over the summer as a result of lengthy
efforts. The head of NPO Energia will be visiting the
Institute this week to further these discussions. You are
also aware that we have yet to pass through the very serious
hurdles attendant to securing export license approval for
the launch of the spacecraft. Despite these facts, you are
quoted as saying that the "Soviet Space Agency has pledged
to provide a rocket free of charge" and that "LEI has secured a firm commitment from the Soviet Space Agency to
launch the satellite in 1992".

In addition, contrary to our discussions and the
language contained in the Memorandum Of Understanding between LEI and SSI, LEI continues to make reference to a 1992
launch date in both the press releases and the UPI quotes.
This has the potential to both a) destroy our credibility
and 2) to block totally any hopes of getting approval for a
non-western bloc launch.

I received an urgent call today from the U.S. Department of Commerce regarding this matter. I was forcefully
warned of the impact that the above inopportune comments has
on our ability to carry out this mission. It is imperative
that you clear any discussions regarding the possibilities
of the launch on a Soviet vehicle with us prior to making
such comments. If pressed on the subject, I suggest that
you simply state that negotiations are underway with several launch service providers including the Soviets.

More generally, we need to immediately correct the
serious violations of our operational agreements evidenced
in these recent activities. For example, the first paragraph of section three of our recent Memorandum of Understanding specifically refers to using the International
Space Year time frame as a launch target (rather than 1992
calendar year.)

LEI also agrees to acknowledge the role of SSI in
initiating and conducting the Lunar Prospector project.
However, neither the press release nor the UPI quotes make
any reference to SSI's role in the project despite references to areas where SSI has almost exclusively, or in some
cases exclusively provided items refered to in the release.

The third paragraph says that both parties agree to
maintain an open flow of information about the project.
Obviously, we need to do this if the project is to survive
and yet were not advised of the change in date of the press
conference until it became impossible for us to participate.
Furthermore, in a chance voice mail comment it was mentioned
that Preston was flying to New York to meet with a potential
sponsor for the project. We were given no notification, no
opportunity to participate, and no basic information about
an activity in our own backyard.

It is particularly disturbing to see these problems arising in light of your own requests to us to increase our sensitivity to recognition of LEI's interest.

I believe that you and we are in fundamental agreement about one thing. We have invested heavily in the success of this project in a multitude of ways and it would be tragic if the project should die as a result of unfortunate statements made in haste as we try to generate much needed support. We take a long view of this mission having worked on it for five years in various incarnations. I understand your view that we desperately need to obtain major funding to now and maintain momentum in order to succeed. However, unless we rectify the present situation and are successful in controlling the damage already done, the project will die anyway.

The purpose of this letter is to put you on notice of the actual and potential effects of the aforementioned activities and statements. These comments are made without malice. We must coordinate our efforts immediately if this effort is to survive.

Sincerely,

Gregg E. Maryniak

Appendix 1-7: A letter that Gregg Maryniak faxed to Preston Carter and me, justifiably complaining about statements Preston had made in our less than successful Lunar Exploration Inc. Press Conference that was held on October 17, 1990 — statements that I, too, was unhappy about. That was the second time in the history of the project that Gregg and I were on the same side of an issue that related to the management of the project, rather than being opponents, as was usually the case (also see www.lunar-research-institute.org).

НАУЧНО-ПРОИЗВОДСТВЕННОЕ
ОБЪЕДИНЕНИЕ
„ЭНЕРГИЯ"
─────

141070 г. Калининград, Московской обл.
Телеграфный «ГРАНИТ»

Gregg Maryniak
Space Studies Institute (SSI)
P.O. Box 82
Princeton, NJ 08542

Dr. Allen Binder
Lunar Exploration Inc. (LEI)
3027 Marina Bay Dr. Suite 110
League City, Tx 77573

Mike Lawson
Felco Inc.
8601 Dunwoody Place, Suite 144
Atlanta, GA 30350

Anthony Arrott
Payload Systems, Inc.
276 Third Street
Cambridge, MA 02142

November 1, 1990

Dear Mr. Maryniak & Dr. Binder

During our visit to Houston we were pleased to see the progress of the Lunar
Prospector project. We wish to commit to launch services. In order to advance our
negotiations beyond our letter of interest of June 28, 1990, NPO Energia would like to
invite SSI, LEI, Felco Inc. and Payload Systems representatives to the U.S.S.R. within
the next 30 days to finalize launch vehicle details. Please send us your travel plans so
that the proper arrangements can be made.

Regards,

Yuri P. Semyenov
General Designer of ENPO

2.11 90

Appendix 1-8: The letter from Yuri Semyenov indicating that NPO Energia wanted to commit to the launch of Lunar Prospector and wanted to invite us to go to Moscow in December 1990 to finalize the deal (also see www.lunar-research-institute.org).

Synthesis Group

Mr. Mike Lawson
President
Space Marketing Concepts
8601 Dunwoody Place #144
Atlanta, Georgia   30350

NOV 28 1990

Dear Mike:

On behalf of the Synthesis Group, I would like to thank you and Jon Reed, Alan Binder, and Preston Carter of Lunar Exploration, Inc., and Greg Maryniak and Chris Faranetta of Space Studies Institute for presenting your Lunar Prospector project to our group.

As you are aware, the Synthesis Group, as charged under President Bush's Outreach Program, has spent the last several months reviewing and evaluating various models and approaches on returning to the Moon and ultimately accomplishing a manned landing on Mars. Your Lunar Prospector project appears to be an innovative and timely (1992 launch projection) mission to initiate the important goals we are recommending for the American space program.

Please keep George Abbey and myself informed of your progress and let either of us know of any assistance we may be toward the success of your project.

Sincerely,

Thomas P. Stafford, Lt. Gen. USAF (Ret.)
Chairman, Synthesis Group

1225 Jefferson Davis Highway, Suite 1501
Arlington, VA 22202
Phone: 557-5544 - FAX: (703) 557-5502

Appendix 1-9: The letter Astronaut Tom Stafford wrote on behalf of the Lunar Prospector Project after we had presented our case to the Synthesis Group that Tom chaired (also see www.lunar-research-institute.org).

National Aeronautics and
Space Administration

Washington, D.C.
20546

JUL 25 1991

Reply to Attn of:

SL

Dr. Alan Binder
12602 Ponderosa Drive
Dickinson, TX 77539

Dear Dr. Binder:

Your letter of June 25, 1991, to Admiral Richard Truly,
reporting on the progress of your planning for the Lunar
Prospector mission, has been referred to this office for reply.

We were interested to hear that your organization, Lunar
Exploration, Inc., which is planning the Lunar Prospector
mission in cooperation with the Space Studies Institute, no
longer plans to use the Apollo Gamma-Ray Spectrometer which NASA
agreed to provide for the mission. While that conclusion may
have been disappointing to you, we certainly understand that an
acceptable modification and refurbishment effort could have been
a substantial undertaking.

On the issue of future NASA support for the Lunar Prospector
mission, the Solar System Exploration Division would consider
the possibility of providing support for the mission on two
conditions:

1. The mission, including the science goals and payload,
    must pass the same critical peer review and evaluation
    process by the planetary science community that is
    applied to all proposed future planetary missions.

2. The mission must be selected for inclusion in the Office
    of Space Science and Applications' Strategic Plan, in
    competition with all other candidate space science
    missions.

We appreciate your interest in lunar exploration. I hope this
letter will be helpful in defining the conditions under which
the possibility of NASA support for the Lunar Prospector mission
could be considered.

Sincerely,

Wesley T. Huntress, Jr.
Director
Solar System Exploration Division
Office of Space Science and Applications

Appendix 1-10: The letter from Wes Huntress in which he responded negatively, in typical NASA bureaucratic lingo, to a
progress report I had sent to NASA Administrator, Admiral Richard Truly somewhat earlier (also see www.lunar-research-insti-
tute.org).

Lockheed Missiles & Space Company, Inc.

Sunnyvale, California 94088-3504 (408) 742-6211

John N. McMahon
President & CEO

July 1, 1992

Dr. Alan Binder
Lunar Exploration Inc. President and
Lunar Prospector Project Manager
Lunar Exploration, Inc.
12602 Ponderosa Drive
Dickinson, TX 77539

Dear Dr. Binder:

In the absence of D. M. Tellep, I am responding to your letter
of July 1 regarding the Lunar Prospector.

We appreciate your interest in this program but we do not
find it within Lockheed's plans to participate at this time.

Thank you for your consideration.

Sincerely,

John N. McMahon

cc: D. M. Tellep
R. P. Parten

Appendix 1-11: The short rejection letter from John McMahon, President and CEO of Lockheed Missiles & Space Company, I received in response to my request that Lockheed give the Lunar Prospector Project a million dollars and other forms of support (also see www.lunar-research-institute.org).

Lunar Prospector

Lunar Exploration, Inc.
12602 Ponderosa Dr.
Dickinson, TX 77539
409/925-7012

Date: July 16, 1993

Dr. Gary Coutler
Code SL
NASA Headquarters
D Street SW
Washington, DC 20546

Dear Dr. Coutler:

Enclosed you will find an unsolicited proposal to the Discovery Program requesting support for the Lunar Prospector (LP) Project. The Project was initiated in 1988 as an attempt to conduct the first privately organized and commercially funded lunar mission. This polar orbit mapping project is being conducted by Lunar Exploration, Inc. (LEI), a non-profit. tax-exempt corporation setup to support the National space effort.

The LEI staff consists mainly of volunteer aerospace engineers from the Johnson Space Center area and scientists form the lunar community. This group of experienced professionals contribute long hours after work, on weekends and even vacations to lend their talents to the development of this exciting venture because they are totally committed to the rekindling of a vigorous space exploration program. This dedicated team has remained intact throughout the "roller coaster" events of five years as promising financial backing again and again failed to materialize. **Our team will make this mission a success for the Discovery program.**

Our goals are to demonstrate that small, lunar (and planetary) missions can be done quickly and inexpensively using existing technology, i.e. ""faster, better, cheaper". Throughout the development of Lunar Prospector we have remained focused on these goals. We believe this project can open the door to a new way of performing space missions: small capable staff, existing technology and modest budgets while providing significant accomplishments. Also, these small missions invite the concept of commercialization.

As you will see from our proposal and the enclosures, we have achieved considerable support from the non-government community, from NASA officials (Adm. Truly, Dr. Goldin, Dr. Cohen, Mr. Huffstetler), many Congressmen and the Russians, and have received much favorable press.

Lunar Prospector is at a high level of maturity - we are ready for spacecraft and instrument construction. Our budget, including the costs of the one year nominal mapping mission, is $19,529,000. We have two competitive bids for launch services of $22 million and $22.5 million or less. Thus, the total cost of Lunar Prospector Project is about $40,000,000. We can, if funded by this fall, be ready for launch in the fall of 1995. Thus, LEI can provide SL with an inexpensive, quick, simple and reliable mission with which to start the Discovery Program and demonstrate to NASA, the Congress, and the public that the Discovery goals are readily achievable.

We are confident that Code SL will recognize the value of Lunar Prospector as the initial Discovery mission.

If you have any question regarding Lunar Exploration, Inc., or the Lunar Prospector Project, please contact me.

Sincerely yours,

Dr. Alan Binder
Lunar Exploration, Inc. President and
Lunar Prospector Project Manager

CC W. Huntress
   D. Goldin
   A. Cohen
   W. Huffstetler
   Congressman J. Brooks
   Senator K. B. Hutchinson

Appendix 1-12: The cover letter for the Unsolicited Proposal I sent to NASA requesting support for the Lunar Prospector Project (also see www.lunar-research-institute.org).

≡⚡ Lockheed *Missiles & Space Company, Inc.*

1111 Lockheed Way, Sunnyvale, California 94088-3504

October 11, 1994

Alan Binder
Principle Investigator
Lunar Explorer Program
Dept. N1-01, Building 107
Lockheed Missiles and Space Co.

Dear Dr Binder:

Lockheed Launch Vehicles and Services is pleased to respond to your request of October 5, 1994. Many of the questions contained in your inquiry will require further technical interchange in order to develop appropriate answers. This letter provides a cost estimate to enable you to move forward with your proposal for a NASA Discovery Program mission phase B study. We will work with you during the study to develop launch requirements, optimize injection strategies and define the interfaces and services to the level required for a fixed price quotation.

The performance requirements stated in your letter can be met with an LLV2 and a STAR 37FM kick motor. This combination will inject a mass of 397kg. on a lunar trajectory with a C3 of -2. This provides nearly 150 kg of margin for payload growth and trajectory trades.

The LLV&S plans for an injection stage are not sufficiently mature to enable the requested price and schedule commitment for a developed stage. Therefore we are proposing to supply an LLV2, and the STAR motor separately and quote the integration of the motor with the satellite/launch vehicle as a separate task. Prior to release at time of injection, the LLV would properly orient the spacecraft/kick motor, spin it up, then separate. The injection burn would be under spacecraft control.

The projected price of a LLV2 is $22M. This includes all launch related costs except reflight insurance if required. The STAR 37 motor can be supplied for an additional $2M. This would include the safe and arm device and lease of the necessary handling equipment, LLV effort in support of the design and integration of the kick motor into the system is estimated at $1M for a total of $25M.

We will assist you during your phase B study to define your requirements and supply the remainder of the data requested. We will also keep you apprised of our planned injection stage as it matures. Potentially it may provide a more cost effective solution to your requirements than the spin stabilized approach.
Sincerely,

Don E. Damon
Program Manager
Lockheed Launch Vehicles and Services

Appendix 2-1: The unsigned letter Don Damon sent to me during the Lunar Prospector Proposal effort in the fall of 1994, confirming that Lockheed Launch Vehicles and Services would launch Lunar Prospector to its translunar trajectory on a Lockheed Launch Vehicle 2 (LLV2) with a Star-37 kick motor for $25 million (also see www.lunar-research-institute.org).

Williamson, Mary Ann

From: Dan Cathcart
Sent: Tuesday, September 23, 1997 8:23 AM
To: Maryann Williamson
Subject: Binder's Ch4 shot

>Mime-Version: 1.0
>Date: Sat, 20 Sep 1997 14:27:24 -0700
>To: dmorse@mail.arc.nasa.gov, Tom.Dougherty@lmco.com
>From: Scott Hubbard <shubbard@mail.arc.nasa.gov>
>Subject: Binder's Ch4 shot
>Cc: sacox@mail.arc.nasa.gov,
>   "Lisa Chu-Thielbar" <lchu-thielbar@mail.arc.nasa.gov>,
>   dcathcart@mail.arc.nasa.gov
>Status:
>
>I am told that Alan appeared on the Channel 4 News last night with an
>interview and video shot of the current spacecraft. It appears that the
>spacecraft video was shot very recently in in Bldg 150. I want this event
>checked and verified. The reason I am concerned is a)We all agreed to
>coordinate PR events which utilize the fully complete spacecraft so as not
>to scoop or undercut each other, b)there are clearly security issues with
>unauthorized news crews shooting in potentially sensitive areas, c)LP is a
>government funded project and it is government policy to not grant
>"exclusives" to any particular media outlet.
>
>If the event occured as described to me then several things follow:
>1)It was my understanding that LMMS was very sensitive to and careful about
>cameras in the spacecraft areas (indeed in all of LMMS). While I don't
>know that I can impact LMMS security I would think that LMMS might want to
>take steps to monitor, control and restrict Binder's/LRI's access to
>spacecraft areas with camera and/or news crews.
>
>2)Further press events must be cleared with the Mission Office and Ames
>Code DX. If this Channel 4 event occurred with Buddy Nelson's knowledge
>and/or assistance then as far as I am concerned he is off the program
>effective   immediately.
>
>3)I want Dan Cathcart to evaulate modifying Binder's LRI subcontract
>modified to clearly establish that widely braodcast media contacts must be
>cleared with the Mission Office. I think that any science release is
>covered, but I am concerned about other activities.
>
>4)It is clearly unacceptable to have this happen in the future -
>particularly with the possibility for similar events in the Ames control
>room. I want Code DX to establish clear guidelines with Security that
>media (especially electronic media) covering LP are absolutely not allowed
>to enter Ames property without the express permission of Code DX and the LP
>Mission Office. I believe that this is SOP, but I want to be sure.
>
>Please report to me as soon as possible on Monday what happened.
>-Scott

Page 1

Appendix 3-1: The email NASA/Ames Scott Hubbard originally sent to Ames's Dan Cathcart in a fit of childish anger, without bothering to find out what the fact of the situation were, and that Dan forwarded to Lockheed's Maryann Williamson, that led to my being locked out of Lockheed like a common criminal (also see www.lunar-research-institute.org).

Subject: ALAN BINDER'S APPEARANCE ON CHANNEL 4/SEPT. 19, 1997
Date: Thu, 25 Sep 1997 18:05:38 -0700 (PDT)
From: David Morse <dmorse@mail.arc.nasa.gov>
To: Tom.Dougherty@lmco.com
CC: buddy1@home.com, shubbard@mail.arc.nasa.gov, ecarter1@mail.arc.nasa.gov,
sacox@mail.arc.nasa.gov, lchu-thielbar@mail.arc.nasa.gov

Folks,
Whoops!

Regarding the subject topic, I think that it is only fair to CONFESS that
Buddy Nelson of Lockheed Martin did, indeed, call me around noon on the day
of the interview and tell me that it was scheduled for later that
afternoon. Frankly, occuring as it did the day before the Ames Open House,
it was in one ear and out the other -- with no apparent slowing down in
between.

But, the fact is, Buddy DID call, I acknowledged that the interview was
going to be conducted, and I offered no objection. Had I given this
additional thought, which I would normally have done, I may (but, perhaps
not -- I'm not the brightest thing!) have questioned the timing or the
advisability of what looks like "an exclusive."   But, in any event, the
fact is I DIDN'T!

>From my limited perspective, MY real concern here (which may differ from
that of others) is not the notification process, but the use of
non-inclusive language by on camera personnel. I know that it comes from
passion for the project and is not intended to be a negative -- but I
continue to urge against it. THAT, to me, is the problem, not the
notification process.

I sincerely apologize for my forgetfulness and for not notifying the
mission office that Lockheed Martin/Buddy Nelson had called me and informed
me of his plan for this interview. I have suggested to Buddy that he drop
me a note (plus my Ames PAO colleague Betsy Carter --
ecarter1@mail.arc.nasa.gov) in writing next time and be sure to copy Scott
Hubbard of the Mission office. That way my schedule, absence, tardiness,
or forgetfulness will not be an issue in our communications and
interrelations.

I regret any inconvenience or frustration that has resulted from my benign
neglect and attention to other things. Sorry! Can we all still be friends
and working "buds?" I hope so!

Cheers. drm

Appendix 3-2: The "Whoops!" email Ames's PR person, David Morse, sent to all the individuals involved in Scott's Hubbard's
fiasco (Appendix 3-1) — except the victim, me — explaining that Lockheed's Buddy Nelson had indeed properly informed
NASA/Ames about my appearance in a Channel 4 TV interview and that he, David, had dropped the ball (also see www.lunar-
research-institute.org).

Subject: FW: Dr. Binder's Access
Date: Tue, 23 Sep 1997 11:15:27 -0700
From: "Nelson. Buddy" <BNelson@svl.ems.lmco.com>
To: buddy1@home.com

```
-----------
From:    Williamson, Mary Ann
Sent:    Tuesday, September 23, 1997 11:12:01 AM
To:      Dougherty, Tom; Garner, Robert
Cc:      Pappas, Jim; Larson, Bergman L; Palochak, John; Nelson, Buddy;
'Cathcart, Dan'; Dunbar, Peter
Subject:      Dr. Binder's Access
Importance:   High
Auto forwarded by a Rule
```

Because of the seriousness of NASA letter to me regarding Dr. Binder's
unauthorized filming of the LP spacecraft by the Channel 4 news group, I
have removed Dr. Binder's access to all buildings here at LM Sunnyvale
except for building 107. Dr. Binder will need to be escorted by Ms.
Berman-Larson for any trips he needs to make to view the spacecraft.
Also, Mr. Nelson will need to be notified each and every time Dr. Binder
shows the spacecraft to any outside group, and Dr. Binder will need to
clear any public releases with both Mr. Nelson, LP Program and NASA
prior to release.

Mr. Palochak and I are relooking Clause 18 (Public Information Release
Policy) of Dr. Binder's subcontract per NASA's request. We are to
provide a response to NASA today.

Appendix 3-3: The email Lockheed's Maryann Williamson wrote in response to the Scott Hubbard's email (Appendix 3-1) that started the lockout procedure that ended with my being locked out of Lockheed like a common criminal for several days (also see www.lunar-research-institute.org).

Lunar Research Institute

Director: Alan Binder, Ph.D.
1180 Sunrise Dr.
Gilroy, CA 95020
(408) 847-0969
Jan. 15, 1998   **CONFIDENTIAL**

Via FAX and U.S. Mail

Dr. Wesley Huntress
Code S
NASA Headquarters
Washington, DC

Dear Wes:

I am writing you to apprise you of a disturbing situation regarding Scott Hubbard's role in the Lunar Prospector (LP) mission and to ask that you immediately remove Scott from the LP Team, both in his capacity as the NASA Program Manager and as one of the Co-Investigators.

I did not bring this to your attention earlier because I only realized in the last few months the full extent to which Scott has been manipulating the management of LP and at that point in time, I did not want the focus of the LP team to be drawn away from the then upcoming critical events of launch and LP's insertion into its mapping orbit. Now that LP has safely started its mapping mission, I am regretfully turning some of my limited time to correcting this situation.

Three years ago, when I added Lockheed-Martin and Ames to my long standing LP Team of Co-Investigators, I asked Scott to be the NASA Center Partner Manager. I did so because it appeared that we shared a common view as to how Discovery Missions should be conducted. This view was <u>exactly</u> that defined in the pre-AO materials, in the first AO and in the NASA pamphlet on the Discovery Program, all of which clearly stated that the **responsibility of the mission was to be in the hands of the Principal Investigator** who selected his team of Co-Investigators, an Industry Partner and, **only if desired, a NASA Center Partner with NASA's role being <u>limited to</u> "<u>minimum</u> oversight, review and program control".**

I was both pleased and assured when you confirmed NASA's commitment to the above principles at the Feb. 28, 1995, Discovery Program news conference, and I quote *"We (NASA) more or less turned the old way of doing business upside down. The old way was community support of NASA missions. The new way is NASA support of community missions. The old way was community participation in NASA missions. The new way is NASA **participation in*** *community missions, and only as an option. In the Discovery Program the federal government is in essence essentially purchasing missions from the university and aerospace community. Discovery missions are to be managed by a single Principal Investigator ... and that PI is solely responsible for the mission."*

While Scott and I maintained an excellent working relationship during the first two years of the program, I gradually became aware during the last year that Scott has been improperly using his position as a NASA official to usurp the responsibility of the mission for himself, to attempt to take on the mantel of the leader of LP and to unilaterally reduce the role of the PI of the mission to that of a traditional project scientist. As one result of two discussions we had about this, I became aware that Scott is driven by an intense desire to rapidly advance within the NASA Ames management hierarchy and to help preserve Ames as a viable NASA Center by demonstrating his capabilities as LP's self-proclaimed leader.

While I do not object to Scott's advancing his career and helping to maintain Ames as a natural outcome of the mutually beneficial partnership as was initially proposed to - and accepted by - your office, I do vehemently object when these efforts are done at the expense of the principles upon which both the Discovery Program and the LP Mission are based. On a personal level, the LP volunteers and I did not work for nine years to have a NASA official, of any rank, come in at the end and take over the leadership of - and the bulk of the credit for - LP.

As partially documented in the enclosures, a few examples of Scott's attempts to take the leadership role of LP for himself began innocently enough by him insisting that he and Sylvia Cox, the NASA management team, be listed first as key personnel on the NASA PR materials (e.g., see 1st attached LP Fact Sheet) and the Lockheed-Martin Project Manager and PI be listed second. This has now been extended to having me and my institute listed third (the excuse is that technically my non-profit, tax exempt corporation, Lunar Research Institute [LRI], is a sub-contractor to Lockheed-Martin) on the new editions of the PR materials printed after LRI had been officially established (e.g., see 2nd attached Fact Sheet).

Similarly, NASA News Releases which originate at Ames with Scott's approval, seldom, if ever, mention the role of the PI, just Scott, Ames and Lockheed-Martin (e.g., see attached NASA NewsRelease from March, 1997)).

About a year ago, Scott stopped Buddy Nelson (a Lockheed PR representative) from responding positively to a Channel 4 TV request to do an interview with me on the now transparent excuse that it would interfere with a NASA Ames news conference planned for March, 1997, during which the spacecraft was first shown to the press and the public. Buddy responded to Scott that he would delay the interview until after the Ames news conference, after which any concern of "exclusivity" is absurd, and at the appropriate time proceeded to get the standard

Lockheed-Martin camera clearance and notify Ames of the Sept. 22, 1997, date (see attached email from Ames' D. Morse to Lockheed-Martin's T. Dougherty, Subject: Alan Binder's appearance on channel 4/Sept. 19, 1997). When Scott heard (not saw) that I was on TV, without even doing me the professional courtesy of calling me and asking me about the interview, he sent the attached email to Ames' Dan Cathcart, who immediately emailed it to Lockheed-Martin's Maryann Williams (see attached email from S. Hubbard to D. Morse, D. Cathcart and others, as forwarded to Maryann, Subject: Binder's Ch4 shot). Cathcart then called and gave Maryann a stern lecture on how I was to be treated and stated that my sub-contract must be unilaterally changed. Maryann called me and said that I had to come to Lockheed immediately. When I arrived, I found that my magnet key card no longer worked! I had been "locked out" of the Lockheed-Martin facilities, preventing me from accessing the very spacecraft on which I worked daily with the engineers. As a direct result of Scott's outrageous, unilateral, and erratic behavior, I was locked out of Lockheed-Martin like a common criminal for a full week, during which I had to be escorted into the various buildings (see attached email from Maryann to Dougherty et al., Subject: Dr. Binder's Access)! As a result of this outrageous series of events and treatment of a PI, I began to seriously question Scott's motives, behavior and leadership role in LP.

When I retired from Lockheed-Martin in August, 1997, and started carrying out my PI duties as the Director of LRI, I asked Scott to have all future printings of NASA PR materials changed to reflect my status with the institute. After this request, Scott has, among other things, refused to have the institute's name added to the new printing of the LP sticker. It still appears that just NASA Ames and Lockheed-Martin are the organizations responsible for LP (see attached copy of the sticker; excuse: the art work could not be changed!).

Later, during launch preparations, Scott blocked having the LRI logo added to the launch vehicle. Several weeks earlier, when I asked to have the logo added to the vehicle, I was informed via Sylvia Cox that it was far too late to do so. While at the Cape, I found that this was not the case and I had a LRI decal made in a few hours and gave it to the launch preparation crew who were still adding contractor and subcontractor decals to the vehicle. A day later I was told that Scott had vetoed the addition of the LRI logo to the rocket. There is simply no rational excuse for excluding the Logo of the institute of the PI from the launch vehicle! This insult is as outrageous as having been locked out of Lockheed-Martin because of Scott's tyrannical behavior.

Not only have Scott's attempts to take credit for LP come to my attention, the community at large has also taken note of it. Two months ago, a friend of mine said that a reporter had asked him "What is going on with Lunar Prospector, why are NASA and Lockheed trying to pretend that Alan Binder does not exist?" Similarly, since the NASA invitations to the launch came out, I have had several calls asking why neither LRI nor the PI are mentioned in either the invitation or the description of the mission enclosed in the invitation.

Because of the magnitude of Scott's interference with my contractual rights and intellectual property rights as the originator and PI of LP, I have ask the LRI lawyers to advise me regarding the legal options that are available to me. Though I do not now intend to take legal action against Scott, I do not exclude the possibility in the future.

As a result of Scott's increasingly disturbing and unethical behavior, I no longer have any personal or professional confidence in his playing any further role in LP. Thus I ask that you immediately removed Scott from the LP management and science teams and immediately prohibit him from any further interference with the operations of the LP mission. I look forward to your prompt response to this urgent matter.

Sincerely yours,

Alan Binder
Lunar Prospector Principal Investigator

cc: Mr. H. McDonald, Director, Ames Research Center
    Mr. J. Muncy, Congressional Aide, Science & Aeronautics Sub-Committee
    Mr. J. Paul, Congressional Aide, House Science Committee
    Mr. T. Greenwalt, Vinson & Elkins
    Mr. D. Weaver, Vinson & Elkins

Appendix 4-1: The letter I sent to Wes Huntress requesting the removal of Scott Hubbard from the Lunar Prospector Project (also see www.lunar-research-institute.org).

Lunar Research Institute

Director: Alan Binder, PhD
1180 Sunrise Dr.
Gilroy, CA 95020
(408) 847-0969

Feb. 12, 1998

Mr. M.R. Brashears
Space & Strategic Missiles Sector
Lockheed-Martin
6801 Rockledge Dr.
Bathesda, MD 20817

Dear Mel:

As you are well aware, Lunar Prospector has successfully begun its mapping mission of the Moon. The flawless performance of the spacecraft and the science instruments is a full conformation of the concepts I had regarding the utility and reliability of small, simple, inexpensive spacecrafts and the quality of Lockheed-Martin engineering and workmanship. Though we are now just one month into the 18 month mapping mission, I have no doubts about its ultimate success and Lockheed-Martin's potential for future missions based on the Lunar Prospector concept.

I want to take this opportunity to thank you for your support when I asked Lockheed to become my Industry Partner just over three years ago. Your foresight paid large dividends for the exploration of the Moon and for Lockheed-Martin.

I also want to take this opportunity to ask for your support in a follow-on matter. As I assume your are aware, I retired from Lockheed-Martin last August and founded the Lunar Research Institute, an Arizona, non-profit, tax exempt corporation [501 (c) (3)] which is dedicated to the scientific study of the Moon and it resources. I am currently conducting the Lunar Prospector Mission on a subcontract from Lockheed-Martin and will receive funding for the data analysis phase of the mission directly from NASA. In order to provide a stable basis from which I can expand the staff and capabilities of the Institute, I am in the process of soliciting philanthropic contributions from various institutions to build an endowment for the Institute.

Given that Lockheed-Martin is getting a $4 million fee for Lunar Prospector, I would like to explore the possibility of Lockheed-Martin contributing $2 million of that fee to the Lunar Research Institute to help start building the endowment. Such a contribution would not only help me in my quest to study the Moon scientifically, but would also help me to develop and promote future exploration missions to the Moon as I did in the case of Lunar Prospector to our mutual benefit.

I again thank your for your support of Lunar Prospector and for your consideration of my request for a philanthropic contribution from Lockheed-Martin to the Lunar Research Institute.

Sincerely yours,

Dr. Alan Binder
Lunar Prospector Principal Investigator

zc: K.M. Henshaw

Appendix 4-2: The letter I sent to Lockheed's Mel Brashears requesting that Lockheed split the $4 million fee it was getting for the Lunar Prospector Project with my non-profit, tax-exempt institute, the Lunar Research Institute (also see www.lunar-research-institute.org).

National Aeronautics and
Space Administration

Headquarters
Washington, DC 20546-0001

Reply to Attn of: SD

FEB 13 1998

Dr. Alan Binder
Principal Investigator
Lunar Prospector
Lunar Research Institute
11805 Sunrise Drive
Gilroy, CA 95020

Dear Dr. Binder:

Thank you for your letter of January 15, 1998. I would like to
congratulate you on the tremendous success of the Lunar
Prospector (LP) mission. After so many years of effort, it must
be particularly gratifying to see your concept for a lunar orbit
mapping mission become a reality. The entire LP team is to be
congratulated on the successful development and launch of the
spacecraft on schedule, within budget, and successfully achieving
the mapping orbit. I look forward to the data return, an answer
to the question of polar ice, and a deeper understanding of the
Moon's origins and evolution.

In reviewing your letter, I am concerned about both the tone of
the document and the issues you raise about NASA's role in the
Discovery program. It is most certainly true that I have
supported and continue to support a strong role for the Principal
Investigator (PI) as the scientific leader of a mission
consortium. However, I must hasten to add that NASA-funded
projects, including Discovery missions, must exist within the
framework established for the oversight and expenditure of public
funds.

In the case of LP, the organization charged by the Office of
Space Science (OSS) with oversight and management responsibility
has been the LP Mission Office located at the Ames Research
Center (ARC). As the agent of NASA Headquarters, the Mission
Office contracted with Lockheed Martin Missiles and Space (LMMS)
to develop the spacecraft, provide the instruments, and,
ultimately, supply data to NASA. Mission operations are being
conducted by a combination of LMMS employees, ARC staff and
facilities, and the science team with you as Mission Director.
It is my understanding that other than the recent change of your
status from an employee of LMMS to Director of the Lunar Research
Institute which will provide your support of mission operations
and data reduction under contract to LMMS, the LP consortium is
functioning essentially as proposed.

While the PI as the central figure in the LP team is accountable
for the scientific success of the mission, the ARC Mission Office
is accountable to NASA Headquarters for overall program success.
Since NASA is required by laws and regulations to perform certain
oversight and fiduciary functions, we do not contemplate changing
the mission office role.   To date, the role of mission manager
has been ably filled by Mr. Scott Hubbard.   We at OSS have every
confidence in Mr. Hubbard's skills and integrity and believe that
he has created a number of innovative techniques for NASA
management of low-cost missions.

It is clear from our knowledge of the parties involved that some
misunderstanding must have occurred.   I ask that you revisit the
issues with Mr. Hubbard with a goal of mutual agreement on the
next steps during the operations phase.   I am confident that we
have the right team in place to achieve full mission success and
begin the process of unraveling the myriad of lunar science
issues facing us.

Sincerely,

Wesley T. Huntress, Jr.
Associate Administrator
    for Space Science

cc:
ARC/200-1/Dr.   McDonald
ARC/200-7/Mr.   Hubbard

Appendix 4-3: Wes Huntress's rejection letter to my request (Appendix 4-1) to have Scott Hubbard removed from the Lunar
Prospector Project (also see www.lunar-research-institute.org).

Lockheed Martin Missiles & Space
1111 Lockheed Martin Way   Sunnyvale, CA 94089
Telephone 408-756-5515   Facsimile 408-742-2858

Michael L. Coats
Vice President
Civil Space Programs

March 10, 1998

Dr. Wesley T. Huntress, Jr.
Associate Administrator for Space Science
National Aeronautics and Space Administration
Headquarters (Code S)
Washington, DC 20546-0001

Dear Dr. Huntress,

The recent letters to you from Dr. Alan Binder highly critical of Mr. Scott Hubbard strike me as unfair and short-sighted.   Dr. Binder has done a truly amazing job of making Lunar Prospector a total success, and his ability to maintain a sharp focus on the mission objectives sets an excellent example for other programs.   Dr. Binder richly deserves all the credit and accolades he is currently receiving.   Likewise, Mr. Hubbard is — and has been — integral to the success of the Lunar Prospector Program, and deserves recognition as well.   The program could not have been accomplished without Mr. Hubbard and his staff at NASA Ames.

The following are specific examples of their contributions:

- The contract, fashioned by Ames, provided timely funding, a motivational fee structure, and no constraints to innovation.   The contractual interface was excellent.

- Highly talented and experienced non-advocate review teams were established to provide well-received technical and programmatic advice.   These reviews were held at critical times in the design, test, and operation phases.

- Mr. Hubbard was totally responsible   for the extensive outreach program established   for Lunar Prospector.   He was also highly involved in the successful public relations program.

- Lockheed Martin was provided access to Ames expertise to support program problems.

- One of the more significant contributions to the program was the provision of the Mission Control Center and the JPL/GSFC services to perform operations. This included facilities, computer systems, personnel, and management.

- Lunar Prospector was not only a faster, better, cheaper spacecraft, constrained by a tight budget and schedule, but was also launched on the first flight of a new launch vehicle (Athena II) and from a new launchpad at Spaceport Florida.

- Mr. Hubbard was able to form an exceptional government, science, and industry team, a goal frequently expoused by NASA. Above all, Mr. Hubbard is the champion of Lunar Prospector at Lockheed Martin, in the press, at NASA HQ, and in the scientific community.

Both Dr. Binder and Mr. Hubbard were — and are — critical to the outstanding success of Lunar Prospector, and both should receive the proper recognition and rewards for their fine work.

Sincerely,

Michael L. Coats

Michael L. Coats, Vice President
Civil Space Programs

cc: Dr. Alan Binder/Lunar Research Institute
      Dr. Earle Hutkins/NASA HQ
      Mr. Scott Hubbard/Ames Research Center
      Dr. Harry McDonald/Ames Research Center

Appendix 4-4: The obsequious letter Lockheed VP, Mike Coats, wrote to NASA Headquarters defending poor Scott Hubbard again my unjust allegations and my request to have him removed from the Lunar Prospector Project (also see www.lunar-research-institute.org).

Lunar Research Institute

Director: Alan Binder, Ph.D.
1180 Sunrise Dr.
Gilroy, CA 95020
(408) 847-0969
March 2, 1998

Mr. Michael L. Coats
Vice President
Civil Space Programs
Lockheed Martin Missiles & Space
1111 Lockheed Martin Way
Sunnyvale, CA 94089

Dear Mike:

Thank you for sending me a copy of the letter you sent to Dr. Huntress on March 10, 1998, in which, in defense of Mr. Hubbard, you enumerate the contributions he and the Ames staff made to the success of Lunar Prospector.

Through, due to your lack of firsthand knowledge of how the program was setup and carriedout, there are gross errors in your assessment of Mr. Hubbard's role in Lunar Prospector, I do not dispute the real contributions that the Ames staff and Mr. Hubbard made to the mission. The concerns I expressed and documented in my letters to Dr. Huntress are with the abuses of authority Mr. Hubbard committed while exercising his role as the NASA Mission Manager, the fact that his activities far exceeded that of "minimum oversight, review and program control" as defined for NASA's role in the Discovery Program, and his denigration of the role the Principal Investigator to that of a project scientist. I have these concerns not only because of their detrimental effect on me, but more importantly because of their detrimental effect on the development of the Discovery Program as a Principal Investigator driven, new way of conducting space exploration.

Though your letter contains the expected response from Lockheed Martin in deference to NASA, I find it unfortunate that in serving Lockheed Martin's self-interests, you completely ignore the serious issues I raised and are only concerned with what you consider to be my unfairness and short-sightedness.

Sincerely yours,'

Alan Binder
Lunar Prospector Principal Investigator

cc: Mr. G.S. Hubbard, Ames Research Center
Dr. W. Huntress, Jr., NASA HQ
Dr. E. Hutkins, NASA HQ
Dr. H. McDonald, Director, Ames Research Center

Appendix 4-5: My reply to Coats's obsequious letter (Appendix 4-4) (also see www.lunar-research-institute.org).

Lockheed Martin Missiles & Space
1111 Lockheed Martin Way   Sunnyvale, CA 94089
Telephone 408·742·5113   Facsimile 408·742·8484

LOCKHEED MARTIN

Janet V. Wrather
Vice President - Communications

September 29, 1998

Alan Binder, Director
Lunar Research Institute
1180 Sunrise Dr.
Gilroy, CA 96020

Dear Alan:

Your letter to Mel Brashears requesting a contribution to the Lunar Research Institute has been referred to Missiles & Space for consideration.

First, congratulations on the phenomenal success of Lunar Prospector. As Principal Investigator for this important scientific endeavor, you are largely responsible for the stellar results that are providing so much new data about the Moon. We at Lockheed Martin are proud to have been able to contribute to this exciting program that continues to unveil discoveries that are astounding the scientific community and the public at large.

As much as we would like to respond positively to your request for funding to further the efforts of the Lunar Research Institute, financial constraints preclude our doing so.

We recently made major financial commitments to several K-12 education projects--a key thrust of Lockheed Martin Corporation. We also must meet ongoing commitments in our local and remote site communities. Because our contributions budget has been trimmed significantly during the last several years, we must unfortunately turn down many viable requests such as yours.

I have taken the liberty of forwarding your letter to Dale Von Haase of Lockheed Martin Corporation. Dale administers funds for research efforts of interest to the Corporation, and will evaluate your request from a Corporate perspective.

In closing, I want to emphasize that we are vigorously promoting the Lunar Prospector program in every public medium possible. I think you will agree that the worldwide coverage is significantly raising the visibility of this vital mission.

Thank you, Alan, for your role in the success of the Lunar Prospector Program. I hope you are able to obtain the funding that will allow you to reach your visionary goals.

Sincerely,

J. V. Wrather
Vice President, Communications

cc: M. Brashears
      M. Henshaw

Appendix 4-6: Lockheed's rejection of my request that Lockheed split the $4 million fee that it was getting for the Lunar Prospector Project with my non-profit, tax-exempt institute, the Lunar Research Institute (see Appendix 4-2) (also see www.lunar-research-institute.org).

National Aeronautics and
Space Administration

Headquarters
Washington, DC 20546-0001

SEP 25 1998

Dr. Alan Binder
Director
Lunar Research Institute
1180 Sunrise Drive
Gilroy, CA 95020

Dear Dr. Binder:

Thank you for your letter dated September 3, 1998, to NASA Administrator Daniel S. Goldin concerning the Lunar Prospector mission.

I have followed the Lunar Prospector mission with great interest, and am pleased to see that it was indeed developed in the Faster, Better, Cheaper mode. As you will recall, the Discovery Announcement of Opportunity, to which your proposal responded, specified an end-to-end mission cost, including data processing to level 1 and basic data analysis, of $69M. That same announcement also specified that all higher-level data processing and further science analysis would be selected via competitive science review, open to the full science community, which of course includes you and your team. As stated in the Announcement of Opportunity, there was no intent to set aside substantial funds exclusively for the Principal Investigator team.

The level of funding currently planned for Lunar Prospector post-mission data processing and analysis is influenced by our tight financial situation, but is commensurate with recommendations from an independent panel of experts with a large amount of relevant experience. I also point out that the Space Science Enterprise has other research and analysis programs, which support topical efforts like cartography.

I look forward to more science discoveries during the completion of this successful Faster, Better, Cheaper mission, and wish you success for further data reduction and analysis.

Sincerely,

George Withbroe
Acting Director
Research Program Management Division
Office of Space Science

Appendix 4-7: The unintelligible letter I got from NASA's George Withbroe in response to my trying to make sure NASA had enough money for the data reduction of Lunar Prospector data, in which it was "clear", if one understood NASA gobbledygook, that there was no money for the reduction of the data (also see www.lunar-research-institute.org).

(LRI) Lunar Research Institute

Alan B. Binder, PhD, Director

Mr. Daniel Goldin   March 21, 2000
Administrator
NASA Headquarters
Washington, DC 20546-0001

Dear Dan:

As the Principal Investigator (PI) of the Lunar Prospector (LP) Mission, I am deeply concerned about the attacks on your Faster, Better, Cheaper (FBC) approach to lunar and planetary exploration missions and the conclusions presented in Tony Spear's *NASA FBC TASK FINAL REPORT*.

As you are aware, long before I proposed LP as a Discovery Program mission, my colleagues and I had developed LP as a private effort to demonstrate that small, inexpensive spacecraft with limited payloads could make major contributions to the exploration of the Moon and planets. When the first Discovery AO was released in the late summer of 1994, the LP payload, spacecraft and mission were well defined at the Phase B level, its cost (including launch) was just $63 million and its Phase C/D development time was just 22 months. As such, LP was the ideal mission to prove your FBC concept and was, of course, selected by the evaluation team to proceed directly to flight (the only Discovery mission to do so). While the Code S goal for LP was primarily to obtain lunar data, my primary goal was to prove that FBC works. That is still my goal, especially in light of the recent Mars Mission failures and the resulting attacks on FBC.

I would like to remind you of the following:

1) As was intended in the original definition of the management of a Discovery mission, I was in charge of the program (not a NASA or a Lockheed manager) and directly responsible to NASA for its success. I was not only the PI, but also the Mission Director and was responsible for - and actively participated in - all aspects of every phase (definition, design, construction, test and flight) of the mission.

2) Despite your original directive that the average total cost of Discovery Missions should only be 30% to 50% of the cost cap, the cost of each of the selected Discovery Missions is close to the $250 million cap - except for LP whose total cost (including its 7 month extended mission) was just $65 million or 25% of the cap.

3) LP's Phase C/D construction time was 22 months, well below the 3-year cap.

4) LP was a simple, single-string spacecraft with no on-board computer (I controlled LP from the ground, one command at a time), constructed from reliable, flight-proven hardware.

5) I flew an essentially flawless 12-month nominal mission (a 100+/-20 km altitude polar orbit) and a 7–month extended mission (a 30+/-15 km altitude polar orbit) without any failures or mishaps.

6) Finally, the global mapping data sets obtained exceed those we originally proposed to NASA by a factor of a least 3 in resolution and at least a factor of 3 in quality.

In summary, the LP mission was the least expensive NASA lunar or planetary mission ever flown, one of the most reliable and productive, and certainly the most cost effective. Given its scientific and programmatic successes, I believe that LP fully validated your FBC concept.

Given my success with LP, I absolutely disagree with the various letters and articles in *AW&ST* and *Space News* attacking FBC. These authors totally ignore the FBC successes and concentrate on the failures in an attempt to return to the old, expensive aerospace corporation way of doing business. I note that, while the science community has been the loser in the recent failures, it is the aerospace community that is attacking FBC, not the scientists. My assessment of the failures is that the aerospace companies are attempting to use old style (big budget), mission management techniques with dispersed responsibility to run FBC missions and that does not work. The failures are not technical in nature - they are due to poor management.

Unfortunately, Tony's report is also an attempt to return to business as usual. In reading through this long and wordy report, I find that the emphasis is on returning the mission management to the NASA, JPL and aerospace mission managers, not to the PI. Nowhere in the report is the concept of the PI even mentioned! While some valid points are made in the report, they are lost in the verbiage, but the message is clear – go forward with FBC, but relax the requirements, give us more money and time and let the mission managers (not PI's) run the missions. Based on my success with LP, I totally disagree with these conclusions.

Given my 10-year efforts to prove that FBC works as you had originally defined it and my concern about the attacks and the NASA report on FBC, I would very much appreciate the opportunity to present my views to you and to others at NASA Headquarters who want FBC to work as originally defined. I expect to be a NASA Headquarters on the March 30 and 31st and, if you would like to hear my views, this would be an opportune time for me to do so.

Sincerely yours,

Alan Binder
Lunar Prospector Principal Investigator

Appendix E-1: The letter I wrote to NASA Administrator, Dan Goldin, defending the "Faster, Better, Cheaper" approach to lunar and planetary missions in response to the attacks on it after the two Mars Mission failures in late 1999 (also see www.lunar-research-institute.org).

TESTIMONY OF

ALAN BINDER, PHD

LUNAR RESEARCH INSTITUTE DIRECTOR,
LUNAR EXPLORATION INC. CEO &
LUNAR PROSPECTOR PRINCIPAL INVESTIGATOR

United States House of Representatives

Committee on Science

HEARING

NASA's MARS PROGRAM AFTER THE YOUNG REPORT: PART II

JUNE 20, 2000

Mr. Chairman and Members of the Committee, I am pleased to have the opportunity to appear before you today to discuss the ramifications of the recent Mars Mission failures and the contrasting successes in the Discovery Program on the Faster, Better, Cheaper approach to space exploration missions. As the Principal Investigator of the highly successful Lunar Prospector Mission, the 3rd mission in the Faster, Better, Cheaper Discovery Program and the 1st to be peer reviewed and competitively selected, I am both deeply concerned about — and strongly disagree with — the main conclusions presented in both the *YOUNG REPORT* and Tony Spear's *NASA FASTER, BETTER, CHEAPER TASK FORCE FINAL REPORT*. In contrast to the recommendations in these reports that call for more money, more NASA oversight, and more management to "insure" that failures do not occur, I decisively demonstrated with Lunar Prospector that inexpensive missions can be successfully defined, developed, and flown with an absolute minimum of both management and NASA oversight if they are managed by an experienced and fulltime Principal Investigator who is supported by a small staff of experienced and competent scientists and engineers. If the Young and Spear recommendations are followed, I firmly believe that we will have started down the slippery path back to the old, expensive, slow way of exploring space. If the Lunar Prospector model is followed and if we return to the Faster, Better, Cheaper concept as originally defined by Mr. Goldin at the beginning of the Discovery Program, I believe that we will achieve both a high rate of success, and a maximum return on investment in the exploration of the Moon and planets.

Before I discuss my experience with Lunar Prospector and the recommendations I have for conducting Faster, Better, Cheaper missions, I would like make the following general comments:

1) Having more money, more management, and more NASA oversight does not insure mission success as witnessed by the failure of the $800 million Mars Observer, the incorrectly finished mirror on the $3 billion Hubble Telescope, the stuck antenna on the $1.3 billion Galileo spacecraft, and other failed or compromised missions of the past.

2) The failures of the Faster, Better, Cheaper Mars Climate Observer and the Mars Polar Lander, as well as the WIRE and Lewis Faster, Better, Cheaper missions, were not caused by hardware problems; they were caused by poor management (as witnessed by the failure to only use the Metric System in the case of the Mars Climate Observer and to properly test in the case of the Mars Polar Lander).After some 40 years of experience, the components used to build spacecraft are highly reliable and will perform as expected if the definition, design, construction, and testing of the missions and spacecraft are properly and competently managed.

3) In contrast to the failures of the Faster, Better, Cheaper Mars Missions and the WIRE and Lewis missions, the four Discovery Program Missions thus far completed (Pathfinder and Lunar Prospector) or well underway (NEAR and Stardust) have been highly successful. Thus any recommendations derived from an investigation of the Mars failures should be considered in light of the contrasting successes in the Discovery Program, as I will do using Lunar Prospector as the example shortly.

4) Regarding the Discovery Program: As originally conceived and defined by Mr. Goldin, the missions of the Faster, Better, Cheaper Discovery Program were to cost, on average, 30% to 50% of the $250 million cap, they were to have limited science objectives, and they were to be lead by their Principal Investigators who were to be "solely responsible to NASA for the success" of their missions. With the exception of Lunar Prospector, and despite Mr. Goldin's directives, the costs of all seven of the other full Discovery Missions selected by NASA's Code S are at or near the cost cap, the mission objectives have become more complex and the role of the Principal Investigator has been increasingly limited - while that of the NASA Program Manager has increased. Thus even in the Discovery Program, there is a creeping and disturbing tendency of returning to "business as usual".

In contrast to the recommendations of the Young and Spear reports, and in light of the above four points, I would like to use my experience as the Principal Investigator of the Lunar Prospector mission to substantiate how I believe Faster, Better, Cheaper Missions can be successfully managed and conducted.

First it is important to note that Lunar Prospector was developed as a private effort, completely outside of the NASA hierarchy and hence completely unencumbered by it.

Six years before I proposed Lunar Prospector as a Discovery Program Mission, my colleagues and I in Houston, TX, together with the Space Studies Institute in Princeton, NJ and several Chapters of the National Space Society, developed Lunar Prospector as a private effort to demonstrate that small, inexpensive spacecraft with limited payloads could make major contributions to the exploration of the Moon and planets. When the first Discovery AO was released in the late summer of 1994, the Lunar Prospector payload, spacecraft and mission were well defined and validated at the Phase B level, its cost (including launch) was just $63 million and its Phase C/D development time was just 22 months. As such, Lunar Prospector was the ideal mission to prove the Faster, Better, Cheaper concept and was selected by the evaluation team to proceed directly to flight (the only Discovery mission to do so). While the NASA Code S goal for Lunar Prospector was primarily to obtain lunar data, my primary goal was to prove that Faster, Better, Cheaper worked. With this in mind, I would like to make the following points:

1) As was intended in the original definition of the management of a Discovery Mission, as the Principal Investigator, I was contractually and directly in charge of the program (not a NASA or a Lockheed manager) and directly responsible to NASA for its success. I was not only the Principal Investigator, but also the Mission Director and so I was responsible for — and actively participated in — all aspects of every phase (definition, design, construction, test and flight) of the mission.

2) The management structure of the program was two-tiered: The Lockheed Martin Project Manager and I directly managed our engineering and support staff of some 35 people and worked intimately with them on every aspects of the spacecraft on a daily basis. There was one responsible engineer for each subsystem of the spacecraft. Every staff member knew exactly what his or her task was and who was in charge. Simultaneously, I frequently interfaced with my Co-Investigators, who were developing the science instruments at their home institutions, to insure that all science instrument issues were properly addressed. Finally, the NASA/Ames Research Center provided the required limited NASA oversight and acted as my contact with NASA Headquarters.

3) Program reviews were contractually limited. On the Spacecraft side, we had just four semiformal reviews — a Technical Design Review before we started construction (Phase C/D), a Test Readiness Review, a Pre-Ship Review prior to shipping the spacecraft to Cape Canaveral, and a Launch Site Readiness Review prior to launch. In addition, after the Lewis failure, NASA imposed a two-day review of the Lunar Prospector spacecraft on the project. Finally we had a Mission Operations Readiness Review before launch.

4) As was consistent with the original directive that the average total cost of Discovery Missions should only be 30% to 50% of the cost cap, Lunar Prospector's total cost was just $63 million (not including an extra $2 million for the 7 month extended mission) or 25% of the cap, and the mission was developed and flown within its original budget. The budget breakdown is: Spacecraft — $20 million, 5 Science Instruments — $4 million, Launch Vehicle — $29 million, 12 months of Nominal Mission Operations - $6 million, and Lockheed Martin Fees — $4 million

5) The Phase C/D construction of Lunar Prospector was completed on schedule in 22 months, well below the 3-year cap imposed by the Discovery Program.

6) Lunar Prospector was a simple, single-string spacecraft with no on-board computer (I controlled Lunar Prospector from the ground, sending one command at a time), constructed from reliable, flight-proven hardware. Similarly, the science instruments were all based of flight proven hardware and concepts.

7) Testing was extensive — I "flew only what was tested and tested everything that flew". Also my Operations Team and I helped conduct the testing, thereby gaining operational experience with the spacecraft before it was ever launched.

8) My small Operations Team and I also trained extensively before launch on a computer model of the spacecraft, during which we validated all of the operational and emergency procedures.

9) I flew an essentially flawless 12-month nominal mission (a 100+/–20 km altitude polar orbit) and a 7-month extended mission (a 30+/–15 km altitude polar orbit) without any failures or mishaps.

10) Finally, the global mapping data sets obtained greatly exceed those we originally proposed to NASA by a factor of a least 3 in resolution and at least a factor of 3 in quality.

In summary, the Lunar Prospector mission was the least expensive NASA lunar or planetary mission ever flown, one of the most reliable and productive, and certainly the most cost effective. Given its scientific and programmatic successes, I believe that Lunar Prospector fully validated the Faster, Better, Cheaper concept and should serve as a model for all Faster, Better, Cheaper Missions.

Given my success with Lunar Prospector, I disagree with the major recommendations of the Young and Spear Reports. Rather than spending more money and time on the missions and having more management and more reviews, the Lunar Prospector experience has shown that inexpensive missions will have a very high probability of success if the following recommendations are followed:

1) The mission should be defined and managed by a full-time, experienced Principal Investigator with the full authority and responsibility to conduct all phases of the mission. He or she must be fully responsible for its success.

2) The mission objectives, payload, spacecraft and mission profile must be kept as simple as possible. They, as well as the budget, must be validated and frozen before Phase C/D. NASA must not be allowed to impose new requirements or change the requirements on the program once Phase C/D has started.

3) The staff must have a sufficient number of experienced, senior engineers to insure that the lessons learned from the past are not ignored or forgotten.

4) A two-tiered management structure must be used so the Principal Investigator and his (small) management staff can work intimately with the engineering and science staff during all phases of the program.

5) Reviews must be limited in scope and number to avoid wasting program time and money. In general, since reviewers cannot delve deeply enough into the fine technical details of the hardware or mission to discover any fatal flaws the system may contain, missions fail despite having frequent and numerous reviews. It is better to have a full-time, independent, experienced, quality control engineer working on the project than to have numerous reviews. Major reviews at critical junctions in the mission development (like those listed in point 3 in the previous section) do serve a useful function if the review team is the same for all reviews so the review team is familiar with all aspects of the program.

6) The flight hardware, software and instruments must be developed using flight proven items and concepts — inexpensive missions can not be used to develop new types of hardware or software.

7) Finally, in order to insure absolute continuity and "no loss of information" during the entire project: The team that defines the mission must define the hardware; the team that defines the hardware must build the hardware; the team that builds the hardware must test the hardware; and the team that tests the hardware must fly the hardware.

Appendix E-2: My testimony to the Congressional Committee on Science in response to the attacks on the "Faster, Better, Cheaper" approach to lunar and planetary missions after the two Mars Mission failures in late 1999 (also see www.lunar-research-institute.org).

The Honorable F. James Sensenbrenner   July 11, 2000
Committee on Science
U.S. House of Representatives
Washington, DC 20515

Dear Mr. Chairman:

Thank you for the opportunity to testify to the Science Committee on the Mars mission failures and their impact on the "Faster, Better, Cheaper" approach to lunar and planetary exploration. I greatly appreciated being invited to testify since one of my goals for Lunar Prospector was to demonstrate how to properly manage and conduct inexpensive exploration missions and your committee meeting gave me an opportunity to present my case.

Though I was pleased with my being able to present my successful approach to space exploration and I felt that your introduction and review of the problem were accurate and correctly addressed the points in question, I believe that the questions asked by the various committee members addressed the wrong issue. Rather than questioning Mr. Goldin and Mr. Stone on how NASA and JPL were going to "fix the problem", the real issue should have been, "Are NASA and JPL going to make the necessary changes in the way they define, manage and carryout "Faster, Better, Cheaper" missions, as clearly demonstrated by Clementine and Lunar Prospector, and if so, how are NASA and JPL going to make these changes? As Dr. Rustan so aptly put it, "...there has to be a change in *culture*...", at NASA, if "Faster, Better, Cheaper" is to work as it did in the Clementine and Lunar Prospector missions.

My decades of experience with NASA, the resistance of NASA's middle management to Mr. Goldin's attempts to implement the required culture changes and the general ineptness of NASA in conducting programs (e.g., the space station) all indicate to me that NASA can not and will not make the necessary changes to make its programs work in a reliable and cost effective way. The only way I see to eliminate the increasingly ineffective way NASA does business and to make space exploration cost effective is to have Congress mandate the commercialization of most of NASA's activities.

In addition to the goal of proving that "Faster, Better, Cheaper" works very well if properly done, I also had as a goal for Lunar Prospector demonstrating the commercial feasibility of such missions, by which I mean that such missions can be done so reliably and at such low cost that they can be financially backed by investors and make NASA's _only_ role that of a customer with no financial risk to the American tax payer.

After having demonstrated with Lunar Prospector that lunar exploration is commercially feasible, I am soliciting Congressional support for a funded "Data Purchase Program" within NASA so that those startup companies (including mine - see the attached Lunar Exploration, Inc. business plan) that are interested in developing a viable commercial space exploration capability have an initial customer with which to start this new arena of business. Once a commercial space exploration capability is firmly established, I believe that the customer base will expand and NASA will become just one of many such customers.

I have discussed this issue on several occasions with Eric Sterner, Richard Oberman and Sharon Hays on the Science Committee staff, as well as the aids to several other Senators and Congressmen. I would greatly appreciate discussing this issue with you personally and testifying to the Science Committee about the value of a Data Purchase program and the value of a viable commercial space exploration capability to the United States' economy.

Respectfully yours,

Alan Binder, PhD
Lunar Prospector Principal Investigator

Appendix E-3: The letter I wrote to Congressman Sensenbrenner after I testified to the Congressional Committee on Science regarding the utility of the "Faster, Better, Cheaper" approach to lunar and planetary missions and the need to reform NASA (also see www.lunar-research-institute.org).

Photograph 1-1: The original Lunar Exploration Inc. (LEI) volunteers that formed the basis of the original Lunar Prospector Engineering Team (LEI photograph, see www.lunar-research-institute.org for color version of this photograph).

Photograph 1-2: Some of the attendees at the Critical Design Review of the Lunar Prospector Spacecraft design was held on June 16, 1990, at the end of the OMNI Systems Inc. spacecraft design effort. Seated from right to left: Andy Abraham (OMNI), John Jordan (OMNI), Jim French (Space Studies Institute), Ian Ayton (OMNI), Bob Noteboom (Lunar Exploration Inc.), and the author (Lunar Exploration Inc.). Standing from right to left: Jim Burke (Space Studies Institute) and Wayne Stevens (OMNI) (OMNI photograph, see www.lunar-research-institute.org for color version of this photograph).

Photograph 1-3: The full-scale, OMNI engineering model of the Lunar Prospector Spacecraft with its science instrument booms extended. The Gamma-Ray Spectrometer (GRS) and its science boom extend towards the foreground. The Magnetometer (MAG) and Electron Reflectometer (ER) and their boom extend back and to the left. The MAG is mounted on a 1-m long MAG extension boom extending upwards from the ER and their common electronics box (CPU) that are mounted together at the end of the main boom. The Neutron Spectrometer (NS) and the Alpha particle Spectrometer (APS) — both hidden behind Ian Ayton — and their boom extend back and to the right. The omni and medium gain antennas extend out the top of the model. One can also see the silvery fuel tanks inside the main structure and the dark blue solar cells mounted on the outside of the solar array drum (OMNI photograph, see www.lunar-research-institute.org for color version of this photograph).

Photograph 1-4: The OMNI engineers standing next to the OMNI spacecraft model with its science instrument booms in the stowed position. From right to left: Wayne Stevens, OMNI's President; Diane Pieczynski, the Communications Engineer; Asif Ansari, the Mechanical Engineer; Andy Abraham, the Controls Engineer; Mike Chobotov, the Systems Engineer and Study Manager; Vladimir Chobotov (Mike's father), consultant; John Jordan, the Propulsion Engineer, and Ian Ayton, who built the OMNI spacecraft engineering model (OMNI photograph, see www.lunar-research-institute.org for color version of this photograph).

Photograph 1-5: Three of the senior members of the Lunar Prospector Team standing next to the OMNI spacecraft model with its science instrument booms in the stowed position. From right to left: Jim Burke and Gregg Maryniak, both from the Space Studies Institute, and the author from Lunar Exploration Inc (OMNI photograph, see www.lunar-research-institute.org for color version of this photograph).

Photograph 1-6: Mike Lawson, President of Space Marketing Concepts of Atlanta, standing at the podium with a video showing the launch of a Soviet rocket, discusses the NPO Energia offer to launch Lunar Prospector at the Lunar Prospector Press Conference held by Lunar Exploration Inc. on October 17, 1990 in Houston. Having given our parts of the Press Conference, Preston Carter (Lunar Exploration Inc.'s Co-Chairman and Lunar Prospector's Project Engineer, to Mike's far left) and the author are seated in front of the white screen. I am complaining to Preston about the gross exaggerations he and Mike had made regarding the certainty of the NPO Energia offer to launch Lunar Prospector and about the status of our fundraising activities — exaggerations that were about to backfire a few minutes after this picture was take (LEI photograph, see www.lunar-research-institute.org for color version of this photograph).

Photograph 1-7: Preston Carter (facing the cameras), to the left of the desktop model of the Lunar Prospector Spacecraft, discussing the mission with some guests at the Post-Press Conference Reception held in Clear Lake, TX, during the evening of October 17, 1990. The author (back to the camera) and David Juist (facing the camera), a lawyer in the Clear Lake area, are discussing his generous offer to do the legal work on the Lunar Exploration Inc. contracts pro bono (LEI photograph, see www.lunar-research-institute.org for color version of this photograph).

Photograph 1-8: The author giving a presentation on the Lunar Prospector Mission at the Post-Press Conference Reception held in Clear Lake, TX, during the evening of October 17, 1990, with desktop model of the spacecraft in the foreground (LEI photograph, see www.lunar-research-institute.org for color version of this photograph).

Photograph 1-9: The Discovery Proposal version of the Lunar Prospector Spacecraft is depicted in this composite image orbiting above the Moon at 100 km. The image consists of an Apollo image of the Moon taken from a 100 km altitude orbit and a computer rendition of the spacecraft (Lockheed image, see www.lunar-research-institute.org for color version of this photograph).

Photograph 1-10: The full-scale engineering model of the Discovery Proposal version of the Lunar Prospector Spacecraft. Note the great similarities between this version of the spacecraft design and the OMNI design as shown in Figures 1-3, 1-4, 1-5, 1-7 and 1-8. In this picture, the Gamma-Ray Spectrometer (GRS) is on the science instrument boom nearest the camera; the Alpha Particle Spectrometer (APS, the instrument at the end of the boom) and the Neutron Spectrometer (NS, the silvery cylinders somewhat nearer the spacecraft than the APS) are on the science boom extending back and to the left; and the Magnetometer (MAG) and Electron Reflectometer (ER) are out of the picture on the science boon extending to the right (Lockheed photograph, see www.lunar-research-institute.org for color version of this photograph).

Photograph 2-1: Shortly after NASA announced that Lunar Prospector had been selected by the NASA Discovery Program for flight, this PR photograph of the principles was taken in front of the full-scale engineering model of the Discovery Proposal version of the Lunar Prospector Spacecraft. Left to right are: Scott Hubbard, the NASA/Ames Project Manager; the author and Lunar Prospector Principal Investigator; and Domenick Tenerelli, the Lockheed Project Manager (Lockheed Martin photograph, see www.lunar-research-institute.org for color version of this photograph).

Photograph 2-2: This oblique overhead shot of the full-scale engineering model of the Discovery Proposal version of the Lunar Prospector Spacecraft shows clearly the scale of the spacecraft and science instrument booms. The Gamma-Ray Spectrometer (GRS) is on the science instrument boom to the lower right; the Alpha Particle Spectrometer (APS, the instrument at the end of the boom) and the Neutron Spectrometer (NS, the silvery cylinders somewhat nearer to the spacecraft than is the APS) are on the science boom extending to the lower left; the Magnetometer (MAG) and Electron Reflectometer (ER) are on the science boom extending to the back. NASA/Ames Project Manager, Scott Hubbard, is on the right of the spacecraft and behind the GRS boom. Lockheed Project Manager, Domenick Tenerelli, is to the left and in front of the model. The author and Lunar Prospector Principle Investigator is in the middle and in front of the model (Lockheed Martin photograph, see www.lunar-research-institute.org for color version of this photograph).

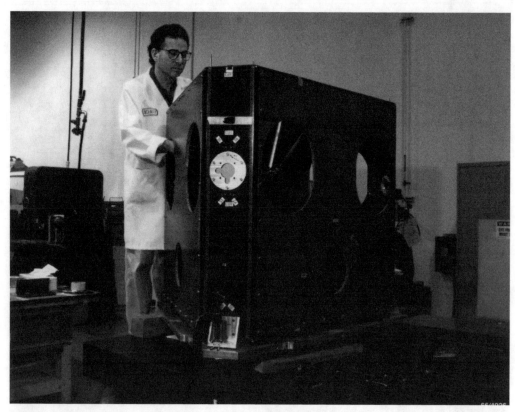

Photograph 3-1: The triangular prism shaped, graphite epoxy, load bearing, main structure of the Lunar Prospector Space-craft. The Lockheed technician is starting the process of very precisely measuring the structure in preparation for the begin-ning of the assembly of the spacecraft. The two large holes in the upper part of each side panel of the structure were cut out to make room for the (three) large fuel tanks, which were too large to fit inside the load bearing structure. The smaller hole near the bottom of each side panel is where one of the three science instrument boom canisters would eventually be attached to the load bearing structure. The circular aluminum boss attached to the upper part of the vertical longeron in the foreground is the external part of one of three such bosses (the internal side of another boss can be seen through the tank cutout, attached to the inner side of a vertical longeron, to the far right of the load bearing structure), which were the front attachment points for the three fuel tanks. Seen through the tank cutout, immediately to the right of the boss on the longeron in the foreground, are two of the three legs of the inverted tripod, the apex of which held three slip bearings that were the attachment points for the backsides of the fuel tanks. The aluminum structure attached at the bottom of the longeron in the foreground is one of the three "feet," or attachment points that were used to attach the spacecraft to the Trans-Lunar Injection Stage by means of three explosive bolts (Lockheed Martin photograph, see www.lunar-research-institute.org for color version of this photograph).

Photograph 3-2: The Lunar Prospector load bearing structure in the hydraulic apparatus that was used to do the static testing of the structure. The static tests were conducted to determine how much the load bearing structure would deform under the loads of the Athena II rocket launch (Lockheed Martin photograph, see www.lunar-research-institute.org for color version of this photograph).

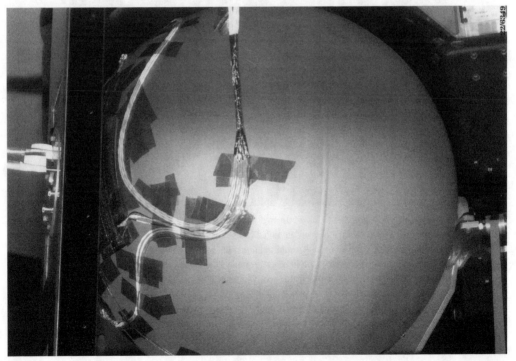

Photograph 3-3: One of the three propellant tanks, wired with its thermostat, thermisters, and heaters, seen temporarily mounted in the load bearing structure during a clearance test. The front of the tank is bolted to the boss on the longeron of the load bearing structure (see Figure 3-1) to the left in the picture and the back of the tank (to the right in the picture) is held in a slip bearing mounted on the inverted tripod at the center on the load bearing structure (Lockheed photograph, see www.lunar-research-institute.org for color version of this photograph).

Photograph 3-4: A propellant tank all dressed up and ready to go. Here, a propellant tank is seen wrapped in its thermal blanket, mounted by its boss to a work stand. The nipple at the (in this photograph) top of the tank would slid into a slip bearing on the inverted tripod in the center of the load bearing structure in order to support the back of the tank. The nipple and slide bearing allowed the tank to be firmly held, while still allowing the tank to expand and contract as the pressure in the tank went up to 450 psi during the fuelling and as the pressure dropped to 150 psi, as the fuel was used up during the mission (Lockheed photograph, see www.lunar-research-institute.org for color version of this photograph).

Photograph 3-5: The Lunar Prospector Spacecraft, with aluminum blocks mounted on and in it, blocks that simulated the masses of the science instruments and their booms on the lower sides of the structure and those of the antennas and the various electronic units on top of the structure, is seen here attached by its three "feet" to the Trans-Lunar Injection (TLI) Stage casing by three explosive bolt, awaiting the drop test. A crane suspends the entire stack, i.e., Lunar Prospector and the TLI Stage, about 10-cm above a thick foam pad. The test was conducted to determine if the spacecraft and TLI Stage casing would separate cleanly when the explosive bolts were blown after the TLI burn. The foam pad was there to absorb the shock of the falling TLI Stage casing, preventing any damage to it and preventing the TLI Stage casing from bouncing back up and hitting the spacecraft, both of which were, of course, flight hardware (we did not have expensive engineering test spacecraft to used during the testing, as is usually the case in more costly programs) (Lockheed photograph, see www.lunar-research-institute.org for color version of this photograph).

Photograph 3-6: The Lunar Prospector Spacecraft and its Trans-Lunar Injection Stage mounted on the shaker, in preparation for the vibration tests. In addition to the aluminum blocks that simulated the masses of the various electronic units, antennas, science instruments, and the science booms (as discussed in the caption of Figure 3-5), one (out of three) solar panel simulator is clearly seen on the left side of the spacecraft structure (Lockheed photograph, see www.lunar-research-institute.org for color version of this photograph).

Photograph 3-7: The Lunar Prospector Spacecraft just after the completion of its wiring. Missing are the science instrument booms and their canisters, which were yet to be mounted on the aluminum disks towards the bottom of the side panels and the solar array panels that would be mounted on the spacecraft much later in the integration and test phases of the program (Lockheed Martin photograph, see www.lunar-research-institute.org for color version of this photograph).

Photograph 3-8: The Space Port Florida commercial launch pad — Pad 46, its gantry to the left, and its blast vent to the right (photograph provided by Karen Ramos, see www.lunar-research-institute.org for color version of this photograph).

Photograph 3-9: Karen Ramos and the author standing at the base of the Pad 46 gantry that was built under Karen's oversight (photograph provided by Karen Ramos, see www.lunar-research-institute.org for color version of this photograph).

Photograph 3-10: The Lunar Prospector Spacecraft as presented to the world at its "Coming Out Press Conference" on March 12, 1997. Except for the missing solar panels and the thermal blanketing, the spacecraft was fully functional. The white, cone shaped, omni and medium gain antenna complex is seen atop the spacecraft. The science instruments are mounted on their respective science instrument booms that are coiled up in their boom canisters — the Alpha Particle Spectrometer (APS)/Neutron Spectrometer (NS) unit faces the camera at the bottom of the spacecraft, the Gamma-Ray Spectrometer (the black cylindrical object) is to the rear and right-hand side of the spacecraft, the Magnetometer (MAG) is the silvery box protruding above the back and left-hand side of the top of the spacecraft, and the Electron Reflectometer (ER) is the object to the back and lower left-hand side of the spacecraft. Two of the three thermal-blanketed propellant tanks can be seen protruding through the propellant tank cutouts in the side panels of the spacecraft's structure and the various electronic units can be seen atop and on the upper front side of the spacecraft structure. Kim Foster is standing to the right of the spacecraft and connected to it by an anti-static electricity line, while the author, standing to the left of the spacecraft and being very careful not to touch it — since I was not connected to it by an anti-static electricity line, is explaining the various parts of the spacecraft to the members of the press (Lockheed Martin photograph, see www.lunar-research-institute.org for color version of this photograph).

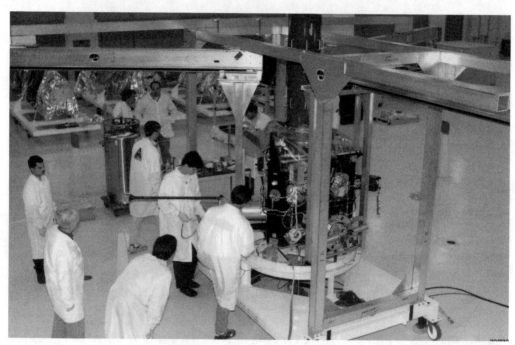

Photograph 3-11: The start of the first science instrument boom deployment test. The large aluminum frame surrounding the spacecraft provided support for the booms during the deployment test, since the 2.5-m long booms could not support their own mass, let alone the mass of the heavy instruments (up to 6.5 kg) in Earth's gravity. At the time this photograph was taken, the author had commanded the release of the Magnetometer (MAG) extension boom, which can be seen extended to the left of the spacecraft and surrounded by Lockheed and Able Engineering technicians — the MAG is the small silvery box at the end of the MAG extension boom (Lockheed photograph, see www.lunar-research-institute.org for color version of this photograph).

Photograph 3-12: The Lunar Prospector Spacecraft as it appeared after the first science instrument boom deployment test was completed. One can see how spindly the booms were and how the aluminum frame held the booms and the heavy science instrument during and after deployment. The boom to the right carries the Alpha Particle Spectrometer (APS) and Neutron Spectrometer (NS), while the other two booms are visible in the background. The circular devices (here seen best immediately behind the NS/APS unit) attached at the junction between the booms and the science instruments, allowed the booms and instruments to rotate freely (four times) as the booms uncoiled and moved outwards, supported by the frames, during the deployment (Lockheed photograph, see www.lunar-research-institute.org for color version of this photograph).

Photograph 3-13: The Gamma-Ray Spectrometer (GRS), before its thermal shield was installed, attached to its boom, which is coiled in its boom canister. The larger diameter cylinder in the middle of the instrument holds the actual Gamma-Ray detector and its anti-coincident shield. The smaller diameter cylinders at the top and bottom of the instrument hold the photomultiplier tubes and pre-amplifiers that detect the light flashes caused when gamma-rays and cosmic rays strike the gamma-ray detector and when cosmic rays strike the anti-coincident shield (Lockheed photograph, see www.lunar-research-institute.org for color version of this photograph).

Photograph 3-14: The Gamma-Ray Spectrometer (GRS) all dressed up in it shiny thermal shield that would keep it at its operational temperature of −28° C to −29° C (Lockheed photograph, see www.lunar-research-institute.org for color version of this photograph).

Photograph 3-15: The Alpha Particle Spectrometer (APS, the square box at the front of the unit) and the Neutron Spectrometer (NS, the two tubes sticking out the sides of the unit), before they were wrapped in their thermal blankets, attached to their boom, which is coiled in its boom canister. The 5 APS detector pairs, located on five faces of the instrument's square housing, are cover with "red-tag" covers to protect them. The red-tag covers were removed for testing and, of course, prior to launch. All such protective covers and devices that were to be removed before flight were red-tagged and all such red-tag items were catalogued and carefully accounted for after their removal just before launch, to absolutely insure that no such red tag devices were left on the spacecraft prior to launch (Lockheed photograph, see www.lunar-research-institute.org for color version of this photograph).

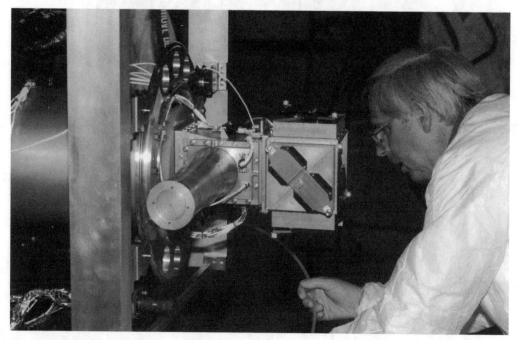

Photograph 3-16: The author photographed while attaching a nitrogen gas purge line to the APS after the first science instrument boom deployment test was completed (photograph provided by Francisco Andolz, see www.lunar-research-institute.org for color version of this photograph).

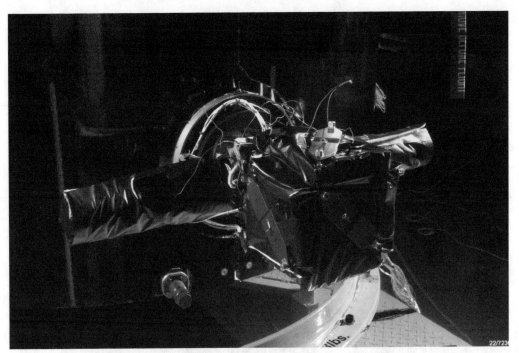

Photograph 3-17: The Alpha Particle Spectrometer (APS) and Neutron Spectrometer (NS) covered with their black blankets that would keep them warm (Lockheed photograph, see www.lunar-research-institute.org for color version of this photograph).

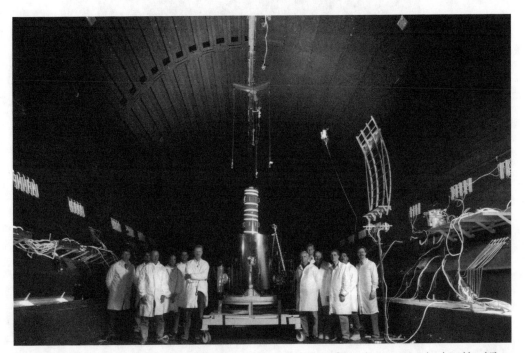

Photograph 3-18: Little Lunar Prospector and the test support crew in the huge (20 m diameter, 25 m long) Lockheed Thermal-Vacuum Test Chamber. The spacecraft has its test solar panels on and a "hat-coupler" covers the omni and medium gain antenna complex. The hat-coupler allowed radio signals to be transmitted to — and received from — the spacecraft antennas without broadcasting the signals to the outside world and hence, interfere with normal civil broadcasts in the vicinity (Lockheed Martin photograph, see www.lunar-research-institute.org for color version of this photograph).

Photograph 3-19: Tom Polette, the author's close friend and, during Phases B/C/D, deputy, photographed behind the Magnetometer (MAG) and Electron Reflectometer (ER), as he worked on the spacecraft. The MAG/ER are seen here mounted on their boom, which is coiled in its boom canister. The MAG is seen at the end of the short MAG extension boom, just above and to the left of Tom's head. The MAG extension boom was held in place for launch by a bracket with two thin wires wrapped around the boom. At the start of the boom deployment sequence, the wires would be cut, on the authors command, by two small explosive devices and the MAG extension boom would swing out and lock into place, extending to Tom's left. The ER detector can be seen on the lower right of the housing and is covered with a red-tag cover. The housing, on which the ER detector and the MAG extension boom are mounted, contains the electronics for the MAG/ER (Lockheed Martin photograph, see www.lunar-research-institute.org for color version of this photograph).

Photograph 3-20: Lunar Prospector, in its full flight configuration with its flight solar panels in place, and its Trans-Lunar Injection (TLI) Stage casing in a Lockheed Acoustic Test Chamber. One of the wiring technicians is connecting the wires between the explosive bolts and the TLI timer. Though the spacecraft is shown here in its full flight configuration, the TLI Stage still has aluminum mass simulators, instead of flight hardware, on it. The acoustic test was the last major test before the spacecraft was shipped to Cape Canaveral for launch preparations and launch (Lockheed Martin photograph, see www.lunar-research-institute.org for color version of this photograph).

Photograph 3-21: Lockheed Project Manager Tom Dougherty (right) and the author (left) in front of a full-scale model of the spacecraft (Lockheed Martin photograph, see www.lunar-research-institute.org for color version of this photograph).

Photograph 3-22: The Lockheed/Lunar Prospector Team that did the final design of the Lunar Prospector Spacecraft, built it, tested it, and got it ready for flight (LRI photograph, see www.lunar-research-institute.org for color version of this photograph).

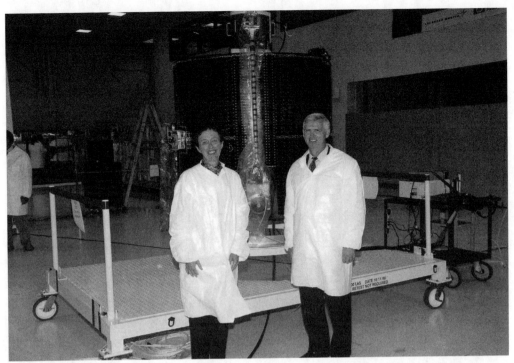

Photograph 3-23: NASA/Ames's Deputy Project Manager, Sylvia Cox, and the author standing in from of the completed Lunar Prospector Spacecraft (Lockheed Martin photograph, see www.lunar-research-institute.org for color version of this photograph).

Photograph 3-24: Members of the Science Team and the author, who were active in the design, construction, integration, and testing of the science instruments. From right to left, Bill Feldman (the Gamma-Ray Spectrometer/Neutron Spectrometer/Alpha Particle Spectrometer Co-Investigator), Bob Lin (Magnetometer/Electron Reflectometer [MAG/ER] Co-Investigator), the author (Lunar Prospector Principle Investigator), David Curtis (MAG/ER Chief Engineer), and Paul Turin (MAG/ER Mechanical Engineer); the person to Paul's right is a technician (Lockheed Martin photograph, see www.lunar-research-institute.org for color version of this photograph).

Photograph 3-25: The senior members of the Lunar Prospector Mission Operations Team. From right to left, Paul Travis (Senior Uplink Controller), the author (Mission Director), Dan Swanson (Dynamics Officer and Deputy Mission Director), and Ric Campo (Senior Uplink controller) (Lockheed Martin photograph, see www.lunar-research-institute.org for color version of this photograph).

Photograph 3-26: Lunar Prospector just after it was secured in its inexpensive, but serviceable, wooden shipping box in preparation for its being shipped in a truck to Cape Canaveral. The hardware in the box had a value of nearly $25,000,000 (photograph by Francisco Andolz, see www.lunar-research-institute.org for color version of this photograph).

Photograph 3-27: Lunar Prospector in its shipping box being secured in the special shipping truck for its trip to Cape Canaveral (photograph by Francisco Andolz, see www.lunar-research-institute.org for color version of this photograph).

Photograph 3-28: The Star-37 rocket motor that would be the heart of the Trans-Lunar Injection (TLI) Stage after it arrival at the Astro Tech spacecraft processing facility near Cape Canaveral. Behind and to the right of the Star-37 rocket is the TLI Stage casing, in which the Star-37 would soon be mounted (photograph by Francisco Andolz, see www.lunar-research-institute.org for color version of this photograph).

Photograph 3-29: Astro Tech technicians preparing to fill Lunar Prospector's three fuel tanks with 137 kg of explosive, toxic, corrosive hydrazine (N_2H_4, a relative to common ammonia, NH_3). Given hydrazine's nasty disposition, the technicians had to wear protective suits and stand behind the blast shield, seen on the left, as they filled the tanks (photograph by Francisco Andolz, see www.lunar-research-institute.org for color version of this photograph).

Photograph 3-30: The TLI Stage is nearly ready to go. A Lockheed technician puts the final touches on the Trans-Lunar Injection (LTI) Stage. The Star-37 rocket motor (whose black engine bell can be seen under the casing) had been mounted in the TLI Stage casing, the red-tagged pyro-devices had been attached, the 3000-psi nitrogen bottles (the dark cylinders, one of which the technician is working on) of the collision avoidance system had been mounted on the right and left sides of the casing, the TLI Stage timer unit had been installed, and the spin-up rockets (one of which is to the immediate right side of the technician's forehead and the other is on the opposite side of the casing) had been mounted. All those components of the TLI Stage were ready to perform their critical jobs in the separation, spin-up, and TLI burn sequence that would propel Lunar Prospector out of its low Earth parking orbit and on its way to the Moon (photograph by Francisco Andolz, see www.lunar-research-institute.org for color version of this photograph).

Photograph 3-31: Laying down on the job? Not really — the technicians, Tim Maloney (lying on the floor just behind the high pressure nitrogen bottle and looking upwards along the Trans-Lunar Injection [TLI] Stage) and the author (lying on the floor to Tim's right) are all trying to make sure the TLI Stage and the spacecraft (not seen atop the TLI Stage) are properly attached to the spin-balance test stand for the critical, final spin balancing of the Spacecraft/TLI Stage stack (photograph by Francisco Andolz, see www.lunar-research-institute.org for color version of this photograph).

Photograph 3-32: Mass Properties Engineer, Al Tilley (standing on the right) and the author (standing on the left) watching the Astro Tech engineers spin-balance the Lunar Prospector/TLI Stage stack — visible on the TV screen (photograph by Francisco Andolz, see www.lunar-research-institute.org for color version of this photograph).

Photograph 3-33: One of the author's favorite photographs of Lunar Prospector and the Trans-Lunar Injection Stage as they stand on the spin-balance table. The Magnetometer (MAG)/Electron Reflectometer (ER) instrument complex is seen mounted on its boom canister on the lower left side of the spacecraft, with the MAG and its MAG extension boom extending to the top of the solar panel drum. The MAG/ER gold-coated foil, thermal blankets, and thermal stripping in place. The Alpha Particle Spectrometer (APS)/Neutron Spectrometer complex is seen on the lower right side of the spacecraft. Looking downwards into the interior of the solar panel drum, one can see the various blanketed electronic units and the white omni and medium gain antenna complex extending upwards from the top of the spacecraft structure. Note that all the red-tagged items, e.g., the APS detector covers, the ER cover, and those on the TLI Stage, have been removed for the spin balancing (photograph by Francisco Andolz, see www.lunar-research-institute.org for color version of this photograph).

Photograph 3-34: Mass Properties Engineer, Al Tilley, standing in front of Lunar Prospector and the Trans-Lunar Injection Stage on the spin-balance test stand (photograph by Francisco Andolz, see www.lunar-research-institute.org for color version of this photograph).

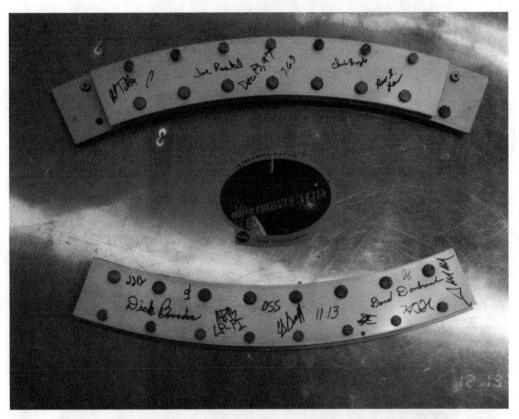

Photograph 3-35: The Trans-Lunar Injection (TLI) Stage ballast weights that were attached to the TLI Stage during the final preparations of the spacecraft and TLI Stage for launch at the Astro Tech spacecraft processing facility near Cape Canaveral. Just before we attached the ballast weights to the TLI Stage, I had all the engineers and technicians present sign the ballast weights. After launch, the signed weights and the TLI Stage initially followed Lunar Prospector as it raced towards the Moon, but because of the decrease in the TLI Stage's velocity caused by the firing of the high-pressure nitrogen jets of the collision avoidance system immediately after spacecraft separation from the spent TLI Stage, the TLI Stage did not reach the Moon. Rather, the TLI Stage went most of the way to the Moon and then started back to Earth, where it entered into — and burned up in — the Earth's upper atmosphere over the Indian Ocean several days after launch (photograph by Francisco Andolz, see www.lunar-research-institute.org for color version of this photograph).

Photograph 3-36: Starting the final stacking of the Athena II rocket's payload. Technicians watch as the fully flight ready, Trans-Lunar Injection Stage is carefully lowered onto the Athena II rockets adapter (photograph by Francisco Andolz, see www.lunar-research-institute.org for color version of this photograph).

Photograph 3-37: Shortly after the Trans-Lunar Injection (TLI) Stage had been attached to the Athena II rocket adapter (Figure 3-36), Tim Maloney watches as the fully flight ready Lunar Prospector Spacecraft is carefully lowered onto the TLI Stage. Visible (slightly out of focus) on the bottom of the spacecraft, mounted on a bracket, is one of the six small rocket engines of the spacecraft. Note that the small rocket engine bell is at a right angle to the long axis of the engine. Also note the separation spring mounted on the attachment bracket just in front of Tim. Three such springs would push Lunar Prospector away from the spent TLI Stage with a resultant separation velocity of about 1-m/sec, a velocity that would be immediately and greatly augmented by the firing of the nitrogen jets of the collision avoidance system, (photograph by Francisco Andolz, see www.lunar-research-institute.org for color version of this photograph).

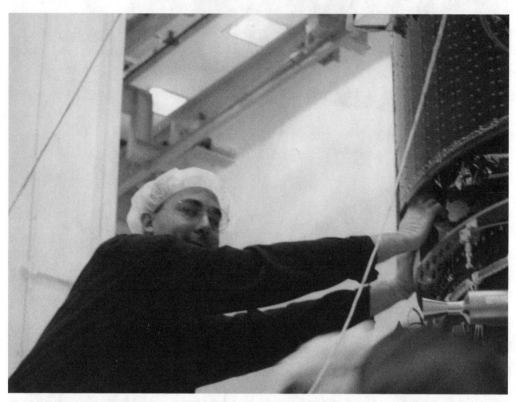

Photograph 3-38: Francisco Andolz, with a smile of satisfaction, helping to attach the Lunar Prospector Spacecraft to the Trans-Lunar Injection Stage, shortly after the photograph in Figure 3-37 was taken. Note the spin-up rocket nozzle that is pointing directly at Francisco (photograph courtesy of Francisco Andolz, see www.lunar-research-institute.org for color version of this photograph)!

Photograph 3-39: The author's favorite photograph of the fully flight ready Athena II rocket payload stack — the Athena II rocket adapter, the Trans-Lunar Injection Stage, and Lunar Prospector. I am pensively and nostalgically taking a long look at the final results of over 9 years of effort and contemplating the coming, complex events that would, hopefully, result in the successful launch and lunar orbit insertion of my beloved spacecraft. This photograph is part of the Lunar Research Institute's (LRI) Lunar Prospector display and also hangs in LRI's main office. I tell visitors, jokingly (since I am an atheist), I am praying to the rocket Gods in this photograph (photograph by Francisco Andolz, see www.lunar-research-institute.org for color version of this photograph).

Photograph 3-40: Shortly before the Astro Tech technicians began the encapsulation process, i.e., putting the Athena II rocket shroud over the payload, part of my proud and happy spacecraft launch preparation crew and I posed before the Lunar Prospector/Trans-Lunar Injection Stage/Athena II rocket adapter stack that would soon be hidden from view by the Athena II rocket shroud, seen almost out of view to the right in this photograph. From right to left, Francisco Andolz, Tim Maloney, Ross Shaw, the author, Kim Foster, Ralph Fullerton, David Curtis, and Joe Rashid (photograph courtesy of Francisco Andolz, see www.lunar-research-institute.org for color version of this photograph and additional Lunar Prospector photographs).

Photograph 3-41: The encapsulation process began as the Athena II launch vehicle engineers hoisted the Athena II shroud from its shipping platform. The two white, vertical structures to the left and right of the Lunar Prospector/Trans-Lunar Injection (TLI) Stage/Athena II rocket adapter stack are two of three guide rails that would ensure the shroud did not accidentally hit the spacecraft or the TLI Stage as the shroud was lowered over the stack (photograph by Francisco Andolz, see www.lunar-research-institute.org for color version of this photograph).

Photograph 3-42: Going, Going, Gone. Slowly, every so slowly, the Athena II rocket shroud was lowered over the Lunar Prospector/Trans-Lunar Injection (TLI)/Athena II rocket adapter stack. Finally, the bottom of Lunar Prospector was no longer visible and I felt a nostalgic pang, knowing I would never see my beloved spacecraft again. Though I would be able to see a small part of the spacecraft through a payload access door at the bottom of the shroud, I would never the see the entire spacecraft again. Several minutes later, the TLI Stage disappeared from view and then the shroud was resting on the basal adapter ring — that Stage of the encapsulation was finished (photograph by Francisco Andolz, see www.lunar-research-institute.org for color version of this photograph).

Photograph 3-43: The shroud, with Lunar Prospector and the Trans-Lunar Injection Stage safely tucked inside, had just been hoisted onto a flatbed truck for its midnight ride to the Athena II rocket that was waiting for its payload at pad 46 at Cape Canaveral (photograph by Francisco Andolz, see www.lunar-research-institute.org for color version of this photograph).

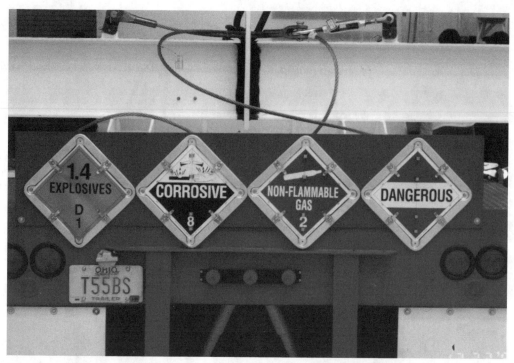

Photograph 3-44: The warning signs on the back of the flatbed truck used to transport the payload to Pad 46 — and we weren't kidding (photograph by Francisco Andolz, see www.lunar-research-institute.org for color version of this photograph)!

Photograph 3-45: The start of "The midnight ride of Paul Re . . . — no, no, of Lunar Prospector." At 1:30 AM, December 23, 1997, the payload convoy was ready to start the several hour journey to Pad 46 (photograph by Francisco Andolz, see www.lunar-research-institute.org for color version of this photograph).

Photograph 3-46: One of four rest and safety check stops on they way to Pad 46. Seen here, immediately behind the flatbed truck with the payload, is the emergency truck (photograph by Francisco Andolz, see www.lunar-research-institute.org for color version of this photograph).

Photograph 3-47: After having arrived safely with the payload at Pad 46, well after sunrise, my tired, but smiling crew, and I posed for a photograph in front of the shrouded payload. From right to left, Gary Schlueter, Ralph Fullerton, Tim Maloney, Kim Foster, the author, and Joe Rashid (photograph by Francisco Andolz, see www.lunar-research-institute.org for color version of this photograph).

Photograph 3-48: The topless Athena II rocket awaiting its payload in the Pad 46 gantry (photograph by Francisco Andolz, see www.lunar-research-institute.org for color version of this photograph).

Photograph 3-49: The hungry alligator that was a few meters from where my crew and I were standing as we watched the payload and shroud being very slowly placed atop the Athena II rocket (photograph by Francisco Andolz, see www.lunar-research-institute.org for color version of this photograph).

Photograph 3-50: After "A hard day's night" Kim took a nap while the alligator in Figure 3-49 eyed him as a possible breakfast snack. Apparently Kim assumed, incorrectly, that we would wake him up if the alligator decided to amble over for a bite (photograph by Francisco Andolz, see www.lunar-research-institute.org for color version of this photograph).

Photograph 3-51: The Athena II rocket with Lunar Prospector in its protective shroud, ready to go to the Moon (photograph by Francisco Andolz, see www.lunar-research-institute.org for color version of this photograph).

Photograph 4-1: Ignition — 6:28:43 PM PST on January 6, 1998 (Lockheed Martin photograph, see www.lunar-research-insti-tute.org for color version of this photograph)!

Photograph 4-2: Liftoff (Lockheed photograph, see www.lunar-research-institute.org for color version of this photograph)!

Photograph 4-3: The blazing trail to the Moon (Lockheed photograph, see www.lunar-research-institute.org for color version of this photograph).

Photograph 4-4: This NASA artist's composite image shows the Lunar Prospector Spacecraft, with science instrument booms deployed, nearing its goal — the Moon (see www.lunar-research-institute.org for color version of this illustration).

Photograph 4-5: Some of the members of the original Lunar Exploration Inc. Team and Bill Feldman at the celebration dinner given by the author on March 18, 1998 at Laundry's in Kemah, TX. From left to right, Bill Feldman, Mike Matthews, the author, Rick Corbell, Larry Spratlin, Andre Sylvester, Graham O'Neil, and Brian Cox (LRI photograph, see www.lunar-research-institute.org for color version of this photograph).

Photograph 4-6: The attendees along with their better halves at the celebration dinner given by the author on March 18, 1998 at Laundry's in Kemah, TX. The author's better half, Rebecca, is standing in the middle of the front row on the author's left (LRI photograph, see www.lunar-research-institute.org for color version of this photograph).

Photograph 4-7: The author sitting inside the Mission Ops Glass Room at his Mission Director's console exactly 325 days, 18 hours, 28 minutes and 15 seconds after spacecraft turn-on (note the Mission Elapse Time clock numbers in the background, outside the Glass Room, and just above my head), checking the spacecraft's engineering data at 10:03 PM PDT. My wife, Rebecca, and I had stopped at Mission Ops on the way home after a weekend vacation at Point Reyes, CA, so I could check on the health of my beloved spacecraft (LRI photograph, see www.lunar-research-institute.org for color version of this photograph).

Photograph 4-8: Shortly after Rebecca had taken the photograph in Figure 4-7, I was ready to leave Mission Ops and Rebecca took this photograph of a very, very tired Mission Director, as I turned away from my console. Despite the restful weekend vacation at Point Reyes, one can easily see in my face the deep fatigue I felt, caused by the intense Mission Operations activities during the previous 11 months and the nearly constant battles I had fought with Lockheed and NASA to keep the program on track during the mission and during the more than three year period between the start of the proposal effort in the fall of 1994 and launch in January 1998 (LRI photograph, see www.lunar-research-institute.org for color version of this photograph).

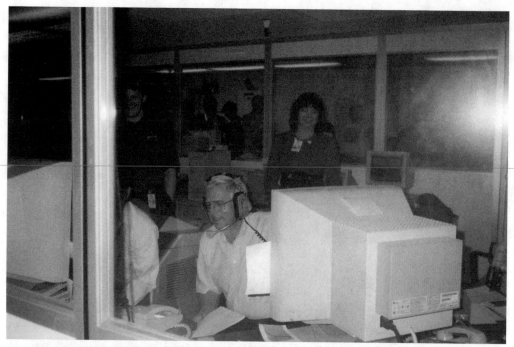

Photograph 4-9: Just before the End-of-Mission commanding session started in the early morning hours of Saturday, July 31, 1999, Mission Controller, Cathy Culver (standing right), the author (seated at my Mission Director's console), Dynamics Officer, Dan Swanson (standing left), and an unidentified Controller (seated in front of Dan), are photographed (from outside the Glass Room), while laughing about some remark as we were preparing for the mission's last commanding session. Other Mission Ops personnel and visitors watch our activities from outside the Mission Ops Glass Room (LRI photograph see www.lunar-research-institute.org for color version of this photograph).

Photograph 4-10: Seated at our consoles inside the Glass Room (photographed from outside the Glass Room), during the commanding of the final Kamikaze burn, from right to left are Dynamics Officer, Dan Swanson, the author and Mission Director, and Senior Uplink Controller, Paul Travis. Other Mission Ops personnel and visitors watch our activities from outside the Mission Ops Glass Room (LRI photograph, see www.lunar-research-institute.org for color version of this photograph).

Photograph 4-11: Several members of the Lunar Prospector Mission Operations crew photographed after the end of the mission, standing behind the seated author and Mission Director. From right to left: David Lozier (Ames Navigation Team member), Dan Swanson (Dynamics officer), Ken Galal (Ames Navigation Team member), Paul Travis (Senior Uplink Controller), John Kohli (Mission Controller), and Howard Wilkinson (LRI photograph, see www.lunar-research-institute.org for color version of this photograph).

See www.lunar-research-institute.org for the global and regional gravity, magnetic, compositional, hydrogen (water ice?) distribution, and radon release maps produced from the data received from Lunar Prospector.